The Fossil Record

The First Record

The
Fossil Record

A SYMPOSIUM WITH DOCUMENTATION
jointly sponsored by
the Geological Society of London
and the Palaeontological Association

Edited by

W. B. HARLAND

C. H. HOLLAND

M. R. HOUSE

N. F. HUGHES

A. B. REYNOLDS

M. J. S. RUDWICK

G. E. SATTERTHWAITE

L. B. H. TARLO

E. C. WILLEY

Published by the

GEOLOGICAL SOCIETY OF LONDON
BURLINGTON HOUSE · LONDON · W 1

1967

The papers in Parts I and III of this volume were presented and discussed at a joint meeting of the Geological Society of London and the Palaeontological Association held in the Department of Geology, University College of Swansea, on 20–21 December 1965.

Published by the Geological Society of London
Burlington House, London W 1

October 1967

Printed in Northern Ireland by
The Universities Press, Belfast

References to this volume

It is recommended that reference to the whole or part of this volume be made in one of the following forms, as appropriate:

HARLAND, W. B. *et al.* (Eds.) 1967. *The Fossil Record.* London (Geological Society), xii + 828 pp.

BANKS, H. P. *et al.* 1967. Thallophyta—1. *In* HARLAND, W. B. *et al.* (Eds.) *The Fossil Record.* London (Geological Society), pp. 163–180.

JOHNSON, H. M. 1967. Family Codiaceae. *In* HARLAND, W. B. *et al.* (Eds.) *The Fossil Record.* London (Geological Society), p. 167.

ARRANGEMENT OF THE VOLUME

(For detailed list of contents see overleaf)

508763

CONTENTS

Part I: Symposium papers

Part II: Documentation of the fossil record

Contents

Part III: Computer analysis

Names of those who contributed to this work

C. G. Adams
D. V. Ager
K. L. Alvin
F. W. Anderson
S. M. Andrews
R. M. Appleby
H. P. Banks
F. T. Banner
P. D. W. Barnard
R. H. Bate
M. Black
P. Brönimann
T. P. Burnaby
P. M. Butler
R. Casey
W. G. Chaloner
A. J. Charig
K. I. M. Chesters
W. J. Clarke
W. A. Clemens
M. G. Collett
J. S. H. Collins
J. C. W. Cope
P. Copper
J. W. Cowie
C. B. Cox
L. R. Cox
R. A. Crowson
D. Curry
J. L. Cutbill
W. T. Dean
D. T. Donovan
C. Downie
G. M. Dunlop
F. E. Eames
G. F. Elliott
R. M. Finks
D. W. Fisher
J. M. McC. Fisher
B. N. Fletcher
B. M. Funnell
B. G. Gardiner

F. R. Gnauck
R. Goldring
S. F. Graham
L. J. Grambast
A. Hallam
J. M. Hancock
W. B. Harland
T. M. Harris
D. Hill
F. Hodson
C. H. Holland
D. A. Hooijer
M. R. House
M. K. Howarth
J. D. Hudson
R. G. S. Hudson
N. F. Hughes
R. P. S. Jefferies
G. A. L. Johnson
H. M. Johnson
E. H. Jope
E. M. Jope
K. A. Joysey
K. A. Kermack
W. S. Lacey
G. P. Larwood
A. J. Lloyd
W. S. McKerrow
A. W. Medd
F. A. Middlemiss
R. S. Miles
L. R. Moore
N. J. Morris
D. E. Owen
A. L. Panchen
B. Patterson
C. Patterson
C. R. C. Paul
G. M. Philip
W. H. C. Ramsbottom
A. B. Reynolds

F. H. T. Rhodes
R. B. Rickards
W. D. L. Ride
W. R. Riedel
J. E. Robinson
W. D. I. Rolfe
R. Ross
A. J. Rowell
M. J. S. Rudwick
A. W. A. Rushton
D. E. Russell
P. A. Sabine
W. A. S. Sarjeant
G. E. Satterthwaite
R. J. G. Savage
F. W. Shotton
E. L. Simons
D. Skevington
J. Smart
A. H. Smout
N. Spjeldnaes
I. Strachan
I. D. Sutton
L. B. H. Tarlo
R. Tavener-Smith
F. M. Taylor
J. T. Temple
L. Thaler
G. Thomas
E. T. Tozer
R. P. Tripp
R. H. Wagner
V. G. Walmsley
C. D. Waterston
A. Wesley
T. Whitworth
B. Wilcock
E. C. Willey
A. Williams
R. J. Wootton
A. D. Wright
C. W. Wright

Preface

THIS VOLUME is in three parts. Part I contains the text of papers given at the symposium meeting; in this sense it is what is generally understood by a symposium in that each paper is the responsibility of the author, who although invited to contribute in a particular field has nevertheless decided for himself how to do this. It thus consists of a series of loosely related papers. Part II, on the other hand, is an integrated compilation, and the introduction explains how this effort in documentation was organized. It does not comment, however, on the labour which made this publication possible; the debt to the many contributors is not in all cases manifest in the length of their initialled work below. Complete coverage was required by the plan for the volume, but this was only possible at great inconvenience to some contributors. Thus, while some contributors may well have been in a position to document the taxa requested with relatively little trouble, others undertook tasks which were far from easy in order to fill the various gaps. In this connexion I should like to pay tribute to the late Dr L. R. Cox, Chairman of the Joint Committee, and to Mr N. J. Morris who completed Dr Cox's contribution after his untimely death; also to Dr G. Thomas for completing the work of the late Professor R. G. S. Hudson in similarly distressing conditions.

Less obvious perhaps is the work done by the Editorial Sub-Committee. The responsibility for the chapters in Part II was divided more or less equally between five sectional editors, as indicated in the table on p. 827. Having decided the policy, which was set out in a series of bulletins to all concerned, each of these five editors approached potential contributors to their sections, and undertook a continuing responsibility to persuade, explain and edit the work for those chapters. This involved a great deal of correspondence and many circulars. In the formulation of policy and initial circulation of bulletins Dr Rudwick also acted as Secretary of the Sub-Committee. For a time when he was ill, and again when he was on sabbatical leave, Mr Hughes fulfilled this function. During my own absence Mr Hughes also undertook some of the duties of Chairman of the Sub-Committee and imparted the necessary degree of impetus and co-ordination. It was soon realized that in order to secure uniformity of presentation in the volume, and particularly of the figures, professional draughting would be necessary, and this was undertaken for the Geological Society by Miss Ailsa B. Reynolds in the Department of Geology at Cambridge. However, it became increasingly evident that agreement between text and figures could only be achieved by a meticulous checking of the submitted charts and text, and whilst the five editors did much of this, a substantial check was also carried out by Miss Reynolds, who in addition kept the files and managed the extensive correspondence. Because of the magnitude of this work, and the short time between receipt of many contributions and going to press, Mr Hughes made it possible for Mr E. C. Willey to assist in rationalizing the references within each of the chapters of Part II and putting their abbreviations, where practicable, into the form of the *World List of Scientific Periodicals* (4th edn, London, 1963–5). The references comprise a substantial part of the bulk and value of this work.

Mr B. Wilcock advised on the format and took initial steps to secure printers, but the main burden fell on Mr G. E. Satterthwaite, his successor as Editor and Executive Secretary of the Geological Society, to negotiate and plan the details of printing, and then to receive the total copy and see it through all stages of production into book form.

Professor O. M. B. Bulman, then Head of the Department of Geology at Cambridge, permitted much of the editorial and office work to be undertaken there, and for the latter Miss J. E. Suttle took much responsibility. The Heads of many other geological institutions have allowed their staff facilities to contribute to this volume, and the Directors of the British Museum (Natural History) and of the Geological Survey (now the Institute of Geological Sciences), have given permission for their staff to publish. This assistance, in respect of all such contributions, is gratefully acknowledged here; the addresses of the contributors listed at the end of each chapter indicate the institutions who have helped in this way.

Dr Funnell and Dr Cutbill, in volunteering to provide a numerical analysis of the data, are fully aware of the limitations which the data themselves impose and are under no illusions about the substantial element of variable palaeontological activity that their analysis reflects. It was not practicable to begin the final computations until the last contribution had come in, which left very little time for the whole operation. Nevertheless, it was felt that such a numerical presentation would be appreciated.

The magnitude of the volume was difficult to estimate accurately until most of the copy had been received, and thus at quite a late stage, when the estimated cost of the volume exceeded first estimates by a substantial margin, Mr Hughes arranged to guarantee the Geological Society a sum to avoid a suggested economy of 50 pages by abbreviating references in Part II (a guarantee later assumed by the Palaeontological Association). Publication of the volume, originally hoped for by the end of 1966 was delayed partly by the late and unpredictable arrival of several contributions and then by the very large number of corrections that were made to the galley proofs. In a work of this kind corrections and improvements can be made almost indefinitely. However useful this work may prove to be, it must contain many inaccuracies. It will be appreciated if those who take the trouble to discover these will communicate them for subsequent publication (see note opposite) to the Geological Society.

W. B. Harland,
Department of Geology,
Sedgwick Museum, Cambridge
22 August 1967

Arrangements for correcting and supplementing the documentation

The Editors will welcome corrections and additions to the documentation from any reader. These should be submitted in typescript, set out in the style of Part II of this volume—attention is drawn to the Introduction (pp. 1–11) and to the Introduction to Part II (pp. 158–159). Such contributions will be considered for publication, with due acknowledgement, in a form to be decided. They should be addressed to:

The Editors, *The Fossil Record*,
Geological Society of London,
Burlington House,
LONDON W 1.

Introduction

THE COUNCIL of the GEOLOGICAL SOCIETY OF LONDON decided that a volume with a palaeontological theme should be the sequel to its volume on *The Phanerozoic Time-scale*. It was thus natural to seek the co-operation of the Palaeontological Association, and a Joint Committee of the two bodies was set up in May 1964, constituted as follows: Dr L. R. Cox (Chairman), Dr C. G. Adams, Dr R. Casey, Dr C. H. Holland, Dr M. R. House, Mr N. F. Hughes, Professor F. H. T. Rhodes, Dr M. J. S. Rudwick, Dr P. A. Sabine, Professor F. W. Shotton, Mr W. B. Harland (Secretary). At the invitation of Professor F. H. T. Rhodes a joint symposium meeting was arranged at Swansea, and held on 20–21 December 1965 (*Proc. geol. Soc. Lond.* no. 1630, 40–41, 1966; McKerrow, W. S., *New Scient.* **20,** 23–4; Harland, W. B., *Nature, Lond.* **209,** 864–6). The task of the Joint Committee was to organize this meeting and to choose a theme. After some discussion it was decided to produce a review of the fossil record, with special reference to ranges of taxa, and an editorial Sub-Committee was appointed to work out the details of what became known colloquially, as the 'Swansea Symposium Volume'. This Sub-Committee was as follows: Mr W. B. Harland (Chairman), Dr C. H. Holland, Dr M. R. House, Mr N. F. Hughes and Dr M. J. S. Rudwick; Dr L. B. H. Tarlo and Dr B. M. Funnell were later co-opted. For the detailed planning of the Swansea meeting the Joint Committee co-opted Dr V. G. Walmsley, who acted as local secretary and, with the help of the University staff at Swansea, looked after the practical details of the meeting which was attended by about 160 people. The texts of the papers presented and some discussion constitute Part I of this volume.

As with *The Phanerozoic Time-scale*, it was the policy of the Geological Society to give priority to the publication of a worth-while volume, leaving it to the meeting to discuss whatever aspects seemed suitable, rather than to let the contents of the volume be dictated by what it was convenient to arrange for a meeting. Thus the Editorial Sub-Committee became responsible to the Publication Committee of the Society, and continued this policy of attempting to assemble in one volume, through the efforts of many specialists, a useful collection of data. It was decided to select a pattern of data which could be largely objective, and to avoid, as far as possible, interpretative opinions. This was partly in order to secure the collaboration of workers with differing outlooks, but mainly because the volume could thereby become a useful reference work. The objectivity lies essentially in the documentation of published records of fossils in their stratigraphical context.

The Fossil Record, pp. 1–11. Geological Society of London, 1967. Printed in Northern Ireland.

Contributors were asked to document the first- and last-known fossil records of taxa in the group for which they were responsible. These records were to be related as precisely as possible to a standard scheme of stratigraphical divisions. The Committee believed that such a compilation would be a valuable initial source of information for a variety of uses, such as the critical evaluation of theories concerning the history of life, and, not least, to draw attention to the deficiencies of our present knowledge. More particularly, they felt that there was a need to collect, in easily accessible form, information on the *known* ranges of taxa, as opposed to the hypothetical ranges often ascribed to taxa in phylogenetic and other interpretations.

Some data on ranges are, of course, available in the *Treatise on Invertebrate Paleontology;* but this does not set out to give detailed or precise documentation, in either stratigraphical or taxonomic terms, of the first- and last-known records of taxa, and does not include full bibliographical references to such records. Some contributors to the chapters on Invertebrata in this volume have adopted, with more or less modification, the schemes of classification used in the *Treatise;* but the aim of the present volume is to provide more detailed documentation of ranges than that available in the *Treatise* or in any compilation easily accessible to the non-specialist. Moreover, this volume deals with all organisms known in the fossil record, both plants and animals, whereas the *Treatise* so far covers only a part of the Invertebrata.

In planning so large an assembly of data, the Editorial Sub-Committee had in mind the possibility of processing the data by computer. At a later stage it was decided to include such a computer analysis of the data within the volume; this appears as Part III. An interim version of this paper, based on the chapters then complete, was presented at Swansea, but the paper now follows the documentation in Part II because in its present form it is based on the figures as finally drawn for Part II and the data could thus not be processed until a late stage in the preparation of the volume. Even so some newly available information was included in the volume, or errors were corrected, after the computing began, thus leading to a very few small discrepancies between the statistical data in Part III and the documentation in Part II. However, these are so slight as to have no perceptible effect on the numerical results.

Choice and treatment of taxa

The Editorial Sub-Committee intended to make the coverage of fossil taxa comprehensive in the sense that so far as possible all taxa would be included, either explicitly, or implicitly by inclusion in other taxa. By giving some indication of the space available to contributors, and by the inevitable limitation of time due to other commitments, a severe restriction was thus enforced on the number of taxa that could be documented. However, it was left to each contributor to decide how many taxa to treat within the systematic groups allotted. Consistency of the level of taxa documented was not expected, and it is therefore diverse. To treat the fossil record fully to species or generic level, or even in many cases to family level, was beyond the resources available. Nevertheless, since it is questionable whether any greater objectivity can be claimed for fossil species or genera than for families or higher taxa, this diversity of treatment can hardly detract from the validity of the documentation. In any case, it leaves the way open for various more detailed studies of particular groups.

The possibility was considered of giving some indication of the nature, richness or completeness of the fossil record, based on the clear impression gained by experts from experience with their own taxa. The progress of life might thus be qualified by some indication of waxing, waning and of acmes. The decision to document only the records of the stratigraphically earliest and latest fossils within a given taxon was based partly on practical and partly on theoretical grounds. The practical consideration was that an additional parameter, even if easy to obtain, would have unduly increased the scale of an already large undertaking. The course chosen also had the advantage of minimizing ambiguity in the request to contributors—namely to document the records of the earliest and latest occurrences of taxa, the level of taxa being decided by themselves.

The theoretical consideration was that it is difficult to devise an agreed, objective means of characterizing the relative diversification and abundance of life from the fossil record—complicated as it is by considerations of both (*a*) the remoteness of the evidence of fossil assemblages from the living communities that gave rise to them, and (*b*) the difficulty of estimating numbers of individuals and weighing them against numbers of taxa. The decision to document terminal records, however, does give some opportunity to demonstrate taxonomic diversification by displaying the ranges of constituent taxa. Such a method can be almost completely objective, in so far as the data treated are restricted to published records—it is thus an analysis of the published fossil record. To achieve this it was necessary in a few cases to publish papers validating new or revised taxa (*Proc. geol. Soc. Lond.* no. 1640, pp. 137–51, 1967).

It is obvious that the intended objectivity of our compilation, being an abstract of the *published* record, is qualified by a degree of subjectivity in the work of the palaeontological authors. To the inevitable natural accidents of preservation are added the human accidents of collection and description stimulated by differing degrees of competition, interest, outlook and resources available in different areas at different times. However, after more than 150 years of dedicated work by hundreds of palaeontologists it seems to the Editors unlikely that the main features of the published record as abstracted here are artifacts, and whatever the problems it must surely help our understanding to review the current state of knowledge from time to time.

Stratigraphical framework

In order to make it easier to compare the stratigraphical ages of the published records documented here, it was obviously desirable to attempt to correlate with a single stratigraphical scale. The Editorial Sub-Committee, whilst recognizing the improbability of general agreement on any scale without many years of patient research and negotiation, devised a scale solely for the purpose of this volume. Indeed, it had to be devised at an early stage, so that contributors could use it in their work. The scale was circulated to contributors in December 1964, and was based on the following principles. Firstly, that as far as possible consecutive divisions approaching the size order of a Jurassic age or stage should be used throughout; 74 such divisions were selected. Secondly, that familiar names should be used for these divisions, but that to avoid any possible misunderstanding, the base of each should be defined as being at a stated horizon or point (selected solely for the purpose of this work); each division would thus be taken to end at the beginning of the next division. Thirdly, that all definitions should be taken in marine successions. Fourthly, that wherever possible definitions should be based on evidence of planktonic or nektonic organisms. The scale as finally used is presented in Table 1. Abbreviations used throughout this volume are given there, and the text-figures plotting graphically the ranges of taxa between first and last records are based on this same scale.

Table 1 gives briefly the definitions of the divisions as used, but inevitably there were several points of difficulty and controversy, and some of the arguments used in the adopted solution are mentioned below. Needless to say, not all the contributors could be satisfied, nor even all the Editors. The Editors, therefore, wish to thank contributors, not only for the work involved in attempting to translate their records from stratigraphical terms familiar to them into a stratigraphical scale that may be unsuitable for their particular taxa, but also for agreeing to accommodate their records in a scale which often was one with which they personally had no sympathy. Such forbearance on their part has been an ingredient of any success this compilation may have. The Editors express their hope, to readers and contributors alike, that acceptance of the stratigraphical conventions in this volume will in no way prejudice efforts being made elsewhere to promote an agreed Standard Stratigraphical Scale.

For the purposes of this volume all records have been made according to the scale-division definitions, e.g. a record from Lias below the base of the Zone of *Psiloceras planorbis*, would be given *in this volume* as Triassic Rhaetian. It is unlikely that there were many problems of this order of magnitude.

For continental sequences it was felt better to accept a low order of accuracy of correlation with the scale division and record it on the marine standard, rather than not to attempt any correlation; contributors were asked to make this attempt.

The abbreviations listed in the second column of Table 1 have been used throughout the text and the figures in Parts II and III without further explanation.

Comments on stratigraphical divisions selected

Period/system and epoch/series names. The placing of such divisions as the Tremadocian and the Danian did not require a decision for the figures, but the choice for use in the text was made by Editorial Sub-Committee majority vote. Discussion

TABLE 1: Stratigraphical scale used in *The Fossil Record*

(1)	(2) Selected unit (stage, series or other division) with abbreviated form used throughout Part II.	(3) Some other divisions included in (but not necessarily equivalent to) the selected units (col. 2). These do not appear on the printed scales	(4) Definition of base of unit of col. 2 (point, or base of the Zone listed)	(5) Notes on definition in col. 4
QUATERNARY	HOLOCENE — Holo		10300 years B.P.	
	PLEISTOCENE — Pleist	(Calabrian)	Zone of *Globorotalia truncatulinoides*	(Base of 'Reuverian' C)
TERTIARY	PLIOCENE — Plioc	(Astian, Piacenzian (Plaisancian))	Zone of *Sphaeroidinella dehiscens*	
	UPPER MIOCENE — U. Mioc	(Messinian, Sahelian, Sarmatian, Pontian)	Zone of *Globorotalia tumida plesiotumida*	
	MIDDLE MIOCENE — M. Mioc	(Vindobonian, Tortonian, Helvetian *pars*)	Zone of *Globigerina nepenthes/ Globorotalia mayeri*	(The Vindobonian may extend just below the base of the *nepenthes/mayeri* Zone)
	LOWER MIOCENE — L. Mioc	(Aquitanian, Burdigalian, Helvetian *pars*)	Zone of *Globorotalia opima opima*	(The Aquitanian may extend down slightly below the base of the *opima* Zone)
	UPPER OLIGOCENE — U. Olig	(Chattian *s.s.*)	Zone of *Globigerina ampliapertura*	
	LOWER and MIDDLE OLIGOCENE — L/M. Olig	(Lattorfian and Rupelian)	Zone of *Globigerina sellii*	(In appropriate facies, Middle Oligocene may be distinguished by the presence of BOTH *Nummulites* and *Eulepidina*)
	UPPER EOCENE — U. Eoc	(Bartonian, Ledian, Priabonian)	Zone of *Globigerapsis seminvoluta*	
	MIDDLE EOCENE — M. Eoc	(Lutetian)	Zone of *Hantkenina aragonensis*	
	LOWER EOCENE — L. Eoc	(Cuisian, Ypresian, Ilerdian *pars*)	Zone of *Globorotalia rex/ wilcoxensis*	
	PALAEOCENE — Palaeoc	(Seelandian, Montian, Landenian, Thanetian, Ilerdian *pars*)	Subzone of *Turborotalia trinidadensis*	(*trinidadensis* is the upper Subzone of the *Globigerina daubjergensis* Zone)
	DANIAN — Dan	(Danian 1–4 type area)	?Zone of *Globigerina eugubina*	

2

5

(1)	(2)	(3)	(4)	(5)
	Selected unit (stage, series or other division) with abbreviated form used throughout Part II.	Some other divisions included in (but not necessarily equivalent to) the selected units (col. 2). These do not appear on the printed scales	Definition of base of unit of col. 2 (point, or base of the Zone listed)	Notes on definition in col. 4
CRETACEOUS	MAESTRICHTIAN — Maestr		Zone of *Pachydiscus neubergicus*	(Zone of *Belemnella lanceolata*)
	CAMPANIAN — Campan		Zone of *Diplacmoceras bidorsatum*	(Zone of *Gonioteuthis granulata*)
	SANTONIAN — Santon		Zone of *Texanites texanus*	(Zone of *Micraster coranguinum*)
	CONIACIAN — Coniac		Zone of *Barroisiceras haberfellneri*	(Zone of *Micraster cortestudinarium*)
	TURONIAN — Turon		Zone of *Mammites nodosoides*	(Zone of *Inoceramus labiatus*)
	CENOMANIAN — Cenom		Zone of *Mantelliceras mantelli*	(Zone of *Schloenbachia varians*)
	ALBIAN — Alb		Zone of *Leymeriella tardefurcata*	
	APTIAN — Apt		Zone of *Prodeshayesites fissicostatus*	
	BARREMIAN — Barrem		Zone of *Paracrioceras strombecki*	
	HAUTERIVIAN — Haut		Zone of *Acanthodiscus radiatus*	
	VALANGINIAN — Valang		Zone of *Kilianella roubaudiana*	
	BERRIASIAN — Berr	(Ryazanian, M. & U. Purbeck)	Zone of *Berriasella boisseri*	
JURASSIC	'TITHONIAN' — 'Tith'	(Volgian, L. Purbeck Portlandian, M. & U. Kimmeridgian)	Zone of *Taramelliceras lithographicum*	(approx. Zone of *Gravesia* spp.)
	KIMMERIDGIAN — Kimm	(L. Kimmeridgian)	Zone of *Pictonia baylei*	
	OXFORDIAN — Oxf		Zone of *Quenstedtoceras mariae*	
	CALLOVIAN — Call		Zone of *Macrocephalites macrocephalus*	
	BATHONIAN — Bath		Zone of *Zigzagiceras zigzag*	
	BAJOCIAN — Bajoc	(Aalenian)	Zone of *Leioceras opalinum*	(*sensu* Arkell 1956)

Period	Stage	Abbr.	Regional equivalents	Zone	Approx. base
TRIASSIC	TOARCIAN	Toarc		Zone of *Dactylioceras tenuicostatum*	
	PLIENSBACHIAN	Pliens		Zone of *Uptonia jamesoni*	
	SINEMURIAN	Sinem		Zone of *Arietites bucklandi*	
	HETTANGIAN	Hett		Zone of *Psiloceras planorbis*	
	RHAETIAN	Rhaet		Zone of *Choristoceras marshii*	
	NORIAN	Nor		Zone of *Heinrichites paulckei*	
	CARNIAN	Carn	(Ischigualasto Fm., Argentina)	Zone of *Trachyceras aon*	
	LADINIAN	Ladin	(Santa Maria Fm, Brazil)	Zone of *Protrachyceras reitzi*	
	ANISIAN	Anis	(Manda Fm., E. Africa)	Zone of *Nicomedites osmani*	
	OLENEKIAN	Olenek	(Cynognathus Zone, S. Africa)	Zone of *Meekoceras gracilitatis*	
PERMIAN	INDUAN	Induan	(Lystrosaurus Zone, S. Africa)	Zone of *Otoceras woodwardi*	
	DZHULFIAN	Dzhulf	(Tartarian; ?Zechstein, Ochoan; ?Tapinocephalus, Endothiodon, Kistecephalus Zones, S. Africa)	Zone of *Cyclolobus*	
	GUADELUPIAN	Guad	(Ufimian, Kazanian, Zechstein, Word, Capitan)	Zone of *Waagenoceras*	
	LEONARDIAN	Leonard	(Artinskian–Kungurian)	Zone of *Perrinites*	(approx. base of *Parafusulina* Zone)
	SAKMARIAN	Sakm	(Upper Wolfcampian)	Zone of *Pseudofusulina moelleri* (Schellw.)	
	ASSELIAN	Assel	(Lower Wolfcampian)	Zone of *Pseudoschwagerina vulgaris* (Tscherb.)	
CARBONIFEROUS	UPPER CARBONIFEROUS	U. Carb	(Kasimovian, Gzelian, Orenburgian, Stephanian, Missourian, Virgilian)	Zone of *Triticites montiparus* (Ehrenb. em. Moeller)	
	MOSCOVIAN	Moscov	(Westphalian C,D?, Atokan, Des Moines)	Zone of *Profusinella prisca* (Deprat)	
	BASHKIRIAN	Bashk	(Namurian C, Westphalian A,B)	Zone of *Pseudostaffella antiqua* (Dutk.)	
	NAMURIAN	Namur	(Namurian A,B)	Entry of *Cravenoceras leion*	(approx. base of *Eumorphoceras* Zone E$_1$)
	VISÉAN	Viséan		Lower Zone of *Beyrichoceras* (B$_1$)	
	TOURNAISIAN	Tourn		Zone of *Protocanites lyoni*	(base of *Gattendorfia* Major Zone)

7

TABLE 1: (*continued*)

(1)	(2) Selected unit (stage, series or other division) with abbreviated form used throughout Part II.		(3) Some other divisions included in (but not necessarily equivalent to) the selected units (col. 2). These do not appear on the printed scales	(4) Definition of base of unit of col. 2 (point, or base of the Zone listed)	(5) Notes on definition in col. 4
DEVONIAN	FAMENNIAN	Famenn		Zone of *Cheiloceras curvispina*	(base of *Cheiloceras* Major Zone) (also entry of *Cyrtiopsis*)
	FRASNIAN	Frasn		Zone of *Pharciceras lunulicista*	(base of *Manticoceras* Major Zone) (= base of Assisse de Frome-lennes) (approx. = base of *Asterolepis radiata* Zone)
	GIVETIAN	Givet		Zone of *Cabrieroceras crispiforme*	(base of *Maenioceras* Major Zone)
	EIFELIAN	Eifel		Zone of *Anarcestes lateseptatus*	(base of *Anarcestes* Major Zone) (i.e. top of Komdel Group, Heisdorfer Schichten, and Zlichov Limestone—boundary 'c' of 2nd Siluro/Devon report to Int. Comm. on Strat.)
	EMSIAN	Ems		Zone of *Mimagoniatites zorgensis*	
	SIEGENIAN	Siegen		Zone of *Acrospirifer primaevus*	(= base of *Acrospirifer pellico* Zone)
	GEDINNIAN	Gedinn		Zone of *Monograptus uniformis*	(approx. base of *Pteraspis (Althaspis) leachi* Zone)
SILURIAN	LUDLOVIAN	Ludl		Zone of *Monograptus deubeli* (Jaeger 1962)	
	WENLOCKIAN	Wenl		Zone of *Cyrtograptus murchisoni*	
	LLANDOVERIAN	Lldov		Zone of *Glyptograptus persculptus*	

8

ORDOVICIAN	ASHGILLIAN	Ashg	(Richmond)	Zone of Dicellograptus complanatus	
	CARADOCIAN	Carad	(Porterfield, Trenton, Eden, Maysville)	Zone of Nemagraptus gracilis	
	LLANDEILIAN	Lldeil		Zone of Glyptograptus teretiusculus	
	LLANVIRNIAN	Llvirn	(Lower Champlainian)	Zone of Didymograptus bifidus	
	ARENIGIAN	Arenig	(Upper Canadian)	Zone of Didymograptus deflexus	(base of original *extensus* Zone of Britain; see also D. E. Jackson 1964, *Bull. Geol. Soc. Amer.* **75**, 523)
	TREMADOCIAN	Tremad		Zone of Dictyonema flabelliforme	
CAMBRIAN	UPPER CAMBRIAN	U. Camb		Zone of Agnostus pisiformis	
	MIDDLE CAMBRIAN	M. Camb		Zone of Paradoxides insularis	(Probably lower than base of *harknessi* Zone)
	LOWER CAMBRIAN	L. Camb		'Zone of Obolella'	(*Olenellus* Subzone thought to be later)
PRE-CAMBRIAN	VARANGIAN	Varang		Base of Tillite-bearing beds in Varanger Fjord	
	PRE-VARANGIAN	Pre-Var		Radiometric date where possible	

of epoch/series (such as the Middle Jurassic) has been avoided by their almost complete omission.

Pre-Cambrian. It was thought practicable to distinguish only the very latest Pre-Cambrian (as Varangian). In the form Varegian this is already used by the Swedish Geological Survey and represents the Period from the onset of the Varangian glaciation in Varangeren, N. Norway, to the base of the Cambrian.

Cambrian. The base of the Cambrian has not been agreed but was drawn to include everything normally placed in the Lower Cambrian. Sub-division of the Cambrian beyond the three-fold grouping of Lower, Middle and Upper was thought desirable but could not be agreed. A scheme for this was submitted later by some contributors and appears in Part II, Chapter 18.

Carboniferous. The use of some Russian marine divisions was accepted because of the fragmentary nature of the marine evidence in Western Europe (even in Spain) and in North America, and because of the need of a succession through into full-marine Permian. Definitions of these divisions were only left in terms of benthonic foraminifera because the cephalopods are still so little known.

Permian. Every attempt was made to use successive divisions in a geographical 'chain'; where the published Eurasian data proved inadequate two American divisions were inserted.

Triassic. Our scale was fixed before the ambiguities in the use of the stages Olenekian and Induan were fully appreciated. As it is, these two divisions of the lower Trias are used according to Kiparisova & Popov (1956 and 1961, *not* 1964). A little later the scheme of Tozer (1965) with Griesbachian, Dienerian, Smithian and Spathian would have been considered.

The correlation of the continental Trias with the marine sequence conforms to that given by C. B. Cox (see p. 77). This procedure has been agreed by the relevant contributors (Chapter 28: A. J. C., C. B. C., L. B. H. T.), except that the Ischigualasto Formation is considered Ladinian by one author (A. J. C.).

Jurassic. The names of divisions follow Arkell (1956) except for the last which is expressed as 'Tithonian' to draw attention to the difficulty of selection and definition. Fossils from the Lithographic Stone of Solenhofen contribute significantly to the record and their age has been adopted as 'Tithonian'.

Tertiary. Although the various European stage-names such as Aquitanian have long been used, they are inherently unsatisfactory owing to restricted facies, gaps and overlaps. It was decided, without adopting stage-names, to define familiar divisions from planktonic foraminifera which can be used in ocean areas as well as in most of the epicontinental basins, although their acceptance for this purpose is not yet universal. Baltic Amber, while mostly occurring in Quaternary deposits, has been somewhat arbitrarily taken as derived from Oligocene (possibly Upper Eocene) deposits.

The following have very kindly assisted the Editorial Sub-Committee in refining the scale, in writing or in discussion: C. G. Adams, D. V. Ager, D. J. Carter, C. B. Cox, J. W. Cowie, J. L. Cutbill, F. E. Eames and colleagues, E. H.

Francis, R. Goldring, J. M. Hancock, F. Hodson, M. K. Howarth, A. J. Rowell, W. D. I. Rolfe, D. E. Russell, D. Skevington, D. B. Smith, I. Strachan, J. T. Temple, E. T. Tozer. The members of the Editorial Sub-Committee, however, are alone responsible for the scale in use.

Index

The possibility of indexing all taxa was precluded by the necessary labour and cost. It was nevertheless thought useful to have a short index of a general nature. This includes entries for authors and contributors, some of whose work is scattered through the volume. The other main body of entries refers to selected taxa in their anglicized form. These are designed to help the non-specialist find the required entries in the volume. It is assumed that the specialist will find his way about the systematic part even if he is in disagreement with the classification adopted. Page references are given to the relevant paper or chapters and not to every mention. Some entries to groups of organisms of undoubted antiquity which are not documented in the volume are included with the words 'not recorded here', to save further search.

THE EDITORS

W. B. Harland, M.A. F.R.A.S. SEC.G.S.
Department of Geology, Sedgwick Museum, Downing Street, Cambridge.

[Professor] C. H. Holland, PH.D. F.G.S.
Department of Geology, Trinity College, Dublin 2, Ireland;
(formerly) Bedford College, Regents Park, London N W 1.

[Professor] M. R. House, M.A. PH.D. F.G.S.
Department of Geology, The University, Hull, Yorkshire;
(formerly) Department of Geology and Mineralogy, Parks Road, Oxford.

N. F. Hughes, M.A. F.G.S.
Department of Geology, Sedgwick Museum, Downing Street, Cambridge.

Ailsa B. Reynolds, B.SC.
Department of Geology, Sedgwick Museum, Downing Street, Cambridge.

M. J. S. Rudwick, M.A. PH.D. F.G.S.
Whipple Museum of the History of Science, Free School Lane, Cambridge;
(formerly) Department of Geology, Sedgwick Museum, Downing Street, Cambridge.

G. E. Satterthwaite, F.R.A.S.
Executive Secretary and Editor, Geological Society of London, Burlington House, Piccadilly, London W 1.

L. B. H. Tarlo, D.SC. PH.D. F.L.S. F.A.Z. F.G.S.
Department of Geology, The University, Reading.

E. C. Willey, B.SC. PH.D. F.G.S.
Department of Geology, University of New England, Armidale, New South Wales, Australia;
(formerly) Department of Geology, Sedgwick Museum, Downing Street, Cambridge.

The symposium meeting

The meeting was organized jointly by the GEOLOGICAL SOCIETY OF LONDON and the PALAEONTOLOGICAL ASSOCIATION, and was held at The University College of Swansea on Monday and Tuesday, 20 & 21 December, 1965 by kind invitation of Professor F. H. T. RHODES, Head of the Department of Geology.

First Session (20 December, 9 a.m. to 1 p.m.)

Professor F. W. SHOTTON, M.B.E. M.A. SC.D. F.R.S., President of the Geological Society, in the Chair.

A welcome on behalf of Professor F. H. T. Rhodes was given by Dr B. Simpson, and some explanatory remarks about the symposium meeting and the volume were made by Mr W. B. Harland.

Paper: *Pre-Cambrian life and the base of the Cambrian*, by Dr J. W. Cowie.

Discussion: Dr T. P. Burnaby, Dr J. W. Cowie, Professor P. C. Sylvester-Bradley. [This paper replaces one which the late Professor W. F. Whittard had agreed to give, before his illness.]

Paper: *The significance of certain trace fossil ranges*, by Dr R. Goldring.

Paper: *Computer analysis of the fossil record*, by Dr J. L. Cutbill and Dr B. M. Funnell.

Discussion: Dr D. V. Ager*, Dr J. L. Cutbill, Dr B. M. Funnell, Mr N. F. Hughes*, Dr P. A. Sabine, Professor F. W. Shotton*, Dr V. G. Walmsley*.

[The paper appearing as Part III of this volume is based on all the data published in Part II, much of which was not available at the time of the meeting when the principles were explained and comments made on a preliminary analysis. The discussion is printed in General Discussion at the end of Part I.]

Paper: *Lower Palaeozoic appearances*, by Dr M. R. House.

Discussion: Dr C. G. Adams, Dr J. W. Cowie, Dr R. A. Crowson*, Dr M. R. House*, Professor F. W. Shotton.

Short contribution: *The origins of some Silurian enteletacean brachiopods*, by Dr V. G. Walmsley.

Discussion: Dr C. G. Adams, Dr D. V. Ager, Dr R. A. Crowson, Dr J. L. Cutbill, Dr B. M. Funnell, Dr J. M. Hancock*, Dr A. Hallam*, Dr M. R. House, Dr J. D. Hudson*, Mr N. F. Hughes, Dr G. A. L. Johnson*, Dr K. A. Joysey, Dr G. Larwood*, Dr W. S. McKerrow, Dr Anderson, Dr M. J. S. Rudwick, Professor A. Seilacher, Dr L. B. H. Tarlo.

[Discussion by Dr Johnson is printed after the paper by Dr House, by Dr Hudson after that by Professor Rhodes, by Dr Larwood after that by Dr Hancock, by Dr Hallam after that by Dr Tarlo and by Dr Hancock in General Discussion.]

---

* Discussion printed.

Second Session (20 December, 2.30 to 6 p.m.)

Dr W. S. McKerrow, Vice-President of the Palaeontological Association, in the Chair.

Paper: *Permian–Triassic changes*, by Professor F. H. T. Rhodes (read by Dr M. J. S. Rudwick).

Paper: *Triassic–Jurassic vertebrate changes*, by Dr C. B. Cox.

Discussion: Dr D. V. Ager*, Dr R. A. Crowson*, Dr J. L. Cutbill, Dr J. M. Hancock*, Dr M. J. S. Rudwick, Dr L. B. H. Tarlo*. [Discussion by Dr Ager, Dr Crowson and Dr Hancock is printed after the paper by Professor Rhodes.]

Paper: *Cretaceous–Tertiary marine faunal changes*, by Dr J. M. Hancock.

Discussion: Professor P. Brönimann*, Dr F. E. Eames, Dr. J M. Hancock*, Professor P. C. Sylvester-Bradley.

Short contribution: *Major features of the evolution of echinoids*, by Dr G. M. Philip.

Short contribution: *Taxonomic rates of evolution in the small Foraminifera* (*Globigerinacea excepted*), by Dr. A. J. Lloyd.

Discussion: Dr J. C. W. Cope*, Dr C. B. Cox*, Dr R. A. Crowson, Dr F. E. Eames, Dr A. Hallam, Dr K. A. Joysey, Dr K. A. Kermack*, Dr W. S. McKerrow*, Professor A. Seilacher, Professor P. C. Sylvester-Bradley, Dr L. B. H. Tarlo*.

[Discussion by Dr Cope, Dr Cox, Dr Kermack, Dr McKerrow and Dr Tarlo is printed after the paper by Dr Cox.]

Third Session (21 December, 9 a.m. to 1 p.m.)

Professor F. W. Shotton in the Chair.

[The session opened with a short business meeting of the Geological Society.]

Paper: *Plant–insect relationships*, by Mr N. F. Hughes and Dr J. Smart.

Discussion: Dr R. A. Crowson*, Dr J. M. Hancock*, Mr N. F. Hughes*, Dr W. S. Lacey*, Professor F. W. Shotton, Dr J. Smart*, Dr N. Spjeldnaes*, Dr R. J. Wootton*.

Paper: *Biochemical evolution and the fossil record*, by Dr L. B. H. Tarlo.

Discussion: Dr T. P. Burnaby*, Dr R. A. Crowson*, Dr J. D. Hudson*, Mrs E. M. Jope*, Professor E. M. Jope*, Dr J. Smart, Professor P. C. Sylvester-Bradley, Dr L. B. H. Tarlo*, Dr V. G. Walmsley*, Dr R. J. Wootton.

Part I
Symposium papers

Introduction to Part I

The order of the Symposium Meeting at Swansea is outlined above (pp. 13–14). This Part contains the papers presented there (except that in Part III), and such discussion as was subsequently submitted in writing. Because the written record was incomplete it has been rearranged for the convenience of readers. Mr James Fisher was unable to present his paper at the meeting but it is printed here.

Life in Pre-Cambrian and early Cambrian times

JOHN WATSON COWIE

CONTENTS

SUMMARY

Physical and chemical conditions which could have favoured the origin of life on Earth are briefly discussed, together with the evidence of the geological record. Free oxygen may be of critical importance as a factor in the early evolution of life. Recent studies of the occurrence of biogenic materials and the micropalaeontology of ancient rocks have led to striking advances in knowledge of Pre-Cambrian life. Plants and protistids are the oldest known fossils. Pre-Cambrian fossil protozoans and most metazoans are the subject of dispute. The remarkable fauna from Ediacara is partly metazoan, but the age may be Cambrian or Pre-Cambrian. Aspects of the problem of the base of the Cambrian System are discussed and the earliest Cambrian taxa are listed. Selected theories which attempt to explain the manner of appearance and character of the early Cambrian fauna are reviewed in a brief conspectus.

1. Introduction

The Pre-Cambrian and Cambrian rocks, and the evidence of life that they contain, present two problems of great interest to palaeontologists and non-palaeontologists alike: the origin of life and the origin of the early Cambrian fauna. Professor Whittard had to cancel his lecture on these topics to the symposium meeting on 'The Fossil Record' due to the illness which had also prevented him from preparing a manuscript or notes. I was invited by the symposium organizers to prepare a lecture and this article: the sole responsibility for both must remain with me (the note in *Proc. geol. Soc. Lond.* 1630, p. 40, was incorrect in this respect). It was my hope that Professor Whittard would be able to criticize the manuscript, but this was prevented by his death; I should like to express my gratitude for all the help he gave me during the last twenty years, as he did for so many others.

The Fossil Record, pp. 17–35. Geological Society of London, 1967. Printed in Northern Ireland.

W. T. Dean, S. C. Matthews, J. W. Murray and R. J. G. Savage kindly read and criticized the manuscript.

2. The origin of life

A starting point of modern scientific discussion on the origin of life is that it was of necessity preceded by geochemical evolution and that biological and chemical evolution were complementary and interwoven. Extra-terrestrial origin of life is left aside here but may gain further support from continuing research on biological material in meteorites or, conceivably, by direct examination of other parts of the solar system. The possibility that meteorites, or at least some of them, represent returning terrestrial matter cannot be excluded (Urey 1966). The emergence of the biosphere was related to the emergence of appropriate quantities of the right organic compounds in a suitable environment of the lithosphere, hydrosphere and atmosphere. Life may be considered to be an inevitable process; bound to appear wherever and whenever conditions are favourable. Whittard (1953, pp. 299–301) discussed the application of Milne's cosmological theory by Haldane to the enigma of the earliest fossils. Whittard's cautious remark that "the danger lies in the possibility that the model is wrong" was amply justified because later he was informed by Professor M. H. L. Pryce, physicist, of an arithmetical error in Milne's theory which made it untenable (Whittard, *verb. comm.*). It is nowadays often postulated that the Earth formed initially as a cold body by accretion and that it has subsequently been heating up as a result of internal radioactive decay and gravitational compression. Uffen (1963, pp. 143–4) suggested that the thermal history of the Earth has determined the origin and development of the Earth's core which could have been a major factor in biological evolution through its control of the main geomagnetic field and consequently of the charged particles which have been able to reach the Earth. If the magnetic field intensity was reduced to zero during geological history then the 'solar wind' of ionizing radiation would have been able to bathe the Earth, exerting a major influence in the evolution of life.

Another limiting environmental factor for the origin and suvival of life is the temperature range. Variations in solar heat radiation may have occurred in the past. Cyclical changes in the sun may have caused fluctuations and an overall rise in the mean earth temperature so that refrigeration prevented life processes before 3000 m.y. ago (Öpik 1958). The Sun's radiation could also have been reduced, and cloud cover increased, by volcanic dust (Wexler 1952). Geologists commonly assume little variation in the mean temperature at the surface or outer part of the earth in the last 3000 m.y. (Rutten 1962, 120–122). The geological record is equivocal and there seems little over-all support for colder conditions in the earlier part of the Pre-Cambrian than in the later. The evidence of palaeomagnetic observations, suggests, however, that the Varangian (late Pre-Cambrian) glaciation extended into equatorial latitudes and may have been more severe than later ice ages (Harland & Rudwick 1964; Öpik 1958). The complex heat balance of the whole earth, including the atmosphere and hydrosphere, has various feed-back mechanisms (Rutten 1962, pp. 122–124) making for stability and perhaps there has been little change in the average surface temperature since well before the origin of life.

The earliest atmosphere probably escaped in part from the Earth's gravitational field and this is indicated by the impoverishment of the proportions of the inert gases (Brown 1952; Fesenkov 1960). Slightly later, major contributions to the primeval atmosphere came ultimately from within the Earth—the phenomenon of 'out-gassing'. Thus the atmosphere and oceanic water may have escaped from the Earth's interior. Theory suggests that the primeval atmosphere contained methane, ammonia, hydrogen and water vapour, whilst carbon dioxide and nitrogen were also present in increasing percentages as time passed. An analogy can be made with the present atmosphere of the major planets. An indication of the existence of some of these substances in the past is suggested by the contents of cavities in crystals. Some of these cavities contain trapped fluids such as water, methane and ethane.

The Earth is distinguished from other planets by its content of free oxygen. The absence of free oxygen from volcanic gases today seems to support the theory that the present free oxygen in the atmosphere did not escape from the interior of the Earth and the element was not present in the primeval atmosphere, only being found at that time in a combined state within the Earth. Free oxygen may have begun to be an atmospheric constituent about 3000 m.y. ago and be largely biological in origin, due directly or indirectly to photosynthesis. In the primeval reducing atmosphere ultraviolet radiation may have acted on carbon dioxide to liberate free oxygen and carbon; this abiogenic process is not operative now due to the subsequent development of an ozone envelope shielding the Earth's surface from the solar ultraviolet radiation. Biogenesis is the hypothesis that living matter arises always from living matter (Oxford Dictionary) and biogenic and abiogenic are used here in a similar sense. This is contrary to Rutten's usage of 'biogenesis' (Rutten 1962, p. 127). Bernal (1960, p. 31) favoured the term biopoesis for life-making. Urey has shown that oxygen production by photodissociation eventually inhibits itself as the oxygen formed prevents penetration of further ultraviolet radiation. This supports the suggestion that free oxygen is largely biogenic. Other sources of free oxygen could have been through the precipitation in water of calcium carbonate and by green plant photosynthesis. Urey (1952B) concluded that if the earth had a primitive reducing atmosphere then organic compounds would have been synthesized in this atmosphere by ultraviolet radiation and electrical discharges. Laboratory experiments by Calvin, Miller, Fox and others support Urey's theories. Model primitive atmospheric gas mixes (CH_4, NH_3, H_2 and H_2O) were subjected either to electron bombardment in a particle accelerator or to electrical discharges, producing amino-acids and simple proteins. Amino-acids can be polymerized to more complex molecules by ultraviolet radiation on a clay base. [These experiments have been reviewed: (Miller & Urey 1959; Horowitz & Miller 1962).] The first steps necessary for the origin of life are now understood experimentally to some degree but many difficult problems remain. The origin of life seems to require a primeval atmosphere with prevailing anoxygenic conditions to avoid dissipation by oxidation of essential life components such as amino-acids and to allow the accumulation of complex organic compounds by abiogenic mechanisms. Evolution from non-living to living is often considered to be inoperative today.

Multiple and repeated origination of life in the past is a theoretical possibility and offers alternative starting points for evolution which may then have been partly parallel and not directly related (Whittard 1953, p. 301) instead of following a dendritic course as is frequently assumed. With more than one time for the origin of life the complete extinction of life could have been followed by a new origin. If repeated extinctions at intervals in Pre-Cambrian times were due to radical geophysical/geochemical changes which caused conditions inimical to life to prevail for a time, then the successive reinstatements of life on a similar course could have occurred because of the continued existence of uniformitarian physico-chemical laws. The existence of a number of fundamental features common to all life on Earth suggests a common origin and there seems on biological grounds to be little demand for more than one origin. The molecular biological evidence of ubiquitous primary structures associated with photosynthesis supports a common, single origin (Echlin 1966).

Physical requirements for the origin of life may be summarized as:

(1) Solar radiation with a wide frequency spectrum at the Earth's surface, including at that time radiation which is now cut off.

(2) Ultraviolet and high-energy radiation or electrical discharges to act on the gases of the primeval reducing atmosphere (CH_4, NH_3, H_2, H_2O, CO_2, N).

(3) The presence of a body of liquid water—sea or lake—probably sheltered and shallow (Miller 1964).

According to Berkner & Marshall (1965) organic compounds synthesized by ultraviolet radiation could have been moved downwards away from ultraviolet damage into regions at depths below about 35 ft where eventually organisms could have formed in visible but non-lethal solar radiation; water would be a suitable shield. Oparin (1960, p. 170) looked for a site where an evolving multi-molecular organic system was separated from its environment by a distinct boundary but could constantly interact with the external environment in the manner of open systems, thus overcoming the difficulty of concentration in a simple liquid medium. By analogy with present day protoplasm which possesses a coacervate structure he postulated coacervate drops as the starting site for the evolution leading to the origin of life. Coacervate drops could fit the aqueous setting at Bernal's suggested locus (1961) of surface-active foam on estuarine muds. The organic molecules could have been sited on templates of platy clay minerals in a regular manner; the clay (? montmorillonite) would have acted as an inorganic catalyst performing the function later carried out by enzymes. Alternatively the absorption of these primary molecules might have occurred on finely-divided quartz which, like living matter, is optically active and asymmetric in structure. Reid (1960, pp. 189–95), however, stresses the important role of sulphur in primitive life.

In all these fields of speculation there is, of course, room for considerable disagreement, and Hinton & Blum (1965) suggested that the first life compounds were synthesized in the atmosphere and then fell into the sea and on to the land. On dry land the organic materials collected in crevices which alternately were wetted and dried out, and there would have been insulated against ultraviolet and high-energy radiation. During periods of dehydration the compounds could have been blown about varying the proportions in the niches giving a far greater variety of reacting systems than would be possible in a continuously wet environment.

The transition, presumably gradual, from a primeval reducing atmosphere to the present atmospheric constitution, with 21% of free oxygen, must, it seems, be closely correlated with the evolution of the metabolism of most forms of life. Berkner & Marshall (1965) calculated that oxygen in the primitive atmosphere about 3000 m.y. ago was about 0·1% of the present concentration. Mainly through photosynthesis the percentage of oxygen could have slowly increased to the 'Pasteur Point' of 1% of present atmospheric concentration allowing the evolution of respiration as a major biological advance. This may have occurred between 1000 and 600 m.y. ago. The Pasteur Point is considered to be the first critical level at which life was still confined to the water but could have survived at very shallow depths because ultraviolet radiation was then largely absorbed by atmospheric oxygen and ozone. Life could then have spread to the surface of the oceans. The accession of oxygen to the atmosphere probably reached its present level with the development of photosynthesizing land floras about 400–450 m.y. ago. The incoming of an oxygenic atmosphere may be recorded by rocks. 'Red beds' may, by their content of iron in a high oxidation state, indicate an oxygenic atmosphere, and they are apparently found only in the late Pre-Cambrian rocks, approximately 1000 m.y. or less in age. With the incoming of oxygen and a decrease in the amount of carbon dioxide an acceleration of precipitation of calcium carbonate may have accounted for the apparent increase in the occurrence of limestone and dolomite in Pre-Cambrian times later than about 1200 m.y.

3. Evidence of life in Pre-Cambrian times

The search for fossils in Pre-Cambrian rocks has been prolonged and probably quite intensive in some areas with the incentive to field investigators that any vestige of evidence may be an important discovery. It seems possible, however, that further intensive searching by skilled and experienced fossil-collectors might produce new worth-while evidence. The factual basis for the existence of life in Pre-Cambrian times has been reviewed a number of times over the past decades and will not be examined in detail here. The most significant contributions have been made by Raymond (1935, 1947), Whittard (1953), Schindewolf (1956), Seilacher (1956), Wilson (1957), Shevyrev (1962), Müller (1964) and Glaessner (1962, 1965, 1966). From these summaries and discussions, based on the great and constantly growing number of scattered records, there is strong factual support for the belief that life existed on earth at least 3000 m.y. ago and increased in complexity and variety until the latest Pre-Cambrian times when metazoan faunas appeared. The criteria for the recognition of Pre-Cambrian fossils, or trace-fossils, are diverse; the rigorous position restated by Cloud (1965) is perhaps less in favour today ". . . in considering what we may accept as unequivocal Precambrian fossils, the crucial point is not whether materials observed might conceivably be of vital origin, [but] whether they could have been produced by non-vital processes . . .".

(A) BIOGENIC MATERIALS IN ANCIENT ROCKS

The search in rocks and fossils of all ages for substances which were derived from, or contributed to, life processes has recently been proceeding at an accelerating rate. The studies initiated by Abelson and others on relict amino-acids do not appear, as yet, to have contributed directly as evidence for Pre-Cambrian and early Cambrian life. It is important to bear in mind that not all complex organic materials and naturally-occurring hydrocarbons found in rocks are necessarily biogenic (Sylvester-Bradley 1964; Ponnamperuma & Pering 1966).

Saturated hydrocarbons—alkanes—with a general formula C_nH_{2n+2} (methane, CH_4, is the simplest) have been found in the Pre-Cambrian Soudan Formation of Minnesota (Meinschein 1965) which is thought to be 2700 m.y. old, and in the Gunflint Formation of Ontario—1900 m.y. old. These substances can be interpreted as chlorophyll-degradation products but are also present in bacteria and animals (Cloud & Hagen 1965). Chlorophyll may break down into porphyrins (Sylvester-Bradley 1964, p. 39) which are readily recognized by their optical characteristics and have been found in ancient rocks. Outstanding contributions to this topic in the last few years include that by Barghoorn *et al.* (1965) on the palaeobiology of the Pre-Cambrian Nonesuch Shale from Michigan which has been dated as 1000 m.y. old and contains indigenous porphyrins produced by primary photosynthetic processes. This is a continuation of earlier work (Meinschein *et al.* 1964) on microfossils, porphyrins and optically active alkanes from the same formation.

Variation of the ratio of carbon isotopes $^{12}C/^{13}C$ has been considered to differentiate biogenic from abiogenic materials (Rankama 1948; Whittard 1953) but in a recent reappraisal Sylvester-Bradley (1964, 39–40) suggested that no clear-cut distinction can be made with carbon isotope ratios. This is in opposition to the views of Silverman (1964) and others.

(B) MICROPALAEONTOLOGY

At the most primitive level the distinctions between living and non-living may be somewhat artificial, but Hedgpeth (1964, p. 11) suggests that the first step across the boundary could have been analogous to the addition of one more grain to a supersaturated mixture. Life in Pre-Cambrian and early Cambrian times could have gradually evolved in biochemistry, symmetry, ethology and ecology. Biochemical evolution was, no doubt, expressed by changes in soft tissue followed by mineral-trapping (e.g. algal stromatolites), tissue-mineralization and eventually into Cambrian and later times by successively chitinous, chitino-phosphatic, calcareous and siliceous skeletal mineralization. Evolution in symmetry perhaps progressed from a centre implying no locomotion to an axis and eventually to bilateral symmetry with mobility (e.g. trilobites). New basic symmetries could have been associated with diversification into new habitats and ways of life.

Until recently, reports of finds of bacteria in Pre-Cambrian rocks were received with scepticism; examples were Cayeux's claims from Brittany and Walcott's from North America. In the last decade better evidence resulting from the use of modern technical equipment has been brought forward. Dombrowski (1963) reported that he had restored bacteria from suspended animation in Pre-Cambrian salt. Evidence of organisms from South Africa, like rod-shaped bacteria and measuring half a micron, was reported by Barghoorn to the annual meeting in 1965 of the Geological Society of America. The age was given as about 3000 m.y. old. The best authenticated Pre-Cambrian microfossils, amongst the oldest known preserved structural evidence of life, have been obtained from the Gunflint Formation black cherts of the iron ore series of southern Ontario. These were first described in modern terms by Tyler & Barghoorn (1954) and there have been later contributions by these authors and others, including Cloud (1965). Both optical and electron microscopy have been used to study these minute (*c.* 1μ) but well-preserved rod-shaped, coccoid, filamentous and spheroidal members of an assemblage which shows affinities with bacteria, fungi and blue-green algae or has no living counterpart. The mean age-determination is 1900 m.y. Many pitfalls attend an investigation involving the application of delicate and complicated techniques to microfossils of this size (Cloud & Hagen 1965, p. 2) and contaminants have been detected in some preparations. The question of contamination in micropalaeontology is pressing and critical, due to the scale of study and the universal presence of micro-organisms in unsterilized terrestrial environments accessible to man: 'sterile' has a very strict meaning in this context, where suspended animation under hostile conditions is a distinct possibility. Research on amino-acids in material extracted from carbonaceous meteorites has led in turn to needed research on the organic content of fingerprints and dust. The implications of this fossil evidence with regard to the availability and importance of oxygen and of other chemical and physical factors is of great interest. No conclusive answer seems to be available yet; Cloud (1965) reiterated the idea that photosynthetic oxygen may have had local effects before becoming a major atmospheric gas. These localized conditions could span the time of Gunflint Formation microfossils (1700–2100 m.y.). If these microfossils include photosynthetic blue-green algae and filamentous organisms (comparable with bacteria and fungi) then perhaps the latter were non-photosynthetic. They all perhaps lived in a loose cellular association which has modern analogies and also has homologies with actual symbiotic relationships between blue-green algae and other organisms today (Echlin 1966).

Possible microfossils have been described by Bailey (1964) from chert in the Lower Proterozoic Roraima Formation in British Guiana. Marshall *et al.* (1964) found pockets of minute red or yellow objects, which may be microfossils, from the cement of a Pre-Cambrian quartzite from West Australia. The age of the mineral grains of the quartzite is thought to be at least 2700 m.y. but there is some doubt as to the age of the cement and hence of the microfossils contained in it. Schidlowski (1965) described probable microscopic bacteria and other elements suggesting the existence of unicellular life at the time of formation of gold conglomerates from the Pre-Cambrian Witwatersrand System of South Africa. Well preserved microfossils from chert facies of the Bitter Springs Limestone of Pre-Cambrian age (? 700–900 m.y.) have been interpreted as algal (Barghoorn & Schopf 1965). Solid hydrocarbons found now in cavities in igneous rocks may have been abiogenic and enabled anoxygenic bacteria to release energy and make essential biochemical compounds (Sylvester-Bradley 1964, pp. 37–42; Ponnamperuma & Pering 1966).

(c) STROMATOLITES

Stromatolites and onkolites, which are considered to be biogenic structures and due to algal activity, have been described in considerable numbers from a high percentage of the regions with Pre-Cambrian sediments. According to Glaessner (1965, 1966) collections by Russian geologists from Eurasian measured sections have enabled them to recognize distinctive zonal assemblages in Proterozoic rocks.

Davidson (1964) reported the find by Ramsay of silicified structures, probably algal, from the Fig Tree Series of the Swaziland System which apparently may be as much as 3500 m.y. old. These could be the oldest organic remains. Finely lamellar stromatolites from dolomites of the Bulawayo area of Rhodesia were ascribed to algal activity by MacGregor (1940). The dolomites apparently occur in isolated outcrops resting on metamorphic and igneous rocks. There is some doubt that the stromatolites are of greater age than pegmatites which intrude the sedimentary series and give an isotope date of 2700 m.y. Cloud (1965, p. 7) points out that the dated pegmatites occur over 500 km. away from the stromatolitic structures. Stromatolites of similar age, greater than 2500 m.y., have been described by Joliffe (1955) from Steep Rock Lake in North America. It seems likely that *Corycium enigmaticum* Sederholm is a true fossil and that these coal-bearing sacs in Pre-Cambrian 'varved schists' probably originated from ancient aegragropilous forms of algae preserved as 'lake-balls' (Ohlson 1962). Algal cysts are included in organic remains described by Pflug (1965) from the Beltian rocks of North America. These Pre-Cambrian stromatolites may have been formed by blue-green algae which today, taking the group as a whole, are more resistant to ultra-violet radiation than most other organisms. This would be an advantage in the primeval conditions outlined earlier in this paper. Recent algal colonies of this type cover themselves either by entrapping or secreting calcium carbonate or silica and this mineralization, seen also in Pre-Cambrian species, could have shaded them from the full spectrum of radiation (Echlin 1966). Early Pre-Cambrian algae could probably have tolerated oxygenic or anoxygenic conditions; their ecosystem may have included herbivores but there is no fossil evidence of this.

(D) PROTOZOA

Pre-Cambrian fossil protozoans have been claimed a number of times, recently by Madison (1957) and Pflug (1965), but claims seem so far to have failed to gain acceptance. The latter author assigns organic remains from the Beltian of North America to cysts of flagellates but other objects are only tentatively suggested as foraminiferid. '*Eozoon canadense*' from the Grenville Series of Canada, radiolarians and foraminiferids described by Cayeux from Brittany and by David & Howchin from southern Australia are now usually thought to be inorganic. Chapman's Australian radiolarians seem to be authentic but their Pre-Cambrian age is disputed. Other examples can be criticized on various grounds.

(E) METAZOA

Many of the earlier claims to have recognized Pre-Cambrian metazoan fossils have not been supported in recent reviews and comments. Serious criticisms have been levelled against '*Atikokania*', 'brachiopods' from the U.S.A. and Australia, '*Beltina*', '*Beaumontia*' and '*Protadelaidea*' to quote a few cases; detailed consideration is not attempted here. The criticisms may be palaeontological or stratigraphical; *Xenusion*, possibly a protonychophoran, cannot it seems be proved to be Pre-Cambrian in age; brachiopods from the Vindhyan of India may not be reliably identified, neither is it clear that they come from Pre-Cambrian strata. Claimed worm tracks and remains discovered in the Pre-Cambrian Belt Series of Montana by Walcott (1899) include examples which Seilacher (1956) considered to be reliable; 'medusae' from the Grand Canyon of the U.S.A. may be trace-fossils of filter-feeding benthonic worms (Seilacher 1953, p. 430).

The soft-bodied metazoan fauna from the Pound Quartzite of Ediacara in South Australia has attracted much attention, particularly through the interpretation by Glaessner in the last six years. The fossils include representatives of coelenterates, annelid worms and several unidentified phyla. The horizon yielding the assemblage which has come to be known as the 'Ediacara fauna' lies 100–200 ft below the top of the Pound Quartzite; undoubted Lower Cambrian brachiopods and archaeocyathids are found about 500 ft above the base of the overlying Ajax Limestone. Beds with Lower Cambrian trilobites occur higher still, above the archaeocyathid carbonates (Glaessner 1960). None of these fossil horizons contains any of the Ediacara fauna. When the earliest finds were made by Sprigg the quartzites were considered to be Lower Cambrian. The revised interpretation of the age to late Pre-Cambrian, now promulgated by Glaessner, is based on a number of criteria, including a claim that no known Cambrian fossils have been found in the Ediacara fauna or below it and the claim that no Ediacara fossils occur in the known Cambrian; apparently suitable sedimentary rocks are available at varying stratigraphical levels above and below the Ediacara fauna horizon. In his most recent paper however, Glaessner (1966, p. 43) mentions a form resembling *Discinella*. This genus is widely found in Cambrian rocks and is regarded as having zonal significance in the Lower Cambrian in some areas (Spizharskiy 1963, p. 1368). The claim by Glaessner that no Cambrian fossils have been found in the Ediacara fauna should now be qualified. The Pound Quartzite contains abundant trace-fossils at the same stratigraphical level as the Ediacara fauna and in higher strata: as noted later in this review such tracks, trails and burrows are found in many parts of the world in very late Pre-Cambrian and in early Cambrian beds. The thickness of strata between the horizon of the Ediacara fauna and the first undoubted Lower Cambrian fossils is 600–700 ft and although this may represent a considerable length of time many critics seem to agree that if the Ediacara fauna horizon is not Lower Cambrian then it is probably quite late in the Pre-Cambrian. Elements of the Ediacara fauna are found in rocks of the Nama Series of South West Africa associated with putative archaeocyathids (Haughton 1959) which normally indicate a Lower Cambrian age. Thus the claim mentioned above that no Ediacara fossils occur in the known Cambrian may be open to doubt also. The Nama Series is dated as younger than 590 m.y. (Cloud 1965; Glaessner 1963, p. 119) or is possibly older (Glaessner 1966). Arguments by Glaessner (1965, p. 167) in favour of a late Pre-Cambrian age include, however, the presence of elements of the Ediacara fauna in the Charnian of England (possibly older than 680 m.y.) and in northern Siberia (670 m.y.). If the age of the base of the Cambrian is between 530 and 600 m.y. (570 m.y. in *Geological Society Phanerozoic Time-Scale* 1964: results published since 1964 tend to support this mean date), then these facts suggest but do not prove that the Ediacara fauna was fossilized before the early Cambrian. It can still be maintained, however, that the stocks of some elements of the Ediacara fauna persisted from Pre-Cambrian into Cambrian times and were available for fossilization along with newly-evolved, Cambrian, elements. The ecological and sedimentary conditions for the occurrence and fossilization of this comparatively rich fauna must have been as unusual in the context of these earlier times as the Burgess Shale of British Columbia in Canada was in Middle Cambrian times. Both presumably represent eco-systems which were almost unique. The Burgess Shale fauna, which is being reinvestigated by Whittington, includes Middle Cambrian zonal trilobites and the age of associated unique faunal elements are not in doubt; the absence (in the main anyway) from the Ediacara fauna of faunal elements which are characteristically Lower Cambrian may indicate that the biofacies is even more unusual, rather than that its age is Pre-Cambrian. The stratigraphical position of the Ediacara faunal horizon seems at present to remain ambiguous.

Edgell (1964) described fossils from Western Australia, collected from a Protero-zoic sequence, including possible medusoid impressions in addition to calcareous algal growths. Several of the coelenterate forms show a strong similarity to those from the Ediacara fauna of South Australia and occupy a similar stratigraphical position near the base of the Cambrian.

Frarey & McLaren (1963) published descriptions of relics of tapering, branching tubes which they claimed to represent fossil metazoans from the early Proterozoic of Canada with an age between 1700 and 2500 m.y. A recent find, briefly reported by McNair (1965), was of primitive, thin-shelled brachiopods with other fossil remnants and trace-fossils from the Shaler Group on Victoria Island in arctic Canada. The validity of the fossils is not in dispute but the claimed Pre-Cambrian age based on stratigraphical and isotopic date considerations is apparently being further investigated. The Shaler Group is overlain unconformably by Middle or Late Cambrian rocks and is intruded by gabbroic sills which give a minimum age of about 650 m.y.

(F) TRACE-FOSSILS

Pre-Cambrian trace-fossils, resulting from the activities of organisms, seem to be found in rocks deposited in the later part of Pre-Cambrian times and most frequently in strata which are stratigraphically not far below the base of the Cambrian System (however that may be defined). Further critical study of their palaeontological and stratigraphical significance is required but the impression certainly arises from a general view of the record that there was a striking increase in tracks, trails and other traces of fossils just before the Cambrian period, that these are of metazoan benthonic life, and that earlier Pre-Cambrian life was planktonic (Seilacher 1956). It seems that a soft-bodied benthos existed shortly before the early Cambrian fauna appeared. Conditions in some locales during Pre-Cambrian times may have militated against the preservation of organisms which occupied ecological niches with low fossilization potentials (Goldring 1965). In another part of this volume, which the writer has been able to see before publication by courtesy of the Editors, Goldring has noted the recognition from the upper Pre-Cambrian of Domichnia (dwelling burrows), Fodinichnia (feeding burrows) and Repichnia (crawling trails).

4. Life in early Cambrian times

(A) THE PROBLEM OF THE BASE OF THE CAMBRIAN SYSTEM

Little progress has been made with the problem since the Paris meeting of the Centre National de la Recherche Scientifique in 1957 (Pruvost 1958). In the context of this symposium, discussion of inorganic criteria is inappropriate but even so it is clear that organic criteria may be affected by tectonic, magmatic, sedimentary, climatic, geophysical and geochemical stability or changes, so that all relevant factors are interrelated and multiple techniques may be needed to solve this awkward stratigraphical problem.

The geological column displays many remarkable contrasts between adjacent parts but perhaps the greatest is between Cambrian and Pre-Cambrian. This is especially true in the classic geological areas of parts of Europe and North America but in many regions of the world the only contrast is in palaeobiology. Originally the contrast was thought to be two-fold; the first occurrence of guide faunas which gave wide, even intercontinental, correlations, and of an unconformable overstep of sedimentary rocks on to the eroded surfaces of rocks with higher tectonic grades which were often metamorphosed. The latter unconformities have, however, been shown in certain cases to be diachronic and this is suspected in many others. In major geosynclines either no major angular unconformity can be found at the appropriate level or the unconformity is separated by a great thickness of strata from the first diagnostic Cambrian fossil horizon. There is now no general recognition of a major, ubiquitous tectonic or sedimentational change at the Pre-Cambrian/Cambrian boundary.

The main difficulties in identification of the base of the Cambrian System seem to be: (*i*) general paucity of early Cambrian fossil evidence, (*ii*) absence of late Pre-Cambrian fossils which can be used for correlation, (*iii*) the inadequacy of recorded field evidence and knowledge of zones in many areas, (*iv*) the lack of correlation between different faunal provinces of the Lower Cambrian (Atlantic, Pacific and Oriental).

Identification of a world-wide synchronous discontinuity, marker horizon or faunal zone to signal the time of the start of the Cambrian period may not be possible at the moment. Even the first preserved occurrences of Lower Cambrian type faunas may be diachronous (Spizharskiy 1963). The procedure adopted recently is to relate the lower boundary of the Cambrian to the appearance of fossils of animals with hard skeletal parts such as trilobites, archaeocyathids, brachiopods and hyolithids; the greatest emphasis is placed on the zonal value of trilobites. The assumption is usually made that all these skeleton-bearing organisms emerged more or less simultaneously. Obvious criticisms of this assumption on theoretical grounds may support the suspicion that the appearance of these earliest Cambrian faunas in the stratigraphical record occurred over a span of time. Radiometric dates suggest the span could be from 600 to 530 m.y. (Spizharskiy 1963, p. 1368; Cowie 1964) but margins of error in these dates are great at this level in the geological column. A special problem of pre-Ordovician dates is the unreliability of the K–A method because of the possibility of argon loss. The evidence of the time of arrival of the first diagnostic Lower Cambrian faunas is inadequate at present on the grounds of stratigraphical correlations or on the basis of radiometric dates. Factors, which by their varied time of arrival in an area could cause the first Lower Cambrian zones to be of different dates at different places, may be: (*i*) the onset of favourable environmental conditions associated in some instances with the breakdown of geographical isolation, (*ii*) the evolution by different animal groups of hard skeletal material, (*iii*) inadequacy of the fossil record due to variations in fossilization potential and factors of preservation. Diachronous first appearance of faunal elements was recognized by Palmer (1965) during intensive study of part of the Upper Cambrian in the Great Basin of the western U.S.A. Other faunas of zonal significance are present too which give chronomeric guidance. He proposed the term biomere for "a regional biostratigraphic unit bounded by abrupt non-evolutionary changes in the dominant elements of a single phylum. These changes are not necessarily related to physical discontinuities in the sedimentary record and they are, or may be, diachronous". It may help investigations to consider the applicability of the biomere concept to some, at least, of the earliest Cambrian faunal assemblages. It has been noted earlier that one of the main difficulties in defining the base of the Cambrian is the absence of late Pre-Cambrian fossils which can be used for correlation. Stromatolites are more widely known than any other organic evidence in the Pre-Cambrian but are not at present relied on for interregional correlation. Micropalaeontology may come to fill the need but the most feasible solution would probably be if metazoan fossils could be used. Glaessner (1965) considered the Ediacara fauna to be a distinctive assemblage that precedes the first Cambrian zonal assemblages. Cloud (1965) maintained that the Ediacara fauna is unsuitable because it may be Cambrian in age and he concluded from his studies of Pre-Cambrian fossils that there are as yet no records of unequivocal metazoa in rocks of undoubted Pre-Cambrian age. Cloud defined the base of the Cambrian as the base of the range-zone of metazoa and the top of the Pre-Cambrian as the top of the range-zone of the stromatolite *Conophyton*. This is indeed a useful suggestion but perhaps a definition which placed the base of the Cambrian between two metazoan zones would be of greater utility if it were possible. The raising of the present base to a higher level between better known faunal zones would still leave unsolved problems at the old level, which would continue to demand attention.

(B) THE EARLIEST CAMBRIAN FAUNA

The earliest Cambrian fauna is more restricted than any later one but continues to impress investigators as a spectacular and striking advance on all earlier, Pre-Cambrian, fossil evidence. Rudwick (1964) put forward a most persuasive argument that ".... even if [metazoan] phyla did appear one by one ... these 25–30 m.y. [Lower Cambrian time] must be compared with the subsequent 500–600 m.y. in which their fossil record is almost unbroken, and with the still longer period of Pre-Cambrian time in which their record is virtually non-existent". There is a discernible tendency amongst palaeontologists in recent years, however, to minimize to a certain degree the speed of the evolutionary advance. Lower Cambrian times represent about 30 m.y. (*Geological Society Phanerozoic Time-Scale* 1964) which is equivalent to almost half the duration of the Cainozoic era. In many discussions the whole Lower Cambrian fauna is taken together; in fact different taxa appear at various heights above the base (*vide* this volume). Early Cambrian faunas are much less varied than later faunas, and major taxa which are absent make a list which is comparable with a list of those present. Nevertheless, there are over 900 species of Lower Cambrian metazoan animals described, whereas Pre-Cambrian metazoan fossils are extremely rare and, some would say, non-existent. The first known trilobites, for example, presumably had a considerable length of time to evolve and this stipulation applies to other phyla as well. Nine phyla may be recognized in the Lower Cambrian, but this is not the most significant fact in this discussion: the detailed composition of the earliest Cambrian faunas should be established and the times of arrival of its component members related to one another and to a standard stratigraphical scale monitored by accurate radiometric dating. This is an outstanding challenge to present and future workers on Cambrian palaeontology, stratigraphy and isotopic dating.

Clastic sediments in the earliest beds of the Lower Cambrian contain worm burrows, and other trace-fossils; archaeocyathids are the earliest fossils in carbonate rocks in some regions. Frequently other phyla appear a little later—sponges, molluscs, echinoderms, brachiopods and arthropods. It is, however, not until the middle of the Ordovician period that the majority of animal phyla are present, about 125 m.y. after the start of the Cambrian period. Only three groups are comparatively abundant in the early Lower Cambrian fauna. Shevyrev (1962, p. 1620) gives the following percentages according to types: arthropods 32, archaeocyathids 30, brachiopods 21, molluscs 10, worms 3, sponges 1, echinoderms 1, coelenterates 1, ? protozoa 1. These are represented by only a very small number of species. Except for trilobites and archaeocyathids most early Cambrian fossils are small. The range of habitats was more limited than in later times. The land was probably devoid of animal and plant life although protistids may have colonized it by then; the sea was apparently the dominant aqueous site. As already suggested, most Pre-Cambrian metazoa may have been small, soft-bodied and planktonic. In contrast the larger, but still in the main small, Lower Cambrian metazoa may have been benthonic and many phyla had evolved skeletal mineralization. The fossil records of taxa given elsewhere in this volume may contribute to an understanding of the earliest Cambrian life: the author has had a partial preview by courtesy of the Editors. The following taxa are considered with varying degrees of certainty to occur at, or close to, the base of the Cambrian:

ARTHROPODA—Olenellidae, Daguinaspidae, Redlichiidae, Neoredlichiidae, Saukiandidae, Gigantopygidae, Despujolsiidae, Palaeomeridae.

ARCHAEOCYATHA—Monocyathidae, Cryptoporocyathidae, Bacatocyathidae, Rhizacyathidae, Capsulocyathidae, Uralocyathidae, Dokidocyathidae, Ajacicyathidae, Cyclocyathellidae, Nochoroicyachidae, Coscinocyathidae, Metacyathidae, Syringocnematidae.

BRACHIOPODA—Botsfordiidae, Obolellidae, Paterinidae, Kutorginidae, Yorkiidae.

WORMS—Tubes of sedentarids are known from the Lower Cambrian but some records may belong to other phyla.

PORIFERA—Lyssacinosa, Heteractinida.

(ECHINODERMATA—Helicoplacidae. *Helicoplacus* is in the Lower Cambrian but occurs 2500 ft above the base of the olenellid-bearing strata and is not, therefore, considered by the author to be earliest Cambrian.)

MISCELLANEA—Hyolithida, Coleolidae, Hyolithelminthes.

TRACE-FOSSILS—Pascichnia, Cubichnia, Domichnia, Fodinichnia, Repichnia. As far as I am aware no metazoan taxa are given a range in this volume which extends back into the Pre-Cambrian, except for worms and trace-fossils. This may be because contributors regard most elements of the Ediacara fauna and allied finds as belonging to otherwise unknown taxa.

A significant step in biochemical evolution is shown by the earliest Cambrian fauna, with the acquisition by many phyla of tissue mineralization and the incoming of skeletal hard parts. At first this seems to have been mainly spicules, chitinous and chitino-phosphatic shells or exo-skeletons, but later calcium carbonate became an important skeletal component with a concomitant trend to thickening. This development of heavy shells may have been related to the appearance of predators, as yet unknown in the fossil record, or to size and the need for support.

The many theories which attempt to explain the manner of appearance and character of the early Cambrian fauna will not be pursued *in extenso* here. Views range between two extremes in interpreting the manner of appearance and character *either* as a rapid and radical change (an evolutionary explosion) *or* as a slow and progressive continuation of the normal course of evolution. The most complete summary of hypotheses was given by Shevyrev (1962) and a valuable contribution was later made by Rudwick (1964). The following brief conspectus is drawn from many sources and is classified under three main headings which are not mutually exclusive. It is not intended to suggest that all these hypotheses are considered tenable, they could be partially incompatible. Shevyrev and Rudwick give references to earlier work; they are not detailed here.

(i) *Environmental*
(Including changes in the physico-chemical state of atmosphere and hydrosphere which gave rise to new ecological niches and ethological modes.)

(a) *Climatic change.* Alterations in the heat available occurred through cyclical variation in the sun's radiation. Variation in shield effect due to change in amount of volcanic dust in the atmosphere, water-vapour cover or atmospheric carbon dioxide. These climatic changes caused ice ages which inhibited or terminated the development of life. The evolution of life had to start again after each Pre-Cambrian ice age. The intervals between ice ages were not long enough to allow the higher forms of life to evolve until the general amelioration which occurred in late Pre-Cambrian times after the Varangian glaciation. A universal warming of the climate at the beginning of the Cambrian period allowed undiscovered Pre-Cambrian equatorial invertebrate stock to migrate to middle latitudes where their descendants are now found fossilized in Cambrian strata.

(b) *Atmospheric oxygen.* Due to the primeval anoxygenic atmospheric state, the land and the upper layers of the water masses were subjected to intense ultra-violet radiation. Rise of biogenic oxygen levels to the Pasteur Point made respiration a feasible metabolic process and provided a screen from ultraviolet radiation. This allowed a 'great quantum jump' in evolution (Berkner & Marshall 1965; Fischer 1965). Animals became more widely distributed and were able to exploit previously unoccupied habitats.

(c) *Extension of epicontinental seas.* Late Pre-Cambrian sedimentary rocks are varied and lacking in abnormalities; they are comparable with their Phanerozoic equivalents. The main faunas of Pre-Cambrian marine fossils will only be found in strata beneath the ocean floors of today, below the Upper Cretaceous rocks which are the oldest series exposed; submarine geological research will provide the evidence. The stock which gave rise to the early Cambrian fauna evolved in late Pre-Cambrian times in small confined regions and only gradually extended its range: this stock has not been discovered. Early Cambrian marine transgressions offered the first opportunity to Pre-Cambrian life, previously confined to deep water, to expand into virgin marine environments with a concomitant accelerated proliferation of new species. This universal transgression was due to eustatic change at the end of the widespread late Pre-Cambrian ice age which terminated perhaps not unduly long before the beginning of the Cambrian period.

(d) *Fossilization potential.* The immediate ancestors of Cambrian metazoa lived in coastal sites or other environments which are not represented among Pre-Cambrian sediments because of the low fossilization potential (Goldring 1965) of these sediments. These littoral organisms could not have drifted into a deeper-water environment to become preserved there.

(ii) *Biochemical and physiological evolution*
(Including the incoming of new modes of internal and external skeletal mineralization.)

The simultaneous appearance of organisms in early Cambrian times with skeletons of diverse composition (chitinous, phosphatic, siliceous, calcareous) shows that the advent of the early Cambrian fauna was not due to a major physico-chemical change of the seas. There is no evidence that Pre-Cambrian sea-water was either poor in calcium or acidic and the evidence of stromatolites and thick limestone strata is against these suggestions. The density of carbonate material depends on the Mg/Ca ratio. Pre-Cambrian seas with a high Mg content produced only a soft ooze: early Cambrian seas had a lower Mg content which favoured the availability of hard carbonate material for skeletal formation (Chilinger & Bissell 1963).

Pre-Cambrian animals existed but were exclusively soft-bodied. Late Pre-Cambrian trace-fossils show that more was involved in the origin of the Cambrian fauna than the mere acquisition of preservable skeletons; soft-bodied trilobites or brachiopods never existed—rigid skeletal supports are needed for viable function in these taxa. The threat of newly-evolved predators in early Cambrian times, whose fossil remains have not been discovered, endowed selective benefits on animals with protective hard parts but this does not explain the appearance of taxa with hard parts whose function is support.

After the concentration of free atmospheric oxygen reached the Pasteur Point, animals moved away from close dependence on photosynthesizing plants to new loci of the air-water interface in either deep or shallow water-bodies. Skeletons then originated, partly as a protection against radiation which at the beginning of the Cambrian period still remained at levels inimical to unshielded life near the surface of water (Fischer 1965). Hard parts were a selective advantage as groups made the change from infauna to epifauna with resultant greater need for support and for weight as an anchoring device in current-swept locales. The colonization of the sea-floor by a previously planktonic fauna became desirable in early Cambrian times due to over-population of surface waters; the discovery of the sea bottom and the littoral zone resulted in competitive situations which encouraged secretion of protective calcareous skeletons in a number of taxa.

(iii) *Extra-terrestrial or non-uniformitarian factors*

Alterations occurred in the heat available through cyclical changes in the Sun's radiation. Chemical processes acquired an increased efficiency as an energy source. Increased rates of mutations were caused by intense cosmic radiation associated with extra-terrestrial events.

In the above remarks qualifying phrases have been omitted not only for the sake of brevity but in order to attempt to sharply focus the nature of the theories, without critical comment.

When the great length of time from the first known evidence of plant and bacterial activity at least 3000 m.y. ago to the first metazoan fossils about 600 m.y. ago is considered, it seems very likely that there must have been some inhibiting environmental factor in operation. Evolution under present-day environmental conditions would hardly be expected to be so slow. It can be argued, however, that the earliest steps were the most difficult and required prolonged operation of natural selection of mutational changes. This extended time span between the origin of life and of the early Cambrian fauna is perhaps one of the most remarkable features of the whole problem. Research on the many unsolved problems concerning life in Pre-Cambrian and early Cambrian times will continue to demand the attention of research scientists in many disciplines for some time yet.

References

AXELROD, D. I. 1958. Early Cambrian marine fauna. *Science, N.Y.* **128,** 7–9.

BAILEY, P. B. H. 1964. Possible microfossils found in the Roraima Formation in British Guiana. *Nature, Lond.* **202,** 384.

BARGHOORN, E. S. & SCHOPF, J. W. 1965. Micro-organisms from the Late Precambrian of Central Australia. *Science, N.Y.* **150,** 337–9.

——, MEINSCHEIN, W. G. & SCHOPF, J. W. 1965. Paleobiology of a Precambrian shale. *Science, N.Y.* **148,** 461–72.

BERKNER L. V. & MARSHALL, L. C. 1965. Oxygen and evolution. *New Scient.* **28,** 415–9.

BERNAL, J. D. 1960. The problem of stages in biopoesis *in* Florkin (1960), *q.v.*

BROWN, H. 1952. Rare gases and the formation of the Earth's atmosphere. *In* KUIPER, G. P. (Ed.) *The Atmospheres of the Earth and Planets.* Chicago (University of Chicago Press).

CHILINGER, G. V. & BISSELL, H. J. 1963. Note of possible reason for scarcity of calcareous skeletons of invertebrates in Pre-Cambrian formations. *J. Paleont.* **37,** 942–3.

CLOUD, P. E. 1965. Significance of the Gunflint (Precambrian) microflora. *Science, N.Y.* **148,** 27–35.

—— & HAGEN, H. 1965. Electron microscopy of the Gunflint microflora: preliminary results. *Proc. natn. Acad. Sci. U.S.A.* **54,** 1–8.

COWIE, J. W. 1964. The Cambrian period. *In* HARLAND, W. B. *et al.* (Eds.) *The Phanerozoic Time-Scale. Q. Jl geol. Soc. Lond.* **120s,** 255–8.

DAVIDSON, C. F. 1964. Uniformitarianism and ore genesis. *Min. Mag., Lond.* **109,** 1–12.

DOMBROWSKI, H. 1963. Bacteria from Paleozoic salt deposits. *Ann. N.Y. Acad. Sci.* **108,** 453–60. New York (John Wiley).

ECHLIN, P. 1966. Origins of photosynthesis. *Sci. Jl, Lond.* **2,** 42–7.

EDGELL, H. S. 1964. Precambrian fossils from the Hamersley Range, Western Australia and their use in stratigraphic correlation. *J. geol. Soc. Aust.* **11,** 235–61.

FESENKOV, V. G. 1960. Some considerations on the primaeval state of the earth. In FLORKIN (1960), *q.v.*

FISCHER, A. G. 1965. Fossils, early life and atmospheric history. *Proc. natn. Acad. Sci. U.S.A.* **53,** 1205–15.

FLORKIN, M. (Ed.) 1960. *Aspects of the Origin of Life.* Oxford (Pergamon Press).

FRAREY, M. J. & McLAREN, D. J. 1963. Possible metazoans from the Early Proterozoic of the Canadian Shield. *Nature Lond.* **200,** 461–2.

GLAESSNER, M. F. 1960. Precambrian fossils from South Australia. *Int. geol. Congr.* **21,** (12), 59–64.

——1962. Pre-Cambrian fossils. *Biol. Rev.* **37,** 467–94.

——1963. Zur Kenntnis der Nama-fossilien südwest-Afrikas. *Annln naturh. Mus. Wien* **66,** 113–20.

——1965. Pre-Cambrian life—problems and perspectives. *Proc. geol. Soc. Lond.* no. 1626, 165–9.

——1966. Precambrian palaeontology. *Earth-Sci. Rev., Amsterdam* **1,** 29–50.

GOLDRING, R. 1965. Sediments into rock. *New Scient.* **26,** 863–5.

HARLAND, W. B. & RUDWICK, M. J. S. 1964. The great Infra-Cambrian ice age. *Scient. Am.* **211,** 28–36.

HAUGHTON, S. H. 1959. An archaeocyathid from the Nama System. *Trans. R. Soc. S. Afr.* **36,** 57–9.

HEDGPETH, J. W. 1964. Evolution of community structure. In IMBRIE, J. & NEWELL, N. (Eds) *Approaches to paleoecology.* New York (John Wiley), pp. 11–8.

HINTON, H. E. & BLUM, M. S. 1965. Suspended animation and the origin of life. *New Scient.,* **28,** 270–1.

HOROWITZ, N. H. & MILLER, S. L. 1962. Current theories on the origin of life. *Fortschr. Chem. org. Naturstoffe* **20,** 423.

JOLIFFE, A. W. 1955. Geology and iron ores of Steep Rock Lake. *Econ. Geol.* **50,** 373–98.

MACGREGOR, A. M. 1940. A Precambrian algal limestone in Southern Rhodesia. *Trans. geol. Soc. S. Africa* **43,** 9–15.

MADISON, K. M. 1957. Fossil protozoans from the Keewatin sediments. *Trans. Ill. St. Acad. Sci.* **50,** 287–90.

MARSHALL, C. G. A., MAY, J. W. & PERRET, C. J. 1964. Fossil microorganisms: possible presence in Precambrian shield of Western Australia. *Science, Wash.* **144,** 290–2.

McNAIR, A. H. 1965. Precambrian metazoan fossils from the Shaler Group, Victoria Island, Canadian Archipelago. *Geol. Soc. Amer.,* Program 1965 Annual Meetings, Abstracts, 106.

MEINSCHIEN, W. G., BARGHOORN, E. S. & SCHOPF, J. W. 1964. Biological remnants in a Precambrian sediment. *Science, N.Y.* **145,** 262.

—— 1965. Soudan Formation: organic extracts of early Precambrian rocks. *Science, N.Y.* **150,** 601.

MILLER, S. L. & UREY, H. C. 1959. Organic compound synthesis on the primitive earth. *Science, N.Y.* **130,** 245.

—— 1964. Liquid water and the origin of life. In MILLER, S. L. *et al.* (Eds.) *Isotopic and cosmic chemistry.* Amsterdam (North-Holland).

MÜLLER, A. H. 1964. Die präkambrische Lebewelt, Erscheinungen und Probleme. *Biol. Rdsch.* **2,** 53–67.

OHLSON, B. 1962. Observations on recent lake balls and ancient *Corycium* inclusions in Finland. *Bull. Commn. geol. Finl.* **196,** 377–90.

OPARIN, A. I. 1960. Biochemical processes in the simplest structures In FLORKIN *q.v.*

ÖPIK, E. J. 1958. Climate and the changing sun. *Scient. Am.* June, 3–8.

PALMER, A. R. 1965. Biomere—a new kind of biostratigraphic unit. *J. Paleont.* **39,** 149–53.

PFLUG, H. D. 1965. Organische Reste aus der Belt Serie (Algonkium) von Nordamerika. *Paläont. Z.* **39,** 10–25.

PONNAMPERUMA, C. & PERING, K. 1966. Possible abiogenic origin of some naturally occurring hydrocarbons. *Nature, Lond.* **209,** 979–82.

PRUVOST, P. 1958. *Les relations entre Précambrien et Cambrien. Problèmes de séries intermédiaires.* Colloques Internationaux. Centre National de la Recherche Scientifique (Paris).

RANKAMA, K. 1948. New evidence of the origin of Pre-Cambrian carbon. *Bull. geol. Soc. Am.* **59,** 389–416.

RAYMOND, P. E. 1935. Pre-Cambrian Life. *Bull. geol. Soc. Am.* **46,** 375–92.

—— 1947. *Prehistoric Life.* Cambridge, Mass.

REID, C. 1960. The relation between primitive and present day photobiological processes. In FLORKIN (1960).

RUDWICK, M. J. S. 1964. The Infra-Cambrian glaciation and the origin of the Cambrian fauna. In NAIRN, A. E. M. (Ed.) *Problems in Climatology.* New York (John Wiley), pp. 150–5.

RUTTEN, M. G. 1962. *The geological aspects of the origin of life on Earth.* Amsterdam (Elsevier).

SCHIDLOWSKI, M. 1965. Probable life-forms from the Precambrian of the Witwatersrand System (South Africa). *Nature, Lond.* **205,** 895–6.

SCHINDEWOLF, O. H. 1956. Über präkambrische Fossilien. In *Geotektonisches Symposium zu Ehren von H. Stille,* 455–80. Stuttgart.

SEILACHER, A. 1953. Über die Methoden der Palichnologie. *Neues Jb. Geol. Paläont. (Abh.* and *Mh.)* **96,** 421–52.

—— 1956. Der Beginn des Kambriums als biologische Wende. *Neues Jb. Geol. Paläont. (Abh.* and *Mh.)* **103,** 155–80.

SHEVYREV, A. A. 1962. The problem of the origin of the early Cambrian fauna. *Geol. Rev.* **6,** 1617–29.

SILVERMAN, S. R. 1964. Investigations of petroleum origin and evolution mechanisms by carbon isotope studies. In CRAIG, H. *et al.* (Eds.) *Isotopic and cosmic chemistry,* Amsterdam (North-Holland), pp. 92–102.

SPIZHARSKIY, T. N. 1963. The boundary between Cambrian and Precambrian. *Geol. Rev.* **7,** 1368–73.

SYLVESTER-BRADLEY, P. 1964. The origin of oil—and life. *Discovery, Lond.* May, 37–42.

TYLER, S. A. & BARGHOORN, E. S. 1954. Occurrence of structurally preserved plants in the pre-Cambrian rocks of the Canadian shield. *Science, N.Y.* **119,** 606–8.

UFFEN, R. J. 1963. Influence of the Earth's core on the origin and evolution of life. *Nature, Lond.* **198,** 143–4.

UREY, H. C. 1952A. The planets, their origin and development. New Haven (Yale University Press).

—— 1952B. On the early chemical history of the Earth and the origin of life. *Proc. natn. Acad. Sci. U.S.A.* **38,** 351.

—— 1966. Biological material in meteorites: a review. *Science, N.Y.* **151,** 157–66.

VINOGRADOV, A. P. 1960. The origin of the biosphere. In FLORKIN (1960), *q.v.*

WALCOTT, C. D. 1899. Precambrian fossiliferous formations. *Bull. geol. Soc. Am.* **10,** 199–244.

WEXLER, H. 1952. Volcanoes and world climate. *Scient. Am.* April, 3–5.

WHITTARD, W. F. 1953. The enigma of the earliest fossils. *Proc. Bristol Nat. Soc.* **28,** 289–304.

WILSON, A. E. 1957. Life in the Proterozoic. In GILL, J. E. (Ed.) *The Proterozoic in Canada.* Special Publication no. 2, Royal Society of Canada, pp. 18–27.

Manuscript submitted June 1966.

J. W. Cowie, PH.D. F.G.S.
Department of Geology, The University, Bristol 8.

The significance of certain trace-fossil ranges

ROLAND GOLDRING

TRACE-fossils (ichnofossils; tracks, trails and burrows) are an important constituent of the fossil record, and although their stratigraphical value is limited, they provide a valuable clue to the environments colonized by different groups of organisms and an indication of the various activity patterns formed by benthonic animals.

Seilacher (1956) demonstrated the wealth and diversity of trace-fossils in the Cambrian, compared with their paucity in the Pre-Cambrian, and indeed was able to say that the Cambrian trace-fossil assemblage was no poorer or less diverse than any which may be collected from younger strata of similar facies such as the Swabian Middle Jurassic. There thus appears to have been an explosive evolution at the beginning of the Cambrian which was not restricted only to the trilobites and other groups developing a hard skeleton, but also involved soft-bodied animals. Forms such as *Dictyodora* and *Phycodes*, presumably constructed by some type of worm, exhibit a feeding pattern with a complexity quite unknown in the Pre-Cambrian. Glaessner (1962) criticised Seilacher's findings on three points. Whereas it is true that Seilacher did compare the Pre-Cambrian trace-fossils with those of the Lower and Middle Cambrian, the increase is equally marked if comparison is made only with the Lower Cambrian forms, but not so if comparison is made with the 'lowest' Cambrian where suitable facies are less well developed in the sections at present known. Concerning Glaessner's other points, publication is awaited that will show evidence of a gradational increase in the number and diversity of trace-fossils into the Cambrian. For this volume Seilacher's thesis must be upheld.

Two other aspects of the stratigraphical range of trace-fossils are significant. Firstly, the range of certain trace-fossils differs markedly from the range of the body-fossils inferred to be responsible for their formation, and secondly, where there appears to be change in the sedimentary facies in which the trace-fossils occur through geological time.

Trace fossils occur virtually only in their position of formation, and so these two aspects may provide some further clues as to the environment in which the organisms lived and, possibly, to changes in the environment. Four examples may be considered (Fig. 1.)

1. Trilobite traces are of quite frequent occurrence in the neritic sandy facies of the Lower Palaeozoic (Seilacher 1955, 1962). None have been recorded from the Middle Devonian upwards, although many sandy developments are present, such as the Famennian Psammites du Condroz and their lateral equivalents in north-west Europe, in which trilobite traces might well be expected. One explanation for their absence from this ecological niche in the Upper Palaeozoic

The Fossil Record, pp. 37–39. Geological Society of London, 1967. Printed in Northern Ireland.

4

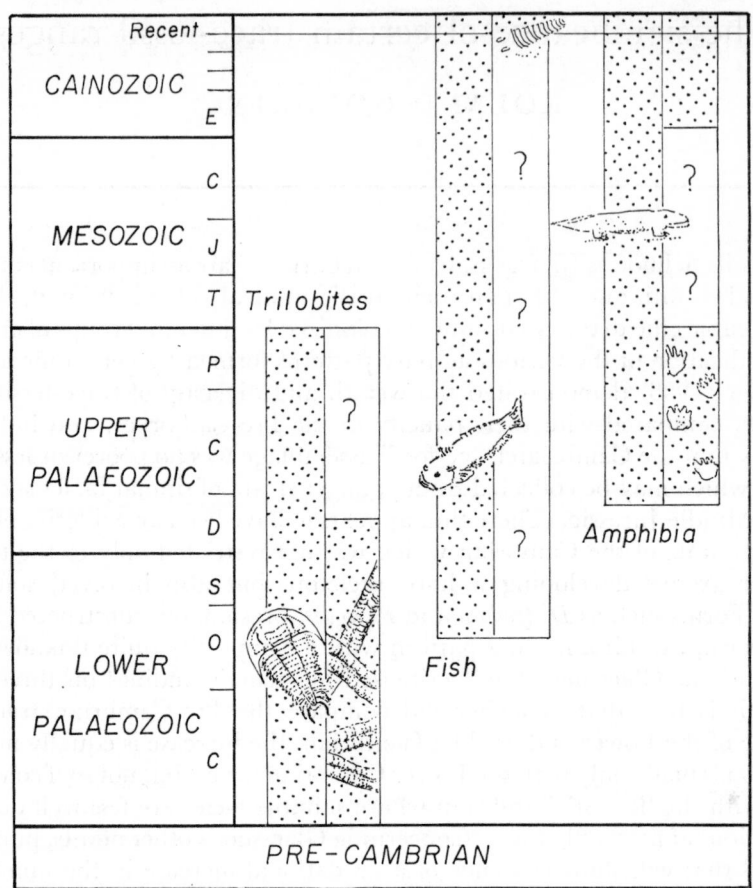

Fig. 1. The range of three groups of trace-fossils compared with the range of the body-fossils inferred to be responsible for their formation.

is that this niche was then scarcely occupied by the trilobites, and was largely vacated by them in the Silurian.

2. Amphibian traces are not infrequent between the Lower Carboniferous and the Triassic, but curiously none have been recorded from the Jurassic or Cretaceous. Again, there is no absence of the facies in which they might have been fossilized if they had continued to move in the same environments as those in which they had moved during the late Palaeozoic and Triassic. This suggests a marked change in the ecological niche occupied by later Palaeozoic amphibia which is well supported by the evidence, sparse though it is, of the body-fossils.

3. Bottom-dwelling demersal fish considerably disturb the sedimentary surface, and something of their activity patterns is known from present-day sediments (Schäfer 1962). Scarcely anything has been recorded of the traces of fossil fish (Goldring, this volume, pp. 622). One explanation for this may be that

the activity traces of fish are frequently too indefinite and irregular for positive determination, but an alternative explanation is that the surfaces on which these fish live have a low fossilization potential and are rarely fossilized. Such an explanation may account for the apparent absence of fish traces from the Lower Devonian, where the ostracoderms, with their presumably sucking mouths, are so important, and the question may be posed whether the sedimentary surfaces on which Old-Red-Sandstone fish lived and fed are ever actually preserved.

4. Limulinid traces are of rather infrequent occurrence, but from the evidence of the trace- and body-fossils it would seem that in the Devonian and Carboniferous they are most characteristic of a non-marine environment (Heide 1951; King 1965). In the Triassic a few species are marine and in younger sediments they appear to have inhabited a brackish or inshore environment (Størmer 1955). The lumulinids thus seem to have changed their environment with time, to some extent.

References

GLAESSNER, M. F. 1962. Pre-Cambrian fossils. *Biol. Rev.* **37,** 467–94, pl. 1.

HEIDE, S. VAN DER. 1951. Les arthropodes du terrain houillier du Limbourg meridional. *Meded. geol. Sticht.* Serie C-IV-3, (5), 1–84.

KING, A. F. 1965. Xiphosurid trails from the Upper Carboniferous of Bude, north Cornwall. *Proc. geol. Soc. Lond.* no. 1626, 162–5.

SCHÄFER, W. 1962. *Aktuo-Paläontologie nach Studien in der Nordsee.* Frankfurt-am-Main (Kramer).

SEILACHER, A. 1955. Spuren und Lebensweise der Trilobiten: Spuren und Fazies im Unter-kambrium. *In* SCHINDEWOLF, O. H. & SEILACHER, A.: Beiträge zur Kenntnis des Kambriums in der Salt Range (Pakistan). *Akad. Wiss. Lit. Mainz, math.-nat. Kl. Abh.* **10,** 86–143, pls. 16–27.

—— 1956. Der Beginn des Kambriums als biologische Wende. *Neues Jb. Geol. Paläont. Abh.* **103,** 155–80, pls. 8, 9.

—— 1962. Form und Funktion des Trilobiten-Daktylus. *Paläont. Z.* (H. Schmidt Festband), 218–27, pls. 24, 25.

STØRMER, L. 1955. Merostomata. *In* MOORE, R. C.: *Treatise on Invertebrate Paleontology*, Part P: *Arthropoda* (2).

Manuscript submitted May 1966.

R. Goldring, PH.D. F.G.S.
Department of Geology, The University, Reading, Berkshire.

Fluctuations in the evolution of
Palaeozoic invertebrates

MICHAEL ROBERT HOUSE

CONTENTS

SUMMARY

The problem of interpreting faunal fluctuations is reviewed and it is stressed that numerical abundance cannot be assessed, and morphological diversity only by comparing taxa or the subjective views of specialists. Comparisons at generic and higher taxon levels are made for the more common Palaeozoic fossil groups for appearance of new and extinction of old stocks. The striking diversification (and often appearance) of many groups with calcareous hard parts during the Ordovician is stressed and related to evidence for particularly widespread shallow seas at that time. In detail, groups do not show precise time agreement in their later evolutionary 'bursts', but significant periods seem to be during the early and mid-Devonian and the early Carboniferous, but these are at taxon grades lower than the Ordovician diversification. For extinctions it is often possible to separate intrataxal, presumably competitive, extinctions during the rapid rise of a group, from extinctions which appear to affect unrelated stocks. Significant periods for the latter are around the mid- and late Devonian and the mid- and late Carboniferous. These extinctions occur *pari passu*, rather than as single catastrophic events. Possible long-continued palaeogeographical causes are considered.

1. Introduction

THE PALAEOZOIC is delimited at its base by the apparently abrupt appearance of abundant hard-shelled marine invertebrates and, at its top, by a much cited diminution and extinction of faunas in the Permian and Trias. These terminal events are reviewed elsewhere in this volume. In this contribution an attempt is made to review the faunal record between these events with particular regard to periods of marked diversification and extinction, the extent to which these may be correlated between groups, and the conclusions and inferences which may be drawn therefrom. Remarks will be restricted to a few of the major groups.

Studies of this sort raise many problems, not least of which lie in the premises. Attempts to analyse the fossil record, either quantitatively or qualitatively, are fraught with uncertainties. It is important therefore, at the outset, to make a few comments on the nature of the data bearing on faunal fluctuations and the conclusions which may reasonably be drawn.

The Fossil Record, pp. 41–54. Geological Society of London, 1967. Printed in Northern Ireland.

1. We have no way of measuring the *abundance* of past organisms.
2. We can only attempt to estimate *variety* among past organisms, and this only by accepting the subjective opinion of a specialist, or the equally subjective and unequal measurement provided by the systematic taxa.
3. The absolute *time range* of organisms will always be uncertain and any generalizations made about time ranges will be interim statements.
4. In the analysis of supposed morphological variation with time, what is being studied is the morphological effects of the *adaptation* of organisms to their environment.

In this contribution an attempt will be made to contrast the data obtained from the systematic taxa at several levels. Emphasis on generic diversification is due rather to higher categories having been dealt with by Newell (1963), and by other contributors to this volume, than that they are regarded as more significant.

A starting point for such discussions must be the symposium on the *Distribution of evolutionary explosions in geologic time* published in 1952. At this symposium, Newell (1952, p. 371) presented a synthesis on periodicity in invertebrate evolution using data at system level on generic distribution. Newell concluded that "Analyses of the better records of the fossil invertebrates show that rise and fall in apparent evolutionary radiation is not at random. In a large proportion of major groups, times of low evolutionary activity tend to coincide. This indicates a common external cause ...". Subsequently Newell (1962, 1963) has analysed the data at family level and has concluded that fluctuation of sea-level is a major factor controlling periodicity in evolution.

On the other hand, discussing Cambro-Ordovician records of graptolites, trilobites and brachiopods, Whittington & Williams (1964, p. 245) remark that their data "simply confirm what is generally known, namely that allegedly significant changes in the inferred evolutionary histories of phyla are out of phase with one another".

It is therefore appropriate to consider the evidence on which these conflicting views are based, in the light of the much more complete documentation assembled for this volume.

2. Periods of diversification

Within the Lower Cambrian faunas are many groups with calcareous hard-parts, but those with chitinoid or organophosphatic tests predominate (Glaessner 1962, p. 486). A striking reversal takes place by the Ordovician, with the rather sudden rise and diversification of calcareous-shelled groups. This broad change is well illustrated at a generic level by Fig. 1. Subsequent periods of significant rise in genera would appear to be the Lower and Middle Devonian and the Lower Carboniferous. These are not correlated with any comparable skeletal factor. For convenience, these fluctuations will be analysed stratigraphically.

(A) CAMBRIAN

The basal Cambrian faunas having been considered by Cowie (this volume, pp. 17–35) and reviewed by Whittard (1953), with additional comments by Glaessner

(1962) and Durham (1964), attention will only be drawn here to certain features of the trilobite evidence, the generic diversification and sudden rise of which is remarkable. Changes during the Cambrian are difficult to document. Whittington (1954, p. 193) wrote that "About half of the 600 or so Cambrian genera are incompletely known and based on poor material, and many have never been placed in any family". Generic details given in the *Treatise* (Moore 1959) enable superfamilies to be placed in order of generic diversity during the three main divisions of the period. During the Lower Cambrian the order is: Ellipsocephalacea (52), Olenellina (23), Redlichiacea (22), Corynexochida (19), Ptychopariacea (17) with other groups substantially lower. In the Middle Cambrian the order is Corynexochida (62), Ptychopariacea (42), Agnostina (32), Anomocaracea (21), Solenopleuracea (20), with other groups lower. The Upper Cambrian order is Solenopleuracea (42), Dikelocephalacea (29), Olenacea (24), Ptychaspidacea (24), Marjumiacea (22) with other superfamilies below ten genera. In view of the overall rise in generic numbers through the Cambrian, these changes would seem clearly to reflect high evolution rates and competition within the group during this period.

(B) ORDOVICIAN

Whether the Tremadocian is included in the Cambrian, as Whittington & Williams (1964, p. 241) recommend, or not, it is clear that in a broad sense the Tremadocian to mid-Ordovician marks a major diversification in marine invertebrate faunas, as has recently been stressed by Newell (1963) and Stubblefield (1960, p. 228). The groups most affected are those with calcareous hard-parts, that is the rugose and tabulate corals and stomatoporoids; the Bryozoa; many groups of the Brachiopoda; among the Echinodermata especially the Crinoidea; and the Nautiloidea. Significant changes also occur in the Trilobita, and there is rapid evolution of the Graptolithina. In attempting to document this diversification, the greatest handicap is lack of detailed stratigraphical record for many of the groups.

Coelenterata. The rise of the rugose corals has been documented by Hill (*in* Moore 1956, p. 253) thus: "The Rugosa first appeared in the Blackriverian strata [more correctly the Black River formation of Caradocian age] in the shallow seas associated with the Appalachian geosyncline and it is quite probable that all three suborders were represented therein". Elsewhere she adds "they immediately spread around the globe". Claims have been made of earlier Russian records, and perhaps this is not unexpected, but the geographical expansion and appearance in significant numbers is a mid- and late Ordovician event. Data at family level by Taylor (this volume, p. 359) show that the main diversification at family level occurred between the Valentian and Gedinnian. This is broadly mirrored at generic level (Fig. 1). A somewhat similar situation is shown by the tabulate corals which first appear in the mid-Ordovician of the U.S.A. with the chaetetids, syringophyllids and auloporids, and almost all other families appearing before the close of the system, by which time they were world-wide in distribution.

Galloway (1957) considers the first authenticated stromotoporoids to be from

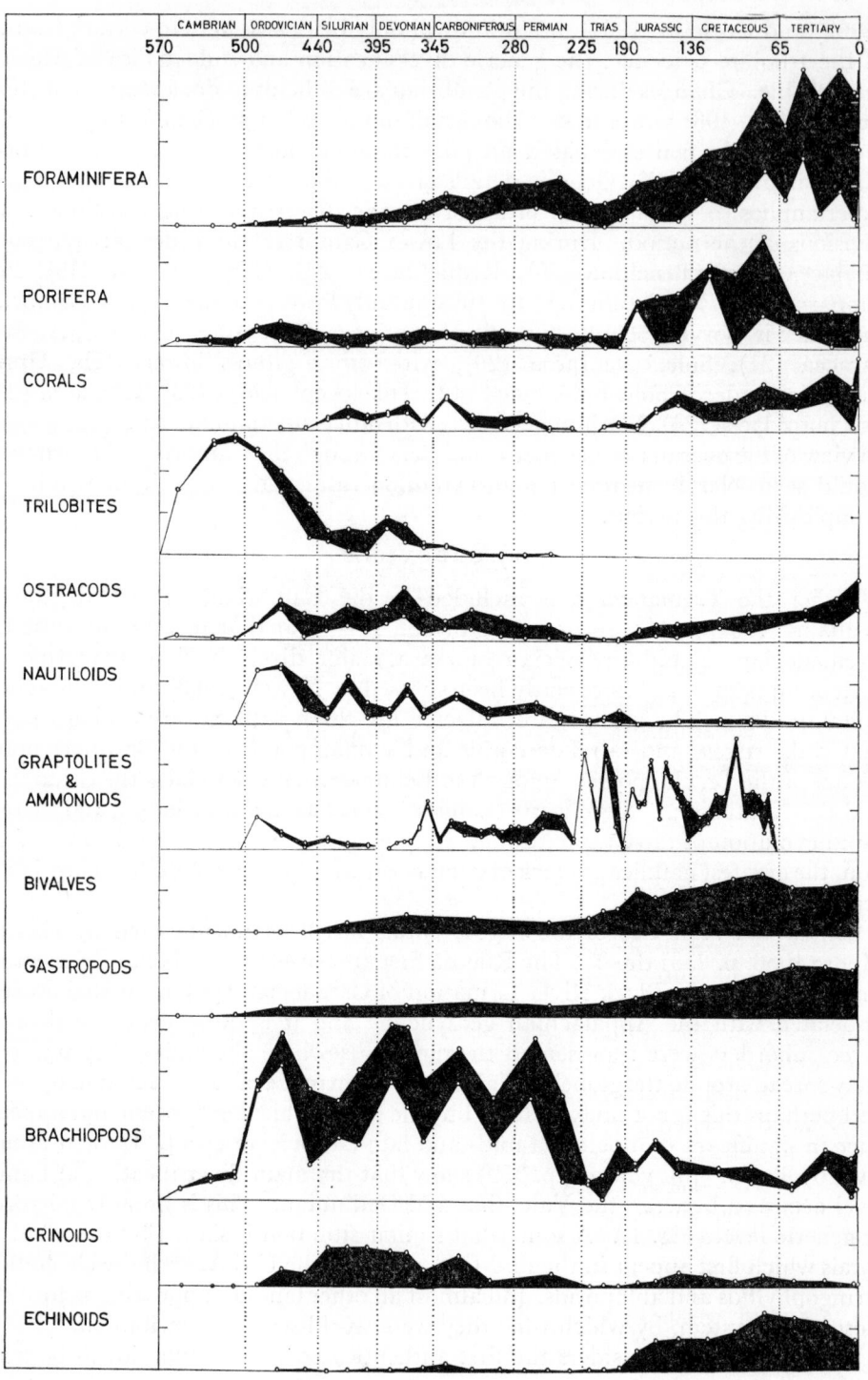

the mid-Ordovician of Vermont, and he doubts Cambrian records of Yavorsky (1932), repeated in the *Osnovy* (Sokolov 1963, p. 160). Thereafter the group diversified enormously through the late Ordovician and Silurian, as was emphasized diagrammatically by Galloway (1957, p. 396).

Trilobites. To comment on the relative merits of the basal Arenigian and basal Tremadocian as marked periods of faunal change introduces the problem of boundary definition. Whittington (1954) made clear that the major break was pre-Tremadocian. Whittard (1960, p. 11 *et seq.*) has also emphasized that the Tremadocian trilobite faunas are more closely related to the Ordovician than Cambrian, but Whittington & Williams (1964) have subsequently doubted this, and quoting several families known in the Ordovician and not yet in the Tremadocian conclude "that the assumption that the Tremadoc trilobite faunas are dominantly Ordovician in type is a matter for debate." Whether one boundary or the other is preferred may still be a matter of debate, nevertheless the contrast between pre- and post-Tremadocian faunas is clear. Also clear is the fact that the Ordovician and Silurian trilobite taxa are relatively stable and persistent. A Tremadocian to Arenigian diversification produced them, and this event would seem to be more significant than any subsequent diversification period.

Cephalopoda. For a broad view of the evolution of the groups of nautiloids we have the reviews of Flower (1955, 1964) and the views of Ruzhentsev (1962) and others in the *Osnovy* and of Teichert and others in the *Treatise* (Moore 1965). These are in general agreement as far as the evolutionary diversification is concerned, that is, that between the Upper Cambrian and Middle Ordovician (essentially Champlainian) all nautiloid orders apart from the Nautilida have appeared. In terms of their generic variety, three quarters of these stocks achieve their greatest diversity in this period also.

Graptolithina. For the graptolites (Bulman, *in* Moore (1955) and Rickards & Skevington (this volume p. 601)) the Tremadocian and Arenegian together form the greatest period of appearances at family level, and they are numerically about equal. In view of the divergent opinions on the status of Silurian genera the apparent agreement between the family and generic date (Fig. 1) may be unreliable. At specific level Dr H. Jaeger (*in litt.*) has informed me that the pattern is very different, this being skewed with a Silurian peak reflecting the large numbers of monograptid species.

Brachiopoda. It is well known that already in the Lower Cambrian articulate and inarticulate brachiopods are present and both calcareously shelled and phosphaticly shelled groups occur. The seven superfamilies which appear in the

---

Fig. 1. Diagram showing the number of genera, for certain common fossil invertebrate marine groups, at various periods in the past. Based on accepted genera in the *Treatise* (Moore 1953–1966) excluding Echinoidea, and *Traité* (Pivetau, 1952, 1953)—groups not yet covered by the *Treatise*. Although drawn as a graph more correctly it should be regarded as a histogram, and the time classes, it will be noted, are not necessarily equal. Each division on the left-hand scale represents fifty genera. For each graph the upper line represents total genera, the lower graph, where present, the number of newly appearing genera.

Lower Cambrian presumably form the base-stock for the subsequent evolution. At the superfamily level, the Middle and Upper Cambrian and the Tremadocian produce, as far as present evidence indicates, only one group each. The major diversification at this level was between the Arenigian and Ashgillian, when 16 superfamilies appear, almost half the complete total for the phylum. Nor is this all; the stocks include the first spire-bearers (Cooper 1956, p. 133) as well as the numerically important dalmanellids and rhynchonellids.

Williams (*in* Whittington & Williams 1964, p. 244) seems to indicate that the Arenig was the period of greatest change, although the appearance of super-families would suggest it was the Caradocian (where five superfamilies appear). Williams writes "if the brachiopod record is also considered, an unequivocal case can be made for relating the Cambro-Ordovician boundary to the base of the Arenig. Only three groups of articulate brachiopods, the orthaceans, syntrophaceans, and the clitambonacean polytoechiids, are known from the Cambrian (including Tremadocian) rocks. Yet during Arenig times they were greatly enlarged by the appearance of such distinctive familial stocks as the skenidiids, dolerorthids, dinorthids, plectorthids, syntrophids, porambonitids, camarellids, clitamonitids and gonambonitids: and were also joined by early representatives of the plectambonitaceans, strophomenaceans, and enteletaceans (=dalmanella-ceans), all of which were pre-eminently characteristic of the Ordovician".

This Ordovician radiation is illustrated, for the Orthacea and Clitambonacea, by diagrams prepared by Cooper & Williams (1952, p. 335). In generic diversity, a decline apparently sets in through the later Ordovician and into the Silurian. This is accompanied by an apparent failure to produce new superfamily taxa during the Silurian.

Bryozoa. Ross (1964) has recently reviewed the Ordovician rise of this group and referred to it as a "burst in evolution". Here also extinctions are high at low taxon levels.

Echinodermata. By the close of the Ordovician, all major groups of echinoderms are known. The extreme diversity, even in the Lower Cambrian, with the Helico-placophora, Eocrinoidea and Edrioasteroidea (Durham & Caster 1963) is sufficient to suggest that records of first appearances of the rarer groups are unlikely to be helpful. Some documentation at other levels is, however, instructive. Ubaghs' data (Pivetau 1953) gives a rise from 4 to 43 genera between the low and mid-Ordovician, but the stratigraphical records are somewhat unreliable. Moore (1952) gives similar evidence for a rather sudden diversification.

(c) ORDOVICIAN–SILURIAN

The Ordovician–Silurian boundary shows no faunal change comparable in magnitude to that of the low Ordovician, neither does the evidence appear to allow the recognition of any widespread break within the Silurian. The rise in the percentage of new genera (Fig. 2) shows remarkable consistency between groups but changes at higher taxon levels are not so clear.

Ordovician rugose coral genera number slightly over a dozen, whilst the Silurian new genera number almost one hundred; this would seem to represent a genuine morphological diversification and Hill gives the culmination as Llandovery. The family data, however, suggests a rather long continued period of family appearance through the Silurian and low Devonian, although the Silurian total is as high as at any stage in the history of the group.

Although the trilobites show an early Silurian rise in the percentage of new genera (Fig. 2), this is misleading as overall there is a substantial fall in total from the late Ordovician (Fig. 1) from 122 to the low Silurian total of 60. This reflects the poorer diversification at higher taxon levels which characterizes the period.

Perhaps the impoverished generic record for the low Silurian nautiloids is largely due to poor documentation, for some orders are unrepresented which are known to survive. A clear mid-Silurian resurgence is shown by all groups, however, especially by the Oncoceratida, Orthoceratida (which are here at generic acme) and Discosorida. After this period there seems to be a general decline.

At specific level the graptolites show greatest numbers in the early and mid-Silurian, but this is scarcely reflected at generic level and not at all at family level. The elaborations are chiefly of the *Monograptus* stock, a well-documented early Silurian radiation.

The brachiopod decline in genera from the late Ordovician (123) to 'early' Silurian (92) is emphasized by the relatively low proportion of new genera appearing (Fig. 2). This is perhaps the more significant when the absence of any new taxa at superfamily level is considered. Stropheodontid radiation is illustrated for the Silurian by Williams (1953, p. 20).

Both the data of Ubaghs (*in* Pivetau 1953) and Moore (1952) suggest the importance of the Silurian in crinoid evolution at levels of genera and above. This is the generic acme for the stock, and the most substantial rise in generic numbers occurs between the later Ordovician and early Silurian.

(d) DEVONIAN

The difficulties in defining faunally the Silurian–Devonian boundary emphasize the absence of major change at this level. Even the long-held view that the extinction of the graptolites occurred at the boundary has now been disproved. Most major early Devonian taxa have origins in the Ordovician. Yet at generic and familial level there seems good evidence for an early Devonian resurgence.

For the corals Hill stresses a "burst of evolutionary activity" for the late early and early Middle Devonian, and five families appear in this time. The generic totals for the early and mid-Devonian are 45 and 67 respectively, the latter just surpassing a mid-Silurian figure of 58; but few experienced in the literature of Devonian corals would give these figures much reliance.

The 93 trilobite genera (66 new) recorded for the Lower Devonian in the *Treatise* represents the highest figure for post-Ordovician times using a triple system division for the counts. At family level a similar increase is shown (Stubblefield 1959, p. 148).

The goniatites appear in the mid-Siegenian as simple primitive types which soon diversify rapidly. Their origin has been traditionally linked with the bactritids because of the shared marginal position for the siphuncle, the egg-shaped protoconch and other characters. Recently Donovan (1964) has peremptorily rejected this view, without additional evidence, and suggested an origin of the group from the Barrandeoceratida and Tarphyceratida, but Erben's elegant work on the morphologically and stratigraphically intermediate forms is sufficient to strengthen farther the accepted view (Erben 1964, 1965). Donovan would also derive the Famennian clymenids from the Oncoceratida, but the early onto-genetic stages link them closely with the goniatites and the writer would draw attention to that group of lowest Famennian tornoceratids in which the suture reverts to a rectilinear form and in which siphuncle migration has been described. This group is both morphologically and stratigraphically intermediate between the goniatites and clymenids and seems a preferable solution to the problem.

The generic data for nautiloids shown a rise from 37 to 93 from low to mid-Devonian. Perhaps this figure is the more indicative when the rise of orthoceratid, nautilid and oncoceratid genera is seen to be matched by an antipathetic decline in the other contemporary orders. This mid-Devonian figure is not subsequently reached by the group.

The low and mid-Devonian figures of 212 and 211 genera for the brachiopods represents the maximum differentiation of the group at any time, if genera be taken as a guide. The low Devonian figure almost doubles that of the Silurian 'average.' At higher taxonomic levels this is illustrated by the appearance through the early and mid-Devonian of the Stenocismatacea, Terebratulacea [for the diversification of which see Cloud (1942)], Productacea and Stropholosacea.

The changes in these four stocks therefore suggest a substantial morphological diversification at low taxon levels in the early and mid-Devonian. When the numerical importance of these groups, as opposed to others in Devonian faunas, is considered this inference is perhaps strengthened.

(E) CARBONIFEROUS

For many groups there would appear to be an impoverished generic record for the Famennian, and this may falsely stress the apparent rise in genera shown by many groups in the early Carboniferous (see Fig. 1); this rise is however also indicated at higher taxon levels.

The appearance of four new rugose coral families in the Tournaisian, unequalled since the low Devonian and never later, represents the final 'burst' in their evolution recognized by Hill. At generic level, the *Treatise* figure of 82 (79 new) represents the acme of the group, and even if it is partly monographic the rise from 22 of the late Devonian is obviously significant when the distinctive structures of the forms involved are considered.

Such a resurgence is not, however, shown by the trilobites, for numerically these are restricted, and the figure of 84% new genera is thus misleading (Fig. 2). Somewhat analogous is the decline in ostracod genera from a mid-Devonian figure of 121 to an early Carboniferous figure of 49 (slightly more than half of which are new). For the trilobites the Devonian extinctions were not recouped.

The early Tournaisian goniatite resurgence is well marked: the more so when the possibility that all are derived from *Imitoceras* is allowed. The apparent rise in nautiloid genera in the low Carboniferous results largely from the high figures for the Orthoceratida (24) and Nautilida (39). Both these groups were well developed in the mid-Devonian, and the poor documentation of Famennian nautiloids is probably responsible for the apparent rise.

At first glance, the apparent decline in brachiopod genera from a late Devonian (mostly Frasnian) figure of 116 to a low Carboniferous figure below one hundred is surprising. The extinctions at high taxon level in the mid- and late Devonian apparently took its toll. Here the consistency of the evidence is comforting, for the Carboniferous faunas have not lacked monographers.

Moore (1952, p. 341) has remarked that the Palaeozoic peak for crinoid species is in the Mississippian, and his evidence gives a decline thereafter until the middle Permian. Whilst the data of Ubaghs (*in* Pivetau 1953, p. 658 et seq.) supports a general decline from 74 genera in the low Carboniferous to less than half that figure for the Permian, the generic peak for the group is Silurian—but in both cases specific and generic diversification is substantially greater than in the late Devonian.

Although the taxon levels involved are generally lower, therefore, some evidence for a low Carboniferous period of diversification is forthcoming. A subsequent decline in the late Carboniferous is shown at generic level by many groups.

3. Periods of extinction

The rapid decline of trilobite genera from the late Cambrian (Fig. 1) is illustrated also by extinctions at higher taxonomic levels (Whittington 1954, p. 195). Whittington (1966, p. 731) has recently observed that "no genera, and members of at most two families may be in common between pre and post Tremadocian faunas". Attention has already been drawn to the apparently intrataxal competition extinctions of trilobite superfamilies within the Cambrian. Palmer (1965) notes an apparently significant break within the Upper Cambrian.

For the groups which become particularly abundant during the Ordovician, several show an initial diversification from which long-persisting stocks emerge, and the phasing of the extinctions of the latter is of particular interest. These groups will therefore be considered separately.

The data of Taylor (this volume, p. 359) for the rugose corals and of Hill (*in* Moore 1956) shows that the Devonian was the most significant extinction period. Some twelve families do not survive the Givetian—by far the most significant break at this level for the group. Few other families survive the Devonian, and the bleakest period is the late Famennian; extinctions affect quite unrelated stocks. At the generic level the *Treatise* data show, of 67 Middle Devonian rugose coral genera, 58 do not survive into the Frasnian (Fig. 3). Further periods of significant generic extinction occur in the low mid-Carboniferous (but with far fewer extinctions at higher taxon levels). Attention may be drawn to the progressive decline in generic numbers from the Lower Carboniferous or, more probably, Namurian.

Analysis of trilobite evolution at family level has been given by Stubblefield

(1959, p. 148). It is interesting that his graphs of family abundance agree closely with those for genera given here (Fig. 1). The number of groups, established in the early Ordovician, which survive into the Devonian is striking, and the Middle and Upper Devonian saw a great extinction of quite major taxa which most stratigraphers would agree were also numerically abundant. Here disappear the Phacopacea, Dalmanitacea, Lichida, Odontopleurida and Illinacea (*contra* Moore 1959 (O), p. 365). This is not a sudden event, but represents extinctions *pari passu*. If any times are particularly significant they are the times of extinction of the calymenids, holomonotids, cheirurids and cyphaspids in the upper Givetian; of the harpids and thysanopeltids in the Upper Devonian and probably late Frasnian; and of the Dalmanitacea and Phacopacea in the late Famennian. In the case of the Phacopacea there is the remarkable trend to blindness in the *Trimerocephalus* group, although the many faceted *Phacops* (*Phacops*) persists into the Wocklumeria Zone.

The family extinctions for the Bryozoa (as a percentage of total present) are highest in the Devonian (37%) and Permian (41%). Owen and Tavenor-Smith's data (this volume, p. 379) suggest that Devonian extinctions are spread rather evenly through the period, perhaps with a maximum in the Eifelian. The generic data differs greatly (Fig. 3), being at a maximum in the Ordovician, as might be expected during a period which Ross calls a "burst in evolution." Caution is probably particularly necessary in this group where monographic treatment is unevenly spread through the Palaeozoic.

At the ordinal level, the nautiloids show greatest diversification in the low–mid–Ordovican with subsequent decline. The generic data are different (Fig. 1) with a peak generic extinction (117) by the close of the Lower Ordovician, presumably related to intrataxon competition. A high rate continues through the Ordovician with subsequent highs in the mid-Silurian and mid-Devonian (79 and 74 genera extinct by the close, respectively). When plotted as a ratio (Fig. 3) the late Silurian and late Devonian are emphasized.

The ammonoid data show two particularly important breaks. The first is at the close of the Givetian, which probably only tornoceratid, anarcestid and prolobitid stocks survived. The next is at the close of the Famennian where, in the opinion of many, only *Imitoceras* survived to give the Goniatitina and prolecantids (although some favour an independent origin for the latter). Also the cylmenids become extinct, making this a critical period for the group comparable with the later Permian and Triassic extinctions. What is striking about the Carboniferous and Permian is the long continuance of taxa at superfamily level (House 1963, p. 159).

As might be expected in a period of major diversification, there are several superfamilies of brachiopods which do not survive the Ordovician, but at generic level the decline is much more striking (Fig. 1). The Trimerellacea, Acrotretacea and Triplesiacea do not survive the Upper Silurian, but these groups were not particularly important numerically: generally extinctions are low and this supports the steady rise in the group's diversification indicated by the generic figures for the mid- and late Silurian (Fig. 1). The most significant extinction

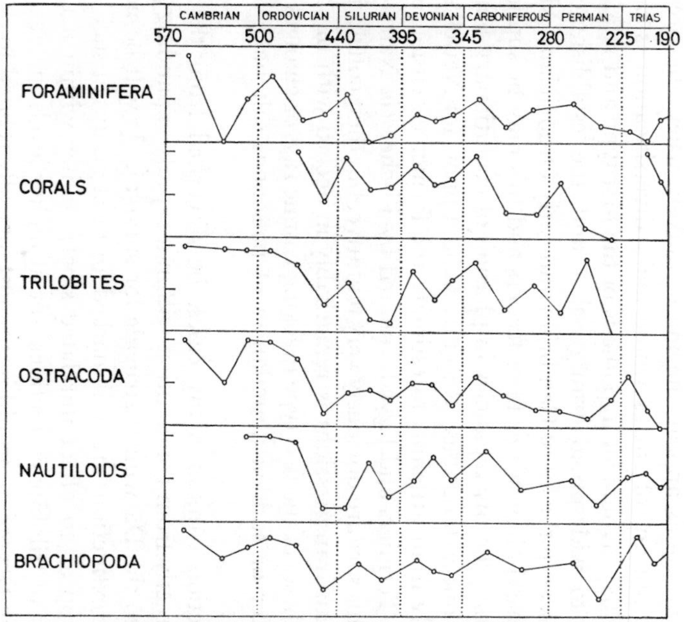

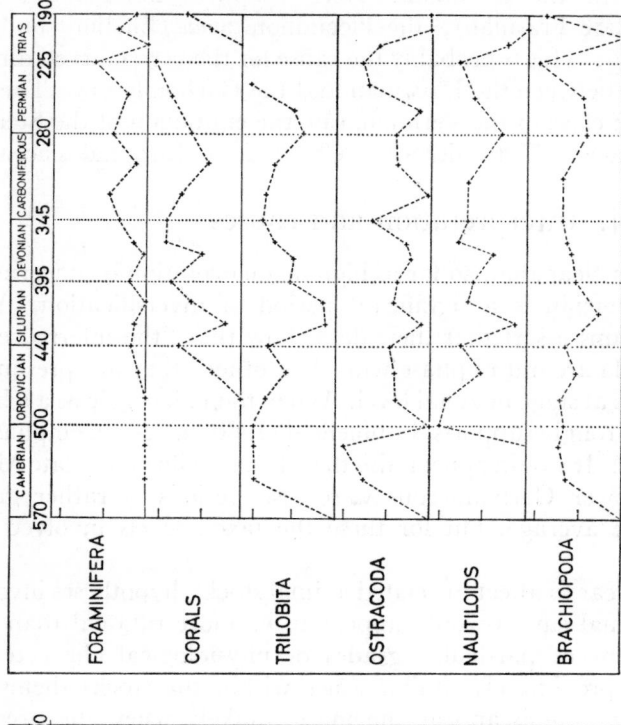

Fig. 3. Showing the percentage of genera becoming *extinct* and *new* genera appearing. Notes as for Fig. 2. The late Permian extinctions are common to all groups, an important subsidiary high occurs in the late Devonian.

Fig. 2. Showing the percentage between *new* and *total* genera during the Palaeozoic for certain groups based on *Treatise* data (Moore, 1953–66). It will be noted that the points are not necessarily equidistant and represent averages for the time unit considered. For each graph the scale units correspond to 50%. High early Ordovician and early Carboniferous figures are common to all groups.

period would seem to be the Devonian. Here disappear the Pentameracea, Atrypacea, Orthacea (late Frasnian); the Plectamonitacea (Eifelian) and Porambonitacea (Siegenian). This is probably the cause for the very marked diminution in generic numbers between the Devonian and the Carboniferous. The final Palaeozoic event, at the close of the Permian, saw the extinction of the Stenocismatacea, Rhynchoporacea, Eichwaldiacea, Chonetacea, Strophalosiacea and Richthofeniacea.

4. Interpretation and causes

From the foregoing it is clear that, so far as high taxon evolution is concerned, in most groups the Ordovician is a significant period of diversification. When Whittington and Williams assert that their data show that "the inferred evolutionary histories of phyla are out of phase with each other" they are presumably speaking of comparisons at stage or zonal level. When the Palaeozoic as a whole is considered, the writer strongly supports Stubblefield (1960, p. 228) in emphasizing the Ordovician changes. It would appear also that the late Silurian to late Middle Devonian, and the Lower Carboniferous were also periods of rather greater diversification than the average, but for these the taxon levels involved were generally lower.

For events which appear to affect unrelated animal stocks, hypotheses involving environmental or external causes would appear to be more rational than those invoking the attainment of particular grades or physiological characters independently and at approximately similar times within the stocks themselves. These latter types of hypothesis appear the more unlikely when the presence, even in the Lower Cambrian, of stocks whose main diversification is later is considered. Newell (1963) favours an hypothesis of the first type and relates the Ordovician radiations to widespread transgression and the establishment of shallow epicontinental seas in the latest Cambrian and early Ordovician. Most of the groups concerned are shallow water filter feeders and this may be supporting evidence. That there may be discrepancies in phasing of evolutionary bursts at stage and zonal level is understandable. Recently some support for Newell's view has come independently from attempts to estimate the former extension of epicontinental seas by the Termiers and Egyed, collated by Fischer (*in* Nairn 1964, p. 469). Estimates of this sort are obviously very tentative, but their conclusion on the extent of Ordovician transgressions is remarkably in accord with the faunal evidence. Other hypotheses of the first type invoking cosmic rays or changes in the constitution of sea-water or sudden abundances of poisonous salt have less to recommend them.

Two types of extinction can, in many cases, be discerned from the data. Extinction resulting directly from competition within a rapidly expanding group bears witness directly to the Darwinian struggle for survival. It will be noticed that generic and higher extinctions are well marked for most groups at such times.

Extinctions which appear to affect unrelated stocks, either within a class— such as the late Cambrian trilobite extinctions—or at higher levels such as those, here documented, of the Devonian, would seem most logically related to external or environmental events. The Devonian and late Carboniferous would appear to be periods characterized by this type of extinction. The evidence shows that the Devonian extinctions, whilst perhaps most marked at the close of the Givetian and Famennian, are spread through the period. It is a gradual decline. The same has been said for the late Carboniferous changes (House, *in* Nairn 1964, p. 575). Newell has related these events to regressions and consequent restrictions of littoral environments. Perhaps the Old Red Sandstone is evidence for this in the Devonian, but then contributory factors may have been the excessive clastic littoral deposits of that time, emphasized by the fact that this environment lay essentially in tropical zones where littoral life would normally have been profuse: hence the effects would have been more marked.

5. References

CLOUD, P. E. 1942. Terebratuloid Brachiopda of the Silurian and Devonian. *Spec. Pap. geol. Soc. Am.*, **38**, 1–182.

COOPER, G. A. & WILLIAMS, A. 1952. Significance of the stratigraphic distribution of brachiopods. *J. Paleont.* **26**, 326–37.

DONOVAN, D. T. 1964. Cephalopod phylogeny and classification. *Biol. Rev.* **39**, 259–87.

DURHAM, J. W. & CASTER, K. E. 1963. Helicoplacoidea: a new class of echinoderms. *Science, N.Y.* **140**, 820–2.

ERBEN, H. K. 1964, 1965. Die evolution der ältesten Ammonoides. *Neues Jb. geol. Paläont. Abh.* **120**, 107–212; **122**, 275–312.

FLOWER, R. H. 1955. Saltations in nautiloid coiling. *Evolution, Lancaster, Pa.* **9**, 244–60.

—— 1964. The nautiloid order Ellesmeroceratida (Cephalopoda). *Men. Inst. Min. Technol. New Mex.* **12**, 1–234.

GALLOWAY, J. J. 1957. Structure and classification of the Stromatoporoidea. *Bull. Am. Paleont.* **37**, 341–470.

GLAESSNER, M. F. 1962 Pre Cambrian fossils. *Biol. Rev.* **37**, 467–94.

HOUSE, M. R. 1963. Bursts in evolution. *Advmt Sci., Lond.* **19**, 155–63.

MOORE, R. C. 1952. Evolution rates among crinoids, *J. Paleont.* **26**, 338–52.

——(Ed.) 1953–1966. *Treatise on invertebrate paleontology.* University of Kansas Press.

NAIRN, A. E. M. (Ed.) 1964. *Problems in Palaeoclimatology.* New York (Interscience).

NEWELL, N. D. 1952. Periodicity in invertebrate evolution. *J. Paleont.* **26**, 371–85.

—— 1962. Paleontological gaps and geochronology. *J. Paleont.* **36**, 592–610.

—— 1963. Crises in the history of life. *Scient. Am.* **208**, 76–92.

PALMER, A. R. 1965. Trilobites of the Late Cambrian pterocephaliid biomere in the Great Basin, United States. *Prof. Pap. U.S. Geol. Surv.* **493**, 1–105.

PIVETAU, J. (Ed.) 1952–3. *Traité de Paléontologie*, vols. 1–3. Paris (Masson).

ROSS, J. P. 1964. Morphology and phylogeny of early Ectoprocta (Bryozoa). *Bull. geol. Soc. Am.* **75**, 927–48.

SOKOLOV, B. S. (Ed.) 1963. *Osnovy paleontologii*, vol. 2. Moscow (Akademii Nauk SSSR).

STUBBLEFIELD, C. J. 1959. Evolution in trilobites. *Q. Jl geol. Soc. Lond.* **115**, 145–62.

—— 1960. Sessile marine organisms and their significance in Pre-Mesozoic strata. *Q. Jl geol. Soc. Lond.* **116**, 219–38.

RUZHENTSEV, V. E. (Ed.) 1962. *Osnovy paleontologii*, vol. 5. Moscow (Akademii Nauk SSSR).

WHITTARD, W. F. 1953. The enigma of the earliest fossils. *Bristol Nat. Soc.* **28**, 289–304.

WHITTARD, W. F. 1960. In *Lexique stratigraphique international*, vol. 1, (7A, IV). Paris (Centre National de la Recherche Scientifique).

WHITTINGTON, H. B. 1954. Trilobite. *In* Status of invertebrate paleontology; 1953, VI. Arthropoda (Ed. Kummel, B.) *Bull. Mus. Comp. Zool. Harv.* **112,** 193–200.

—— 1966. Phylogeny and distribution of Ordovician trilobites. *J. Paleont.* **40,** 696–737.

—— & WILLIAMS, A. 1964. The Ordovician Period, *Q. Jl geol. Soc. Lond.* **120 S,** 241–54.

WILLIAMS, A. 1953. North American and European stropheodontids: their morphology and systematics. *Mem. geol. Soc. Am.* **56,** 1–67.

Manuscript submitted October 1966.

[Professor] M. R. House, M.A. PH.D. F.G.S.
Department of Geology, The University, Kingston upon Hull, Yorkshire.

DISCUSSION

Dr R. A. CROWSON remarked that the dramatic rise of some groups ought logically to be correlated with the decline of others. In the Palaeozoic, the Cephalopoda would probably be the most formidable predators in the seas when they first appeared in the Ordovician. Later, in the Devonian, the diversification of the fishes might have had a similar effect. Other marine groups might be expected to be affected by the rise of these groups.

Dr J. W. COWIE asked how the apparently sudden incoming of various sub-divisions of the nautiloids was related to the problem of the Cambro–Ordovician boundary in North American carbonate sequences.

Dr G. A. L. JOHNSON asked Dr House if he would enlarge on his remarks made towards the end of his paper regarding the mid-Ordovician expansion of faunas and its correlation with widespread marine conditions; surely the important influence here was the widespread development of epicontinental seas. The development of this shallow-water marine environment had important bearing on the expansion of the shelly faunas and Maslov has suggested that important physiological changes took place in the algae under these conditions at this time.

Dr HOUSE agreed with Dr Crowson that a correlation of rise and decline would be expected. It had been argued in the paper that Cambro–Ordovician groups show some such antipathetic relation, particularly the trilobite decline and the rise of calcareous forms. But whether this was due to predation alone was uncertain and for several reasons seemed unlikely.

The comments made on the rise of the Nautiloidea were based mainly on the work of Flower who suggests that main radiation is Canadian. In fact, the richest faunas are from the carbonate facies, and relation of this to the European sequence is uncertain in detail. The generalization, however, seems inescapable.

In reply to Dr Johnson the AUTHOR said he agreed that the most important factor in the Ordovician may well have been the development of widespread Ordovician shallow seas and he drew attention again to the graphs of Egyed and Strackov bearing on this.

The origins of some Silurian enteletacean brachiopods

VICTOR GORDON WALMSLEY

In the charts which have been prepared to illustrate the Symposium Volume, the Brachiopoda have been treated only down to superfamily level. This seems to be a wise decision so far as the Enteletacea are concerned because my own studies of some of the Silurian and Lower Devonian members of this superfamily have shown that detailed revision at the species level leads to revision at the generic, sub-family and family levels.

The starts and ends of ranges of sub-families and families thus depend on prior revision of the species involved, and for the Silurian and Lower Devonian much of this work is only now in preparation for publication. Some examples may clarify the problem.

Work on some 50–60 species of enteletacean brachiopods has led to suggested phylogenies and consequently the re-assignment of certain species to different, and in some instances new, genera. New species of isorthids, now being described, extend the range of *Isorthis* back to the earliest Silurian, where it appears to be derived from *Dalmanella*. The re-assignment of other Silurian species from *Dalmanella* to *Isorthis* and *Salopina* results in a contraction of the range of *Dalmanella* and the extension of *Salopina*, hitherto known only from the Ludlovian. In a joint study with Boucot and Harper, the range of *Salopina* is now recognized as extending from Upper Llandovery to at least Eifelian. Some Wenlockian species at present referred to *Dalmanella* may in fact belong to *Onniella*. This re-assignment is not yet certain but if confirmed, has the effect of extending the Ordovician genus *Onniella* into late Wenlockian. The resserellid group including a new genus now being proposed appears to start in the late Llandovery and extend into early Devonian. These changes in the ranges of genera, the extension of *Isorthis*, *Salopina* and possibly *Onniella* and the reduction of *Dalmanella*, naturally affect the sub-families to which they are assigned. The occurrence of *Isorthis* in the earliest Silurian extends the range of the Isorthinae.

If *Salopina* is assigned to the Drabovinae as is proposed (Walmsley, Boucot & Harper, in preparation), the range of this sub-family, previously regarded as Ordovician, is extended to at least Eifelian. Moreover, the family assignment of the Drabovinae is in doubt. According to whether it is placed in the Schizophoriidae or the Dalmanellidae, the ranges of these families may also be affected.

The Fossil Record, pp. 55–56. Geological Society of London, 1967. Printed in Northern Ireland.

These few examples from a part only of the proposed phylogenetic and taxonomic revision of some of the Silurian and Lower Devonian Enteletacea may be taken to show how necessary is an overhaul at the species level before ranges of genera, sub-families and families can be accepted with any confidence.

Manuscript submitted May 1966.

V. G. Walmsley, PH.D. F.G.S.
    Department of Geology, University College, Swansea.

Permo–Triassic extinction

FRANK HAROLD TREVOR RHODES

CONTENTS

1. Introduction

The Permo–Triassic extinction of many fossil groups is one of the most striking events in the history of life: a 'crisis in earth history' which marked the end of an era. Major groups of organisms, which had dominated life in the Palaeozoic seas, became extinct in late Permian times. Organisms as different as fusulinids, rugose corals, trilobites, eurypterids, dalmanelloid and productoid brachiopods, blastoids, inadunate, flexibilate and camerate crinoids, trepostome and crypto-stome bryozoans were all involved. Yet it is easy to over-dramatize this extinction; it was less taxonomically widespread in its effects, less sudden in its onset, less simultaneous in its influence and less geographically universal in its operation than is usually claimed. Land plants showed no dramatic episode of extinction, and land animals were little reduced, although they showed rapid turnover changes in most groups: some of the marine invertebrates involved were represented only by

The Fossil Record, pp. 57–76. Geological Society of London, 1967. Printed in Northern Ireland.

very restricted relict faunas, although others were widespread and diversified groups of varying ecological preferences.

The purpose of the present paper is to analyse the detailed patterns of this extinction, both between and within the various taxa of organisms involved, and to seek to discover their relationships to each other and to the physical changes in the environments in which they lived.

2. Characteristics of Permian faunas: patterns of extinction

It is sometimes suggested that the whole Permian period was one of dwindling numbers of species and of isolated, specialized faunas. This is not the case, although there are certainly many areas of the world where Permian strata are continental in origin, and others where they are only poorly fossiliferous. In areas of true marine sedimentation, however, there was a great variety of Permian invertebrates: the west Texas, Timor and Salt Range Permian deposits provide familiar examples. Indeed, there are probably rather more Permian species described than there are Pennsylvanian.

Foraminifera, which had undergone an impressive late Palaeozoic expansion, displayed greater generic diversity in the Permian than in any earlier period, but they were reduced in numbers in late Permian to Triassic times. The most important groups to become extinct were the fusulinids and neoschwagerinids, but, although 15 genera disappeared in late Permian times, almost twice as many related genera had become extinct at earlier epochs of the Permian period. Numbers of hyperamminid, textularid, ophthalmid and trochamminid genera also suffered extinction, but the degree of turnover was no greater than that at other system boundaries.

Sponges were little affected by late Palaeozoic changes, but bryozoans underwent drastic reduction, both in numbers of genera and in higher taxa. This followed a period of relative stability in the general characters of late Palaeozoic faunas and the numbers of genera involved. Brachiopods were greatly reduced in late Permo–Triassic times, and the long-ranging productoids and orthoids became extinct, but both groups showed no gradual or sudden reduction in generic diversity before their mass extinction, and in both the numbers of Permian genera substantially exceeded the numbers of Pennsylvanian genera.

Blastoids reached their greatest generic diversity in Permian times, even though they became extinct in the same period. Permian crinoids were a more generically diverse group than at any time since the early Mississippian, but they suffered decimation at the close of the period (p. 60). Echinoids, which had displayed little generic variety in late Palaeozoic times, persisted with little change through late Permian events.

Gastropods and pelecypods, both groups with a relatively conservative Palaeozoic history, survived late Permian times with little modification, but underwent marked expansion in early Mesozoic times. Ammonoids underwent marked reduction in late Permian times. Of the 12 Permian families, only a handful of medlicottids and the otoceratids survived into the Triassic. Nautiloids were much less affected than were ammonoids. The 30 Permian genera were very slightly exceeded in numbers by Triassic genera, but Scythian nautiloids were represented by only 14 species, in contrast to some 76 in the succeeding Anisian epoch. Of the Scythian genera, all were new, although they were members of Palaeozoic families.

Trilobites became extinct in late Permian times, but this involved the extinction of only a few forms of phillipsiids. The group had suffered its biggest decline during the Lower Palaeozoic, and by early Carboniferous times only a small remnant survived. Ostracods also dwindled markedly in generic diversity in Permo–Triassic times. [Data for above groups from House (1963), Newell (1952), Thompson (1948), Kummel (1953) and original.]

'Fish' were relatively less influenced by late Permian extinction. Placoderms did become extinct, but they were represented in the Permian only by the relict acanthodians. Sharks were much reduced, but their decline was no new feature: it had begun in the Carboniferous. Crossopterygian bony fish became virtually extinct, and, although primitive actinopterygians continued, there was a marked relative decline in the numbers of new genera in Upper Carboniferous and Permian times. Most of the late Palaeozoic Chondrichthyes were marine, and most of the Osteichthyes fresh-water.

Simpson (1952) has provided detailed data on vertebrate evolution. One feature is particularly revealing in the present discussion. In the Carboniferous both first and last appearances of 'fish' (in a broad sense) dropped to a minimum, reflecting the fact that the successful Devonian forms persisted with comparatively little change. This minimum persisted for genera from the Pennsylvanian to the Permian. In the Permian, however, last-appearance rates of orders per million years increased markedly, with no comparable increase in first appearances. Indeed, this is the only period in the whole history of the groups in which last order appearances exceeded first order appearances. Succeeding Triassic times were marked by a complete reversal of the relationship, first appearance rates for orders far exceeding those of last appearances.

This distinction between the mere number of taxa in any period and their time of origin is of value in assessing evolutionary change. It is frequently said that tetrapods were little affected by late Palaeozoic extinction. This is broadly true, but it is also true that their rate of 'turnover' was abnormally high. The rates of first and last appearances of orders were equal for Upper Carboniferous times, and both were unusually high in Permian–Triassic times, indicating that their marked diversity involved a sequence of orders which replaced each other in very rapid succession.

The implications of this survey are clear. Permian times did not witness a gradual dwindling of most of the stocks that became extinct towards the close of the period. The Permian period is marked by an episode of evolutionary diversification as conspicuous as those of the Ordovician, Silurian, Mississippian or Jurassic. Of the groups that became extinct or underwent drastic reduction, only the trilobites and placoderms, and to a much lesser extent the brachiopods and bryozoans, were in decline in generic diversity before the period began.

This does not imply that their final extinction was catastrophic. The Permian period probably lasted some 45 m.y., and Upper Permian times probably represented about a third of that period. Various groups became extinct at slightly different times—e.g. the American or European dalmanellids (Cooper & Williams 1952, figs. 10, 11)—or greatly different times (e.g. the blastoids in North America and those in south-east Asia) in different areas. Other groups such as the fusulinids showed a slow decline. There are 40 genera of Permian fusulinids, distributed through 4 zones; 5 of these genera became extinct in the lowest zone, 9 in the succeeding zone and 11 in the next. Of the 15 genera that became extinct within the uppermost zone, only 4 extended as far as the top. This pattern of piecemeal extinction is wholly disguised by a description of 'sudden' fusulinid extinction at the close of the Permian. Any view of extinction depends partly upon the level of heirarchies used in the description and both the magnitude and the catastrophic nature of any episode are exaggerated by the 'lumping' of the taxonomic or stratigraphic categories involved.

The level of extinction in Permian times was not abnormally severe; admittedly there was a marked bulk reduction in the number of genera of some, but by no means most, 'doomed' stocks during Permian times: rugose corals, and to a lesser extent the ostracods, are the only conspicuous examples. But these declines, both individually and collectively, were not obviously more harsh than those of such earlier periods as the late Silurian or late Devonian, which both these groups had endured, but survived.

The problem seems to be not Permian extinction, but lack of rapid Triassic replacement.

One feature of Permian extinction may be the effects of the relative dearth of new genera in most groups in Upper Carboniferous times. For these were times of little change in many marine invertebrates. The ratio of new to total genera reached an all-time low in Upper Carboniferous times for no fewer than seven groups (trilobites, corals, crinoids, echinoids, ammonoids, gastropods and pelecypods); in four other groups (ostracods, bryozoa, brachiopods and nautiloids) it formed part of a depressed 'trough' or was continuous with the Permo–Trias low, which is the only one by which it was exceeded [data from Newell (1952), fig. 10]. It is possible, though by no means probable, that some delayed effect of this Pennsylvanian conservatism was a factor in Permo–Trias extinctions.

3. Extinction in Upper Palaeozoic crinoids: a case history

One of the difficulties in making an accurate census of the evolutionary development of any major group is that of evaluating the taxonomic data. One of the comparatively few groups where such data are available is the crinoids, thanks largely to the authoritative studies of Moore (1950, 1952, 1955A) from whose works (and the references he cites) data for the present review are drawn. They have been modified only by regarding his 'Middle' Permian as 'Upper' Permian, the rich Timor faunas from Basleo, Bitauni and Amarossi being generally regarded as of Upper Permian age (*see* Moore 1952, p. 342); even if this conclusion is not accepted, the interpretation given here will not be affected. There will, however, be a gap in information of 'Upper' Permian faunas.

(A) THE GENERAL PATTERN OF CRINOID EXTINCTION

The extinction of the dominant subclasses of Palaeozoic crinoids did not result from a gradual dwindling in numbers of species. No fewer than 325 species of Permian crinoids are known, most of them Eurasiatic in origin. This compares with 275 species in the Pennsylvanian (Moore 1952, p. 342). There were far more species of Upper Permian age than of Upper Devonian, yet from the 100 or so species of Upper Devonian age there developed the 1000 species of the Mississippian. Clearly, therefore, Permian extinction involved no gradual decline. The absence of direct Triassic survivors does not seem to be the result of any dearth of potential ancestors.

The same is true at the generic level. Upper Permian crinoids were represented by more genera, 125, than any other time in the history of the group [Moore (1955A, figs. 4*a*, 4*b*) shows a slightly lower total for the whole system], except for the Middle Silurian, which just exceeded that number, and the Lower Mississippian, which equalled it. This implies that extinction followed a period of unusual faunal diversity, and that it was not the result of restricted variety. The same general feature is seen in the history of several other groups.

(B) EXTINCTION IS NOT THE EXCEPTION, BUT THE RULE

Late Permian extinction does not seem to have been relatively more severe in its effects than extinction in earlier or later periods. One of the most striking features of Moore's graph of generic distribution (1955A, fig. 4*a*) is the 'catastrophic' reduction in numbers near the boundaries of most of the systems. This is a puzzling feature, and one that is somewhat difficult to explain, though it may be largely a reflection of the original 'diastrophic' selection of system boundaries. If this is the case, it should tend to disappear with further collection. It may also be the result of 'real' physical control, if we accept the suggestion that the middle of periods coincided with maximum extent of epicontinental seas, which, in some cases and in some areas, they did. Whatever the explanation of this feature, one must, for the present, accept it.

The simplest way to compare this 'normal' extinction at successive periods is to calculate the percentage extinction of new and 'hold-over' genera from the mid periods at the early and late period boundaries (Table 1). This indicates that the percentage extinction of late Permian times was not much greater in its severity than extinction in most earlier periods. The extinction rate for genera between earlier periods was high, the 'average' percentage of new genera in the total genera in the various earlier periods after their Ordovician origin being 75 per cent. Although it was 100 per cent in Triassic times, it must be borne in mind that the total number of genera known from that period is only 8, and this small number could have important implications upon the interpretation of the figure. Furthermore, the figure for Ordovician times (not included in the above average) was 100 per cent when some 65 new genera were involved.

TABLE 1: Distribution of Palaeozoic crinoid genera
(Based on data from Moore, 1955A)

	No. of new genera	No. of hold-over genera	Total genera	No. of new genera as percentage of earlier period total	No. of new genera as percentage of period total	Total no. of genera as percentage of earlier period total	No. of hold-over genera as percentage of earlier period total
TRIASSIC	8	0	8	8%	100%	8%	0%
PERMIAN	71	29	100	92%	71%	130%	38%
PENNSYLVANIAN	45	32	77	32%	51%	55%	23%
MISSISSIPPIAN	104	35	139	78%	75%	104%	26%
DEVONIAN	96	37	133	89%	72%	123%	34%
SILURIAN	100	8	108	154%	93%	166%	123%
ORDOVICIAN	65	0	65	—	100%	—	—

If this is the case, then it may be that late Permian extinction involved no substantial difference in kind or degree of causes from the extinction of earlier periods. The problem, therefore, is not so much to account for late Permian extinction, which seems little more drastic than that of earlier periods, but to account for the lack of Triassic replacements.

(C) PATTERNS OF EXTINCTION WITHIN SUBCLASSES

The advantage of studying the history of intermediate taxa is that they provide (to a greater or lesser extent) a more refined indication of phyletic development than the crude counts involved by including all genera in a single class. They also substantiate the broad conclusions (A, B) drawn on the basis of the class census. Thus, the inadunate crinoids of the late Permian were represented by more species than at any other epoch of their history, except the Lower Mississippian. Similarly, although the numbers of late Permian camerate crinoid species (35) were smaller than those of Mississippian, Devonian and Silurian faunas, it is noteworthy that their earlier history clearly shows that extinction is not the inevitable result of low specific diversity. This group had survived Pennsylvanian and early Permian times with an average of less than 10 contemporary species, while the 340 mid-Silurian species had arisen from a stock of only 5 in the early Silurian, and the 225 mid-Devonian species from only 5 in the late Silurian. The same general pattern is seen in the Flexibilia which were represented in the Permian by 12 genera, in contrast to only 3 genera in the Pennsylvanian.

(D) EVOLUTIONARY PATTERN AT THE FAMILY LEVEL

There is some evidence that kladogenetic branching is typical of the early, rather than later, evolutionary history of many groups. Thus the diplobathrid Camerata (Ordovician to Mississippian) are represented by 8 families, all of which arose by Silurian times, only three of them surviving that period, and only one surviving the Devonian. The monobathrid camerate crinoids (Ordovician to Permian) were represented by 21 families, 20 of which had developed by earliest Mississippian times. The Inadunata were represented by 53 families, but only 8 of these appeared in Middle Mississippian or later times. Of the 6 families of Flexibilia, all are of Silurian or earlier origin. It may be significant, and not merely a reflection of circular reasoning, that the inadunate crinoids were the dominant late Palaeozoic forms, outnumbering all other species by 230:94 in the Permian and 225:21 in the Pennsylvanian.

It is not clear to what extent the structural differentiation represented by the recognition of new families is a morphological response to new environmental conditions, but it is possible that the general lack of such family origins in Late Palaeozoic times may be a reflection of the decline of ecological innovation.

Dr Raymond C. Moore (personal communication 1965) could detect no significant ecological differences between the subclasses of Palaeozoic crinoids, all of which are represented in the Permian faunas of Timor.

(E) GEOGRAPHICAL FEATURES OF EXTINCTION

One of the most striking features of the late Permian history of the crinoids is their restriction to Timor. Such limited geographical distribution was unique in their history, and cannot be wholly explained by lack of collecting from appropriate beds of similar age in North America and Europe, limited as these are. This is in contrast to the apparent absence of Asiatic representatives in the much smaller number of species known from the early and middle Permian (45 and 88 respectively) which may be the result of inadequate collections. Only 155 of the 285 late Permian species were of Eurasiatic genera, the rest being members of cosmopolitan genera.

Such geographical restriction may well be a critical, though not lethal, factor in extinction. Many periods of Mesozoic and Cainozoic time were marked by a comparable dominance of Eurasiatic species. In the early stages of the history of most marine invertebrates, geographical restriction seems to be the general rule and clearly has no adverse effects on later expansion. It seems no more likely that it could be a decisive factor in the extinction of established groups. Probably the delicate interaction of physical and biological factors, within a reasonably large biotope, are more important than its absolute size.

(F) ORIGINS OF TRIASSIC CRINOID FAUNAS

The impression sometimes given is that Triassic faunas of some groups, such as crinoids, appear to arise spontaneously, without any trace of possible ancestors. Moore's views on the subject are as follows (personal communication, 1965):

"A Lower Triassic crinoid assemblage is nonexistent in the record. The Middle Triassic genus—and species—poor echinoderm fauna consists of a little more than *Encrinus, Dadocrinus, Isocrinus* and *Pentacrinus*, all of which can be classed as inadunates or slightly modified inadunates. Certainly camerates and typical flexibles are lacking in the Triassic. The articulates are arbitrarily and somewhat artificially segregated as a subclass. With little doubt, most post-Palaeozoic crinoids are descendants of inadunate stocks. A few Jurassic and Cretaceous forms (e.g. *Phyllocrinus, Eugeniacrinites*, possibly even reef-dwelling crinoids like *Cyathidium*) display earmarks of the Flexibilia but differ greatly from Palaeozoic (except some Permian) genera. It is thinkable that bourgueticrinids and other post-Palaeozoic crinoids with elliptical stems bearing a fulcral ridge on their columnal facets are long-after follow-ups of platycrinitid-type camerates. In short, a case can be made, I think, for Articulata as a hodge-podge of derivatives from all three Palaeozoic crinoid subclasses, though typical representatives of each and all have disappeared."

63

Such a view from the leading crinoid authority has important implications in the understanding of Permo–Triassic faunal changes, and makes any 'neocatastrophic' interpretation more difficult to accept: and this in spite of the fact that crinoids have been used as one of the cornerstones of such an interpretation.

4. The character of early Triassic faunas

Early Triassic faunas, though relatively widespread, are marked by their limited number of major groups, their lack of variety and their general homogeneity. Foraminifera, bryozoa, crinoids and corals, which in both earlier and later times were diverse and numerous, are unknown from Lower Triassic strata. Sponges, brachiopods, asteroids, ophiuroids, echinoids and ostracods are known only from a very small number of forms. Only a single type of shark is known from Triassic deposits. These faunas are dominated by molluscs, especially ammonites, but also to a lesser extent by nautiloids, pelecypods and gastropods. These latter were the groups of marine invertebrates least affected by the Permian extinction.

The general sequence of Triassic faunas clearly suggests some ecological replacement of earlier Palaeozoic forms. Pelecypods, and to some extent gastropods, replaced brachiopods as the dominant thick-shelled benthos. Scleractinian corals replaced the rugose forms as reef builders, crustaceans became the dominant arthropod components of neritic faunas.

5. New faunas from Transcaucasia

The foregoing account of Permo–Triassic changes is one which represents the most commonly accepted interpretation of the fossil record. Recently, however, the description of marine Permo–Triassic faunas from Transcaucasia has provided new information of the greatest importance. Ruzhentsev & Sarytcheva (1965) have given a detailed account of the faunal succession of these strata, which involves major modification of the generally accepted ranges of a number of invertebrate groups. The validity of their conclusions depends on the acceptance of their correlation of the strata involved, but on the data available they appear to have selected the most logical boundary between the Permian and the Trias.

If this is so, the revisions involved in faunal ranges are far reaching. Fusulinids suffered their greatest extinction at the close of the Guadelupian, finally dwindling to extinction in Dzhulfian times. Rugose corals not only survived into the Trias, but are represented by very similar forms (even including some identical species) in the Dzhulfian and Induan. There are seven common nautiloid genera in the two epochs, and three ammonite orders survived into the early Trias, the change in ammonite faunas at the Triassic boundary being no sharper than that at any other system boundary. Bryozoans, though rare in the transition zone, are represented by several common species, as are brachiopods. Productoids carry over into the Trias, while trilobites become extinct well before the end of the Permian. There are 13 ostracod species common to both the Upper Permian and Lower Trias.

These new ranges give a very different impression of Permo–Triassic changes. They prove beyond all reasonable dispute the lack of abrupt or catastrophic faunal change at the system boundaries. It may seem difficult to reconcile them with traditional views, and expecially with the findings of Schindewolf (1954, 1962) for the Salt Range section, where he found all 51 species of the Dzhulfian Upper Productus Limestone to have become extinct by the end of the Permian, the 16 species of the overlying Induan all being new. If one accepts the adequacy of Schindewolf's collecting, which there is no reason to question, the absence of transition in one section is no reason for denying it in another. The most reasonable interpretation of the Salt Range section seems to be that it represents a paraconformity, as Newell (1962) and others have already argued; this has been confirmed by Kummel & Teichert (1966).

Even if the interpretation of the age of the Transcaucasian fauna is questioned (e.g. Chao 1965, p. 1825), the piecemeal pattern of 'Late Palaeozoic' extinction, whatever the precise age involved, is clearly reinforced by the Russian discoveries.

6. Distribution of Lower Triassic strata

One possible explanation of the paucity of Lower Triassic faunas is the paucity of outcrops of strata of that age, as discussed in general terms by Gregory (1955). Some writers have suggested that there are probably no areas in which marine Upper Permian and Lower Triassic deposits lie conformably together; while this is true for most areas, it may not be true for all. There are some regions in the western United States where there is apparent conformity, including southeastern Idaho, where some 5000 feet of Lower Triassic strata overlie the Permian. Central east Greenland (Trumpy 1961) and parts of Indonesia (Sumatra, the Ceram–Timor–Celebes area) and Malaysia (Riow Archipelago, south to Bangka, Billinto) may have continuous marine sedimentation (Umbgrove 1938), although there is some doubt as to this interpretation. Even in such classic Upper Permian areas as that of Timor, however, the localities are few and the detailed correlation obscure.

In some of these areas it is difficult to establish undoubted relationships with the underlying Permian faunas. The same difficulty exists in most of the other areas. Dunbar (1961, p. 227) has commented on the difficulties in correlation of the Upper Permian of Greenland with other areas, its closest similarities being not with beds of supposedly comparable age in the standard American section, but with the Zechstein of Germany and England. He is cautious in interpreting the Greenland Permo–Triassic succession as transitional, even though Trumpy (1961) claims the East Greenland succession to be conformable "and without a gap" in some localities.

Kummel & Teichert (1966) have given a detailed account of the Permo–Triassic sequence in the Salt Range and in the Trans-Indus Ranges of West Pakistan. This has been an area in which Schindewolf (1954) and others have claimed essentially continuous Permo–Triassic sedimentation without any real faunal continuity. Kummel & Teichert have shown that strata with Triassic *Ophioceras* Zone cephalopods overlie the highest Permian and underlie the

65

"Lower Ceratite Limestone" of Waagen, which most observers had regarded as the local base of the Triassic System. They have also shown that, although there is generally a sharp environmental change represented by the Permo–Triassic boundary strata, small assemblages of typically Permian brachiopods (*Enteletes, Spirigerella, Crurithyris, Orthotetina* and *Linoproductus*) are sometimes found in the lowermost strata of the *Ophiøceras* Zone. Cooper (*in* Kummel & Teichert 1966) suggests a Middle rather than Upper Permian 'aspect' for this fauna, but mentions that the presence of clay balls, broken fossils and coarse detritus in the limestone matrix, as well as the absence of spines on the productids, may indicate some reworking. Those fossils occur at two localities, nearly 50 miles apart, in the lowest (dolomitic) unit of the lowest Triassic Kathwai member. Although they are most abundant at the base of the unit, they have also been found to six feet above the base. Kummel regards these as reworked Permian faunas, but Teichert regards at least some of them as indigenous to the Triassic.

The work of Kummel & Teichert is thus of considerable importance in the present discussion. Their precise recognition of the Permo–Triassic boundary differs from that of most earlier authors, and reveals an abrupt lithofacies change between the adjacent strata of the two systems, the white sandstone of the Upper Permian Chhidru Formation, and the basal dolomite of the Kathwai Member of the Lower Triassic Mianwali Formation. The apparent 'gradation' between Permo–Triassic strata has resulted from the earlier misplacement of the boundary.

The bulk of the Permian fauna disappears almost everywhere several feet below the top of the Permian system, at the base of the white sandstone mentioned above, although in one locality this unit contains a number of typical Permian brachiopod genera. This observation at least disposes of the interpretation of the Salt Range–Sunghar Range succession as continuous in any meaningful ecological sense. Kummel and Teichert interpret the boundary as representing a paraconformity of unknown magnitude. Furthermore, if the undoubted Permian brachiopods in the basal Triassic are in fact survivors, rather than being reworked, Triassic ophiceratids must have existed together with them for a period of several thousand years after the abrupt Permo–Triassic lithofacies change.

The situation seems to be that the absence of undoubted transitional Permo–Triassic deposits (except for Transcaucasia) may make the abruptness of the faunal change more apparent than real, but enough Lower Triassic fossil localities are now known to make the existence, though not the speed, of a marked faunal change undoubted. A further complication is the present inadequate state of knowledge of Lower Triassic cephalopod sequences and correlations (Kummel & Steele 1963). Chao's suggestion (1965) that the Dzhulfian Beds are of Kazanian age, being separated by a major non-sequence from 'true' lower Triassic strata, may imply a greater stratigraphic break than has been generally assumed to exist in most areas.

7. Causes of extinction

Extinction itself is seldom simple. The extinction of a population involves as many delicate and complex physical and biological interactions as its survival.

Apart from the intricacy of the factors involved, and the apparent uniqueness of each specific case, extinction may reflect either evolutionary change or cessation. As a taxon undergoes phyletic evolution, it produces a new taxon by its own extinction. In other cases, extinction involves the disappearance of the lineage which the taxon represents.

It seems unlikely that any single factor is sufficient to account for all cases of extinction or that all larger episodes of extinction must be the results of similar causes. It has also been shown that Late Permian extinction was not conspicuously more severe than that of earlier periods of time, and may therefore require no special causal explanation. But it may be that unusual factors were involved in the lack of rapid replacement, which seems to be the most conspicuous feature of Permo–Triassic faunal changes.

(i) *'Neocatastrophism'*

'Neocatastrophist' hypotheses are best represented by the writings of Schindewolf (1962, and earlier references therein). The term is a little ambiguous, but it is used here in a restricted sense to denote the postulate of instantaneous mass extinction. Schindewolf has argued that, in at least some areas, there is no evidence of physical unconformity at era or period boundaries characterized by major faunal changes. Schindewolf suggests that this apparent sedimentary continuity implies that the organic discontinuity is real, rather than apparent, representing a true biological hiatus, rather than non-preservation of a once continuous lineage. Newell (1956; 1962, p. 606) has argued convincingly against this view, stressing the common occurrence of paraconformities in what are apparently continuous rock successions. One need not argue that all such successions must conceal breaks, however, although Newell's arguments are very strong. Even if some successions of Permo–Triassic marine strata were shown to be continuous, this would in no way prevent the possibility of migration of new faunas from other areas. Extinction may well have been very rapid in some late Permian groups, but it was certainly not instantaneous, nor, as Schindewolf's own tables show, was replacement instantaneous (Schindewolf 1962, fig. 2). This does not affect the validity of Schindewolf's views on the mechanism of replacement, which are discussed below (p. 68); but it does contradict his interpretation of the nature of replacement, as sudden, widespread and more or less instantaneous.

(ii) *Extra-terrestrial factors*

A number of authors have, at various times, suggested that Permo-Triassic faunal changes were so extreme that some extra-terrestrial agency must be involved to account for them (e.g. Schindewolf 1954, 1962; Stechow 1954; Wilser 1931). There are good reasons for rejecting all such explanations, quite apart from the Ockhamian economy to which we should remain committed. Certainly such cosmic variations may, and probably have, occurred, but the length of time over which the extinctions took place makes it seem wholly unlikely that any such factor could have been the chief agent. If the effects were so lethal as the proponents of these hypotheses claim, it seems unlikely that certain families, genera and species could have withstood their influence for millions of years longer than others. Furthermore, if radiation was the agent, its effects should be far more conspicuous upon terrestrial organisms than upon aquatic ones. Clarke (1939) and others have shown that water of only a few metres depth is an effective filter of such radiation. But it was marine organisms which were most affected: terrestrial organisms were little influenced at this period of time.

Schindewolf (1954, p. 182) has suggested another possible effect of radiation would be to increase mutation rates and thus produce the 'rapid differentiation' of Triassic times; but the big problem is the lack of early Triassic differentiation, not the excess of it. Even then, it seems to be stretching the argument beyond its limits to suggest that radiation, lethal to so many taxa, may affect others only as a mutational stimulant. Nor can we accept the premise that increased mutation rate, if it ever occurred, would necessarily produce an increase in evolutionary rate. Newell (1956) and George (1958) have also dealt with these problems.

(iii) *Plankton reduction*

Bramlette's hypothesis of a sudden reduction in plankton supply (Bramlette 1965A, B) has much to make it attractive. A major break in the oceanic food chain would have far-reaching consequences for other groups, but whatever its merits for other periods, there is no evidence available for or against such a relationship in Permo–Triassic times.

(iv) *Climatic changes*

One common suggestion is that changes in climate may have produced late Palaeozoic extinction; but again, terrestrial organisms (especially plants), which should indicate the existence of extremely rapid or intense climatic changes in late Palaeozoic times, provide little or no support for this view. Stokes (1960, pp. 438–40) has suggested that diastrophic changes may have influenced oceanic circulation, which might in turn have produced a lowering of sea-water temperature. Such changes would, however, inevitably control land climates, and, if they were sudden, should be reflected by land plants.

In a more general sense, late Palaeozoic times were indeed marked by climatic extremes. The major glaciation of Gondwanaland, and the widespread development of continental red beds, are two reflections of this. How far these factors, as such, influenced marine faunas, is difficult to determine; the only valid comparison we can make is with the Pleistocene glaciation, which involved changes in sea level of the order of 300 ft. This had marked effects on the distribution and survival of many marine organisms, but its net effects seem of a different order of magnitude from those of late Palaeozoic times.

Some have suggested the Permo–Triassic climatic changes may have reduced the salinity of the oceans (e.g. Beurlen 1965). This might have resulted from melting of the late Palaeozoic glaciers, from a reduction in terrigenous salt supplies from arid lands, or perhaps even from the locking-up of salt in late Palaeozoic evaporites. The greatest effects of these changes would be upon stenohaline forms;

yet some of the most stenohaline groups, such as cephalopods, were least influenced by Permo–Triassic changes (Ruzhentsev & Sarytcheva 1965).

Fischer (*in* Nairn, 1964) argued for reduced oceanic salinity, as a result of evaporite formation producing 'pockets' of dense brine on the ocean floors. He argued that those aquatic forms least affected by the late Permian extinctions were euryhaline, whereas those most affected were stenohaline. This is broadly true, but it certainly cannot be the whole explanation. Nautiloids, which were almost totally unaffected, can scarcely be regarded as very different in their tolerance from ammonoids; ostracods are generally amongst the more euryhaline forms, and yet were 'decimated' (Fischer's phrase).

Fischer has argued that the cosmopolitan and meagre Lower Triassic faunas reflect uniform and peculiar conditions. The great rarity or virtual absence from the Lower Triassic of many groups well represented in Upper Permian and Middle Triassic faunas, tends to support this. Most Lower Triassic marine faunas are virtually restricted to bivalve molluscs, ammonoids and inarticulate brachiopods. Fischer regards the early Triassic 'marine faunas' as derived largely from brackish or lagoonal Permian ancestors. Here again, ammonoids and pelecypods make strange bed-fellows in terms of salinity tolerances. Teichert (*in* Nairn 1964, p. 576) has stressed that the presence of a rich echinoid fauna in the lowest Triassic of the Salt Range scarcely indicates reduced salinity, and Lowenstam (*in* Nairn 1964, p. 576) has shown that the scanty oxygen isotope ratios available for the period imply no salinity changes.

(v) *Orogeny*

The view that world-wide, instantaneous diastrophism or orogeny brought about faunal change (both in extinction and rapid evolution, e.g. Strakhov (1948)) was once popular; but there is now overwhelming evidence that such physical changes (e.g. volcanic poisoning of Pavlov (1924) and the isotopic effects of Ivanova (1955)) are neither universal nor instantaneous (e.g. Henbest 1952; Spieker 1956; Westoll 1954; George 1958). For example, to correlate the Variscan orogeny, which lasted from early Carboniferous to late Permian times, with late Permian extinction, implies a plasticity of interpretation of both time and the geographical effects of orogeny that are unacceptable. Indeed, the most severe deformational phases of the Variscan were completed in most areas by early Permian times; while in the western United States mid-Triassic tectonism was far more severe than that of Permo–Triassic transitional time.

(vi) *Racial senescence*

The concept of racial senescence is more of a straw man than a serious hypothesis, yet it seems to have influenced much thinking (see Hawkins 1950, p. 6). Certainly some Permian groups were small in numbers and of limited distribution, some had had a long earlier history (the trilobites are perhaps the best examples), but, even if this is what is meant by 'senility', the phrase is wholly inappropriate for many of the groups which suffered extinction. Permian crinoids, blastoids, foraminifera, dalmaneloids, productoids and other groups display an evolutionary 'vigour' which is far more remarkable than the questionable 'senility' of a few restricted groups.

(vii) *Biological factors*

Nicol (1961) has stressed the need to assess ecologic relationships between organisms involved in periods of extinction. This is never easy, although some food chains have been tentatively reconstructed. On balance, Permo–Triassic extinctions seem to have had a more profound effect upon benthic than upon planktonic or nektonic organisms. This may be a reflection of the fact that at that period, as in later periods, the numbers of taxa of benthic forms far exceed those of pelagic forms, although the latter involve enormous numbers of individuals. Certainly ammonites, which were largely pelagic, shared a similar fate to benthic forms. Whether sessile benthic forms were more affected by extinction than vagrant forms is a particularly difficult question. There is some suggestion that they were (gastropods and pelecypods, for example) being much less influenced than were corals, brachiopods, crinoids and bryozoa; but whether this is a case of cause and effect is more difficult to judge.

(viii) *Eustatic changes in sea level*

The effects of eustatic changes in sea level were conspicuous in late Palaeozoic and early Triassic times. Various authors have pointed out that the restriction of shallow seas, and the high emergent continents of those times, combined to produce a quantitatively unique environment (Newell 1956, 1962; Moore 1954, 1955B; Kummel 1961). Moore has argued that "regression of a shallow sea inevitably produces crowding together of populations so that weaker, less well adapted, marine invertebrates should be weeded out. It seems reasonable to construe times of marine regression as more significant in terms of accelerated evolution than times of marine transgression." (Moore 1954, p. 259; Moore 1955B, p. 483.) Moore's 'accelerated evolution' in this sense implies more rapid extinction.

Rutten (1955) has argued against this thesis, partly on the grounds that transgression of shelf seas does not necessarily supply the genetically isolated niches supposed (by Rutten) to be essential for evolution. Moore (1955) has challenged the view that speciation necessarily requires either a very long period of time or particular conditions of geographical isolation. Newell (1956) has argued that if the shallow shelf seas were destroyed by a eustatic drop in sea level of, say, 100 fathoms, it seems unlikely that neritic benthic faunas would re-establish themselves on the continental slope; even though the shallow depths would still be available, the steeply sloping bottoms would produce a quite different environment. Reduction of optimum population size has particularly severe effects in those aquatic groups in which the chance union of gametes is involved, which will vary logarithmically with population density. This may produce an ultimate biological cause of extinction in a population which has been reduced in numbers of physical causes (see also Kummel (1961, p. 214) and Ruzhentsev & Sarytcheva (1965)).

It seems to the writer that the piecemeal pattern of extinction of, say, the fusulinids is far too extensive in time and uneven in its effects to attribute to a single period of eustatic change in later Permian times.

Perhaps the only relatively recent comparison that we can make is that of the changes in sea level involved during the Pleistocene, which were of some 300 ft. These did not bring about any substantial mass extinctions of either terrestrial or marine organisms.

This neither proves, nor even implies, that there is no connexion between diastrophism and evolution. Local fluctuations in sea level are clearly of major importance in creating and destroying a great variety of different environments. Hallam (1961) and others have shown the influence of such movements on ammonite evolution. But the effects are neither simple nor uniform. The origin of some groups, the extinction of others and the acme of still others have all been correlated with similar eustatic changes. This variety of effects, as well as the piecemeal character of extinction, seem to make the dependence of mass extinction on extreme eustatic fall altogether too simple, though there may be a more general—and much more complex—connexion between them.

8. Towards a synthesis

What then has to be explained? Firstly, the degree and extent of late Permian and early Triassic extinction. This was certainly not instantaneous, it was taxonomically uneven in its effects, and it involved some groups that were already in decline or limited in their geographical distribution, or sometimes both. But it was unusually widespread in its effects. Permo–Triassic extinctions are, like C. S. Lewis' view of miracles, not so much unique, but magnified, and perhaps accelerated, examples of events that are commonplace in the everyday history of life. Perhaps we need no 'special' explanation over and above the explanation of normal extinction (imponderable as that is).

Secondly, the Triassic was also relatively unremarkable. Triassic first appearances are less difficult to interpret, given Permian extinction. Indeed, to the writer it is not the appearance of new taxa, but the time-lag between the disappearance and replacement of the old that is unusual. But such time lags are known in other parts of the column. The ecological replacement of ocean-going reptiles by marine mammals is a familiar example. In Triassic times, even in forms which 'replaced themselves' by the rise of new groups within the same phylum, a conspicuous time lag appears to have existed (corals, bryozoa, brachiopods and crinoids are examples; ammonites are a major exception). To what extent limitation in outcrops of early Triassic rocks are responsible for this is not clear, but it is regarded as an unlikely 'total' explanation. The discovery of Permian elements in the Transcaucasian and possibly the Himalayan Lower Triassic faunas greatly reduces both the size and the regularity of the gap, but does not altogether remove it.

It seems unlikely that there is a simple answer to the difficult questions of extinction. The restriction of late Permian sea-ways, and extreme geographic and oceanographic conditions were unusual, if not unique, terrestrial conditions. Ruzhentsev & Sarytcheva (1965) have shown that Dzhulfian sediments lack rudaceous deposits and are often very thinly developed (measuring from a few

71

score to a few hundred metres in thickness) in contrast to those of earlier stages of the Permian, which are measured in thousands of metres. Certainly these, and probably other, factors interacted to produce the piecemeal extinction of Permo–Triassic times, but there is no evidence that any single factor was of decisive importance.

The homogeneity and lack of diversity of early Triassic faunas seems to be a real feature, and not only an effect of limited outcrops or collecting, although the Transcaucasian faunas have changed our understanding of the exact nature of this. This may be the more direct result of palaeogeographical conditions, though clearly in intricate association with biological and perhaps other physical components. Early Triassic faunas may reflect partial adaptation to the limited deeper waters and perhaps reduced salinity. Examples are the changes in molluscs, the virtual absence of corals in most areas and the survival of some of the more tolerant ostracod species (Ruzhentsev & Sarytcheva 1965).

The homogeneity and lack of variety of Lower Triassic faunas may also be a reflection of the limited extent of shelf seas.

9. Conclusion

This analysis has shown that Permo–Triassic times were not marked by any 'instantaneous' extinction of large numbers of organisms. Certainly several major taxa of Palaeozoic invertebrates became extinct, but the pattern of extinction shows little uniformity. Geographical differences, piecemeal survival of different genera and species, the marked absence of major changes in terrestrial biotas, the recognition of paraconformities in areas once thought to display continuous sedimentation, the suggested extended ranges of many 'Permian' groups into the 'Lower Triassic' of Transcaucasia and the provisional and imprecise nature of Permo–Triassic zonation all argue against any catastrophic view of Permian–Triassic extinction. They also seem to make any single cause of extinction unlikely. Late Palaeozoic extinction rates were by no means unique, and the character of early Triassic faunas is best explained by the multiple interactions of a wide variety of physical and biological factors; but to select any one of these as decisive seems to neglect the complexity of adjustment and response involved in both extinction and survival.

Furthermore, it is particularly difficult in the Permo–Trias to distinguish the 'real' biological extinction of organisms from the variety of effects of geological non-preservation, which have led to oversimplification in the interpretation of the character of extinction. The increasing recognition that late Palaeozoic extinction was neither uniform in its effects, nor instantaneous in its action, the presence of numbers of typical Palaeozoic faunal elements as early Triassic survivors, and the virtual absence of any undisputed Permo–Triassic transitional marine sequences, all suggest that the sharpness of the faunal break has been exaggerated by non-preservation. In this sense, but in this sense only, can restricted late Palaeozoic seas as yet be accepted as the 'cause' of this rapid extinction.

This is not to deny that there was a major decline of Palaeozoic taxa in Permo–Triassic times. This seems to me to be an inevitable conclusion from our present data, however inadequate their detail may be. Furthermore, it was a decline whose total magnitude was probably greater than any that had preceded it, and also perhaps greater than any that followed it (though that of the late Cretaceous was broadly comparable). The decline was followed by the rise of new taxa, whose bulk diversity (measured in generic and family totals) was less than that of its immediate predecessors. None of this is in dispute. But there is no evidence that Palaeozoic extinction was qualitatively, rather than quantitatively, different from that of any other period. Indeed, most periods seem to end with just such an episode of extinction and replacement, though its cause is far from clear and it is probably, at least in part, exaggerated by both our stratigraphical practice and by non-preservation. The pattern, as opposed to the extent, of Permo–Triassic extinction is not different from any of the vast number of other episodes of extinction that make up the fossil record, and probably demands no additional explanation. Even in the case of recently extinct species there is little agreement as to the particular cause of extinction, and it is scarcely surprising that we remain ignorant of the causes of this 'routine, every-day' extinction of fossil species. Our difficulty in interpreting Permo–Triassic faunal changes appears to stem directly from this basic ignorance, rather than from the operation of any unique physical or biological influences in Permo–Triassic times.

ACKNOWLEDGEMENTS. I am deeply grateful to Dr Martin Rudwick, of the University of Cambridge, who read this paper for me at the symposium for which it was written; to Dr Raymond C. Moore, of the University of Kansas, for his advice on Permo–Triassic crinoid faunas; and to Dr Bernhard Kummel, of Harvard University, for his advice on the Permo–Triassic succession of West Pakistan. The paper was written during the early part of the tenure of a National Science Foundation Senior Visiting Scientist Research Fellowship of Ohio State University, which I acknowledge with gratitude.

10. References

BEURLEN, K. 1965. Der Faunenschnitt an der Perm–Trias Grenze. *Z. dt. geol. Ges.* **108**, 88–9.

BRAMLETTE, M. N. 1965A. Mass extinctions of Mesozoic biota. *Science, N.Y.* **150**, 1240.

—— 1965B. Massive extinctions in biota at the end of Mesozoic time. *Science, N.Y.* **148**, 1696–9.

CHAO, KING-KOO 1965. The Permian ammonoid-bearing formations of south China. *Scienta sin.* **14**, 1813–26.

CLARKE, G. L. 1939. The utilization of solar energy by aquatic organisms. In *Problems in Lake Biology. Publs. Am. Ass. Advmt Sci.* **10**, 27–38.

COOPER, G. A. & WILLIAMS, A. 1952. Significance of the stratigraphic distribution of brachiopods. *J. Paleont.* **26**, 326–37.

DUNBAR, C. O. 1961. Permian invertebrate faunas of central east Greenland, *in* Raasch, G. D. (Ed.): *Geology of the Arctic*, vol. 1. University of Toronto Press, pp. 224–30.

GEORGE, T. N. 1958. Rates of change in evolution. *Sci. Prog., Lond.* **46**, 409–28.

GREGORY, J. T. 1955. Vertebrates in the geologic time scale, *in* Poldervaart, A. (Ed.): *Crust of the Earth. Spec. Pap. geol. Soc. Am.* no. 62, 593–608.

HALLAM, A. 1961. Cyclothems, transgressions and faunal change in the Lias of north-west Europe. *Trans. Edinb. geol. Soc.* **18**, 124–74.

HAWKINS, H. L. 1950. Earth movements and organic evolution: Introduction. *Int. Geol. Congr.* **18**(12), 5–6.

HENBEST, L. G. 1952. Significance of evolutionary explosions in geologic time. *J. Paleont.* **26**, 298–318.

HOUSE, M.R. 1963. Bursts in evolution. *Advmnt. Sci., Lond.* **19**, 499–507.

IVANOVA, E. A. 1955. Concerning the problem of the relations of evolutionary stages of the organic world with evolutionary stages of the earth's crust. *Dokl. Akad. Nauk SSSR* **105**, 154–7.

KUMMEL, B. 1953. American Triassic coiled nautiloids. *Prof. Pap. U.S. geol. Surv.* no. 250.

—— 1961. *History of the Earth.* San Francisco (Freeman).

—— & Steele, G. 1962. Ammonites from the *Meekoceras gracilitatus* Zone at Crittenden Spring, Elko County, Nevada. *J. Paleont.* **36**, 638–703.

—— & C. TEICHERT. 1966. Relations between the Permian and Triassic formations in the Salt Range and Trans-Indus Ranges, West Pakistan. *Neues Jb. Geol. Palaönt. Abh.* **125**, 297–333.

MOORE, R. C. 1950. Evolution in the Crinoidea in relation to major palaeogeographic changes in earth history. *Int. geol. Congr.* **18**(12), 27–53.

—— 1952. Evolution rates among crinoids. *J. Paleont.* **26**, 219–318.

—— 1954. Evolution of late Paleozoic invertebrates in response to major oscillations of shallow seas. *Bull. Mus. comp. Zool. Harv.* **112**, 259–86.

—— 1955A. Invertebrates and geologic time scale. In Poldervaart, A. (ed.): *Crust of the earth. Spec. Pap. geol. Soc. Am.* no. 62, 547–74.

—— 1955B. Expansion and contraction of shallow seas as a causal factor in evolution. *Evolution, Lancaster, Pa.* **9**, 482–3.

NAIRN, A. E. M. (Ed.). 1964. *Problems in Palaeoclimatology.* New York (Interscience, Wiley).

NEWELL, N. D. 1952. Periodicity in invertebrate evolution. *J. Paleont.* **26**, 371–85.

—— N. D. 1956. Catastrophism and the fossil record. *Evolution, Lancaster, Pa.* **10**, 97–101.

—— 1962. Paleontological gaps and geochronology. *J. Paleont.* **36**, 592–610.

—— 1965. Mass extinctions at the end of the Cretaceous period. *Science, N.Y.* **149**, 922–4.

NICOL, D. 1961. Biotic associations and extinction. *Syst. Zool.* **10**, 35–41.

PAVLOV, A. P. 1924. About some still little studied factors of extinction. In Pavlov, M. B. *Causes of animal extinction in past geologic epochs.* Moscow (State Publishing House), pp. 89–130.

RUTTEN, M. G. 1955. Evolution and oscillations of shallow shelf seas. *Evolution, Lancaster, Pa.* **9**, 481–2.

RUZHENTSEV, B. E. & SARYTCHEVA, T. T. 1965. Development and change of marine organisms at the Paleozoic and Mesozoic boundary. *Trudy paleont. Inst.* **108**, 1–431.

SCHINDEWOLF, O. H. 1954. Über die möglichen Ursachen der grossen erdgeschichtlichen Faunenschnitte. *Neues Jb. Geol. Palaönt Abh.* **10**, 457–65.

—— 1962. Neokatastrophismus? *Z. dt. geol. Ges.* **114**, 430–45.

SIMPSON, G. G. 1952. Periodicity in vertebrate evolution. *J. Paleont.* **26**, 358–70.

SPIEKER, E. M. 1956. Mountain-building chronology and nature of geologic time scale. *Bull. Am. Ass. Petrol. Geol.* **40**, 1769–815.

STECHOW, E. 1954. Zur Frage nach Ursache des grosen Sterkens am Ende der Kreidezeit. *Neues Jb. Geol. Palaönt. Mh.* 183–6.

STOKES, W. L. 1960. *Essentials of Earth History.* Englewood Cliffs, N.J. (Prentice-Hall).

STRAKHOV, H. M. 1948. *Principles of Historical Geology,* pt. II. Moscow (State Geological Publishing House).

THOMPSON, M. L. 1948. Studies of American fusulinids. *Paleont. Contr. Univ. Kans.* Protozoa, Art. I, 1–184.

TRÜMPY, R. 1961. Triassic of Greenland In Raasch, G. D. (ed.): *Geology of the Arctic.* University of Toronto Press, pp. 248–54.

UMBGROVE, J. H. F. 1938. Geological history of the East Indies. *Bull. Am. Ass. Petrol. Geol.* **22**, 1–70.

WESTOLL, T. S. 1954. Mountain revolutions and organic evolution. *In* Huxley, J., Hardy, A. C. & Ford, E. (Eds.): *Evolution as a process.* London (Allen & Unwin).

WILLIAMS, A. 1957. Evolutionary rates in brachiopods. *Geol. Mag.* **94,** 201–11.

WILSER, J. L. 1931. *Lichtreaktionen in der Fossilen Tierwelt.* Berlin (Verlag von Gebrüder Borntraeger.)

Manuscript submitted June 1966.

[Professor] F. H. T. Rhodes, D.SC. PH.D. F.G.S.

Department of Geology, University College of Swansea, Singleton Park, Swansea, Glamorgan, Wales.

DISCUSSION

Dr J. M. HANCOCK mentioned that the work of Trümpy on the Triassic ammonite succession in east Greenland suggests that there are probably three ammonite zones missing at the base of the Trias in the Salt Range of the Himalaya. This may explain, in part, the abrupt faunal change that Schindewolf reports at the boundary between the Permian and the Trias in the Salt Range.

Dr D. V. AGER, in connexion with Dr Rudwick's comment on the recent discovery of productid and other typically Permian brachiopods in the Lower Triassic beds of Transcaucasia, drew attention to Professor Trümpy's record, several years ago, of productids in the Lower Trias of East Greenland, and more recently Kummel and Teichert have a similar record from the Salt Range of West Pakistan. There now seemed to be no major group of brachiopods which terminated actually at the Permo–Triassic boundary.

Dr J. D. HUDSON commented that some speakers had appeared to imply that nothing drastic had happened to various invertebrate groups at, for instance, the Permo–Triassic boundary, although their habitats, the shallow continental shelves, had almost disappeared. It seemed to the speaker that if, as he believed, such habitats really had been greatly diminished, something of great significance to the animal populations, though perhaps not to the distribution of named taxa, had clearly happened.

If changes in the geological environment, in this case rising and falling sea level, interacted at all with animal populations and their evolution, and hence with the fossil record, we must expect to find that they also affected the availability of evidence for reconstructing that record. We could not hope both to observe the effects of diminished continental shelves *and* to find a widespread record of those shelves.

This made it difficult, though hopefully not impossible, to sort out real changes from artefacts of deficient observation in cases of this kind.

Dr R. CROWSON asked whether coral reefs persist anywhere in the world in late Permain and early Triassic times? Coral reefs are a very important type of habitat, and if they disappeared at this time it may have had major effects on other animals.

Professor RHODES later contributed the following reply:

I am grateful for Dr Hancock's observation that there may be a disconformity involving the absence of three ammonite zones at the base of the Salt Range Triassic succession. If this proves to be the case, then Kummel and Teichert's discovery of 'Permian' brachiopods in the lower Triassic is even more remarkable. These authors have shown that there is certainly a paraconformity in the Salt **Range** section, Lower Triassic granular dolomites resting on white sandstones. Furthermore, the affinities of the Lower Triassic brachiopods, whatever their origin, seem to be closer to late Dzhulfian brachiopod faunas from Armenia, than to those of the underlying Salt Range Permian.

I know of no Late Permian or Early Triassic reefs, but I hope the coelenterate and carbonate specialists may be able to give an authoritative answer to Dr Crowson's interesting question.

Dr Ager's observation that no major brachiopod group became extinct at precisely the Permo–Triassic boundary is a welcome confirmation of my general thesis that extinction was gradual and piecemeal, rather than rapid and universal. It differed in magnitude but not in kind from other episodes of extinction in the fossil record. It is for this reason that I find it difficult to accept Dr

Hudson's suggestion that something 'drastic' happened at the Permo–Triassic boundary. Certain typical Palaeozoic groups (conodonts, trepostome bryozoans and some brachiopods, for example) carried through into the Triassic. Other major taxa, which did become extinct, did so before and after the Permo–Triassic boundary. I agree fully with Dr Hudson's observation of the paucity of the record of this particular period of geological time. Only about a dozen Late Permian sequences have been described, and there are still fewer of early Triassic age. Of the four areas of once supposedly continuous sedimentation, two are now regarded as probably discontinuous, a third is in non-marine strata and opinion is somewhat divided on the precise ages of strata in the remaining area. Certainly Late Permian times were marked by extensive marine regression and the Permo–Triassic faunal 'gap' is partly a result of lack of outcrop, but I remain sceptical about both the extent and the influence of the regression as such. The very fact that we have even a few exposures of this age indicates that in at least some localities Late Permian–Early Triassic seas covered a greater area than do the oceans of today. Nor do I believe that we can find any single explanation such as regression to account for the high rate but spasmodic pattern of Permo–Triassic extinction on the one hand, or the radically different fates of related groups in similar environments on the other. Why, for example, should the ammonites suffer near-extinction in Late Permian times, but the nautiloids remain relatively unaffected?

Changes in terrestrial vertebrate faunas during the Mesozoic

C. B. COX

CONTENTS

SUMMARY

The precise time-range of any terrestrial group is difficult to establish, due to the uncertainties of preservation and discovery and due to the difficulty of ascertaining the relative ages of faunas from different areas. Differences between such faunas may be due to ecological and zoogeographical factors as well as to age differences. Even when a relative time-sequence has been established, it is difficult to correlate this with the standard section for the period; this is particularly true for the Triassic faunas.

As seen in the South African record, the climate became progressively hotter and drier from the Carboniferous Dwyka glaciation until the deserts of the Upper Triassic. The earliest Triassic fauna is a swamp fauna which still included elements of most of the more conservative, synapsid reptiles. During the remainder of the Triassic, these synapsids were gradually replaced by the evolving diapsids. The more primitive members of the Diapsida were themselves replaced in the Jurassic by more progressive members of the group.

The earliest mammals, those of the Triassic and Jurassic, were probably homoiothermal though not viviparous. None larger than a cat is known until immediately after the disappearance of the dinosaurs. The reasons for this apparent inability of somewhat larger (e.g. pig-sized) mammals to co-exist with the dinosaurs are not obvious.

1. Introduction

No OTHER geological period witnessed as many changes in its vertebrate fauna as did the Triassic. Reptile history is largely the story of two great adaptive radiations, that of the synapsid or mammal-like reptiles, and that of the diapsid reptiles, including the dinosaurs and their relatives. The radiation of the synapsids reached its peak during the late Permian, when these reptiles provided the dominant terrestrial vertebrate fauna, including many different types both herbivorous and carnivorous. The Triassic sees the virtual extinction of the synapsids and the beginning of that radiation of the archosaurian reptiles which, from the late Triassic onwards, provided the bulk of the terrestrial vertebrate fauna. Though it was not until post-Cretaceous times that the archosaurs were replaced by the radiation of the mammals, the earliest known mammal is also found in an Upper Triassic deposit. The only time at which the lepidosaurian reptiles provided a prominent component of the terrestrial vertebrate fauna was during the Triassic, when the rhynchosaurs flourished. In the seas, the plesiosaurs

The Fossil Record, pp. 77–89. Geological Society of London, 1967. Printed in Northern Ireland.

and ichthyosaurs both appeared during the Triassic and, finally, the earliest known chelonian is also of Triassic age.

The patterns of evolutionary change and faunal replacement in the Mesozoic can only be understood if the ranges in time of the different reptilian groups are first established. This, in itself, raises several problems. Even if the whole of the Earth's surface is considered, many periods of the Earth's history are not represented by fossil-bearing strata. Even where such strata are known, particular faunal elements may not be found until after many years of collecting. For example, until a few years ago it was usual to refer to the phytosaurs as a Northern Hemisphere group, unknown in the Gondwana continents; however, they have now been discovered in Madagascar (Guth 1963). Similarly, though rhynchosaurs had been found in Africa, India, Britain and South America, they were unknown in North America until their recent discovery in Nova Scotia (Baird 1962). Gaps of this kind in the record are doubtless often due to the strictly limited ecological range of any fossil fauna. In the Santa Maria Formation of Brazil, the herbivorous element in the reptilian fauna is represented in two localities by dicynodonts; in the third locality, in contrast, dicynodonts are absent and the herbivores are instead represented by rhynchosaurs (Cox 1965, p. 509). In other cases the absence of a particular group seems quite inexplicable. To take the rhynchosaurs again, the group is quite unknown from the fairly abundant mid-Norian Stubensandstein fauna of Germany, though they are found in the very similar fauna of the Lossiemouth Beds of Scotland, which seem to be of the same age (Walker 1961).

The question of the age of these Lossiemouth Beds introduces the second major difficulty in defining the range in time of a particular group: that of establishing the relative ages of faunas from different areas. A complete and continuous record of successive fossil faunas does not exist in any single part of the world. As can be seen from Table 1, the known terrestrial vertebrate faunas of the Triassic and Jurassic are all of strictly limited time-span, and many gaps exist in the fossil record of every continent. Some of the known faunas contain an extremely limited ecological range of animals (e.g. that of the Lower Jurassic fissure-fillings of the Somerset area), while others have only recently been discovered and their fauna is as yet incompletely known (e.g. the Puesto Viejo fauna of Argentina, and the Kota and Yerrapalli faunas of India) (Jain, Robinson & Chowdhury 1962, 1964).

Occasionally, the history of a particular group of vertebrates is known so well that the group itself can be used as a standard. Faunas which contain primitive members of that group are then presumably of earlier date than those containing more advanced forms; Gregory (1962) has recently used the phytosaurs in this way. However, the patterns of evolution of the vertebrates are rarely sufficiently simple or well documented for this method to be widely applicable. Usually, comparative dating relies upon a comparison of the faunas as a whole, and an analysis of the differences between them. Some of these differences may be due to the faunas being of different age; others may, as already noted, be ecological. Other differences may be zoogeographical, so that a particular group may be absent from one fauna because it had not colonized the continent in question.

TABLE 1. The main Triassic and Jurassic deposits which contain terrestrial vertebrates. Arrows indicate the range of uncertainty of the stratigraphical position of the deposits concerned.

	S. AMERICA	N. AMERICA	EURASIA	INDIA	AFRICA
U. JURASSIC		Morrison	Solenhofen Oxford Clay		Tendaguru
M. JURASSIC			Stonesfield Slate		Morocco Madagascar
L. JURASSIC		Navajo	Fissure fillings	Kota	
RHAETIC		Kayenta Dinosaur Canyon	Rhaetic; Lufeng		↑ ?
NORIAN		Portland Arkose Newark, etc. Popo Agie	Stubensandstein Blasensandstein	↑ ? Maleri	Cave Sandstone U. Red Beds Passage Beds
CARNIAN	Ischigualasto			↓ ?	
LADINIAN	Santa Maria				↓ ?
ANISIAN					Manda
SCYTHIAN	Puesto Viejo		Er-Ma-Ying; VI Sinkiang; V	Yerrapalli Panchet	Cynognathus zone Lystrosaurus zone

Though only those differences which result from a discrepancy in age are significant in dating the fauna, it is not always possible to distinguish these from differences due to ecological or zoogeographical variations. For example, the Manda fauna of East Africa differs from the Santa Maria fauna of South America; this may be because it is of slightly earlier age, or because the fauna of Africa was slightly more conservative than the contemporary fauna of South America (Cox 1965). Similarly, where a climatic change has occurred, two faunas which differ in age may also necessarily differ in their ecological character. Where one is dealing with a fairly continuous record from a single area, the climatic change may be comparatively clear, so that it does not greatly complicate the task of correlating the faunas, e.g. the changes in the climate of southern Africa from the Upper Carboniferous to the Upper Triassic, which will be described below.

Where both the faunas involved include a fairly wide range of vertebrate groups and are of similar ecological type, it may be possible to estimate their relative ages with some confidence—e.g. the Norian faunas of North America and Europe, which appear to be contemporary in age (Gregory 1962; Walker 1961). In other cases, where a fauna is known from a very small number of specimens, or is of very limited ecological range, or differs greatly in its ecology from other faunas of the same period, it may not be possible to estimate its age except within very wide limits. Two examples of such faunas are shown in Table 1: the Maleri fauna of

India (Chowdhury 1965) and the faunas of the Cave Sandstones, Upper Red Beds and Passage Beds of South Africa (Charig, Attridge & Crompton 1965).

Even when all the known terrestrial vertebrate faunas have been arranged, as far as possible, in their correct temporal sequence, one is still faced with the problem of correlating this relative sequence with the stages of the standard succession for the period. This is particularly difficult in the case of the German Triassic standard succession. The lowest portion of this, the Bunter, consists of fresh-water deposits (the lower half of which are non-fossiliferous). This is followed by the marine Muschelkalk deposits, which in turn are followed by the mainly continental deposits of the Keuper. As a result of these extreme ecological changes, it is very difficult to correlate non-European terrestrial faunas with the standard German sequence, since only the German Upper Triassic Keuper contains an ecologically comparable fauna. Terrestrial vertebrate faunas similarly cannot be correlated with the French marine Alpine ammonite sequence.

Though they cannot, then, be followed in Europe, the changes in the terrestrial vertebrate faunas of the early Triassic are well represented by the extensive series of deposits in southern and east-central Africa. The Lower Triassic reptilian zones of the South African Karroo (the Lystrosaurus zone and the Cynognathus zone) can be related to the standard German Triassic by indirect means, as follows. A primitive capito sauroid amphibian, *Wetlugosaurus*, is found in Greenland above a zone containing the ammonite genus *Proptychites* (Säve-Söderbergh 1935). This ammonite genus is a zone-fossil which indicates a Gyronitan age (Spath 1934), i.e. Induan or Lower Scythian in other terminologies. *Wetlugosaurus*, which may then be accepted as of Induan age, occurs also in the Lystrosaurus zone of South Africa. Above this zone is the Cynognathus zone, in which *Wetlugosaurus* is absent and slightly more advanced capitosauroids such as *Parotosaurus* appear. *Parotosaurus* is known also from the German Upper Bunter. It seems reasonable, therefore, to regard the South African Cynognathus zone and the German Upper Bunter as both of Upper Scythian, Olenekian, age; the non-fossiliferous German Lower Bunter may be regarded as equivalent to the South African Lystrosaurus zone, i.e. of Lower Scythian, Induan, age.

2. Mesozoic faunal changes

In order to understand the faunal changes of the South African Karroo series, it is necessary to begin even earlier in time than the Lystrosaurus zone, as conditions in that zone seem to be the culmination of a progressive change in climate, flora and fauna which commenced with the Carboniferous Dwyka glaciation. From that time, the climate of southern Africa appears to have become progressively warmer and wetter until Lystrosaurus zone times. Three main habitats seem to have been present in the Upper Permian Tapinocephalus, Endothiodon and Kistecephalus zones of the Karroo (Plumstead 1963):

(1) Small fresh-water lakes;
(2) Extensive low-lying ground with mud-swamps, and a flora consisting mainly of the small horsetail *Schizoneura*;

(3) Drier ground with *Glossopteris* woodland; the trees have clear growth-rings, implying a markedly seasonal climate (Lacey 1961).

As might be expected, it is the lowland swamp-fauna which is most abundantly preserved in the fossil record. The pareiasaurs and dinocephalians are the herbivores of the lowest zones, but by Kistecephalus zone times these have been almost wholly replaced by a varied array of both large and small dicynodonts. The main carnivores are the gorgonopsids and the therocephalians.

If the Lystrosaurus zone fauna is compared with that of these earlier zones, three obvious differences can be seen (Parrington 1948). Firstly, the carnivorous gorgonopsids and therocephalians have been replaced by the bauriamorphs (themselves a progressive derivative of the therocephalians) and by the cynodonts. (Both these two groups appear first in the earlier zones, but are there less common and varied). Secondly, these Lystrosaurus zone carnivores are all of small size. Thirdly, the small dicynodonts are absent (with the exception of one rare genus) and the dicynodonts are represented only by the aberrant hippopotamus-like genus *Lystrosaurus*. Other semi-aquatic elements in the fauna are the archosaurian reptile *Chasmatosaurus* and several genera of large labyrinthodont amphibians.

As Parrington (1948, p. 442) has stated "The elimination of all non-aquatic forms of any size at the beginning of the Trias, together with the abundance of the aquatic *Lystrosaurus*, suggests that there was a great increase in the extent of the swamps and that the remaining areas of dry land were of small size though they may have been numerous". As Parrington notes, this environmental change appears to have been surprisingly widespread, as this *Lystrosaurus–Chasmatosaurus* fauna is present also in Sinkiang, western China.

Higher ground must, of course, have existed around the *Lystrosaurus* swamps, as is shown by the presence in the swamp deposits of large trunks of the conifer-like tree *Dadoxylon* (again, with marked seasonal growth-rings). The unknown fauna of these uplands must have included dicynodonts, since large terrestrial members of this group are found again in the succeeding Cynognathus zone fauna, and these are unlikely to have evolved from the specialized genus *Lystrosaurus*.

Though large dicynodonts reappear in the Cynognathus zone, the smaller dicynodonts do not. It is impossible to tell whether this was due to some change in the flora, or whether they were not sufficiently agile to evade the more advanced predators which were beginning to appear. (It may be significant that these smaller dicynodonts were replaced ecologically by two herbivorous or omnivorous branches of their more agile, basically carnivorous relatives, the cynodonts.) The new predators of the Cynognathus zone are the early pseudosuchians, which replace both the synapsid bauriamorphs and the early archosaur *Erythrosuchus*. The Cynognathus zone itself marks the beginning of drier conditions, and from then onwards the climate of southern Africa seems to have become progressively drier. The flora changes, also, to one dominated by the seed-fern *Dicroidium* (also known as *Thinnfeldia*). This climatic change culminates in the Upper Triassic hot deserts of the Red Beds and Cave Sandstones.

In South Africa itself, the Lower Triassic Cynognathus zone is followed by the poorly-fossiliferous Molteno Beds. However, further north in Tanzania, the

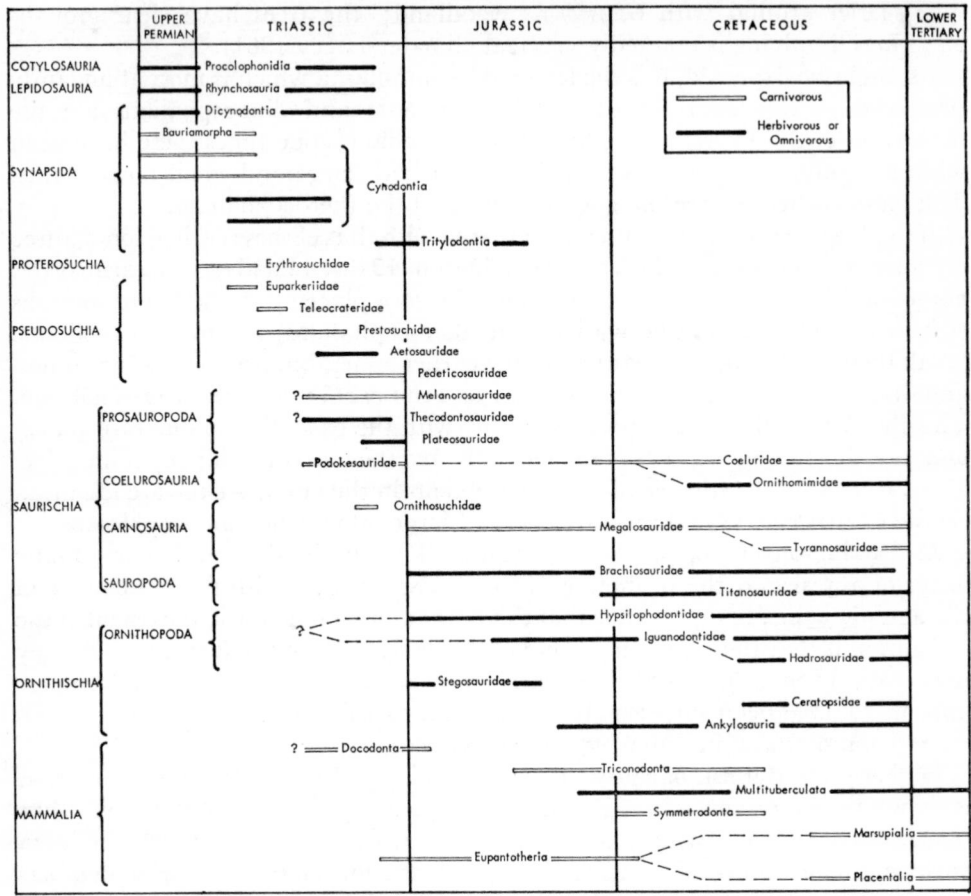

F ɪ ɢ. 1. Time ranges of the Mesozoic terrestrial vertebrates. Some groups appear for the first time in the Passage Beds or Red Beds of South Africa; the uncertain geological age of these faunas is indicated by a question mark (?).

Manda Formation has a fauna which appears to be rather more advanced, but which does also contain the Cynognathus zone dicynodont genus *Kannemeyeria* (Cruickshank 1965). Cynodonts, too, continue into the Manda Formation, but two new faunal elements appear: more advanced pseudosuchian reptiles, and rhynchosaurs.

The rhynchosaurs are a very distinctive element; they are very specialized herbivorous lepidosaurs, found only in the Triassic. Romer (1960) has even suggested that they are restricted to the Middle Triassic. However, they are found in Scotland with the pseudosuchian *Stagonolepis*, which is very closely related to the genus *Aëtosaurus* of the German mid-Norian Stubensandstein (Walker 1961) and they are also found in the Indian Maleri Formation with the labyrinthodont amphibian *Metoposaurus*, which is also an Upper Triassic form

(Chowdhury 1965). There seems, in any case, little reason for thinking that their evolution was in any way connected with the ebb and flow of the Muschelkalk Sea over Europe.

The Manda Formation is usually regarded as the beginning of Anisian, Middle Triassic, times. This is supported by the close similarity between *Mandasuchus* (Charig 1966) from the Manda Formation, and *Ticinosuchus* (Krebs 1965) from Monte San Giorgio, Switzerland. This latter is from a stratum in a mainly marine series and can be definitely assigned to the Anisian.

Faunas similar to that of the Manda Formation are known also in Brazil and Argentina, but no genera are common to these different areas. The fauna of the Brazilian Santa Maria Formation seems to be slightly more advanced than that of the Manda Formation, and that of the Argentinian Ischigualasto Beds seems a little more advanced again, as it contains saurischians. It seems probable, therefore, that these three faunas may form a series, but it is impossible to be sure whether the latest of them (the Ischigualasto fauna) should be regarded as of late Middle Triassic (i.e. Ladinian) age or of early Upper Triassic (i.e. Carnian) age. As argued in an earlier paper (Cox 1965), the similarity between *Aetosauroides* from Ischigualasto and *Aëtosaurus* from the German Norian Stubensandstein makes the later date somewhat more likely.

Another series of faunas which appears to be later than that of the Manda Formation is that of the South African Passage Beds, Red Beds and Cave Sandstones (Charig, Attridge & Crompton 1965). Unfortunately, these beds are rather poorly fossiliferous, and their fauna is of rather restricted nature. That of the lowest, the Passage Beds, is difficult to date, as it contains both cynognathid cynodonts (otherwise unknown later than the Anisian Manda Formation) and footprints apparently made by sauropod dinosaurs (otherwise unknown before the Jurassic). It is particularly unfortunate that these faunas are so difficult to date accurately, for the Passage Beds also contain the earliest known prosauropods, including both melanorosaurs and thecodontosaurs, while the succeeding Red Beds contain both the earliest known ornithischians (e.g. *Lycorhinus*, Crompton & Charig 1962) and the earliest known mammal, *Erythrotherium* (Crompton 1964).

As already mentioned, these Upper Triassic South African desert sandstone beds represent the culmination of the progressive increase in aridity which began in the Lower Triassic. It seems reasonable to correlate the appearance of a variety of archosaurian reptiles (both pseudosuchians and early dinosaurs) with this climatic change. It is clear that this new reptile fauna at first co-existed with the more archaic procolophonid–rhynchosaur–synapsid fauna. Elements of both faunas are found together in the Norian Lossiemouth Beds of Scotland (Walker 1961) and in the probably Carnian Ischigualasto Beds of Argentina (Cox 1965). The variety of pseudosuchians and saurischians that appears in Norian times also implies that these groups must have had a considerable earlier history. This history is largely unknown, presumably because these fundamentally active and fast-moving groups, comparable to the modern ungulates, may have evolved on higher ground, whilst most of the Lower and Middle Triassic faunas represent lowland environments.

Until recently, it was thought that the dinosaurs evolved (probably polyphyleti-cally) from the later, Upper Triassic members of the Pseudosuchia. It is now clear that the dinosaurs themselves had already appeared by this time, and that their ancestry must instead be sought in forms such as the Lower Triassic genus *Euparkeria* (Walker 1964). Many of the Upper Triassic genera which were formerly placed in the Pseudosuchia are now themselves regarded as saurischian dinosaurs, or as early members of the Crocodilia and unrelated to the dinosaurs. The only Upper Triassic terrestrial forms which are still regarded as pseudo-suchians are the carnivorous aëtosaurids, which seem to have died out, like the procolophonid–rhynchosaur–dicynodont–cynodont complex, after mid-Norian Stubensandstein times. The extinction of all these groups was probably due to competition from ecologically equivalent groups amongst the saurischian and ornithischian dinosaurs, whose unquestioned dominance dates from this time (the Upper Norian–Rhaetic; Chowdhury 1965) and continues throughout both the Jurassic and the Cretaceous. As can be seen from Fig. 1, the dinosaurs included medium-sized and large forms in both herbivores and carnivores.

Compared with the dinosaurs, the smaller components of the Jurassic terrestrial fauna are much less readily found, and much less completely preserved, so that they are far less well known. For example, six families of lizard appear suddenly in the Upper Jurassic, so that this group must have originated much earlier—as is in any case indicated by the presence of an ancestral form in the Triassic. Similarly, several families of mammal are known from the Rhaetic/Jurassic boundary, and nine families had differentiated by the beginning of the Cretaceous.

Compared with the dramatic faunal changes of the Triassic, very little change seems to have taken place during the Jurassic and Cretaceous. Except for the stegosaurs, all the dinosaur lines which had appeared in the Jurassic survived into the Upper Cretaceous. Only three new dinosaur groups evolved during the Cretaceous; as Russell has suggested, the appearance of at least two of these (the hadrosaurs and the ceratopsians) seems to be correlated with the great change in plant life which occurred "at about the middle of the Cretaceous period, when the angiosperms gradually but decisively displaced the gymnosperms as the dominant form of plant life" (Russell 1965, p. 499).

3. Significance of the faunal changes

In broad outline, the changes in terrestrial vertebrate faunas which took place during the Mesozoic were as follows. The earliest faunas, those of the lower Triassic, were mainly composed of members of the successful Permian reptile groups, the cotylosaurs and the synapsids, plus the aberrant rhynchosaurid lepidosaurs. The radiation of the archosaurian reptiles did not take place until the Triassic itself. The more archaic Permian relicts, the less progressive pseudo-suchian archosaurs, and the early prosauropod saurischians had all disappeared by the end of the Triassic. The saurischians and ornithischians formed the dominant medium and large-sized elements of the terrestrial fauna throughout the remainder of the Mesozoic. Only then did the little mammals, which had appeared in much earlier Triassic times, in turn undergo a great adaptive radiation to recolonize the ecological niches left vacant by the vanished dinosaurs.

These changes pose several questions. Why did the more archaic groups die out during the Triassic? Since both archosaurs and the mammals appeared in the Triassic, why did the archosaurs provide only the medium and large-sized elements of the Jurassic and Cretaceous fauna, and the mammals provide only the small elements? Finally, of course, why did the archosaurs themselves die out at the end of the Cretaceous?

Though many explanations for the last of these questions have been put forward during the last 50 years or so, a new and attractive hypothesis has recently been suggested by Russell (1965). Some earlier workers have suggested that the dinosaurs may have been homoiothermal (i.e. could preserve their body temperature at a more or less constant level, irrespective of environmental temperature changes) and hence could maintain a fairly constant level of activity. Russell further points out that they lacked the external insulating layer, such as hair or feathers, possessed by the living homoiothermal mammals and birds. If the climate became cooler, such an animal would not be able to reduce its heat loss by increasing its external insulation, as did the woolly rhino or the woolly mammoth during the Pleistocene Ice Ages. Nor, since the normal functioning of its physiological processes would depend on the maintenance of its body temperature, would such a dinosaur be able to adjust to the new conditions by reducing its rate of metabolism and activity, as does a non-homoiothermal animal. Russell therefore suggests that the imperfectly homoiothermal dinosaurs were vulnerable to any such climatic change, and that their extinction may have been caused by a progressive decrease in the prevailing temperature and humidity-level, and accentuation of the climatic seasons.

It seems possible that differences in physiological processes and tolerances may help to explain some of the other questions posed above. For example, it seems reasonable to assume that reptiles such as the cotylosaurs and early synapsids, were poikilothermal (i.e. could not, if environmental temperatures changed, preserve a constant level of body temperature). This might *a priori* be expected in such early tetrapods, while their clumsy construction also suggests that their capability for fast, continuous locomotion was strictly limited, as it is in modern poikilothermal reptiles. It is not, then, surprising that these archaic reptiles should have been gradually replaced during the Triassic by the more physiologically advanced archosaurs and mammals.

To turn now to the ecological relationships between the archosaurs and the mammals, it seems clear that the differences between the thermo-regulatory characteristics of these two groups would have led to considerable differences in their ecological potentialities. In the absence of any insulatory covering to the body surface, a large animal is in some ways at a considerable advantage compared with a smaller one, because it will have a smaller surface-area : volume ratio. Though, under identical conditions, it will lose heat at the same rate (per cm^2 of body surface) as will the smaller animal, this will represent a smaller fraction of its total thermal capacity, and its temperature change will therefore be smaller. This was clearly shown by Colbert, Cowles & Bogert (1946) who found that, under similar conditions, the temperature of a 13 000 g alligator rose by 1 °c every $7\frac{1}{2}$ minutes, while that of a 50 g alligator rose by 1 °c in only $1\frac{1}{2}$ minutes. Extrapolating these results to estimate the rate of temperature change of a dinosaur weighing *c.* 9 000 kg, Colbert *et al.* estimated that its temperature would probably have changed by 1 °c in about 86 hours. The size of these archosaurs must therefore in itself have permitted the maintenance of a fairly stable level of body temperature, whether or not such active physiological mechanisms as shivering were also present. As Colbert *et al.* suggest, the resulting physiological advantage for the large individual was probably the cause of the appearance of the extremely large Mesozoic archosaurs[1].

Conversely, of course, the smaller individual is far more affected by change in external temperatures. Even in climates which were in general warm or even hot, temperatures might frequently fall, during the night or during rainstorms, to levels at which a small archosaur lacking any insulatory body covering might find it impossible to maintain its body temperature at the 'normal' level. If, as in modern homoiotherms, such a change in body temperature interfered with the normal functioning of the body's physiological processes, such a small archosaur would be at a disadvantage compared with either a small mammal, whose insulation of hair would greatly reduce its heat-loss during these colder periods, or with a poikilothermal reptile such as the Jurassic lizards. The limiting factor was probably the size of the young, rather than of the adult, animal; even if an adult dinosaur only three feet long were able to tolerate the fluctuations in environmental temperatures, its four-inch-long hatchlings might well have found them fatal.

In considering the problems of competition between dinosaurs and mammals, one cannot assume that these early mammals possessed all the characteristics of the modern members of the group. The marsupials and the placental mammals appear to have separated by Upper Cretaceous times (Simpson 1961). The presence of hair, sweat glands, a diaphragm and enucleate red blood corpuscles in both groups strongly suggests that their common ancestor had already developed an homoiothermal metabolism. On the other hand, the two groups had evolved differing methods in coping with the problem of maintaining the temperature of developing and newly-born or newly-hatched homoiotherms. Though the presence of milk glands in both marsupials and placentals suggests that some form of parental care and early nourishment of the young had developed in their common Mesozoic ancestor, the pattern of early development is very different in the two groups. Instead of remaining within the uterus, in placental fashion, the young marsupial is born at a relatively early stage of development and undergoes further development within the pouch. These differences between the two groups appear to be due to a difference in the relationships of their genital and urinary

---

[1] Though there is at least one concomitant disadvantage: the amount of heat generated during exercise depends on body volume, and will therefore be greater in a large animal, whose lower surface-area : volume ratio will simultaneously make it more difficult to dissipate this heat via the skin.

ducts (Wood Jones 1943), and suggest that their common Mesozoic ancestor had not yet developed full viviparity. Instead, these early mammals were probably more like the monotremes, which still lay an egg in reptilian fashion and afterwards keep it warm by behavioural adaptations, as do the birds.

It may, then, be that the somewhat delayed success of the mammals was, in part at least, because they did not develop mammalian reproductive methods until a considerable time after they had developed the osteological and physiological characteristics of mammals. Even if this is so, it must still be admitted that the marsupials and placentals are likely to have developed their characteristic reproductive methods by Upper Cretaceous times.

One can, then, suggest some possible factors which may help to explain the comparative lack of success of the earlier Mesozoic mammals, and to explain why no small-sized dinosaurs seem to have existed. However, there still seems to be no obvious reason for the failure of the mammals to provide any larger sized elements in the Mesozoic fauna. Such large mammals, including both carnivores (the creodonts) and herbivores (the early ungulates) do rapidly appear in the Paleocene, immediately after the disappearance of the dinosaurs. The multituberculate mammals, though of small size during the Mesozoic, also produce much larger genera (e.g. *Taeniolabis*) in the early Paleocene. These facts do seem to indicate that it was only the presence of the dinosaurs that prevented the appearance of larger mammals during the late Mesozoic. However, the reason for this is not apparent; the mammals appear to have been homoiothermal, like the dinosaurs, and to have had the additional advantages of external insulation and, in the Upper Cretaceous at least, of viviparous reproductive methods.

References

BAIRD, D. 1962. Rhynchosaurs in the late Triassic of Nova Scotia. Abstract in *Programme of 1962 Meeting.* Washington (Geological Society of America).

CHARIG, A. J. 1966. Preliminary note on the archosaurs in the Manda Formation (Middle Trias) of Tanzania. *Palaeontology* [in press].

——, ATTRIDGE, J. & CROMPTON, A. W. 1965. On the origin of the sauropods and the classification of the Saurischia. *Proc. Linn. Soc. Lond.* **176**, 197–221.

CHOWDHURY, T. R. 1965. A new metoposaurid amphibian from the Upper Triassic Maleri Formation of Central India. *Phil. Trans. R. Soc.* (B) **250**, 1–52.

COLBERT, E. H., COWLES, R. B. & BOGERT, C. M. 1946. Temperature tolerances in the American alligator and their bearing on the habits, evolution and extinction of the dinosaurs. *Bull. Am. Mus. nat. Hist.* **86**, 327–74.

Cox, C. B. 1965. New Triassic dicynodonts from South America, their origins and relationships. *Phil. Trans. R. Soc.* (B) **248**, 457–516.

CROMPTON, A. W. 1964. A preliminary description of a new mammal from the Upper Triassic of South Africa. *Proc. zool. Soc. Lond.* **142**, 441–52.

—— & CHARIG, A. J. 1962. A new ornithischian from the Upper Triassic of South Africa. *Nature, Lond.* **196**, 1074–7.

CRUICKSHANK, A. R. I. 1965. On a specimen of the anomodont reptile *Kannemeyeria latifrons* (Broom) from the Manda Formation of Tanganyika, Tanzania. *Proc. Linn. Soc. Lond.* **176**, 149–57.

GREGORY, J. T. 1962. The genera of phytosaurs. *Am. Jl Sci.* **260,** 652–90.

GUTH, C. 1963. Au sujet de restes de reptiles de Madagascar. *C.r. hebd. Séanc. Acad. Sci., Paris* **256,** 2661–3.

JAIN, S. L., ROBINSON, P. L. & CHOWDHURY, T. K. R. 1962. A new vertebrate fauna from the early Jurassic of the Deccan, India. *Nature, Lond.* **194,** 755–57.

——, —— & —— 1964. A new vertebrate fauna from the Triassic of the Deccan, India. *Q. Jl geol. Soc. Lond.* **120,** 115–124.

KREBS, B. 1965. *Ticinosuchus ferox* nov. gen. nov. sp. Ein neuer Pseudosuchier aus der Trias des Monte San Giorgio. *Schweiz. palaeont. Abh.* **81,** 1–140.

LACEY, W. S. 1961. Studies in the Karroo floras of Rhodesia and Nyasaland. Part 1. A geological account of the plant-bearing deposits. *Proc. Trans. Rhod. scient. Ass.* **49,** 26–53.

PARRINGTON, F. R. 1948. Labyrinthodonts from South Africa. *Proc. zool. Soc. Lond.* **118,** 426–45.

PLUMSTEAD, E. P. 1963. The influence of plants and environment on the developing animal life of Karroo times. *S. Afr. Jl Sci.* **59,** 147–52.

ROMER, A. S. 1960. Explosive evolution. *Zool. Jb.* (Abt. 1) **88,** 79–90.

RUSSELL, L. S. 1965. Body temperature of dinosaurs and its relationships to their extinction. *J. Paleont.* **39,** 497–501.

SÄVE-SÖDERBERGH, G. 1935. On the dermal bones of the head in labyrinthodont stegocephalians and primitive Reptilia with special reference to Eotriassic stegocephalians from East Greenland. *Meddr Grønland* **98,** No. 3, 1–211.

SIMPSON, G. G. 1961. Evolution of Mesozoic mammals. K. vlaam. Acad. Wet. Lett. sch. Kunst. Belg.; *Int. Coll. Evol. Mammals* **1,** 57–95.

SPATH, L. F. 1934. *Catalogue of the fossil Cephalopoda of the British Museum (Natural History), Part IV. The Ammonoidea of the Trias.* London (H.M.S.O.).

WALKER, A. D. 1961. Triassic reptiles from the Elgin area: *Stagonolepis, Dasygnathus* and their allies. *Phil. Trans. R. Soc.* (B) **244,** 103–204.

—— 1964. Triassic reptiles from the Elgin area: *Ornithosuchus* and the origin of carnosaurs. *Phil. Trans. R. Soc.* (B) **248,** 53–134.

WOOD JONES, F. 1943. *Habit and Heritage.* London (Kegan Paul).

Manuscript submitted May 1966.

C. B. COX, M.A. PH.D. F.Z.S.
Department of Zoology, King's College, Strand, London W C 2.

DISCUSSION

Dr K. A. KERMACK congratulated Dr Cox on his paper, but wished to comment on the neat lining-up of continental and marine formations in which Dr Cox had indulged. While this probably made it easier to draw the table on the blackboard, it had no basis in reality and could be most misleading. By and large continental deposits did not show exact correlation with the marine stages, and the failure to appreciate this fact might only cause needless confusion.

Dr Cox, in reply, agreed that one could not expect marine and continental stages to show any exact correlation. However, since few people are familiar with all the names of the local geological formations in the different continents, he had felt that it would be useful to show some more familiar framework of reference. The table does emphasize those fauna whose age is particularly uncertain, and Dr Cox felt that this, with his long account of the difficulties involved in any kind of correlation, should be sufficient warning.

Dr L. B. H. TARLO said that the Triassic Period was for vertebrate palaeontologists especially interesting, since it witnessed the eclipse of the once dominant mammal-like reptiles and the rise of the dinosaurs and their relatives, with a brief interregnum of lizards between these two major dynasties.

It was also during the Trias that attempts to establish a modern terrestrial vertebrate food-chain were finally successful. Similarly, in the seas the vertebrates reached the peak of the marine food-chain pyramid during this period. With the return of bony fish to the seas, the marine and littoral reptiles were primarily fish-eaters, although eventually such pelagic forms as the ichthyosaurs and pliosaurs became cephalopod eaters.

Dr J. C. W. Cope asked Dr Tarlo on what evidence he based his statement that ichthyosaurs and pliosaurs fed on cephalopods? To the speaker's knowledge the only record of an ammonite showing evidence of attack by a reptilian predator was the recent description of a shell of the Cretaceous genus *Placenticeras* bearing clear evidence of having been bitten by a mosasaur. Apart from this evidence he knew of no other record, nor had he seen any ammonite showing evidence of reptilian predation. The peg-like teeth of these marine reptiles would leave unmistakable marks on an ammonite shell, and in this connexion would one not expect a mollusc-eating reptile to be equipped with palatal crushing teeth?

In the speaker's own experience of the British Upper Kimmeridge Clay, there are three horizons completely devoid of ammonites—and it is only these three horizons which have yielded ichthyosaur or pliosaur remains. Two conclusions could be drawn from this—either the reptiles devoured all the ammonites from these horizons (and then died of starvation), or they did not eat ammonites.

Considering next the belemnites, the speaker was aware of reports of belemnite guards in the stomach of an ichthyosaur, but in the case of the Kimmeridge Clay, belemnites were unlikely to be a source of food for reptiles as they appeared to be completely absent from the fauna.

In view of the fact that there are several reported instances of swarms of ammonites clustered round reptilian remains, which have been interpreted as being ammonites feeding on the reptiles, could it be that the situation was the reverse of what Dr Tarlo suggested?

Dr Tarlo stated briefly that the cephalopod diet of ichthyosaurs and pliosaurs was inferred from preserved stomach contents consisting of myriads of chitinous hooks from cephalopod tentacles.

Dr D. V. Ager has since submitted the observation on the uniqueness of the bitten ammonite from South Dakota described by Kauffman and Kesling: It seemed incredible that, if this were a normal food relationship, more ammonites have not been found bitten in this way. What is more, the one known example does not seem to record a very successful encounter from the mosasaur's point of view. The reptile seems to have taken at least 16 bites at the ammonite without managing to crush the shell, and to have broken two of his teeth in doing so! Dr Ager suggested that this was perhaps an unusual encounter brought about by special circumstances.

Dr W. S. McKerrow said that he thought that extinction of an earlier group usually preceded the expansion of a group of animals into new environments. Dr Cox and Dr Tarlo have spoken of one group 'ousting' another; had they any evidence for this?

Dr Cox, in reply, referred to the gradual replacement of the more archiac procolophonid-rhynchosaur-synapsid fauna by the early archosaurs and to the replacement of these by more advanced archosaurs.

Some Cretaceous–Tertiary marine faunal changes

JOHN MICHAEL HANCOCK

CONTENTS

SUMMARY

The progressive disappearance of ammonites and belemnites is described in some detail. The Tertiary range of some of the common Cretaceous echinoids is discussed. References are given for the planktonic foraminifera. It is concluded that the late-Cretaceous disappearances were not simultaneous, were preceded by geographical contraction, and cannot be explained catastrophically.

1. Introduction

THE MAIN differences between Cretaceous and Tertiary marine faunas are well enough known. It has long been recognized that a striking number of groups of animals disappear near the close of the Cretaceous, particularly if the Maestrichtian is accepted as the highest stage of the Cretaceous, and any strata classed as Danian or Montian is placed in the Tertiary: Grossouvre (1897, pp. 72–3) quoted the ammonites, belemnites, rudists and inocerami. These and other changes are readily apparent from the range-charts in this volume. Therefore the taxa considered in this paper are limited to those for which the author feels he can give a fuller picture. Ager and others have already remarked that the supra-generic appearances and disappearances in these charts conceal many changes, whilst Walmesley has pointed out that the assignment of a single species to a different family may markedly change the total ranges of two families.

2. Ammonites

(A) GENERAL

Judged by the number of families, the Upper Cretaceous shows a tailing-off from 22 in the Cenomanian to 11 in the Maestrichtian, although most of this decrease

The Fossil Record, pp. 91–104. Geological Society of London, 1967. Printed in Northern Ireland.

was pre-Santonian (Fig. 1). In genera there is a fall from about 78 in the Campanian to about 34 in the Maestrichtian. This makes the Maestrichtian age low in number of families and markedly low in number of genera for the Cretaceous period, although the Berriasian has only about 35 genera spread amongst 9 families. From the data given by Wright (this volume, p. 445) one could presume that about 23 genera do not range above the Lower Maestrichtian, leaving only

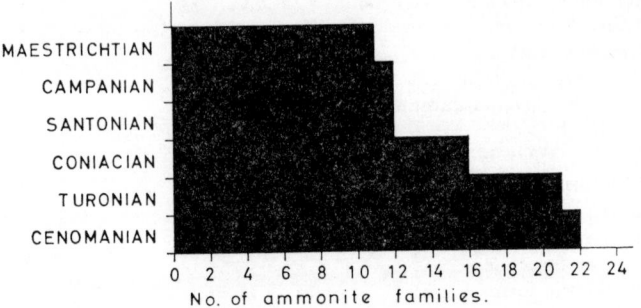

Fig. 1. Number of ammonite families in the stages of the Upper Cretaceous. Data taken from Fig. 151 in Arkell *et al.* (1957).

11 genera in the Upper Maestrichtian (although these genera are still spread amongst 5 superfamilies). The decline in ammonite genera is probably spread over the Maestrichtian age, rather than a sudden disappearance at the end of the age. But the numbers of ammonite genera quoted above for the Lower and Upper Maestrichtian must be regarded as approximations: the ammonite zonation of the Maestrichtian as a whole is very poorly known.

(B) REGIONAL VARIATIONS

At the beginning of the Maestrichtian ammonites had an essentially world-wide distribution, but there are no Upper Maestrichtian ammonites known from:

(i) *New Zealand.* The list given by Wellman (1959, p. 137) of ammonites from the Haumurian includes five species which he recognizes "have lower Maestrichtian affinities"; the others with stratigraphical value are probably Campanian.

(ii) *Western Australia.* See Spath (1941).

(iii) *Southern India.* The youngest ammonites are found in the Valudayur Beds of the Ariyalur State; most of the fauna, including the youngest elements, is Lower Maestrichtian. Spath (1941, p. 51) quotes *Sphenodiscus siva* (Forbes) as an Upper Maestrichtian species, but apart from comparable forms in the Lower Maestrichtian of Balúchistán, the species is unknown outside southern India.

(iv) *Zululand.* It is not certain if any of the ammonites are post-Campanian (Spath 1921, pp. 264–72).

(v) *Graham Land, Antarctica.* The youngest fauna here is Middle Campanian (Howarth 1958, p. 15).

(vi) *California.* The youngest ammonite—*Eubaculites ootacodensis* (Stoliczka)— is a form believed to range from the highest Campanian to Lower Maestrichtian (Matsumoto 1959, pp. 166–71; 1960A, pp. 44–5, pls. 1 and 2).

(vii) *Vancouver Island, British Columbia.* See Usher (1952).

In several regions the existence of Upper Maestrichtian ammonites is doubtful, or the representation is very limited:

(i) *Japan.* Lower Maestrichtian ammonite faunas occur, but Upper Maestrichtian is doubtful (Matsumoto 1960B, pp. 51–2).

(ii) *Madagascar.* The only evidence of Upper Maestrichtian is two isolated specimens of *Sphenodiscus* (Collignon 1954). There is a rich fauna of Lower Maestrichtian ammonites (Collignon 1959; Besairie & Collignon 1959).

(iii) *Angola.* There is a good Lower Maestrichtian ammonite fauna but the only evidence for possible Upper Maestrichtian is one specimen of *Sphenodiscus* (Howarth 1965). Wright (this volume, ch. 15) also quotes *Neophylloceras* and *Paraphylloceras* from the Upper Maestrichtian of Angola, but Howarth (1965) indicates that these need not be later than Lower Maestrichtian.

(iv) *Nigeria.* Most of the Maestrichtian ammonites are Lower Maestrichtian. There is a single specimen of *Sphenodiscus* cf. *pleurisepta* (Conrad) (Reyment 1955, p. 89) which Reyment (1956) uses to mark a Zone of *Sphenodiscus* aff. *pleurisepta*. In Mexico and the Gulf Coast the Pleurisepta Zone is the highest zone of the Upper Maestrichtian (Böse & Cavins 1927, p. 50; Young 1960), but Reyment correlates it with the Zone of *Discoscaphites nebrascensis* in the western interior of the U.S.A. which may or may not be Upper Maestrichtian (*vide infra*).

(v) *Spain.* Wiedmann (1959) records *Pachydicus llarenai* Wiedmann (one specimen ?) from the Upper Maestrichtian of Zumaya on the north coast of Spain,

(vi) *West Greenland.* Here there are several Maestrichtian ammonite faunas and the youngest with *Scaphites (Discoscaphites) waagei* Birkelund and *S. (D.) angmartussutensis* Bireklund correlates with the Zone of *Discoscaphites nebrascensis* of the western interior of the U.S.A. (Birkelund 1965).

(vii) *Western interior of the U.S.A.* (Dakota, eastern Montana and eastern Wyoming). The Fox Hills Sandstone (which partly overlies and partly passes eastwards into the Pierre Shale, and partly underlies and partly passes westwards into the non-marine Hell Creek (Lance) Formation) contains a succession of four ammonite zones, of which the top zone is that of *Discoscaphites nebrascensis*. Cobban & Reeside (1952, p. 1026) considered the Fox Hills fauna to be competely upper Maestrichtian, whilst Jeletzky (in Cobban & Reeside 1952, p. 1027) considered it largely Lower Maestrichtian, but thought it possible that the highest zone might be Upper Maestrichtian. Jeletzky (1962, p. 1008, Fig. 1) now places all four zones in the Lower Maestrichtian.

Only in northern Mexico and the Gulf Coast of the United States (and possibly Balúchistán) are there sufficient ammonites to build a zonal succession for the Maestrichtian. In Mexico, Böse & Cavins (1927) have divided the stage into five zones, and Young (1960) has used this zonation in the Gulf Coast. There seems no reason to doubt that their Zone of *Sphenodiscus pleurisepta* is approximately equivalent to that of *Sphenodiscus binckhorsti* of the Upper Maestrichtian of the type area.

There is a limited ammonite fauna in the type Maestrichtian of Limburg which does not include ammonite-bearing Lower Maestrichtian (Grossouvre 1908; Schmid 1959) (the Lower Maestrichtian Kunrade Limestone and Gulpen Chalk do not form part of the type succession). The Upper Maestrichtian of the southern part of the Polish platform has yielded *Discoscaphites constrictus* var. *vulgaris* and one specimen of *Sphenodiscus binckhorsti* Böhm (Pozaryski 1959, p. 167). In the Soviet Union Upper Maestrictian ammonites are recorded, but the author agrees with Jeletzky (1962, p. 1013) that the Russian belemnite Zone of *Belemnella casimirovensis* probably includes some Lower Maestrichtian. In the Crimea, Moskvin & Naidin (1959) record Lower Maestrichtian ammonites such as *Pachydiscus neubergicus* Hauer, and *Echinocorys ciplyensis* Lambert, with *Belemnella arkhangelskii* Naidin (= *Belemnella casimirovensis* ? and vars.). The ammonite *Libycoceras berisensis* Awad and Nain is found in the highest Maestrichtian of Egypt (Upper Sharawana Shale), and may also occur in Transjordan (El-Naggar 1966; Spath 1941).

In Balúchistán the beds with *Sphenodiscus 'ubaghsi'* and *Indoceras baluchistanense* Noetling are probably Upper Maestrichtian; they overlie beds with a Lower Maestrichtian ammonite fauna, although revision of these faunas is needed (Noetling 1903; Vredenburg 1908).

(c) RECORDS OF DANIAN AMMONITES

Yanshin (1960) has resurrected the idea that ammonites range into the Danian. He quotes two regions:

(i) *Egypt* and *Libya*. Zittel's Beds with *Exogyra overwegi* von Buch (Overwegischichten) were called by him Danian but they include Maestrichtian and even Campanian. They contain *Libycoceras*, *Baculites* and *Inoceramus*. A Danian age for these beds was accepted by Quaas, Wanner and Blanckenhorn, but the Campanian–Maestrichtian age of the horizons with ammonites has been confirmed by the foraminiferal dating of El–Naggar (1966).

(ii) *Western Pyrenees*. Seunes (1890) quoted *Hamites* and various species of *Pachydiscus* from the lower Danian, but in his stratigraphical table he equates lower Danian with Maestrichtian, and some of the *Pachydiscus* spp. also occur in the Calcaire à Baculites in the Cotentin. His upper Danian with *Echinocorys pyrenaicus* Seunes, he equates with the Garumnian; it contains no ammonites.

Daguin (1942, 1948) has recorded *Hamites* cf. *cylindraceus* var. *gigantea* Daguin from the Danian at Bidart near Biarritz. The Danian is said to be characterized by *Jeronia pyrenaica* and *Nautilus danicus*, but the Danian dating of the hamitid (not collected by Daguin himself) seems to be based on accepting Seunes' upper Danian (= Garumnian) as being true Danian; Szöts (1959) has shown that even the Middle Garumnian is still Maestrichtian.

There are to date no unquestionable records of post-Maestrichtian ammonites.

3. Belemnites

In the early Cenomanian the world distribution of belemnites is only slightly more limited than in the Aptian–Albian as shown by Stevens (1963, fig. 7; 1965,

TABLE 1: Belemnite zones of the Maestrichtian stage. Although some diagrams attempt to show equivalent ammonite zones, these are not sufficiently well known in Europe to permit this.

Upper Maestrichtian	*Belemnella casimirovensis*
	Belemnitella junior
Lower Maestrichtian	*Belemnella occidentalis cimbrica*
	Belemnella lanceolata

fig. 42). *Neohibolites* is known from the Cenomanian of northern Europe, Algeria, Tunisia, Madagascar, California and South America. It is possible that *Dimitobelus* ranges into the Cenomanian in New Guinea (Stevens 1965, p. 163) and it is certainly found in the Cenomanian of New Zealand. In southern India the last Cretaceous belemnites are *Parahibolites* from the Upper Albian.

During the later Upper Cretaceous there are two distinct and geographically separate subfamilies of belemnites: the Dimitobelinae, largely or entirely confined to New Zealand, and the Belemnitellinae, known from Venezuela, United States, Canada, Greenland, northern Europe and extending eastwards to the northern Causcaus and the Urals. Above the Cenomanian the Dimitobelinae are completely confined to New Zealand; the last species, *Dimitobelus hectori* Stevens, may not range above the Lower Maestrichtian.

In Europe a useful zonal succession of Belemnitellinae in the Maestrichtian has been worked out by Naidin (1952, 1964), Naidin & Nerodenko (1957), Kongiel (1962), Birkelund (1957), Schmid (1959) and Jeletzky (1951, 1958) as shown in Table I, although the different workers do not all use the same index species.

During the Lower Maestrichtian these Belemnitellinae were common everywhere in northern Europe, and *Belemnitella americana* (Morton) and *B. bulbosa* Meek are found in the U.S.A. In the Upper Maestrichtian the Belemnitellinae are confined to Europe, and even here are of limited distribution, being common only in Poland, the Russian Platform, Crimea and the northern Caucasus. In eastern Belgium *Belemnitella* ex gr. *junior* Nowak is quite common in the Craie tigrée and the Craie grossière (Schmid 1959). *Belemnella casimirovensis* (Skolozdrówna) is scarce in Md of the Maastricht Tuff of Limburg. In Denmark, Birkelund had six specimens of *Belemnitella junior* and 24 usable specimens of *Belemnella casimirovensis*. But the representation of Upper Maestrichtian sediments is limited: in north Germany it is only known from Hemmoor; in the Mons Basin there is only the thin lenticle of the Tuffeau de St. Symphorien, and in England there is none at all: all these areas have rich Lower Maestrichtian belemnite faunas.

But the belemnites do not die out at the end of the Cretaceous: *Bayanoteuthis* from the Upper Eocene of Bremier, France, and also known from the Eocene of Italy and Bavaria, is a typical belemnite. This genus was put by Naef (1922) into the Belemnitidae, and by Jeletzky (1965) into the suborder Belemnitina, although Roger (1952) placed it in the Neobelemnitidae.

4. Sepiids

The order Sepiida is thought to be derived from a member(s) of the Belemnitida. The earliest example is probably *Voltzia* from the Upper Oxfordian of Cuba (Donovan, this volume, p. 465). If Jeletzky is correct in doubting Jurassic and Cretaceous records of sepiids, *Belocurta* from the Paleocene of Israel is the earliest (Avnimelech 1958); the first *Belemnosella* is about the same age. Some 12 genera had appeared before the end of the Eocene. All these are classed as Belemnoidea by some authors (Roger 1952; Avnimelech 1958). In the author's opinion the aragonite guard of the Tertiary sepiids separates them sharply from the Belemnitidae.

5. Other Mollusca

The changes in Denmark have been reviewed by Rosenkrantz (1960), who records 31 genera of bivalves and 34 genera of gastropods which range from Cretaceous (or earlier) to post-Danian, but no rudists or *Inoceramus* occur above the Maestrichtian. In a review of the literature Naidin (1960) could find no authentic examples of post-Maestrichtian rudists or *Inoceramus*. But Kopp (1959) lists a number of records of post-Maestrichtian *Inoceramus* from the Mediterranean region: *I. regularis* d'Orbigny from the Danian of Algeria, Anatolia and Egypt, and Eocene *Inoceramus* from Thrace and Spain. Some of these are of the same breed as the so-called Danian ammonites from Egypt, and may be discounted. The best documented example is of four specimens of *Inoceramus*, identified as *I. balticus* Böhm, collected by Kopp himself from marls which are probably Middle Lutetian, in the coastal outcrop of the Eocene basin of Berango, north of Bilbao.

The relative upper limit of *Inoceramus* and the ammonites seems to vary from region to region. Thus in New Zealand the ammonites and belemnites (themselves Lower Maestrichtian) range above the highest *Inoceramus*—*I. matotorus* Wellman (Wellman 1959, p. 137). In Nigeria Reyment (1956) has a Zone of *Inoceramus coxi* above the highest ammonites in the Zone of *Sphenodiscus* aff. *pleurisepta* (possibly Upper Maestrichtian).

6. Echinoids

From Table 2 it can be seen that there is an unusually large number of families (8) disappearing at the end of the Cretaceous, and that spread over the Paleocene and Eocene there is a greater number of appearances (12). This marked change at the Maestrichtian–Paleocene boundary is seen also at specific level in the Maastricht region: of the 32 species in the Maestrichtian and the 14 species in the Dano–Montian, only one species—*Temnocidaris danica* (Desor)—is common to the two stages (Meijer 1965).

Such assessments do not take into account the relative abundance of the different echinoids. In the Senonian–Maestrichtian of northern Europe at least, the majority of individuals belong to only two genera—*Micraster* and *Echinocorys*. Both these genera persist into the Tertiary. *Micraster* and descendants or close relatives of *Micraster* (*Brissopneustes* and *Cyclaster* [classed by Mortensen as a Brissid]), range up to the Middle Eocene in the Mediterranean region, India and

TABLE 2: Disappearance and appearance of families of Echinoidea in the late Cretaceous and early Tertiary; data from Philip (this volume, p. 586).

Disappearing	*Appearing*
at the top of the Santonian:	in the Santonian:
Pseudodiamatidae	Brissidae
	Palaeostomidae
at the top of the Maestrichtian:	
	in the Upper Maestrichtian:
Orthopsidae	Fibulariidae
Acrosaleniidae	
Conulidae	
Discoididae	
Galeritidae	in the Paleocene:
Holectypidae	
Clypeolampadidae	Conoclypidae
Nucleolitidae	
	in the Lower Eocene:
in the Middle Eocene:	Pericosmidae
	Echinometridae
Micrasteridae	
	in the Middle Eocene:
	Spatangidae
	Scutellidae
	Loveniidae
	Palaeopneustidae
	in the Upper Eocene:
	Clypeasteridae
	Laganidae
	Neoleganidae
	Neolampadidae
	Maretiidae

? Madagascar (Davies 1935; Mortensen 1950). *Cyclaster* is found in the Janjukian (Upper Oligocene and Lower Miocene) of Australia (Fell 1953 [he also records *Hemiaster* and *Nucleopygus* (= *Nucleolites*)]), and *Cyclaster recens* Mortensen is a living species in the Indo-Malayan region (Mortensen 1951).

Echinocorys is widespread in the Danian (lower Paleocene) but becomes rare in undisputed Paleocene. It is recorded by Moskvin & Naidin (1960) from "indisputable Paleocene" of the Crimea, Caucasus, Transcaspia and the south-eastern part of the Russian Platform. *'Oolaster' matseensis* v. Laube from the Paleocene of Salzburg, Austria, is an *Echinocorys* (N. B. Peake, personal communication), but there are no reliable younger records. Records of *Echinocorys* from the Oligocene of New Zealand (Fell 1953; Rosenkrantz 1960) refer to specimens which, though possibly descendants of *Echinocorys*, should not be included in that genus (N. B. Peake, personal communication). A collection of these New Zealand specimens has recently been examined by W. J. Clarke & F. E. Eames: "All the specimens labelled 'Probably *Echinocorys* but *Holaster spatangiformis* Hutton', '? *Echinocorys*' and '*Echinocorys scutatus*' have an anterior sulcus and their periprocts are terminal-supramarginal, not inframarginal, indicating that they do not belong to the genus *Echinocorys*. However, comparison with the type specimens of *Duncaniaster australis* (Duncan) from the Eocene of Australia, the type species of *Duncaniaster*, indicates that the New Zealand specimens have the same morphological characters and belong to that genus" (Eames 1967).

Of considerable interest is the work of Poslavskaia & Moskvin (1960) on the Holasteroids and Spatangoids at horizons around the Cretaceous–Tertiary boundary in eastern Crimea, western Georgia, northern Caucasus and Transcaspia. In these regions there is no real change of facies between the Danian and overlying horizons. Eleven genera die out below the top of the Maestrichtian (*Holaster, Cardiaster, Offaster, Galeola, Paronaster, Stegaster, Seunaster, Guettaria, Pseudoffaster, Infulaster, Isomicraster*) [although this number of genera would be less if there had not been so much taxonomic splitting of the Campanian–Maestrichtian echinoids]; seven genera persist from the Maestrichtian into the Danian (*Echinocorys, Homoeaster, Coraster, Ornithaster, Galeaster, Hemiaster* and *Cyclaster*) and are abundant in the Danian; three genera first appear in the Danian (*Isaster, Garumnaster* and *Basseaster;* Poslavskaia and Moskvin also quote *Protobrissus*, but Villatte (1964) has pointed out that their *Protobrissus* is really a *Micraster*); ten genera known from the Danian are also found in "indisputable Paleocene" (*Echinocorys, Coraster, Ornithaster, Homoeaster, Galeaster, Isaster, Hemiaster, Micraster* (*Protobrissus* of Poslavskaia and Moskvin) and *Garumnaster*. This gives a rather different picture of early Tertiary changes in the echinoid fauna from the work of Ravn (1927, 1928), who worked on the echinoids of the type Danian where the facies has some similarity with the underlying Maestrichtian, but there is a strong change of facies at the top of the Danian. Of the irregular echinoids Ravn notes three genera which die out at the top of the Maestrichtian—*Conulus, Conulopsis* and *Cardiaster;* two genera which die out at the top of the Danian—*Globator* and *Galeaster;* and five genera which persist from Maestrichtian to post-Danian; there are no new genera appearing in the Danian [*Conulus* and *Conulopsis* of Ravn are both *Galerites;* true *Conulus* dies out near the top of the Campanian.].

It is well known that the Australasian region is important for Cretaceous-type echinoids surviving into the Tertiary, but assessment of them is bedevilled by different meanings being given to genera such as *Holaster* and *Cardiaster*. A more uniform picture should emerge when Philip has completed his work on the Tertiary echinoids of south-east Australia.

7. Foraminifera

(A) BENTHIC FORMS

During the Paleogene there are different faunas of the larger benthic foraminifera in the Americas, Tethys and Indo-Pacific regions (C. G. Adams, personal communication). The data given by Eames (this volume, p. 314) shows that amongst the larger foraminifera 26 genera die out in the Maestrichtian, and 14 genera appear in the Paleocene. But the Paleocene appearances are almost entirely Upper Paleocene: there are very few records of large benthic foraminifera from the Lower and Middle Paleocene.

There seems to be relatively little work on the smaller benthic foraminifera.

(B) PLANKTONIC FORMS

Planktonic foraminifera first appear in the Lower Cretaceous (Bolli, Loeblich & Tappan 1957). Their relatively wide geographical distribution, their abundance, and the limited vertical range of many forms, have led to the Maestrichtian–Paleocene faunas being studied by many workers (see particularly Subbotina

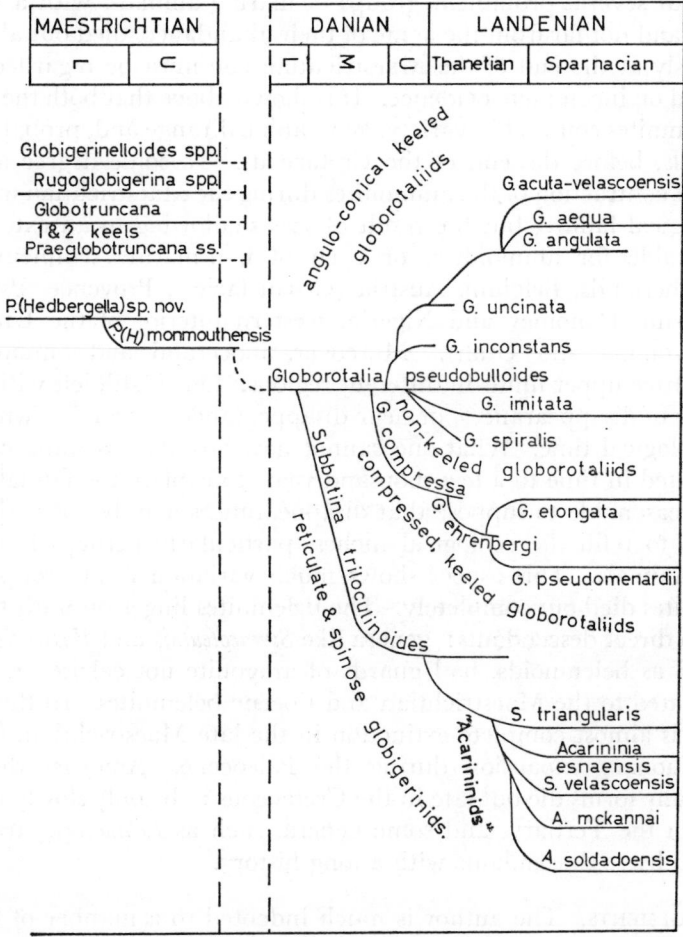

FIG. 2. Suggested morpho-phylogenetic development of Lower Tertiary Globigerinacea: after Berggren (1962A, Fig. 3) with modifications kindly supplied by W. A. Berggren.

1960; Berggren 1962A, 1962B, 1965A, 1965B; El-Naggar 1966). There is wide agreement that important changes occur at the Maestrichtian–Paleocene boundary, but varying interpretations of possible homeomorphs have made for less agreement about the details. Of the more prominent genera it is agreed that *Pseudotextularia* and *Globotruncana* die out in the Maestrichtian, and many authors would add *Rugoglobigerina*, *Praeglobotruncana* and *Heterohelix*. In the Paleocene are found the first *Globorotalia*, but the appearance of true *Globigerina* is argued over.

Berggren's ideas of the morpho-phylogenetic development of the important superfamily Globigerinacea are shown in Fig. 2.

8. Conclusions

Any idea that several prominent groups of marine animals, with a world-wide distribution and not far from the acme of their abundance, died out abruptly and simultaneously at the end of the Maestrichtian age must be regarded as a false picture based on incomplete evidence. It is shown above that both the ammonites and the belemnites contract in variety, geographical range and, probably, number of individuals, before the end of the Cretaceous. To some degree at least the geographical contraction of the ammonites during the Maestrichtian was not some innate biological failure, but the result of seas shallowing to an extent to make them unsuitable for ammonites, or even of non-marine sedimentation, e.g. Poland, Netherlands, Belgium, Austria (Gosau facies), Provence, Pyrenees and northern Spain, Dahomey and Nigeria, western interior of the United States (eastern Wyoming and Utah). Moreover, inocerami and ammonites have different relative upper limits in different regions. One is still left with a remarkable number of disappearances, or near disappearances, occurring within a short range of geological time. What one cannot now postulate is some catastrophic event(s) limited in time to a few thousand years to explain the faunal changes.

It seems reasonable to suppose that disappearances may be more sudden than appearances to refill the ecological niches, particularly perhaps in the case of planktonic animals. This aspect shows much variation from group to group. The ammonites died out completely. The belemnites linger on until the Eocene, but leave no direct descendants: genera like *Styracoteuthis* and *Vasseuria* which are often classed as belemnoids, had guards of aragonite not calcite, and are only remotely related to the Maestrichtian and Eocene belemnites. In the Globigerinacea there is almost complete extinction in the late Maestrichtian, followed by rapid evolutionary expansion during the Paleocene. Amongst the irregular echinoids many forms die out late in the Cretaceous to be only slowly replaced by new forms in the Tertiary, and some genera, such as *Echinocorys*, trail into the Tertiary and leave descendants with a long history.

ACKNOWLEDGEMENTS. The author is much indebted to a number of friends and colleagues for information and advice, including C. G. Adams, W. A. Berggren, F. E. Eames, R. P. S. Jefferies, N. B. Peake and C. W. Wright.

References

ARKELL, W. J. *et al.* 1957. Cephalopoda Ammonoidea. *Treatise on Invertebrate Paleontology*, L4. Kansas University Press.

AVNIMELECH, M. 1958. A new belemnoid genus from the Paleocene of Israel. *Bull. Res. Coun. Israel* (G) **7,** 61–5.

BERGGREN, W. A. 1962A. Some planktonic foraminifera from the Maestrichtian and type Danian stages of southern Scandinavia. *Stockh. Contr. Geol.* **9,** 1–106.

—— 1962B. Stratigraphic and taxonomic–phylogenetic studies of Upper Cretaceous and Paleogene planktonic foraminifera. *Stockh. Contr. Geol.* **9,** 107–29.

—— 1965A. The Maestrichtian, Danian and Montian stages and the Cretaceous–Tertiary boundary. *Stockh. Contr. Geol.* **11,** 103–76.

—— 1965B. Some problems of Paleocene–Lower Eocene planktonic foraminiferal correlations. *Micropaleontology* **11,** 278–300.

BESAIRIE, H. & COLLIGNON, M. 1959. Le Système Crétacé à Madagascar. *Int. geol. Congr.* **20,** El Sistema Cretacico 2, 135–98.

BIRKELUND, T. 1957. Upper Cretaceous belemnites from Denmark. *Biol. Skr. Dan. Vid. Selsk.* **9,** 1–69.

—— 1965. Ammonites from the Upper Cretaceous of West Greenland. *Medd. Grønland* **179,** (7), 1–192.

BOLLI, H. M., LOEBLICH, A. R. JR. & TAPPAN, H. 1957. Planktonic foraminiferal families Hantkeninidae, Orbulinidae, Globorotaliida and Globotruncanidae. *Bull. U.S. natn. Mus.* **215,** 3–50.

BÖSE, E. & CAVINS, O. A. 1927. The Cretaceous and Tertiary of southern Texas and northern Mexico. *Univ. Texas Bull.* **2748,** 7–142.

COBBAN, W. A. & REESIDE, J. B. JR. 1952. Correlation of the Cretaceous formations of the western interior of the United States. *Bull. geol. Soc. Am.* **63,** 1011–44.

COLLIGNON, M. 1954. La question du Maestrichtien malgache (Madagascar). *Int. geol. Congr.* **19,** (21), 137–43.

—— 1959. Corrélations sommaires entre les dépôts du Crétacé supérieur de Madagascar et ceux de l'Europe Occidentale, en particulier de la France. *Comptes Rend. Cong. Soc. Sav.— Dijon* **1959**—*Colloque sur le Crétacé Supérieur Français* 41–52.

DAGUIN, F. 1942. Sur des restes de Céphalopodes déroulés de grande taille dans le Crétacé supérieur des Pyrénées occidentales. *C.r. Somm. Séanc. Soc. géol. Fr.* **1941,** 132–3.

—— 1948. L'aquitaine Occidentale. *Géologie régionale de France,* vol. 5. Paris (Hermann).

DAVIES, A. M. 1935. *Tertiary Faunas—I. The composition of Tertiary faunas.* London (Murby).

EAMES, F. E. 1967. The Tertiary–Cretaceous boundary. *J. geol. Soc. India* (in the press).

EL-NAGGAR, Z. R. 1966. Stratigraphy and planktonic foraminifera of the Upper Cretaceous–Lower Tertiary succession in the Esna-Idfu region, Nile valley, Egypt, U.A.R. *Bull. Br. Mus.* (*Nat. Hist.*) *Geol.,* Supplement 2.

FELL, H. B. 1953. The origin and migrations of Australasian Echinoderm faunas since the Mesozoic. *Trans. R. Soc. N.Z.* **81,** 245–55.

GROSSOUVRE, A. de 1897. Sur la limite du Crétacé et du Tertiaire. *Bull. Soc. géol. Fr.* (3) **25,** 57–80.

—— 1908. Description des Ammonitides du Crétacé Supérieur du Limbourg Belge et Hollandais et du Hainaut. *Mém. Mus. Hist. nat. Belg.* **4,** 1–39.

HOWARTH, M. K. 1958. Upper Jurassic and Cretaceous ammonite faunas of Alexander Land and Graham Land. *Scient. Rep. Falkld Isl. Depend. Surv.* **21,**

—— 1965. Cretaceous ammonites and nautiloids from Angola. *Bull. Brit. Mus.* (*Nat. Hist.*) (*Geol.*) **10,** 337–412.

JELETZKY, J. A. 1951. Die Stratigraphie und Belemnitenfauna des Obercampan und Maastricht Westfalens, Nordwestdeutschlands und Dänemarks sowie einige allgemeine Gliederungs-Probleme der jüngeren borealen Oberkreide Eurasiens. *Beih. geol. Jb.* **1.**

—— 1958. Die jüngere Oberkreide (Oberconiac bis Maastricht) Südwestrusslands und ihr Vergleich mit der Nordwest-und Westeuropas. *Beih. geol. Jb.* **33.**

JELETZKY, J. A. 1962. The allegedly Danian dinosaur-bearing rocks of the globe and the problem of the Mesozoic–Cenozoic boundary. *J. Paleont.* **36,** 1005–18.

—— 1965. Taxonomy and phylogeny of fossil Coleoidea (-Dibranchiata). *Geol. Surv. Pap. Can.* **65–2,** 72–6.

KONGIEL, R. 1962. On belemnites from Maestrichtian, Campanian and Santonian sediments in the Middle Vistula valley (Central Poland). *Pr. Muz. Ziemi* **5,** 3–148.

KOPP, K. O. 1959. Inoceramen im Tertiär des Mittelmeerraumes. *Neues Jb. Geol. Paläont, Mh.* **1959,** 481–92.

MATSUMOTO, T. 1959. Upper Cretaceous ammonites of California, Part I. *Mem. Fac. Sci. Kyushu Univ.* Ser. D, **8,** 91–171.

—— 1960A. Upper Cretaceous ammonites of California, Part 3. *Mem. Fac. Sci. Kyushu Univ.* Ser. D, spec. vol. **2,** 1–204.

—— 1960B. Cretaceous–Tertiary boundary in the Japanese islands. *Int. geol. Congr.* **21,** (5), 50–6.

MEIJER, M. 1965. The stratigraphical distribution of Echinoids in the Chalk and Tuffaceous Chalk in the neighborhood of Maastricht (Netherlands). *Meded. geol. Sticht.* (N.S.) **17,** 21–5.

MORTENSEN, TH. 1950–51. *A monograph of the Echinoidea,* vol. 5, parts 1 & 2. Copenhagen (Reitzel).

MOSKVIN, M. M. & NAIDIN, D. P. 1959. Stratigraphie du Crétacé supérieur de la plate-forme russe, de la Crimée et du Caucase du Nord. *Comptes Rend. Cong. Soc. Sav.—Dijon 1959—Colloque sur le Crétacé Supérieur Français* 497–522.

—— & —— 1960. Danian and adjoining deposits of Crimea, Caucasus, the Transcaspian region and the south-eastern part of the Russian platform. *Int. geol. Congr.* **21,** Reports of Soviet Geologists (5), 15–40. [In Russian with English summary.]

NAEF, A. 1922. *Die Fossilen Tintenfische.* Jena (Gustav Fischer).

NAIDIN, D. P. 1952. [Belemnites of the Upper Cretaceous of the western Ukraine.] *Trudy mosk. geol.-razv. Inst.* **27,** 4–125. [In Russian.]

—— 1960. Concerning the boundary between the Maestrichtian and Danian stages. *Int. geol. Congr.* **21,** Reports of Soviet Geologists (5), 41–6. [In Russian with English summary.]

—— 1964. [Upper Cretaceous Belemnitella and Belemnella of the Russian Platform and some adjoining regions.] *Byull. mosk. Obshch. Ispÿt. Prir.* (Geol. sect.) **39,** 85–97. [In Russian.]

—— & NERODENKO, V. M. 1957. [The belemnites of the Maestrichtian of the Ukrainian lowland.] *Dokl. Akad. Nauk SSSR* **112,** 115–7. [In Russian.]

NOETLING, F. 1903. Uebergang zwischen Kreide und Eocaën in Baluchistan. *Zentbl. Miner. Geol. Paläont.* **1903,** 514–23.

POSLAVSKAIA, N. A. & MOSKVIN, M. M. 1960. [Echinoids of the order Spatangoida in Danian and adjacent deposits of Crimea, Caucasus and the Transcaspian region.] *Int. geol. Congr.* **21,** Reports of Soviet Geologists (5) 47–82. [In Russian with English summary.]

POZARYSKI, W. 1959. Stratigraphie du Crétacé epicontinental en Pologne. *Int. geol. Congr.* **20,** El Sistema Cretacico 1, 149–69.

RAVN, J. P. J. 1927. De irregulaere Echinider i Danmarks Kridtaflejringer. *Communs. paléont. Mus. Miner. Géol. Univ. Copenh.* **27,** 307–54.

—— 1928. De regulaere Echinide i Danmarks Kridtaflejringer. *Communs. paléont. Mus. Minér. Géol. Univ. Copenh.* **29,** 1–62.

REYMENT, R. A. 1955. The Cretaceous Ammonoidea of southern Nigeria and the southern Cameroons. *Bull. geol. Surv. Nigeria* **25.**

—— 1956. On the stratigraphy and palaeontology of the Cretaceous of Nigeria and the Cameroons, British West Africa. *Geol. Fören. Stockh. Förh.* **78,** 17–96.

ROGER, J. 1951. Sous-classe des Dibranchiata. *In* Piveteau, J. (Ed.): *Traité de Paléontologie,* vol. 2, pp. 689–755.

ROSENKRANTZ, A. 1960. Danian Mollusca from Denmark. *Int. geol. Congr.* **21** (5), 193–8.

SCHMID, F. 1959. Biostratigraphie du Campanien–Maastrichtien de N E du la Belgique sur la base des Bélemnites. *Annls Soc. géol. Belg.* (B) **82,** 235–56.

SEUNES, M. J. 1890. Recherches géologiques sur les terrains Secondaires et l'Eocène inférieur de la region sous-Pyrénéenne du sud-ouest de la France (Basses-Pyrénées et Landes). *Annls. Mines Carbur., Paris* (8) **18**, 209–458.

SPATH, L. F. 1921. On Cretaceous Cephalopoda from Zululand. *Ann. S. Afr. Mus.* **12**, 217–321.

—— 1941. On Upper Cretaceous (Maestrichtian) Ammonoidea from Western Australia. *J. Proc. R. Soc. West. Aust.* **26**, 41–57.

STEVENS, G. R. 1963. Faunal Realms in Jurassic and Cretaceous Belemnites. *Geol. Mag.* **100**, 481–97.

—— 1965. The Jurassic and Cretaceous belemnites of New Zealand and a review of the Jurassic and Cretaceous belemnites of the Indo-Pacific region. *Palaeont. Bull., Wellington* **36**.

SUBBOTINA, N. N. 1960. [Pelagic foraminifera of the Paleogene deposits of the southern part of the U.S.S.R.] (In) *Paleogene deposits of the south European part of the USSR* Moscow (Akademii Nauk SSSR), pp. 24–36. [In Russian.]

SZÖTS, E. 1959. Note sur la limite entre Crétacé et Tertiaire dans les environs des petites Pyrénées. *Comptes Rend. Cong. Soc. Sav.—Dijon 1959—Colloque sur le Crétacé Supérieur Français* 671–3.

USHER, J. L. 1952. Ammonite faunas of the Upper Cretaceous Rocks of Vancouver Island, British Columbia. *Bull. geol. Surv. Can.* **21**.

VILLATTE, J. 1964. Observations à propos d'une étude sur des Echinides du Paléocène de la Crimée, du Caucase ét des régions transcaspiennes. *C.r. Somm. Séanc. Soc. géol. Fr.* **8**, 315–6.

VREDENBURG, A. W. 1908. The Cretaceous Orbitoids of India. *Rec. geol. Surv. India* **36**, 171–213.

WELLMAN, H. W. 1959. Divisions of the New Zealand Cretaceous. *Trans. R. Soc. N.Z.* **87**, 99–163.

WIEDMANN, J. 1959. Le Crétacé supérieur de l'Espagne et du Portugal et ses Céphalopodes. *Comptes Rend. Cong. Soc. Sav.—Dijon 1959—Colloque sur le Crétacé Supérieur Français* 709–64.

YANSHIN, A. L. 1960. Stratigraphic position of the Danian stage and the problem of the Cretaceous–Paleogene boundary. *Int. geol. Congr.* **21**, Reports of Soviet Geologists (5), 5–14. [In Russian with English summary.]

YOUNG, K. 1960. Later Cretaceous ammonite successions of the Gulf Coast of the United States. *Int. geol. Congr.* **21**, (11), 251–60.

Manuscript submitted June 1966.

J. M. Hancock, M.A. PH.D. F.G.S.
Department of Geology, King's College, Strand, London W C 2.

DISCUSSION

Dr G. P. LARWOOD said that during Cretaceous time the Bryozoa underwent a marked change. In the Lower Cretaceous the Cyclostomata were varied and abundant, especially in littoral and neritic marine sediments. The first Cheilostomata appeared in the Middle Albian increased swiftly in numbers and variety during the Cenomanian. By Coniacian–Santonian times they equalled the Cyclostomata in abundance and from the late Santonian onward the Cheilostomata were dominant among the Bryozoa. There seemed to be no clear correlation between increasing temperatures during the Upper Cretaceous, based on oxygen-isotope studies, and phases of diversification in the Bryozoa at that time.

Dr F. E. EAMES remarked that Dr Hancock's contribution mainly concerned the ammonites which became extinct at the end of the Mesozoic. It was, however, necessary to draw attention to the fact that many groups of characteristic Cretaceous fossils (e.g. bryozoans, dromiid crabs, brachiopods, etc.) continued into the Danian, which, as originally described by Desor, was a "new stage of the chalk". In spite of the massive extension of *Globotruncana* and ammonites at the end of the Maestrichtian, it seemed to him that the Danian was the last sub-division of the Cretaceous. Typical Tertiary type faunas (e.g. *Alveolina*, *Nummulites*, *Discocyclina*, *Assilina*) do not appear until the Upper Palaeocene. The relatively poorly fossiliferous rocks between the top of the Maestrichtian and the Upper Palaeocene seems, on the sum total of the palaeontological evidence, to belong in its lower part to the Cretaceous (Danian) and in its upper part to the Tertiary (L. Palaeocene).

Professor BRÖNIMANN asked Dr Hancock for the reasons which made him accept the Eocene belemnites of Italy and France to be *in situ*.

Dr HANCOCK, in reply to Professor Brönimann, said that he had not checked the possibility that the specimens of *Bayanoteuthis* might be derived from pre-Eocene rocks. The fact that the same genus is recorded from the Eocene of three countries had dulled his critical faculty. However, one might now add that if *Bayanoteuthis* is not a genuine Eocene belemnite, it is difficult to know whence it could have been derived. It is morphologically distinct from any other described belemnoid, and it seems difficult to believe that the only occurrences of a distinct taxon are as derived fossils.

The points raised by Dr Eames were dealt with in the paper.

Major features of the evolution of echinoids

GRAEME MAXWELL PHILIP

The general shortcomings of compilations presented in this volume have been discussed by other contributors. Similar limitations exist for the ranges of echinoid families presented in Chapter 22 of Part II. However, the writer suspects that the data reveal real features of the evolution of the class, which are worthy of comment because the pattern of the evolution differs from that of other invertebrates.

The first feature can be seen from the range charts in Chapter 22. In their pattern of extinction echinoids appear to have paid scant attention to the traditional faunal crises at the end of the Palaeozoic and Mesozoic eras.

The second feature is seen on examining the appearances of 75 families recognized in this compilation. These appearances in time may be tabulated thus:

	New families
Cainozoic	26
Cretaceous	22
Jurassic	19
Triassic	2
Permian	1
Carboniferous	1
Devonian	1
Silurian	1
Ordovician	2

Prior to the Jurassic, on the average, slightly more than one echinoid family appeared per geological period. The Jurassic marks a fundamental change in this pattern, for during that period and thereafter there is a striking increase in the tempo of evolution. This change was of profound importance, for in the Jurassic we find the appearance of all major groups of diadematacoid regular and irregular echinoids (except the clypeasteroids which first appear in the Upper Cretaceous).

In a volume such as this, it is perhaps appropriate to speculate as to the causes of this sustained post-Triassic evolutionary burst.

In terms of adaptation, there can be no doubt that the expansion and diversification of irregular echinoids is related to the acquisition of a burrowing mode of life which enabled this branch of the class to explore a new ecological setting. This, however, cannot be argued for the parallel expansion of the diadematacoid regular echinoids. Here it rather seems that the Palaeozoic regular urchins, because of their organization, could not favourably compete with other benthonic organisms. It was not until advances in organization (such as stabilization of the

The Fossil Record, pp. 105–106. Geological Society of London, 1967. Printed in Northern Ireland.

apical system and the number of columns of coronal plates, development of external gills, and the development of a perignathic girdle) were achieved that this could take place. In this context it should be noted that the Mesozoic diversification of echinoids cannot be correlated with the extinction of any Palaeozoic group of similar ecological adaptation.

In conclusion, attention must be directed to the incomplete nature of the Triassic record. In faunas of this age we might expect to trace the origins of the Jurassic radiation. Present knowledge is tantalizing and so fragmentary that it probihits decisions on some of the outstanding problems of echinoid phylogeny.

Manuscript submitted September 1966.

G. M. Philip, M.SC. PH.D. F.G.S.
Geology Department, University of New England, Armidale, New South Wales, Australia.

Plant–insect relationships in
Palaeozoic and later time

NORMAN FRANCIS HUGHES & JOHN SMART

SUMMARY

Events in the history of land plants and of insects are discussed, with particular reference to fossil evidence from Palaeozoic rocks. Some possible relationships are suggested, although it is acknowledged that evidence on many points is as yet insufficient.

Introduction

LAND plants and insects clearly diversified at about the same time in the Palaeozoic, and some members of each group subsequently were and are closely connected. This paper is an attempt to synthesize across traditional boundaries by two authors in different subjects after they have held several discussions. No attempt has been made to merge their views, which are in part complementary and are here presented in sequence as they were at the Swansea meeting.

Evolution of the insects

There have been four major episodes in the evolution of insects. First, evolution of primitive wingless hexapodous insects from multi-legged ancestral Insect–Myriapod stock that, presumably, was terrestrial or perhaps subterranean (Ghilarov 1959) in its mode of life; there are no fossils relating to this stage, but it probably took place at the same time that the plants and arachnids invaded the land from the aquatic environment. Second, evolution of winged, flying, insects from primitive hexapods; winged insects are found in the Namurian Carboniferous and there is an abundant fauna in the Bashkirian but the events leading up to this are practically unrepresented in the fossil record. Third, a peak in diversity of orders of insects occurs in the Permian when many old orders present in the Carboniferous had not yet become extinct and most of the more recently evolved Orders were already present. Fourth, one may say that in the Jurassic the general facies of the insect fauna was very similar to that of today with the notable exception of the nectar-feeding Lepidoptera and such insects as have become especially adapted to life in a world dominated by Mammals whose bodies they parasitize and whose excreta they consume.

The fossil record of insects is very discontinuous because the nature of their bodies is such that they will only be fossilized under particularly favourable circumstances. Fossils are known from many places but the bulk of them come from a very limited number of localities where they occur in large numbers. In the past many descriptions of fossils have left much to be desired. Recently, however, careful re-examination of important described material has yielded interesting and valuable results. Details of structure passed over by early authors are being

The Fossil Record, pp. 107–117. Geological Society of London, 1967. Printed in Northern Ireland.

ascertained; features to which earlier authors attached importance are, in some cases, being discovered to be misinterpretations of closely adjacent fossils unrelated to the insect (Carpentier, 1943, 1948, 1961, 1965; Carpentier 1953; Carpentier & Lejeune-Carpentier 1949, 1952; Demoulin 1956, 1960; Laurentiaux 1952, 1953; Rohdendorf 1962).

There was a vast and varied insect fauna fully established in the Bashkirian Carboniferous. This is not just an array of species but a diversity of taxonomic segregates of ordinal status and the divergence fully established between the Palaeopterous orders, which (with the possible exception of some advanced Megasecoptera) cannot reflex the wings over the abdomen when resting, and the Neopterous orders, which (with the exception of a few highly evolved types where the condition is secondary, e.g. butterflies) do reflex the wings over the abdomen when at rest.

Coupled with the occurrence of some fossils in the Namurian this suggests that the main evolution of the winged insects took place in the early Carboniferous and/ or the later Devonian. Rohdendorf (1961) has, in fact, described a fossil from the Devonian that appears to be a winged insect but the nature of the specimen is such that details necessary to enable the insect to be compared with other orders of insects are not known.

Such a time-table would also allow of the evolution of early stages, the nymphs or larvae, re-adapted to the aquatic environment. Relatively few nymphs of either the extant or extinct orders are known as fossils, but it has frequently been conjectured, by analogy with the life histories of the Ephemeroptera (Mayflies) and the Odonata (Dragon-flies), that the nymphs of the other, extinct Palaeopterous orders (e.g. Palaeodictyoptera, Megasecoptera, Protodonata, etc.) were also secondarily aquatic in their mode of life, as is the case in the extant Mayflies and Dragon-flies.

Typical of the Carboniferous insect fauna are Dictyoptera (Cockroaches), Palaeodictyoptera, Megasecoptera, some primitive Orthopteroid insects, (Grass-hoppers), a few primitive Ephemeroptera (Mayflies), some early Odonata (Dragon-flies) and some dragon-fly-like insects that were co-lateral lines of development and not ancestral to the Dragon-flies of the present day. There were also present the earliest representatives of the holometabolous insects which at the present day have complex life-histories with a larva very different from the imago in its structure and mode of life, and a resting pupa intervening between the two.

The environment of all these insects was the tropical swamp-forest of the Carboniferous. Many of the predators of modern terrestrial insects were completely absent. However, in addition to the Dragon-flies and their allies, the Megasecoptera appear to have been predatory, at least in their imaginal stage— their mode of life in the immature states is unknown. In general the environment must have offered a great variety of niches for exploitation by a group such as the insects, which always seem ready to radiate into available unoccupied territory.

The Dictyoptera probably found their living in the litter of the forest floor in much the same way as do their living representatives. There are species of extant Cockroaches that enter water.

The Palaeodictyoptera have no living representatives; the impression is of rather heavy-bodied insects that, if not flying, would perch with out-stretched wings on the fructifications of plants and investigate these with their rostrate mouth-parts to obtain pollen and spores for food. The immature stages could have had the same habit of crawling on the vegetation but we know nothing of them (Carpenter 1948). Something is known of their body structure (Brongniart 1894; Tillyard 1932) and a re-examination of described fossils is revealing more detail than originally described (DeMoulin 1960; Laurentiaux 1952). Most of the fossils are, however, isolated wings or parts thereof, but these reveal sufficient diversity to show that the Bashkirian fauna of Palaeodictyoptera was one that must have undergone considerable evolution and that the discovery of fossils of ancestral forms in Namurian or even earlier strata may be hoped for.

The internal classification of the Order Palaeodictyoptera presents difficulties; it is probably best to retain the order (Kukalova 1963) till more information is available and to resist any temptation to give ordinal status to segregates within it.

The Palaeodictyoptera were at their peak in the late Carboniferous; the last of them is from the Guadeloupian Permian. It has been suggested that if their nymphs were aquatic the changes in climate may have cut down the available breeding grounds; more recently Laurentiaux (1952, 1953) has suggested that it was the floristic changes at the end of the Carboniferous that caused their decline, on account of the disappearance or increasing rarity of plants upon which they had become dependent by various adaptive processes.

The Megasecoptera, all extinct before the end of the Permian, were lightly built insects that give an impression of efficient flight. Some, possibly all, had raptorial fore-legs; probably they were predators and, presumably, attacked other insects.

By analogy with living forms the primitive Orthopteroids of the Carboniferous probably lived much as the long-horned grasshoppers of today; these crawl about in vegetation from ground level to forest canopy at all stages of their life-histories.

Extant Ephemeroptera have degenerate mouth-parts in the imaginal and pre-imaginal stages, of which both, unique amongst living insects, have fully developed wings capable of flight; these two instars do not feed and are, as their name implies very short-lived in typical species. In living forms the immature stages, prior to the pre-imago, are all aquatic nymphs fully adapted to the aquatic environment; there is no pupal stage. Tillyard (1932) has observed that some of the more primitive extant Mayflies are longer lived in the imaginal and pre-imaginal stages than those more highly evolved and that, in some fossils at least, the mouth-parts are "by no means obsolete". Nymphs, almost certainly those of Ephemeroptera and equally certainly adapted to an aquatic environment, have been found in the Russian Permian (Tschernova 1962). The manner of life of the earliest Ephemeroptera from the Commentry deposits (Carb.-U. Carb) must remain a matter of conjecture; it is, however, unlikely that they would be predatory on other insects.

There is no reason to suppose that the ancestral Dragon-flies in the Bashkirian Carboniferous lived in any other way than do the present day representatives of

109

the Odonata. The environment would certainly be well suited to the carnivorous habits of both the strong-flying, insect-catching, imagines and the active, aquatic, predatory, nymphs that we are familiar with today.

Whether such groups as the Protodonata, best thought of as colateral to the evolutionary line of the Odonata, were similar in habit to the Odonata of today is more conjectural. Their grouping alongside the Odonata is based mainly on the fact that their wings are rather like those of Dragon-flies. This could be due to convergence. Where the fossils of these consist of more than wings, recent work Carpenter 1961; Carpentier 1953; Carpentier & Lejeune-Carpentier 1949, 1952; Laurentiaux 1953) indicates that they had rather large, heavy bodies and that the familiar restorations of them [e.g. the original restoration of *Meganeura moyni* (Brongniart 1884), with its 60 cm. wing-span (Brongniart 1894)] showing an elongate dragon-fly-like creature, with a slim body suited to very active flight, are erroneous. The mouth-parts were of the kind usually associated with the predatory mode of life in insects. The nymphs of these insects are unknown.

[J.S.]

Interpretation from Recent plants and insects

Many Recent insects are involved with certain Angiosperm groups in connection with pollination, seed dispersal and general plant control; the phytophagous insects involved in this last are: gross indiscriminate feeders such as the locust (Homoptera), plant-bugs (Hemiptera) which are specific, and others of various groups which eat plant reproductive organs. Perhaps the majority of angiosperms of the Recent equatorial lowland forest are concerned in some way, but it is debatable whether this is a Recent phenomenon only, a situation which has existed since land plants arose, or a situation which has changed throughout by evolution in the broadest sense.

To make the following argument clearer, certain author-prejudices should be admitted even if there is no space to justify them. First, among angiosperms the large arborescents of the equatorial forest were primitive and herbs are derived; very many families show a spectrum of genera and species of decreasing size (but often of increasing abundance and distribution) from tropics to temperate climates, e.g. the Graminae. Second, the lowland climax forest is the only habitat which could have been of geological importance; all others such as temperate, and altitude, and fresh-water were derived, and thus out of the main stream of plant evolution. Palaeobotanical material, both macrofossil and palynological, which probably almost entirely represents lowland forest, is therefore fully relevant. Third, entomophilous (insect-pollinated) angiosperms are primitive, using flower attraction by colour, size or smell in decreasing order of subtlety for everything down to the Diptera. Anemophilous (wind-pollinated) angiosperms are derived by reduction of flower perianth. Thus far only there is general agreement with the stimulating work of Corner (1964). Fourth, there were no angiosperms before the Albian, but from then onwards successive angiosperm groups (judged mainly from palynological characters) started in equatorial regions amd migrated polewards [idea of Axelrod (1959), although he did not have any palynological evidence]. Fifth, that although no plant extinctions are shown in the documentation (this volume, Part II) for the Tertiary, and few for the Mesozoic, this may well be inaccurate and mainly due to the deplorable habit among palaeobotanists of naming fossils (organ taxa) into *extant* formal taxa on limited evidence and *without* at the same time changing the circumscription of the taxon concerned (cf. Hughes 1963).

The problem seems to be that while steady improvement in interpretation of post-Aptian floras is probable, there is immediate difficulty with the pre-Albian Mesozoic floras composed entirely of gynmosperms and pteridophytes. The descendants of these plants (from which at least some parallels *have* to be drawn) are virtually confined now to derived or secondary habitats (temperate, altitude, etc.); it is therefore very difficult to reconstruct lowland forests dominated by such plants. Further, recent insects are also observed to have little connexion with the descendant gymnosperms in recent temperate habitats, but does this also automatically apply to the Mesozoic equatorial lowland forest gymnosperms about the ecology of which so relatively little has yet been discovered? It also happens that early Cretaceous insect records are very few indeed, although at least the Middle Purbeck beds of Britain are now transferred to the Cretaceous.

Features of Palaeozoic plants

In the Devonian there were sufficient trees by Frasnian times to satisfy the initial requirement of height for the promotion of insect flight. These included *Callixylon* (*Archaeopteris*), *Eospermatopteris*, *Lepidosigillaria* and *Protolycopodiopsis*. Of these only *Eospermatoperis* is recorded from the Givetian, but even earlier *Pseudosporochnus* may have reached a height of nine feet [see Banks (this volume, Part II, Chapter 4, and personal communication)]. The leaves of these plants were either microphylls or megaphylls with a very little-expanded leaf lamina. Seeds have still not been found although increasing variety of megaspores is recorded. In default of any positive evidence of their feeding even on the mainly scattered sporangia, late Devonian insects were probably only wingless crawlers; it is unnecessary to postulate long evolution for a character such as wings, to which traditional systematics may give undue weighting.

In early Carboniferous times, the expanded leaf-lamina (*Sphenopteris* s. 1.) was widespread, and there were many surprisingly elaborate seeds. The tall-tree (probably equatorial) coal-swamp forests provided the still-air habitat for the flight of many Palaeoptera with large unfolded wings like Recent dragon-flies (Odonata); these are well-known to have reached unusual size, but unfortunately the wings which are the principal fossils can only represent a short phase at maturity of such insects. The other habitat specifically provided by these forests was the mass of fallen but not decayed vegetation (of coal), probably lying in water. The Dictyopteran insects and their larvae (like Recent cockroaches) could well have been general trash-feeders, and there was presumably the possibility for separate aquatic larval stages in such a swamp environment.

By Viséan times the variety of pteridospermous seeds (more correctly ovules) is considerable (Andrews 1963). They were integumented, with variously arranged micropyles which probably often carried a drop of fluid at maturity; *Salpingostoma* from the Scottish Calciferous sandstone was perhaps the most elaborate. The most obvious variable character, however, in the numerous genera consists of hairs and other processes on the enclosing cupule which were so arranged as some kind of protection that would at the same time permit entry of pollen to the micropyle. Although there may well be other 'physical' explanations, it seems worth considering whether these structures may have been connected with the protection of ovules from foraging, but not specially adapted, crawling insects. It may possibly have been only later that plants resorted to greater production of ovules as a defense. The backwardly projecting glandular hairs which cover *Physostoma* (Westphalian) may have had such a function, and as yet no purpose has been suggested for the scattered capitate glands of *Lagenostoma*. At the same time there was a parallel development in the 'seed-bearing' lycopods; *Lepidocarpon* apparently had nothing more than the great depth of the 'micropylar slit', but the cones were probably borne in the main tree canopy; *Miadesmia* on the other hand, which may well have been borne on a low shrub or herb, has an elaboration of processes comparable with the pteridosperms mentioned.

The pollen of these pteridosperms is, with two exceptions, difficult to distinguish from pteridophyte spores and presumably both were wind-distributed. The early saccate pollen such as *Florinites* was probably adapted for micropyle flotation, much as is the conifer pollen later; but *Monoletes*, from the pteridospermous male organ *Dolerotheca*, is inexplicably large (up to 200 μ) and also incorporates distal germination by a colpus. This could perhaps indicate crawling-insect pollenation in the Medulloseae in which the rather large ovules (unlike those of the Lyginopterideae mentioned above) did not particularly bear distal processes. In *Trigonocarpon* a thick fleshy sarcotesta and an inner hard sclerotesta already suggest a reliance on somewhat larger animals for seed distribution.

A single Carboniferous fern spore *Raistrickia* from the plant *Senftenbergia* (Schizeaceae) bears heavy blunt baculae which may indicate insect distribution; although this type of spore continues through the Permian and Mesozoic it is never numerically important. Recent *Anemia* from the same family has completely striate spores borne in sporangia aggregated on a low insect-visited spike. Similar spores are known from the Late Jurassic onwards, and are particularly common in the whole of the Cretaceous. Rather curiously striate sculpture is common in the Permian throughout the world, but in the totally unrelated group of saccate pollen. No physical explanation for this striation has been offered, and a biological connexion seems on general grounds to be much more likely.

Features of Mesozoic and Tertiary plants

The dominant gymosperms of the Mesozoic include conifers, ginkgos and cycadophytes with much thicker leaf and other cuticles than most subsequent angiosperms or the Mesozoic ferns. In the Cycadales, *Beania* carried large relatively unprotected fruits (Harris 1961) which were probably the food of vertebrates; the pollen was small and generalized. In the Benettitales, however, *Cycadeoidea* bore much more protected smaller fruits set among the leaf bases of the short low stem, and very large (up to 80μ) elongated pollen grains. The insects concerned may have been only beetles which scramble, bite and break rather indiscriminately, but which probably moved pollen effectively. The few living Chlamydosperms are insect-pollinated, and although the fossil evidence is mainly from pollen, the group appears to have been more important in the Mesozoic than it is now.

Although the ephemeral flower is the least likely plant organ to be preserved fossil, evidence of leaves, etc., suggests that the Magnoliaceae and similar plants were among the earliest (late Cretaceous) angiosperms. The large flowers of some Recent species of the family are probably pollinated by crawling insects, but caution is necessary in transferring this to fossils in which the flower is not known; in the living members of the family Malvaceae, the temperate *Althaea* (the hollyhock) is pollinated by crawling insects but some tropical species of *Hibiscus* are pollinated by birds.

In Tertiary times, as indicated by the amber preservations, insects were greatly diversified below the level of documentation given in Part II, Chapter 19 of this volume, and so also were the plants of the angiosperm equatorial forests, complete with epiphytes, lianes, etc.

[N.F.H.]

General conclusions

1. Devonian insects will have moved into a competition-free land habitat, but presumably with land plant débris at the base of the food chain.

2. The specialized swamp forests of the Carboniferous may have provided the first cases of some insect dependence on living plants as opposed to plant débris, and even the first plant use of insect pollination; but in general, although insect groups had reached the stage of providing their own predator members, the degree of engagement with plants was probably small.

3. The important Early Permian climatic changes led to extinctions, but where there was continuity of plants and insects as in Central Asia (Angara Permian province) there was steady development of new types, particularly including the very specialized sucking mouth-parts of the Hemiptera. The floras concerned were no longer dominated by the very thick-barked lycopods of the Carboniferous.

4. Triassic and Jurassic insects clearly progressed from the Permian, although our knowledge of the plants is restricted by the necessity of using comparisons with temperate descendants which are even less relevant because of the probable weakness of latitudinal climatic zonation in the Mesozoic. It is hard to believe that plants and insects were in any way less related at this time.

5. The very great mid-Cretaceous floral change to angiosperm domination was probably connected with an unusual temperature-high period culminating in the Early Tertiary. The probable insect-pollination of the early angiosperms is not yet proved, but such late orders as the Hymenoptera and Diptera were already in the record before the advent of angiosperms.

6. Tertiary plants show steady response to the formation of latitudinal floral province belts on the approach of glaciation. The amber deposits, and the Oeningen beds among others, indicate insect specializations such as seed distribution by the Hymenoptera which match the plant diversity.

7. The insectivorous Nepenthaceae and Sarraceniaceae do not appear to have any fossil record.

8. Although many of the most interesting details remain to be inserted, and although many important connexions with other animal groups have been neglected, the general story appears to be a steady progression of increasing interdependence between living plants and certain insects, starting however from non-dependence.

References

ANDREWS, H. N. 1963. Early seed plants. *Science, N.Y.* **142,** 925–31.

AXELROD, D. I. 1959. Poleward migration of early angiosperm floras. *Science, N.Y.* **130,** 203–7.

BRONGNIART, C. 1884. Sur un gigantesque neurorthoptere, provenant des terrains houillers de Commentry (Allier). *C.R. Acad. Sci., Paris* **98,** 832–3.

—— 1894. Recherches pour servir à l'histoire des insectes fossiles des temps primaries. *Bull. Soc. Industr. Minerale* **7,** (4), 124–615, pls. 17–53; Thèse, Faculté de Science, Université de Paris, no. 821, 1–494, pls. 1–37. Sainte-Etienne (Theolier). [References in the literature are usually to the *Thèse*, since this is the form usually available, See Carpenter (1943), below.]

CARPENTER, F. M. 1943. Studies on carboniferous insects from Commentry, France—I: Introduction and families Protagriidae, Meganeuriae and Campylopteridae. *Bull. geol. Soc. Amer.* **54,** 527–54.

—— 1948. The supposed nymphs of the Palaeodictyoptera. *Psyche* **55** (1), 41–50.

—— 1961 [for 1960]. Studies on North American Carboniferous insects—1: the Protodonata. *Psyche* **67**(4), 98–110.

—— 1965. Studies on North American Carboniferous Insects—4. the Genera *Metropator, Eubleptus, Hapaloptera Hadentomum. Psyche* **72** (2), 175–90.

CARPENTIER, F. 1953. Sur une figure récente de Meganeurula gracilipes Handl. (Pronodonate du Houiller) *Bull. Ann. Soc. Entom. Belg.* **89** (78), 183–4.

—— & LEJEUNE–CARPENTIER, M. 1949. Conformation de l'abdomen d'un insecte Protodonate du Stéphanien de Commentry (Allier, France). *Ann. Soc. géol. Belg. Brussels* (B) **72,** 317–26.

—— & —— 1952. Structure du thorax des Meganeurides (Protodonates). *Trans. Int. Congr. Entomol.* **9,** (1), 161–4.

CORNER, E. J. H. 1964. *The life of plants.* London (Weidenfeld & Nicholson).

DEMOULIN, G. 1956. Nouvelles recherches sur *Tripolosoba pulchella* (Brongniart) (Insectes Ephéméroptères). *Bull. Inst. Sci. nat. Belg.* **32** (14), 1–8.

—— 1960. Quelques remarques sur un insecte fossile abracadabrant: *Lycocercous goldenbergi* (Brongniart, 1885). *Bull. Inst. Sci. nat. Belg.* **36**(44), 1–4.

GHILAROV, M. S. 1959. Adaptations of insects of soil dwelling. *Proc. Int. Congr. Zool.* **15,** 354–7.

HARRIS, T. M. 1961. The fossil cycads. *Palaentology* **4,** 313–23.

HUGHES, N. F. 1963. The assignment of species of fossils to genera. *Taxon* **12,** 336–7.

KUKALOVA, J. 1963. To the taxonomy of Palaeodictyoptera (Insecta.) *Zvlást. Otisk Vestniku. Ústředního Úst. Geol.* **38**(3), 197–200.

LAURENTIAUX, D. 1952. Découverte d'un rostre chez *Stenodictya lobata* Brgt. (Paléodictyoptère Sténodictyide) et le probleme des Protohémiptères. *Bull. Soc. géol. France* (6)**2,** 233–47.

—— 1953. Insectes *in* PIVETEAU, J. (Ed.): *Traité de Paléontologie,* vol. 3, 397–527.

ROHDENDORF, B. B. 1961. The description of the first winged insect from the Devonian beds of the Timan (Insecta, Pterygota). *Ent. Obozr., Moscow* **40,** 485–9. [In Russian; English summary.]

—— (Ed.) 1962. Arthropoda: Tracheates and Chelicerates. *Osnovi Paleontologii: Tracheata i Chelicerata.* Moscow (Akademii Nauk SSSR). [In Russian.]

TILLYARD, R. J. 1932. Kansas Permian insects—15: the order Plectoptera. *Amer. J. Sci. New Haven, Conn.* (5) **23**, 97–134; 237–72.

TSCHERNOVA, O. A. 1962. Order Ephemeroptera in ROHDENDORF, B. D. (Ed.): *Osnovi Paleontologii.* Moscow (Akademii Nauk SSSR), pp. 55–64. [In Russian.]

Manuscript submitted June 1966.

N. F. Hughes, M.A. F.G.S.
   Department of Geology, Sedgwick Museum, Downing Street, Cambridge.
J. Smart, PH.D. F.L.S. F.Z.S.
   Department of Zoology, Downing Street, Cambridge.

DISCUSSION

Dr R. J. WOOTTON, in reply to an observation by the President, said that although deposits with insects are rare, where they do occur it is sometimes quite possible to find insect fragments piled close enough together for many to occur on a small piece of rock. This is perhaps the result of drifting at the time of fossilization.

Dr N. SPJELDNAES asked if there was any evidence of Carboniferous seeds having been bitten.

Dr R. A. CROWSON commented that Professor John Walton had told him of some cases.

Dr W. S. LACEY recalled finding in Rhodesia, in Karroo rocks of Permian age, leaves of *Glossopteris* with cut away and incised margins having all the appearances of having been browsed by animals, possibly by insects. Although the type of damage was similar to that produced by caterpillars, for example, at the present day, it was not certain in the case of the *Glossopteris* leaves that it was due to insect feeding.

Dr J. M. HANCOCK, speaking from acknowledged ignorance of both plants and insects, wondered why there has been little evolution of insects since the beginning of the Jurassic, when the Angiosperms did not appear until the Albian. Even allowing that the Gymnosperms used insects to effect fertilization, he would have expected some insect evolution to occur alongside this important plant innovation.

Mr N. F. HUGHES in answer considered that the rarity of Cretaceous insect fossils and the level of taxon here selected for record precluded, as yet, any solution of this interesting problem.

Dr R. J. WOOTTON said that it was important not to lay too much stress on Upper Carboniferous insect faunas when forming conclusions about the nature of primitive insects, and when considering questions like the origin of flight. Some Upper Carboniferous insects were no doubt rather primitive, but the fauna as a whole was already diverse and well-advanced. Several widely differing orders, including wing-folding forms, are represented in Namurian and Lower Bashkirian beds, and the presence in the Lower Permian of Coleoptera, Mecoptera and Neuroptera suggests, as strongly as the supposedly Carboniferous raphidioid *Fatjamoptera*, that complete metamorphosis with a pupal stage had arisen before the Carboniferous ended.

With such diversity it is certain that insects were feeding in many ways and at many levels within the population. The big Protodonata were probably aerial carnivores, and it is probably misleading to account for the presence of less active palaeopterous forms like the Palaeodictyoptera by assuming a lack of predators.

It is certain, indeed, that the variety of Upper Carboniferous insects was far greater than we knew. He would be glad if Mr Hughes or Dr Smart would tell them if all the productive insect beds of this age were laid down under coal-swamp conditions. If so, insects elsewhere might have been very different.

Dr L. B. H. TARLO pointed to the Amphibia as active predators and asked if there were soil predators of any kind present.

Dr J. SMART said that Snodgrass (1930, 1935) had outlined the commonly accepted theory of the origin of the wings of insects from the paranotal folds of the meso- and meta-thoracic segments. Briefly it is that with paranotal folds on the thorax the primitive insect was able to exercise some control over its movements as it leapt amongst vegetation or fell from the vegetation to the ground. From this gliding stage to a flying insect is a matter of selection pressures in favour of bigger and better paranotal folds, articulated and provided with some form of power and responses to nervous reactions to enable controlled movement through the air, or flight, to be accomplished.

It is not difficult to conceive what the selection pressures on these ancestral forms might be. Escape from predators (e.g. amphibia, arachnids, and perhaps ancestral insects themselves), access to food, the meeting of the sexes, search for oviposition sites and dispersal, are among the most obvious.

What has proved difficult is to suggest the selection pressures and evolutionary steps involved in the development of paranotal folds to a size when they began to have any effective function as gliding organs.

An elegant theory to account for the development of the paranotal folds through stages within which they could have no aerodynamic significance has however, recently been propounded by Alexander & Brown (1963). The development steps are as follows:

(1) The ancestral Myriapod-Insect moves from the aquatic into the terrestrial environment.

(2) The ancestral insect develops the hexapedal gait and modifications of the three thoracic segments take place to provide more efficient skeleto-muscular mechanisms for the legs. Possibly some dorso-ventral flattening of the body related to living in the surface layers of the soil, in litter or escape into crevices.

(3) Further modification of the thoracic exoskeleton, including development of paranotal folds related to: (a) improved leg movement, (b) shadow elimination, (c) crevice dwelling, (d) armouring.

(4) Further development of the paranotal folds for the purpose of presence-signalling to bring the sexes together for reproductive ends.

(5) Jumping and falling, become gliding when the paranotal folds are large enough to function aerodynamically.

(6) Full articulation of the wing and flight.

The important novel idea put forward by Alexander & Brown (1963) is the fourth listed above. In the aquatic environment the sex products are not at risk of immediate destruction by desiccation if merely passed out into the water; the matter of their conjunction may be left to chance. In the terrestrial environment it becomes essential that the sexes achieve proximity in order that the male sex cells be passed directly into the female's body or that they be deposited in such a place and manner that she will take them up into her body immediately.

Extant insects use a great variety of sensory communication channels to achieve this proximity of the sexes; these include, for instance, the use of scents, stridulation and sight. However, the very early terrestrial insect had probably to rely on sight, since the visual is a communication channel that it could have carried straight over from life in the aquatic environment. The suggestion made by Alexander & Brown (1963) is that the development of the paranotal folds was favoured by the possibility that the larger and more conspicuous the paranotal folds the more easily would male and female find each other! Slight movement of the folds would also be an advantage hence incipient articulation.

These theories assume that the ancestral insect was of a size such as we usually associate with every-day extant insects. Such size, and its accompanying weight, could give the paranotal folds aerodynamic significance in a free-fall and visual significance over reasonable distances. It is worth noting that in the extant orders of winged insects, with one exception only the final, sexually mature, instars have fully developed wings and powers of flight. The exception are the the Ephemeroptera (May Flies) where the penultimate instar has wings and can fly.

Another theory has been put forward by Wigglesworth (1963a, b). This theory assumes the ancestral insect to have been of very small size so that any increase of surface area, such as would be provided by paranotal folds, would give air-lift in a slight wind and so provide a mechanism for the dispersal of the species.

Unfortunately there is no fossil available of anything that can be considered as representative of the ancestral insect form; all these theories therefore remain speculative.

References

ALEXANDER, R. D. & BROWN, W. L. 1963. Mating behaviour and the origin of insect wings. *Occasional papers of the Museum of Zoology, University of Michigan*, no. 628; 1–19.

SNODGRASS, R. E. 1930. How insects fly. *Smiths. Rept.* 1929; 383–421.

SNODGRASS, R. E. 1935. *Principles of Insect Morphology*. New York (McGraw-Hill).

WIGGLESWORTH, V. B. 1963a. Origin of wings in insects. *Nature, Lond.* **197;** 97–98.

WIGGLESWORTH, V. B. and others. 1963b. The origin of flight in insects. *Proc. R. ent. Soc., Lond.*, (c) **28** (6); 23–32.

Biochemical evolution and the fossil record

LAMBERT BEVERLY HALSTEAD TARLO

CONTENTS

SUMMARY

From the sequences of amino-acids in protein molecules and their substitutions in different parts of the molecule, it can be shown how, for example, the four polypeptide chains of the respiratory pigment haemoglobin can be derived from one another, and ultimately from myoglobin. Zuckerkandl & Pauling have estimated the times at which the four chains found in human haemoglobin are likely to have originated—the alpha chain 650 m.y. ago, gamma 380 m.y., beta 150 m.y. and delta 35 m.y. These dates coincide exactly with the first records of crossopterygian fish (380 m.y.) and the anthropoids (35 m.y.) and approximately with the placental mammals (135 m.y.). However, this approach can only be vindicated if it can be applied to proteins actually preserved in the fossil record. The only important protein so preserved is collagen and there are considerable problems still to be overcome in its study (viz. the differential breakdown of the amino-acids with the consequent alteration of the molecule, and also contamination from amino-acids derived from organic debris in the surrounding sediments). With the aid of the 'Technicon automatic Amino-Acid Analyzer' it is hoped to eventually resolve these problems. If an evolutionary picture can be built up for collagen, on the lines of that already begun for haemoglobin, and if in the meantine the exact fate of collagen in geological time can be established, it may eventually be possible to test theories of biochemical evolution by direct reference to fossil proteins.

1. Introduction

WORK in recent years has led biochemists confidently to predict the path of synthesis of complex organic molecules such as proteins. Although it is possible to make in the laboratory the constituent amino-acids of proteins, the search still goes on for the exact mechanism that could produce their peptide links. Proteins are essentially composed of varying combinations of about twenty different amino-acids, the sequence of which is believed to reflect the genetic code of the animal in question. Thus from a comparative study of the sequences of amino-acids in particular protein molecules in both primitive and advanced living animals, it is possible to infer the mutational changes that must have occurred in the past. Already the study of the structure of the respiratory pigment, haemoglobin, has enabled a hierarchy of evolutionary changes to be documented, and

The Fossil Record, pp. 119–132. Geological Society of London, 1967. Printed in Northern Ireland.

attempts have also been made to extend these results theoretically to the fossil record. Now that it is generally recognized that certain proteins can be preserved in rocks, the possibility (albeit a faint one) arises of actually testing the conclusions of biochemists by direct analyses of fossil proteins. It is too early yet to know whether such an endeavour can ever be crowned with success. Indeed, as far as palaeontology is concerned the stage has been reached where we are only now becoming aware of the magnitude of the problems involved. The entire subject is only beginning to undergo its first birth pangs and it will be many years before it even reaches its infancy.

2. Biochemical evolution

Comparative biochemistry in general is by no means a new subject and considerations of biochemical evolution have long exercised the minds of scientists. Baldwin (1949) and Florkin (1949) have both lucidly discussed the major outlines and have attempted, moreover, to do so in the framework provided by geologists. More recently there has appeared the monumental comprehensive treatise on comparative biochemistry edited by Florkin & Mason (1963). In spite of the great value of these works, caution must be exercised in interpreting the results, since similar biochemical adaptions may be evolved independently. This should occasion no surprise, as quite unrelated groups of animals may possibly share common metabolic pathways.

Perhaps the most significant advance in recent years has been in what Crick has termed 'protein taxonomy'. This consists of plotting the sequence of amino-acids making up the proteins of an organism and comparing such sequences between species. It is believed that these sequences are the most delicate expression possible of the character of any animal and hence vast amounts of evolutionary information are likely to be hidden away within them. So far this type of work has only been started with the respiratory pigment haemoglobin and the closely related myoglobin.

In man there are besides myoglobin, three types of haemoglobin. They all possess 4 protein chains made up of various amino-acids, which together with a haem group form one large molecule. Human embryos have haemoglobin consisting of 2 alpha chains plus 2 gamma chains, while at birth they change over to the adult haemoglobins which consist of 2 alpha chains plus 2 beta chains. Frequently adults possess a haemoglobin in which there are 2 delta chains instead of the beta chains.

Ingram (1961) postulated that during the course of evolution of these chains from a single chain such as is found in myoglobin, the gene responsible for the synthesis of the proteins mutated, and was duplicated and translocated, forming two different genes. One of the two genes so formed appears to have evolved into one controlling the synthesis of present-day myoglobin, while the other became the gene for the haemoglobin alpha chain. This latter gene is thought to have evolved in such a way that it was capable of reproducing itself, so that the alpha chain became twinned, forming 2 identical chains. This same type of mutation is presumed to have occurred again to produce paired gamma chains, and then again to give rise to the beta chain gene. Later, the beta chain gene mutated to give rise to the delta.

By observing the differences in the constituents of the haemoglobin protein chains in the various groups, it can be shown for example that the gorilla beta chain differs from the human by the substitution of one amino-acid at only one site; the pig chain differs from that of man at 14 sites, and the horse chain at 26 sites (Zuckerkandl 1965). The number of differences in the chain indicates roughly how far each of these animals are separated from man on a phylogenetic tree.

This method of comparing chains has been used by Zuckerkandl & Pauling (1962, 1965) to estimate the number of years required to produce an *effective* evolutionary change at one site on the chain.

[This is in contrast to the more normal mutation, which may render the protein unstable, for example the substitution of methionine for valine in position 98 of the human beta-chain causes 'inclusion-body anaemia' (Carrell, Lehmann & Hutchinson 1966).]

Since it is generally accepted from palaeontological evidence that horses, pigs, cattle and rabbits had a common ancestor about 80 million years ago, and since the mean value for the number of apparent amino-acid substitutions and hence changes per chain is 11, then it is believed that the average time required for each mutation was approximately 7 m.y. This figure has then been used to estimate roughly the time that has elapsed since the 4 principal types of chain seen in human haemoglobin made their appearances. Thus since there are 10 differences between the beta and delta chains and to exhibit 10 differences each gene line need undergo only 5 changes, it is therefore implied that the divergence took place some 35 m.y. ago, in fact at the time when the higher primates made their first appearance in the fossil record (Simons, this volume). The beta and gamma chains exhibit differences at 37 sites indicating a divergence 150 m.y. ago, which is reasonably close to the appearance of the first placental mammals (Kermack, this volume). The origin of the beta chain itself from the alpha is similarly calculated to have occurred 380 m.y. ago at the time when the crossopterygian fishes appeared (Andrews, this volume). Finally the origin of haemoglobin from myoglobin is supposed to have taken place some 650 m.y. ago. As is demonstrated in Fig. 1, the changes in the evolution of the haemoglobin molecule do not co-incide with the origin of any of the major vertebrate taxa such as Amphibia, Reptilia and Mammalia, but if Pauling's calculations are on the right lines, they do appear to agree in a most striking manner with several major advances in vertebrate history.

It is necessary at this stage to remember that this type of extrapolation of the results of biochemists to the sequence observed in the fossil record is entirely speculatory. Although serious criticism can be levelled at this approach, because of the large number of variables involved, nevertheless it does provide for the integration of biochemical data in a general palaeontological framework. Unfortunately there is, as yet, no evidence that haemoglobin can be preserved in the

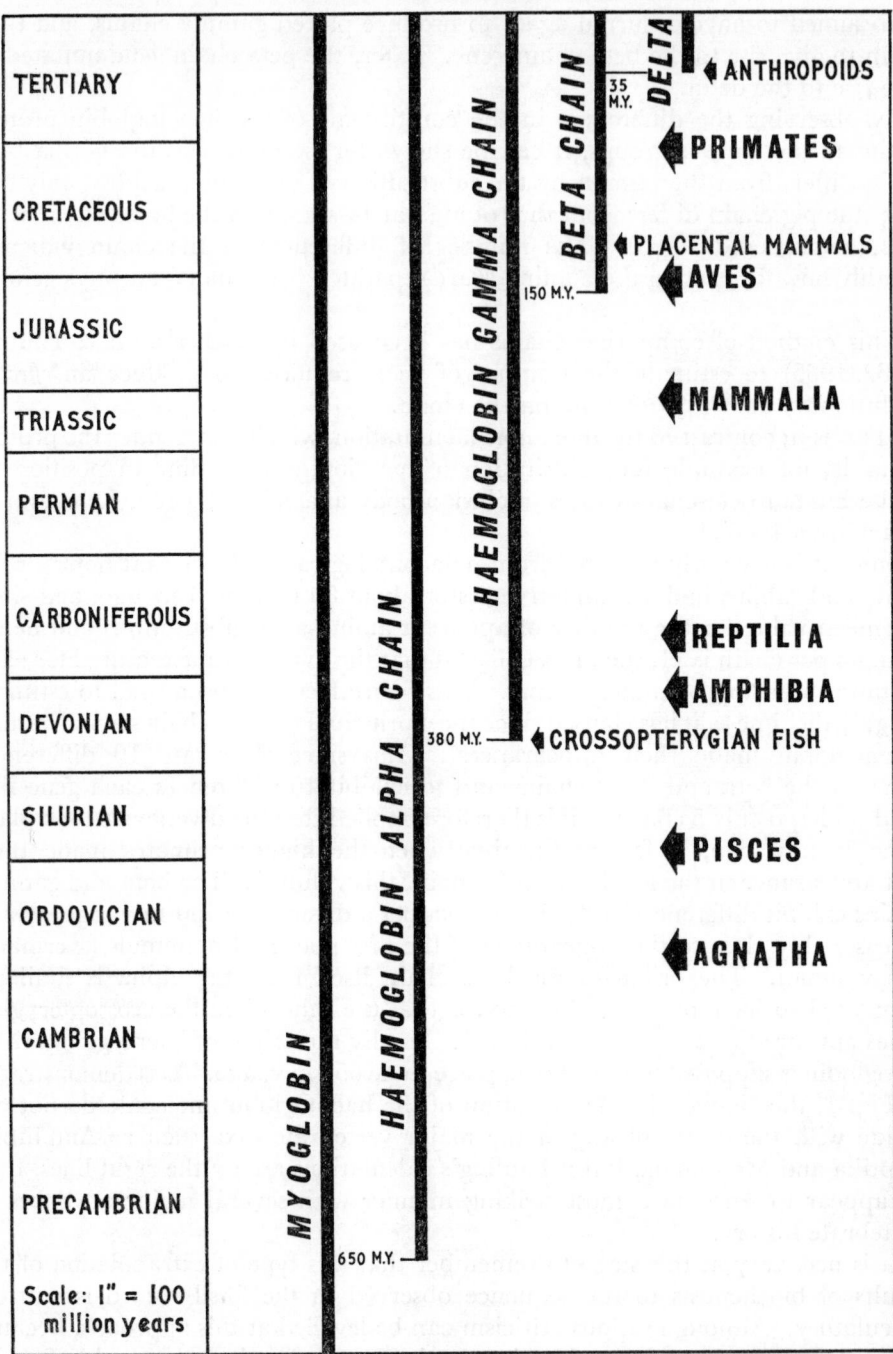

Fig. 1. Evolution of human haemoglobin chains during geological time according to calculations of Zuckerkandl & Pauling, with origins of selected vertebrate taxa inserted from documentation of present volume.

fossil record; nonetheless certain proteins do survive in fossil material and the following section discusses current study on them and on the theoretical possibilities of future research.

3. Fossil proteins

(i) *Historical introduction.* To date the only important recognizable protein to have an appreciable fossil record is collagen, on fibres of which calcium phosphate is laid down in the hard tissues of all the vertebrates. The first indication that residual organic matter survived in fossil calcified tissues was a comment by Bennett in the discussion of a paper on fossil fish teeth at the beginning of the century (Humphreys 1908). However, it was not until Abelson (1956, 1957, 1963) analysed qualitatively a series of fossils by means of paper chromatography and demonstrated the presence of up to 8 different amino-acids that Bennett's inferences were confirmed. Subsequently Moss (1961) and Tarlo & Mercer (1961) produced decalcified sections of Devonian dermal bone using routine histological techniques. It was evident that there was sufficient organic matrix surviving to allow the fossils to be treated, as if they were tissues of living animals. Little, Kelly & Courts (1962) published a photograph of decalcified Miocene mammal bone showing the fibrillar nature of the matrix suggesting collagen, and later Isaacs, Little, Currey & Tarlo (1963) from electron and x-ray diffraction studies confirmed the presence of collagen in decalcified bone from the Triassic and the Devonian. Wyckoff, Wagner, Matter & Doberenz (1963) studies early Pleistocene mammal bone and demonstrated a banding in the fibrils of about 600 Å thus indicating a shrinkage in the molecule, since fresh collagen has a banding of 640 Å. Shackleford & Wyckoff (1964) observed in Miocene bone a further shrinkage to 500 Å. Ho (1965) published a series of quantitative amino-acid analyses of Upper Pleistocene bone which were consistent with the collagen pattern, although he noted that there was a differential loss of certain amino-acids such as hydroxyproline. Quantitative analyses of earlier fossil tissues have recently been published by Armstrong & Tarlo (1966) and these are discussed below.

(ii) *Problems involved.* Since the work of Abelson (1956, 1957, 1963) it has been accepted that amino-acids can be extracted from the organic residue of fossils. Abelson claimed that the amino-acids he found were generally the more stable ones. In order to confirm this, he carried out a series of 'accelerated ageing tests' and he concluded that the more unstable amino-acids were arginine, aspartic acid, lysine, phenylalanine, serine, threonine and tyrosine. The more stable were alanine, glutamic acid, glycine, isoleucine, proline and valine. Although there are differences in the relative stability of the different amino-acids, one must be especially cautious when interpreting results of so-called 'ageing' tests since they may not reflect what happens under geological, as opposed to laboratory, conditions. Furthermore, when W. G. Armstrong repeated Abelson's paper chromatography analyses he identified the majority of the supposedly unstable amino-acids listed by Abelson, and in our more recent work measurable quantities of all the so-called unstable amino-acids have been extracted. Clearly, considerably more work is required to establish the relative stability of the different amino-acids under geological conditions.

This whole problem is complicated by the sedimentary conditions of preservation, since certain rocks—such as shales and ashphalt—will preserve organic materials more efficiently than others. Therefore it is necessary to make comparative analyses of fossils from different types of rock. A further complication is added to this problem, since Erdman, Marlett & Hanson (1956) were able to extract from both recent and Oligocene sediments the same amino-acids identified from fossils by Abelson.

As the products of decay of proteins will contain amino-acids, and all proteins are composed of vaying combinations of these same 'building bricks', the identification of specific amino-acids is usually in itself of no real significance. It is only possible to draw worthwhile conclusions if one can ascertain the relative proportions of the different amino-acids concerned. By obtaining quantitative results both from the fossils and the surrounding sediments, one can attempt to ascertain their ultimate source (i.e. from general organic debris in the rock or from the particular fossils being investigated). Fortunately, techniques have advanced sufficiently for this now to be possible, but these bring their own inherent problems. It now becomes necessary to guard against contamination by fingerprints from handling the material, or even by minute dust particles from leaving it exposed in the open for any length of time. However, these are comparatively minor problems which do not alter the major ones of contamination from amino-acids in the enclosing sediment and differential breakdown of the amino-acid components of the original proteins.

4. Methods

The method of amino-acid analysis described below is by column chromatography, which is based on the same principles as paper chromatography but has the added advantage of giving quantitative as well as qualitative results. The equipment used in this work is the 'Technicon automatic Amino-Acid Analyzer', a simplified explanatory diagram of which is given in Fig. 2. Before the fossil material can be analysed, it is necessary for it to be suitably prepared. First of all five to ten grams of the fossil are broken up in a micropulverizer, in this case a vertically oscillating ball-mill. Five grams of the resulting powder are hydrolysed in 30–40 ml of concentrated hydrochloric acid, together with a few drops of *n*-octanol to prevent foaming. The mixture is refluxed for 24 hours and the hydrolysate dried in a vacuum desiccator, over phosphorus pentoxide to remove the water and caustic-soda pellets to neutralize the hydrochloric acid. The dried product is dissolved in 20–30 ml of distilled water and the solution is run through an ion-exchange column to remover the anions, the cations and amino-acids remaining on the column. Elution with $4N$ ammonia preferentially releases the amino-acids and these are evaporated to dryness on a rotary evaporator, which at the same time removes the ammonia.

The dried preparation is then taken up into a suitable volume and applied to the separating column of the Analyzer. This consists of an ion-exchange resin column, in which the amino-acids 'attach' themselves to particles of the resin, and can only be freed by solutions of particular values of pH. From the 'autograd', a buffer of continually varying pH is pumped through the column and as a result the individual amino-acids separate out and emerge independently at the bottom (see Fig. 2). From here, they are fed through a proportioning pump, where the colorimetric reagent nin-hydrin is automatically mixed in the right proportions.

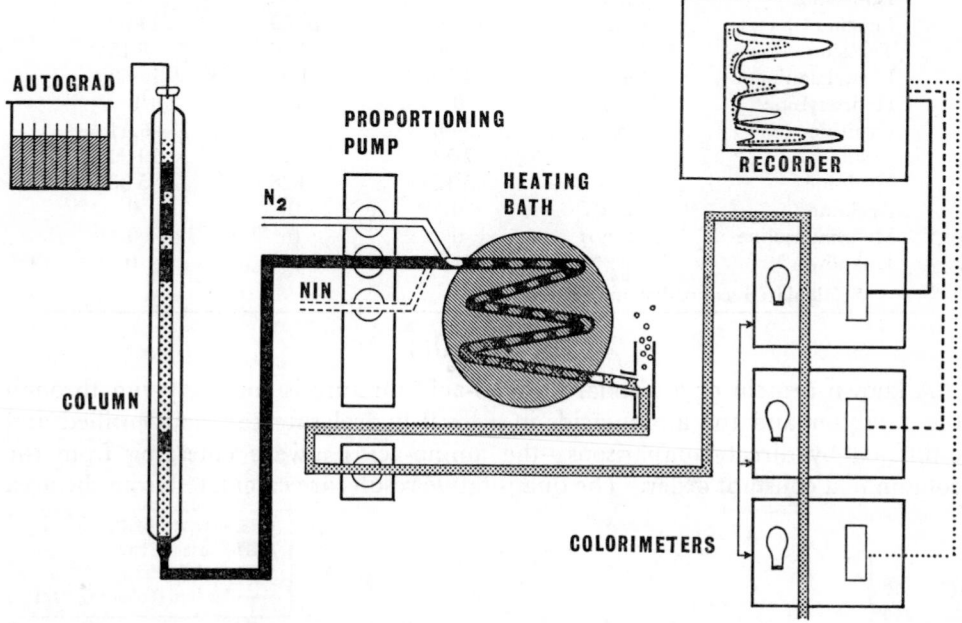

FIG. 2. Simplified diagram of 'Technicon automatic Amino-Acid Analyzer', based on drawing on pp. 4–5 of 'Analyzer' brochure (published by permission of Technicon Instruments Company Ltd.).

For technical reasons, and to prevent undue diffusion, it is necessary to introduce regularly spaced bubbles of nitrogen into the stream. The segmented stream so produced is fed through a long coil in a heating bath (10–15 min at 90 °c) where the characteristic colour develops. This is generally purple with a wavelength of about 570 mμ, but for two amino-acids, proline and hydroxypoline, a yellow colour develops (wavelength of 440 mμ). After removal of the nitrogen bubbles. the coloured stream is fed in series through three colorimeters, two of which are set to measure at 570 mμ at two different concentrations, and one at 440 μ at one concentration. Signals from the photoelectric cells measure the intensity of the colour, and are recorded on a graph–each individual amino-acid being marked by three coincident peaks (one for each colorimeter).

TABLE 1: Micrograms amino-acid per 5 g fossil specimen

Amino-acid		Pliosaur tooth	Pliosaur bone	Conodonts
Aspartic acid	(ASP)	13·84	10·12	2·00
Threonine	(THR)	3·38	2·98	1·19
Serine	(SER)	6·54	3·36	2·21
Glutamic acid	(GLU)	21·54	21·92	3·09
Proline	(PRO)	3·28	7·14	trace
Glycine	(GLY)	13·62	10·43	4·50
Alanine	(ALA)	16·12	16·57	3·65
Valine	(VAL)	8·58	9·02	3·05
Iso-leucine	(I-LEU)	7·34	5·90	6·82
Leucine	(LEU)	13·10	10·89	14·00
Tyrosine	(TYR)	4.66	3·80	8·15
Phenylalanine	(PHE)	4·50	4·96	16·68
Hydroxylsine	(HYLYS)	0	0	0
Ornithine	(ORN)	5·08	1·19	3·44
Lysine	(LYS)	7·52	7·16	19·00
Histidine	(HIS)	5·12	3·26	5·90
Arginine	(ARG)	0	0	0
Hydroxyproline	(HYPRO)	0	0	0
Unknowns*		1·24	4·07	0

*Calculated as nor-leucine equivalents.

5. Results

A known protein or a standard amino-acid mixture is routinely run through the Analyzer and the amino-acids in a fossil hydrolysate can be identified and estimated by direct comparisons—the amino-acids always emerging from the column in a constant order. The quantitative results are calculated from the area

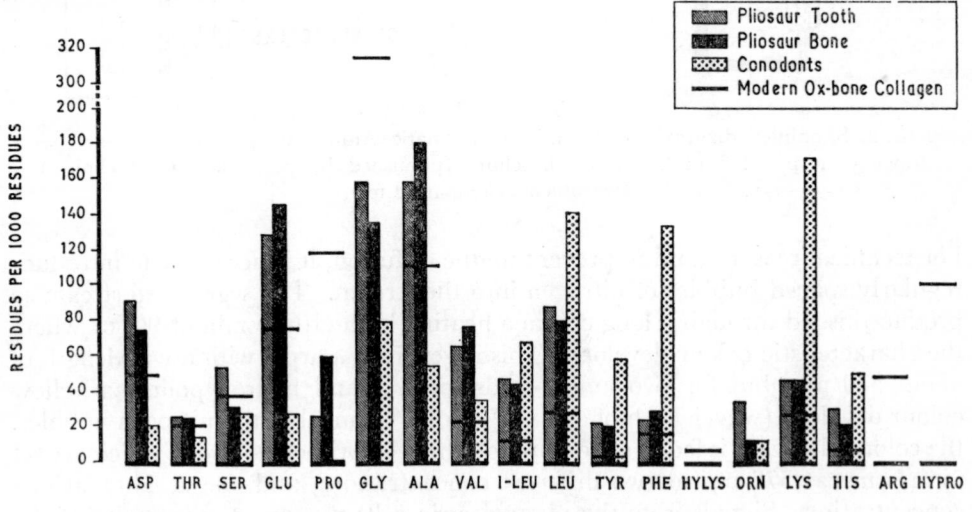

FIG. 3. Amino-acids in fossil calcified tissues expressed as residues per 1000 residues (published by permission of Dr W. G. Armstrong and the Editor of *Nature*).

within the peaks, and Table 1 gives such results in micrograms per five grams of fossil.

A more visual presentation of these results is shown in Fig. 3, where the relative proportions of the amino-acids to one another are plotted—being expressed as residues per thousand total residues. This method of portraying the results gives a much clearer indication of the compositional affinity. Note the fossil bone and tooth results approximate very closely to each other. However, they do not give a compositional profile comparable to collagen; hydroxylysine and hydroxy-proline are absent and there is not the expected large amount of glycine. This disparity may well be due to the differential breakdown of certain of the amino-acids (Armstrong & Tarlo 1966). There is also the likelihood that we may be

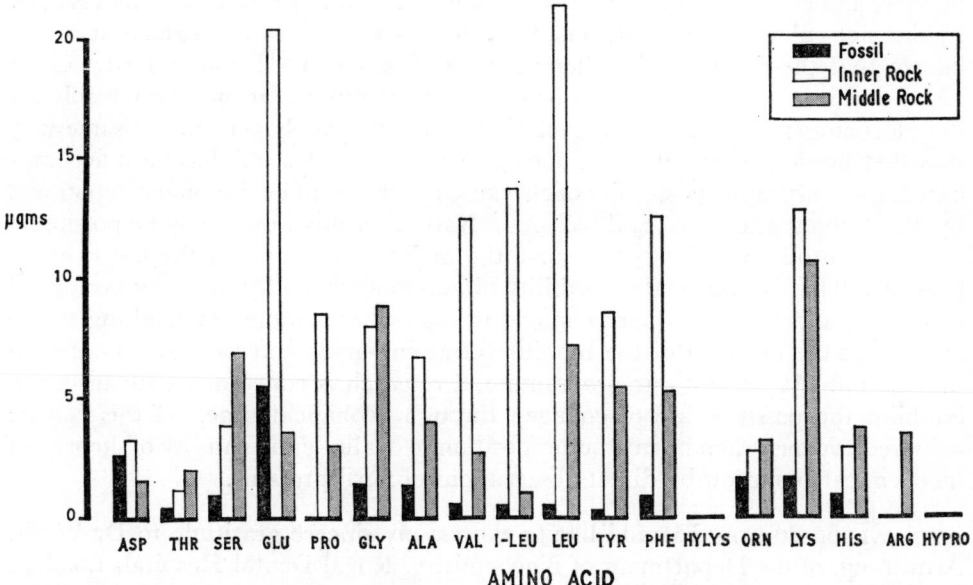

FIG. 4. Amino-acids per 5 g fossil or rock sample (published by permission of Dr W. G. Armstrong and the Editor of *Nature*).

dealing with contamination from the surrounding sediment. When Armstrong & Tarlo (1966) analysed the enclosing sediments, it was found that there was a concentration of several amino-acids immediately adjacent to the bone, and there was the very strong impression that amino-acids may have exhibited a large degree of mobility both in and out of sediment and fossil. This is clearly shown in Fig. 4—'inner rock' being from 2–5 mm from the fossil, 'middle rock' about 2 cm away.

6. Conclusions

Collagen, which is the main constituent of all connective tissues and accounts for a third of all protein in the body, only survives in the fossil record because it forms the organic matrix on which calcification takes place. In some way or other the apatite crystallites must lock in and protect this fibrous protein (Tarlo & Mercer 1966). At present a great deal is known about the structure of collagen—the molecule consists of three polypeptide chains each one forming a left-handed helix, thereafter being wound round each other in a right-handed helix (Gross, 1963). The sequence of amino-acids in the individual chains has still to be worked out. By comparison the haemoglobin molecule is a relatively simple one—each chain having a molecular weight of only 17,000. Noda (1955) calculated that the molecular weight of collagen from rat tail tendon was 700,000. Other workers have suggested a figure of 360,000. Even in this case, it is clear that the task of producing a similar scheme to that already done for haemoglobin almost defies imagination. Nevertheless, the whole subject of 'protein taxonomy' is only in its infancy, and one can look forward with confidence to this problem being resolved by the molecular biologists at some time in the distant future. Already it is well known that there are many different types of collagen (Harkness 1961; Gross 1963) and it seems reasonable to believe that, eventually, it may be possible for the biochemists to work out an evolutionary story for collagens in the same way that they are now doing for the haemoglobins. Once this task has been accomplished, there arises the possibility of checking the resultant evolutionary hypotheses by direct observations on fossil collagen. Naturally, this would only be possible if in the meantime we are able to solve the major problems that the fossil record presents. That is, the relative stability of amino-acids under differing geological conditions and the consequent changes in the collagen molecule resulting therefrom; also the problem of the mobility of amino-acids and the dangers of contamination. At present our programme of research is concerned with trying to establish the possible fate of collagen through geological time. If this can be achieved, we may then be in a better position to evaluate the validity of theories of biochemical evolution by direct observations of fossil proteins.

ACKNOWLEDGEMENTS. I would like to express my sincere gratitude to Dr W. G. Armstrong, of the Department of Biochemistry, Royal Dental Hospital, London, for his patient help and guidance, and also to Dr Kitty Little and Mr J. R. Mercer for useful discussions. Mrs Beryl J. H. Tarlo conducted much of the research into the literature and the article is consequently based in large measure on her endeavours. Miss Jennifer Middleton prepared the text-figures and Mr L. J. Evans, of Technicon Instruments, gave permission to publish the diagram of the 'Analyzer'.

7. References

ABELSON, P. H. 1956. Paleobiochemistry. *Scient. Am.* **195,** 83–90.

—— 1957. Organic constituents of fossils. *Mem. geol. Soc. Am.* **67,** 87–92.

—— 1963. Geochemistry of amino-acids, 431–455. In I. A. Breger (Editor): *Organic Geochemistry.* Oxford (Pergamon Press).

ARMSTRONG, W. G. 1966. Preparation of Calcified and fossil hard tissues for amino acid analysis. *4th Amino-acid colloquium.* Technicon Instruments, pp. 45–53.

—— & Tarlo, L. B. H. 1966. Amino-acid components in fossil calcified tissues. *Nature, Lond.* **210,** 481–482.

Baldwin, E. 1949. *An introduction to comparative biochemistry*. Cambridge (Cambridge University Press).

Braunitzer, G., Hilse, K., Rudloff, V. & Hilschmann, N. 1964. The Haemoglobins, pp. 1–71. In Anfinsen, C. B., Anson, M. L., Edsall, J. J. & Richards, F. M. (Eds.): *Advances in protein chemistry*, Vol. 19. New York (Academic Press).

Carrel, R. W., Lehmann, H. & Hutchinson, H. E. 1966. Haemoglobin Köln (β-98 valine → methionine): an unstable protein causing inclusion-body anaemia. *Nature, Lond.* **210,** 915–916.

Erdman, J. G., Marlett, E. M. & Hanson, W. E. 1956. Survival of amino acids in marine sediments. *Science, N.Y.* **124,** 1026.

Florkin, M. 1949. *Biochemical Evolution.* New York (Academic Press).

—— 1960. *Unity and diversity in biochemistry.* Oxford (Pergamon Press).

Florkin, M. & Mason, H. S. 1963. *Comparative biochemistry—a comprehensive treatise.* Vols. I–VII. New York (Academic Press).

Gross, J. 1961. Collagen. *Scient. Am.* **204,** 120–130.

—— 1963. Comparative biochemistry of collagen, 307–346. In M. Florkin & H. S. Mason (Eds.): *Comparative biochemistry,* Vol. 5. New York (Academic Press).

Gustavson, K. H. 1956. *Chemistry and reactivity of collagen.* New York (Academic Press).

Harkness, R. D. 1961. Biological function of collagen. *Biol. Rev.* **36,** 399–463.

—— 1966. Collagen. *Sci. Prog., Lond.* **54,** 257–274.

Ho, T.-Y. 1965. The amino acid composition of bone and tooth proteins in late Pleistocene mammals. *Proc. natn. Acad. Sci. U.S.A.* **54,** 26–31.

Humphreys, J. 1908. The teeth of fossil fishes. *Proc. R. Soc. Med.* **1,** 7–16.

Ingram, V. M. 1961. Gene evolution and the haemoglobins. *Nature, Lond.* **189,** 704–708.

Isaacs, W. A., Little, K., Currey, J. D. & Tarlo, L. B. H. 1963. Collagen and a cellulose-like substance in fossil dentine and bone. *Nature, Lond.* **197,** 192.

Little, K., Kelly, M. & Courts, A. 1962. Studies on bone matrix in normal and osteoporotic bone. *J. Bone Jt. Surg.,* (B) **44,** 503–519.

Moss, M. L. 1961. The initial phylogenetic appearance of bone: an experimental hypothesis. *Trans. N.Y. Acad. Sci.* (ser. 2) **23,** 495–500.

Noda, H. 1955. Physico-chemical studies on the soluble collagen of rat-tail tendon. *Biochim. biophys. Acta* **17,** 92–98.

Randall, J. T. 1953. *Nature and structure of collagen.* London (Butterworths).

Shackleford, J. M. & Wyckoff, R. W. G. 1964. Collagen in fossil teeth and bones. *J. Ultrastruct. Res.* **11,** 173–180.

Tarlo, L. B. H. & Mercer, J. R. 1961. A note on the histological study of fossil dentine. *Proc. geol. Soc. Lond.* no. 1590, 127–128.

—— & —— 1966. Decalcified fossil dentine. *Jl R. microsc. Soc.* **86,** 137–40.

Wyckoff, R. W. G., Wagner, E., Matter, P. & Doberenz, A. R. 1963. Collagen in fossil bone. *Proc. natn. Acad. Sci. U.S.A.* **50,** 215–218.

Zuckerkandl, E. 1965. The evolution of haemoglobin. *Scient. Am.* **212,** 110–118.

Zuckerkandl, E. & Pauling, L. 1962. Molecular disease, evolution and genic heterogeneity, pp. 189–225. In Kasha, M. & Pullman, B. (Eds.): *Horizons in biochemistry.* New York (Academic Press).

—— & —— 1965. Evolutionary divergence and convergence in proteins, 97–166. In Bryson, V. & Vogel, H. J. (Eds.): *Evolving genes and proteins.* New York (Academic Press).

Manuscript submitted June 1966.

L. B. H. Tarlo, d.sc. ph.d. f.l.s. f.a.z. f.g.s.
Department of Geology, The University, Reading; Royal Dental Hospital of London, Leicester Square, London w c 2.

DISCUSSION

Professor E. H. JOPE said that he was very pleased to hear Dr Tarlo emphasizing the importance of intact protein molecules, with their potential of stored genetic information, which was after all what they were largely interested in, and for which they must therefore exploit them. This information was of course entirely dispersed when we had nothing but amino-acid analyses, but we should not neglect peptide fragments—whether products of natural or of laboratory enzymatic breakdown.

He thought that we sometimes allowed ourselves to be side-tracked when we criticized the stimulating, pioneer—if somewhat philosophical—approach of Pauling and Zuckerkandl to the complexities of haemoglobin molecular ancestry. In any case it was on the insoluble, rather intractable, structural proteins that we had to focus our attention. Dr Tarlo's firm reference to Crick's remarks on proteins as a store-house of genetic information was very salutary.

Dr R. A. CROWSON said that he doubted the Zuckerkandl–Pauling hypothesis of a proportionality of amino-acid substitutions to time in proteins such as haemoglobin. If this principle implied that vertebrate haemoglobin and myoglobin diverged ancestrally far back in the Pre-Cambrian, then he thought that this should be taken as evidence against the Zuckerkandl–Pauling hypothesis rather than in favour of a Pre-Cambrian origin of the Vertebrata.

Dr T. P. BURNABY asked whether the various forms of the haemoglobin molecule were thought to have any adaptive significance, or whether the evolutionary changes were the result of a purely stochastic or random process. He said there were some newly-developed techniques of multivariate analysis which should be particularly helpful in interpreting and comparing fossil and recent amino-acid spectra while eliminating disturbing factors such as differential decomposition and contamination by the enclosing sediments. He offered assistance in this connexion.

Dr V. G. WALMSLEY remarked that Dr Tarlo's very recently obtained results suggesting the probable presence of collagen in conodonts were of considerable interest. It was not, however, as he had understood Dr Tarlo to imply, the first time this result had

been obtained. In 1963 Dr E. Hare and Dr K. Towe at Caltech had investigated a sample of conodonts supplied by Professor F. H. T. Rhodes and in a written communication to Professor Rhodes they had stated that they believed that a collagen-like protein was present and they had drawn conclusions similar to Dr Tarlo's. The speaker could not say whether the results had been published.

Mrs E. M. JOPE said that her own observations certainly suggested variable preservation of protein in Recent as well as in fossil shell. Foucart had now observed on Ordovician and Silurian graptolites a residual amino-acid content released only after hydrolysis. If this indeed reflected intact protein molecules, it opened the possibility of comparing fossil genera through peptide mapping. She had recently been examining the protein web remaining after EDTA treatment of Recent brachiopod shells; amino-acid analyses (like Hare's on lamellibranchs) showed protein complexities in the layers, and starch-gel electrophoresis was showing soluble acidic and basic fractions from the webhomogeneous proteins to be further characterized by peptide mapping. But it remained to be seen how far this could be carried with the fossil material.

Dr A. HALLAM described an apparent instance of biochemical evolution in the Mollusca, based on X-ray fluorescence studies of the strontium content of aragonitic cephalopod shells, undertaken in collaboration with Dr N. B. Price (Hallam & Price 1966). Most aragonite-secreting invertebrates, together with calcareous algae, had a skeletal (Sr/Ca) ratio similar to that of sea water, but the advanced molluscs (i.e. excluding the Polyplacophora) and fish had an appreciably lower ratio, signifying to Lowenstam (1963A) an increase in power of discrimination by more advanced biochemical systems against ions from the external aqueous medium. Lowenstam (1963B) had further shown an increase with age in the Sr/Ca ratios of aragonitic fossil gastropods and had suggested that this reflected biochemical evolutionary changes of increased discrimination against Sr relative to Ca from the late Palaeozoic to the present.

A number of Mesozoic ammonites were analysed at Edinburgh together with Recent Nautilus and found to have a Sr/Ca ratio similar to other cephalopods, bivalves and gastropods living at the present day. Certain excellently preserved goniatites from the Carboniferous of Scotland had a slightly higher but comparable ratio, but orthocone nautiloids from the same bed have a significantly higher ratio, intermediate between the advanced group of living molluscs and the more primitive Polyplacophora. Following Lowenstam, this may be tentatively interpreted as signifying that, at least in this discriminatory capacity, the Scottish Palaeozoic nautiloids had more primitive biochemical systems than living nautiloids and contemporary ammonoids.

References

HALLAM, A. & PRICE, N. B. 1966. Strontium content of recent and fossil aragonitic cephalopod shells. *Nature, Lond.* **212**, 25–7.

LOWENSTAM, H. A. 1963A. Biological problems relating to the composition and diagenesis of sediments. *In* T. W. Donnely (Ed.): *The Earth Sciences*. Rice Univ. Semicent. Publications.

—— 1963B. Sr/Ca ratio of skeletal aragonite from the Recent marine biota at Paula and from Fossil gastropods. *In* H. Craig, S. L. Miller & G. J. Wasserburg (Eds.): *Isotopic and cosmic chemistry*. Amsterdam (North-Holland).

Dr J. D. HUDSON drew attention to the work of Dr P. E. Hare and others on the organic matrix of mollusc shells as paralleling the work described by Dr Tarlo on the biochemistry of hard parts of (mainly) vertebrates. It had been shown that the amino-acid spectra of hydrolyzed protein from the aragonitic layers of *Mytilus* shells differed from those of the calcitic layers; a result of interest in view of suggestions that the organic matrix plays a part in the nucleation of aragonite versus calcite in shell structures. Genera, regarded as primitive, from different molluscan classes gave similar amino-acid spectra; they also resembled one another in having nacreous or partly nacreous shells with high organic contents. In contrast, specialized genera with mainly crossed-lamellar shell structure gave low organic contents and different spectra. It seemed that mollusc shell protein was a more variable substance (or substances) than vertebrate collagen and that the variation was linked with shell structure and phylogenetic position. This work promised to throw new light on the origin of that part of the animal from which palaeontologists had to try to reconstruct the whole.

A major difficulty in applying these methods directly to the fossil record was that it appeared that, even in mineralogically unaltered shells which yielded physically well-preserved sheets of organic matrix on decalcification, the protein had generally suffered considerable chemical change during diagenesis. Preliminary results from some Jurassic *Mytilus* examined by the speaker showed their organic carbon reduced to about one fifth of that expected by comparison with modern shells, and organic nitrogen still more drastically reduced to one twentieth or less of the probable original content. The composition of the degraded organic matrix was perhaps comparable to that of the insoluble kerogen of sedimentary rocks. Such changes in the organic matrix were unfortunate from the palaeontological viewpoint and it was to be hoped that exceptions would be found, but they might yield useful information on the nature of diagenetic processes in the rocks concerned.

References

HARE, P. E. 1963. Amino-acids in the proteins from aragonite and calcite in the shells of *Mytilus californianus*. *Science N.Y.* **139**, 216–7.

—— & ABELSON, P. H. 1964. Proteins in mollusk shells. *Annual Report of the Geophysical Laboratory for 1963*. Washington (Carnegie Institution), pp. 267–70.

Dr TARLO thanked Mrs Jope, Dr Hallam and Dr Hudson for their contributions on proteins and biochemical evolution in the invertebrates which helped to correct the balance of his own paper which dealt exclusively with the vertebrates, and even then with only two proteins.

In reply to Dr Crowson he stressed that the suggested divergence of myoglobin and haemoglobin in the Pre-Cambrian in no way implies such an early origin for the vertebrates. The evolution of efficient respiratory pigments can be expected to have taken place in the proto-chordates long before vertebrate status was ever achieved.

In reply to Dr Burnaby, he thought that all too little was known of the significance of the configuration of the haemoglobin molecule, and of the amino-acid substitutions that have occurred, and thanked him for his offer of assistance.

To Dr Walmsley's reference to the identification of amino-acids in conodonts by American workers, he replied that no valid conclusions could be drawn from such results unless they were quantitiative. Hydroxylysine, which is unique to collagen, had not yet been extracted from known collagenous fossil material. He thought that the first quantitative amino-acid analysis from conodonts had been obtained by Dr Armstrong and himself. He had not intended to imply that their results indicated the presence of a collagenous matrix in conodonts: he was non-commital.

Since the meeting Dr Tarlo has written in connexion with Professor Jope's remarks that Dr Armstrong had in fact succeeded in obtaining peptide maps of Pleistocene mammal bone and it was hoped to extend this aspect to earlier fossils. He added that the preliminary results by Armstrong and himself suggest that the protein matrix is unlikely to be collagen.

Fossil birds and their adaptive radiation

JAMES FISHER

CONTENTS

SUMMARY

The history of the systematic listing of fossil-bird taxa is briefly reviewed, and the radiation of avian palaeospecies discussed. Their strati-graphical succession in the Mesozoic and Cainozoic is then presented in some detail.

---

1. Introduction

It is scarcely more than a century and a quarter since the first avian palaeospecies, *Larus toliapicus* König 1825, was formally named under the systematic rules. Since then the science of palaeornithology has advanced, but in a somewhat inconsistent and globally uneven fashion, and has produced between 880 and 900 palaeospecies likely to be agreed as valid among working bird palaeontologists. This is about a tenth of the acceptable number of neospecies, that is to say species known to have lived since 1600*. Of these neospecies about 90 (85–95) are now believed extinct, and over 800 are also known from fossil or subfossil material of the Quaternary. Though a few neospecies have been formerly recorded from fully Pliocene horizons, such material as has lately been re-examined belongs to palaeospecies.

The first important global bird fossil systema was that of Lydekker in 1891, a year in which he also produced a list of British fossil birds (Lydekker 1891), and in which the Ameghino (1891) and Moreno–Mercerat (1891) lists of Argentine fossil birds were also published. Previously Milne-Edward's classic catalogue and plates of the fossil birds of France (Milne-Edwards 1867–71) had astonished the systematic world. Wetmore produced a succession of deeply scholarly summaries of the fossil birds of North America (Wetmore 1927, 1940, 1956). The standard textbook of Lambrecht (1933) has recently been reprinted in response to increasing public demand, and remains the only treatment of palaeornithology

---

* This definition is not offered as a blanket definition for palaeozoology. Many workers, e.g. Brodkorb, take the Linnean year 1758. All birds extinct since 1600 seem to have been at least described from life or skins as well as bones, and this 'year after which the colours are known' has been adopted by the International Union for Conservation of Nature and Natural Resources.

The Fossil Record, pp. 133–154. Geological Society of London, 1967. Printed in Northern Ireland.

with full systema, diagnoses, adaptive and historical discussion and bibliography. Advances in the systema since Lambrecht's great offering were described and discussed in some detail by Wetmore (1951). More recent systematic summaries and discussions at the level of taxa higher than the genus have been offered, amongst others, by Storer (1960) and Fisher & Peterson (1964), the latter with the first world maps of fossil sites outside the present neofaunal limits. Since 1963 Brodkorb has begun to publish his most valuable *Catalogue of fossil birds* of which three substantial parts have already appeared (Brodkorb 1963, 1964, 1967): it contains no diagnoses but is a nomenclator and geographer of the palaeospecies and fossil neospecies to warm a scholar's heart.

Most of those mentioned above have discussed the light that fossil studies throw on the evolution and adaptive radiation of birds, either in the works cited or others such as Lydekker (1896) and Wetmore (1928, 1929). Besides these, stimulating papers and booklets have come from Howard (1947, 1950), Swinton (1958) and Kuhn (1965).

It is not surprising that the depth of investigation of the world's great fossil aviafaunas shows some remarkable differences, depending as it does on the distance of museums, seats of learning and palaeornithologists from field material. Only in North America is there a close-knit school of learned enthusiasts with copious comparative material, and a satisfying published palaeofauna of the Nearctic. The Palaearctic avifauna shows signs of having been capriciously worked, in comparison. British Tertiary material has been scarcely examined in the twentieth century, and the results of British and Irish Quaternary investigations have been published in archaeological and other journals and largely seem to have escaped ornithologists' notice. The major British text-books of Witherby and Bannerman, and the now obsolete *Check-list* of the British Ornithologists' Union, ignore fossils—unlike their American counterparts. The late Kalmán Lambrecht still inspires critical work in Hungary; but palaeornithologists, on the whole, sleep in the rest of Europe. The greatest and most peculiar of all the avifaunas, the Neotropical, has its Phororhacologists (or to be possibly more precise, Phorusrhacologists), but enjoys no great organized programme of new research. The Australasian palaeofauna has lately been reworked by a growing group of natives and some Holarctic visitors, though little is yet published. Material from the Oriental and Ethiopian fossil sites is going to waste, though; and as far as the writer can discover the only palaeospecies so far described from continental Africa south of the Sahara are *Struthio oldawayi* Lowe 1933, *Gigantornis eaglesomei* Andrews 1916 and *Anas luederitzensis* Lambrecht 1929—but three, each from a different locality; and four birds have been referred to living species. The palaeontologist in search of described Ethiopian material must go to that of Eocene–Miocene France!

2. Radiation of birds

The geological pattern as assembled is, then, heavily weighted in favour of fossils likely to be found in the regions now inhabited by the Holarctic fauna. It is also (obviously) heavily weighted in favour of the more fossilizable taxa of birds. The species of the Anatidae constitute only 1·7 % of the neofauna, but no less than 10 % of the aggregate palaeofauna. Nature can scarcely ever have given us a proper sample of the avifauna of any time at any horizon; the favoured candidates were nearly always the bigger birds—the marsh-birds, water-birds, shore-birds and continental-shelf sea-birds, and the birds of prey that preyed upon them. The fossil avifaunas that have the most 'normal' distribution are doubtless the freak ones like that of the Uppermost Pleistocene–Holocene tarpits of Rancho la Brea in California.

It is lucky that *Archaeopteryx*, which seems to have been a woodland-type bird, was clumsy enough to fall thrice into the kind of lagoonal mud we could find it in later. Apart from this *no strictly land bird of any sort* has been believably detected in any horizon between the 'Tithonian' Jurassic and the Lower Eocene, apart from the Palaeocene Diatrymiformes. The writer excludes the Upper Cretaceous *Caenagnathus* as he shares the doubts of many scholars as to whether this mandibular mystery is a bird.

All the Cretaceous birds are water-birds or marsh-birds or mud-birds, and we must judge them rather specially. *Gallornis*, the earliest, is doubtless correctly referred by Brodkorb to his new Torotigidae—an early family based on a proto-flamingo. This Neocomian or possibly Valangian genus (if we can accept the taxonomic signs of the proximal end of a femur) was already highly specialized, and as a proto-flamingo was probably toothless and possibly even an alga-sifter.

Enaliornis of the Albian was next—the British early bird. The writer feels with Storer (1960) and his predecessors that it was an Hesperornithiform diver and unlikely to have been stem to the Gaviiformes, which may more likely have enjoyed their convergent specialization towards diver form from the Palaeocene, unless *Lonchodytes* (see below) be a true link.

The Coniacian brings in the vintage early birds of Marsh. Still toothed (we do not know the skull of *Enaliornis*) the Hesperornithidae show dead-end flightless specialization, and became extinct in the Campanian. The Baptornithidae (not known to be toothless or toothed) last to the Maestrichtian, and may or may not have been ancestors of the grebes. The Ichthyornithiformes appear in the Coniacian, but in full anatomical glory; and by Gregory (1952) were elegantly demonstrated to have confused an earlier generation of palaeontologists by borrowing the teeth of baby mosasaurs. They were probably toothless, and quite modern-style, simple, gull-like, flying sea-birds, and suitable candidates for stem to the Charadriiformes and a whole bunch of other taxa adapted in different ways.

In the Santonian the appearance of Plataleae seems to indicate a common flamingo–stork–ibis stem earlier, from which Anseriformes (first Upper Eocene) could also have arisen, or be about to arise. Suloids appear in the Maestrichtian at the same time as Lonchodytids which could be Hesperornithiform hangovers or Gaviiform precursors. The Maestrichtian also brings us the rails and the Charadriiformes proper.

135

FIG. 1. [Taxa in square brackets known only as extant and not plotted unless sole known representatives of order.]

Archaeopterygiformes   1 Archaeopterygidae.

Struthioniformes   2 Eleutherornithidae, 3 Struthionidae.

Rheiformes Rheidae   4 Opisthodactylinae, 5 Rheinae.

Tinamiformes   6 Tinamidae.

Casuariiformes   7 Dromornithidae, 8 Dromiceiidae, 9 Casuariidae.

Aepyornithiformes   10 Aepyornithidae.

Apterygiformes   11 Dinornithidae, 12 Emeidae, 13 Apterygidae.

Sphenisciformes   14 Spheniscidae.

Procellariiformes   15 Diomedeidae, 16 Procellariidae, 17 Oceanitidae, 18 Pelecanoididae.

Phoenicopteriformes   19 Torotigidae, 20 Scaniornithidae, 21 Telmabatidae, 22 Agnopteridae, 23 Phoenicopteridae, 24 Palaelodidae.

Anseriformes   25 Anatidae, 26 Anhimidae.

Odontopterygiformes   27 Odontopterygidae, 28 Pseudodontornithidae.

Pelecaniformes   29 Elopterygidae, 30 Sulidae, 31 Pelecanidae, 32 Pelagornithidae, 33 Phalacrocoracidae, 34 Anhingidae, 35 Cyphorinthidae, 36 Fregatidae, 37 Phaethontidae, 38 Cladornithidae.

Hesperornithiformes   39 Baptornithidae, 41 Hesperornithidae, 53 Enaliornithidae.

Podicipitiformes   40 Podicipitidae (41 see above).

Falconiformes   42 Neocathartidae, 43 Teratornithidae, 44 Cathartidae, 45 Acciptridae, 46 Pandionidae, 47 Falconidae, 48 Sagittariidae.

Ciconiiformes   49 Plegadornithidae, 50 Ardeidae, 51 Plataleidae, 52 Ciconiidae [Scopidae, Balaenicipitidae].

Gaviiformes   53 (see Hesperornithiformes), 54 Lonchodytidae, 55 Gaviidae.

Ichthyornithiformes   56 Ichthyornithidae, 57 Apatornithidae.

Diatrymiformes   58 Gastornithidae, 59 Diatrymidae.

Gruiformes   in Cariamidae 60 Bathornithinae, 61 Cariaminae and 62 Psilopterinae, in Phorusrhacidae 63 Phorusrhacinae and 64 Brontornithinae, 65 Cunampaiidae, 66 Idiornithidae, 67 Rallidae, 68 Geranoididae, 69 Eogruidae, [Psophiidae], 70 Aramidae, 71 Ergilornithidae, 72 Gruidae, [Eurypygidae, Rhynochetidae, Heliornithidae], 73 Turnicidae, 74 Otididae, [Mesitornithidae ? Galliform].

Psittaciformes   75 Psittacidae.

Columbiformes   76 Raphidae, 77 Columbidae, 78 Pteroclidae.

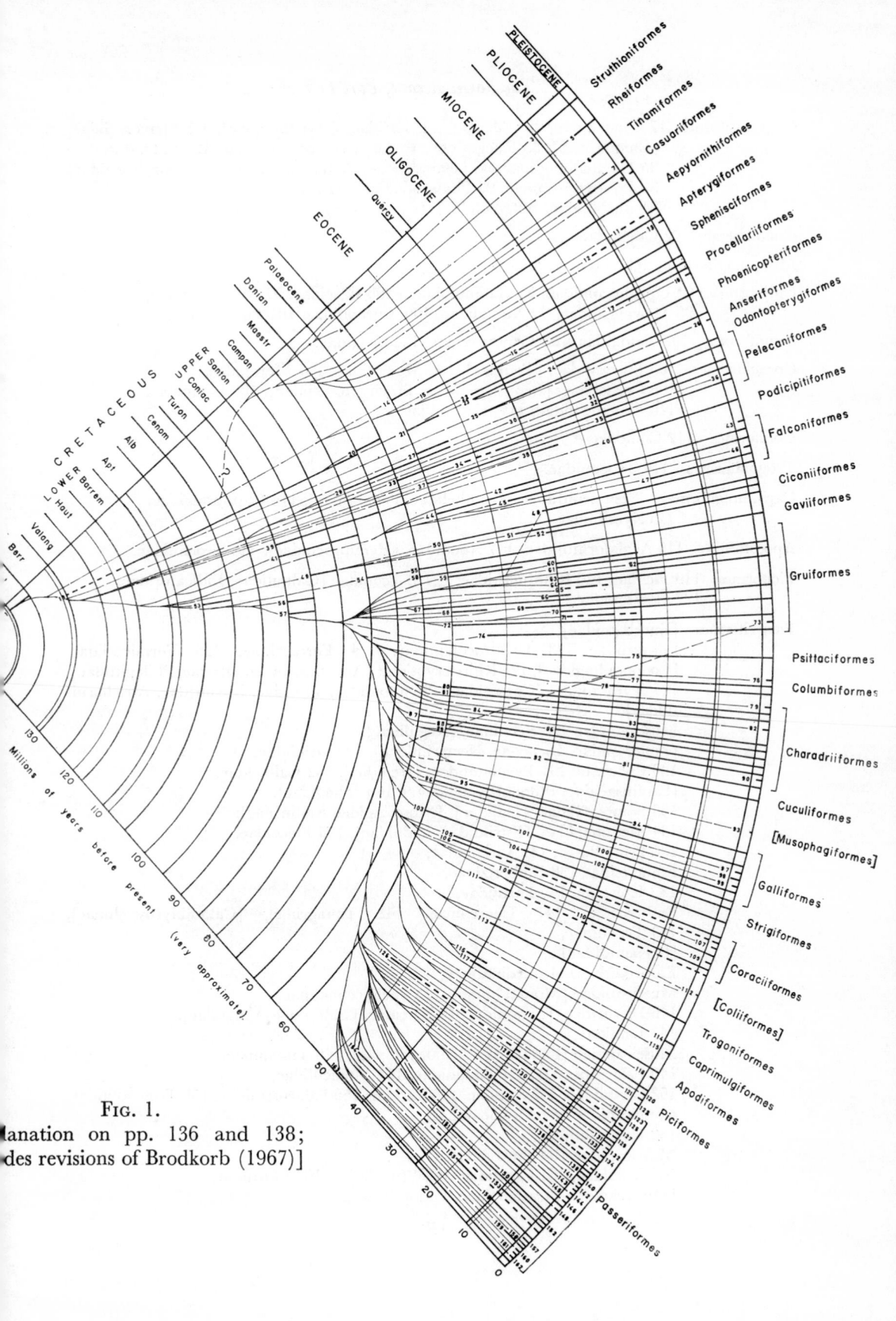

FIG. 1.
[Expl]anation on pp. 136 and 138;
[inclu]des revisions of Brodkorb (1967)]

Charadriiformes   79 Jacanidae, 80 Alcidae, 81 Laridae, [Rynchopidae], 82 Stercorariidae, [Chionididae], 83 Rhegminornithidae, [Thinocoridae], 84 Rostratulidae, 85 Haematopodidae, 86 Charadriidae, 87 Scolopacidae, 88 Recurvirostridae, 89 Presbyornithidae, 90 Phalaropodidae, [Dromadidae], 91 Burhinidae, [Glareolidae]. (Cimolopterygidae not plotted.)

Cuculiformes   92 Cuculidae.

Musophagiformes   93 Musophagidae.

Galliformes   94 Opisthocomidae, 95 Gallinuloididae, 96 Cracidae, 97 Megapodiidae, 98 Meleagrididae, 99 Numididae, 100 Tetraonidae, 101 Phasianidae.

Strigiformes   102 Tytonidae, 103 Protostrigidae, 104 Strigidae.

Coraciiformes   105 Bucerotidae, [Todidae], 106 Momotidae, 107 Meropidae, 108 Coraciidae, [Leptosomatidae, Brachypteraciidae], 109 Upupidae, 110 Phoeniculidae, 111 Alcedinidae.

Coliiformes   112 Coliidae.

Trogoniformes   113 Trogonidae.

Caprimulgiformes   [Steatornithidae, Aegothelidae, Podargidae], 114 Caprimulgidae, 115 Nyctibiidae.

Apodiformes   116 Aegialornithidae, 117 Apodidae, [Hemiprocnidae], 118 Trochilidae.

Piciformes   119 Picidae, 120 Ramphastidae, 121 Bucconidae [Galbulidae, Indicatoridae], 122 Capitonidae.

Passeriformes   [Eurylaimidae], Furnariidae 123 Dendrocolaptinae, 124 Furnariinae, 125 Formicariidae, [Conopophagidae], 126 Rhinocryptidae, [Acanthisittidae, Pittidae, Philepittidae], 127 Tyrannidae, [Cotingidae, Phytotomidae, Pipridae, Menuridae, Atrichornithidae].
Muscicapidae 128 Sylviinae, [Regulinae],
[Zosteropidae, Dicaedae, Nectariniidae], 129 Oriolidae,
130 Corvidae, 131 Pycnonotidae, [Irenidae], 132 Callaeidae,
[Paradisaeidae, Ptilonorhynchidae, Campephagidae],
133 Bombycillidae, [Dulidae], [Muscicapidae Malurinae],
134 Meliphagidae, [Estrildidae, Viduidae], 135 Ploceidae,
136 Fringillidae, 137 Vireonidae,
Emberizidae 138 Emberizinae,
139 Icteridae, 140 Parulidae,
Emberizidae 141 Coerebinae, 142 Tanagrinae, [Catamblyrhynchinae], 143 Tersininae,
[Drepanididae],
Emberizidae 144 Cardinalinae,
Muscicapidae [Monarchinae], 145 Pachycephalinae,
146 Dicruridae, [Artamidae, Cracticidae, Grallinidae, Vangidae],
147 Laniidae,
Muscicapidae [Panurinae, Orthonychinae], 148 Timaliinae,
149 Palaeospizidae, 150 Alaudidae, 151 Motacillidae,
152 Certhiidae, 153 Sittidae, 154 Paridae, 155 Palaeoscinidae, 156 Troglodytidae,
Muscicapidae 157 Muscicapinae,
158 Hirundinidae,
Muscicapidae 159 Turdinae,
160 Mimidae, 161 Cinclidae, 162 Prunellidae, 163 Sturnidae,
[Muscicapidae Picathartinae, Polioptilinae].

138

In so far as the biassed record of the rocks shows anything, it shows the completion of the main ordinal streams of avian evolution by the Eocene. Perching Non-passerines like kingfishers and hornbills appear by the middle Eocene, as probably do primitive Passerines ('*Hebe*', ? Rhinocryptidae). Advanced (Oscine) Passerines appear by the Upper Eocene. By Oligocene times almost every major order of birds is represented in the fossil record.

No family of birds of the 155 surviving in the neofauna is represented in the fossil record before the Phalacrocoracidae, Rallidae and Scolopacidae of the Maestrichtian and the Gaviidae of the Palaeocene; but Lower Eocene times have added (to our present proof) ten more. By the Lower/Middle Oligocene fossil members of 43 such families are known, by the Lower Miocene 57, by the Lower Pliocene 67, from deposits before A.D. 1600, 107, and 48 families are so far unknown from fossils or subfossils, as far as the writer can discover. The number of families accepted in the present systema is 198, of which 42 were evidently extinct by 1600.

The count of Fisher & Peterson (1964) of acceptable bird palaeogenera described by 1962 was 331, of neogenera 2128. Authorities of the calibre of Mayr (1963), however, believe that modern reassessments of generic status may bring the neogenera down to *c.* 1750. Of the 2128 Fisher–Peterson neogenera, material from the Upper Eocene has been doubtfully referred to the living genus *Limosa* (Ledian). However the Eocene–Oligocene threshold (Quercy) brings in *Milvus*, *Pterocles*, *Bubo* and *Asio*, and by the Lower/Middle Oligocene 9 neogenera were living, by the Lower Miocene 27, by the Lower Pliocene 69, by the Upper Pliocene 81. So far, deposits from the Villafranchian Pleistocene to A.D. 1600 have shown about 426 neogenera (of which about 106 are Passeriform).

Figure 1 superposes a hypothetical evolutionary tree on the plot of the listed taxa in a highly approximate chronological frame. The suggested relationships have necessitated a presentation of the taxa in a different arrangement from that adopted in Chapter 29 of Part II, which is the systema devised by Fisher & Peterson (1964) with minor modifications from Wetmore (1960), the present editors of the Peters *Checklist of the* [living] *birds of the world* (1931 on) and recent International Ornithological Congress resolutions. This classification tries to follow Simpson's principle (Simpson 1945, p. 13) that 'good classification is conservative', and that its primary purpose is 'simply to provide a convenient, practical means by which zoologists may know what they are talking about and others may find out'. The hypothetical tree is not another alternative classification, but a model which attempts to express some of what is now guessed to be the phylogenetic tree of birds from the evidence of palaeontology, anatomy (especially the anatomy of vestiges and believed non-adaptive structures), zoology, geographical distribution, serum chemistry, parasites, behaviour, etc. The bibliography cites important recent contributions in most of these spheres: and it must be remembered that the palaeontologists' rôle as a phylogeneticist is confined to one main band in the spectrum of descent relationships, even if it is practically the only one available to him.

3. Stratigraphical succession of avifaunas

At this point it may be best to summarize the acceptable palaeontological material actually named by 1963, including a few 'species' as yet without trivial adjectives—notably the important Lower Oligocene *Eogrus* sp. Wetmore 1934, Lower Miocene *Sylvia* sp. Lambrecht 1933 and Lower Miocene *Passer* sp. Lambrecht 1933. Among named material rejected for various reasons are the following:

Based solely on fossil tracks: *e.g. Ornithichnites, Ornithoidichnites, Ignotornis, Urmiornis abeli.*

Based solely on fossil feathers or their impressions: *e.g. Ornitholithes* and *Fontinalis* (first described as a moss).

Based solely on eggshell material: *e.g. Psammornis.*

Non-avian, or probably so: *e.g. Palaeonornis, Laopteryx, Protornis bavarica* (reptile), *Cimoliornis, Caenagnathus, Diatryma filifera* (bryophyte), *Protorhee* (camelid).

Incertae sedis: *e.g. Palaeolestes gorei, Colinus eatoni, Yalavis, Laornis, Eopteryx, Falco falconellus, Anas benedeni, Palaeoapterodytes, Pelophilus radoboyensis* (first described as a frog), *Fringilla trochanterica, Metapteryx, Turdus bresciensis.*

Nomina nuda vel vana: *e.g. Argala, Otis brevipes, Ptenornis.*

In the following list the census numbers the species *recorded* in each horizon, except that species recorded from more than one horizon (about 30) are included in the census only from the earliest.

(A) MESOZOIC AVIFAUNAS

JURASSIC

'TITHONIAN'. 1 (or 2) species, *Archaeopteryx lithographica* (Archaeopterygidae).

CRETACEOUS

NEOCOMIAN (Berriasian–Valanginian–Hauterivian–Barremian). 1 species, *Gallornis straeleni* (Torotigidae) is provisionally referred to Valanginian.

APTIAN. No known avian fossil.

ALBIAN. 2 species of *Enaliornis* (Enaliornithidae).

CENOMANIAN. No known avian fossil.

TURONIAN. No known avian fossil.

CONIACIAN. 12 species: *Baptornis* 1 (Baptornithidae), *Hesperonis* 3 (Hesperornithidae), *Ichthyornis* 7 (Ichthyornithidae) and *Apatornis* 1 (Apatornithidae); all in the Niobrara fm. of Kansas save 1 sp. *Ichthyornis.*

SANTONIAN. 1 species, *Plegadornis* (Plegadornithidae).

CAMPANIAN. 2 species, *Coniornis* (Hesperornithidae) and *Parascaniornis* (Torotigidae).

MAESTRICHTIAN. 17 species, *Neogaeornis* 1 (Baptornithidae), *Apatornis* 1 (Apatornithidae), *Lonchodytes* 2 (Lonchodytidae), *Elopteryx* 1 (Elopterygidae), *Torotix* 1 (Torotigidae), *Cimolopteryx* 3 and *Ceramornis* 1 (Cimolopterygidae), *Palaeotringa* 3 (Scolopacidae), *Telmatornis* 2 (Rallidae) and *Graculavus* 2 (Phalacrocoracidae).

(B) TERTIARY AVIFAUNAS

DANIAN. 1 species, *Scaniornis* (Scaniornithidae).

PALAEOCENE. 7 species in 3 families. First Gaviid, Gastornithids and Diatrymid in Cernaysian fms. of France.

EOCENE

The Gruid *Eobalearica* (Turkestan) is of uncertain horizon.

LOWER EOCENE. 26 species in 19 families; plus first Spheniscid, New Zealand. First Rheid and sole Telmabatid Casamayor fm., Argentina. In London Clay of England 7 spp. fauna with the first Phaethontid, an Elopterygid, the sole Odontopterygid, the first Ardeid and first Cathartid, a Gastornithid and the first Larid. In Wyoming first Cracid in Willwood fm., sole Geranoidid in Greybull fm., and in Wasatch fm. 8 spp. fauna with first Gruid, 2 Rallids, 4 Diatrymids and first Protostrigid. In France a Diatrymid in Ypresian fm. In Utah first Presby-ornithids (2) and first Alcids (2) in Colton and lower Green River fms.

MIDDLE EOCENE. 26 species in 16 families. Sole Eleutherornithid in Eger-kingen fm., Switzerland. Last Diatrymids in Mont d'Or, France and Manasquan marl, New Jersey. First Diomedeid in Ameki fm., Nigeria. Last Elopterygids (2) in Bruxellian fm. of Belgium (U. Eoc. London Clay sp.) and Steinbruch coarse chalk fm. of Rumania. First Anhingid in freshwater fishbeds of Sumatra. In Bridger fm. of Wyoming 14 spp. fauna with 2 Ardeids, first Gallinuloidid (also in U. Green River fm.), same cracid as in L. Eoc. Willwood fm., 6 Gruids, last (3) Protostrigids, first Momotid (cf.). In Lutetian fms. of Germany 5 spp. fauna with Cathartid, Gruid, first Otidid, first Rostratulid and first Bucerotid. A Gruid in the Parisiano of Italy. '*Hebe*' *schucherti*, which cf. Rhinocryptid and if so earliest known Passeriform, may be from Green River fm. of Wyoming and if so of this or L. Eoc. horizon.

UPPER EOCENE. 30 species in 21 families. Spheniscids (2) in New Zealand & Australia. First Aepyornithid in Egypt, ? Libya, Algeria and Arabia. In Lower Headon (Bartonian) fm. of England 9 spp. fauna with Gaviid, Phalacrocoracid, first Plataleid, first Agnopterid, first Phoenicopterid, first Accipitrid, 2 Gruids and last Gastornithid. In Montmartre (Ledian) fm. of France 12 spp. fauna with Agnopterid, same Accipitrid as in Bartonian England, 2 Gallinuloidids, 2 Rallids, a Scolopacid, a Bucerotid, the first Parid (cf.) and the first (3) Sturnids. First Anatid in Uinta C fm. of Utah. Sole Neocathartid in Washakie B fm. of Wyoming. In Irdin Manha fm. of Inner Mongolia, first Eogruid and a Rallid. An Alcid in Arago fm. of Oregon. In fish-bearing and Matt schists of Switzerland *Protornis* 2 spp., cf. first Alcedinids.

UPPERMOST EOCENE AND LOWEST OLIGOCENE

QUERCIAN. The phosphorites of the Quercy district of south-central France, have the second largest and most comprehensive fossil avifauna known from the Tertiary, with 44 species (plus 2 also in other U. Eoc. horizons) in at least 18 families, though its probably Passeriform material has not yet been formally named. A century of work by Milne-Edwards, Gaillard and others has demon-strated, on the avian evidence alone, an essentially inland forest and open wetland Ethopian fauna, fossilized in strata conformably spanning the Ledian–Tongrian (Stampian) threshold. The array consists of an Ardeid, the first (3) Ciconiids,

3 Cathartids, the first Sagittariid, 3 Accipitrids (one other species also found in Bartonian of England and Ledian of France), 9 Gaillinuloidids, a Gruid also found in Bartonian of England, the 7 Idiornithids (a Ralloid family unknown from any other formation), 2 Rallids, a Scolopacid, the first (2) Pteroclids, the first Cuculid, the first (5) Strigids, the 2 Aegialornithids (an Apodid or Apodoid family unknown from any other formation), the first Apodid and the first (3) Trogonids.

OLIGOCENE.

LOWER AND MIDDLE OLIGOCENE. 53 species (plus 1 also in U. Eoc.) in 31 families. Of Spheniscids one in New Zealand's Kakanui limestone; this species also in Moerewhenna greenstone with 4 other penguin species and a Diomedeidid; one Moerewhenna penguin also found in Wharekuri limestone and later Waitakian fm. with a sixth L./M. Oligoc. penguin. The sole Ergilornithids (2, S. E. Gobi) are of L. Oligoc. horizon. In Fayum fm. of Egypt an Aepyornithid, an Ardeid and a Ciconiid. In Deseado fm. of Argentina 15 spp. fauna with sole Cladornithid, a Ciconiid, a Phoenicopterid, 2 Anatids, 2 Cathartids, the first Aramid, the first Cariamid, the first (2) Phororhacids and the first (3) Cariamids. In Tongrian fm. of France (incl. Ronzon) 6 spp. fauna with first Sulid, 2 Phoenicopterids, an Anatid, a Cathartid and the first Charadriid. In the Lower Hampstead Beds of England an Agnopterid also found in England's Bartonian U. Eoc. In the Chadron fm. of Colorado, South Dakota or Nebraska 2 Cathartids, a Gallinuloidid, a Rallid and the first Bathornithid. In the Cypress Hills fm. of Saskatchewan the first Phasianid, a Scolopacid and a Cuculid. From Outer Mongolia, an Eogruid in the Ardyn Obo fm.

Faunas above (except Waitakian = M) are regarded as L. Oligoc. L. and M. Olig. is Wyoming's White River fm., whence a Gaviid and a Phalacrocoracid; and L. or M. Oligoc. is Atala fm. of Argentina, whence sole Cunampaiid. Regarded as M. Oligoc. is Rupelian fm. of Belgium, whence first Procellariid, an Anatid, a Charadriid and a Larid; and the *Oreodon* bends of the lower Brule and White River fms. of South Dakota, Colorado and Wyoming, whence 3 Accipitrids and a Cracid.

UPPER OLIGOCENE. 17 species in 12 families. Florissant Lake bed fm. of Colorado (may be M. Oligoc.) has a Charadriid and the sole Palaeospizid (Passeriform). The Upper Brule fms. of Wyoming and South Dakota show an Acciptrid, a Cracid, 2 Aramids and the last (3) Bathornithids. In Oregon the Lower John Day fm. has a Charadriid and a Larid. In the Old World Chattian horizons, or their equivalent, show a Sulid, a Gallinuloidid and a Phasianid in France; an Anatid in Czechoslovakia; the last Agnopterid and an Anatid in Kazakhstan.

MIOCENE.

The Pseudodontornithid *Pseudodontornis*, formerly of uncertain horizon and place, has lately been found in S. Carolina Hawthorne, U. Mioc. Of uncertain horizon within the Miocene are a Cariamid (Patagonia) and an Alcid (North Carolina).

LOWER MIOCENE. 130 species in 44 families. The Spheniscids have a broad representation with 1 in the Balcombian fm. of Australia, 7 in the Seymour Island beds of Seymour Island off Graham Land, Antarctica and 15 species in the Juliense Patagonian fm. of Argentina. Also from the Argentinian Patagonian are a Procellariid, 2 Phorusrhacids and a Cariamid. The biggest fauna, of 57 species, comes from the Aquitainian of France, with a Gaviid, a Procellariid, the first Pelecanid, 2 Phalacrocoracids, 2 Ciconiids, 2 Plataleids, 5 of the first Palaelodids, a Phoenicopterid, 4 Anatids, a Sagittariid, 5 Accipitrids, 3 Gallinuloidids, 2 Gruids, 2 Rallids, an Otidid, 3 Scolopacids, the first Burhinid, 3 Larids, a Pteroclid, the first Columbid, the first Psittacid, the first (2) Tytonids, a Strigid, 2 Apodids, a Trogonid, the first Phoeniculid, the first (2) Picids, and in the Passeriformes the first certain Motacillids (2), Laniid, Muscicapid Sylviine (cf.) and Ploceid (cf.). Five of these same species are found also in the equivalent Hydrobienkalk fm. of Germany, which yields also another Anatid; and one in an Aquitanian equivalent of Czechoslovakia, which also yields another Anatid. Yet another Anatid is found in the Aquitanian of Italy. This European Aquitanian avifauna smells strongly Ethiopian.

The Aquitainian equivalents of North America include the Upper John Day formation of Oregon, whence the first Podicipitid and a Phalacrocoracid; the Rosebud fm. of South Dakota, whence another first Palaelodid, 5 Anatids, an Accipitrid, a Cracid, the first Tetraonid, a Phasianid and a Strigid; probably later are the lower Harrison beds of the Arikaree fm. of Nebraska with 3 Accipitrids, a Cracid, a Tetraonid and the first Haematopodid. Probably a full equivalent of the later European Burdigalian is the Hawthorne fm. of Florida (and South Carolina), whence a Procellariid, one of the two known Cyphornithids (S.C.), a Sulid, a Phalacrocoracid, a Ciconiid and a Rhegminornithid.

Burdigalian species from France are Procellariids, the sole Pelagornithid and a Sulid; and from Czechoslovakia an Accipitrid and a Scolopacid. The Tick Canyon Accipitrid from California may be at a Burdigalian or lower Helvetian horizon. Other lower Miocene formations hard to horizon within it are the Carmanah Point beds of British Columbia with the only other member of the (so far) peculiarly L. Mioc. Cyphornithids; the Etadunna fm. of Australia with 2 Phoenicopterids; South-west Africa's Kalahari fm. with an Anatid; the Thomas Farm beds of Florida with 3 Accipitrids and a Cracid; and the Kolozsvár fm. of Hungary (possibly U. Oligoc.) with a Rallid.

MIDDLE MIOCENE. 75 species in 30 families (plus 8 also in L. Mioc.). In the Helvetian of France a 19 spp. fauna with a Phalacrocoracid, 2 Ardeids, an Anatid, 2 Accipitrids, 6 Phasianids, 3 Rallids, a Scolopacid, a Cuculid, a Strigid and the first Corvid; and doubtless also Passeriform are "*c.* 13 spp". cf. Fringillidae *sensu lato* badly needing re-investigation. In North American equivalent, Calvert fm. of Maryland, a Procellariid, 2 Sulids (one of them also in Kirkwood fm. New Jersey) and an Alcid. Probably spanning Helvetian and Tortonian horizons are the Sheep Creek beds of Nebraska, whence 3 Accipitrids, a first Falconid, a Phasianid, an Aramid and a Psittacid; and the Monte Leon–Santa Cruz–Cuevian fms. of Argentina whence a 16 spp. fauna with a Pelecanid, a Plataleid,

2 Anatids, 2 Accipitrids, a first Falconid, a Cracid, 3 Phorusrhacids and 5 Caria-mids. From the La Venta beds (Honda group) of Columbia comes the first Opisthocomid.

In the later M. Mioc. the Tortonian of France shows a 25 spp. fauna with the last Pelagornithid (cf. the same species as the first in the Burdigalian L. Mioc.), a Ciconiid, 2 Anatids, 2 Accipitrids, 9 Phasianids (2 spp. also found in the earlier Helvetian), 3 Scolopacids, 2 Larids (also L. Mioc.), a Tytonid, 2 Strigids, an Apodid and a Picid; and the Tortonian of Germany shows 2 more Phasianids. In California the Mohnian (equivalent to uppermost Helvetian and Tortonian) has the unique Palaeoscinid (Passeriform); and the Temblor fm. (= Tortonian–Vindobonian) has an 8 spp. fauna with a Diomedeidid, 3 Procellariids, a Sulid, an Anatid, a Scolopacid and an Alcid. The only European Vindobonian material appears to be from Germany, with a Phasianid also found in the Helvetian and Tortonian of France, and a metacarpal which has been referred to the Passeriform Fringillids *sensu lato*.

UPPER MIOCENE. 47 species in 22 families (plus also in L. Mioc. (cf. some species) and 3 in M. Mioc.) No Passeriformes have so far been recorded, unless the Gabbro fm. of Italy, cf. L. Plioc, is U. Mioc. In California the Barstow lake bed fm. yields a Palaelodid (possibly the same as a L. Mioc. species) and a Cracid; the Capistrano fm the first Oceanitid; the Monterey shale fm. a Procellariid, 3 Sulids and the 2 Pseudodontornithids; the Sisquoc fm. 3 Sulids (one also in Monterey fm.); the Modelo fm. a Phalacrocoracid. In Nebraska the Barstovian has a Larid; the lower Snake Creek fm 2 Accipitrids, and the Sheep Creek or Marshland fm. a Tetraonid; another Tetraonid is found in the Mascall fm. (= Sarmatian) of Oregon.

In Europe Germany's Oberfalz lignite has a Phalacrocoracid, 2 Ardeidids and an Anatid; its upper freshwater silt fm 2 Pelecanids, an Ardeidid, a Palaelodid, 5 Anatids (one also in the previous fm.) and an Otidid; its upper marine silt an Ardeidid; and its Munich Flinz an Anatid. Belgium has an Anatid and a Rallid in the Bolderian and an Anatid in the Anversian sands; Switzerland 2 Anatids, and a Phasianid in the Sarmatian Ohningen chalk fm. referred to a species also found from the Helvetian to Vindobonian M. Mioc. The typical Pontian fauna is represented by a Phalacrocoracid, a Ciconiid, 4 Phasianids, a Gruid, an Otidid, a Scolopacid and a Strigid in the Ukraine, 2 Phasianids in Greece (one also found Ukraine), and a Rallid in Spain. Also on the U. Mioc. list are the last Eogruid from Tung Gur, Mongolia and a Phorusrhacid from Arroyo Roman, Uruguay.

PLIOCENE.

Of uncertain horizon are a Cathartid from the Tarija Valley, Bolivia and a Larid from kieselguhr in Georgia, U.S.S.R.

LOWER PLIOCENE. 72 species in 33 families plus 1 U. Mioc. species. New Zealand has a Spheniscid in Waitotaran fm. and the first Emiid in Gleniti fm. (may be U. Mioc). Australia has the first Dromiceiid in Mampuwurdu fm. The Siwalik beds of India have a first Struthionid, 2 Pelecanids and a Ciconiid. The

Pannonian Pikermi (*Hipparion*)–Ertemte–Eppelsheim (*Deinotherium*) horizons have yeilded another first Struthionid and 2 Ciconiids in Greece; another first Struthionid in Inner Mongolia; an Anhingid, an Anatid, a Gruid (also known from U. Mioc.) and a Strigid in Hungary; an Anatid and a Gruid in Germany; and a Falconid in Kazakhstan. From the Meotian fm. of the Ukraine comes a Pelecanid and Phalacrocoracid; and from the Maragha fm. of Iran a Gruid. In Italy the earliest Alaudid (Passeriform) comes from the Gabbro fm., which may possibly be U. Mioc.—also from this fm. comes a Motacillid; in the Messiniano fm. we find a Rallid, a Scolopacid, another Alaudid, and the first Sittid; in lignite an Anatid. Many workers refer the Messiniano and Meotian to uppermost Mioc., pre-Pontian and Pikermi to Pontian.

Of the New World L. Plioc. faunas the most comprehensive is the 16 spp. array of the Bone Valley guano in Florida, with 2 Gaviids, a Podicipitid, a Diomedeid, 3 Sulids, a Phalacrocoracid, an Ardeid, a Phoenicopterid, an Anatid, a Haematopodid, 2 Scolopacids, a Larid and an Alcid. Florida's Alachua clay fm. shares the Phalacrocoracid and has another Ardeid, another Scolopacid and the earliest certain (Emberizine) Emberizid. The lower Juntura fm. of Oregon provides a Phalacrocoracid, the last Palaelodid, 3 Anatids and a Rallid. California's Repetto fm. has a Procellariid, Ricardo fm. an Anatid and Black Hawk fm. a Gruid. Nevada's Esmeralda fm. has an Anatid, Nebraska's upper Snake Creek fm. 2 Accipitrids, a Cracid and a Gruid. South Dakota's L. Ash Hollow fm. has an Anatid, and its Ogallala fm. an Accipitrid; other Ogallala birds are an Anatid, an Accipitrid, a Gruid and another earliest Emberizid in Kansas. New Mexico's Santa Fé fm. has an Accipitrid. In Argentina the Mesopotamian fm. has 2 Phorusrhacids, the Andalgala' fm. a Cariamid.

MIDDLE PLIOCENE. 35 species in 18 families (plus 3 also L. Plioc). Those (Piacenzan or Plaisancian) of Europe have a Gaviid, a Podicipitid, a Phalacrocoracid, a Falconid and an Alcid in Italy; and 2 Phasianids and a Corvid in France. In North America the San Diego fm. of California holds 2 Gaviids (one also Etchegoin fm., as well as L. Plioc), a Podicipitid, a Procellariid, 2 Sulids, a Phalacrocoracid, 4 Alcids and a Tytonid. Oregon has a Phalacrocoracid (also L. Plioc.) in the U. Juntura fm., an Anatid and a Phasianid in the McKay beds, an Accipitrid in the Drewsey fm. (also L. Plioc.) and a Scolopacid in the Hemphillian fm. From the Chalk Hills fm. of Idaho comes a Phalacrocoracid; from the Kern River fm. of California a Cathartid; from the Hemphill fm. of Texas the Anatid also found in the McKay beds; and from the Chihuahua fm. in Mexico a Phoenicopterid. A Rheid, the first (3) Tinamids, a Cathartid, 2 Cariamids and 2 Phorusrhacids seem to be the only known M. Plioc. South American bird fossils.

UPPER PLIOCENE. 15 species in 9 families (plus one cf. also L. Plioc.) if we assign the Rexroad, Kansas and Benson (San Pedro Valley) faunas to the Villafranchian Pleistocene. The Gray Ranch fm. of Arizona has a Rallid. In Europe the Diomedeid in England's Coralline Crag may also be represented in L. Plioc, Florida. Germany's Rippersroda lignite has an Ardeid. The Astian fms. of France have an Anatid, a Turdine Muscicapid (probably without justification referred to the neospecies *Monticola solitarius*) and a Corvid; those of Italy 2 Anatids, a Corvid and a bone fragment cf. Fringillidae *sensu lato*.

(c) QUATERNARY AVIFAUNAS

PLEISTOCENE—HOLOCENE.

Dating from the Villafranchian and its probable Nearctic equivalent the Rexroadian-? Blancan to A.D. 1600, well over a thousand formations, prehistoric and archaeological sites have disclosed bones of about 270 acceptable palaeospecies and an array of neospecies which brings the total to over eleven hundred. Of the 155 families doubtless living in this period 48 appear to be so far unrepresented in the fossil record. Only three flightless taxa appear to have become extinct in the Pleistocene—in the L. Pleist. the Psilopterinae and in the U. Pleist. the Dromornithidae and Phorusrhacidae. The vast thermal-soaring Teratornithids, flightless Aepyornithids, Emeids and Dinornithids and peculiar Raphids did not disappear until the Holocene and the invasion of North America and the colonization of some islands by man.

A breakdown of the fossil and sub-fossil material available for the periods, described to 1964 and analysed by the writer* is:

		PALAEOSPECIES	NEOSPECIES Extinct	NEOSPECIES Living	TOTAL
Palaearctic		29	1	341	371
Nearctic		97	3	276	376
Neotropical W. Indies & Bermuda		21	1	65	87
Continental		27	—	168	195
Ethiopian Islands		21	15	16	60
Continental		1	—	4	5!!
Oriental		2	—	22	24!
Australia (2 neospp. on islands.)		43	—	6	49!
New Zealand		40	8	63	111
All Villafr.–L. Pleist.		46	—	173	219
M. Pleist.		50	1	158	209
U. Pleist.†	a.	149	6	572	727
	b.	115	2	565	682
Holo (incl. prehist.)	a.	92	27	466	585
Non-passerine		253	25	604	882
Passerine		19	2	204	225
All species		272	27	808	1107

† *a*: including, *b*: excluding New Zealand birds on the Pleist–Holo threshold.

VILLAFRANCHIAN AND LOWER PLEISTOCENE. These are grouped together as recent radio datings of putative Villafranchian correlates of North America appear to confuse, rather than simplify the position of aviferous deposits such as the San Pedro Valley fm. of Benson in Arizona (*c.* 7 spp.); the Hagerman Lake beds fm. of Hagerman in Iadaho (*c.* 16 spp.) and the Rexroadian fm. of Rexroad in Kansas (*c.* 25 spp.). Combining the so-far-determined species of these and other comparable horizons (*e.g.* Blanco Canyon in Texas), with those of the L. Pleist. (*sensu lato*) Nearctic faunas of California (Tulare, Santa Barbara fms.),

* As part of a work in progress on Pleist–Holo extinction.

Nebraska (Nebraskan), New Jersey (Bridgeton), Pennsylvania (cave deps.) and Texas (Cita Canyon Beds) we have a fauna of 44 species, of which 27 are palaeospecies.

The Lower Pleistocene of the Palaearctic has a stronger known fauna of 173 determined species, of which 15 are palaeospecies; the true Villafranchian, however, is scarcely represented. This is thanks to the work, over some years, of Čapek and Kretzoi on the Biharian (Cromerian) fauna of Püspokfürdö (now known as Betfia) in Rumania (*c.* 52 spp.), and of Serebrovsky and Burchak–Abramovich on the Kirov beds of Binagady near Baku in Azerbaijan (*c.* 107 spp.). Small English avifaunas are known from the Günzian–Cromerian of Norfolk–Suffolk (*c.* 12 spp.), and from the cave deposits of Clevedon, Somerset, whose *c.* 22 bird species are probably from a L. Pleist, horizon.

Outside the region presently occupied by the Holarctic fauna scarcely any Lower Pleistocene birds are described: the Neotropical birds are but two palaeospecies; the Ethiopian birds one palaeospecies, one neospecies; the Australian birds one palaeospecies, one neospecies. The writer knowns of no others yet published.

MIDDLE PLEISTOCENE. The described Palaearctic Holsteinian and Rissian avifauna consists of 77 determined species, of which 7 are palaeospecies; it is not very strong, therefore, though good faunas have been described by Tchernov from the horizons of mid (*c.* 37 spp.). and upper (*c.* 21 spp.). Acheulean culture in the cave deposits of Mugharet Oumm Qatafa in Israel. Perhaps the last Palaearctic examples of the Pleistocene trend towards gigantism and 'dead-end specialization' come from this sub-period, from the cave deposits of Malta which yielded to Lydekker, Bate and others amongst other palaeospecies a swan whose linear dimensions were about a third larger than its congener *Cygnus olor* and a *Gyps* vulture about a fifth larger than the largest living species *Aegypius monachus*. The Maltese swan, if it could fly, may have been the heaviest bird that ever did; *C. olor* is doubtless the heaviest that does. Other avifaunas, not fully determined, come from river-gravels in England and Russia.

The determined Nearctic Yarmouthian and Illinoian avifauna consist of 146 species, of which 43 are palaeospecies and one the extinct passenger pigeon. California's Upper Palm Spring fm. at Vallecito Creek yields *c.* 7 spp.; Oregon's famous and long-worked Fossil Lake fm. *c.* 63 (critically summarized by Howard); but perhaps the finest avifauna sample has been, mainly lately, described with care by Brodkorb and fellow-workers from Florida's Illinoian Arredondo Clay of Arredondo (43 spp.), Haile (28+ spp.) and other sites, and from the Reddick beds (54 spp).

Outside the Holarctic the certain Middle Pleistocene avifauna appears to consist of 4 species in the post-Walsingham beds of Bermuda.

UPPER PLEISTOCENE. The Eemian (Ipswichian) and Würmian deposits of the Palaearctic, and their equivalents in Asia, have yielded a total of 285 determined species, of which but 7 are palaeospecies and one, the great auk, is an extinct neospecies. About twenty-five deposits have avifaunas of over 25 spp., among them: probably of Eemian horizon the Mousterian faunas of Čertova

Dira (*c.* 72 spp.) and Sipka (*c.* 31 spp.) in Czechoslovakia worked by Woldirch and Capek; the Eemian–early Würmian faunas of the Grotta Romanelli in Italy (*c.* 52 spp. found by Regália and Blanc), and of the Monaco caves of Grimaldi (*c.* 54 spp., Boule), Menton (*c.* 25 spp., Rivière) and l'Observatoire (30 spp., Boule); an upper Levalloiso-Mousterian fauna with an early Würm correlation in the Kebara Cave, Israel (*c.* 55 spp., Tchernov) and the late Würmian faunas of Pálffy (*c.* 44 spp., Čapek, Lambrecht, etc.) and Pilisszántó (*c.* 73 spp. Lambrecht, Jánossy) in Hungary, others probably of this horizon in Italy (*c.* 28, 79 & 88 spp., Regália), a palaeolithic site in the Crimea (68 spp., Tugarinov, Gromov), Schweizersbild's Magdalenian fauna in Switzerland (*c.* 26 spp., summarized by Lambrecht). In Britian and Ireland the *c.* 57 spp. of Chudleigh Cave in Devon (E. T. Newton) are Eemian or early Würmian; other biggish faunas are probably mainly late Würmian (though some caves have several horizons), such as those of Wye Valley caves in Herefordshire (*c.* 34 spp., Bate Newton) and caves in Clare (*c.* 41 spp.) and Sligo (31 spp.) whose material was determined mainly by Scharff.

The Sangamonian and Wisconsinian (incl. Iowan and Bradyan) deposits of the Nearctic have yielded 232 determined species of birds, of which 38 are palaeospecies and one an extinct neospecies. The Nearctic sample appears smaller than that of the equivalent Palaearctic; but the non-passerine species numbers (189P, 181N) are very similar, which shows that the on the whole more recent North American workers have applied less attention or (more probably) more critical standards of acceptance to the determination of the much more difficult passerines which are of approximately equal weight in the two living faunas. The principal workers are, or have been, Brodkorb, Compton, De May Holman, Howard, McCoy & Miller, Sibley, Wetmore and Woolfenden. The principal faunas are found in:

California: Palos Verdes sands, Manix Lake beds, cave deposits and the tarpits of Carpinteria (*c.* 54 spp.), McKittrick (*c.* 69) and Rancho la Brea (*c.* 147).

Florida: Pamlico fm., *e.g.* Itchtucknee River (49), Rock Spring (*c.* 39) and Seminole Field (*c.* 49); also Melbourne beds. Nevada; New Mexico and Texas; cave deps.

The cave deposits of Shelter cave in New Mexico are probably of the earliest Holocene rather than the uppermost Pleistocene, and the famous tarpit fauna of Rancho la Brea, with its vast assembly of mammals and birds appears from recent ^{14}C datings to embrace deposits probably from over 16 000 B.P. in the late upper Pleistocene to less than 4250 B.P. in the Holocene. From Howard's careful analysis it seems clear that a Holocene group of pits may have a fauna of well over 50 bird species, of which at least 10 are palaeospecies, among them several last 'markers' of the typical Pleistocene fauna with gigantic elements, such as the Brea stork *Ciconia maltha*. The rather larger predecessor of the California condor *Gymnogyps amplus*, the huge Teratorn *Teratornis merriami* (its even bigger congener *T. incredibilis* persisted until the U. Pleist. and was the largest known bird of prey with a *c.* 16 ft. wingspan), other biggish extinct raptors and the Brea turkey *Parapavo californicus*. The collapse of the 'Rancholabrean' mammal fauna in the same period was even more spectacular. Flint (1957, p. 468) wrote that "probably many of these extinctions in both Europe and North America were the result of the hunting activities of prehistoric man". The mammal markers tell us this clearly, but the bird markers also say so. Man arrived in N. America *c.* 10 000 years before the Pleist–Holo threshold. He became an active hunter in the Palearctic at the Middle–Upper Pleist threshold; it is interesting that the last detectable 'Rancholabrean' bird marker in Europe, the giant Maltese vulture *Gyps melitensis* (see above), last appears in an horizon in the Grotte de Grimaldi, Monaco, not older than early Würmian and possibly Eemian.

The Neotropical bird fauna of the Upper Pleistocene consists of 166 determined species, of which 28 are palaeospecies, in continental deposits. The best faunas are in the Pampean deposits of Luján in Argentina (*c.* 23 spp., Ameghino, Moreno, Mercerat in the last century) and the cave deposits of Lagao Santa in Brazil (*c.* 126 spp. in the Lapa da Escrivania, mainly Winge, also in the last century); and in the cave deposits of San Josecito in Nuevo Léon, México (34 spp., mainly L. H. Miller). In the West Indies Cuban deposits referred sometimes to the Pleistocene are probably all Holocene, but the Banana Hole horizon on New Providence I., Bahamas, cf. early Wisconsinian but probably Sangamonian (pre-Pamlico) has an interesting fauna of 15 spp. of which 8 are palaeospecies (Brodkorb).

The continental Ethiopian bird fauna of the Upper Pleistocene consists of but three determined neospecies, as far as the writer can discover. Further comment seems unnecessary. The Ethiopian islands of Ascension, St. Helena, Madagascar, Mauritius and Rodriguez all have strongish fossil faunas, but as uppermost Pleistocene horizons may only be present in the deposits of the first three, and all are mainly or entirely Holocene, these, like the Quaternary deposits of New Zealand, will be discussed under the next heading.

The writer can find but 24 species of birds (one a passerine) that have been determined from deposits of Quaternary age in the region now occupied by the Oriental fauna. One hornbill is from a prehistoric site (Borneo), as also is the fowl *Gallus gallus* (Asian mainland). Eleven neospecies are from horizons which I have been unable to determine within the Pleistocene, including the only passerine (a drongo). The remaining eleven are from the Upper Pleistocene and include only two palaeospecies, which are of 'Rancholabrean' character. One is the giant stork *Leptoptilos titan* from the classic Solo River beds of Java (Wetmore). The other is the Chinese ostrich, *Struthio anderssoni*, whose bones and more often fossil eggs have been found rather widely in China and were also in prehistoric deposits, and which appears to have been sub-domesticated through the Han period (2nd cent. B.C. to 3rd cent. A.D.) and probably survived at least until the T'ang period (7th to 10th cent. A.D.).

Australia's named upper Pleistocene bird fauna was nearly all determined by DeVis sixty years ago and more, mostly from the Darling Downs (Chinchilla) beds of Queensland and from the Malkuni fauna in the Katipiri sands of Eyrean South Australia. Of the 45 species in the combined fauna, no less than 42 are palaeospecies, of which may have 'Rancholabrean' character. None is a passerine; it is probable that DeVis may have concentrated on determinable palaeospecies; but equally certain that (with its marsupial mammals) the Australian fauna suffered a sudden débacle similar to but deeper than that of Rancho la Brea, and that this can be probably attributed to the arrival of hunting man, possibly as long ago as 20 000 B.P. The full publication of new recent Eyrean investigations is awaited.

HOLOCENE AND PREHISTORIC

This period, as analysed and here defined, covers Europe to the end of the Iron Age, including as such the Roman and Dark Age Periods of Britain and Ireland, the pre-Columbian Americas and the pre-(Western) colonization period of New Zealand and other islands.

The Palaearctic fossil and subfossil fauna of this period has been determined as 193 bird species, of which the only palaeospecies (extinct before 1600) is *Struthio anderssoni* (which extended into the Palaearctic) and the only extinct neospecies *Pinguinus impennis*, the great auk. While there is much fossil evidence of climatic distributional changes, and withdrawals of vulnerable species at the edge of their range (e.g. *Pelecanus crispus* from Western Europe and Britain in the Iron Age), the fauna, as a whole and in its balance, has remained late Pleistocene, doubtless because it had ceased to be a Pleistocene fauna, in the 'Rancholabrean' sense, early in the Upper Pleistocene.

Records are scattered over many archaeological sites, and scores must be 'buried' in archaeological literature from palaeontologists, judging by the writers' comparison of the material in British archaeological and speleological literature with the entries in (for instance) the *Zoological Record*. Some good avifaunas are:

Mesolithic: Puskaporos (*c.* 60 spp.) and Remetehegy (*c.* 50) in Hungary (Čapek, Kormos, Lambrecht).

Mesolithic culture, towards or in Neolithic period: the classic sites of Ertebølle (26 spp.); also cf. here Mejlgaard (26 spp.) and Solager (31 spp.), also in Denmark (all Winge).

Azilian Neolithic: combined fauna of sites in England (Durham), Scotland and Ireland (*c.* 27 spp.).

Neolithic–Bronze Age: combined fauna of English (Norf.–Cambs.) peats of this period (*c.* 21 spp.).

Neolithic–Bronze Age: site in Crimea (*c.* 27 spp., Voistvenski).

Late Iron Age: Glastonbury in England (*c.* 31 spp., Andrews).

Roman: combined fauna of England, Monmouth and Scotland (*c.* 40 spp.).

Also Jarlshof in Shetland (Platt, Hamilton); *c.* 21 spp. at Bronze Age–Broch culture horizon, *c.* 6th to 1st cent. B.C.; 29 spp. at Viking–Norse horizon, *c.* 10–11th cent. A.D.

The Nearctic fauna of this period consists of 191 defined species, of which 16 are palaeospecies and 3 extinct neospecies (great auk, passenger pigeon, Carolina parakeet). Contemporary with the Holocene fauna of Rancho la Brea (see above) was a prehistoric midden of Archaic culture at Five Mile Rapids in Oregon with *c.* 18 spp., of which one was a palaeospecies and another evidently intermediate between *Gymnogyps californianus* and its doubtless direct ancestor the extinct *G. amplus* (L. H. Miller). In Illinois (Baker, Parmalee) an Archaic site of rather later date at Modoc had *c.* 17 spp. and a site of Middle Mississippi culture (*c.* 1200–1550 A.D.) at Cahokia had 23 spp., including the extinct passenger pigeon and Carolina parakeet, and the ivory-billed woodpecker whose continental race now lives no nearer than the Gulf coast (*c.* 10 birds at present). Later than the late Rancho fauna, but long before our calendar era, are the 56 spp. of the Emeryville Indian shellmound in California (Howard). Within our calendar era, and ranging in age from 0 to 1800 A.D. (most around 1000 A.D.) are 6 Eskimo sites in Alaska (Friedmann) with faunas (all neospecies) of *c.* 38, *c.* 53, *c.* 31, *c.* 35, 25 & 36 spp.

Some of the Brazilian cave deposits examined by Winge were referred to Holocene horizons, and these contained 33 neospecies, the only subfossil records for the period from the Neotropical continent; but from the west Indian islands a fine combined pre-Columbian fauna is available of over 85 species, 13 being palaeospecies and one an extinct neospecies, the Cuban red macaw *Ara tricolor*. The faunas (Wetmore, Brodkorb) come from the Bahamas, Cuba, Puerto Rico (50 spp.) and St. Croix and St. Thomas in the Virgin Islands. Some of the fauna, e.g. gaint barn owls, was 'Rancholabrean' and the palaeospecies were doubtless aided to extinction by the original human colonists. Much of it is believed to date from *c.* 3000–1500 B.P.

No continental Ethiopian Holocene fossil bird seems to be recorded; but lately Ashmole and his colleagues of the B.O.U. Centenary expedition have excavated bones on Ascension Island and St. Helena from horizons which, mainly Holocene and some quite recent, may also just go back to the uppermost Pleistocene. The elephant bird fauna of Madagascar, determined at the most important deposit, Sirabé, by Andrews in the last century, may also be partly uppermost Pleistocene but is mainly Holocene; and the subfossil beds of Mauritius and Rodriguez, with their dodo faunas, are doubtless quite Holocene (determined mainly by Milne-Edwards, Günther, E. T. Newton, Lydekker and Gadow in the last century and later partly by Rothschild and Hachisuka). A summary of the determined fauna of the Atlantic islands is Ascension 8 spp. with 1 extinct neospecies; St. Helena, with 1 palaeospecies and 1 extinct neospecies; and of the Indian Ocean islands Madagascar 20/9/2, Mauritius 18/9/6 and Rodriguez 11/1/8. The combined fauna is 60 spp./21 palaeospp. /15 extinct neospp. The last 'Rancholabrean' elements on these relatively recently human-colonized islands were, in fact, all neospecies; for the last and greatest elephant bird *Aepyornis maximus* (the largest bird recorded, weighing nearly half a ton) probably survived on Madagascar until the first half of the seventeenth century; the last dodo *Raphus cucullatus* was seen alive on Mauritius in 1681; and the last solitaire *Pezophaps solitaria* (another Raphid) on Rodriguez *c.* 1791. The third known Raphid *R. solitarius*, which survived until 1746 on Réunion, is not known as a fossil; the island should be dug over. Amsterdam island (Indian Ocean,

Jouanin and Paulian) has a late prehistoric subfossil fauna of 9 spp., probably all living neospp.

We finally come to New Zealand, with its great moa fauna, and birds in mammal niches in a community which evolved, after ancestral colonization, six of the taxa listed in this essay in the Tertiary (Fleming 1962A, in an admitted "educated guess", believes the 3 ratite families are of Cretaceous origin). Unfortunately no fully Tertiary deposit containing any community of land birds has yet been discovered in New Zealand, despite over a century of bone hunting inspired largely by the widespread remains of moas. The oldest Emeid, *Anomalopteryx antiquus*, it is true, is based only on a tibia and parts of a metatarsus found in a bed of clay believed to be Upper Miocene or Lower Pliocene under a lava flow near Timaru, South Island. Oliver (1949) refers the North Island deposits of Hunterville and Nga Rata to 'Pliocene', the papa sea-cliff beds near Nukumaru to 'early Pliocene' and a deposit at Mangaonoko to 'Pliocene'. The first and second contain remains of the extinct Emeid moa neospecies *Euryapteryx gravis*, the second of the flightless goose palaeospecies *Cnemiornis gracilis* which did not become extinct until the later Holocene, the third and fourth of the Dinornithid moa palaeospecies *Dinornis novaezealandiae* (lately *ingens*) which did not become extinct until after the Polynesian colonization. All but the Nukumaru beds are very doubtfully earlier than the uppermost Pleistocene; I know not what to make of the Nukumaru record (ignored by Brodkorb 1963). Fleming (1962B), professional geologist and scholar of birds, resolutely states that "it is doubtful if any *major* source of extinct bird bones so far known in New Zealand is as old as early or even mid-Holocene in age, let alone Pleistocene". Following his lead, I have analysed the aviferous deposits of New Zealand from the investigations and systemae of, amongst others, Archey, Bourne, Brodkorb, Dawson, Duff, Eyles, Falla, Fleming, Gurr, Oliver, Scarlett, Trotter, Williams and Yaldwyn. The deposits of the two main islands and Stewart Island can be assigned with reasonable certainty to (*a*) the Older Holocene, when they contain material (often cave material) relatively highly fossilized and so remarked upon in the literature. This period may embrace some Uppermost Pleistocene (last Glacial) horizons equivalent to 'Würm 3', though this by no means proved; (*b*) the younger Holocene before the human colonization in *c*. 950 A.D., when they are characterized by a relatively low degree of fossilization, and by the absence of human traces and the presence of any one of five 'marker' moa species unknown from any human-associated site and which possibly became extinct, naturally, before the advent of man; (*d*) prehistoric (i.e. pre-Cook) sites recognised as such from human material (middens most often) or horizons ^{14}C dated after 950 A.D. The deposits of the Chatham Islands (*c*) in time probably embrace the periods of (*b*) and (*d*). The number of species represented are shown in the table on the next page.

There is no passerine in (*a*), 1 passerine palaeosp. in (*b*) and (*c*), and 8 passerine spp. in (*d*) and (*e*) of which one is a palaeosp. and another an extinct neosp. Of the 26 moas in (*e*), 23 are found in (*a*), 24 in (*h*), 21 in (*d*); but only 3 (neospecies) provedly persisted until after 1600; the Emeids *Megalapteryx didinus*

Fossil birds and their adaptive radiation

	PALAEO-SPECIES	NEOSPECIES Extinct	NEOSPECIES Living	TOTAL
(a) Main islands' older deposits, of uppermost Pleistocene? and earlier Holocene age	31	3	8	42
(b) Main islands' younger Holocene deposits, probably older than 950 A.D.	30	4	9	43
(c) Chatham Islands' deposits, probably embracing (b) and (d): 11 seabirds.	7	3	18	28
(d) Main islands' Holocene deposits known to have been formed since the human colonization in c. 950 A.D. (prehistoric)	28	6	48	82
(e) Combined avifauna (a) to (d)	40	8	63	111

(after 1785—after Cook—by ^{14}C) and *Euryapteryx gravis* (in a moa-hunter midden of early European times), and the Dinornithid *Dinornis torosus* (to *c.* 1670 by ^{14}C). The New Zealand 'Holocene' avifauna was spread over 200 sites known to the writer from publications by 1965. None of these has more than 25 species save the classic Pyramid Valley swamp site in South Island, whose horizons, now systematically excavated, have been ^{14}C-dated from *c.* 1000 B.C. to *c.* 1670 A.D. Its birds were 44 species; of the 36 fully determined 14 were palaeospp., 2 others extinct neospp.

There is no doubt that the 'Rancholabrean' phase of the New Zealand avifauna lasted through the Pleistocene until a thousand years ago, and was brought to a crashing end by the Polynesian colonists before Europeans came to their assistance. Recognizing that the *natural* colonization of New Zealand by birds (from Australia especially) is a continuing process, which has been quite marked during the years of European observation, it can be estimated that the indigenous breeding avifauna of the main islands and the Chathams (but not including the other outliers) was not much more than 150 species, over 20 moas included, when the Polynesians arrived in *c.* 950. Since that time at least 48 species have become globally extinct, 8 of them since 1600; and up to 10 others have become extinct in the archipelago, though not globally. So at least a third of the higher vertebrate fauna of New Zealand was removed by man, even allowing for some natural extinction. In historical times there have been additions, which include at least 8 natural colonists and 35 aliens established after introduction, and in some cases are self-spread to Chatham Islands (and the smaller outliers, to distances of 600 miles). So the avifauna may once again approach its Pleistocene size: though it can never regain its Pleistocene shape and quality.

ACKNOWLEDGEMENTS. I have to thank Dr Beverly Tarlo of Reading University and Dr Pierce Brodkorb of the University of Florida for much patient help and advice, and Dr Roger Tory Peterson of Old Lyme, Connecticut, for encouragement and helpful disputation. I am also indebted to the Zoological Society of London, and its Librarian, for the swift satisfaction of my bibliographical needs.

4. References

AMEGHINO, F. 1891. Enumeración de las aves fósiles de la República Argentina. *Rev. Argent. Hist. nat.* **1**, 441–53.

BRODKORB, P. 1963. Catalogue of fossil birds, Part 1 (Archaeopterygiformes through Ardeiformes). *Bull. Florida St. Mus. biol. Sci.* **7**, 179–293.

—— 1964. Catalogue fossil birds, Part 2 (Anseriformes through Galliformes). *Bull. Florida St. Mus. biol. Sci.*, **8**, 195–335.

—— 1967 (1966). Catalogue of fossil birds, Part 3 (Ralliformes, Ichthyorniformes, Charadriiformes). *Bull. Florida St. Mus. biol. Sci.* **11**, 99–220.

FISHER, J. & PETERSON, R. T. 1964. *The world of birds*. London (Macdonald).

FLEMING, C. A. 1962A. History of the New Zealand land bird fauna. *Notornis* **9**, 270–4.

—— 1962B. The extinction of moas and other animals during the Holocene period. *Notornis* **10**, 113–7.

FLINT, R. F. 1957. *Glacial and Pleistocene geology*. New York (John Wiley).

GREGORY, J. T. 1952. The jaws of the Cretaceous toothed birds, *Ichthyornis* and *Hesperornis*. *Condor* **54**, 73–88.

HOWARD, H. 1947. A preliminary survey of trends in avian evolution from Pleistocene to Recent time. *Condor* **49**, 10–13.

—— 1950. Fossil evidence of avian evolution. *Ibis* **92**, 1–21.

KUHN, O. 1965. *Die fossilen Vögel*. Krailling-München (Verlag Oeben).

LAMBRECHT, K. 1963. *Handbuch der Palaeornithologie*. Berlin (Borntraeger).

LYDEKKER, R. 1891. *Catalogue of the fossil birds in the British Museum*. London (British Museum (Nat. Hist.)).

—— 1896. Fossil birds. In NEWTON, A. (Ed.): *A dictionary of birds*. London (Black), pp. 277–89.

MAYR, E. 1963. *Animal species and evolution*. Cambridge, Mass. (Harvard University Press).

MILNE-EDWARDS, A. 1867–71. *Recherches anatomiques et paléontologiques pour servir a l'histoire des oiseaux fossiles de la France*, Vols. 1 & 2.

MORENO, F. P. & MERCERAT, A. 1891. Catálogo de los Pájaros fósiles de la República Argentina. *An. Mus. La Plata Sec. Paleont.* part 1.

OLIVER, W. R. B. 1949. The moas of New Zealand and Australia. *Dom. Mus. Bull.* **15**, 1–206.

SIMPSON, G. G. 1945. The principles of classification and a classification of mammals. *Bull. am. Mus. nat. Hist.* **85**, 1–350.

STORER, R. W. 1960. Adaptive radiation in birds *and* The classification of birds. In Marshall, A. J. (Ed.): *Biology and comparative physiology of birds*. London (Black), pp. 15–93.

SWINTON, W. E. 1958. *Fossil birds*. London (British Museum (Nat. Hist.)).

WETMORE, A. 1928. Prehistoric ornithology in North America. *J. Wash. Acad. Sci.* **18**, 145–58.

—— 1929. Birds of the past in North America. *Rep. Smithson Inst.* (1928), 377–89.

—— 1940. A check-list of the fossil birds of North America. *Smithson. misc. Collns* **99**, 1–81.

—— 1951. [Presidential address]. Recent additions to our knowledge of prehistoric birds 1933–1949. *Int. Orn. Congr.* **10**, 51–74.

—— 1956. A check-list of the fossil and prehistoric birds of North America and the West Indies. *Smithson. misc. Collns* **131**, 1–105.

—— 1960. A classification for the birds of the world. *Smithson misc. Collns* **139**, 1–37.

Manuscript submitted May 1966.

JAMES M. McC. FISHER, M.A. F.R.G.S. F.L.S F.Z.S.
Ashton Manor, Northampton.

GENERAL DISCUSSION

The following discussion was contributed either after the paper on computer analysis (later rewritten with new data as Part III) or in general discussion. These contributions are placed here because they discuss general principles. They were placed here and thus taken out of their context in the meeting when it became clear that a complete record of the discussion was impracticable.

Professor F. W. SHOTTON noted that the smoothed curve presented by Funnell & Cutbill that showed the rate of diversification had a marked bend around the Trias, with the implication that after that time diversification had proceeded at a reduced rate. The time-scale had been constructed on the basis of a unit of time for each stage and he wondered if the use of a radiometric scale of time would accentuate or diminish or even eliminate this apparent difference of behaviour in the earlier and later Phanerozoic.

Dr D. V. AGER welcomed the interesting study by Funnell and Cutbill of the psychology of palaeontologists. He was particularly struck by the bimodal distribution demonstrated by them for all invertebrates, and the way this contrasted with the more even curve for the vertebrates. The speaker suggested that this reflected nothing more than the nature of the fossil record in the U.S.A., with its diversity of forms in the Palaeozoic and Tertiary, but great deficiency of marine facies and faunas in the Mesozoic. He did not think it had any world-wide significance.

It had been suggested that the family categories he used in the analysis of the fossil record were in some way less subjective than genera. This he did not believe. If one considered the particular group—the Rhynchonellacea—with which he was most familiar, taxonomic record and the actual record were completely at variance with each other at all levels.

The taxonomic record of families gave two large peaks, like those for the invertebrates as a whole, one in the middle to late Palaeozoic, the other in the Tertiary. These showed little if any relevance to the realities of rhynchonellid diversity and abundance, and resulted entirely from the work of two specialists who had proposed 14 out of the 19 relevant family names. Similarly, the much discussed 'evo-lutionary burst' in mid-Ordovician times was also clearly seen in the taxonomic record of the rhynchonellids, but resulted from a single publication.

In fact, most specialists would agree that the rhynchonellids arose as very minor elements in the Ordovician brachiopod faunas and only very slowly increased in numbers and in diversity through Palaeozoic times. Their only 'sudden' evolutionary burst came at the end of Frasnian times, when they seem to have made a 'take-over bid' for the ecological niches previously occupied by the atrypids. This is seen in Canada, Belgium, Germany and Australia, but makes no showing in the taxonomic record at family or even generic level. The rhynchonellids were apparently unaffected by the end of the Palaeozoic; and the supposed contrast between Palaeozoic and Mesozoic faunas results partly from our lack of knowledge of Lower and Middle Triassic representatives, and partly from the differences in approach, classification, terminology and prejudice of Palaeozoic and Mesozoic workers The rhynchonellids in fact came out of this gap in the record very much as they went into it, and continued their progressive diversification. In later Mesozoic times they seem to have suffered a gradual eclipse by the Tere-bratuloidea and from those benthonic molluscs which took over from both.

The beginning of the Tertiary Era saw a marked diminution in the abundance, diversity and distribution of the rhynchonellids, at least in the most-studied parts of the world. This is in marked contrast to the further diversification suggested by the mere list of family names available. The truth is probably somewhere between the two, but nearer the first, for in the right facies the Tertiary rhynchonellids do seem to continue the Meso-zoic story down to the present day.

Summing up, it may be said that the main

events in the history of the rhynchonellids—their gradual increase and decline, their spurt in the Famennian and their slump in the Palaeogene—are not shown up by any counting of taxonomic heads.

On the basis of this sort of observation, Dr Ager did not think that *The Fossil Record* should be taken too seriously or used as a basis for idle theorizing.

In connexion with the diversity of the taxonomic record in relation to epeirogenic seas Dr Ager remarked that this probably reflected the concentration of taxonomic palaeontologists rather than the extent of the epeirogenic seas.

Dr V. G. WALMSLEY pointed out that the estimate of the average duration of Lower Palaeozoic stages as 15 to 30 m.y. each could be somewhat misleading for the late Silurian. According to the figure given in *The Phanerozoic Time-scale* the total duration of Silurian time appeared to be 20 or 40 m.y. depending on whose figures were accepted. What proportion of Silurian time was attributable to the Ludlovian was arguable but on the basis of graptolite evolution, one quarter was probably the right order of magnitude. This meant allowing 5 to 10 m.y.

for the Ludlovian of which the four stages would on average seem to have lasted $1\frac{1}{4}$ or $2\frac{1}{2}$ m.y. each. This estimate was considerably less than the average figures suggested.

Mr N. F. HUGHES said that in constructing the stratigraphical scale, the committee took note of Dr Walmsley's difficulty and avoided the use of the term 'stage' [see column 2 of Table 1, Introduction].

Dr R. A. CROWSON said that no speaker at this symposium had given a reasonable explanation of extinction of anything. Professor Sylvester-Bradley's suggestion of tabulating origins, extinctions, etc., of taxa against a time-scale in years is rather like making a table of establishment or extinction of status, governments, languages, industries, etc., against centuries—a procedure whose value he doubted for the understanding of human history.

Dr J. M. HANCOCK emphasized a point already made by several speakers: the appearance and disappearance of different taxa is only one aspect of the relative success of different animals. Human beings are one of the most successful animals living to-day, but they are only one species in a table.

The Fossil Record

Part II

Documentation of the fossil record

PLANTAE

Chapters 1–7

Edited by N. F. HUGHES

INVERTEBRATA

Chapters 8–24

Edited by M. R. HOUSE, C. H. HOLLAND & M. J. S. RUDWICK

VERTEBRATA

Chapters 25–30

Edited by L. B. H. TARLO

Introduction to Part II

In this part will be found some details of published records of fossils arranged systematically in 30 chapters. An attempt has been made to cover the whole fossil record of the plant and animal kingdoms by documenting representative taxa at levels selected in each case by the contributor.

For each taxon treated the stratigraphically earliest (**First**) and latest (**Last**) published records are given. The references documenting these records have been selected so as to include a leading or key reference in each case, without attempting a bibliography. The references are grouped at intervals within each chapter and are abbreviated according to the *World List of Scientific Periodicals* (4th edn.), 1963–5. Where the taxon is **Extant** this is indicated without a reference.

Contributors have attempted to refer all records to a stratigraphical age on the standard scale adopted for this volume; this scale is explained in the Introduction (p. 3), and is used throughout in the standard abbreviated form shown in Table I (pp.5–9).

The charts throughout Part II plot the data given in the text in uniform manner on this stratigraphical scale. Each chart is divided into two parts, part A for the Pre-Cambrian to Carnian, and part B for the Norian to Holocene or Recent. Parts A and B of each Figure are printed on the left- and right-hand pages respectively, and each stratigraphical division is in register throughout the volume. All divisions are drawn equal, without any implication of equality in the time they represent.

The fossil records are plotted on this scale according to conventions illustrated opposite. Each taxon selected is represented by one vertical line only, designed to show in visual form the total known stratigraphic range as documented in the text. No attempt has been made to indicate abundance of subordinate taxa or individuals at any time, or continuity of record between terminal records.

The usual procedure in plotting the lines has been to draw the line from the base of the stratal division of the earliest record to the top of the stratal division of the youngest (figure opposite, taxa 1, 4, 7); in a few cases a specified position within a stratigraphical division is shown for a terminal record (taxa 2, 5 in figure).

One or both ends of a line may be broken into dashes: this indicates that in the opinion of the contributor there is doubt about the precise age of the first or last record, either (*a*) on grounds of uncertain stratigraphic dating of the formation concerned, or (*b*) on grounds of dubious identification of the specimens or their dubious assignment to the taxon concerned. Examples are given in the figure (taxa 3, 6). If a dubious record is stratigraphically far removed from other more definite records, it may be shown separate from the rest of the line, though connected by a thin dashed guide line (see figure, taxa 8, 9). Similar thin dashed lines, running obliquely from one line towards another, indicate possible phylogenetic connections, where these have been suggested by the contributor (see figure, taxa 10, 11).

In general, taxa with no record earlier than 'Recent' (Holocene) are not shown on the charts.

QUAT.: Holo   7   9

Pleist

Plioc   3

U.Mioc

M.Mioc

L.Mioc

TERTIARY: U.Olig

L/M.Olig

U.Eoc

M.Eoc

L.Eoc

Palaeoc   1   11

Dan   2   6   8

Maestr

Campan

Santon

Coniac   10

CRETACEOUS: Turon

Cenom   4   5

Alb

Apt

Barrem

Haut

Valang

Berr

1. Taxon first recorded from Aptian, last from Danian.

2. Taxon first recorded in a formation considered by the contributor to be *Upper* Cenomanian; last recorded in a formation considered similarly to be *Lower* Maestrichtian.

3. First record is Upper Cretaceous, a more precise age not being given; last record is Miocene, unspecified.

4. First and last records (may be a single record), Albian.

5. First and last records (or a single record), Upper Albian.

6. First and last records both given as Upper Cretaceous, without more precise age.

7. Taxon first recorded in Albian, and still extant. This may indicate a taxon with a relatively continuous record, but it may refer to a single (but definite) record in the Albian, of a taxon otherwise only known in the living state.

8. Definite records Cenomanian to Maestrichtian inclusive; the Valanginian record may belong to this taxon, but its validity is regarded as questionable by the contributor.

9. Barremian record belongs to extant taxon; no intermediate records.

10 & 11. Taxon 10, Hauterivian to Turonian, is considered by the contributor to be ancestral to taxon 11, Turonian to Danian.

The Fossil Record, Part II

PLANTAE

PLANTAE

Introduction. The classification of plants into higher taxa is not stable owing to the as yet far less complete use of fossil information than is the case with animals. For this reason, Chapters 1–7 have been arranged for ease of location of information rather than as an expression of confidence in currently used groupings such as 'gymnosperms', 'hydropterid ferns', etc. Some arbitrary decisions have had to be made concerning the placing of certain Devonian land plants. Several small changes in arrangement have been made editorially at a late stage in order to achieve a better balance between chapters.

The level of taxon recorded varies, for different special reasons, from the class in some gymnosperms to the genus in dinoflagellates and acritarchs. It is hoped that any dissatisfaction will be expressed in subsequent amplification of this first attempt to deal with palaeobotanical data in this way. Contributors have also been urged to decide independently how much information from dispersed miospores could usefully be included.

It is hoped that the whole plant section of the volume will serve to show that plant evolution was not 'slow' but was both interesting and eventful, and that consequently it can contribute increasingly to stratigraphy.

N. F. H.

CHAPTER 1

Thallophyta—1

Contributors: H. P. BANKS, K. I. M. CHESTERS, N. F. HUGHES,
G. A. L. JOHNSON, H. M. JOHNSON & L. R. MOORE

This chapter includes all benthonic algae (planktonic algae are in Chapter 2), the family Prototaxitaceae, bacteria and fungi. In some of these groups the fossil record is very inadequate, and the method of documentation has been varied accordingly.

THE CALCAREOUS ALGAE

Algae are the only fossil group which have a widespread development in the Precamb. The earliest fossil records, dating from at least 2700 m.y., are stromatolites possibly belonging to the Chlorophyceae and Cyanophyceae. Definite cellular microorganisms, including *Gunflintia*, *Animikiea* and *Archaeorestis* identified as blue-green algae, have been found in the Gunflint Chert, M. Precamb, Canada, and are 1900 m.y. old (Barghoorn and Tyler 1965; Cloud 1965). Even at the earliest period there seems to have been considerable diversity in the group and since then continuous evolutionary progress has taken place. Divergence, convergence and parallelism of form and habit in the different classes of algae during their geological history is striking (Fritsch 1948). Thus the structural pattern of the Chlorophyceae, Cyanophyceae and in most part the Rhodophyceae is remarkably parallel from unicellular motile and colonial, through filamentous to complex thalloid forms.

The great majority of living algae do not produce skeletons but of the known fossil algae almost every genus is calcareous and many are important rock builders. Maslov (1961) has shown that carbonates can be deposited by algae in six different ways. Of these the "mixed" or "stromatolitic" process and the "biochemical" process are most important in the Precamb. The "organic" and "physiological" processes emerged in the Camb but the "stromatolitic" process was probably dominant as late as the Silurian. Since then the "organic" process has been gaining importance and the "stromatolitic" process is restricted to limited occurrences at the present time. To what extent the evolution of the various classes of fossil algae is connected with these changes in carbonate deposition is obscure.

Genetic classification of the fossil algae is largely subjective owing to the great antiquity of the group and the origin of even the more recent families is shrouded in uncertainty. Lack of colour pigments and reproductive structures further adds to the difficulties of classification in the fossil algae. The classification used here is adapted from Papenfuss (1955) and Pia (1927). We are much indebted to Dr J. H. Price (British Museum of National History, London) who kindly supplied the authorities of the living families of calcareous algae. [H.M.J. & G.A.L.J.]

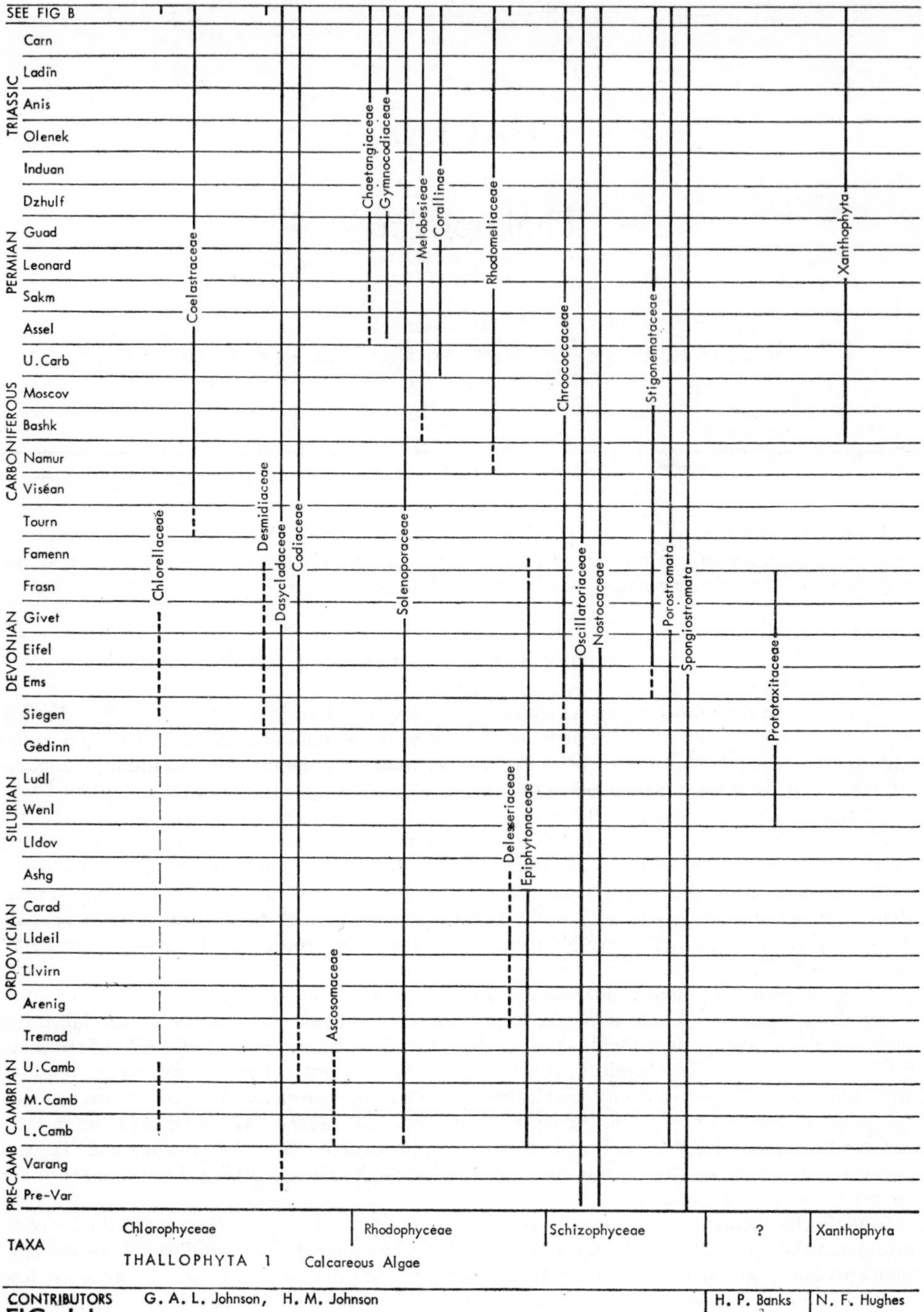

THALLOPHYTA 1   Calcareous Algae

CONTRIBUTORS   G. A. L. Johnson, H. M. Johnson   H. P. Banks   N. F. Hughes

FIG. 1.1A

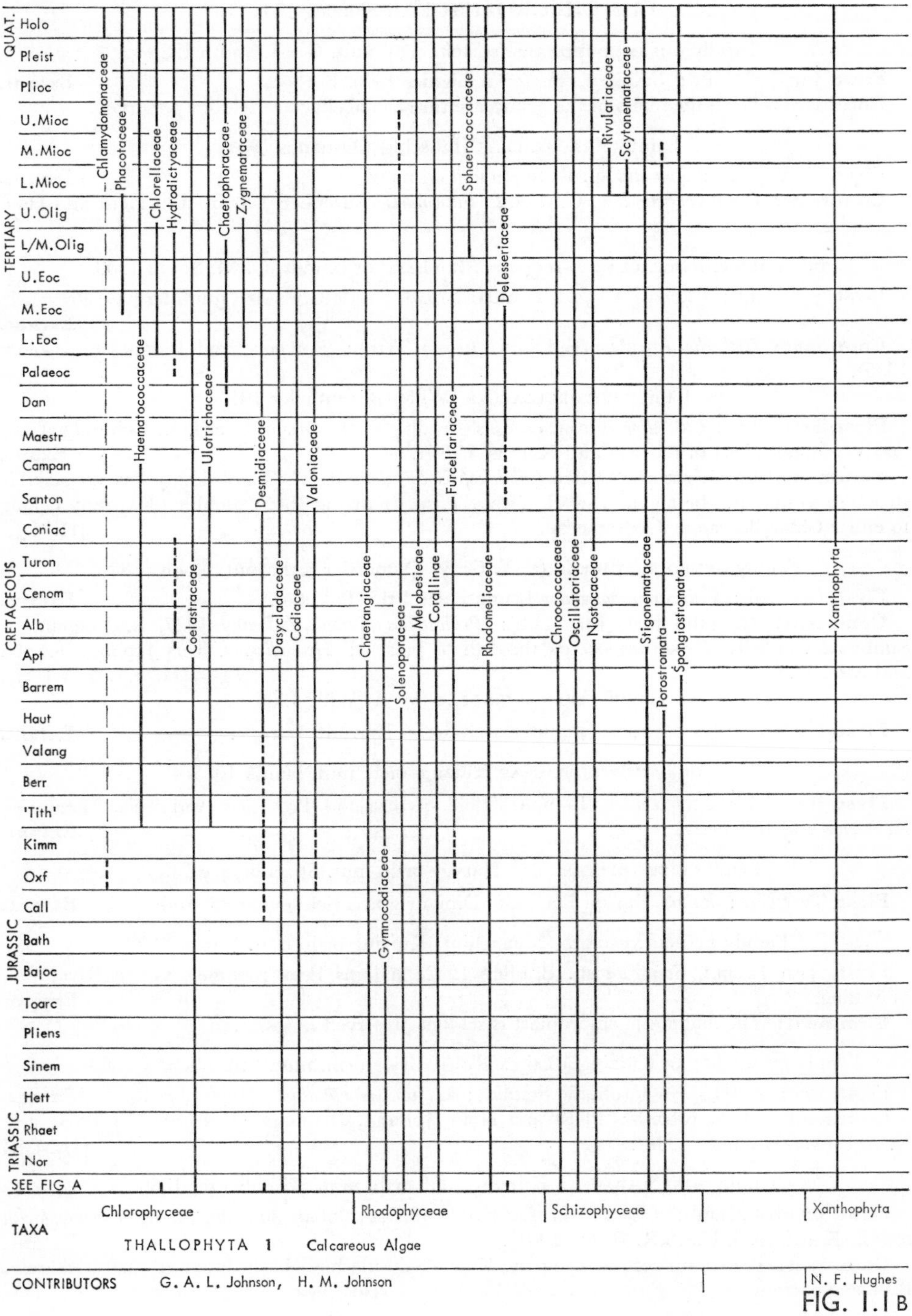

QUAT.	Holo	
	Pleist	
	Plioc	
TERTIARY	U.Mioc	
	M.Mioc	
	L.Mioc	
	U.Olig	
	L/M.Olig	
	U.Eoc	
	M.Eoc	
	L.Eoc	
	Palaeoc	
	Dan	
	Maestr	
	Campan	
	Santon	
	Coniac	
CRETACEOUS	Turon	
	Cenom	
	Alb	
	Apt	
	Barrem	
	Haut	
	Valang	
	Berr	
	'Tith'	
	Kimm	
	Oxf	
	Call	
JURASSIC	Bath	
	Bajoc	
	Toarc	
	Pliens	
	Sinem	
	Hett	
TRIASSIC	Rhaet	
	Nor	
	SEE FIG A	

Column labels (left to right):
Chlamydomonaceae, Phacotaceae, Chlorellaceae, Hydrodictyaceae, Chaetophoraceae, Zygnemataceae, Haematococcaceae, Ulotrichaceae, Desmidiaceae, Valoniaceae, Sphaerococcaceae, Delesseriaceae, Furcellariaceae, Rivulariaceae, Scytonemataceae, Coelastraceae, Dasycladaceae, Codiaceae, Chaetangiaceae, Solenoporaceae, Melobesieae, Corallinae, Rhodomeliaceae, Chroococcaceae, Oscillatoriaceae, Nostocaceae, Stigonemataceae, Porostromata, Spongiostromata, Gymnocodiaceae, Xanthophyta

TAXA	Chlorophyceae	Rhodophyceae	Schizophyceae	Xanthophyta

THALLOPHYTA 1   Calcareous Algae

CONTRIBUTORS   G. A. L. Johnson, H. M. Johnson   N. F. Hughes

FIG. 1.1 B

The Fossil Record, Part II

Class CHLOROPHYCEAE Kützing 1833

Family CHLAMYDOMONACEAE Stein orth. mut. G. M. Smith 1920

First, Jur Oxf-'Tith': *Gleocystis oxfordiensis* Lignier 1906, Europe.   **Extant.**

Comment: Fossil members of the group are rare as flagellae are seldom preserved.

Family PHACOTACEAE (Bütschli) Oltmanns 1904

First, Tert M.Eoc: *Phacotus* sp. Rutte 1953, Germany.   **Extant.**

Comment: Fossil records few, U.Mioc *P. lenticularis* (Ehrenberg) Stein, also Pleist and Holo examples.

Family HAEMATOCOCCACEAE (Trevisan) Marchand orth. mut. G. M. Smith 1950

First, Jur 'Tith': *Globochaete alpina* Lombard 1938, Sainte Crois de Quintillargues, Provence.   **Extant.**

Comment: *Globochaete* widespread in U.Jur in Tethys, Provence and Indonesia. (Colom 1955).

Family CHLORELLACEAE (Wille) Brunnthaler 1913

First, Tert L.Eoc: *Chlorellopsis coloniata* Reis (Bradley 1929), Green River Fm., Colorado, Utah and Wyoming; Tert of Bavaria and Kansas, U.S.A.   **Exant.**

Comment: Camb record "? like *Chlorellopsis coloniata* Reis" (Bigot 1929) has no cellular structure so may not be algal. Dev cf. *Tetraedon.* sp. (Kützing 1845; Bohlin 1901) may belong to either Chlorellaceae or Oocystaceae.   [H.M.J.]

Family HYDRODICTYACEAE (S. F. Gray) Dumortier orth. mut. Cohn 1880

First, Cret Alb: *Pediastrum boryanum* Brunnthaler 1915, Pakistan.   **Extant.**

Comment: Doubtful first, Jur 'Tith': *Pediastrites kidstoni* Zalessky 1927, L. Volgian, nr Simbirsk, U.S.S.R. *Pediastrum* occurs through to present; *Hydrodictyon*, Tert Japan. (Koriba and Miki 1959).   [H.M.J. & N.F.H.]

Family COELASTRACEAE (West) Wille 1906

First, Carb Tourn-Viséan: *Lageniastrum macrosporae* Renault, Europe.   **Extant.**

Family ULOTRICHACEAE Kützing orth. mut. Haulk 1883

First, Jur 'Tith': *Eothrix alpina* Lombard 1938, Switzerland, Provence, Andalusia, Apennines, N. Africa and Indonesia.   **Extant.**

Family CHAETOPHORACEAE Harvey orth. mut. Stizenberger 1860

First, Tert Dan: *Palaeachyla* sp. Pia 1936, Diniyur gp., Trichinopoly, S. India.   **Extant.**

Family ZYGNEMATACEAE (Meneghini) Kützing orth. mut. Engler 1898

First, Tert L.Eoc: *Spirogyra* sp. Bradley 1962, Wilkins Peak member, Green River fm., Wyoming.   **Extant.**

Comment: The diagnostic chloroplast is seldom preserved in fossils.

Family DESMIDIACEAE Kützing 1833 ex Ralfs (1848) orth. mut. Stizenberger 1860

First, Dev: *Arthrodesmus* (probable desmid); U.Jur: *Xanthidium pilosum* Ehrenb.   **Extant.**

Comment: Other records: Pleist and Holo, Jutland, Denmark (Fjerdugstadtl 1954) and N. Alps (Messikommer 1938).   [H.M.J.]

Family DASYCLADACEAE Kützing 1833 orth. mut. Stizenberger 1860

First, Camb L.Camb: *Lenaella reticulata* Korde 1959, Atdaban fm, Siberia, and *Cambroporella tuvensis* Korde 1950, U.S.S.R. (Endo 1961).   **Extant.**

Comment: Pre-Camb records from the Kola Peninsula have been dated at 1720–1780 m.y. B.P. and include cf. *Dasyporella* Pia and the Tribe Cyclocrineae Pia (Lyubtsov 1964). Few Palaeozoic genera, divergence in Permian. Fossil genera numerous compared with only 10 living genera.   [H.M.J. & G.A.L.J.]

Family CODIACEAE (Trevisan) Zanardini 1843

First, Camb-Ord: *Palaeoporella variabilis* Stolley 1893, Late Camb. or basal Ord, Sweden, Norway and Texas.   **Extant.**

Comment: Pre-Camb *Oldhamia* and *Palaeorivularia* may be primitive codiaceans or the latter may be a red alga (C. L. Fenton 1943, Endo 1961). Abundant in present oceans mostly non-lime-depositing.

Family VALONIACEAE Nägeli 1847

First, Jur Oxf-'Tith': *Pycnoporidium lobatum* Yabe and Toyama 1928, Torinosu Lst, Abukama Mountainlands, Japan and Spain. *P. melobesioides* (Pfender), France.   **Extant.**

Comment: *P. toyamai*, Perm, has doubtful generic assignment. *P. lobatum* and *P. melobesioides* extend to L. Cret. *P. sinuosum* J. H. Johnson and Konishi L. Cret, Guatemala. No known Tert forms, living forms mostly tropical.

Family ASCOSOMACEAE Lorenz 1904

First and **Last,** Camb: *Ascosomia phaneroporata* Lorenz 1904 and *Mitscherlichia chinensis* Lorenz 1904, Tschang-duang, N. China.

Class RHODOPHYCEAE Ruprecht 1901

Family CHAETANGIACEAE Kützing orth. mut. Hauck 1883

First, Perm: *Hapalophlaea scissa* Pia 1935, Sumatra.   **Extant.**

Family GYMNOCODIACEAE Elliott 1955

First, Perm: *Gymnocodium bellerophontis* (Rothpletz 1894) Pia 1920, S. Europe, India, Japan and Texas, U.S.A.

Last, Cret Apt: *Permocalculus irenae* Elliott 1958.

Comment: Family regarded first as Dasycladaceae, then Codiaceae, next red algae (Chaetangiaceae Pia 1937) and finally raised to separate family (Elliott 1955).

Family SOLENOPORACEAE Pia 1927

First, Camb L.Camb: *Solenopora* sp., N.W. Beardmore Glacier, Antarctica (Priestley and David 1910); *S. tjanshanica* Vologdin 1955, Russia; *S.* sp., Angara R., Siberia (Maslov 1937).

Last, Tert Mioc: *Neosolenopora vinassi*, Italy, France and Cuba.

Comment: Camb records few; Ord and Sil records rare at first later few genera only but widespread, abundant and rockbuilders. Classification controversial, either sub-family of Corallinaceae (Maslov 1956) or a separate family (Pia 1927, J. H. Johnson 1959).

Family CORALLINACEAE (Lamouroux) Harvey 1849

First, Carb Bashk-Moscov: *Archaeolithophyllum missourensum* J. H. Johnson 1956, Exline Lst, Carroll Co., Missouri; *A. delicatum* J. H. Johnson 1956, Colinsville Lst, Illinois, also New Mexico and Texas. Carb. *Komia abandans* Korde 1951, N. Urals, Russia and Japan.   **Extant.**

Comment: Sub-family Melobesieae U.Carb to Recent as given above. Sub-family Corallinae ?U.Carb to Recent; *Archamphiroa* ?U.Carb, *Amphiroa* Cret. Melobesieae contains *Archaeolithothamnium*, Jur to Recent, of uncertain phylogeny, which gave rise to *Lithothamnium* in L.Jur. Sub-family widespread by U.Cret, tropics to polar regions by M.Eoc. Corallinae most abundant in Tert, widespread in present oceans.

Family FURCELLARIACEAE Greville orth. mut. Kylin 1932

First, Jur Oxf-'Tith': *?Nipponophycus ramosus* Yabe and Toyama 1928, Torinosu Lst, Japan.
                                                                                                  Extant.

Family SPHAEROCOCCACEAE Dumortier orth. mut. Cohn 1872

First, Tert Olig: *Spherococcites cartilagineus* Unger.   **Extant.**

Family RHODOMELIACEAE (J. Agardh) Harvey 1849

First, Carb Namur-U.Carb: *Donezella lutegrini* Maslov 1927, K_1 and K_4 Donetz Basin, U.S.S.R. **Extant.**

Comment: Only fossil record is Palaeozoic unless *Lomentarites borneti*, U.Trias, belongs to this family.

Family DELESSERIACEAE Bory orth. mut. Nägeli 1847

First, Ord: ?*Delesserites silicifolia* Ruedemann 1925, New York. **Extant.**

Comment: *Delesseria friedaui* Unger and *D. fulva* Lesqu., U.Cret constitute the earliest definite record of this family.

Family EPIPHYTONACEAE Korde 1955

First, Camb L.Camb: *Epiphyton benignum* Korde 1959, Kuznetsk, Russia; *E. grande* and *E. fasciculatum* Gordon 1921, boulders dredged from the Weddel Sea.

Last, Dev Givet-Famenn: *Epiphyton budyricus* Antropov 1955, E. Russian Platform, Urals, Kuznetz Basin and Central Asia.

Comment: Constituent genera *Epiphyton* and *Chabakovia*. *Epiphyton* abundant in Camb. and is sometimes a rock-builder.

Class SCHIZOPHYCEAE Cohn 1880

Family CHROOCOCCACEAE Nägeli 1849

First, Dev: *Microcystis* Kutzing 1833. **Extant.**

Comment: Continuous records Dev. to Present. [H.M.J.]

Family OSCILLATORIACEAE (S. F. Gray) Dumortier 1898

First, Pre-Camb: *Animikiea septata* Barghoorn 1965 (cf. *Lyngbya* Ag. and Cf. *Oscillatoria*) c. 1900 m.y., Gunflint Fm, Ontario, Canada; *L. ochracea* Ashley 1937, Kundelungu Series, Lake Tanganika, N. Rhodesia. **Extant.**

Comment: M.Camb *Marpolia spissa* Walcott, Burgess Sh, other records Dev to Present.

[H.M.J. & G.A.L.J.]

Family NOSTOCACEAE Dumortier ex. Engler 1892

First, Pre-Camb: *Filamentella marima* Pflug 1965, Missoula Group, Belt Series, Montana. **Extant.**

Family RIVULARIACEAE Kützing ex. Bornet et Flahault 1887

First, Tert Mioc: *Rivularia haematites* Geither 1930, Baden, Germany, and *Ternithrix compressa* Reiss, Rhine, Germany. **Extant.**

Family SCYTONEMATACEAE Kützing ex. Bornet et Flahault 1887

First, Tert Mioc: *Scytonema julianum* Geither 1930, Baden, Germany. **Extant.**

Family STIGONEMATACEAE Kirchner 1898

First, Derv Ems-Eifel: *Langiella scourfieldi* Croft and George 1959, and *Kidstoniella fritschi* Croft and George 1959, Rhynie Chert, Aberdeenshire, Scotland. **Extant.**

[H.M.J.]

Family POROSTROMATA Pia 1927

First, Camb L.Camb: *Girvanella sinensis* Yabe 1912, *G. manchurica* Yabe and Ozaki 1930, San-yu-tung Province, Hapei and S. Manchuria; *Girvaneila* sp. Flinders Range, Kimberley and McDonnell Ranges, Australia, also Manto Fm, Shangtung, China; *G. mexicana* J. H. Johnson 1952, *G.* cf. *sinensis* Yabe 1912, Camb Mexico; *Uranovia granosa* Korde 1958, *Globuloella butomensis* Korde 1958, *Batomella zelanovi* Korde 1958 and *Visheraia* sp. Korde 1958, Camb, Siberia.

Last, Tert Mioc: *Dimorphostroma palatinum* Reis 1923 and *Brachydactylus radialis* Reis 1923, Germany.

Chapter 1: Thallophyta—1

Family SPONGIOSTROMATA Pia 1927

First, Pre-Camb: *Corycium enigmaticum* Sederholm 1911, Archean (2200–3000 m.y.), Ajonokka E. Shore, Lake Nasijarvi, Finland; Stromatolites, Archean (more than 2700 m.y.), Dolomite Series, Bulawayo, S. Rhodesia; *Collenia* sp. and *Conophyton* sp., Pharusian (more than 2000 m.y.), Sahara, N. Africa. **Extant.**

[H.M.J. & G.A.L.J.]

Class UNCERTAIN

Family PROTOTAXITACEAE Pia 1927

First, Sil Wenl: *Prototaxites hicksii* (Etheridge) Pia, at base of Denbighshire Grits, Cyrtograptus murchisoni Z., Corwen, North Wales, Britain (Hicks 1881, Kräusel & Weyland 1934).

Last, Dev Frasn: *Protoaxites southworthii* Arnold, Kettle Point black sh, Lambton County, Ontario, Canada (Arnold 1952).

Comment: The family Protaxitaceae, as used here, includes *Nematothallus* Lang, 1937 which occurs in the Dev Siegen-Gedin, Wales. It is possible that the family will be split ultimately into two or more groups when sufficient data are available. [H.P.B.]

Class XANTHOPHYTA (Heterocontae)

First, Carb Bashk: *Pila* and *Reinschia* Bertrand and Renault, Boghead Cannel Coal (Torbanehill Mineral), base of Coal Measures, West Lothian, Scotland (Blackburn & Temperley 1936). **Extant.**

Comment: These algae are taken to resemble closely *Botryococcus braunii* Kützing (extant) and other similar records come from most later periods (Traverse 1955). These algae probably occurred also in the early Carb, but *Gleocapsamorpha* from the Kuchersite, Ord, Estonia, has been omitted. [N.F.H.]

REFERENCES

ARNOLD, C. A. 1952. A specimen of *Prototaxites* from the Kettle Point black shale of Ontario. *Palaeontographica*, **93B**, 45–56.

BRADLEY, W. H. 1962. A chloroplast in *Spirogyra* from the Green River Formation of Wyoming. *Amer. J. Sci.*, **260**, 455–459.

BARGHOORN, E. S. & TYLER, S. A. 1965. Micro-organisms from the Gunflint Chert. *Science, N.Y.*, **147**, 563–577.

BLACKBURN, K. B. & TEMPERLEY, B. N. 1936. *Botrycoccus* and the algal coals. *Trans. R. Soc. Edinb.*, **58**, 841–868, 2 pls.

BIGOT, A. 1929. Les Récifs en coupole du Cambrien de Carteret et les Récifs de *Chlorellopsis*. *C.r. hebd. Séanc. Acad. Sci.*, Paris **189**, 816–7.

BOHLIN, K. 1901. *Utleart till de gröna algemas och arkegoniatemas fylogeni*. Thesis, Lund (publ. by author).

CLOUD, P. E. 1965. Significance of the Gunflint (Precambrian) microflora. *Science, N.Y.*, **148**, 27–35.

COLOM, G. 1955. Jurassic-Cretaceous plelagic sediments of the western Mediterranean and the Atlantic area. *Micropaleontology*, **1**, 105–124.

ELLIOTT, G. F. 1955. The Permian calcareous algae *Gymnocodium*. *Micropaleontology*, **1**, 83–90.

—— 1958. Algal debris-facies in the Cretaceous of the Middle East. *Palaeontology*, **1**, 254–259.

ENDO, R. 1961. Phylogenetic relationships among the calcareous algae. *Sait. Univ. Sci. Rep. Ser. B.,* Comm. Vol. Prof. R. Endo, 1–52.

FENTON, C. L. 1943. Precambrian and early Palaeozoic algae. *Amer. Midl. Nat.,* **30**, 83–111.

FJERDUGSTADTL, E. 1954. The sub-fossil algal flora of Lake Bolling. *K. danske vidensk. selsk. (biol.),* **7**, 56.

FRITSCH, F. E. 1948. *The structure and reproduction of the Algae.* 2 vols., Cambridge University Press.

HICKS, H. 1881. On the discovery of some remains of plants at the base of the Denbighshire Grits near Corwen, North Wales. *Q. Jl geol. Soc. Lond.,* **37**, 482–496.

JOHNSON, J. H. 1959. A review of the Silurian (Gotlandian) Algae. *Colorado Sch. Mines Quart.,* **54**, 1–55.

JOHNSON, J. H. 1962. The algal genus *Lithothamnium* and its fossil representatives. *Colorado Sch. Mines Quart.,* **57**, 1–111.

KORDE, K. B. 1950. Algal remains in the Cambrian of the Kazaskhstan. *Dokl. Akad. nauk SSSR, Earth Sci. Ser.,* **73**, 809–812. [in Russian]

KORIBA, K. & MIKI, S. 1959. On *Paleodictyon* and fossil *Hydrodictyon. Yabe Jubilee Pub.,* **1**, 55.

KRÄUSEL, R. & WEYLAND, H. 1934. Algen im deutschen Devon. *Palaeontographica,* **79B**, 131–142.

KUTZING, F. T. 1845. Die kieselschaligen lanen oder Diatomeen. *Ber. Verhandl. Akad. Wiss.,* Berlin.

LANG, W. H. 1937. On the plant remains from the Downtonian of England and Wales. *Phil. Trans. Roy. Soc. Lond.,* 227B, 245–291.

LYUBTSOV, V. V. 1964. Organic remains in most ancient sedimentary and metamorphic sequences of the Kola Peninsula. *Int. Geol. Rev.,* **6**, 1408–1412.

MASLOV, V. P. 1937. On the Palaeozoic rock-building algae of east Siberia. Moscow Univ. Palaeont. Lab., Problems Palaeont., 2–3, 342–348, 12 pls. [In Russian]

—— 1956. Fossil Calcareous algae in the U.S.S.R. *U.S.S.R. Acad. Sci., Proc. Inst. Geol. Sci.,* **160**, 1–301. [in Russian]

—— 1961. Algae and the deposition of carbonates. *Izv. Akad. nauk SSSR Geol. Ser.,* **12**, 66–70.

MESSIKOMMER, E. 1938. Beitrag zur Kenntnis. der fossilen und subfossilen Desmidaceen. *Hedwigia,* Dresden, **78**, 107–201.

PAPENFUSS, G. F. 1955. Classification of the algae *in Centenary volume* (1853–1953), 115–224. California Acad. Sci., San Fransisco.

PFLUG, H. D. 1965. Organische Reste aus der Belt-Serie (Algonkium) von Nordamerika. *Paläont. Z.,* **39**, 10–25.

PIA, J. 1927. Thallophyta *in* Hirmer, M. (1927) "*Handbuch der Palaeobotanik.*" vol. 1, 1–136. Munich and Berlin.

PRIESTLEY, R. E. & DAVID, T. W. E. 1910. Geological notes of the British Antarctic Expedition 1907–1909. 11th *Cong. Geol. Int.*

RAO, L. R. 1952. Recent discoveries of fossil algae in India. *Palaeobot.,* **1**, 386–391.

TRAVERSE, A. 1955. Occurrence of the oil-forming alga *Botryococcus* in lignites and other Tertiary sediments. *Micropalaeontology,* **1**, 343–350, 1 pl.

YABE, H. 1952. A brief summary of the studies of rock forming calcareous algae in Japan. *Palaeobot.,* **1**, 443–447.

FOSSIL BACTERIA

Unequivocal evidence of the presence of bacteria or their spores in the fossil state presents difficulties due to (1) their recognition in view of minute dimensions; (2) their identification dependent upon a morphologic similarity to present-day forms; (3) the delimitation of related and often associated known forms e.g. bacteria, actinomycetes, fungi; (4) absence of knowledge of the forms of ancient life with the functions of bacteria; (5) the problem of possible contamination. In a few instances there is undoubted proof through the detailed recognition by the application of electron-microscopy, and by the application of biochemical techniques; the viability of some fossil bacteria has been demonstrated (Dombrowski). The accepted common forms, of bacteria, e.g. coccoid, bacilloid, filamental, or spirillar have all been recorded, as have their distinctive arrangements such as diplococcoid, staphylococcoid, streptococcoid and the several bacilloid arrangements. The preservation varies from the presence of an actual cell wall, to mineral replacement of this wall, or to sheath-like covering of the wall. In many instances the pathological association with bone, or plant tissue, and the resulting lesions on these materials have provided strong evidence for the presence and activity of bacteria. By analogy with the functions of modern forms so the associations recorded have been referred to autotrophic or chemautotrophic forms, or to groups which include iron bacteria, nitrate and sulphate reducing bacteria, calcareous bacteria and saprophytic forms e.g. (Pia 1928). The possible remains of bacteria have been recorded from limestones, cherts, iron and manganese ores, phosphorites, bauxites, tonsteins, oil shales, coal, vertebrate remains, coprolites, plant tissues and invertebrate skeletons; these occurrences range in age from Pre-Cambrian to the present. The presence of living bacteria in various modern and recent sediments, sulphur deposits, iron deposits, tufa and peats provides an analogy with past occurrences. The most important work on fossil bacteria was that of Renault (1896–1901) and the majority of important references to fossil bacteria are contained in Meschinelli (1902), Pia (1928), Zobell (1957), Kusnetzov, Ivanov and Lyalikova (1963). The recent work of Barghoorn and Tyler (1963, 1965), and Cloud (1965), Barghoorn and Schopf (1965) refer to Pre-Cambrian investigations. The literature contains frequent reference to the presence of unnamed forms which may be bacteria; other workers have noted a resemblance to modern forms and referred to the occurrence in that manner e.g. similar to *Crenothrix, Siderocapsa, Sphaerotilus,* or *Lyngbia.* Few records refer to the occurrence in a taxonomic manner. An important recent exception is the work of Schopf, Ehlers *et al.* 1965 in which by the application of electron microscopy utilising replica techniques, the authors demonstrated the presence of bacteria in iron pyrites of Carboniferous age. Sheath bacteria referred to *Sphaerotilus catenulatus* n. sp. were recognised as allied to modern bacteria, e.g. *Sphaerotilus natans* Kutzing or *Cladothrix dichotoma* Cohn. Spiral thread bacteria referred to *Gallionella pyritica* n. sp. closely resembled the modern forms of *Gallionella ferruginea* Ehrenberg; the authors were confident of

FORMATION	BACTERIAL REMAINS	RECORD
Oligocene	*Bacillus Zilianus* Renault	
	B. Grand 'Euryi Renault	
Eocene	*Micrococcus lignitum* Renault	
	M. paludis Renault	
	Bacilli resembling *B. subtilus*	Bradley 1931
Cretaceous	*Micrococcus* I	Ellis 1914
	Bacillus I	Ellis 1914
	Bacillus II	Ellis 1914
Jurassic	*Micrococcus trigeri* Renault	
	M. sarlatensis Renault	
	Actinomycites (a)	Ellis (1914)
	Iron bacteria (bauxites Mesozoic)	Vologdin in Kuznetzov 1963
Trias	—	
Permian	*Micrococcus lepidophagus* var. *a–g* Renault & Roche	
	M. petrolei Renault	
	Bacillus circulans (Dombrowski)	
	B. granosus Renault	
	B. permiensis Renault	
	B. gamma Renault	
	B. Tieghemi Renault	
	B. Colletus Renault	
	B. lalleyensis Renault	
	B. flaccidus Renault	
	B. lepidophagus arcuatus Renault	
	Filamentous sheaths, bacterial rods	Vologdin in Kuznetzov 1963

FORMATION	BACTERIAL REMAINS	RECORD
Carboniferous	*Micrococcus devonicus* var. *a, b.* Renault	
	M. esnostensis var. *a, b.* Renault	
	M. priscus Renault	
	M. priscus var. *a.* Renault	
	M. Zeilleri var. *a, b.* Renault	
	M. carbo Renault	
	M. Guignardi Renault	
	M. hymenophagus Renault	
	M. hymenophagus var. *a.* Renault	
	M. scoticus var. *a, b.* Renault	
	Bacillus amylobacter Van Tieghem	
	B. exiguus Renault	
	B. moscovianus Renault	
	B. gamma Renault	
	B. gamma var. *tenuis* Renault	
	B. ozodeus Renault	
	B. gomphosoideus Renault	
	B. vorax Renault	
	Sphaerotilus catenulatus	Schopf, Ehlers, Stiles, Birle
	Gallionella ferruginea	Schopf, Ehlers, Stiles, Birle
	Sulphur bacteria ?*Beggiatoa*	
Devonian	Bacterium strain VIII/D (Salt)	Dombrowski 1963
	Iron Bacteria	Vologdin in Kuznetzov 1963
Silurian	Bacterium strain XV/1 (Salt)	Dombrowski 1963
Ordovician	—	—
Cambrian	Filamentous iron bacteria (Bauxite)	Vologdin in Kuznetzov 1963
	Coccoid, bacilloid forms, iron bacteria (Phosphorite)	Vologdin in Kuznetzov 1963
Pre-Cambrian		
Biwabik (U. Huronian)	Iron bacteria (resembling *Chlamydothrix*) Bacilli	Gruner, 1922
Gun Flint (U. Huronian)	Bacteria (resembling *Crenothrix polyspora*)	Barghoorn & Tyler 1965
	Metallogenium personatum Perfilyev	Cloud 1965
	Entosphaeroides amplus Barghoorn (?bacteria)	Barghoorn & Tyler 1965
	Eoastrion bifurcatum Barghoorn	Barghoorn & Tyler 1965
	Eoastrion simplex Barghoorn (Actinomorphic affinity)	Barghoorn & Tyler 1965
	Coccoid forms (resembling *Siderocapsa* and *Siderococcus*)	Barghoorn & Schopf 1965
	Rod shaped cells (resemble *Sphaerotilus natans*)	Barghoorn & Schopf 1965
	Micrococcus sp.	Walcott 1915
	Bacterium strain XXX/1 (Salt)	Dombrowski 1963

[L. R. M.]

generic recognition, but despite a strikingly similar habit believed the specific identification to be unwarranted.

Other segmented microbes of a highly distinctive character were not finally identified but their probable affinity with members of the sulphur bacteria represented by forms such as the modern *Beggiatoa* was noted. The authors draw attention to the remarkable geological stability of both environment and organisms which appears to have existed over a period of at least 300 m.y.

The preparation of a list of occurrences is fraught with difficulty and ranges are unknown. The above record arranged in stratigraphic order is not intended to be exhaustive and the identification is that of the author recording the occurrence. [L.R.M.]

REFERENCES

Barghoorn, E. S. & Schopf, J. W. 1965. Electron Microscopy of Fossil Bacteria Two Billion Years Old. *Science Report*, Sept. 1965, pp. 1365–1367.

—— & Tyler, S. A. 1963. Fossil organisms from Pre-Cambrian Sediments. *Ann. N.Y. Acad. Sci.*, **108,** 451–452.

—— & Tyler, S. A. 1965. Microorganisms from the Gunflint Chert. *Science, N.Y.*, **147,** 563–577.

Bradley, W. H. 1931. Origin and Microfossils of the Oil Shale of the Green River Formation of Colorado and Utah. *Prof. Pap. U.S. geol. Surv.*, **168,** pp. 1–57.

Cloud, P. E. 1965. Significance of the Gunflint (Precambrian) Microflora. *Science, N.Y.*, **148,** 27–35.

Dombrowski, H. 1963. Bacteria from Palaeozoic Deposits. *Ann. N.Y. Acad. Sci.*, **108,** 453–460.

Ellis, D. 1914. Fossil microorganisms from the Jurassic and Cretaceous Rocks of Great Britain. *Proc. Roy. Soc. Edinb.*, **35,** 110–133.

Gruner, J. W. 1922. The origin of sedimentary iron formations: The Biwabik formation of the Mesaba Range. *Econ. Geol.*, **17,** 407–460.

Kuznetzov, S. I., Ivanov, M. V. & Lyalikova, N. N. 1963. *Introduction to Geological Micro-biology.* McGraw-Hill. 252 pp.

Meschinelli, A. 1902. *Fungorum fossilum omnium hucusque cognitorum iconographia.* Vicetiae.

Pia, J. 1928. Die Vorzeitlichen Spaltpilze und Ihre Lebensspuren. *Palaeobiologica*, **1,** 457–474.

Renault, B. 1896a. Recherches sur les Bactéricées fossiles. *Annls. Sci. nat. R. 8, Botan*, **2,** 275.

—— 1896b. *Bassin houiller et permien d'Autun et d'Épinac.* Fasc. 4, flore fossile, 2me partie. Études gîtes minér. de la France, publication of Minist. des Travaux, Paris.

—— 1899. Sur quelques Microorganisms des combustibles fossiles. *Bull. Soc. Ind. minér. St-Etienne*, R. 3, **13,** 865, and **14,** 5.

—— 1901. Du role de quelques bacteriacées fossiles au point de vue geologique. *8th Int. geol. Congr.*, **1,** 646.

Schopf, J. M., Ehlers, E. G., Stiles, D. V. & J. D. Birle. 1965. Fossil iron bacteria preserved in pyrite. *Proc. Am. Phil. Soc.*, **109,** 288–308.

Vologdin, A. G. 1947. Quoted in Kuznetzov, S. I., Ivanov, M. V. & Lyalikova, N. N., 1963.

Walcott, C. D. 1915. Discovery of Algonkian Bacteria. *Proc. U.S. natn. Acad. Sci.*, **1,** 256.

Zobell, C. E. 1957. Bacteria. *Mem. geol. Soc. Am.*, **67,** pp. 693–698.

FUNGI

The fossils of fungi consist of petrifactions of complete mycelia etc. which are rare, of spores which usually have few characters and are difficult to classify, and of organs of other plants attacked by fungi which leave recognisable damage. The fragmentary fossil record has been fitted for convenience into the classification of Recent fungi given by Hawker (1966).

Fossil mycorrhiza have been described from the Carb onwards by Andrews and Lenz (1943), Halket (1930), and others, but no attempt has been made to deal with them separately here. Sclerotinites (Stach 1957) and *Palynomorphites* (Moore 1963) have not been classified.

The higher fungi (Ascomycetes, Basidiomycetes) are not well represented before the Cret.

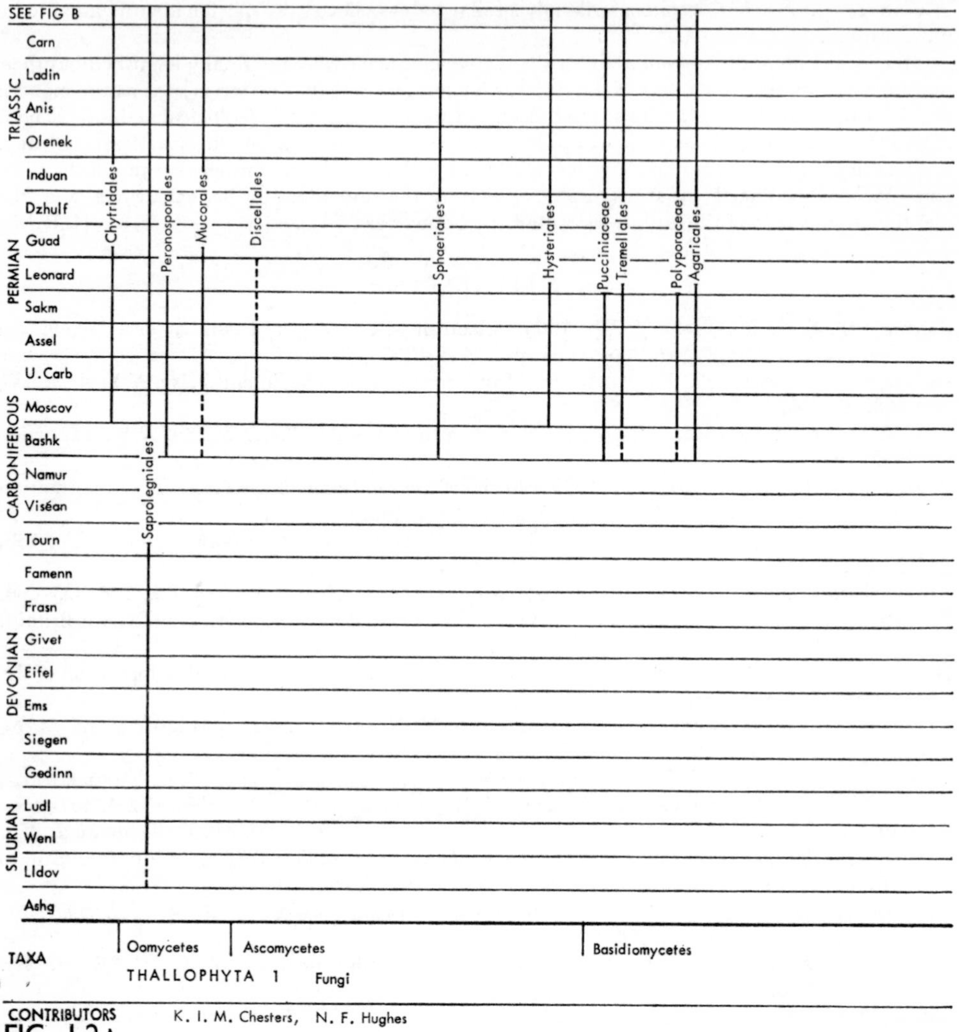

SEE FIG B
Carn
Ladin
Anis
Olenek
Induan
Dzhulf
Guad
Leonard
Sakm
Assel
U.Carb
Moscov
Bashk
Namur
Viséan
Tourn
Famenn
Frasn
Givet
Eifel
Ems
Siegen
Gedinn
Ludl
Wenl
Lldov
Ashg
TRIASSIC
PERMIAN
CARBONIFEROUS
DEVONIAN
SILURIAN
Chytridales
Peronosporales
Mucorales
Discellales
Saprolegniales
Sphaeriales
Hysteriales
Pucciniaceae
Tremellales
Polyporaceae
Agaricales
TAXA
Oomycetes
Ascomycetes
Basidiomycetes
THALLOPHYTA 1
Fungi
CONTRIBUTORS
K. I. M. Chesters, N. F. Hughes

FIG. 1.2A

Division PHYCOMYCETES

Although ?Phycomycetes has been mentioned for the Pre-Camb fossils of the Gunflint Chert, Huronian, Canada (Tyler and Barghoorn 1954), Barghoorn and Tyler (1965) favour algal (or uncertain) origin for most of the fossils.

Class CHYTRIDIOMYCETES

Order CHYTRIDALES

First, Carb Moscov: *Urophlyctites oliverianus* Magnus (on *Alethopteris* leaves), *U. stigmariae* Weiss and *Oochytrium lepidodendroni* Renault (on lycopods), Westphalian Coal Measures, Western Europe (see Hirmer 1927). **Extant.**

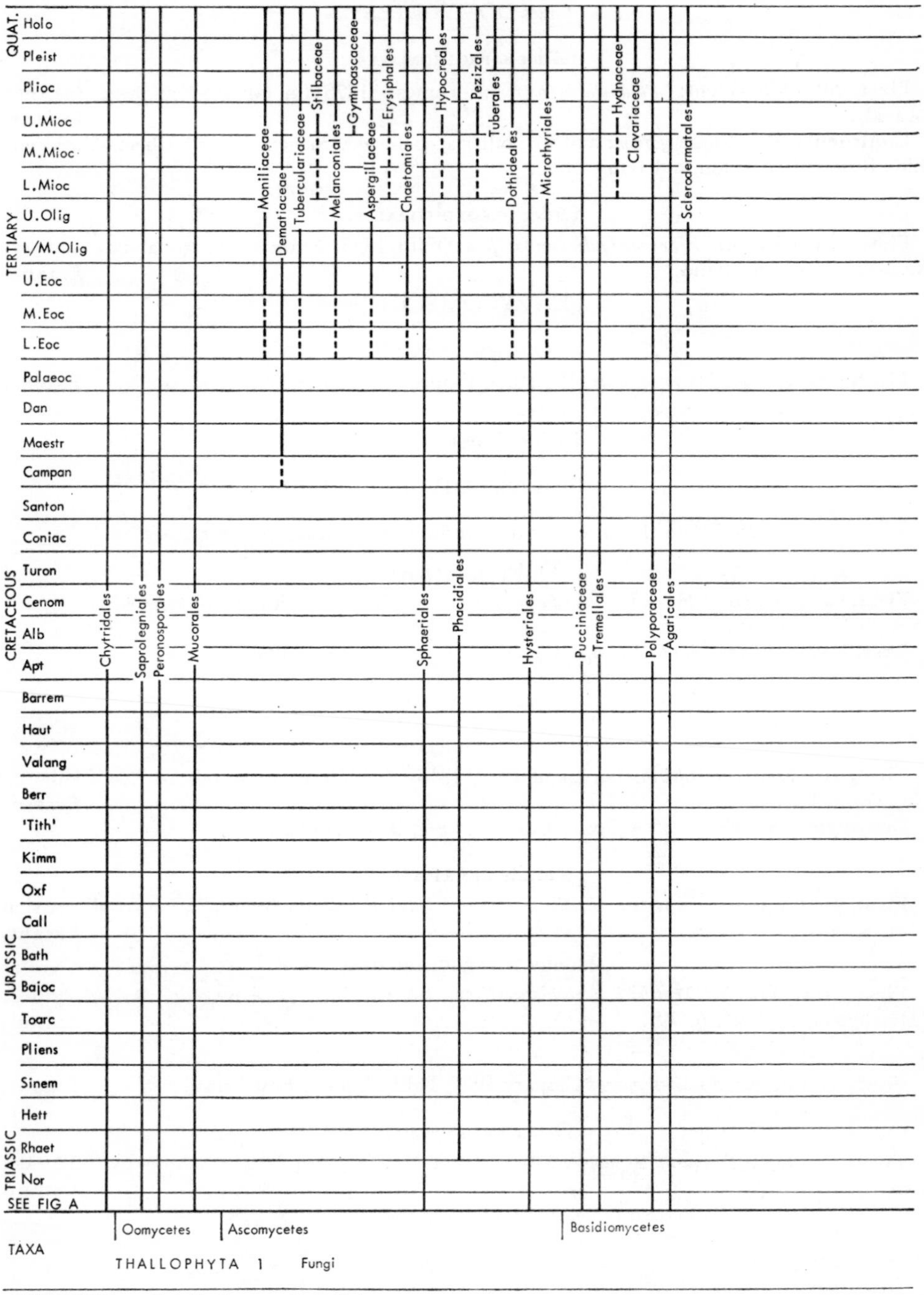
QUAT.
Holo
Pleist
Plioc
U.Mioc
M.Mioc
L.Mioc
TERTIARY
U.Olig
L/M.Olig
U.Eoc
M.Eoc
L.Eoc
Palaeoc
Dan
Maestr
Campan
Santon
Coniac
CRETACEOUS
Turon
Cenom
Alb
Apt
Barrem
Haut
Valang
Berr
'Tith'
Kimm
Oxf
Call
JURASSIC
Bath
Bajoc
Toarc
Pliens
Sinem
Hett
TRIASSIC
Rhaet
Nor
SEE FIG A
Chytridales
Saprolegniales
Peronosporales
Mucorales
Moniliaceae
Dematiaceae
Tuberculariaceae
Stilbaceae
Melanconiales
Gymnoascaceae
Aspergillaceae
Erysiphales
Chaetomiales
Sphaeriales
Hypocreales
Phacidiales
Pezizales
Tuberales
Dothideales
Hysteriales
Microthyriales
Pucciniaceae
Tremellales
Hydnaceae
Clavariaceae
Polyporaceae
Agaricales
Sclerodermatales
Oomycetes
Ascomycetes
Basidiomycetes
TAXA
THALLOPHYTA 1 Fungi

CONTRIBUTORS K. I. M. Chesters, N. F. Hughes

FIG. 1.2B

Class OOMYCETES

Order SAPROLEGNIALES

First, Sil Lldov-Wenl: *Palaeachlya perforans* Duncan 1876 (in *Goniophyllum pyramidale*, not located). **Extant.**

Comment: *Palaeomyces gordoni* and five other species, Dev Siegen, Rhynie Chert, Aberdeenshire, Scotland (Kidston and Lang 1921).

Order PERONOSPORALES

First, Carb Bashk: *Peronosporoides carbonifera* Smith 1896, Main seam, Annandale Colliery, Nr. Kilmarnock, Scotland. **Extant.**

Class ZYGOMYCETES

Order MUCORALES

First, Carb: *Mucorites combrensis* (Renault), France (Meschinelli, A. 1898, p. 9). **Extant.**

Division 'HIGHER FUNGI'

Class ASCOMYCETES

?Subclass (Form Class) DEUTEROMYCETES (Fungi imperfecti)

Order DISCELLALES

First, Carb Moscov: *Excipulites punctatus* Grand'Eury 1877 (on pinnules of *Pecopteris pluckeneti*), Westphalian, France.

Last, Perm: *E. callipteridis* Europe and North America (White 1899).

Order MONILIALES

Family MONILIACEAE

First, Tert Eoc: *Cladosporites fasciculatus* Berry 1916a, (on lauraceous wood), M Eoc, Claiborne Gp, Texas, U.S.A. **Extant.**

Comment: *Ramularites oblongisporus* Caspary, Olig, Baltic Amber.

Family DEMATIACEAE

First, Cret Campan-Maestr: *Trichosporites conwentzi* Felix (on *Cedroxylon*), Ryedal, Sweden (Stopes 1913). **Extant.**

Family TUBERCULARIACEAE

First, Tert Eoc: *Dictyosporites loculatus* Felix (in wood of Rhamnaceae) Baku, Caspian (Meschinelli, A. 1898, p. 79). **Extant.**

Family STILBACEAE

First, Tert Mioc: *Stilbites succini* Caspary 1907, Baltic Amber, East Prussia. **Extant.**

Order MELANCONIALES

First, Tert Eoc: *Pestalozzites sabalana* Berry 1916a (Leaf spot on *Sabalites*), Alum Bluff, Florida, U.S.A. **Extant.**

Subclass EUASCOMYCETES

Order PLECTASCALES

Family GYMNOASCACEAE

First, Tert U.Mioc: *Ctenomyces serratus* Eid., Randecker Maar, Germany (Rüffle 1963). **Extant.**

Chapter 1: Thallophyta—1

Family ASPERGILLACEAE

First, Tert Eoc: *Cryptocolax clamensis* and *C. parvula*, Oregon, U.S.A. (Scott 1956).   **Extant.**
Comment: *Penicillites curtipes* Berkeley, Tert Olig, Baltic Amber, East Prussia (Hirmer 1927).

Order ERYSIPHALES

First, Tert Mioc: *Erysiphites melilli* Pampaloni 1902, Melilli, Italy.   **Extant.**

Order CHAETOMIALES

First, Tert Eoc: *Caenomyces annulata* Berry 1916b, Lagrange fm (Wilcox), Tennessee, U.S.A.
Extant.

Order SPHAERIALES ("Pyrenomycetes")

First, Carb Bashk: *Sphaerites feistmantelianus* (Rabenhorst), Bohemia (Meschinelli, A. 1898, p. 41). Also, *Depazites rabenhorsti* Geinitz (on fern foliage), Carb (Hirmer 1927).   **Extant.**
Comment: *Chaetosphaerites pollenismilis* (spores), Carb Tourn, Spitsbergen (Playford 1962). Some Mesozoic Pyrenomycetes; abundant in Tertiary.

Order HYPOCREALES

First, Tert Mioc: *Melanosporites stefani* Pampoloni 1902, Melilli, Sicily, Italy.   **Extant.**

Order PHACIDIALES

First, Trias Rhaet: *Xylomites intermedius* Nathorst, Germany (Meschinelli, A. 1898).   **Extant.**

Order PEZIZALES

First, Tert Mioc: *Pezizites candidus* Goeppert and Berendt, Baltic Amber (Hirmer 1927).
Extant.

Comment: Discomycetes (Phacidales to Tuberales) poorly represented by fossils.

Order TUBERALES (Truffles)

First, Quat Pleist: *Cenococcum geophilum* Fries, but regarded as doubtful Pyrenomycetes by Hirmer (1927).   **Extant.**

Subclass LOCULO-ASCOMYCETES

Order DOTHIDEALES

First, Tert Eoc: *Dothidites nerii* Bureau and Patouillard, France (Meschinelli, A. 1898, p. 44).
Extant.

Comment: *Dothidea borealis*, Mioc, Iceland (Heer 1868).

Order HYSTERIALES

First, Carb Moscov: *Hysterites cordaitis* Grand'Eury 1877, France.   **Extant.**

Order MICROTHYRIALES

First, Tert Eoc: *Asterina* sp., Eoc?, Tennessee, U.S.A. (Dilcher 1963). Also *Microthyriacites cooksoni* Rao 1959, and *M. sahnii* Rao 1959, Eoc, Palana, Bikaner, India.   **Extant.**
Comment: *Phragmothyrites eocenica* Edwards 1922, Mull, Scotland, may prove to be pre-Eocene.

Class BASIDIOMYCETES

Subclass HETEROBASIDIOMYCETES

Order UREDINALES Family PUCCINIACEAE

First, Carb Bashk: *Anthracomyces cannallensis* Renault and *Teleutosporites milloti* Renault (in *Lepidostrobus*), France (Hirmer 1927).   **Extant.**
Comment: Next record Late Cret, *Puccinites cretaceus* Velenovsky (Frič & Bayer 1901).

The Fossil Record, Part II

Order TREMELLALES

First, Carb: *Myxomycetes mangini* Renault (Dacryomycetaceae?) (Meschinelli, A. 1898, p. 71).
Extant.

Subclass HOMOBASIDIOMYCETES

Order POLYPORALES

Family HYDNACEAE

First, Tert Mioc: *Hydnites argillae* (Ludwig), Germany (Meschinelli, A. 1898, p. 8).
Extant.

Family CLAVARIACEAE

First, Quat Pleist: *Clavaria turbinata* Murr 1926, Hotting breccia, Austria. **Extant.**

Family POLYPORACEAE

First, Carb Bashk-Moscov: *Dactyloporus archaeus* Herzer 1893, Ohio, U.S.A., and *Pseudopolyporus carbonicus* Hollick 1910, West Virginia, U.S.A. **Extant.**
Comment: Next record Mesozoic, China (Hsü 1953).

Order AGARICALES

First, Carb Bashk: *Archagaricon bulbosum* and other spp., Hancock and Atthey 1869, Cramlington, Northumberland, England. **Extant.**
Comment: Next records Tert Mioc, *Agaricites* spp (Hirmer 1927); ?*Agaricus* cf. *melleus*, Mesozoic, Karlsdorf, (Felix 1894).

Order SCLERODERMATALES

First, Tert Eoc: *Scleroderma einosporites* Rouse 1962 (spores), Brothers Creek, British Columbia, Canada. **Extant.**
Comment: *Geaster florissantensis* Cockerell 1908, Mioc, Colorado, U.S.A.

[K.I.M.C. & N.F.H.]

REFERENCES

ANDREWS, H. N. & LENZ, L. W. 1943. A Mycorrhizome from the Carboniferous of Illinois. *Bull. Torrey bot. Club*, **70**, 120–125.

BARGHOORN, E. S. & TYLER, S. A. 1965. Micro-organisms from the Gunflint Chert. *Science, N.Y.*, **147**, 563–577.

BERRY, E. W. 1916a. The physical conditions and age indicated by the flora of the Alum Bluff formation. *Prof. Pap. U.S. geol. Surv.*, **98.**

BERRY, E. W. 1916b. The Lower Eocene Floras of southeastern North America. *Prof. Pap. U.S. geol. Surv.*, **91.**

BERRY, E. W. 1916c. Remarkable fossil fungi. *Mycologia*, **8**, 73–79.

CASPARY, R. 1907. Die flora des Bernsteins und anderer fossiler Harze des ostpreussischen Tertiärs. *Abh. preuss. geol. Landesanst.* (new series), **4**, 1–181.

COCKERELL, T. D. A. 1908. The fossil flora of Florissant, Colorado. *Bull. Am. Mus. nat. Hist.*, **24**, 71–110.

DILCHER, D. L. 1963. Eocene Epiphyllous Fungi. *Science, N.Y.*, **142**, 667–669.

DUNCAN, P. M. 1876. On some unicellular algae parasitic within Silurian and Tertiary Corals. *Q. Jl. geol. Soc. Lond.*, **23**, 205 et seq..

EDWARDS, W. N. 1922. An Eocene microthyriaceous Fungus from Mull, Scotland. *Trans. Br. mycol. Soc.*, **7**, 66–72.

ELLIS, D. 1917–18. Phycomycetous fungi from the English Lower Coal Measures. *Proc. R. Soc. Edinb.*, **38**, 130–45.

FELIX, J. 1894. Studien über fossile Pilge. *Z. dt. geol. Ges.*, **46**, 269–280.

FRIČ, A. & BAYER, E. 1901. Studien im Gebeite der böhmischen Kreideformation. *Arch. naturw. Landes Durchforsch. Böhm.*, **9**, no. 2.

GRAHAM, A. 1962. The role of fungal spores in palynology. *J. Paleont.*, **36**, 60–68.

GRAND'EURY, C. 1877. Flora Carbonifère du dépt de la Loire et du centre de la France. *Mém. prés. div. Sav. Acad. Sci. Inst. Fr.*, **24**, 624 pp., 33 pls.

HALKET, A. C. 1930. The rootlets of *Amyelon radicans* Will; their anatomy, their apices and their endophytic fungus. *Ann. Bot.*, **44**, 865–905.

HANCOCK, A. & ATTHEY, T. 1869. On some curious fossil fungi from the Black Shales of the Northumberland Coalfield. *Ann. Mag. nat. Hist.* (4), **4**, 221–228.

HAWKER, L. E. 1966. *Fungi*. Hutchinson, London.

HEER, O. 1868. *Flora Fossilis Arctica, Vol.* 1. Schulthess, Zürich.

HERZER, H. 1893. A new fungus from Lower Coal Measures (Tuscarawas County, Ohio). *Am. Geol.*, **11**, 365–366.

HIRMER, H. 1927. *Handbuch der Paläobotanik*. Oldenburg, Münich and Berlin.

HOLLICK, A. 1910. A new fossil Polypore *Pseudopolyporus carbonicus* Hollick. *Mycologia*, **2**, 93–95.

HSU, J. 1953. On the occurrence of a fossil wood in association with fungous Hyphae from Chimo of East Shantung. *Palaeont. sin.*, **1**, 84–86.

HUTCHINSON, S. A. & WALTON, J. 1953. A presumed Ascomycete from the Upper Carboniferous. *Nature, Lond.*, **172**, 36–37.

KIDSTON, R. & LANG, W. H. 1921. On Old Red Sandstone Plants showing structure, from the Rhynie Chert Bed, Aberdeenshire, Part V. The Thallophyta occurring in the Peat Bed. *Trans. R. Soc. Edinb.*, **52**, 855–902.

MESCHINELLI, A. 1898. *Fungorum fossilium omnium hucusque cognitorum Iconographia*. Vicetiae, 144 pp, 31 pls.

MESCHINELLI, L. 1898. Contributo alla micologia fossile. Su alcuni funghi terziari del Piedmonte. *Atti Ist. veneto Sci.*, **9**, 7, 769–75, 2pl.

MOORE, L. R. 1963. Microbiological colonization and attack on some Carboniferous Miospores. *Palaeontology*, **6**, 349–372.

MURR, J. 1926. Neue Übersicht über die fossile Flora der Hottinger Breccie. *Jb. geol. Bundesanst., Wien*, **76**, 153–70, 2pls.

PAMPALONI, L. 1902. I resti organici nel disodile de Melitti in Sicilia. *Palaeontogr. ital.*, **8**, 121–130.

PLAYFORD, G. 1962. Lower Carboniferous Microfloras of Spitsbergen. *Palaeontology*, **5**, 550–618.

RAO, A. R. 1959. Fungal remains from some Tertiary deposits of India. *Palaeobotanist*, **7**, 43–46.

ROUSE, G. E. 1962. Plant microfossils from the Burrard Formation of British Columbia. *Micropaleontology*, **8**, 187–218.

RUFFLE, L. 1963. Die obermiozäne Flora vom Randecker Maar. *Paläont. Abh.*, **1**, pt. 3.

SACCARDO, P. A. 1897. *Syloge Fungorum*. Patavii.

SCOTT, R. A. 1956. *Cryptocolax*, a new genus of fungi (Aspergillaceae) from the Eocene of Oregon. *Am. J. Bot.*, **43**, 589–593.

SMITH, JOHN. 1896. On the discovery of Microscopic Plants in the fossil amber of the Ayrshire Coalfield. *Trans. geol. Soc. Glasg.*, **10**, 318–322.

STACH, E. 1957. Die Anschliff-Sporendiagnose des Ruhrkohlenflözes Baldur. *Palaeontographica*, **102B**, 71–95.

STOPES, M. 1913. *Catalogue of the Mesozoic plants in the British Museum: The Cretaceous flora, Part* 1, *Bibliography, algae and fungi*, 281 pp., 2 pls. London, British Museum (Natural History).

179

TYLER, S. A. & BARGHOORN, E. S. 1954. Occurrence of structurally preserved plants in Pre-Cambrian Rocks of the Canadian Shield. *Science, N.Y.*, **119,** 606–608.

WHITE, D. 1899. Fossil Flora from the Lower Coal Measures of Missouri. *Monogr. U.S. geol. Surv.*, **37,** 467 pp., 73 pls.

[Professor] H. P. Banks
  Department of Botany, Cornell University, Ithaca, N.Y., U.S.A.

K. I. M. Chesters, PH.D.
  Department of Palaeontology, British Museum (Natural History), Cromwell Road, London SW 7.

N. F. Hughes, M.A. F.G.S.
  Department of Geology, Sedgwick Museum, Downing Street, Cambridge.

G. A. L. Johnson, PH.D. F.G.S.
  Department of Geology, University Science Laboratories, South Road, Durham.

H. M. Johnson, M.SC. PH.D. F.G.S.
  Department of Geology, University Science Laboratories, South Road, Durham.

[Professor] L. R. Moore, D.SC. PH.D. F.G.S.
  Department of Geology, The University, Mappin Street, Sheffield 1.

CHAPTER 2

Thallophyta—2

Contributors: M. BLACK, C. DOWNIE, R. ROSS & W. A. S. SARJEANT

For convenience, certain unicellular planktonic algae and their associates have been assembled here separately from the remainder of the thallophytes. The acritarchs are included here because of their Mesozoic and later association with dinoflagellates, although they are almost certainly polygenetic.

In the coccoliths and dinoflagellates, taxa have been recorded at a lower level than elsewhere in the volume because of current difficulties in their classification and because of their increasing stratigraphical interest.   [N.F.H.]

Class CHRYSOPHYCEAE

Order CHRYSOMONADALES

Suborder COCCOLITHINEAE

Genera which can with reasonable confidence be regarded as fossil Chrysophyceae have been placed in one or other of the families used for living plants; to these the extinct Discoasteraceae should probably be added. Under the heading *genera incertae sedis* is a list of nano-fossils which are commonly preserved in close association with calcareous planktonic algae, but whose systematic relationships are in doubt; some of these may indeed be the remains of animals.

Where the stratigraphical or geographical range of a taxon is known to extend beyond the limits mentioned in published records, the extended range is also given. A number of recently proposed genera whose stratigraphical ranges cannot be established without substantial nomenclatural revision of pre-existing taxa have been omitted, since such a revision is beyond the scope of this work.

Family COCCOLITHACEAE
(= Coccolithidae Poche 1913)

Genus ALVEARIUM Black 1965
First and **Last,** Jur Hett: *A. dorsetense* Black, L. Lias, Dorset, England (Black 1965).

Genus ARKHANGELSKIELLA Vekshina 1959
First, Cret Turon: *A. obliqua* Stradner, Klementer Schichten, Austria (Stradner 1964).
Last, Cret U. Maestr: *A. cymbiformis* Vekshina, Denmark, Siberia and elsewhere (Bramlette and Martini 1964).

Genus ASPIDORHABDUS Hay & Towe 1962
First and **Last,** Tert M. Eoc: *H. ovalis* Hay & Towe, Donzacq, France (Hay & Towe 1962).

The Fossil Record, pp. 181–210. Geological Society of London, 1967. Printed in Northern Ireland.

The Fossil Record, Part II

Genus BISCUTUM Black 1959

First, Cret Cenom: *B. testudinarium* Black, Totternhoe Stone, England (Black & Barnes 1959).

Last, Cret Maestr: *B. [Discoaster] floridum* (Gorka), Poland (Gorka 1957); also Trimingham Chalk, England.

Genus BLACKITES Hay and Towe 1962

First, Tert M. Eoc: *B. spinosus* (Deflandre), Donzacq, France (Deflandre & Fert 1954; Hay & Towe 1962).

Last, Tert U. Eoc: *B. spinosus* (Deflandre), Marnes à Ph. ludensis, France.

Genus CALCIDISCUS Kamptner 1952

First, Tert Eoc: *C. uniforatus* Kamptner, deep-sea cores, Pacific (Kamptner 1963).

Last, Quat Holo: *C. quadriforatus* Kamptner, deep-sea cores, Pacific and Atlantic (Kamptner 1963).

Comment: Mainly Tert Plioc and Quat Pleist; not known living.

Genus CALYPTROLITHUS Kamptner 1948

First, Tert Palaeoc: *C. subtilis* Kamptner, deep-sea cores, Pacific (Kamptner 1963).

Extant (= isolated coccoliths of *Calyptrosphaera* Lohmann etc.).

Genus COCCOLITHUS Schwarz 1894

First, Jur Pliens: *C. opacus* Stradner, Lias alpha 3, Germany (Stradner 1963).   **Extant.**

Genus COLVILLEA Black 1964

First, Cret Cenom: *C. barnesae* Black, Cambridge Greensand, England (Black 1964).

Last, Cret Maestr: *C. barnesae* Black, dredged chalk, Iberian Seamounts (Black 1964). Also Stevns Klint, Denmark, and Trimingham Chalk, England.

Genus CREPIDOLITHUS Noël 1965

First, Jur Hett: *C.* cf. *crassus* (Deflandre), L. Lias, Dorset, England.

Last, Jur Toarc: *C. crassus* (Deflandre), Vassy, Yonne, France (Noël 1965).

Genus CRETARHABDUS Bramlette & Martini 1964

First, Cret Campan: *C. decorus* (Deflandre), widely distributed (Bramlette & Martini 1964).

Last, Cret Maestr: *C. splendens* (Deflandre), Maestricht Chalk, Holland, and elsewhere; widely distributed (Bramlette & Martini 1964).

Comment: Main development in Cret Maestr, with five species. Specimens in Tert M. Eoc at Donzacq, France, are believed to be re-worked from Cret.

Genus CRIBROSPHAERA Arkhangelski 1912

(= *Cribrosphaerella* Deflandre 1952 under Zoological Rules)

First, Cret Cenom: *C. murrayi* Arkhangelski, Saratov, Russia (Arkhangelski 1912). Also Cambridge Greensand, England (Black 1965).

Last, Cret Maestr: *C. ehrenbergi* Arkhangelski, Poland, Russia and elsewhere (Gorka 1957).

Comment: *C. turgida* Kamptner Tert Paleoc and other species without a central sieve-plate are here excluded.

Genus CRICOLITHUS Kamptner 1958

see *Cyclolithus* Kamptner. The elliptical forms, originally included in *Cyclolithus*, have not all been transferred to *Cricolithus*, and it is at present impracticable to give separate ranges for the two genera.

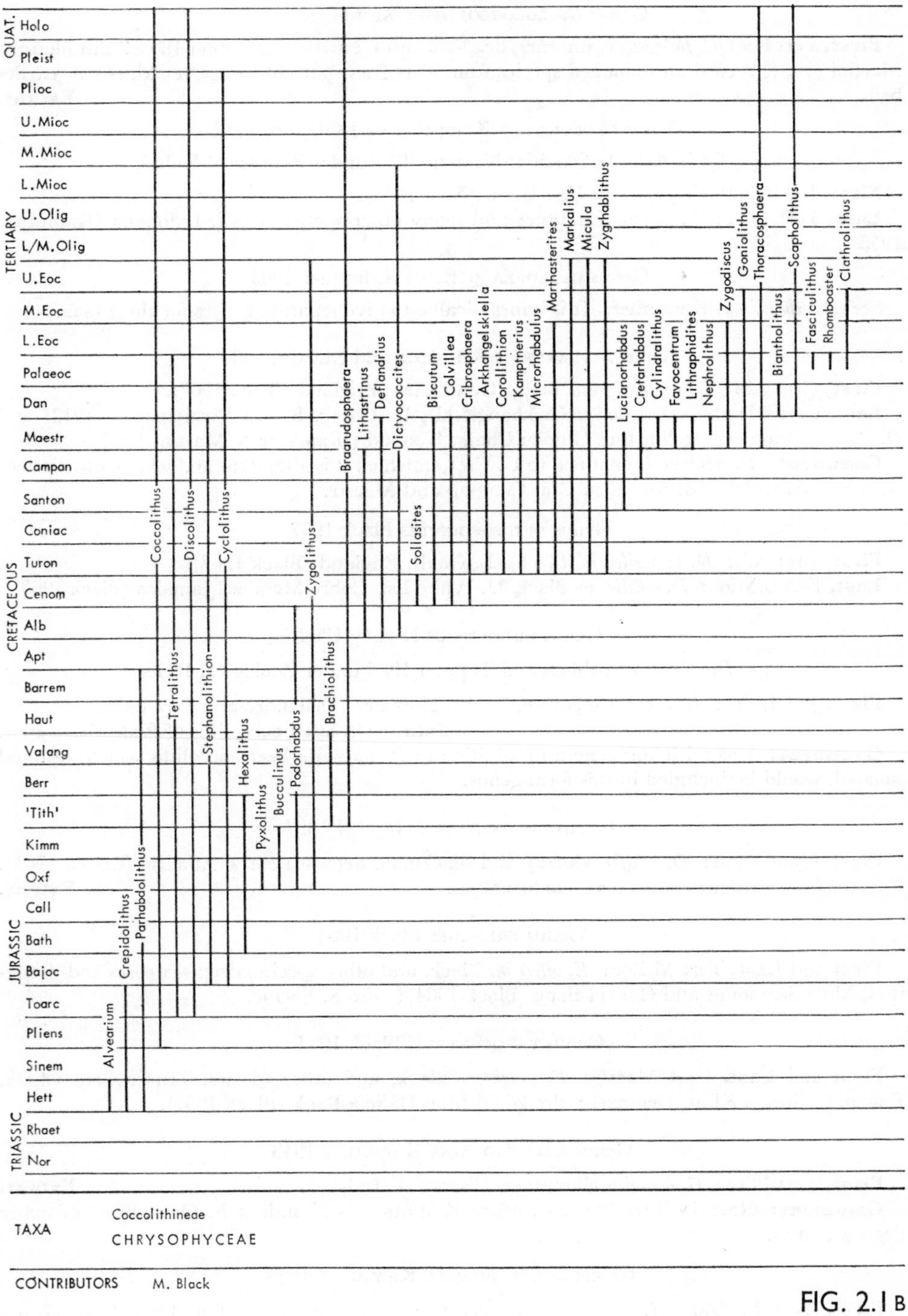
QUAT.
Holo
Pleist
Plioc
U. Mioc
M. Mioc
L. Mioc
TERTIARY
U. Olig
L/M. Olig
U. Eoc
M. Eoc
L. Eoc
Palaeoc
Dan
CRETACEOUS
Maestr
Campan
Santon
Coniac
Turon
Cenom
Alb
Apt
Barrem
Haut
Valang
Berr
'Tith'
JURASSIC
Kimm
Oxf
Call
Bath
Bajoc
Toarc
Pliens
Sinem
Hett
TRIASSIC
Rhaet
Nor
Alvearium
Crepidolithus
Parhabdolithus
Coccolithus
Tetralithus
Discolithus
Stephanolithion
Cyclolithus
Hexalithus
Pyxolithus
Bucculinus
Podorhabdus
Zygolithus
Brachiolithus
Braarudosphaera
Lithastrinus
Deflandrius
Dictyococcites
Sollasites
Biscutum
Colvillea
Cribrosphaera
Arkhangelskiella
Corollithion
Kamptnerius
Microrhabdulus
Marthasterites
Markalius
Micula
Zygrhablithus
Lucianorhabdus
Cretarhabdus
Cylindralithus
Favocentrum
Lithraphidites
Nephrolithus
Zygodiscus
Goniolithus
Thoracosphaera
Bianthoithus
Scapholithus
Fasciculithus
Rhomboaster
Clathrolithus
TAXA
Coccolithineae
CHRYSOPHYCEAE
CONTRIBUTORS
M. Black

FIG. 2.1 B

Genus CYCLOCOCCOLITHUS Kamptner 1954

First, Tert Eoc: *C. formosus* Kamptner, deep-sea cores, Pacific (Kamptner 1963). Bramlette & Martini (1964) record an unnamed species from Tert Dan, but not from Cret Maestr or earlier beds. **Extant.**

Genus CYCLOLITHUS Kamptner ex Deflandre 1952

(= *Cyclolithella* Loeblich & Tappan 1963 under Zoological Rules)

First, Jur Bajoc: *C. simplex* Noël, Algeria (Noël 1956).
Last, Tert Plioc: *C. acutus* Kamptner and many other species, Rotti, Indonesia (Kamptner 1955).

Genus CYCLOPLACOLITHUS Kamptner 1963

See *Cyclococcolithus* Kamptner. It is impracticable to give separate ranges for these taxa.

Genus DEFLANDRIUS Bramlette and Martini 1964

First, Cret Alb: *D. cantabrigensis* Black, Gault Clay, England (Black 1967).
Last, Cret Maestr: *D. cretaceus* (Arkhangelski), U. Chalk, Russia (Arkhangelski 1912) and *D. spinosus* Bramlette & Martini, Gulpen Chalk, Holland (Bramlette & Martini 1964).
Comment: *D. cretaceus* is confined to U. Cret, in which it is abundant and widely distributed. *D. spinosus* is widely distributed in Cret Campan and Maestr.

Genus DICTYOCOCCITES Black 1967

First, Cret Alb: *D. burwellensis* (Black), L. Gault, England (Black 1967).
Last, Tert L.Mioc: *D. antillarum* Black, U. White Lst, Cobre Member, Jamaica (Black 1967).

Genus DISCOLITHUS Huxley 1868

(= *Discolithina* Loeblich and Tappan 1963 under Zoological Rules)

First, Jur Toarc: *D. cancer* Deflandre, Urkut, Hungary (Deflandre and Fert 1954).
                                        Extant (Isolated coccoliths of *Pontosphaera* etc.).
Comment: Several living genera in addition to *Pontosphaera* bear coccoliths which, if found isolated, would be included in this form-genus.

Genus DISCOSPHAERA Haeckel 1894

First, Quat Pleist: *D. tubifer* Murray and Blackman, deep-sea cores, Atlantic (Cohen 1965). Records from earlier deposits need confirmation. **Extant.**

Genus ERICSONIA Black 1964

First and **Last,** Tert M.Eoc: *E. alternans* Black, and other species, deep-sea cores and dredgings, Muir Seamount and Galicia Bank (Black 1964); also S. Pacific.

Genus FAVOCENTRUM Black 1964

First and **Last,** Cret Maestr: *F. laughtoni* Black, and other species, Trimingham Chalk, England; Stevns Klint, Denmark; dredgings from Galicia Bank (Black 1964).

Genus GEPHYROCAPSA Kamptner 1943

First, Tert Plioc: *G. oceanica* Kamptner, Cisano, N. Italy. **Extant.**
Comment: Rare in Tert Plioc. *G. aperta* Kamptner is abundant in Quat Pleist of many deep-sea cores.

Genus HELICOSPHAERA Kamptner 1954

First, Tert L. Eoc: *H. seminulum* Bramlette and Sullivan, Lodo Fm, Unit 3, California (Bramlette and Sullivan 1961). **Extant.**

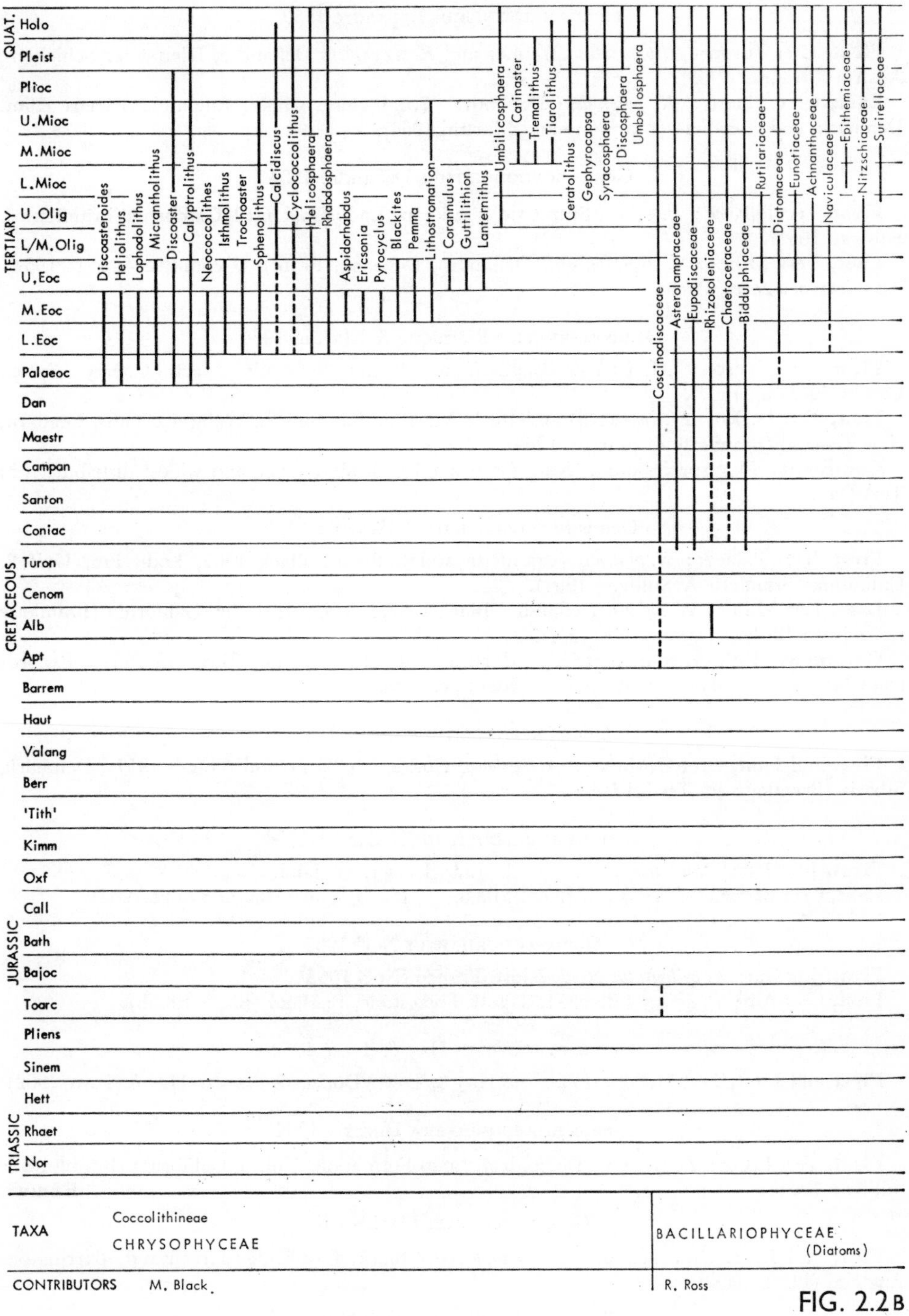
QUAT.
Holo
Pleist
Plioc
U.Mioc
M.Mioc
L.Mioc
U.Olig
L/M.Olig
U.Eoc
M.Eoc
L.Eoc
Palaeoc
TERTIARY
Dan
Maestr
Campan
Santon
Coniac
Turon
Cenom
Alb
Apt
CRETACEOUS
Barrem
Haut
Valang
Berr
'Tith'
Kimm
Oxf
Call
Bath
Bajoc
Toarc
Pliens
Sinem
Hett
JURASSIC
Rhaet
Nor
TRIASSIC
Discoasteroides
Heliolithus
Lophodolithus
Micrantholithus
Discoaster
Calyptrolithus
Neococcolithes
Isthmolithus
Trochoaster
Sphenolithus
Calcidiscus
Cyclococcolithus
Helicosphaera
Rhabdosphaera
Aspidorhabdus
Ericsonia
Pyrocyclus
Blackites
Pemma
Lithostromation
Corannulus
Gutilithion
Lanternithus
Umbilicosphaera
Catinaster
Tremalithus
Tiarolithus
Ceratolithus
Gephyrocapsa
Syracosphaera
Discosphaera
Umbellosphaera
Coscinodiscaceae
Asterolampraceae
Eupodiscaceae
Rhizosoleniaceae
Chaetoceraceae
Biddulphiaceae
Rutilariaceae
Diatomaceae
Eunotiaceae
Achnanthaceae
Naviculaceae
Epithemiaceae
Nitzschiaceae
Surirellaceae
TAXA
Coccolithineae
CHRYSOPHYCEAE
BACILLARIOPHYCEAE
(Diatoms)
CONTRIBUTORS
M. Black
R. Ross

FIG. 2.2B

Genus KAMPTNERIUS Deflandre 1959

First, Cret Turon: *K. punctatus* Stradner and *K. magnificus* Deflandre, Klementer Schichten, Austria (Stradner 1963).

Last, Cret Maestr: *K. magnificus* Deflandre, Trimingham Chalk, England; Stevns Klint, Denmark, and elsewhere (Bramlette and Martini 1964).

Genus LOPHODOLITHUS Deflandre 1954

First, Tert Palaeoc: *L. nascens* Bramlette & Sullivan, Lodo Fm, Unit 2, California (Bramlette & Sullivan 1961).

Last, Tert M.Eoc: *L. mochlophorus* Deflandre, Donzacq, France (Deflandre & Fert 1954). Also deep-sea cores, Pacific.

Genus MARKALIUS Bramlette & Martini 1964

First, Cret Turon: *M. inversus* Bramlette & Martini, Belemnite Marls, Cherry Hinton, Cambridge, England.

Last, Tert U.Eoc: *M. inversus* Bramlette & Martini, diatomite in Waiareka Tuffs, Oamaru, New Zealand (Bramlette & Martini 1964).

Comment: One species only. Rare Cret, maximum abundance and widest distribution in Tert Dan.

Genus NEOCOCCOLITHES Sujkowski 1931

First, Tert Palaeoc: *N. protenus* (Bramlette and Sullivan) Black 1967, Lodo Fm, Unit 2, California (Bramlette & Sullivan 1961).

Last, Tert M.Eoc: *N. dubius* (Deflandre) Black 1967, Kreyenhagen Fm, California (Bramlette & Sullivan 1961).

Comment: Re-worked in Tert Olig (Martini 1960) and Tert Mioc (Stradner 1963). Records from Mesozoic probably based upon mis-identifications.

Genus NEPHROLITHUS Gorka 1957

First and **Last,** Cret U.Maestr: *N. barbarae* Gorka, Chalk, Poland (Gorka 1957), Denmark, Siberia (Bramlette & Martini 1964).

Genus PARHABDOLITHUS Deflandre 1952

First, Jur Hett: *P. marthae* Deflandre, L. Lias, Dorset, England.

Last, Cret Barrem: *P. embergeri* (Noël), Bakony Mts, Hungary (Baldine Beke 1964).

Genus PODORHABDUS Noël 1965

First, Jur Oxf: *P. cylindratus* Noël, Niort, France (Noël 1965).

Last, Cret Alb: *P. albianus* Black, L. Gault, Folkestone, England (Black 1966b).

Genus PYROCYCLUS Hay & Towe 1962

First and **Last,** Tert M.Eoc: *P. inversus* Hay & Towe, Donzacq, France (Hay & Towe 1962).

Genus RHABDOSPHAERA Haeckel 1894

First, Tert L.Eoc: *R. perlonga* (Deflandre), Lodo Formation, Unit 3, California (Bramlette & Sullivan 1961). **Extant.**

Genus SOLLASITES Black 1966

First and **Last,** Cret Cenom: *S. barringtonensis* Black, Cambridge Greensand, Barrington, England (Black 1966b).

Genus SYRACOSPHAERA Lohmann 1902

First, Tert Plioc: *S. pulchra* Lohmann, deep-sea cores, Pacific (Kamptner 1963). **Extant.**

Genus TIAROLITHUS Kamptner 1958

First, Tert M.Mioc: *T. medusoides* (Kamptner), deep-sea cores, Experimental Mohole, Pacific (Martini & Bramlette 1963).

Last, Quat Holo: *T. medusoides* (Kamptner), deep-sea cores, Pacific and S. Atlantic (Kamptner 1963).

Comment: Four other species confined to Quat Pleist; none known living. *Calcidiscus obscurus* Deflandre & Fert May belong to this genus (Hay and Towe 1962); if so the first appearance would be Tert M.Eoc.

Genus TREMALITHUS Kamptner ex Deflandre 1952 emend. Kamptner 1963

First, Tert M.Mioc: *T. umbrella* Kamptner, Badener Tegel, Austria (Kamptner 1948).

Last, Quat Pleist: *T. honestus* Kamptner, deep-sea cores, Pacific (Kamptner 1963).

Comment: Stratigraphical ranges based upon older records can be misleading, since *Tremalithus* was formerly used for the isolated coccoliths of *Coccolithus* and several other genera. *T. quadriturgestus* Kamptner 1963 should probably be excluded from the genus as re-defined in 1963.

Genus UMBELLOSPHAERA Paasche 1955

First, Quat Holo: *U. tenuis* (Kamptner), deep-sea ooze, Atlantic (Markali & Paasche 1955).
Extant.

Genus UMBILICOSPHAERA Lohmann 1902

First, Tert Olig: *U. dilatata* Kamptner, deep-sea cores, Pacific (Kamptner 1963).   **Extant.**

Genus ZYGODISCUS Bramlette & Sullivan 1961

First, Cret Maestr: *Z. pseudanthophorus* Bramlette & Martini, Gulpen Chalk, Holland (Bramlette & Martini 1964).

Last, Tert L.Eoc: *Z. adamas* Bramlette & Sullivan, Lodo Fm, Unit 3, California (Bramlette & Sullivan 1961).

Genus ZYGOLITHUS Kamptner ex Deflandre 1952

First, Jur Oxf: *Z. erectus* Deflandre, Calvados, France. (Deflandre & Fert 1954).

Last, Tert U.Eoc: *Z. aureus* Stradner, Bruderndorf, Austria (Stradner 1962).

Comment: Common in the Mesozoic and early Tert; above Tert Eoc rare and mostly re-worked. Records of autochthonous species from Tert Mioc of Austria and Tert Plioc of Indonesia have not been confirmed by recent work. Living genera bearing superficially similar coccoliths e.g. *Zygosphaera* are probably unrelated.

Genus ZYGRHABLITHUS Deflandre 1959

First, Cret Turon: *Z. turriseiffeli* (Deflandre), M.Chalk, Burham, England (Deflandre & Fert 1954).

Last, Tert U.Eoc: *Z. bijugatus* (Deflandre), diatomite in Waiareka Tuffs, Oamaru, New Zealand (Deflandre & Fert 1954).

Family BRAARUDOSPHAERACEAE

(= Braarudosphaeridae Deflandre 1947)

Genus BRAARUDOSPHAERA Deflandre 1947

First, Jur Tith: *B. bigelowi* (Gran & Braarud), Algeria (Noël 1956).   **Extant.**

Comment: The long time-range of *B. bigelowi* is exceptional; other species, mainly L.Tert, were short-lived.

Genus MICRANTHOLITHUS Deflandre 1950

First, Tert Palaeoc: *M. pinguis* Bramlette & Sullivan, and numerous other species, Lodo Fm, Unit 2, California (Bramlette & Sullivan 1961).

Last, Tert U.Eoc: *M. vesper* Deflandre, boreholes in N. Germany (Martini 1958).

Genus PEMMA Klumpp 1953

First, Tert M. Eoc: *P. rotundum* Klumpp, marls of Holzmannberg, Austria (Stradner & Papp 1961).

Last, Tert U. Eoc: *P. papillatum* Martini, Yazoo Marl, Mississippi (Martini 1959).

Family CALCIOSOLENIACEAE Kamptner 1937

Genus CALCIOSOLENIA Gran 1912

Comment: Isolated coccoliths of early species are included in the form-genus *Scapholithus*, (*q.v.*). **Extant.**

Genus SCAPHOLITHUS Deflandre 1954

First, Tert Dan: unnamed species, Clayton Fm, Alabama (Bramlette & Martini 1964).

Extant (isolated coccoliths of *Calciosolenia* etc.).

Comment: Frequent in Quat Holo deep-sea oozes; rare in Tert.

Family THORACOSPHAERACEAE Schiller 1930

Genus THORACOSPHAERA Kamptner 1927

First, Cret Maestr: *T. operculata* Bramlette & Martini, Prairie Bluff Fm, Alabama (Bramlette & Martini 1964). **Extant.**

Family DISCOASTERACEAE

(= Discoasteridae Tan 1927)

Genus DISCOASTER Tan 1927

First, Tert Paleoc: *D. helianthus* Bramlette & Sullivan, Thanet Sands, England; Lodo Fm, Unit 1, California (Bramlette & Sullivan 1961).

Last, Tert Plioc: *D. brouweri* Tan, deep-sea cores up to Plioc-Pleist boundary, Atlantic and Pacific (Ericson *et al.* 1963; Riedel *et al.* 1963; Wray & Ellis 1965).

Genus DISCOASTEROIDES Bramlette & Sullivan 1961

First, Tert Paleoc: *D. megastypus* Bramlette & Sullivan, Lodo Fm, Unit 1, California (Bramlette & Sullivan 1961).

Last, Tert M. Eoc: *D. kuepperi* (Stradner), Lutetian marls, Mattsee, Austria (Stradner 1961).

Comment: Re-worked in Yazoo Form., Tert U. Eoc, of Mississippi (Levin 1965).

Genus MARTHASTERITES Deflandre 1959

First, Cret Turon: *M. furcatus* Deflandre, Borehole Ameis 1, Austria (Stradner 1963).

Last, Tert L. Eoc: *M. tribrachiatus* (Bramlette & Riedel), Lodo Fm, Unit 3, California (Bramlette & Riedel 1954); London Clay, England (Bramlette & Sullivan 1961).

Comment: Re-worked in Tert Olig and Mioc, Austria (Stradner & Papp 1961).

Genera INCERTAE SEDIS

Genus BIANTHOLITHUS Bramlette & Martini 1964

First and **Last,** Tert Dan: *B. sparsus* Bramlette & Martini, U. Dan Chalk, Copenhagen. Denmark; and elsewhere (Bramlette & Martini 1964).

Genus BRACHIOLITHUS Noël 1958

First, Jur Tith: *B. quadratus* Noël, and other species, Kef Talrempt, Algeria (Noël 1958).

Last, Cret Valang: species and locality as above.

Genus BUCCULINUS Noël 1956

First and **Last,** Jur Oxf-Kimm: *B. algeriensis* Noël and *B. hirsutus* Noël, Algeria (Noël 1956).

Genus CATINASTER Martini & Bramlette 1963

First and **Last,** Tert M. Mioc: *C. calyculus* and *C. coalitus* Martini & Bramlette, Lengua Fm, Trinidad (Martini & Bramlette 1963).

Genus CERATOLITHUS Kamptner 1950

First, Tert U. Mioc: Unnamed species common in cores from the Experimental Mohole, E. Pacific (Martini & Bramlette 1963).
Last, Quat Holo: *C. cristatus* Kamptner, common in Holo deep-sea oozes; possibly extant, but the living organism is unknown.

Genus CLATHROLITHUS Deflandre 1954

First, Tert Palaeoc: *C. ellipticus* Deflandre, Lodo Fm, Unit 2, California (Bramlette & Sullivan 1961).
Last, Tert M. Eoc: *C. minutus* Bramlette & Sullivan, Domengine Sst., California (Sullivan 1965).

Genus COCCOLITHITES Kamptner 1955

An artificial genus for the temporary reception of imperfectly known fossil coccoliths whose status remains doubtful. Its time-range is equal to that of the families considered above (Jur Hett to Quat Holo).

Genus CORANNULUS Stradner 1962

First and **Last,** Tert U. Eoc: *C. germanicus* and *C. arenarius* Stradner, boreholes in N. Germany; Bruderndorf, Austria (Stradner 1962).

Genus COROLLITHION Stradner 1961

First, Cret Turon: *C. signum* and *C. exiguum* Stradner, Salzburg, Austria (Stradner 1963).
Last, Cret Maestr: *C. exiguum* Stradner, U. Maestr Chalk, Holland (Bramlette & Martini 1964).

Genus CYLINDRALITHUS Bramlette & Martini 1964

First, Cret L. Maestr: *C. serratus* Bramlette & Martini, Gulpen Chalk, Holland (Bramlette & Martini 1964).
Last, Cret U. Maestr: *C. gallicus* (Stradner), Prairie Bluff Fm, Alabama (Bramlette & Martini 1964).

Genus FASCICULITHUS Bramlette & Sullivan 1961

First and **Last,** Tert Palaeoc: *F. involutus* Bramlette & Sullivan, Lodo Fm, Unit 2, California (Bramlette & Sullivan 1961).

Genus GONIOLITHUS Deflandre 1957

First, Cret L. Maestr: *G. fluckigeri* Deflandre, Ripley Fm, Alabama (Martini 1964).
Last, Tert M. Eoc: *G. fluckigeri* Deflandre, boreholes in NW Germany (Martini 1964). Also re-worked in Tert Olig.

Genus GUTTILITHION Stradner 1962

First and **Last,** Tert U.Eoc: *G. cassum* Stradner, Bruderndorf, Austria (Stradner 1962).

Genus HELIOLITHUS Bramlette & Sullivan 1961

First, Tert Paleoc: *H. riedeli* Bramlette & Sullivan, Lodo Fm, Unit 1, California; Thanet Sands, England (Bramlette & Sullivan 1961).
Last, Tert M. Eoc: *H. helianthus* Hay & Towe, Donzacq, France (Hay & Towe 1962).

Genus HEXALITHUS Gardet 1955

First, Jur Bath: *H. lecali* Gardet, Austria (Stradner 1963).
Last, Jur Tith: *H. hexalithus* Noël, Kef Talrempt, Algeria (Noël 1956).
Comment: Re-worked in Tert Mioc of Algeria (Gardet 1955).

Genus ISTHMOLITHUS Deflandre 1954

First, Tert L. Eoc: *I. unipons* Bramlette & Sullivan, Lodo Fm, Unit 3, California (Bramlette & Sullivan 1961).
Last, Tert U. Eoc: *I. recurvus* Deflandre, diatomite in Waiareka Tuffs, Oamaru, New Zealand; Austria, Denmark, Germany and elsewhere (Deflandre & Fert 1954; Martini 1958; Stradner 1964).

Genus LANTERNITHUS Stradner 1962

First and **Last,** Tert U. Eoc: *L. minutus* Stradner, Bruderndorf, Austria (Stradner 1962).

Genus LITHASTRINUS Stradner 1962

First, Cret Haut: *L. septentrionalis* Stradner, Germany (Stradner 1963).
Last, Cret Camp: *L. floralis* Stradner, Haidberg, Austria (Stradner 1962).

Genus LITHOSTROMATION Deflandre 1942

First, Tert M. Eoc: *L. perdurum* Deflandre, Assilina Marls, Holzmannberg, Austria (Stradner & Papp 1961).
Last, Tert U. Mioc: *L. perdurum* Deflandre, Sarmatian, Matzen, Austria, possibly re-worked (Stradner & Papp 1961).

Genus LITHRAPHIDITES Deflandre 1963

First, Cret Apt: *L. carniolensis* Deflandre, Carniol, France (Deflandre 1963). Also Speeton Clay and Sutterby Marl, England
Last, Cret Maestr: *L. quadratus* Bramlette & Martini, Maestr Chalk, Holland (Bramlette & Martini 1964).

Genus LUCIANORHABDUS Deflandre 1959

First, Cret Sant: *L. cayeuxi* Deflandre, Chalk France, England and elsewhere (Deflandre 1959).
Last, Cret L. Maestr: *L. cayeuxi* Deflandre, Chalk, England, Denmark and elsewhere (Bramlette & Martini 1964).
Comment: Confined to Upper Chalk; not recorded Cret Coniac or Cret U. Maestr. Abrupt appearance in rock-forming quantities, and equally abrupt extinction.

Genus MICRORHABDULUS Deflandre 1959

First, Cret Turon: *M. nodosus* Stradner, Klementer Schichten, Austria (Stradner 1963).
Last, Cret Maestr: *M. stradneri* Bramlette & Martini, Maestr Chalk, Holland, and elsewhere (Bramlette & Martini 1964).

Genus MICULA Vekshina 1959

First, Cret Turon: *M. staurophora* (Gardet) Chalk, Rouen, France (Caratini 1963).
Last, Tert U. Eoc: *M. swasticoides* (Martini), boreholes in N. Germany (Martini & Stradner 1960).

Genus PYXOLITHUS Deflandre 1954

First and **Last,** Jur Oxf: *P. problematicus*, Oxfordian Marls, Calvados, France (Deflandre & Fert 1954).

Genus RHOMBOASTER Bramlette & Sullivan 1961

First and **Last,** Tert Palaeoc: *R. cuspis* Bramlette & Sullivan, Lodo Fm, Unit 2, California (Bramlette & Sullivan 1961).

Genus SPHENOLITHUS Deflandre 1952

First, Tert L. Eoc: *S. radians* Deflandre, Lodo Fm, Unit 3, California (Bramlette & Sullivan 1961).

Last, Tert U. Mioc: *S. abies* Deflandre, El Medhi, Algeria (Deflandre & Fert 1954).

Genus STEPHANOLITHION Deflandre 1939

First, Jur Bajoc: *S. speciosum* Deflandre, Tagremaret, Algeria (Noël 1956).

Last, Cret Maestr: *S.* cf. *laffittei* Noël, Maestricht Chalk, Holland (Bramlette & Martini 1964).

Genus TETRALITHUS Gardet 1955

First, Jur Toarc: *T. pyramidus* Gardet, Tagremaret, Algeria (Noël 1956).

Last, Tert Palaeoc: *T. quadratus* Stradner, Eitelgraben nr. Salzburg, Austria (Stradner & Papp 1961).

Comment: Extensively re-worked in Tert, e.g. Molasse of Vienna Basin, Sahelian of N. Africa.

Genus TROCHOASTER Klumpp 1953

First, Tert L. Eoc: *T. operosus* (Deflandre), Lodo Fm, Unit 3, California (Sullivan 1965).

Last, Tert U. Eoc: *T. simplex* Klumpp, Kiel, Germany (Klumpp 1953).   [M.B.]

REFERENCES

ARKHANGELSKI, A. D. 1912. [Upper Cretaceous deposits of east European Russia.] *Mater. Geol. Ross.*, **25**, 1–631 [in Russian].

BALDINI BEKE, M. 1964. [Unterkretazische Coccolithophoriden Fauna aus Ungarn.] *Földt. Évk.* [for 1962], 133–44. [In Hungarian with German summary].

BLACK, M. 1964. Cretaceous and Tertiary coccoliths from Atlantic seamounts. *Palaeontology*, **7**, 306–16.

—— 1965. Coccoliths. *Endeavour*, **24**, 131–137.

—— 1967. New names for some coccolith taxa. *Proc. geol. Soc. Lond.*, no. 1637, 139–145.

—— 1967c. The genus *Neococcolithes* Sujkowski. [In preparation].

—— & BARNES, B. 1959. The structure of coccoliths from the English Chalk. *Geol. Mag.*, **96**, 321–8.

BRAMLETTE, M. N. & MARTINI E. 1964. The great change in calcareous nannoplankton fossils between the Maestrichtian and Danian. *Micropaleontology*, **10**, 271–322.

—— & RIEDEL, W. R. 1954. Stratigraphic value of discoasters and some other microfossils related to recent coccolithophores. *J. Paleont.*, **28**, 385–403.

—— & SULLIVAN, F. R. 1961. Coccolithophorids and related nannoplankton of the early Tertiary in California. *Micropaleontology*, **7**, 129–88.

CARATINI, C. 1963. Etude des coccolithes du Cénomanien supérieur et du Turonien de la région de Rouen. *Publication du laboratoire de Géologie Appliquée, Université d'Alger*, 5–61.

COHEN, C. L. D. 1965. Coccoliths and discoasters from Adriatic bottom sediments. *Leid. geol. Meded.*, **35**, 1–44.

DEFLANDRE, G. 1959. Sur les nannofossiles calcaires et leur systématique. *Revue Micropaléont.*, **2**, 127–52.

—— & FERT, C. 1954. Observations sur les coccolithophoridés actuels et fossiles en microscopie ordinaire et électronique. *Annls Paléont.*, **40**, 117–76.

—— 1963 Sur les Microrhabdulidés, famille nou velle denannofossiles calcaires. *C. R. Acad. Sci.* **256**, 3484–6.

ERICSON, D. B., EWING, M., & WOLLIN, G. 1963. Pliocene-Pleistocene boundary in deep-sea sediments. *Science, N.Y.*, **139**, 727–37.

GARDET, M. 1955. Contribution à l'étude des coccolithes des terrains néogènes de l'Algérie. *Publs. Serv. Carte géol. Algér.*, N.S., Bull. **5**, 447–550.

GORKA, H. 1957. Coccolithophoridae z gornego Mastrychtu Polski Sredkowej. *Acta palaeont. pol.*, **2**, 236–84.

HAY, W. W. & TOWE, K. M. 1962. Electron microscopic examination of some coccoliths from Donzacq (France). *Eclog. geol. Helv.*, **55**, 497–518.

KAMPTNER, E. 1948. Coccolithen aus dem Torton des Inneralpinen Wiener Beckens. *Sber. öst. Akad. Wiss.*, Abt. 1, **157**, 1–16.

—— 1955. Fossile Coccolithineen-Skelettreste aus Insulinde. *Verh. K. ned. Akad. Wet.*, Afd. natuurk. (2), **50** no. 2, 1–87.

—— 1963. Coccolithineen-Skelettreste aus Tiefseeablagerungen des Pazifischen Ozeans. *Annln naturh. Mus. Wien*, **66**, 139–204.

KLUMPP, B. 1953. Beitrag zur Kenntnis der Mikrofossilien des Mittleren und Oberen Eozän. *Palaeontographica*, Abt. B., **103**, 377–406.

LEVIN, H. L. 1965. Coccolithoporidae and related microfossils from the Yazoo Formation (Eocene) of Mississippi. *J. Paleont.*, **39**, 265–72.

MARKALI, J., & PAASCHE, E. 1955. On two species of *Umbellosphaera*, a new marine coccolithophorid genus. *Nytt Mag. Bot.*, **4**, 95–100.

MARTINI, E. 1958. Discoasteriden und verwandte Formen in NW-deutschen Eozän (Coccolithophorida) I Teil. *Senckenberg. leth.*, **39**, 353–88.

—— 1959. Der stratigraphische Wert von nannofossilien im nordwestdeutschen Tertiär. *Erdöl Kohle*, **12**, 137–40.

—— 1960. Braarudosphaeriden, Discoasteriden und verwandte Formen aus dem Rupelton des Mainzer Beckens. *Notizbl. hess. Landesamt. Bodenforsch. Wiesbaden*, **88**, 65–87.

—— 1964. Ein vollständiges Gehäuse von *Goniolithus fluckigeri* Deflandre, *Neues Jb. Geol. Paläeont.*, *Abh.*, **119**, 19–21.

—— & BRAMLETTE, M. N. 1963. Calcareous nannoplankton from the Experimental Mohole drilling. *J. Paleont.*, **37**, 845–56.

NOËL, D. 1956. Coccolithes des terrains jurassiques de l'Algérie. *Publs Serv. Carte géol. Algér.*, N.S., Bull. **8**, 303–45.

—— 1958. Etude des coccolithes du Jurassique et du Crétacé inférieur. *Publs Serv. Carte géol. Algér.*, N.S. Bull, **20**, 155–96.

—— 1965. Note préliminaire sur les coccolithes jurassiques. *Cah. Micropaléont.*, Sér. 1, **1**, 1–12. C.N.R.S., Paris.

RIEDEL, W. R., BRAMLETTE, M. N., & PARKER, F. L. 1963. "Pliocene-Pleistocene" boundary in deep-sea sediments. *Science, N.Y.*, **140.**, 1238–40.

STRADNER, H. 1961. Vorkommen von Nannofossilien im Mesozoikum und Alttertiär. *Erdöl-Z.*, 77, 77–88.

STRADNER, H. 1962. Uber neue und wenig bekannte Nannofossilien aus Kreide und Alttertiär, *Verh. Bundesanst. Wien*, **2**, 363–377.

—— 1963. New contributions to Mesozoic stratigraphy by means of nannofossils. *6th Wld. Petrol. Congr.*, Paper 4 [Preprint], 1–16.

—— 1964. Die Ergebnisse der Aufschlussarbeiten der OMV AG in der Molassezone Niederösterreichs in dem Jahren 1957–1963. Teil III: Ergebnisse der Nannofossilien-Untersuchungen. *Erdöl-Z.*, **80**, 133–139.

—— & PAPP, A. 1961. Tertiäre Discoasteriden aus Osterreich und deren stratigraphische Bedentung. *Jb. geol. Bundesanst. Wien*, Sonderband **7**, 1–160.

Sujkowski, Zb. 1931. [Etude pétrographique du Crétacé de Pologne. La série de Lublin et sa comparaison avec la craie blanche.] *Bull. serv. géol. Pologne*, **6**, 485–628 [in Polish with French summary].

Sullivan, F. R. 1965. Lower Tertiary nanno-plankton from the California Coast Ranges. II Eocene. *Univ. Calif. Publs geol. Sci.*, **53**, 1–75.

Wray, J. L. & Ellis, C. H. 1965. Discoaster extinction in neritic sediments, northern Gulf of Mexico. *Bull. Am. Ass. Petrol. Geol.*, **49**, 98–9.

Class BACILLARIOPHYCEAE (Diatoms)

Families as in Papenfuss 1955, except that Anaulaceae and Euodiaceae are included in Biddulphiaceae. The Diatom-like organisms from Camb, Tannu-Ola Mts, U.S.S.R., reported by Vologdin (1962) are impossible to assign to any group. As well as the doubtful records from Jur Toarc under Coscinodiscaceae, Cayeux 1892 reported unidentified diatoms from Jur Oxf, Ardennes, France and Belgium and this record also is doubtful.

Family COSCINODISCACEAE Kützing 1844

First, Cret Apt-Turon: *Coscinodiscus* Ehrenberg, Rolling Downs Fm, Queensland, Australia (Dun, Rands & David 1901). Also Cret Alb: *Craspedodiscus incurvus* Forti & Schulz and four other species (three other genera), Gault, Hanover, Germany (Forti & Schulz 1932). **Extant.**
Records from Jur Toarc (Rüst 1885; Rothpletz 1897) are not undoubted diatoms.

Family ASTEROLAMPRACEAE H. L. Smith 1872

First, Cret Turon: *Actinoptychus* Ehrenberg, U. Turon, Valtirov, near Usti nad Labem, Czechoslovakia (Wiesner 1936). **Extant.**

Family EUPODISCACEAE Kützing 1844

First, Cret Turon: *Aulacodiscus* Ehrenberg, U. Turon, Valtirov, near Usti nad Labem, Czechoslovakia (Wiesner 1936). **Extant.**

Family RHIZOSOLENIACEAE De Toni 1890

First, Cret Coniac-Campan: *Pseudopyxilla aculeata* Jousé and four species of *Pterotheca* Grunow, Senonian, Northern Urals, U.S.S.R. (Jousé 1951b). Hanna's (1927) records of *Kentrodiscus* Pantocsek (2spp), *Pseudopyxilla russica* (Pantocsek) Forti and *Pterotheca* Grunow (2spp) from Moreno Shale, California may be contemporary but this formation is probably Cret Maestr. All above are almost certainly spores of Rhizosoleniaceae. First record of ordinary frustules L.Mioc: *Rhizosolenia inermis* Castracane and two other species, Sendai lst, Japan (Brun & Tempère 1889, p. 73). *Dactyliosolen priscus* Forti & Schulz 1932, Cret Alb, is very doubtfully Rhizosoleniaceae, but *Ditylum cornutum* Forti & Schulz 1932, Cret Alb, Gault, Hanover, is probably spore of Rhizosoleniaceae. **Extant.**

Family CHAETOCERACEAE H. L. Smith 1872

First, Cret Coniac-Campan: *Goniothecium odontella* Ehrenberg, Senonian, Northern Urals (Jousé 1951b). This is almost certainly spore of Chaetoceraceae. First record of ordinary frustules L.Eoc.: *Chaetoceros clavigerum* Grunow, 1884, Franz-Josefs Land, Jutland, and Ulyanovsk Province, U.S.S.R. (for date seen Reinhold 1945). **Extant.**

Family BIDDULPHIACEAE Kützing 1844

First, Cret Turon: *Biddulphia* Gray and *Triceratium* Ehrenberg, U. Turon, Valtirov, near Usti nad Labem, Czechoslovakia (Wiesner 1936). **Extant.**

Family RUTILARIACEAE Pantocsek ex De Toni 1894

First, U. Eoc: *Rutilaria radiata* Grove & Sturt and *Rutilaria lanceolata* Grove & Sturt, Waiareka Volcanic Fm, Oamaru, South Island, New Zealand (Grove & Sturt 1886; for formation and date see Gage 1957); three other species of *Rutilaria* occur in this deposit. Also *Rutilaria* sp. (misidentified as *R.longicornis* Brun & Tempère), Kamyshlov, Sverdlovsk Province, U.S.S.R. (Jousé 1955). **Extant.**

Family DIATOMACEAE Dumortier 1823

First, Palaeoc: *Grunowiella palaeocenica* Jousé, *Raphoneis elliptica* Jousé and *Sceptroneis wittii* Jousé, E. slope of northern Urals, U.S.S.R., and *Sceptroneis grunowii* Anissimova, Ulyanovsk and Sverdlovsk provinces, U.S.S.R. (Jousé 1951a). **Extant.**

Family EUNOTIACEAE Kützing 1844

First: U.Eoc: *Eunotia striata* (Grove & Sturt) Grunow 1888, Waiareka Volcanic Fm, Oamaru, South Island, New Zealand (Grove & Sturt 1887a as *Euodia striata* Grove & Sturt; for formation and date see Gage 1957). **Extant.**

Family ACHNANTHACEAE Kützing 1844

First, U.Eoc: *Cocconeis costata* Gregory, *Cocconeis grevillei* W. Smith (as *Campyloneis argus* Grunow), *Cocconeis nodulifer* Grove & Sturt and *Cocconeis psuedomarginata* Gregory, Waiareka Volcanic Fm, Oamaru, South Island, New Zealand (Grove & Sturt 1886, 1887b,c; for formation and date see Gage 1957). **Extant.**

Cocconeis barbadensis Grev. and *Cocconeis naviculoides* Grev. are Naviculaceae.

Family NAVICULACEAE Kützing 1844

First, L.Eoc: *Navicula hennedyi* W. Smith and *Navicula praetexta* Ehrenberg (Witt 1885) and *Navicula simbirskiana* Pantocsek 1889. Ulyanovsk Province, U.S.S.R. (for date see Reinhold 1945). **Extant.**

Family EPITHEMIACEAE Grunow 1860

First, L.Mioc: *Epithemia argus* Kützing and nine other species, Aquitanian, Ménat, Cantal, and Fontgrand, Lozère, France (Lauby 1910, p. 336). **Extant.**

Family NITZSCHIACEAE Grunow 1860

First, U.Eoc: *Nitzschia grovei* Grunow 1888 (as *Amphiprora rugosa* Petit by Grove & Sturt 1887b) and *Nitzschia grundleri* Grunow (Grove & Sturt 1887b), Waiareka Volcanic Fm, Oamaru, South Island, New Zealand (for formation and age see Gage 1957). *Nitzschia antiqua* Grove & Sturt is not Nitzschiaceae. **Extant.**

Family SURIRELLACEAE Kützing 1844

First, U.Olig: *Campylodiscus thuretii* Brébisson, *Surirella brunii* Héribaud and *Surirella striatula* Turpin, U. Stampian, Puy-de-Mur, France (Lauby 1910, pp.338–340). **Extant.** [R.R.]

REFERENCES

BRUN, J. & TEMPÈRE, J. 1889. Diatomées fossiles du Japon. *Mém. Soc. Phys. Hist. nat. Genève*, **30**(9), 1–75, pl. 1–9.

CAYEUX, L. 1892. Sur la présence de nombreuses Diatomées dans les gaizes jurassiques et crétacées du Bassin de Paris. De l'existence de Radiolaires dans les gaizes crétacées de ce même Bassin. *Ann. Soc. géol. Nord*, **20**, 57–60.

DUN, W. S., RANDS, W. H. & DAVID, T. W. E. 1901. Note on the occurrence of Diatoms, Radiolaria, and Infusoria in the Rolling Downs Formation (Lower Cretaceous), Queensland. *Proc. Linn. Soc. N.S.W.*, **26**, 299–309, pl. 17–19.

FORTI, A. & SCHULZ, P, 1932. Erste Mitteilung über Diatomeen aus dem Hannoverschen Gault. *Beih. bot. Zbl.*, **50**, 241–246, taf. 3.

GAGE, M. 1957. The Geology of Waitaki Subdivision. *Bull. geol. Surv. N.Z.* new ser., **55**, 1–135.

GROVE, E. & STURT, G. 1886. On a fossil marine diatomaceous deposit from Oamaru, Otago, New Zealand. Part I. *J. Quekett microsc. Club, ser.* 2, **2**, 321–330, pl. 18–19.

—— & —— 1887a. Ibid. Part II. *J, Quekett microsc. Club, ser.* 2, **3**, 7–12, pl. 2–3.

—— & —— 1887b. Ibid. Part III. *J. Quekett microsc. Club, ser.* 2, **3**, 63–78, pl. 5–6.

—— & —— 1887c. Ibid. Appendix. *J. Quekett microsc. Club, ser.* 2, **3**, 131–148, pl. 10–14.

GRUNOW, A. 1884. Die Diatomeen von Franz Josefs-Land. *Denkschr. Akad. Wiss. Wien*, **48**, 53–109, taf. 1–5.

—— 1888. [Review of] GROVE, E. and STURT, G., On a fossil marine diatomaceous deposit from Oamaru, Otago, New Zealand . . . Part III and appendix. *Bot. Zbl.*, **34**, 34–41.

HANNA, G. D. 1927. Cretaceous Diatoms from California. *Occ. Pap. Calif. Acad. Sci.*, **13**, 1–48, pl. 1–5.

JOUSÉ, A. P. 1951a. Diatomeae aetatis Palaeocaeni Uralh septentrionalis. *Notul. syst. Inst. cryptog. Horti bot. petropol.*, **7**, 24–42.

—— 1951b. Diatomeae et Silicoflagellatae aetatis Cretae superne e montibus Uralensibus septentrionalis. *Notul. syst. Inst. cryptog. Horti bot. petropol.*, **7**, 42–65.

—— 1955. Species novae Diatomacearum aetatis Paleogenae. *Notul. syst. Inst. cryptog. Horti bot. petropol.*, **10**, 81–103.

LAUBY, A. 1910. Recherches paléophytologiques dans le Massif Central. *Bull. Serv. Carte géol. Fr.*, **20**, 1–398, p. 1–15.

PANTOCSEK, J. 1889. *Beiträge zur Kenntniss der Fossilen Bacillarien Ungarns*, 2. 123 pp., 30 pl. Nagy-Tapolcsány.

PAPENFUSS, G. F. 1955. Classification of the Algae. *In*, *A Century of Progress in the Natural Sciences*, 115–224. California Academy of Sciences, San Francisco.

REINHOLD, T. 1945. Het voorkomen van Diatomeen-houdend Palaeoceen-Eoceen. *Verh. geol.-mijnb. Genoot. Ned.* (Geol. Ser.), **14**, 391–401.

ROTHPLETZ, A. 1897. Ueber die Flysch-Fucoiden und einige andere fossile Algen, sowie über liasische Diatomeen führende Hornschwämme. *Z. dt. geol. Ges.*, **48**, 854–914, taf. 22–24.

RÜST, D. 1885. Beiträge zur Kenntniss der fossilen Radiolarien aus Gesteinen des Jura. *Palaeontographica*, **31**, 271–321, taf. 26–45.

VOLOGDIN, A. G. 1962. Diatomoobraznyye organizmy kembriya khrebta Tannu-Ola v Tuve. *Dokl. Akad. nauk SSSR*, **146**, 909–912. (Engl. Transl. in *Dokl. Akad. Sci. U.S.S.R., Earth Sci. Sect.* **146**, 178–181.)

WIESNER, H. 1936. Sur la découverte de Diatomées et autres microfossiles peu connus dans le crétacé supérieur de la Bohême. *Annls. Protist.* **5**, 151–156, pl. 6–7.

WITT, O. N. 1885. Ueber den Polierschiefer von Archangelsk-Kurojedowo im Gouv. Simbirsk. *Zap. imp. miner. Obschch.*, ser. 2, **22**, 137–177, taf. 6–12.

Class DINOPHYCEAE Pascher

Fossil dinoflagellates fall into three groups, according to shell composition. Genera with siliceous shells are known, both living and fossil, and with calcareous shells in the fossil state; both groups have been little studied and appear rare. In contrast, genera with shells of organic constitution are a major component of the present-day plankton; and fossils of similar composition are comparably abundant.

Dinoflagellates were first recorded fossil by Ehrenberg (1838a) and were long thought distinct from a group of spiny microfossils of similar constitution and occurrence, latterly termed "hystrichospheres". However, in 1961 Evitt conclusively demonstrated that, on the basis of ornament pattern and openings of constant shape and position (archaeopyles), the majority of post-Palaeozoic "hystrichospheres" and of the previously recognized dinoflagellates were in fact the abandoned cysts of dinoflagellates (Evitt 1961b).

Until recently, palynologists have attempted to fit the fossils into the classification system used by neontologists (cf. Eisenack 1961b, 1964). However, since cysts and motile stages may prove dissimilar in morphology when linkage can be proved; since a single motile "genus" may form more than one type of cyst; since a single type of cyst may be produced by more than one motile genus; and since the affinities of many fossil genera are unlikely ever to be demonstrated, it is

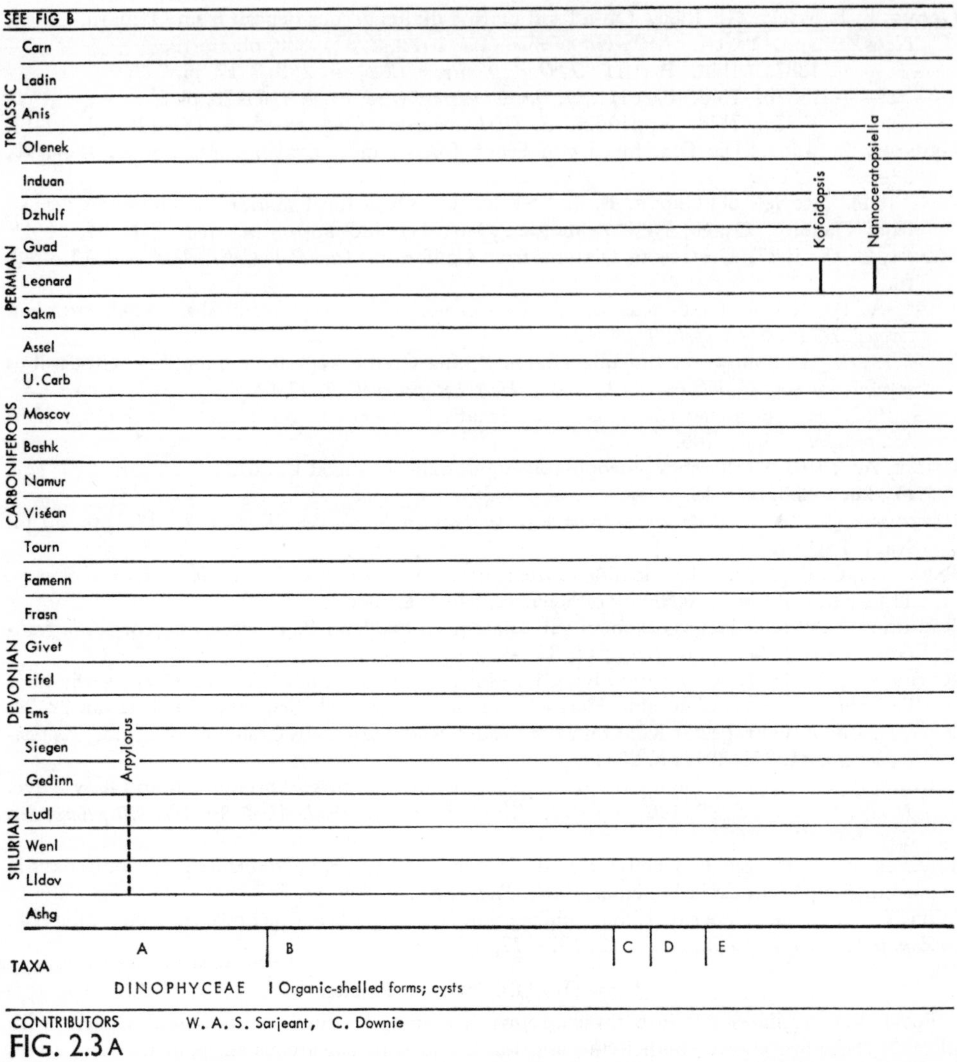

| | | A | B | | | | C | D | E |

DINOPHYCEAE I Organic-shelled forms; cysts

CONTRIBUTORS W. A. S. Sarjeant, C. Downie

FIG. 2.3 A

clear that the existing classification is in urgent need of overhaul. Establishment of a separate classification for the cysts, based on morphology alone, is clearly necessary; since the nomenclatural rules preclude use of morphogenera as types for families, a different system of suprageneric groupings must be utilized.

The earliest undoubted dinoflagellate is *Arpylorus antiquus*, from the Silurian of Tunisia, a cyst characterized by a precingular archaeopyle and tabulation vestiges (Calandra 1964). No other dinoflagellates have been certainly identified until the Permian. (Belloy Formation, Canada-Jansonius 1962; Wellington Formation, Leonard., Kansas-Tasch 1963a). It is probable that a number of acritarch genera are in fact dinoflagellate cysts; but this is not capable of conclusive demonstration. Since only a single genus would be featured, no distribution table is therefore given for the Lower Palaeozoic.

References in the text are quoted in the form employed by Downie and Sarjeant (1964). [Norris & Sarjeant (1965) and Oyen (1964) have also been used. Ed.].

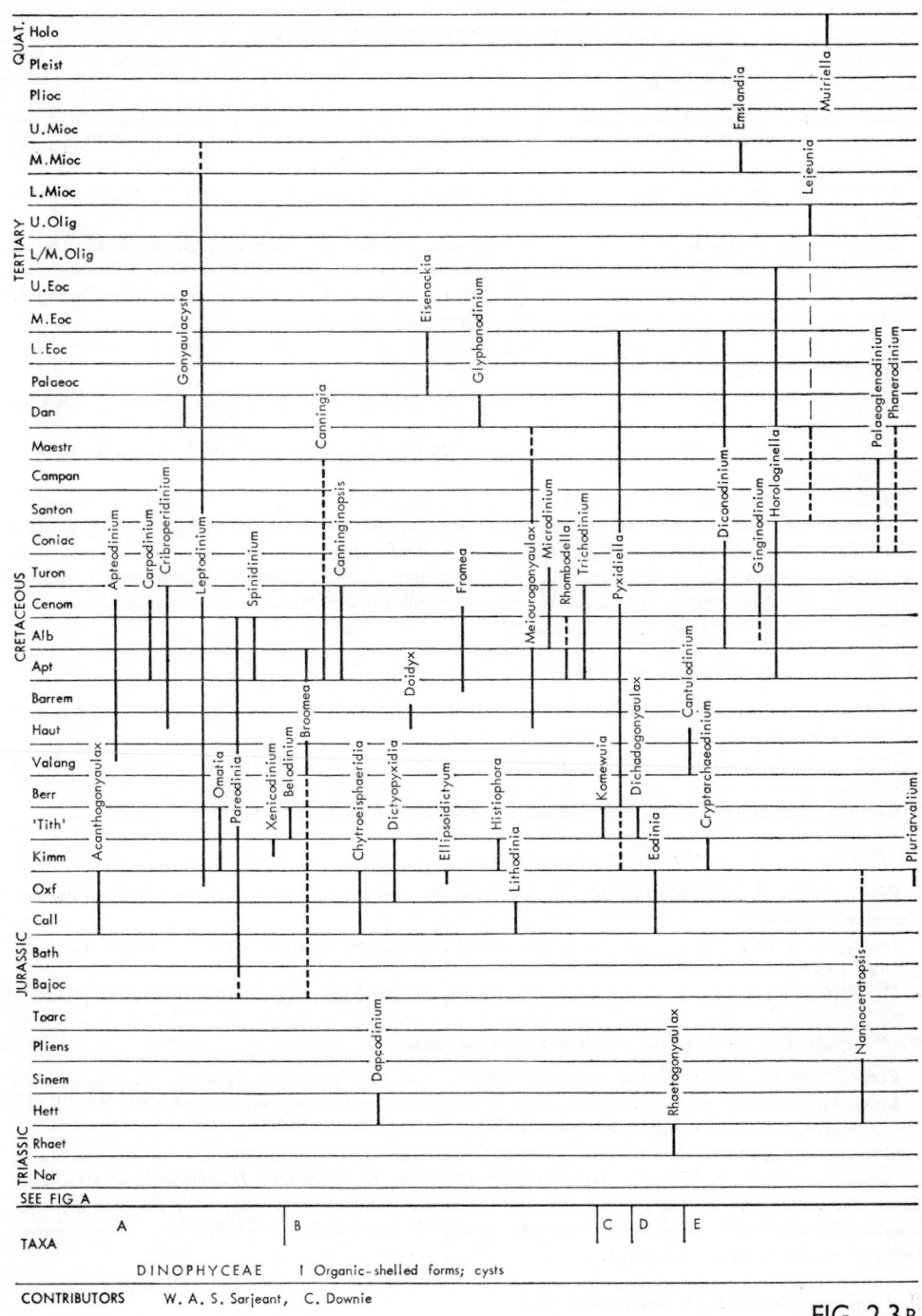

FIG. 2.3 B

197

The Fossil Record, Part II

A. Proximate cysts: archaeopyle precingular

First, Sil: *Arpylorus antiquus* Calandra, Mecheguig I boring, Tunisia. (Calandra 1964). No subsequent records till Jur Baj; *Gonyaulacysta cladophora* (Deflandre), cherts (Valensi 1953). At peak abundance Jur Oxf-Cret Alb.

Last, M. Mioc: *Gonyaulacysta tenuitabulata* (Gerlach), N.W. Germany (Gerlach 1961)-possibly reworked?

Constituent genera, *Acanthogonyaulax* Sarjeant, *Apteodinium* Eisenack, *Arpylorus* Calandra, *Carpodinium* Cookson & Eisenack, *Cribroperidinium* Sarjeant, *Gonyaulacysta* Deflandre emend. Sarjeant, *Leptodinium* Deflandre emend. Sarjeant, ?*Omatia* Cookson & Eisenack, *Pareodinia* Deflandre, *Spinidinium* Cookson & Eisenack, ?*Xenicodinium* Klement.

B. Proximate cysts: archaeopyle apical

First, Jur Hett: *Dapcodinium priscum* Evitt. Lias Alpha, Denmark (Evitt 1961a). Probably at peak abundance Cret Valang-Alb.

Last, L. Eoc: *Eisenackia crassitabulata* Deflandre & Cookson, Dilwyn Clay, Victoria (Deflandre & Cookson 1955).

Constituent genera, *Belodinium* Cookson & Eisenack, *Broomea* Cookson & Eisenack, *Canningia* Cookson & Eisenack, *Canninginopsis* Cookson & Eisenack, *Chytroeisphaeridia* Sarjeant, *Dapcodinium* Evitt, *Dictyopyxidia* Eisenack, *Doidyx* Sarjeant, *Eisenackia* Deflandre & Cookson, *Ellipsoidictyum* Klement, *Fromea* Cookson & Eisenack, *Glyphanodinium* Drugg, *Histiophora* Klement, *Lithodinia* Eisenack, *Meiourogonyaulax* Sarjeant, *Microdinium* Cookson & Eisenack, *Rhombodella* Cookson & Eisenack, *Trichodinium* Eisenack & Cookson.

C. Proximate cysts: intercalary archaeopyle

First, U. Jur: *Pyxidiella pandora* Cookson & Eisenack, Dingo Siltstone, W. Australia; Era River district, Papua (Cookson & Eisenack 1958).

Last, L. Eoc: *Pyxidiella scrobiculata* (Deflandre & Cookson), Dilwyn Clay, Victoria (Deflandre & Cookson 1955).

Constituent genera, *Komewuia* Cookson & Eisenack, *Pyxidiella* Cookson & Eisenack.

D. Proximate cysts: cingular or epitractal archaeopyle

First, Trias Rhaet: *Rhaetogonyaulax chaloneri, R. rhaetica* Sarjeant, Cotham Beds, England (Sarjeant 1963).

Last, Jur 'Tith': *Dichadogonaulax pannea* and *D. schizoblata* (Norris), Lower Purbeck, England (Norris 1965).

Constituent genera, *Dichadogonyaulax* Sarjeant, *Eodinia* Eisenack, *Rhaetogonyaulax* Sarjeant.

E. Proximate cysts: mode of archaeopyle formation uncertain

First, Perm Leonard: *Nannoceratopsiella permiana* Tasch, Wellington, Kansas. (Tasch 1963a).

Last, Holo: *Muiriella plioplax* Churchill & Sarjeant, freshwater peats dated (500–3000 B.C.) Western Australia (Churchill & Sarjeant 1963).

Constituent genera, *Cantulodinium* Alberti, *Cryptarchaeodinium* Deflandre, *Diconodinium* Eisenack & Cookson, *Emslandia* Gerlach, *Ginginodinium* Cookson & Eisenack, *Horologinella* Cookson & Eisenack, *Kofoidopsis* Tasch, *Lejeunia* Gerlach, *Muiriella* Churchill & Sarjeant, *Nannoceratopsiella* Tasch, *Nannoceratopsis* Deflandre emend. Evitt, *Palaeoglenodinium* Deflandre, *Phanerodinium* Deflandre, *Pluriarvalium* Sarjeant.

F. Proximochorate cysts: precingular archaeopyle

First, Jur Oxf: *Hystrichosphaera ramosa* (Ehrenberg), Upper Calcareous Grit, England (Sarjeant 1960c). Continuously abundant since Cret. Barr.   **Extant.**

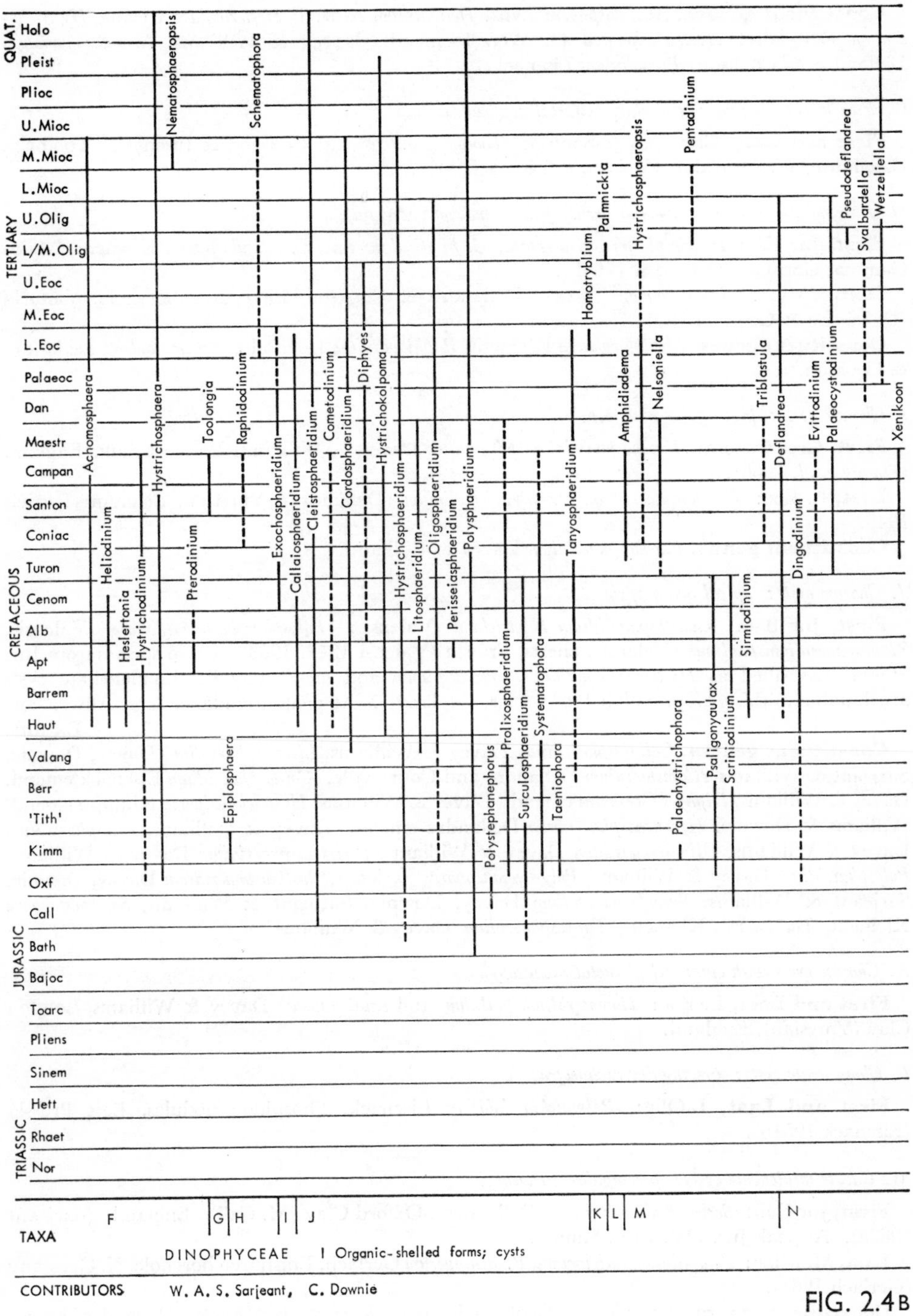
QUAT.
Holo
Pleist
Plioc
U.Mioc
M.Mioc
L.Mioc
TERTIARY
U.Olig
L/M.Olig
U.Eoc
M.Eoc
L.Eoc
Palaeoc
Dan
Maestr
Campan
CRETACEOUS
Santon
Coniac
Turon
Cenom
Alb
Apt
Barrem
Haut
Valang
Berr
'Tith'
Kimm
Oxf
JURASSIC
Call
Bath
Bajoc
Toarc
Pliens
Sinem
Hett
TRIASSIC
Rhaet
Nor
Achomosphaera
Heliodinium
Heslertonia
Hystrichodinium
Hystrichosphaera
Nematosphaeropsis
Pterodinium
Toolongia
Epiplosphaera
Raphidodinium
Schematophora
Exochosphaeridium
Callaiosphaeridium
Cleistosphaeridium
Cometodinium
Cordosphaeridium
Diphyes
Hystrichokolpoma
Hystrichosphaeridium
Litosphaeridium
Oligosphaeridium
Perisseiasphaeridium
Polysphaeridium
Polystephanephorus
Prolixosphaeridium
Surculosphaeridium
Systematophora
Taeniophora
Tanyosphaeridium
Homotryblium
Palmnickia
Amphidiadema
Hystrichosphaeropsis
Nelsoniella
Pentadinium
Palaeohystrichophora
Psaligonyaulax
Scriniodinium
Sirmiodinium
Triblastula
Deflandrea
Dingodinium
Evittodinium
Palaeocystodinium
Pseudodeflandrea
Svalbardella
Wetzeliella
Xenikoon
TAXA
F
G
H
I
J
K
L
M
N
DINOPHYCEAE
I Organic-shelled forms; cysts
CONTRIBUTORS
W. A. S. Sarjeant, C. Downie

FIG. 2.4B

Constituent genera, *Achomosphaera* Evitt, *Heliodinium* Alberti, *Heslertonia* Sarjeant, *Hystrichodinium* Deflandre, *Hystrichosphaera* O. Wetzel emend. Davey & Williams, *Nematosphaeropsis* Deflandre & Cookson, *Pterodinium* Eisenack.

G. Proximochorate cysts: cingular/epitractal archaeopyle

First and **Last,** Cret Coniac-Santon: *Toolongia medusioides* Cookson & Eisenack. Toolonga Calcilutite, W. Australia (Cookson & Eisenack 1960a).

H. Proximochorate cysts: mode of archaeopyle formation uncertain

First, Jur Kimm: *Epiplosphaera areolata, E. bireticulata* and *E. reticulospinosa* Klement, Malm Gamma, Germany (Klement 1960b).

Last, ?Mioc: *Schematophora speciosa* Deflandre & Cookson, Birregurra borehole, Victoria (Deflandre & Cookson 1955).

Constituent genera, *Epiplosphaera* Klement, *Raphidodinium* Deflandre, *Schematophora* Deflandre & Cookson.

I. Chorate cysts: precingular archaeopyle

First, Cret Cenom: *Exochosphaeridium phragmites* Davey & Williams, Lower Chalk, England (Davey *et al.* 1966).

Last, L. Eoc: *Exochosphaeridium pseudhystrichodinium* (Deflandre), Ypresian, Belgium (Pastiels 1948).

Constituent genus, *Exochosphaeridium* Davey & Williams.

J. Chorate cysts: apical archaeopyle

First, Jur Bath: *Cleistosphaeridium polytrichum* (Valensi), ?*Polysphaeridium deflandrei* (Valensi), ?*Polysphaeridium paulinae* (Valensi), cherts, France (Valensi 1947, 1953). [Two species from Jur. Sinem., described as *Hystrichosphaeridium caminuspinum* and *langi*, may be dinoflagellate cysts attributable to this group. (Wall 1965; Lias, England)]. At peak abundance Cret Alb-Paleoc.
Extant.

Constituent genera, *Callaiosphaeridium* Davey & Williams, *Cleistosphaeridium* Davey, Downie, Sarjeant & Williams ?*Cometodinium* Deflandre and Courteville. *Cordosphaeridium* Eisenack emend. Davey & Williams, *Diphyes* Cookson emend. Davey & Williams, *Hystrichokolpoma* Klumpp emend. Williams & Downie, *Hystrichosphaeridium* Deflandre emend. Davey & Williams, *Litosphaeridium* Davey & Williams, *Oligosphaeridium* Davey & Williams, *Perisseiasphaeridium* Davey & Williams, *Polysphaeridium* Davey & Williams, *Polystephanephorus* Sarjeant, *Prolixosphaeridium* Davey, Downie, Sarjeant & Williams, *Surculosphaeridium* Davey, Downie, Sarjeant & Williams, *Systematophora* Klement, *Taeniophora* Klement, *Tanyosphaeridium* Davey & Williams.

K. Chorate cysts with cingular/epitractal archaeopyles

First and Last, L. Eoc: *Homotryblium pallidum* and *tenuispinisum* Davey & Williams, London Clay (Ypresian), England.

L. Chorocavate cysts: precingular archaeopyle

First and Last, L.Olig: *Palmnickia lobifera* Eisenack, Phosphate nodules, East Prussia (Eisenack 1954b).

M. Cavate to bicavate cysts: precingular archaeopyle

First, Jur Call: *Scriniodinium luridum* (Deflandre), Oxford Clay (M. Call.), England. (Sarjeant 1962a). At peak Jur. Oxf.-Cret. Santon.

Last, M. Mioc: *Pentadinium laticinctum, P. taeniagerum* Gerlach, Emsburen borehole, N. Germany (Gerlach 1961).

Constituent genera, *Amphidiadema* Cookson & Eisenack, *Hystrichosphaeropsis* Deflandre emend. Sarjeant, ?*Nelsoniella* Cookson & Eisenack, ?*Palaeohystrichophora* Deflandre emend. Deflandre &

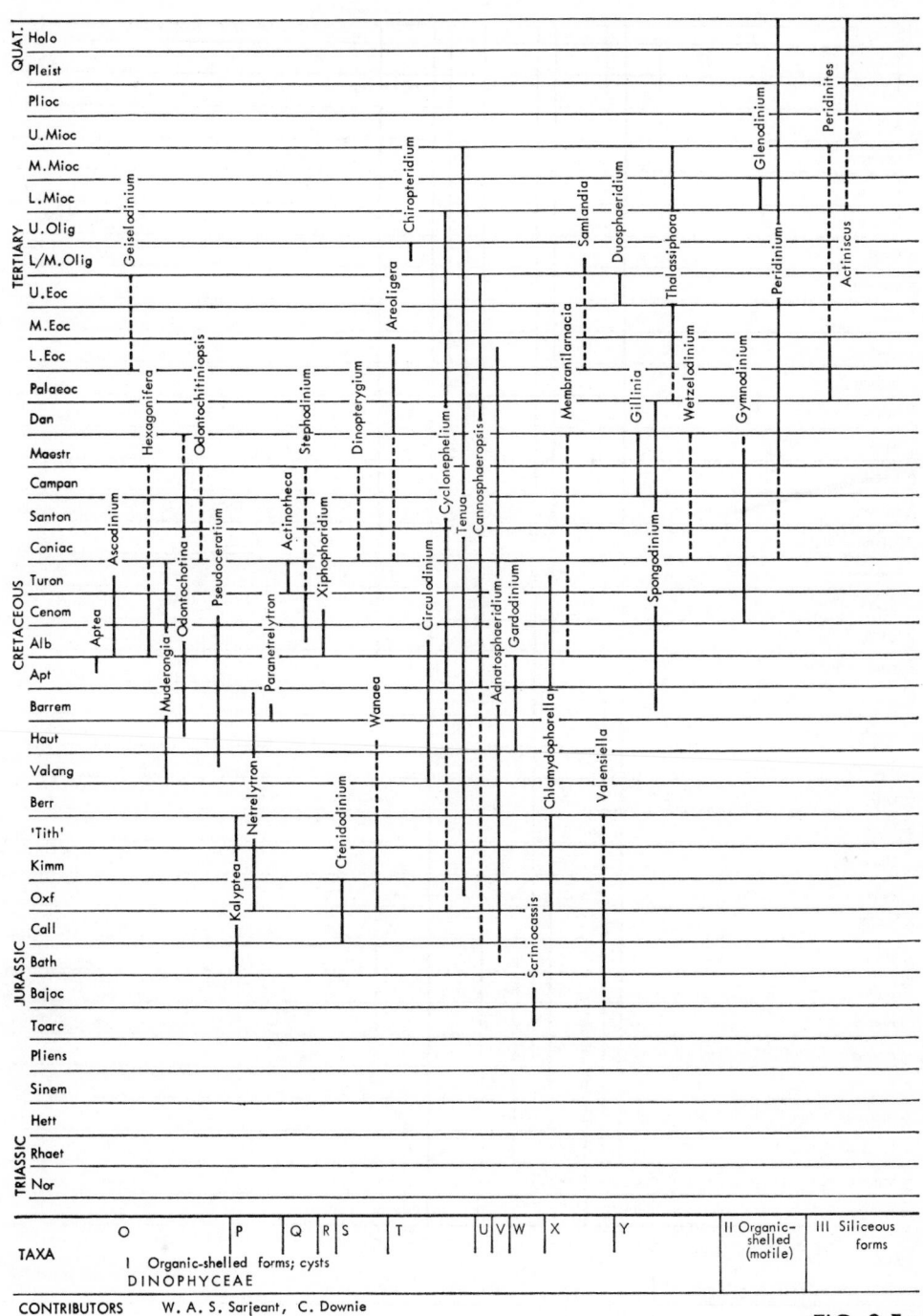

FIG. 2.5 B

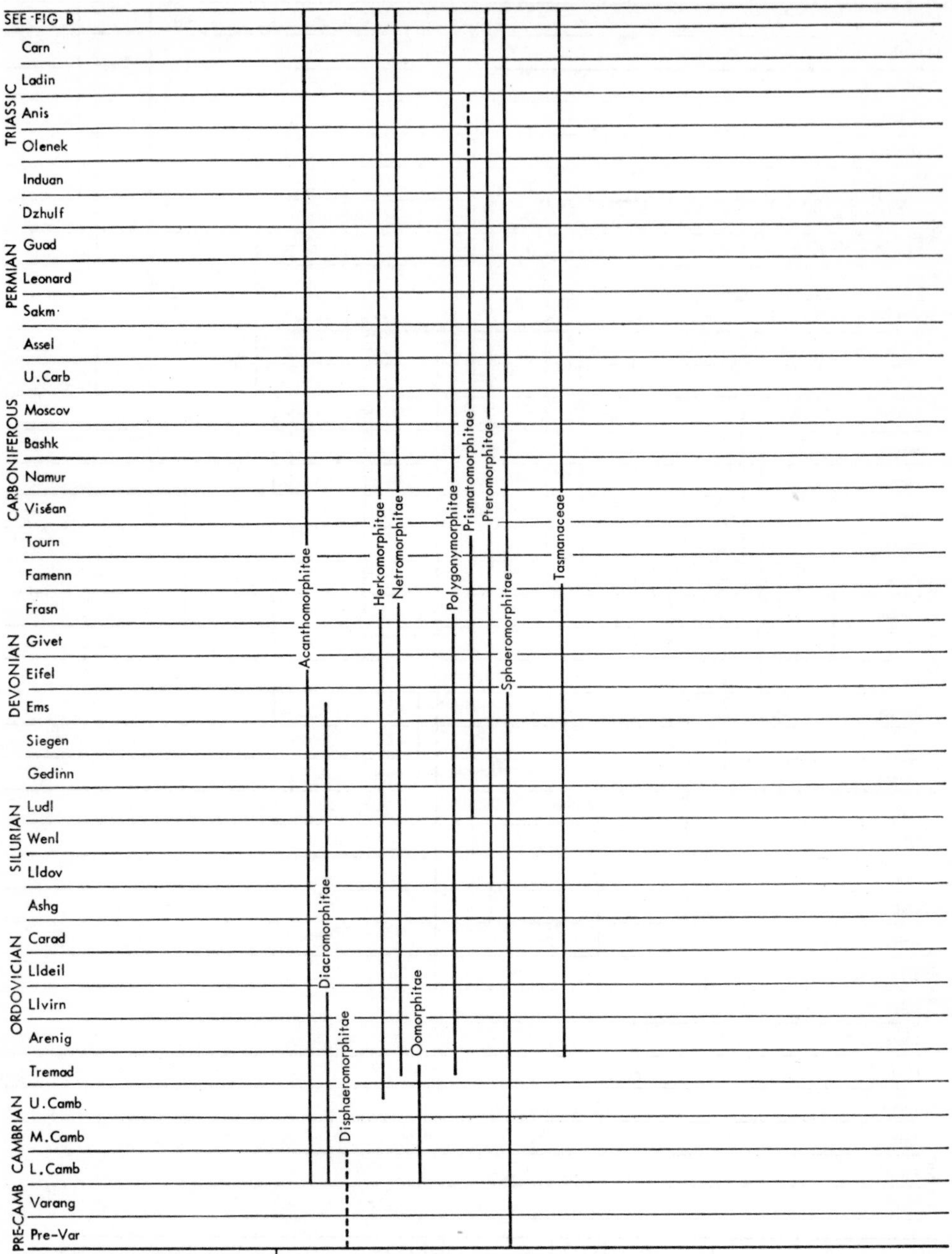

FIG. 2.6A

	TAXA	IV Calcareous forms
		DINOPHYCEAE
		ACRITARCHA
	CONTRIBUTORS	C. Downie, W.A.S.Sarjeant

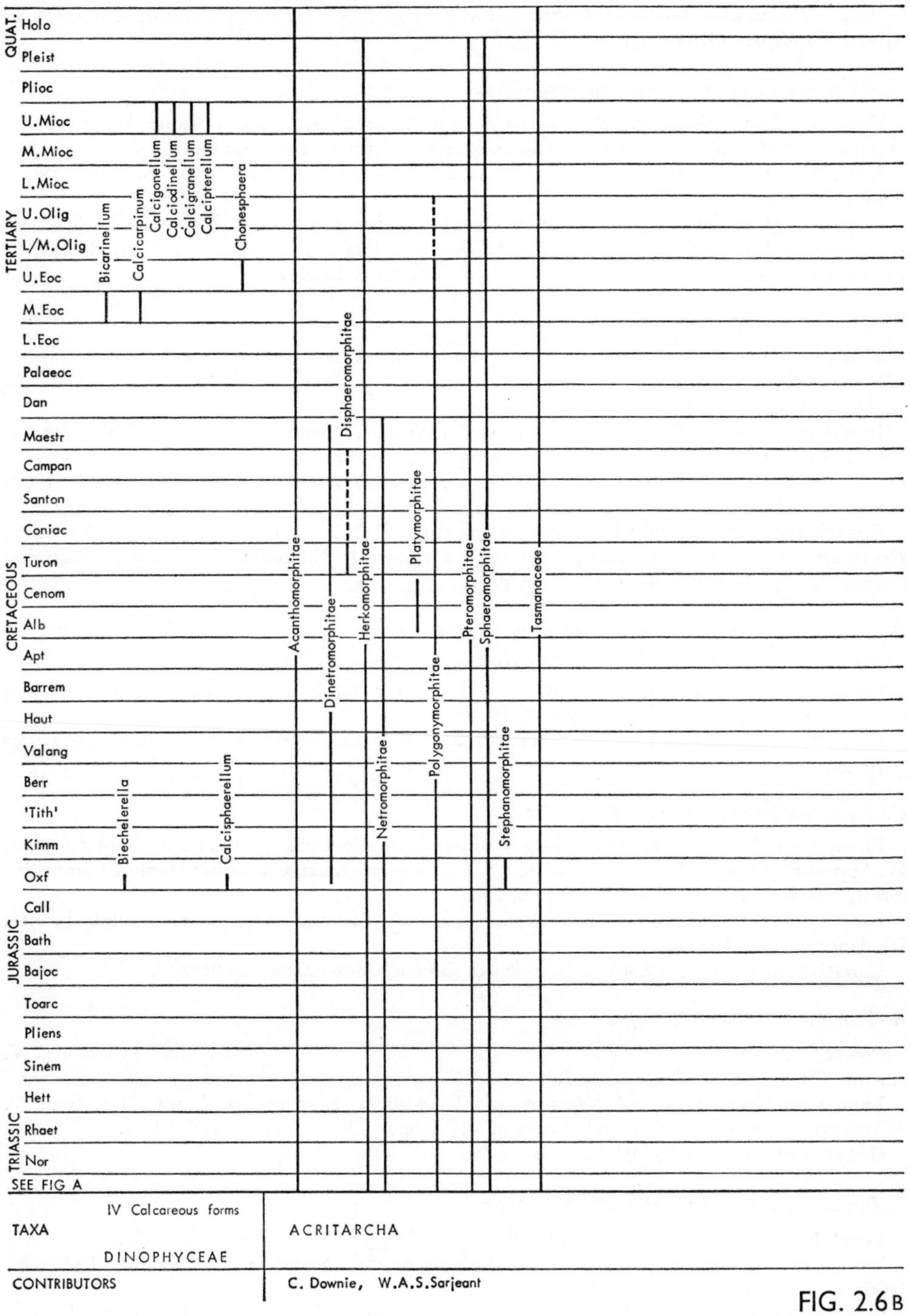
QUAT.
Holo
Pleist
Plioc
U.Mioc
M.Mioc
L.Mioc
TERTIARY
U.Olig
L/M.Olig
U.Eoc
M.Eoc
L.Eoc
Palaeoc
Dan
CRETACEOUS
Maestr
Campan
Santon
Coniac
Turon
Cenom
Alb
Apt
Barrem
Haut
Valang
Berr
'Tith'
Kimm
Oxf
JURASSIC
Call
Bath
Bajoc
Toarc
Pliens
Sinem
Hett
TRIASSIC
Rhaet
Nor
SEE FIG A
Bicarinellum
Calcicarpinum
Calcigonellum
Calciodinellum
Calcigranellum
Calcipterellum
Chonesphaera
Biechelerella
Calcisphaerellum
Acanthomorphitae
Dinetromorphitae
Disphaeromorphitae
Herkomorphitae
Netromorphitae
Platymorphitae
Polygonymorphitae
Pteromorphitae
Sphaeromorphitae
Stephanomorphitae
Tasmanaceae
TAXA
IV Calcareous forms
DINOPHYCEAE
ACRITARCHA
CONTRIBUTORS
C. Downie, W.A.S.Sarjeant

FIG. 2.6B

Cookson, *Pentadinium* Gerlach, *Psaligonyaulax* Sarjeant, *Scriniodinium* Klement, ?*Sirmiodinium* Alberti, *Triblastula* O. Wetzel.

N. Cavate to bicavate cysts: intercalary archaeopyle

First, U. Jur: *Dingodinium jurassicum* Cookson & Eisenack, Dingo Siltstone, W. Australia; borehole, Omati, Papua (Cookson & Eisenack 1958). At peak Cret. Senton.-U. Eoc.

Last, Holo: *Wetzeliella* cf. *symmetrica*, post-Pleistocene clay, England (Sarjeant 1965). (Probably extant).

Constituent genera, *Deflandrea* Eisenack, *Dingodinium* Cookson & Eisenack, ?*Evittodinium* Deflandre, *Palaeocystodinium* Alberti, *Pseudodeflandrea* Alberti, *Svalbardella* Manum, *Wetzeliella* Eisenack emend. Williams & Downie, *Xenikoon* Cookson & Eisenack.

O. Cavate to bicavate cysts: apical archaeopyle

First, Cret Valang: *Muderongia simplex* Alberti, *M. tetracantha* (Gocht) and *M. tomaszowense* Alberti; Schünow and Dabendorf borings, Germany; Tomaszow, Poland, (Alberti 1961). At peak Cret Haut-Cenom.

Last, Cret Campan: *Odontochitina operculata* (O. Wetzel), limest. Poland (Gorka 1963); several vaguely dated records from unlocated flints, possibly post-Campan. Three species from Eocene non-marine sediment (*Geiselodinium eocenium*, *G. geiseltalense* and *G. hallense* Krutzsch 1962: Germany) are doubtfully referred to this group.

Constituent genera, *Aptea* Eisenack, *Ascodinium* Cookson & Eisenack, ?*Geiselodinium* Krutzsch, *Hexagonifera* Cookson & Eisenack, *Muderongia* Cookson & Eisenack, *Odontochotina* Deflandre, *Odontochitiniopsis* Eisenack, *Pseudoceratium* Gocht.

P. Cavate to bicavate cysts enclosed in mucilaginous envelopes

First, Jur Bath: *Kalyptea jarassica* Alberti, Dogger, Germany (Alberti 1961).

Last, Cret Barrem: *Netrelytron trinetron* Sarjeant, *Paranetrelytron strongylum* Sarjeant, Speeton Clay (M. Barrem), England (Davey *et al.* 1966).

Constituent genera, ?*Kalyptea* Cookson & Eisenack, *Netrelytron* Sarjeant, *Paranetrelytron* Sarjeant.

Q. Pterocavate cysts: archaeopyle precingular

First, Cret ?U.Alb-Cenom: *Stephodinium australicum* Cookson & Eisenack, Subiaco Bore, W. Australia, (Cookson & Eisenack 1962b); *Stephodinium europaicum* Cookson & Hughes, Cambridge Greensand, England (Cookson & Hughes, 1964).

Last, Cret ?Campan: *Stephodinium coronatum*, *S. pellucidum* Deflandre, Senonian flints, France. (Deflandre 1936c, 1943a).

Constituent genera, *Actinotheca* Cookson & Eisenack, *Stephodinium* Deflandre.

R. Pterate cysts: apical archaeopyle

First, Cret Alb: *Xiphophoridium alatum* (Cookson & Eisenack), Lower Gearle Siltstone, W. Australia (Cookson & Eisenack 1962a).

Last, Cret Cenom: *Xiphophoridium alatum* (Cookson & Eisenack), Osborne Formation, W. Australia: Lower Chalk, England (Cookson & Eisenack 1962a; Davey *et al.* 1966).

Constituent genus, *Xiphophoridium* Sarjeant.

S. Pterate cysts: precingular/epitractal archaeopyle

First, Jur Call: *Ctenidodinium ornatum* (Eisenack), Dogger, Baltic (Eisenack 1935).

Last, Cret ?Campan: *Dinopterygium cladoides* Deflandre, Senonian flint, France (Deflandre 1936c).

Constituent genera, *Ctenidodinium* Deflandre, *Dinopterygium* Deflandre, *Wanaea* Cookson & Eisenack.

T. Marginate cysts: apical archaeopyle

First, Jur Oxf: *Cyclonephelium densebarbatum* Cookson & Eisenack, Alexander Formation, W. Australia (Cookson & Eisenack 1962b). At peak Cret Apt-Campan.

Last, M. Mioc: *Tenua hystrix* Eisenack, Emsbüren bore, N. Germany (Gerlach 1961); possibly reworked?

Constituent genera, *Areoligera* Lejeune-Carpentier, *Chiropteridium* Gocht, *Circulodinium* Alberti, *Cyclonephelium* Deflandre & Cookson, *Tenua* Eisenack.

U. Trabeculate cysts: precingular archaeopyle

First, Jur Call: ?*Cannosphaeropsis perforata* and ?*C. speciosa* Alberti, Upper Dogger, Hildesheim and Gölzow borings, Germany (Alberti 1961).

Last, U.Eoc: *Cannosphaeropsis reticulensis* Pastiels, in Conow boring, Germany. (Alberti 1961).

Constituent genus, *Cannosphaeropsis* O. Wetzel emend. Williams & Downie. (Many species, including the Jur forms, may well prove referable to *Adnatosphaeridium*).

V. Trabeculate cysts: apical archaeopyle

First, Jur ?Bath: *Adnatosphaeridium caulleryi* (Deflandre), cherts, presumed U. Bath.-Call., France (Valensi 1955b).

Last, L. Eoc: *Adnatosphaeridium multispinum, A. patulum, A. vittatum* Williams & Downie, London Clay (Ypresian), France (Davey *et al.* 1966).

Constituent genus, *Adnatosphaeridium* Williams and Downie.

W. Membranate cysts: archaeopyle precingular?

First, Jur Toarc: *Scriniocassis weberi* Gocht, Lias Zeta, Germany (Gocht 1964).

Last, Cret Apt: *Gardodinium eisenacki* Alberti, in Werle boring, Germany (Alberti 1961).

Constituent genera, *Gardodinium* Alberti, *Scriniocassis* Gocht.

X. Membranate cysts: apical archaeopyle

First, Jur Bajoc: *Valensiella ovula* (Deflandre), Oolites with *Parkinsoni parkinsoni* (U. Bajoc.), N. France (Deflandre 1947d)

Last, L. Olig: *Samlandia chlamydophora* Eisenack, phosphate nodules, East Prussia (Eisenack 1954b).

Constituent genera, *Chlamydophorella* Cookson & Eisenack, *Membranilarnacia* Eisenack, *Samlandia* Eisenack, *Valensiella* Eisenack.

Y. Cysts: not classifiable

The following cyst genera cannot at present be incorporated into the above classification, either through incomplete understanding of structure and archaeopyle formation or because they represent morphological types not yet distinguished: *Duosphaeridium* Davey & Williams, *Gillinia* Cookson & Eisenack, *Spongodinium* Deflandre, *Thalassiphora* Eisenack & Gocht, *Wetzelodinium* Deflandre.

II. ORGANIC-SHELLED FORMS: MOTILE STAGES

A group of organic-shelled genera, recorded in the fossil state, have not yet been convincingly demonstrated to be cysts and may indeed constitute fossils of the motile stage. They comprise the presumed fossil representatives of four living genera.

Order PERIDINIALES

Suborder GYMNODINIINEAE

Family GYMNODINIACEAE

First, Cret Cenom: *Gymnodinium westralium* Cookson & Eisenack, Gearle Siltstones, W. Australia (Cookson & Eisenack 1958). *Gymnodinium dabendorfense* Alberti 1961, Cret Valang, Germany, is incorrectly placed in this genus. No post-Cretaceous records. **Extant.**

Suborder PERIDINIINEAE

Family GLENODINIACEAE

First, L. Mioc: *Glenodinium smreczyniense* Woloszynska, sands, Poland (Mackó 1957). No other fossil records. **Extant.**

Family PERIDINIACEAE

First, Cret ?Coniac: *Peridinium cinctum* Ehrenberg, *P. conicum* (Gran), *P. damasii* Lejeune-Carpentier, *P. galeatum* Lejeune-Carpentier, *P. illustrans* O. Wetzel, *P. pyrophorum* Ehrenberg, *P. subconicoides* Lejeune-Carpentier, Senonian flints, Belgium, France and Germany. Genus also recorded from Olig and Holo. **Extant.**

III. SILICEOUS FORMS: MOTILE STAGES

Fossil dinoflagellates of wholly siliceous composition occur as entire thecae (*Peridinites* Lefèvre) and as discrete skeletal elements (*Actiniscus* Ehrenberg). In addition, two Jur genera, *Lithodinia* and *Eodinia* Eisenack, supposedly have an admixture of silica in their dominantly organic shells; however it is considered appropriate that these genera should be grouped with organic-shelled forms, in view of the difficulties of confirming this.

A. Entire thecae

Order PERIDINIALES

Suborder PERIDINIINEAE

Family Peridinitaceae nom. nov. ≡ Lithoperidiniaceae Deflandre. (The family name Lithoperidiniaceae, used hitherto, is based on the invalid generic name *Lithoperidinium* Deflandre and must thus be abandoned).

First, Palaeoc: *Peridinites rossicus* (Deflandre), diatomite, Kuznetsk, U.S.S.R. (Deflandre 1940b). Subsequent records from L. Tert, Barbados (Lefèvre 1933c) and Tert, New Zealand (Deflandre 1933). No post-Tert records.

B. Discrete elements

Order PERIDINIALES

Suborder GYMNODINIIAEAE

Family GYMNASTERACAE

First, Mioc: *Actiniscus sirius*, ?*A. stella*, *A. tetrasterias* Ehrenberg, from Virginia, U.S.A. (Ehrenberg 1854). **Extant.**

206

IV. CALCAREOUS FORMS: MOTILE STAGES

Order PERIDINIALES

Suborder CALCIODINELLIINEAE

Family CALCIODINELLIIACEAE

First, Jur Oxf: *Biechelerella jurassica, Calcisphaerellum flosculus* Deflandre, clays, N. France (Deflandre 1948c).

Last, U. Mioc: *Calcigonellum infula, Calciodinellum operosum, Calciogranellum limbatum, Calcipterellum colomi,* Deflandre: Sahelian diatomite, Algeria (Deflandre 1948c).

Constituent genera, *Bicarinellum* Deflandre, *Biechelerella* Deflandre, *Calcicarpinum* Deflandre, *Calcigonellum* Deflandre, *Calciodinellum* Deflandre, *Calcigranellum* Deflandre, *Calcipterellum* Deflandre, *Calcisphaerellum* Deflandre, *Chonesphaera* Klumpp. [W.A.S.S. & C.D.]

Group ACRITARCHA Evitt 1963

After demonstration of the dinoflagellate affinity of the typical "hystrichospheres" (such as *Hystrichosphaera* itself), a residue of genera remained that had been previously called hystrichospheres but whose affinity could not be proved. They are of similar shell constitution and morphology; however, whilst their relationships have not been determined, it is highly probable that they constitute a polyphyletic assemblage. Under the terms of the "International Code of Botanical Nomenclature", form genera cannot be used as types for families; moreover, any classification carrying an implication of natural affinity would have been most undesirable. They are thus now treated as a Group, the Acritarcha (Greek, "uncertain origin"), divided into Subgroups containing forms closely similar in morphology; the Subgroups are without designated types, so that the transfer away of constituent genera, following any future demonstration of affinity, is facilitated (Evitt 1963a; Downie, Evitt & Sarjeant 1963). The history of research is treated fully by Sarjeant (1965).

References to 1963 are listed fully in Downie & Sarjeant (1964) and are here quoted in the form adopted in that work. [Norris & Sarjeant (1965) has also been used.—Ed.].

Group ACRITARCHA Evitt 1963

Subgroup ACANTHOMORPHITAE D.,E. & S.

First, L. Camb: *Archaeohystrichosphaeridium dorofeevi* Tim., *A. innominatum* Tim., *A. oblongum* Tim., *A. stipiforme* Tim. *A. vologdense* Tim., *A. ianischewskyi* Tim., Blue Clay Fm, U.S.S.R. (Timofeyev 1959).

Extant, Rossignol (1964) records *Baltisphaeridium* from Mediterranean; McKee, Chronic, and Leopold (1959) record *?Micrhystridium* from Pacific.

Subgroup DIACROMORPHITAE D.,E. & S.

First, L. Camb: *Lophodiacrodium tosnaense* (Tim.), Blue Clay Fm, U.S.S.R. (Timofeyev 1959).
Last, Dev Ems.: *Lophodiacrodium pepino* Cramer, La Vid Sh, Spain (Cramer 1964).

Subgroup DINETROMORPHITAE D.,E. & S.

First, Jur Oxf.: *Diplotesta glaessneri* Cooks. & Eis., Alexander Fm, Australia (Cookson & Eisenack 1960b).
Last, Cret Maestr: *Korojonia dubiosa* Cooks. & Eis., Korojon Calcarenite, Australia (Cookson and Eisenack 1958).

The Fossil Record, Part II

Subgroup DISPHAEROMORPHITAE D.,E. & S.

?First, Pre-Camb Pre-Var-L. Camb: *Megasacculina atava* Naum., and *Protoarchaeosacculina atava* Naum., Riphean, U.S.S.R. and Torridonian, Scotland, (Naumova 1961, Naumova and Pavlovski 1961). *Archaeodiscina granulata* Naum., Blue Clay, U.S.S.R. (Naumova 1960).

First, Cret Turon: *Disphaeria macropyla* Cooks. & Eis., Gearle Siltstone, Australia, (Cookson and Eisenack 1960a).

Last, Cret ?Campan: *Disphaeria macropyla* Cooks. & Eis., Molecap Greensand, Australia (Cookson & Eisenack 1960b).

Subgroup HERKOMORPHITAE D.,E. & S.

First, U. Camb: *Cymatiogalea membrasnacea* (Naum.), U.S.S.R. (Naumova 1950).

Last, Pleist: *Cymatiosphaera* cf. *parva* Sarjeant and *C. nekovda* Ross., Israel, (Rossignol 1962, 1964).

Subgroup NETROMORPHITAE D.,E. & S.

First, Ord Tremad: *Leiofusa squama* Deunff, Algeria (Deunff 1961a).

Last, Cret Maestr: *Leiofusa lidiae* Górka, Poland (Górka 1963).

Subgroup OOMORPHIIAE D.,E. & S.

First, L. Camb: *Ooidium bicorne* Tim., *Zonooidium strobiliforme* Tim., *Z. guttiforme* Tim., and *Z. mirabile* Tim., Blue Clay Fm, U.S.S.R. (Timofeyev 1959).

Last, U. Camb: *Ooidium rossicum* Tim., *O. sablincaense* Tim., *Zonooidium guttiforme* Tim. and *Z. scutellatum* Tim., Obolus Sst, U.S.S.R. (Timofeyev 1959).

Subgroup PLATYMORPHITAE D.,E. & S.

First, Cret Alb: *Halophoridia xena* Cooks. & Eis., Australia (Cookson and Eisenack 1962b).

Last, Cret Cenom: *Platycystidia diptera* Cooks. & Eis. and *Trigonopyxidia ginella* Cooks. & Eis., Australia (Cookson and Eisenack 1960a).

Subgroup POLYGONYMORPHITAE D.,E. & S.

First, Ord Tremad: *Veryhachium minutum* Downie, Shineton Shs, England (Downie 1959).

Last, Olig: *V. trispinosum* (Baksi), Barail Series, India (Baksi 1962).

Subgroup PRISMATOMORPHITAE D.,E. & S.

First, Sil Ludl: *Polyedrixium rabians* Cram. and *P. tetrahedroide* Cram., San Pedro Fm, Spain (Cramer 1964).

Last, Trias Olenek-?Anis: *Staplinium hexaeder* Jan., Toad/Grayling Fm, Canada. (Jansonius 1962).

Subgroup PTEROMORPHITAE D.,E. & S.

First, Sil Lldov: *Pterospermopsis onondagaensis* Deunff, Belgium. (Stockmans and Williere 1963).

Last, Pleist: *Pt. vancampoae* Rossignol, Israel, (Rossignol 1964).

Subgroup SPHAEROMORPHITAE D.,E. & S.

First, Pre-Camb Pre-Var: *Huroniospora macroreticulata* Bargh., *H. microreticulata* Bargh. and *H. psilata* Bargh., Gunflint Fm, Canada, $2,000 \times 10^6$ years (Barghoorn & Tyler 1965).

Last, Pleist: *Leiosphaeridia bentori* Ross. and *Leiosphaeridia scrobiculata* (Defl. & Cooks), Israel, (Rossignol 1964).

Subgroup STEPHANOMORPHITAE D.,E. & S.

First and **Last,** Jur Oxf: *Stephanelytron caytonense* Sarj., *S. redcliffense* Sarj. and *S. scarburghense*, Sarj., Oxford Clay, England (Sarjeant 1961a).

Miscellaneous Algae; Family TASMANACEAE

A group of organic-shelled algae, spherical to disk-shaped and typified by the genus *Tasmanites*, were formerly regarded as hystrichospheres; however, Wall (1962) has since demonstrated the affinity of *Tasmanites* to the living species *Pachysphaera pelagica* Ostenfeld, a green alga. The latter is allocated by many specialists to the Class Chlorophyceae, but this allocation is not universally accepted. Provisionally, therefore, the systematic placing of these organisms must be treated as tentative.

Family TASMANACEAE Sommer 1956

First, Ord Tremad: *Tasmanites* sp. Reg., Ceratopyge Lst., Sweden (Regnéll, 1955).

Extant. [C.D., W.A.S.S.]

REFERENCES

BARGHOORN, E. S. & TYLER, S. A. 1965. Microörganisms from the Gunflint chert. *Science, N.Y.,* **147,** 563–577.

CALANDRA, F. 1964. Sur un présumé Dinoflagellé, *Arpylorus* nov. gen. du Gothlandien de Tunisie, *C.r. hebd. Seanc. Acad. Sci., Paris,* **258,** 4112–4114.

COOKSON, I. C. & HUGHES, N. F. 1964. Microplankton from the Cambridge Greensand (mid-Cretaceous). *Palaeontology,* **7,** 37–59.

CRAMER, F. H. 1964. Microplankton from three Palaeozoic formations in the Province of Léon (N.W. Spain). *Leid. geol. Meded.,* **30,** 262–361, pl. 1–24.

DAVEY, R. J., DOWNIE, C., SARJEANT, W. A. S., & WILLIAMS, G. L., 1966. Studies on Mesozoic and Cainozoic dinoflagellate cysts. *Bull. Brit. Mus. nat. Hist.,* Supp. **3,** 1-242, pls 1-26.

DOWNIE, C., EVITT, W. R. & SARJEANT, W. A. S. 1963. Dinoflagellates, hystrichospheres and the classification of the Acritarchs. *Stanford Univ. Publs (Geol. Sci.),* **7,** 1–16.

——, & SARJEANT, W. A. S., 1964. Bibliography and index of fossil dinoflagellates and acritarchs. *Mem. geol. Soc. Am.,* 94, 1–180.

EISENACK, A. 1964. Erörterungen über einige Gattungen fossiler Dinoflagellaten und über die Einordnung der Gattungen in das system. *Neues Jb. Geol. Paläont., Mh.* for 1964, 321–336.

GOCHT, H. 1964. Planktonische Kleinformen aus dem Lias/Dogger Grenzbereich Nord- und Süddeutschlands. *Neues Jb. Geol. Paläont., Abh.,* **119,** 113–133.

NORRIS, G. 1965. Archaeopyle structures in Upper Jurassic dinoflagellates from Southern England. *N.Z. Jl Geol. Geophys.* (In press).

NORRIS, G., & SARJEANT, W. A. S., 1965. A descriptive index of genera of fossil Dinophyceae and Acritarcha. *Palaeont. Bull., Wellington,* **40,** 1–72.

OYEN, F. H. VAN. 1964. *C.I.M.P. Groupe 9. Résumé de la réunion de travail, des 25 et 26 Novembre 1964, au Laboratoire Central de la C.E.P. a Bordeaux.* Pau (Commission Internationale sur la Microflore du Paléozoique). 1–62.

REGNELL, G. 1955. *Leiosphaera* (Hystrichosph.) aus unter-Ordovizischen Kalkstein in SO-Schönen, Schweden. *Geol. För. Stockh. Förh.,* **77,** 545–6.

ROSSIGNOL, M. 1964. Hystrichosphères du Quaternaire en Mediterranée orientale, dans les sédiments Pléistocènes et les boues marines actuelles, *Rev. Micropaléont.* 7, 83–99, pl. 1–3.

SARJEANT, W. A. S. 1965. The Xanthidia. *Endeavour,* 24, 33–9, 2 pl.

SOMMER, F. W. 1956. South American Paleozoic Sporomorphae without haptotypic structures. *Micropaleontology,* **2,** 175–81, pl. 1–2.

WALL, D. 1962. Evidence from recent plankton regarding the biological affinities of *Tasmanites* Newton and *Leiosphaeridia* Eisenack. *Geol. Mag.,* **99,** 353–62, pl. 17.

—— 1965. Microplankton, pollen and spores from the Lower Jurassic in Britain. *Micropaleontology,* **11,** 151–190.

M. Black, M.A. F.G.S.
Department of Geology, Sedgwick Museum, Downing Street, Cambridge.
C. Downie, PH.D. F.G.S.
Department of Geology, The University, Mappin Street, Sheffield 1.
R. Ross, PH.D. F.L.S.
Department of Botany, British Museum (Natural History), Cromwell Road, London s w 7.
W. A. S. Sarjeant, PH.D F.G.S.
Department of Geology, The University, Nottingham.

CHAPTER 3

Bryophyta and Charophyta*

Contributors: L. J. GRAMBAST & W. S. LACEY

Division BRYOPHYTA Schimper 1879

Section 1

Class HEPATICOPSIDA Rothmaler 1951

Order JUNGERMANNIALES Engler 1892

First, Dev Frasn: *Hepaticites devonicus* Hueber 1961, base of Onteora "Red beds", Senecan Series (Frasn), South Mountain, Schoharie County, New York State (Hueber 1961).   **Extant.**
Comment: Few records of Hepaticopsida in Palaeozoic. Earliest are all sterile forms and satisfactory classification is not possible until reproductive structures are available. Most are referred provisionally to Jungermanniales Anacrogynae on the basis of vegetative morphology. Hueber (1961) compares *Hepaticites devonicus* with present genera *Pallavicinia* (Gray) Carr. and *Metzgeria* Raddi. From U. Carb, Shropshire, England Walton (1925, 1928) describes *Hepaticites kidstoni, H. lobatus, H. langi, H. metzgerioides* compared respectively with present genera *Treubia, Fossombronia, Riccardia (Aneura),* and *Metzgeria.* Jungermanniales Acrogynae (Leafy Liverworts) are recorded with certainty only since Tert Eoc, mainly from Baltic Amber (Caspary 1886, 1906; Steere 1946; Mägdefrau 1957; Savicz-Ljubitzkaja and Abramov 1959; Czeczott 1959).

Order MARCHANTIALES Engler 1892

First, M. Trias: *Hepaticites cyathodoides* Townrow 1959, Waterfall locality, Burnera, U. Umkomaas, Natal, South Africa, exact horizon uncertain but probably Molteno Series (Townrow 1959).   **Extant.**
Comment: Earliest records are all sterile forms and satisfactory classification is not possible until reproductive structures are available. From U. Carb, Dollar, Scotland, Walton (1949) records cf. *Hepaticites* sp. which, if bryophyte at all, bears some resemblance to present genus *Riccia* (Ricciaceae, Marchantiales) but also to *Riccardia* (Jungermanniales Anacrogynae). Likewise, *Marchantites lorea* Zalessky, M. Perm, Bardinsky, Urals, U.S.S.R. (Zalessky 1937) cannot be satisfactorily placed. Townrow (1959) compares *Hepaticites cyathodoides* with present genus *Cyathodium* (sometimes placed in Targioniaceae). Later Mesozoic records of marchantialean affinity include *Ricciopsis* (cf. Ricciaceae) and *Marchantiolites* (cf. Marchantiaccae), Trias-Jur

---

* These two groups are placed together in this chapter for convenience; no connexion is implied. Ed.

The Fossil Record, pp. 211–217. Geological Society of London, 1967. Printed in Northern Ireland.

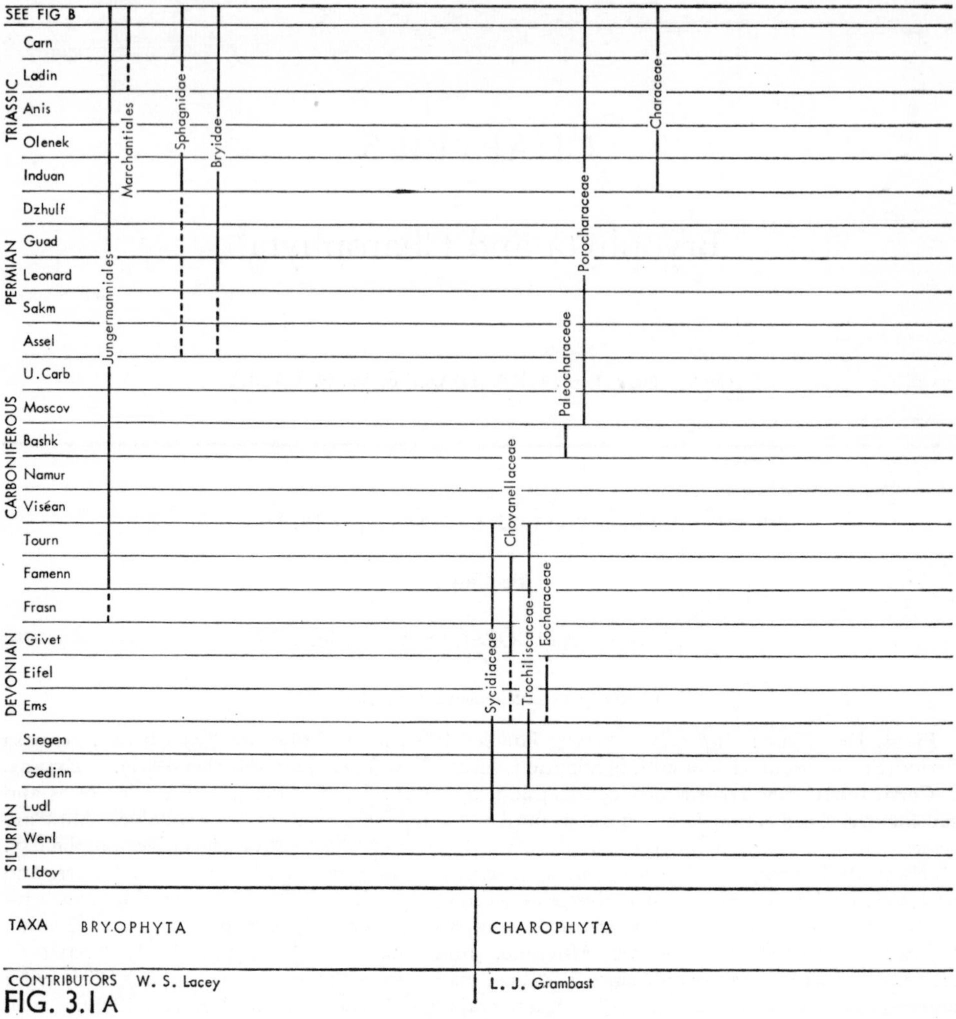

SEE FIG B

Time scale (left column):

TRIASSIC — Carn, Ladin, Anis, Olenek, Induan
PERMIAN — Dzhulf, Guad, Leonard, Sakm, Assel
CARBONIFEROUS — U.Carb, Moscov, Bashk, Namur, Viséan, Tourn
DEVONIAN — Famenn, Frasn, Givet, Eifel, Ems, Siegen, Gedinn
SILURIAN — Ludl, Wenl, Lldov

Range bars (taxa): Marchantiales, Sphagnidae, Bryidae, Jungermanniales, Characeae, Porocharaceae, Paleocharaceae, Chovanellaceae, Eocharaceae, Sycidiaceae, Trochiliscaceae

TAXA	BRYOPHYTA	CHAROPHYTA
CONTRIBUTORS	W. S. Lacey	L. J. Grambast

FIG. 3.1A

(Rhaeto-Liassic), Scania, Sweden (Lundblad 1954); *Hepaticites*, Jur Bajoc, Yorkshire, England (Harris 1941, 1961); and *Marchantites* (cf. Marchantiaceae), L. Cret, Patagonia (Lundblad 1955).

Order SPHAEROCARPALES Cavers 1910

First, Trias Rhaet: *Naiadita lanceolata* Buckman 1850, emend. Harris 1938, "*Naiadita Bed*", Cotham Beds, U. Rhaetic, Somerset east of Mendip Hills to Worcestershire and Warwickshire, England (Harris 1937, 1938, 1939). **Extant.**

Comment, *Naiadita lanceolata* Buckman is one of the few early Bryophytes in which the reproductive organs (except antheridia), and the sporophyte, are known. Harris (1938) considers it to be a submerged water liverwort, and refers it tentatively to the Riellaceae of the Sphaerocarpales. Savicz-Ljubitzkaja and Abramov (1959) point out, however, that *Naiadita* distinctly differs from Sphaerocarpales in several respects.

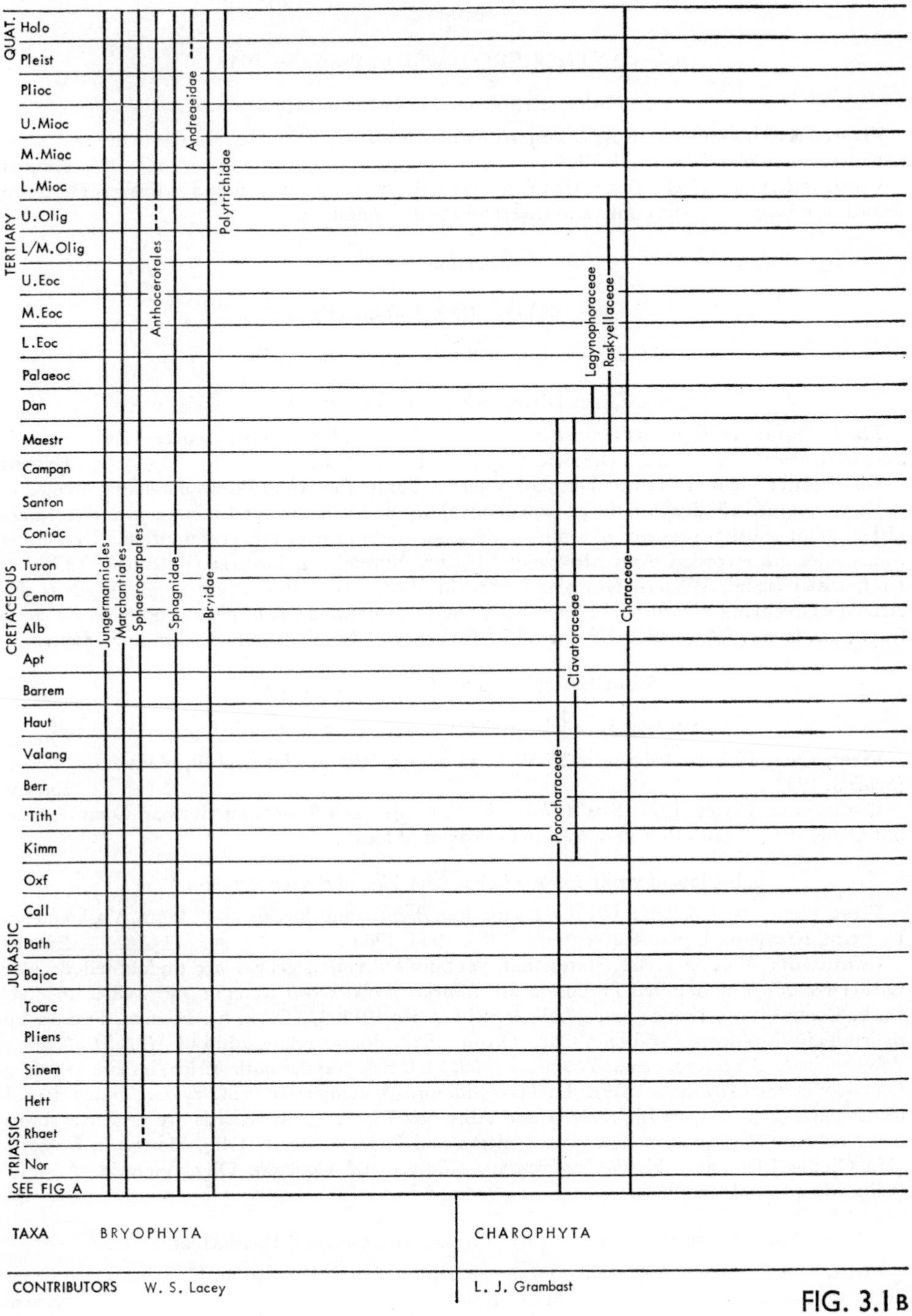

A stratigraphic range chart. The vertical axis shows geological periods and stages from bottom to top:

TRIASSIC: Nor, Rhaet
JURASSIC: Hett, Sinem, Pliens, Toarc, Bajoc, Bath, Call, Oxf, Kimm, 'Tith', Berr, Valang, Haut, Barrem, Apt, Alb
CRETACEOUS: Cenom, Turon, Coniac, Santon, Campan, Maestr, Dan, Palaeoc
TERTIARY: L.Eoc, M.Eoc, U.Eoc, L/M.Olig, U.Olig, L.Mioc, M.Mioc, U.Mioc, Plioc, Pleist
QUAT.: Holo

Also at bottom: SEE FIG A

Taxa columns (BRYOPHYTA): Jungermanniales, Marchantiales, Sphaerocarpales, Sphagnidae, Bryidae, Anthocerotales, Andreaeidae, Polytrichidae

Taxa columns (CHAROPHYTA): Porocharaceae, Clavatoraceae, Lagynophoraceae, Raskyellaceae, Characeae

TAXA	BRYOPHYTA	CHAROPHYTA
CONTRIBUTORS	W. S. Lacey	L. J. Grambast

FIG. 3.1 B

Section 2

Class ANTHOCEROTOPSIDA Proskauer 1957

Order ANTHOCEROTALES Muller 1940

First, Tert U. Olig-Mioc: *Rudolphisporis rudolphi* Krutzsch 1963, Eastern Germany and Mioc, near Warsaw, Poland (Stuchlik 1964). **Extant.**

Comment, Gams (1932) stated that Anthocerotales had never been found as fossils. The above records are based on spores only and therefore open to question.

Section 3

Class BRYOPSIDA Rothmaler 1951

Sub-Class SPHAGNIDAE sensu Parihar 1959

(=SPHAGNALES Dixon 1932; SPHAGNOBRYA Smith 1955)

First, Perm: *Protosphagnum nervatum* Neuburg 1956 and two other genera (*Vorcutannularia*, *Jungagia*), Perm, Angaraland, U.S.S.R. (Neuburg 1956, 1960). **Extant.**

Comment: Neuburg's three Permian genera consitute the group Protosphagnales, erected on basis of presumed affinity with the present genus *Sphagnum* Ehrh. Savicz-Ljubitzkaja and Abramov (1959) point out that presence of a midrib does not conform with this presumption. Undoubted Sphagnales are recorded from Mesozoic; L. Jur, Nuremberg, Bavaria (Reissinger 1950), U. Cret, Disko Island, Western Greenland (Arnold 1932, 1947), but Steere (1946) suggests that Arnold's Greenland record could have been due to contamination of coal samples by *Sphagnum* fragments. Genus *Sphagnum* is widespread in Tert (Savicz-Ljubitzkaja and Abramov 1959).

Sub-Class ANDREAEIDAE sensu Parihar 1959

(=ANDREAEALES Dixon 1932; ANDREAEOBRYA Smith 1955)

First, Quat Pleist: *Andreaea rothii* Web. et Mohr, Riss glacial deposit, Zamszany, Poland (Szafran 1952). **Extant.**

Comment: Dixon (1927) lists *Andreaea huntii* Limpr. as a fossil from German Quat deposits, but Gams (1932) states that these records were not of fossils.

Sub-Class BRYIDAE sensu Engler, Melchior and Werdermann 1954

First, Perm: *Intia, Salairia, Uskatia, Polyssaievia, Bachtia,* and *Bajdaievia,* L. Perm, Vorkouta and U. Perm, Kuznetsk, U.S.S.R. (Neuburg, 1955, 1956, 1960). **Extant.**

Comment: Watson (1964) states that Neuburg's Permian genera are undoubted Bryidae. Earlier records of undoubted Bryopsida are *Muscites polytrichaceus* Renault and Zeiller 1888, U. Carb, Commentary, France and *M. Bertrandi* Lignier 1914, U. Carb, St. Etienne, France, but their affinity is obscure (Walton 1928). Dixon (1927) doubts relationship of *M. polytrichaceus* to Polytrichidae. *Muscites guescelini* Townrow 1959, M. Trias, Natal, South Africa, is close to present Leucodontaceae (Townrow 1959). U. Tert, widespread, many records of Bryidae, some referable to present genera (Savicz-Ljubitzkaja and Abramov 1959). Most records are of sterile forms; two fertile are *Plagiopodopsis cockerelliae* (Britton and Hollick) Steere, Olig, Florissant, Colorado (MacGinitie 1953) and *Muscites yallournensis* Clifford and Cookson, Olig, Victoria, Australia (Clifford and Cookson 1953).

Sub-Class POLYTRICHIDAE sensu Engler, Melchior and Werdermann 1954

First, Tert U. Mioc: *Polytrichites spokanensis* Britton, Latah Formation, U. Mioc, Deep Creek, north west of Spokane, Washington State (Knowlton 1926). **Extant.**

Comment: Jovet-Ast (personal communication) points out that this record might not be the first for Polytrichidae, since other genera are known in Tert but without details of horizon.

Steere (1946) states that this plant resembles a *Polytrichum* fairly closely, but is unusually small for that genus. *Muscites convolutus* Mägdefrau, Tert Eoc, from Baltic Amber, also resembles present genus *Polytrichum* but cannot be satisfactorily classified (Mägdefrau 1957). The assignment of the Carboniferous *Muscites polytrichaceus* Renault and Zeiller 1888 to Polytrichidae is unsubstantiated.

REFERENCES

ARNOLD, C. A. 1932. Microfossils from Greenland Coal. *Pap. Mich. Acad. Sci.*, **15,** 51–61.

—— 1947. *An Introduction to Palaeobotany.* McGraw-Hill, New York.

CASPARY, R. 1886. Einige neue Pflanzenreste aus dem samländischen Bernstein. *Schr. phys.-ökon. Ges. Königsb.*, **26.**

—— 1906. Die Flora des Bernsteins und anderer fossiler Harze des ostpreussischen Tertiärs (bearb. von R. Klebs). *Abh. preuss. geol. Landesanst.* N.F., H. 4.

CLIFFORD, H. T. & COOKSON, I. C. 1953. *Muscites yallournensis*, a fossil moss capsule from Yallourn, Victoria. *Bryologist*, **56,** 53–55.

CZECZOTT, H. 1959. The flora of the Baltic amber and its age. *Pr. Muz. Ziemi*, **4,** 119.

DIXON, H. N. 1927. In JONGMANS, W. J. *Fossilium Catalogus*. II. Plantae, 13, Muscineae, 1–116.

GAMS, H. 1932. in VERDOORN, F. *Manual of Bryology*. XI. Quaternary Distribution, 297–322.

HARRIS, T. M. 1937. *Naiadita*, a strange fossil Bryophyte. *Rep. Br. Ass. Advmt. Sci. Nottingham.*

—— 1938. *The British Rhaetic Flora*. British Museum (Natural History), London.

—— 1939. *Naiadita*, a fossil Bryophyte with reproductive organs. *Anns. Bryol.*, **12,** 57–70.

—— 1941. On two species of Hepatics from the Yorkshire Jurassic Flora. *Ann. Mag. Nat. Hist.*, ser. 11, **9,** 393–401, text figs 1, 2.

—— 1961. *The Yorkshire Jurassic Flora*. 1. British Museum (Natural History), London.

HUEBER, F. M. 1961. *Hepaticites devonicus*, a new fossil Liverwort from the Devonian of New York. *Ann. Mo. bot. Gdn.*, **48,** 125–132, pl. 1.

KNOWLTON, F. H. 1926. Flora of the Latah Formation of Spokane, Washington, and Coeur d'Alene, Idaho. *Prof. Pap. U.S. geol. Surv.*, **140,** 17–81.

KRUTZSCH, W. 1963. *Atlas der mittel- und jungtertiären dispersen Sporen- und Pollen- sowie der Mikroplankton formen des nördlichen Mitteleuropas. Verb. deutscher Verlag der Wissenschaften*, **2.** *Die Sporen der Anthocerotaceae und der Lycopodiaceae*; Deutscher Verlag der Wissenschaften, Berlin.

LUNBLAD, B. 1954. Contributions to the geological history of the Hepaticae. Fossil Marchantiales from the Rhaeto-Liassic Coal Mines of Skromberga (Province of Scania, Sweden). *Svensk bot. Tidskr.*, **48**(2), 381–417, pl. 1–4.

—— 1955. Contributions to the geological history of the Hepaticae. II. On a fossil member of the Marchantineae from the Mesozoic plant-bearing deposits near Lago San Martin, Patagonia (Lower Cretaceous). *Bot. Notiser*, **108,** 22–39, pl. 1–3.

MACGINITEE, H. D. 1953. Fossil Plants of the Florissant Beds, Colorado. *Publs Carnegie Instn.*, **599.**

MÄGDEFRAU, K. 1957. Flechten und Moose in baltischen Bernstein. *Ber. dt. bot. Ges.*, **70,** 433–435.

NEUBURG, M. F. 1955. Bryophytes from Permian sediments of the U.S.S.R. *Dokl. Akad. nauk SSSR*, **107,** 321–324. [In Russian.]

—— 1956. Discovery of Scale Mosses in Permian Sediments of the U.S.S.R. *Dokl. Akad. nauk SSSR*, 107. [In Russian.]

—— 1960. Leafy shoots of mosses in Permian deposits of Angaraland. *Trudÿ geol. Inst., Leningr.*, **19,** 104 pp. [In Russian.]

REISSINGER, A. 1950. Die "Pollenanalyse" ausgedehnt auf alle Sedimentgesteine der geologischen Vergangenheit. *Palaeontographica*, **90B,** (13), 99, pl. 11–19.

SAVICZ-LJUBITZKAJA, L. I. & ABRAMOV, I. I. 1959. The Geological Annals of Bryophyta. *Revue bryol. lichen.*, N.S., **28,** 330–342.

STEERE, W. C. 1946. Cenozoic and Mesozoic Bryophytes of North America. *Am. Midl. Nat.*, **36,** 298–324.

STUCHLIK, L. 1964. Pollen Analysis of the Miocene Deposits at Rypin. *Acta palaeobot., Cracov.,* **5,** 1–111, Pl. 1–25.

SZAFRAN, B. 1952. Pleistocene Mosses from Poland and the adjacent eastern territories. *Biul. pánst. Inst. geol.,* **68,** 5–36.

TOWNROW, J. A. 1959. Two Triassic Bryophytes from South Africa. *Jl. S. Afr. Bot.,* **25,** 1–22, pl. 1.

WALTON, J. 1925. Carboniferous Bryophyta. I. Hepaticae. *Ann. Bot.,* **39,** 563–572, pl. 13.

—— 1928. Carboniferous Bryophyta. II. Hepaticae and Musci. *Ann. Bot.,* **42,** 707–716, pl. 12.

—— 1949. A thalloid plant (cf. *Hepaticites* sp.) showing evidence of growth *in situ,* from the Coal Measures of Dollar, Clackmannanshire. *Trans. geol. Soc. Glasg.,* **21,** 278–280.

WATSON, E. V. 1964. *The Structure and Life of Bryophytes.* Hutchinson. London.

ZALESSKY, M. D. 1937. Sur la distinction de l'étage Bardien dans le Permien de l'Oural et sur sa flore fossile. *Problemÿ Paleont.,* **2–3.**   [W.S.L.]

Division CHAROPHYTA

Class CHAROPSIDA

Order SYCIDIALES Mädler 1952

Family SYCIDIACEAE Peck 1934

First, U.Sil: *Pseudosycidium* (=*Sycidium?*) *sp.* Karpinsky in Hacquaert 1932, Turkestan.

Last, Carb Tourn: *Sycidium foveatum* Peck 1934 and *S. clathratum* Peck 1934, Sylamore fm, basal Mississippian, Missouri.

Note: *Pseudosycidium* illustrated only from sections and not described. *Sycidium* well known from M. Dev, Eifel, Germany, and U.S.S.R. (Croft 1952).

Family CHOVANELLACEAE Grambast 1962

First, M.Dev: *Chovanella burgessi* Peck et Eyer 1963, Watt Mountain fm, Alberta and Callaway Lst fm, Missouri.

Last, Dev Famenn: *Chovanella kovalevi* Reitlinger et Jartzeva 1958 and three other species, Khovansk Beds, Tula region, Ukrain (Peck et Eyer 1963a).

Order TROCHILISCALES Mädler 1952

Family TROCHILISCACEAE Peck 1934

First, Dev Gedinn: *Trochiliscus podolicus* Croft 1952, Downtonian, Podolia.

Last, Carb Tourn: *Karpinskya laticostata* (Peck 1934) Grambast 1962, Sylamore fm, basal Mississippian, Missouri (Peck 1934, Croft 1952).

Order CHARALES

Family EOCHARACEAE Grambast 1959

First and **Last,** M. Dev: *Eochara wickendeni* Choquette 1956, Elk Point Group, Alberta (Grambast 1962).

Family PALEOCHARACEAE Pia 1927

First and **Last,** Carb Bashk: *Paleochara acadica* Bell 1922, lower part of Coal Measures, Nova Scotia, Canada (Peck et Eyer 1963b).

Family POROCHARACEAE Grambast 1962

First, Carb Moscov: *Stomochara moreyi* (Peck 1934) Grambast 1962, Lagonda fm, Pennsylvanian, Missouri, extending to L.Permian (Peck et Eyer 1963b).

Last, Cret Maestr: *Porochara sp.,* Bégudien-?Rognacien, Corbières, France (Grambast 1961).

Chapter 3: Bryophyta and Charophyta

Family CLAVATORACEAE Pia 1927

First, Jur Kimm: *Echinochara spinosa* Peck 1957, Morrison fm of Colorado, Wyoming and Dakota.

Last, Cret Maestr: *Septorella brachycera* Grambast 1962, Rognacien, Provence, France (Grambast 1962).

Family LAGYNOPHORACEAE Stache 1889

First and **Last,** Cret Maestr–Tert Dan: *Lagynophora liburnica* Stache 1889 and 4 other species, Liburnian, Cosina Beds, Corgnale, near Trieste, Italy (Grambast 1962).

Note: the significance of *Lagynophoraceae* and their value as distinct family is questionable.

Family RASKYELLACEAE Grambast 1957

First, Cret Maestr: *Saportanella maslovi* Grambast 1962, Bégudien, Provence, France.

Last, Tert U.Olig: *Rantzieniella nitida* Grambast 1962, Chattian-Aquitanian, Paulhiac, Lot-et-Garonne, France.

Comment: the main genus is *Raskyella* Grambast 1954, Eocene (Grambast 1962).

Family CHARACEAE L. Cl. Richard 1815

First, Trias Induan: *Sphaerochara wetlugensis* Saïdakovsky 1960, Great Donbass, U.S.S.R.

Extant.

Comment: The occurrence of the family in Triassic fms is unquestionable but the involved forms are rare and little known. True *Characeae* play a very unobtrusive part in the Jur and L. Cret. They begin to be more abundant in the M. Cret and are most diversified in the Eoc. Still well represented in the Olig, they greatly decrease from the Mioc onwards (Grambast 1964).

REFERENCES

CROFT, W. N. 1952. A new *Trochiliscus* (Charophyta) from the Downtonian of Podolia. *Bull. Br. Mus. (nat. Hist.), Geol.,* **1,** 189–220.

GRAMBAST, L. 1961. Remarques sur la systématique et la répartition stratigraphique des *Characeae* pré-tertiaires. *C. r. somm. Soc. géol. Fr.,* 1961, no. 7, 200–202.

—— 1962. Classification de l'embranchement des Charophytes. *Naturalia monspel.,* Bot., **14,** 63–86.

—— 1964. Précisions nouvelles sur les tendances évolutives dans l'embranchement des Charophytes. *Naturalia monspel.,* Bot., **16,** 273–279.

PECK, R. E. 1934. The North American Trochiliscids, Paleozoic Charophyta. *J. Paleont.,* **8,** 83–119.

—— & EYER, J. A. 1963a. Representatives of *Chovanella,* a Devonian Charophyte in North America. *Micropaleontology,* **9,** 97–100.

—— & EYER, J. A. 1963b. Pennsylvanian, Permian and Triassic Charophyta of North America. *J. Paleont.,* **37,** 835–844.   [L. J. G.]

[Professor] L. J. Grambast
    Institute Botanique, 5 Rue Auguste Bronnsenet, Montpellier, Hérault, France.
W. S. Lacey, PH.D. F.L.S. F.G.S.
    Department of Botany, University College of North Wales, Bangor, N. Wales.

CHAPTER 4

Pteridophyta—1

Contributors: H. P. BANKS, W. G. CHALONER & W. S. LACEY

In this chapter are recorded the microphyllous pteridophytes, leaving the ferns to Chapter 5. *Psilotum* has been omitted as it has no fossil record.

As in other chapters, much dispersed spore information cannot be included as the affinities are not known with sufficient accuracy.

Class PSILOPHYTOPSIDA

This class is here treated precisely as a group of plants, and not as a label for any Silurian or Devonian plants which are difficult to classify. *Pseudosporochnus* is recorded with Cladoxylaceae (Chap. 5), *Protopteridium* and allies are presumed to be close to Progymnospermopsida (Chap. 6), and Asteroxylaceae are treated separately below. Some other Devonian plants which are not yet well enough known, have been omitted. [N.F.H.]

Family RHYNIACEAE Kidston & Lang 1920

First, Sil Ludl: *Cooksonia* cf. *hemispherica* Lang, Pridoli strata, upper Budnany stage, Pristiograptus-ultimus Z., Central Bohemia (Obrhel 1962).

Last, Dev Frasn: *Taeniocrada lesquereuxi* White, Catskill beds = Chemung Fm, Pennsylvania (White 1903).

Comment: Family here includes plants with naked stems and terminal sporangia primarily from Lower Devonian strata. Occurs in Britain, Europe, North America, Australia, USSR. Other genera here included are *Rhynia* Kidston & Lang, *Horneophyton* K & L, *Hicklingia* K & L, *Eogaspesiea* Daber, *Hedeia* Lang & Cookson, *Yarravia* L & C.

Family ZOSTEROPHYLLACEAE Kräusel 1938

First, Dev Gedinn-Siegen: *Zosterophyllum australianum* Lang & Cookson, Centennial beds, Victoria, Australia, *Z. fertile* Leclercq, assise de St. Hubert, Belgium, *Z. llanoveranum* Croft & Lang, Senni beds, Wales, *Z. myretonianum* Penh., Caledonian Lower Old Red Sst Scotland (Walton 1964).

Last, Dev Siegen-Ems: *Zosterophyllum rhenanum* Kr. & W., Wahnbach beds, Germany, and *Bucheria ovata* Dorf, Beartooth Butte Fm, Wyoming. *Bucheria? valdei* Stockmans, Dev Famenn, is probably not a *Bucheria*, as its author suggested (Walton 1964).

Comment: Family here includes only the two genera listed, with naked stems and sporangia grouped into a "spike". Occurs in North America, Europe, Britain, Australia, U.S.S.R.

The Fossil Record, pp. 219–231. Geological Society of London, 1967. Printed in Northern Ireland.

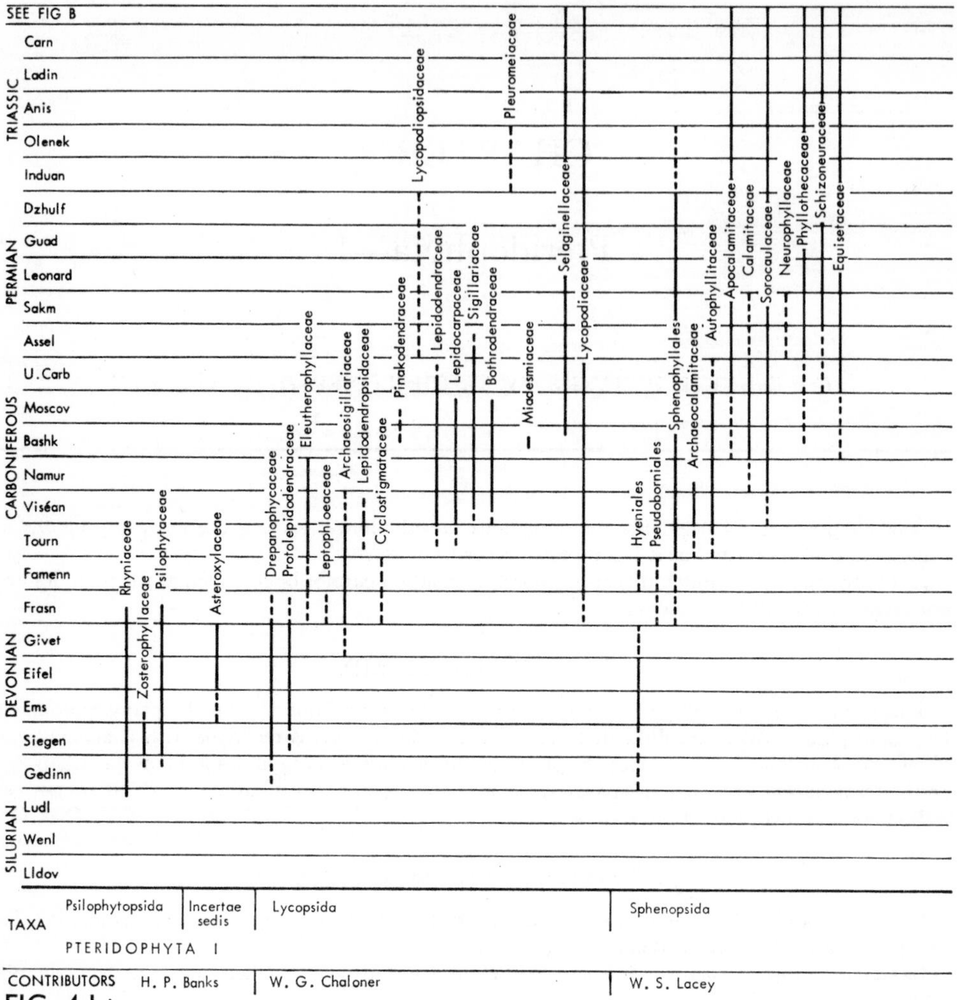

SEE FIG B

TRIASSIC
Carn
Ladin
Anis
Olenek
Indvan
Dzhulf

PERMIAN
Guad
Leonard
Sakm
Assel

CARBONIFEROUS
U.Carb
Moscov
Bashk
Namur
Viséan
Tourn
Famenn
Frasn

DEVONIAN
Givet
Eifel
Ems
Siegen
Gedinn

SILURIAN
Ludl
Wenl
Lldov

Lycopodiopsidaceae
Pleuromeiaceae
Selaginellaceae
Lycopodiaceae
Lepidodendraceae
Lepidocarpaceae
Sigillariaceae
Bothrodendraceae
Miadesmiaceae
Pinakodendraceae
Eleutherophyllaceae
Archaeosigillariaceae
Lepidodendropsidaceae
Cyclostigmataceae
Leptophloeaceae
Protolepidodendraceae
Drepanophycaceae
Asteroxylaceae
Psilophytaceae
Rhyniaceae
Zosterophyllaceae
Sphenophyllales
Archaeocalamitaceae
Hyeniales
Pseudoborniales
Autophyllitaceae
Apocalamitaceae
Calamitaceae
Sorocaulaceae
Neurophyllaceae
Phyllothecaceae
Schizoneuraceae
Equisetaceae

TAXA	Psilophytopsida	Incertae sedis	Lycopsida	Sphenopsida
	PTERIDOPHYTA I			

| CONTRIBUTORS | H. P. Banks | W. G. Chaloner | | W. S. Lacey |

FIG. 4.1A

Family PSILOPHYTACEAE Zimmermann 1930   (See **note** on p. 231)

First, Dev Siegen: *Psilophyton princeps* Dawson, Senni beds, Wales, and *Gosslingia breconensis* Heard, Senni beds, Wales (Croft & Lang 1942).

Last, Dev Frasn: *Psilophyton princeps* Dawson, Oneonta Fm, New York State (Hueber & Grierson 1961).

Comment: Family as revised here includes two genera whose sporangia are scattered laterally along the stem and branches. Two other genera, unpublished, from New York State (Dev Frasn) and Gaspé Peninsula (Dev Ems) display the same characteristic. *Gosslingia* is known only from Wales; *Psilophyton* is world-wide in the northern hemisphere but specimens with sporangia attached have been found only in Wales, on Gaspé Peninsula, and near James Bay, Canada.

Two families excluded from Psilophytopsida: Pseudosporochnaceae (Leclercq and Banks, 1962; *Pseudosporochnus nodosus* sp. nov., a Middle Devonian plant with cladoxylalean affinities; Palaeontographica B 110, 1–34, pl. 1–10) and Asteroxylaceae (Lyon, A. G. 1964; Probable fertile region of *Asteroxylon mackiei* K & L; Nature 203, 1082–3. pl. 1.)

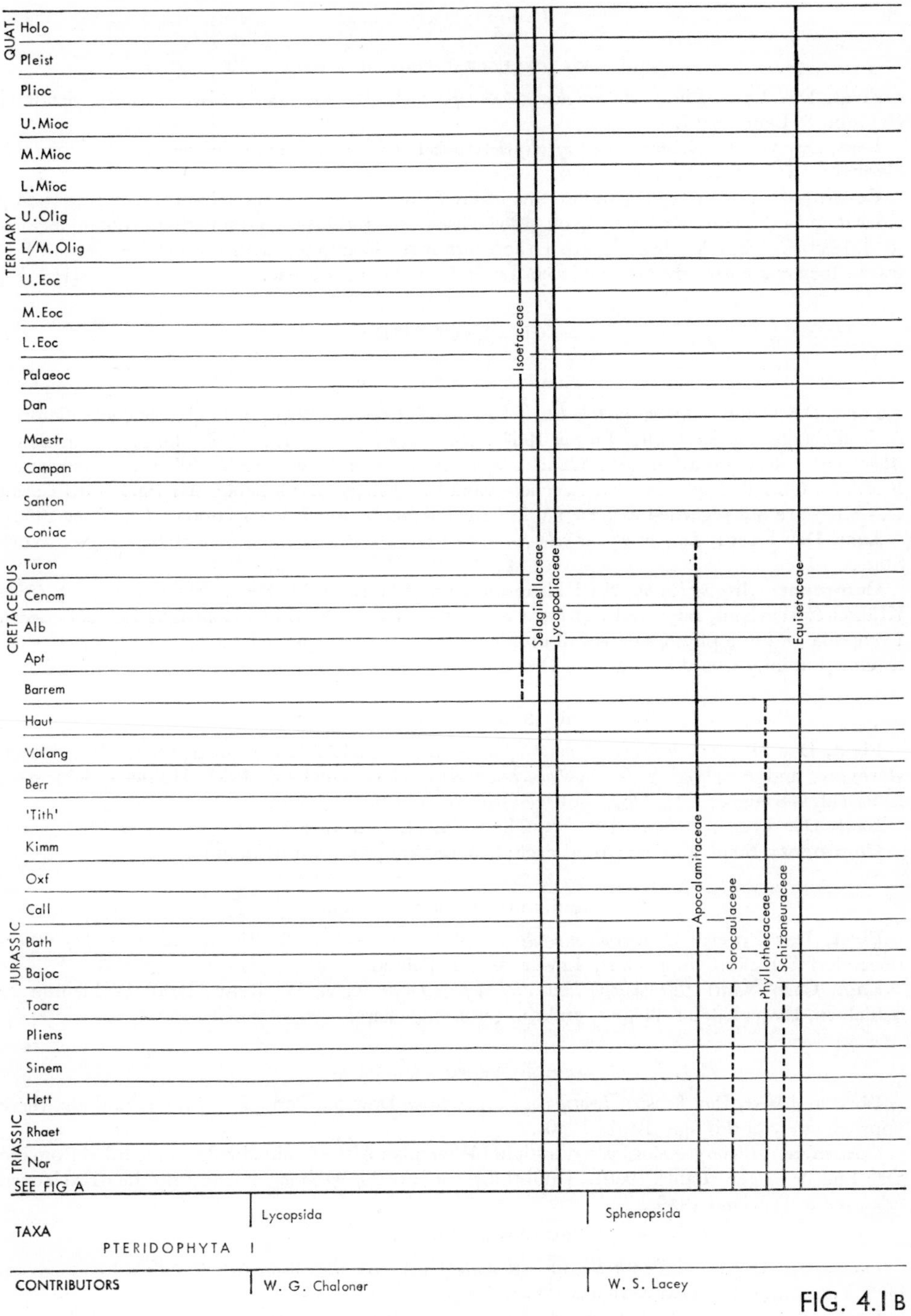
QUAT.
Holo
Pleist
Plioc
U.Mioc
M.Mioc
L.Mioc
TERTIARY
U.Olig
L/M.Olig
U.Eoc
M.Eoc
L.Eoc
Palaeoc
Dan
Maestr
Campan
Santon
Coniac
CRETACEOUS
Turon
Cenom
Alb
Apt
Barrem
Haut
Valang
Berr
'Tith'
Kimm
Oxf
Call
JURASSIC
Bath
Bajoc
Toarc
Pliens
Sinem
Hett
TRIASSIC
Rhaet
Nor
SEE FIG A
Isoetaceae
Selaginellaceae
Lycopodiaceae
Apocalamitaceae
Sorocaulaceae
Phyllothecaceae
Schizoneuraceae
Equisetaceae
TAXA
PTERIDOPHYTA I
Lycopsida
Sphenopsida
CONTRIBUTORS
W. G. Chaloner
W. S. Lacey

FIG. 4.1 B

Group INCERTA SEDIS

Family ASTEROXYLACEAE Kidston & Lang 1920

First, Dev Ems—Eifel: *Asteroxylon mackiei* K & L, Rhynie chert, Aberdeenshire, Scotland (Kidston & Lang 1920).

Last, Dev Givet: *Asteroxylon elberfeldense* Kräusel & Weyland, Honseler beds, near Elberfeld, Germany (Kräusel & Weyland 1926).

Comment: Palynological studies now in progress indicate that the Rhynie chert is probably older than Middle Old Red Sst. Lyon (1964) discovered recently sporangia that probably belong to *A. mackiei*. They are lateral rather than terminal. Combined with the lobed stele and leaf traces, they emphasize the lycopodiaceous affinity of Asteroxylaceae. [H.P.B.]

Class LYCOPSIDA

Family DREPANOPHYCACEAE

First, Dev Gedin: *Baragwanathia longifolia* Lang & Cookson 1935, Jordan River Beds, Victoria, Australia (age not Sil Ludl; Jaeger 1962). *B. oehlheyi* Hundt 1952 (Sil Llandov, Germany), *Aldanophyton* Kryshtofovich (M. Cam U.S.S.R.), *Saxonia* Roselt 1962 (Sil Ludl Germany), *Boiophyton* Obrhel (Ord Llanvirn Czechoslovakia) and *Akdalophyton* Senkevich 1963 (Ord Carad U.S.S.R.) are not regarded as acceptable vascular plants, much less lycopods (Chaloner 1960).

Last, Dev Frasn: *Drepanophycus colophyllus* Grierson & Banks 1963, Seneca Series, New York State.

Comment: *Asteroxylon mackiei* Kidston and Lang (? L. or M. Dev.), but not *A. elberfeldense* Kräusel & Weyland, may well represent a lycopod (Lyon 1964), but its assignation as between Lycopsida and Psilophytopsida is still problematical. If it were to be regarded as a lycopod, then its closest affinity would be with the Drepanophycaceae.

Family PROTOLEPIDODENDRACEAE

First, Dev Siegen: *Sugambrophyton pilgeri* Schmidt 1954, Hamberg-Schichten, Heckersdorf, Germany, and *Protolepidodendron wahnbachense* Kräusel & Weyland, 1932, Honseler Schichten, Elberfeld, Germany (? M. Dev., but see Grierson and Banks 1963).

Last. Dev Frasn: *Colpodexylon deatsii* Banks 1944, Delaware River Flags, New York State.

Comment: Some authors would exclude *Sugambrophyton* from the family.

Family ELEUTHEROPHYLLACEAE

First, Dev Frasn: *Zimmermannia eleutherophylloides* Gothan & Zimmermann 1932, Ober-Bögendorf Schiefern, Bögendorf, Lower Silesia, Poland.

Last, Carb Nam: *Eleutherophyllum drepanophyciforme* R. & W. Remy 1960, Waldenburger Schichten, Lower Silesia, Poland, and the genus elsewhere.

Family LEPTOPHLOEACEAE

First and last, Dev Frasn: *Leptophloeum rhombicum* Dawson, Perry Fm, Maine, and elsewhere approximately of this age (Banks 1960).

Comment: *Blasaria* Zalessky, a questionable member of the family, has been recorded from the Dev Ems or Siegen (Banks 1960). Doubtful records of *Leptophloeum* extend into the Carb Tourn (Kräusel & Weyland 1949).

Family ARCHAEOSIGILLARIACEAE

First, Dev Givet: *Archaeosigillaria vanuxemi* (Goeppert) Kidston, Moscow Fm, Erian Series, New York State (Grierson & Banks 1963).

Last, Carb Viséan: *A. stobbsi* Lacey 1962, Lower Brown Limestone, Dyserth, North Wales.

Comment: ?*A. picosensis* Kräusel & Dolianiti (Dev Gedin or Ems, Brazil) and *A. serotina*

(Gothan) Kräusel & Weyland 1949 are regarded as doubtful records of the genus (and hence family).

Family LEPIDODENDROPSIDACEAE

First. Carb Tourn: *Lepidodendropsis vandergrachti* Jongmans *et al* 1937 and other sp., Pocono Fm, Pennsylvania (Read 1955).

Last, Carb Viséan: *L. jonesi* Lacey 1962, L. Brown Lst, Dyserth, N. Wales.

Comment: *L. arborescens* (Sze) Jongmans (Dev Givet or Eifel) and other Dev records cannot be assigned to this genus or family with certainty (cf. Banks 1960).

Family CYCLOSTIGMATACEAE

First and **Last,** Dev Frasn or Famenn: *Cyclostigma kiltorkense* Haughton, Kiltorkan Beds, Co. Kilkenny, Ireland (Johnson 1913).

Comment: Separation of this family and the next on vegetative material is very unsatisfactory. L. Carb records (e.g. *C. ungeri* Jongmans *et al* 1937), Carb Tourn, are doubtful, and may equally represent the following family. Early Dev records (cf. Grierson & Banks 1963) are even more doubtful.

Family PINAKODENDRACEAE

First, Carb Bashk: *Pinakodendron musivum* Weiss, Charbonnages de Mariement, Westphalian B, Hainaut, Belgium (Martens 1935) and similar horizons elsewhere.

Last, Carb Moscov: *Omphalophloios anglicus* (Sternb.) Kidston, Radstock Group, Somerset, Britain, and elsewhere (Cambier and Renier 1912).

Family LYCOPODIOPSIDACEAE

First and **Last,** Perm: *Cyclodendron, Lycopodiopsis* and *Lycopodiophloios* from the Lower Karroo Fm, S. Africa, various localities in other parts of Africa and other Gondwanan continents, probably of approximately equivalent age (Edwards 1952, Kräusel 1961).

Comment: Relative ages of the earliest and latest records uncertain. The entire family appears to be restricted to Gondwanaland, and equally, it is doubtful whether true Lepidodendraceae or Sigillariaceae are known from any Gondwanan area. *Tundrodendron* Neuburg 1960a, Perm, U.S.S.R. is comparable but as its reproductive structures are unknown, and in view of its disjunction from the Gondwanan distribution of the Lycopodiopsidaceae, it is here excluded from that family.

Family LEPIDODENDRACEAE

First. Carb Tourn: *Lepidophloios kilpatrickense* Smith 1962, Cementstone Group, Dunbartonshire, Scotland and the genus and *Lepidodendron* elsewhere in numberous localities, of undifferentiated L. Carb age.

Last, Perm: *L. tripunctatum* Stockmans & Mathieu 1957, Assise de Tang Chia Chwang, China (the genus elsewhere, Stephanian, e.g. Lee 1964, Wagner 1964). A strict sense of the family is followed here (cf. Eulepidodendraceae Danzé-Corsin 1958) excluding the many lepidodendrids lacking either a clear abscission scar or parichnos, and better regarded as Lepidodendrales *incertae sedis*.

Comment: The earliest record is selected as showing both internal anatomy and clear leaf abscission and parichnos. Earlier records of *"Lepidodendron"* include *Lepidodendropsis, Lepidosigillaria, Archaeosigillaria* and various unassignable partially decorticated forms cf. *Knorria*. Petrified axes without external features (e.g. *"Lepidodendron"* boylensis Read, *"L"*. novalbaniensis Read & Campbell from the L. Carb/Dev transition) are not accepted as record of the family. Later records probably represent other genera of Lepidodendrales not included in this family *s.s.*, such as *Viatscheslavia* and *Lophoderma* in the N. hemisphere and Lycopodiopsidaceae in Gondwanaland. In the strict sense of the family used here, its distribution was probably exclusively northern hemisphere. The family reached its acme in the Carb Bashk—Moscov.

Family LEPIDOCARPACEAE

First, Carb Tourn: *Lepidocarpon wildianum* Scott 1901, Pettycur Lst, Fifeshire, Scotland.

Last, Carb Moscov: *L. palmerensis* Leisman & Spohn 1962, Desmoines Series, Kansas, and other spp. elsewhere, U.S.A.

Family SIGILLARIACEAE

First, Carb Viséan: *Sigillaria* sp., Black Lst., Teilia, N. Wales, (Walton 1931).

Last, Perm ? Assel: *Sigillaria brardi* Brongnt., L. Rotliegenden, W. Germany (Gothan & Remy 1957). Earlier, Dev records (e.g. "*Sigillaria*" *gilboensis* Goldring), are not accepted as record of this genus (see Grierson & Banks 1963).

Comment: The family reaches its acme in the Carb Bashk—Moscov; it is almost entirely (? exclusively) N. Hemisphere in its distribution.

Family BOTHRODENDRACEAE

First, Carb Viséan: *Bothrodendron depereti* Vaffier, Calciferous Sst Series, Scotland and N. England (Crookall 1964).

Last, Carb Moscov: *Bothrodendron punctatum* L. and H., "Westphalian D, South Wales" (Crookall 1964). Later records, e.g. Carb U. Carb: Virgil Series (Cridland *et al.* 1963) need confirmation.

Comment: Separation of this family from the Cyclostigmataceae in sterile material is unsatisfactory. Pre-Carboniferous species attributed to *Bothrodendron* probably represent the Cyclostigmataceae.

Family PLEUROMEIACEAE

First and **Last,** Trias Induan or Olenek: *Pleuromeia sternbergi* (Münster) Corda, Buntsandstein, Saale and elsewhere, Germany (Mägdefrau 1931) and *P. rossica* Neuburg 1960b (approximately equivalent age, U.S.S.R.).

Family MIADESMIACEAE

First and **Last,** Carb Bashk: *Miadesmia membranacea* Bertrand, L. Coal Measures, Westphalian A, Staleybridge, Cheshire, and elsewhere, England (Benson 1908).

Family ISOETACEAE

First, Cret Barrem: *Nathorstiana arborea* Richter, Quedlinburg Sst, Quedlinburg, Germany (Mägdefrau 1932). **Extant** (*Isoetes, Stylites*).

Comment: *Isoetites s.s.* Münster does not appear until the Cret (? U. Cret, e.g. *I. serratus* Brown 1939). Earlier records of *Isoetes* or *Isoetites* (e.g. Trias, Bock 1962) and other genera attributed to the family (*Lepacyclotes* Emmons, Trias; Brown 1958) are not accepted as secure evidence of the family. Present distribution of the family worldwide, tropical and temperate.

Family SELAGINELLACEAE

First, Carb Bashk: *Selaginellites suissei* Zeiller, Barnsley Bed, Westphalian B, Yorkshire, England (Chaloner 1954). **Extant** (*Selaginella*).

Comment: Distinction between *Selaginellites* and living *Selaginella* is arbitrary. Present distribution is worldwide, but chiefly tropical.

Family LYCOPODIACEAE

First, Dev Frasn: *Lycopodites oosensis* Kräusel & Weyland 1937, Ooser Plattenkalk, Budesheim-Oos, Eifel, Germany. **Extant** (*Lycopodium, Phylloglossum*).

Comment: The distinction between *Lycopodites* and *Lycopodium* is arbitrary. Present distribution of the family is worldwide, temperate and tropical. [W.G.C.]

Chapter 4: Pteridophyta—1

Class SPHENOPSIDA Scott 1909

Order HYENIALES sensu Boureau 1964

First, L. Dev: *Hyenia elegans* Kräusel and Weyland 1926, Harz, Germany (Mägdefrau 1938). *Protohyenia janovii* Ananiev 1957, L. Dev, Western Siberia, U.S.S.R., may be the oldest member of the Hyeniales (Delevoryas 1962) but is excluded by Boureau 1964.

Last, Dev Givet: *Calamophyton bicephalum* Leclercq and Andrews 1960, Carrières Brandt, Goé, Belgium; and *Hyenia vogtii* Høeg 1942, uppermost M. Dev, Mimerdalen, Spitsbergen.

Constituent families: Hyeniaceae Kräusel and Weyland 1926, L. and M. (but characteristically M.) Dev, Norway, Germany, Belgium, Spitsbergen, France, Argentina, U.S.S.R.; Calamophytaceae Kräusel and Weyland 1926, M. Dev, Belgium, Germany. Eviostachyaceae F. Stockmans 1948, Dev Famenn, Belgium, is intermediate between Hyeniales and Sphenophyllales, but grouped with Hyeniales by Boureau 1964.

Order PSEUDOBORNIALES Nathorst 1902

First and Last, U. Dev: *Pseudobornia ursina* Nathorst 1894, Bear Island, Arctic Ocean (Nathorst 1894, 1902). Records from U. Dev "Braunwachen" of Lerchenberg and Weinberg, Thuringia, Germany (Mägdefrau 1936) and U. Dev, Huron Member, Ohio Shale, N. Ohio; Genessee Formation, New York State (White *in* Kindle 1912) are unsubstantiated (Mamay 1962). Records from Ireland and Eastern Siberia (Zimmermann 1959) are erroneous (Mamay 1962) but Boureau 1964 cites a record from Minusinsk, Siberia due to Ananiev. Precise age of record from northeastern Alaska (Mamay 1962) is not known.

Constituent families: a single monotypic family Pseudoborniaceae Nathorst 1902. *Prosseria grandis* Read 1953, U. Dev, Genessee Group, New York State, may be pseudobornialean (Mamay 1962).

Order SPHENOPHYLLALES sensu Boureau 1964

First, U. Dev: *Sphenophyllum subtenerrimum* Nathorst 1902, Bear Island, Arctic Ocean (Nathorst 1902); also U. Dev, Bulgaria and Fammen, Belgium (Boureau 1964). *Sphenophyllostachys tumbana* (Remy and Spassov 1959) U. Dev, Tumba, Bulgaria may be the cone of *Sphenophyllum subtenerrimum* (Boureau 1964).

Last, Perm: *Sphenophyllostachys simoni* Remy, U. Autun, Crock, Thuringia, Germany (Remy 1961); *Sphenophyllum tenuifolium* Fontaine and White 1880 also occurs in Perm, U. Autun, France (Zeiller 1892). *Sphenophyllum tomiensis* (Gorelova 1962) U. Perm, Kuznetzk and Tunguska basins, U.S.S.R. may be last record, but horizon not known with precision.

Constituent families: (as in *Traité de Paléobotanique*, Tome III, Boureau 1964), Sphenophyllaceae, U. Dev to Perm, widespread; Cheirostrobaceae, monotypic family, L. Carb, Scotland (Scott 1897); Tristachyaceae, monogeneric family, U. Carb-Perm, Cracow, Poland (Lilpop 1937) and Perm, U. Autun, Crock, Thuringia, Germany (Remy and Remy 1961). Prynadaiaceae, U. Perm, Anhui, China and L. Trias, Madygen, Southern Ferghana, Southern Siberia, U.S.S.R. (Sixtel 1956) is grouped with Sphenophyllales by Boureau 1964.

Order EQUISETALES sensu Boureau 1964

A large Order, with nine Families (as in *Traité de Paléobotanique*, Tome III, Boureau 1964), but only one extant genus.

Family ARCHAEOCALAMITACEAE Stur 1875

First, Carb Tourn: *Archaeocalamites radiatus* (Brongniart 1828) Stur 1875, Culm, Germany and Austria (Stur 1875).

Last, Carb Namur: *Archaeocalamites lohesti* Renier 1910, Assise de Chokier, Belgium (Renier 1910) and *A. bryrichii* Weiss 1884, Namur, Lower Silesia (Weiss 1884).

Comment, widespread in Asia Minor, Europe, Spitsbergen, Greenland and N. America, L. Carb to Namur A. Records from U. Dev are not substantiated: *A. transitionis* Roemer 1854, given as U. Dev-Culm, Europe and Spitsbergen, by Boureau 1964 is cited as a synonym of *A. radiatus*

225

by Jongmans 1911 and is not listed by Leistikow 1959. Hirmer 1927 gives U. Dev–L. Carb for *Asterocalamites scrobiculatus* (Schlotheim) Zeiller, a synonym of *A. radiatus* (Brongniart) Stur, but Zimmermann 1959 gives ?U. Dev–L. Carb. *Pothocites* Paterson 1841 is probably a fructification of Archaeocalamitaceae (Chaphekar 1965).

Family AUTOPHYLLITACEAE Radchenko 1960a

First, Carb Tourn: *Suvundukia aciculata* Zalessky 1948, near the river Aschtschepa-Ssu, Karaganda, S. Urals, U.S.S.R., (Zalessky 1948).

Last, Carb U. Carb: *Autophyllites furcatus* Grand'Eury 1890, Stephanian, Gard, France (Grand'Eury 1890).

Comment, includes several taxa formerly referred by Hirmer 1927 to Archaeocalamitaceae. Widespread in N. Asia and Europe.

Family APOCALAMITACEAE Radchenko 1957

First, Carb Bashk-Moscov: *Angarotheca originalis* Chachlov 1948, Middle Mazurian (M. Carb), Kuzbass, U.S.S.R. (Chachlov 1948).

Last, Cret Turon: *Neocalamites barcenai* Maldonado-Koerdell 1949, Coahuila, N.E. Mexico (Maldonado-Koerdell, 1949).

Comment, the Family is widespread in the Far East, Asia Minor, S. Africa, U.S.S.R., Europe, Greenland, U.S.A. and Mexico; it includes many species of the predominantly U. Trias-L. Jur genus *Neocalamites* Halle 1908, formerly referred to Equisetaceae by Hirmer 1927.

Family CALAMITACEAE sensu Boureau 1964

First, Carb Namur: *Calamites* (sub-genus *Mesocalamites* Hirmer 1927) *cistiiformis* Stur 1877, Namur A, Silesia and Great Britain (Hirmer 1927) and many other species of *Mesocalamites* in the Namur, of Asia Minor, Europe, U.S.S.R. and U.S.A. (Boureau 1964). Species listed by Hirmer 1927 as L. Carb are Namur.

Last, L. Perm: *Calamites* (sub-genus *Stylocalamites*) *cisti* Brongniart 1828, widespread in Europe and North America, and many other species of the compression sub-genus *Stylocalamites* Weiss 1884; also *Arthropitys bistriata* (Cotta) Goeppert 1864, occurring in Europe and North America, and many other species of this petrifaction sub-genus (Boureau 1964).

Comment, an extremely large, unwieldy Family including many compression and petrifaction genera, subgenera and species; widespread in and characteristic of U. Carb-Perm Coal deposits of the Northern Hemisphere.

Family SOROCAULACEAE Radchenko 1956

First, Carb Viséan: *Koretrophyllites vulgaris* Radchenko 1955, L. Carb, Kuznetz and Minusinsk, basins U.S.S.R. (Radchenko 1957).

Last, Trias-Jur: *Neokoretrophyllites annularioides* Radchenko 1960, Trias, Kuznetz and Tunguska basins, Siberia, U.S.S.R. (Radczhenko 1960b). Boureau 1964 states that this sub-genus of *Koretrophyllites* is known from the Rhaetic-Lias, Greenland and the Urals, U.S.S.R. but gives no details.

Comment, virtually all the numerous records of representatives of this Family are from the U.S.S.R.

Family NEUROPHYLLACEAE Kon'no 1941

First and Last, L. Perm: *Neurophyllum koreanicum* Kon'no 1941, L. Perm, Jido Series, Tyosen, Korea (Kon'no 1941).

Comment, this family appears to be intermediate between Sorocaulaceae and Schizoneuraceae (Boureau 1964).

Family PHYLLOTHECACEAE sensu Boureau 1964

First, Carb: *Phyllotheca deliquescens* (Goeppert 1843) Schmalhausen 1879, Kuzbass and Minusinsk basins, U.S.S.R. (Schmalhausen 1879). *Phyllotheca paulinensis* Mamay and Read 1956,

Carb, Spotted Ridge Formation, Oregon, U.S.A. seems doubtfully assigned to *Phyllotheca* (Boureau 1964).

Last, L. Cret: *Phyllotheca whaitsi* Seward 1907, 'Wealden', Uitenhage Series, Cape Province, South Africa (Seward 1907). Several *Phyllotheca* species are also reported from Jur, China, France and Italy (Boureau 1964).

Comment, a predominantly Permian Family, widespread in the Southern Hemisphere and peninsular India (Gondwanaland), but present also in China, U.S.S.R., Europe and N. America.

Family SCHIZONEURACEAE sensu Boureau 1964

First, U. Carb.-L. Perm: *Schizoneura africana* Feistmantel 1889, L. Karroo, South Africa and *S. gondwanensis* Feistmantel 1876 in *Glossopteris* flora of India, Australia, Madagascar (Boureau 1964).

Last, L. Jur: *Schizoneura kuhni* Kräusel 1958, Lias, Sassendorf, Bamberg, Germany (Kräusel 1958).

Comment, a predominantly Permian Family, the genus *Schizoneura* Schimper and Mougeot 1844 being an important constituent of S. Hemisphere *Glossopteris* floras, but also occurring in the N. Hemisphere, particularly in the Far East, and extending into the Jurassic in Europe.

Family EQUISETACEAE sensu Boureau 1964

First, Carb Bashk-Moscov: *Equisetites hemingwayi* (Kidston 1892) Seward 1898, Middle Coal Measures, Monckton Main Colliery, Barnsley, Yorks., England (Seward, 1898). Boureau 1964 states that U. Carb records of *Equisetites* are suspect and does not list *E. hemingwayi*, but Jongmans 1911 and Seward 1933 retain this genus. Boureau 1964 also states that *Equisetites* is only poorly represented in Perm of the N. Hemisphere and not at all in S. Hemisphere. If *E. hemingwayi* is not confirmed, *E. contractus* Goeppert 1864, Perm, Silesia and *E. elongatus* and *E. striatus* Perm, U.S.A. (Fontaine and White 1880) are first records. **Extant.**

Comment, a characteristically Triassic Family, represented by *Equisetites* Sternberg 1833 widespread in Europe, Middle and Far East, U.S.S.R., Greenland, Spitsbergen, U.S.A. and Argentina. Present distribution represented by the single genus *Equisetum* L., with about 25 spp., found in all parts of the world except Australia and New Zealand. [W.S.L.]

REFERENCES

ANANIEV, A. P. 1957. [New fossil plants from the Lower Devonian of Torgachino in the southeastern part of West Siberia]. *Bot. Zh. SSSR*, **42**, 691–702, 5 figs., 1 pl. (Russian.)

BANKS, H. P. 1944. A New Devonian Lycopod Genus from southeastern New York. *Am. J. Bot.*, **31**, 649–59.

—— 1960. Notes on Devonian Lycopods. *Senckenberg. leth.*, **41**, 59–88.

BENSON, M. 1908. *Miadesmia membranacea* Bertrand; a new Palaeozoic Lycopod with seed-like structure. *Phil. Trans. R. Soc.*, **199B**, 409–25.

BOCK, W. 1962. A study on Fossil *Isoetes*. *J. Paleont.*, **36**, 53–59.

BOUREAU, E. 1964. *Traité de Paléobotanique. Tome III*. Masson, Paris.

BROWN, R. W. 1939. Some American Fossil Plants belonging to the Isoetales. *J. Wash. Acad. Sci.*, **29**, 261–9.

—— 1958. New Occurrences of the fossil quillworts called Isoetites. *J. Wash. Acad. Sci.*, **48**, 358–61.

CAMBIER, R. and RENIER, A. 1912. Observations sur *Cyclostigma Macconochiei* Kidston et *Omphalophloios anglicus* Sternberg. *Mém. Soc. géol. Belg.*, **3**, 57–87.

CHACHLOV, V. A. 1948. [Contributions to the knowledge of the fossil flora in the Kamerovsk region of the Kuznetz Basin]. *Trudỹ tomsk. gos. Univ.*, **99** (Russian).

CHALONER, W. G. 1954. Notes on the Spores of Two British Carboniferous Lycopods. *Annl. Mag. nat. Hist.*, ser. 12, **7**, 81–91.

—— 1960. The origin of Vascular Plants. *Sci. Prog., Lond.*, **191**, 524–34.

CHAPHEKAR, M. 1965. On the genus *Pothocites* Paterson. *Palaeontology*, **8,** 107–112; pl. 18.

CRIDLAND, A., MORRIS, J. E. & BAXTER, R. W. 1963. The Pennsylvanian Plants of Kansas and their Stratigraphic Significance. *Palaeontographica*, **112B,** 58–92.

CROFT, W. N. and LANG, W. H. 1942. The Lower Devonian flora of the Senni Beds of Monmouthshire and Breconshire. *Phil. Trans. R. Soc.*, **231B,** 131–163, pl. 9–11.

CROOKALL, R. 1964. Fossil Plants of the Carboniferous Rocks of Great Britain (2nd Secn.). *Mem. geol. Surv. U.K. (Palaeont.)*, **4** (3), 217–354.

DANZÉ-CORSIN, P. 1958. Nouvelle Classification des Lépidophytes du Primaire connues en empreintes. *C. r. hebd. Séanc Acad. Sci., Paris*, **247,** 1226–9.

DELEVORYAS, T. 1962. *Morphology and Evolution of Fossil Plants*. Holt, Rinehart and Winston. New York.

EDWARDS, W. N. 1952. *Lycopodiopsis*, A southern Hemisphere Lepidophyte. *Palaeobotanist*, **1,** 159–64.

FONTAINE, W. M. and WHITE, I. C. 1880. The Permian or Upper Carboniferous flora of West Virginia and Southwest Pennsylvania. *Rep. Prog. 2nd. geol. Surv., Pennsylvania*, 1–143, Harrisburg.

GOEPPERT, H. R. 1864. Die fossile Flora der Permischen Formation. *Palaeontographica*, **12,** 1–316, pl. 1–46.

GORELOVA, S. G. 1962. *in* GORELOVA, S. G. & RADCHENKO, G. P. [Les plantes les plus important des sédiments du fermier Supérieur du District montagneux a Aitai-Saiansk]. *Trudȳ vses. nauchno-issled. géol. Inst.*, 79, 44–45, pl. 1. (Russian).

GOTHAN, W. & REMY, W. 1957. Steinkohlenpflanzen. Essen. 1–248.

—— & ZIMMERMAN, F. 1932. Die Oberdevonflora von Liebichau und Bögendorf (Niederschlesien). *Arb. Inst. Paläobot.*, **2,** 103–130.

GRAND'EURY, C. 1890. *Géologie et Paleontologie du Bassin Houiller du Gard.* 1–354. Paris and St. Etienne.

GRIERSON, J. D. & BANKS, H. P. 1963. Lycopods of the Devonian of New York State. *Palaeontogr. am.*, **4** (31), 217–95.

HIRMER, M. 1927. *Handbuch der Paläobotanik.* I. Munich & Berlin.

HØEG, O. A. 1942. The Downtonian and Devonian flora of Spitsbergen. *Skr. Norg. Svalbard-. Og Ishavs-Unders.*, **83,** 1–228, 35 text figs., pl. 1–62.

HUEBER, F. M. 1964. The psilophytes and their relationship to the origin of ferns. *Mem. Torrey bot. Club*, **21,** No. 5, 5–9. pl. 1.

—— and GRIERSON, J. D. 1961. On the occurrence of *Psilophyton princeps* in the early Upper Devonian of New York. *Am. J. Bot.*, **48,** 473–479, pl. 1–3.

HUNDT, R. 1952. *Von den Ältesten Landpflanzen.* 1–44. Leipzig.

JAEGER, H. 1962. *Das Silur (Gotlandium) in Thüringen und am Ostrand des Rheinischen-schiefergebirges (Kellerwand, Marburg, Giessen).* 108–35. Symposiums-Band der 2e Internationalen Arbeitstagung über die Silur/Devon-Grenze und die Stratigraphie von Silur und Devon, Bonn-Bruxelles 1960. Stuggart 1962.

JOHNSON, T. 1913. On *Bothrodendron (Cyclostigma) kiltorkense* Haughton, sp. *Scient. Proc. R. Dubl. Soc.* (n.s.), **13,** 500–528.

JONGMANS, W. J. 1911. Anleitung zur Bestimmung der Karbonpflanzen West-Europas. I. Thallophyta, Equisetales, Sphenophyllales. *Meded. Rijksopspor. Delfstoff.*, 3.

——, GOTHAN, W. & DARRAH, W. C. 1937. Beitrage zur Kenntnis der Flora der Pocono Schichten aus Pennsylvanien und Virginia. *2ᵉ Congr. Avanc. Étud. Statigr. Carb.*, **1,** 423–44.

KIDSTON, R. and W. H. LANG. 1920. On Old Red Sandstone plants showing structure from the Rhynie chert bed, Aberdeenshire. Part 3. *Asteroxylon mackiei* K & L. *Trans. R. Soc. Edinb.*, **52,** 643–680.

KINDLE, E. M. 1912. The stratigraphic relations of the Devonian shales of Northern Ohio. *Am. J. Sci.*, **200,** 187–213.

KON'NO, E. 1941. On *Neurophyllum koreanicum*, gen. et sp. nov. from the Lower Permian beds of Northern Tyosen (Korea). *Mem. Fac. Sci. Kyushu Univ.*, **1,** 23–51; pl. 1–11.

KRÄUSEL, R. 1958. Die Juraflora von Sassendorf bei Bamberg. I. Sporenpflanzen. *Senckenberg. leth.*, **39** (1/2), 67–103.

—— 1961. *Lycopodiopsis Derbyi* Renault und einige andere Lycopodiales aus den Gondwana-Schichten. *Palaeontographica*, **109B**, 62–92.

—— and H. WEYLAND. 1926. Beiträge zur kenntnis der Devonflora II. *Abh. Senckenb. Naturf. Ges.* **40**, 115–155.

—— & —— 1932. Pflanzenreste aus dem Devon IV. *Protolepidodendron* Krejci. *Senckenbergiana*, **14**, 391–403.

—— & —— 1937. Pflanzenreste aus dem Devon X. Zwei Pflanzenfunde im Oberdevon der Eifel. *Senckenbergiana*, **19**, 338–55.

—— & —— 1949. *Gilboaphyton* und die Protolepidophytales. *Senckenbergiana*, **30**, 129–52.

LACEY, W. S. 1962. Welsh Lower Carboniferous Plants. I. The Flora of the Lower Brown Limestone in the Vale of Clwyd, North Wales *Palaeontographica*, **111B**, 126–160.

LANG, W. H. 1937. On the plant-remains from the Downtonian of England and Wales. *Phil. Trans. R. Soc.*, **227B**, 245–291. pl. 8–14.

—— & COOKSON, I. C. 1935. On a flora, including vascular plants associated with *Monograptus*, in rocks of Silurian age, from Victoria, Australia. *Phil. Trans. R. Soc.*, **224B**, 419–449.

LECLERCQ, S. & ANDREWS, H. N. 1960. *Calamophyton bicephalum*, a new species from the Middle Devonian of Belgium. *An. Mo. Bot. Gdn.*, **47**, 1–23, 16 text figs., pl. 1–5.

LEE, H. H. 1964. The Succession of Upper Palaeozoic Plant Assemblages of North China. 5ᵉ *Congr. Avanc. Étud. Stratigr. Carb.*, **2**, 531–7.

LEISMAN, G. A. & SPOHN, P. A., 1962. The Structure of a *Lepidocarpon strobilus* from Southeastern Kansas. *Palaeontographica*, **111B**, 113–25.

LEISTIKOW, K. U. 1959. *Archaeocalamites* und Archaeocalamitaceae. *Taxon*, **8**, 48–52.

LILPOP, J. 1937. New plants from the Permo-carboniferous rocks of Poland. *Bull. int. Acad. pol. Sci. Lett.*, **1B**, 1–10; 3 textfigs., pl. 1.

LYON, A. G. 1964. The probable fertile region of *Asteroxylon mackiei* K & L. *Nature, Lond.*, **203**, 1082–1083.

MÄGDEFRAU, K. 1931. Zur Morphologie und phylogenetischen Bedeutung der fossilen Pflanzengattung *Pleuromeia*. *Beih. bot. Zbl.*, **48**, 119–40.

—— 1932. Uber *Nathorstiana*, eine Isoetaceae aus dem Neokom von Quedlinburg am Harz. *Beih. bot. Zbl.*, **49**, 706–718.

—— 1936. Die Flora des Oberdevons in östlichen Thüringer Wald. *Beih. bot. Zbl.*, **56**, 213–228.

—— 1938. Eine Halophyten-flora aus dem Unterdevon des Harzes. *Beih. bot. Zbl.*, **56**, 243–251, pl. I-II.

MALDONADO-KOERDELL, M. 1949. Nueva equisetal del Cretacio superior de Coahuila, Mex. *Bol. Asoc. Mex. Geol. Petrol.*, **1**, 27–34.

MAMAY, S. H. 1962. Occurrence of *Pseudobornia* Nathorst in Alaska. *Palaeobotanist*, **11** (1,2), 19–22.

—— and READ, C. B. 1956. Additions to the flora of the Spotted Ridge Formation of Central Oregon. *Prof. Pap. U.S. geol. Surv.*, **274** (1), 211–226, 4pl.

MARTENS, M. P. 1935. La fructification de *Pinakodendron Ohmanni*. *Annls Soc. Scient. Brux.* (B), **55**, 206–214.

NATHORST, A. G. 1894. Zur Paläozoischen Flora der Arktischen Zone. *K. Svenska Vetensk-Akad. Handl.*, **26** (4).

—— 1902. Zur Fossilen Flora der Polarländer. Zur Oberdevonischen Flora der Bäreninsel. *K. Svenska Vetensk.-Akad. Handl.*, **36**(3), 1–60, pl. 1–14.

NEUBURG, M. F. 1960a. Permian Flora from the Pecherskogo Basin. *Trudy̆ geol. Inst. Leningr.*, **43**, 3–64. [In Russian]

—— 1960b. *Pleuromeia* Corda from the Lower Triassic shales of the Russian Platform. *Trudy̆. Geol. Inst., Leningr.*, **43**, 65–92. [In Russian]

OBRHEL, J. 1962. Die Flora der Pridoli-Schichten (Budnany-Stufe) des mittelböhmischen Silurs. *Geologie* **11**, 83–97, pl. 1–2.

RADCHENKO, G. P. 1956. *in Materialy po Paleontologii.* V.S.E.G.E.I. new palaeontological series, no. 12, Moscow.

—— 1957. [Morphological and anatomical features of some Carboniferous plants from the Kuznetz Province]. *in A.N.Kryshtofovich Commemorative Volume,* pp. 33–54, Inst. Bot. Komarov, Akademii Nauk SSSR, Moscow. [In Russian]

—— 1960a (with M. O. BORSUK). [New representatives of the Autophyllitaceae from the Karaganda Basin] in MARKOVSKY, B. P. (Editor) [*New Species of ancient plants and invertebrates in the USSR, Volume 1*]. V.S.E.G.E.I., Moscow. (Russian)

—— 1960b. [New *Neokoretrophyllites*] in MARKOVSKY, B. P. (Editor) [*New species of ancient plants and invertebrates in the USSR, Volume 1*]. V.S.E.G.E.I., Moscow (Russian).

READ, C. B. 1953. *Prosseria grandis,* a new genus and species from the Upper Devonian of New York. *J. Wash. Acad. Sci.,* **43,** 13–16.

—— 1955. Floras of the Pocono Formation and Price Sandstone in Parts of Pennsylvania, Maryland, West Virginia and Virginia. *Prof. Pap. U.S. geol. Surv.,* **263,** 1–32.

REMY, R. 1961. Beiträge zur Flora des Autuniens III. *Mber. dt. Akad. Wiss. Berl.,* **3** (5–6), 331–336, 2 pl.

—— & REMY, W. 1960. *Eleutherophyllum drepanophyciforme* n. sp., aus dem Namur A von Niederschlesien. *Senckenberg. leth.,* **41,** 89–100.

—— & —— 1961. Beiträge zur Flora Autuniens II. *Mber. dt. Akad. Wiss. Berl.,* **3** (3–4), 213–225, 4 pl.

REMY, W. & SPASSOV, C. 1959. Der paläobotanische Nachweis von Oberdevon in Bulgarien. *Mber. dt. Akad. Wiss. Berl.,* **1** (6), 380–387, 1 text fig., 2 pl.

RENIER, A. 1910. *Asterocalamites lohesti* n.sp. du Houiller sans houille (H I a) du bassin d'Anhee. *Mem. Soc. géol. Belg.,* **2** (2), 31–34, pl. VI.

ROEMER, F. A. 1854. Beiträge zur geologische Kenntnisse der Nord-west Harzegebirges. *Palaeontographica,* **3,** 45, pl. 7.

ROSELT, G. 1962. Über die ältesten Landpflanzen und eine mögliche Landpflanze aus dem Ludlow Sachsens. *Geologie* **11,** 320–33.

SCHMALHAUSEN, J. 1879. Jura-Flora Russland. *Zap. imp. Akad. nauk, ser.* 7, **27** (4), 12–14.

SCHMIDT, W. 1954. Pflanzen-Reste aus der Tonschiefer-Gruppe (Unteres Siegen) des Siegerlandes. I. Sugambrophyton pilgeri n.g. n. sp., eine Protolepidodendraceae aus den Hamberg-Schichten. *Palaeontographica,* **97B,** 1–22.

SCOTT, D. H. 1897. On *Cheirostrobus,* a new type of fossil cone from the Lower Carboniferous strata (Calciferous Sandstone Series). *Phil. Trans. R. Soc.,* **189B,** 1–34.

—— 1901. On the Structure and Affinity of Fossil Plants from the Palaeozoic Rocks IV. The seedlike fructification of *Lepidocarpon. Phil. Trans. R. Soc.,* **194B,** 291–333.

—— 1909. *Studies in Fossil Botany.* Vol. 2. Edn. 2, London.

SENKEVICH, M. A. 1963. New finding of Upper Ordovician flora in Kazakhstan. *Izv. Akad. nauk SSSR, geol. Ser.,* **5,** 67–81. (English translation from the Russian, 1965, in *Int. Geol. Rev.,* **7** (3) 476–85).

SEWARD, A. C. 1898. *Fossil Plants.* I. C.U.P.

—— 1907. Fossil plants from South Africa. *Geol. Mag.,* **34,** 481, pl. 20.

—— 1933. *Plant Life through the Ages.* C.U.P.

SIXTEL, T. A. 1956. In *Materially po Paleontologii* (New families and genera). V.S.E.G.E.I., new palaeontology series, issue No. 12, 219–220; text-fig. 5, plate 37.

SMITH, D. L. 1962. The stems of three species of Lepidodendrid from the Scottish Lower Carboniferous. *Ann. Bot.* (n.s.), **26,** 533–49.

STOCKMANS, F. 1948. Végétaux du Dévonien Supérieur de la Belgique. *Mem. Mus. r. Hist. Nat. Belg.,* **110,** 1–85, pl. 1–14.

—— & MATHIEU, F. 1957. La flore paléozoïque du Bassin houiller de Kaiping (Chine). *Publ. Ass. Etud. Paléont.* **32,** 1–89.

STUR, D. 1875. Die Kulm-flora des Mährisch-Schlesischen Dachschiefers. *Abh. geol. Reichsanst., Wien.,* **8,** 2–19, pl. 1–5.

WAGNER, R. H. 1964. Stephanian Floras in N.W. Spain, with special reference to the West-phalian D-Stephanian A boundary. *5th Congr. Avanc. Etud. Stratigr. Carb.*, **2**, 835–51.

WALTON, J. 1931. Contributions to the Knowledge of Lower Carboniferous Plants—Pt. III. *Phil. Trans. R. Soc.*, **219B**, 347–79.

—— 1964. On the morphology of *Zosterophyllum* and some other early Devonian plants. *Phyto-morphology*, **14**, 155–160, fig. 1–3.

WEISS, C. E. 1884. Beiträge zur fossilen Flora Steinkohlen-Calamarien. *Abh. geol. Spezkarte Pruess. Thüring. Staat.*, **5** (2), 1–204.

WHITE, D. 1903. Description of a fossil alga from the Chemung of New York with remarks on the genus *Haliserites* Stbg. *Rep. N.Y. St. Mus. nat. Hist.* for 1901, 593–605, pl. 3–4.

ZALESSKY, M. D. 1948. Über einen neuen Vertreter der Sphenophylleae *Suvundukia aciculata* gen. nov. et sp. nov. *Neues Jb. Geol. Paläont., Mh.*, (1–4), 42–46.

ZEILLER, R. 1892. *Basin Houiller et Permien de Brive. Etudes gîtes mineraux de la France.*

ZIMMERMANN, W. 1959. *Die Phylogenie der Pflanzen.* Gustav Fischer Verlag, Stuttgart.

[Professor] H. P. Banks
Department of Botany, Cornell University, Ithaca, N.Y., U.S.A.
W. G. Chaloner, PH.D. F.G.S.
Department of Botany, University College, London W C 1.
W. S. Lacey, PH.D. F.G.S.
Department of Botany, University College of North Wales, Bangor, N. Wales.

Note on the Family PSILOPHYTACEAE

Following re-investigation of *Psilophyton* Dawson (F. M. Hueber & H. P. Banks 1967, *Taxon* **16**, 81–5) and recent unpublished work by W. S. Lacey and El-Saadawy suggesting that *Nothia* Lyon 1964 belongs to this family, Banks (1967, in press) will propose a new family name based on *Gosslingia*.

[H.P.B.]

CHAPTER 5

Pteridophyta—2

Contributors: H. P. BANKS, M. G. COLLETT, F. R. GNAUCK & N. F. HUGHES

Introduction. The genera *Archaeopteris* and *Callixylon* have been included under Progymnosperm-opsida in Chapter 6. The Stauropteridaceae have been retained in this chapter in spite of uncertainty about the meaning of their heterospory.

The classification of the Filicales follows Holttum (1949), and the arrangement of other groups follows Sporne (1962).

Class PTEROPSIDA

Order CLADOXYLALES

Family CLADOXYLACEAE Hirmer 1927

First, Dev Givet: *Pseudosporochnus verticillatus* (Krejci) Obrhel and *P. chlupaci* Obrhel, Srbsko strata, Central Bohemia, *P. nodosus* Leclercq and Banks, Synclinorium de la Vesdre, Belgium, *Xenocladia medullosina* Arnold, Ludlowville Fm, western New York State.

Last, Carb Viséan: *Vöelkelia refracta* (Gœpp) Solms, Glatzisch-Falkenberg, Silesia.

Comment: Cladoxylaceae is known from petrified axes (Bertrand 1935) except for one species of *Pseudosporochnus* and one of *Cladoxylon*. Both external morphology and internal structure are known for *P. nodosus* Leclercq and Banks 1962 and *C. scoparium* Krausel and Weyland.

Order COENOPTERIDALES

Family TRIMEROPHYTACEAE Banks 1967

First, Dev Siegen: *Dawsonites arcuatus* Halle, Senni beds, Wales (Croft and Lang 1942).

Last, Dev Eifel: *D. arcuatus* Halle, Jemelle, Belgium (Stockmans 1940).

Comment: One other genus *Trimerophyton*, Dev Ems, Gaspé only (Hopping 1956), included in this new family. Both genera formerly in Psilophytopsida but now shown to have complex morphology and anatomy associated with coenopterid-type ferns (Banks 1964, Hueber 1964). Occurs chiefly in Dev Ems.

Family ARACHNOXYLACEAE Arnold 1940

First, Dev Givet: *Arachnoxylon kopfi* (Arnold) Read 1938, Leicester member, Moscow Fm, New York State.

Last, Dev Frasn: *A.* sp., Sherburne Fm (Lodi ls.), New York State (Banks *et al.*, 1959).

The Fossil Record, pp. 233–245. Geological Society of London, 1967. Printed in Northern Ireland.

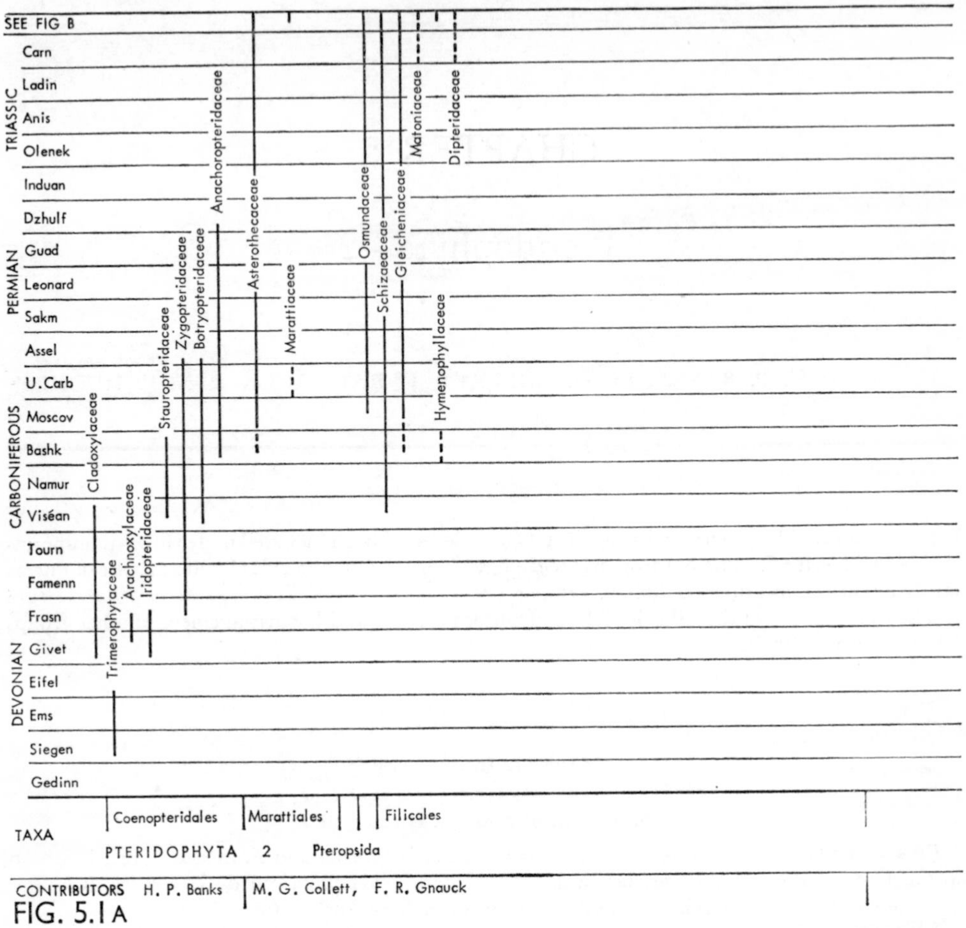

FIG. 5.1 A

Comment: The family is confined to New York State and is based on petrifactions of small axes (Banks *et al.* 1959).

Family IRIDOPTERIDACEAE Arnold 1940

First, Dev Givet: *Reimannia aldenense* Arnold 1935, Ludlowville Fm, western New York State.

Last, Dev Frasn: *R. aldenense*, Sherburne Fm (Lodi ls.), central New York State (Banks *et al.*, 1959).

Comment: Family includes only *Reimannia*, and *Iridopteris eriensis* Arnold which is confined to Moscow Fm, Dev Givet. Family reported only from New York State and based on petrifactions of small axes (Banks *et al.* 1959). *Reimaniopsis indianensis* (R & C) Hoskins & Cross (Syn. *Reimannia indianensis* Read & Campbell) Famenn-Tourn is excluded.

Family STAUROPTERIDACEAE Hirmer 1927

First, Carb Viséan: *Stauropteris burntislandica* Pettycur ls., U. Oil Sh Group, Pettycur, Scotland (Surange 1952a).

Last, Carb Bashk: *Stauropteris oldhamia* Binney, Upper Foot Coal Seam, Westphalian A, Oldham, England (Surange 1952a).

Comment: *Stauropteris* is the only genus included in this family.

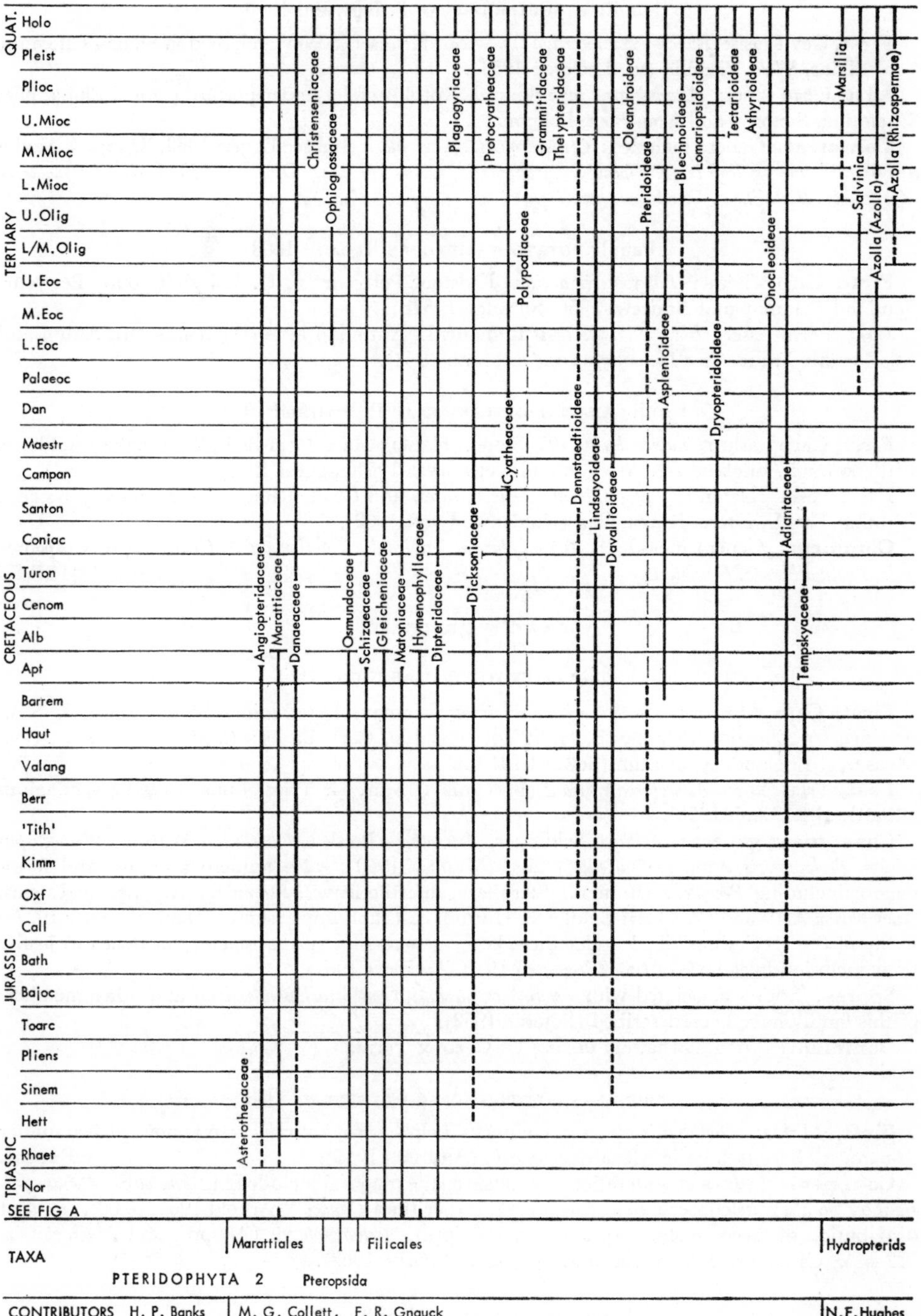
QUAT.
Holo
Pleist
Plioc
U.Mioc
M.Mioc
L.Mioc
U.Olig
L/M.Olig
U.Eoc
M.Eoc
L.Eoc
Palaeoc
Dan
Maestr
Campan
Santon
Coniac
Turon
Cenom
Alb
Apt
Barrem
Haut
Valang
Berr
'Tith'
Kimm
Oxf
Call
Bath
Bajoc
Toarc
Pliens
Sinem
Hett
Rhaet
Nor
TERTIARY
CRETACEOUS
JURASSIC
TRIASSIC
SEE FIG A
Asterothecaceae
Angiopteridaceae
Marattiaceae
Danaeaceae
Christenseniaceae
Ophioglossaceae
Osmundaceae
Schizaeaceae
Gleicheniaceae
Matoniaceae
Hymenophyllaceae
Dipteridaceae
Plagiogyriaceae
Dicksoniaceae
Protocyatheaceae
Cyatheaceae
Polypodiaceae
Grammitidaceae
Thelypteridaceae
Dennstaedtioideae
Lindsayoideae
Davallioideae
Oleandroideae
Pteridoideae
Asplenioideae
Blechnoideae
Lomariopsidoideae
Dryopteridoideae
Tectarioideae
Athyrioideae
Onocleoideae
Adiantaceae
Tempskyaceae
Marsilia
Salvinia
Azolla (Azolla)
Azolla (Rhizospermae)
TAXA
Marattiales
Filicales
Hydropterids
PTERIDOPHYTA 2
Pteropsida
CONTRIBUTORS H. P. Banks
M. G. Collett, F. R. Gnauck
N. F. Hughes

FIG. 5.1 B

Family ZYGOPTERIDACEAE P. Bertrand 1909

First, Dev Frasn: *Rhacophyton incertum* (Dawson) Kräusel & Weyland, Saxton Shales, Chemung Fm, Elkins, West Virginia (see Leclercq 1951).

Last, Perm Assel: *Asterochlaena laxa* Stenzel, Rothliegende, upper porphyry zone, Floha, near Chemnitz, Saxony, and Neu-Paka, Bohemia.

Comment: Genera included: *Clepsydropsis, Ankyropteris* (but see Eggert 1963, Eggert & Taylor 1966), *Metaclepsydropsis, Diplolabis, Asteropteris, Asterochlaena, Dineuron, Etapteris, Corynepteris, Zygopteris, Biscalitheca, Monoscalitheca.*

Family BOTRYOPTERIDACEAE Renault 1883

First, Carb Viséan: *Botryopteris antiqua* Kidston, Pettycur ls., U. Oil sh Group, Pettycur, Scotland (Mamay and Andrews 1950, Surange 1952b).

Last, Perm Assel: *Botryopteris forensis* Renault, L. Autunian beds (Wolfcampian), Autun and St. Etienne, France (see Delevoryas and Morgan 1954).

Family ANACHOROPTERIDACEAE P. Bertrand 1909

First, Carb Bashk: *Tubicaulis sutcliffii* Stopes, Halifax Hard Coal Beds, Westphalian A, Shore, Littleborough, England (see Morgan and Delevoryas 1954, Eggert 1959).

Last, Perm ?Dzhulf: *Tubicaulis africanus* Holden and Croft, Ruhuhu beds (Karroo system), Ruhuhu, Southwestern Tanganyika (Holden & Croft 1962).

Comment: Genera included: *Anachoropteris, Tubicaulis, Chorionopteris, Grammatopteris, Apotropteris, Psalixochlaena, Gyropteris.* [H.P.B.]

Order MARATTIALES

Family ASTEROTHECACEAE (Stur) 1883

First, Carb Moscov: *Cyathotrachus altissimus* Mamay, Des Moines Series, Iowa, U.S.A., petrified fructification (Mamay S. H. 1950). Possibly, Carb Bashk: *C. altus* Watson, L. Coal Measures, England, synangium (Seward 1910).

Last, Trias Nor: *Asterotheca meriani* (Brongniart) Stur, U. Trias, Lunz, Austria, synangium (Bhardwaj & Singh 1956).

Constituent genera: *Acitheca* Schimper, *Asterotheca* Presl, *Cyathotrachus* Watson, *Ptychocarpus* Weiss, *Scolecopteris* Zenker, *Sturiella* Weiss, (Mamay 1950); also numerous organ- and form-genera including *Pecopteris* (Brongn.) Sternberg, infertile leaves, *Psaronius* Cotta, petrified stems, *Megaphyton* Artis and *Caulopteris* Lindley & Hutton, casts and impressions of stems (Hirmer 1927); many of the species described under these latter genera show no satisfactory evidence to justify their inclusion in the Marattiales (Seward 1910, Andrews 1961).

Spores: Spores associated with *Asterotheca meriani, Cyathotrachus altissimus* and other members of this family have been described (Potonié 1962).

Comment: Prominent family during U. Carb & Perm.

Family ANGIOPTERIDACEAE Christensen 1938

First, ?Trias: *Danaeopsis* sp., see comment below. *Angiopteridium* spp. now placed under *Marattiopsis* here treated in Marattiaceae q.v. (Andrews 1955). **Extant.**

Comment: From a consideration of Triassic fertile material included in *Danaeopsis*—"*Danaeopsis* may be a Triassic forerunner of *Angiopteris* rather than *Danaea*" (Arnold 1964, p. 60). Present distribution of three genera *Angiopteris* (c. 100 spp.), *Archangiopteris* (?4 spp.) and *Macroglossum* (?2 spp.) Old World, Polynesia to Madagascar (Sporne 1962).

Family MARATTIACEAE Kaulfuss 1824

First, Trias Rhaet: *Marattiopsis hoerensis* (Schimper) Thomas, Rhaet, Greenland, fertile leaf fragments (Andrews 1961). Not all spp. of *Marattiopsis* justify inclusion in Marattiaceae sensu stricto (Seward 1910). Possibly U. Carb *Marattiotheca grand'euryi* Schimper belongs here (Andrews 1955). **Extant.**

Spores: Spores associated with *M. hoerensis* etc. described (Potonié 1962).

Comment: Present distribution of single genus *Marattia* (c. 60 spp.) pan-tropical south to New Zealand (Sporne 1962).

Family DANAEACEAE (Christensen) Sporne 1962

First, Jur: *Danaea microphylla* Raciborski, Jur, Poland (Seward 1910). *Danaeites sarepontanus* Stur, M. Carb, Saar, Germany and *Danaeopsis fecunda* Halle, Trias Rhaet, Scania, Sweden are of doubtfully danaeaceous affinity (Hirmer 1927). (See also note under Angiopteridaceae, above.) **Extant.**

Spores: Spores associated with *D. fecunda* etc. described (Potonié 1962).

Comment: Present distribution of single genus *Danaea* (32 spp.) confined to New World (Sporne 1962).

Family CHRISTENSENIACEAE (Christensen) Sporne 1962

No known fossil record.

Comment: Present distribution of sole species *Christensenia aesculifolia* (Blume) Maxon confined to Indo-Malayan region (Sporne 1962).

Order OPHIOGLOSSALES

Family OPHIOGLOSSACEAE (Presl) 1836

First, Tert Eoc: *Ophioglossites eocena* Massalongo, Eoc, Monte Bolca, Italy (Andrews 1955). *O. antiqua* Renault, Carb, cannot be regarded as a member of this family (Seward 1910, Hirmer 1927). **Extant.**

Comment: Present distribution of three genera *Botrychium* (35 spp.) cosmopolitan, *Ophioglossum* (45 spp.) widespread and *Helminthostachys* (1 sp.) restricted to Indo-Malaysia and Polynesia (Sporne 1962).

Order OSMUNDALES

Family OSMUNDACEAE (R. Brown) 1810

First, Carb Moscov: *Discopteris karwinensis* Stur, middle U. Carb, Kattowitz, Silesia, fertile leaf fragments. Other spp. described from material of the same age in Silesia, and from Bohemia, France and Asia (Hirmer 1927). *Thamnopteris schlechtendalii* (Eichwald) Brongniart, U. Perm, Kamskowothin, Russia, petrified stem. Material of ± same age contains numerous spp. described under five additional genera *Petcheropteris*, *Zalesskya*, *Chasmopteris*, *Bathypteris* and *Anomorrhoea* (Andrews 1961). L. Carb records including *Todea lipoldi*, sterile leaf impressions; *Todeopsis primaeva*, petrified sporangia; and *Kidstonia heracleensis*, fertile leaf fragments, are not osmundaceous (Seward 1910). **Extant.**

Spores: Associated spores include examples of *Cladotheca*, *Osmundopsis* and *Todites* from Trias Rhaet and Jur (Potonié 1962).

Comment: Fossil representatives of the family were prominent and widespread particularly during the Mesozoic (Andrews 1961). Present distribution of three genera *Osmunda* (14 spp.) widespread in both hemispheres, *Leptopteris* (6 spp.) confined to Australasia and South Sea Islands, and *Todea* (1 sp.) S. Africa and Australasia (Sporne 1962).

Order FILICALES (= Eufilicinae–Homosporous)

Family SCHIZAEACEAE Martius 1834

First, Carb Viséan: *Senftenbergia sturi* (Sterzel) Radforth, L. Carb, Cuthill Rocks near Mussel-burgh, Scotland, fertile leaf fragments (Radforth 1939). Spp. of *Senftenbergia* also described from Yorkshire, England; Saar, Germany and elsewhere (Hirmer 1927). **Extant.**

Spores: Associated spores of *S. sturi* and many other fossil members of the family described (Potonié 1962).

Comment: Family well represented in Mesozoic floras by *Klukia* and extant genera *Lygodium* and *Anemia* appearing in Jur. Present distribution of four genera *Lygodium* (39 spp.) pan-tropical extending as far as N.Z. and Japan, *Anemia* (90 spp.) mainly tropical America extending through Africa and Madagascar to India, *Schizaea* (30 spp.) Southern Hemisphere and *Mohria* (1 sp.) tropical and S. Africa (Copeland 1947).

Family GLEICHENIACEAE (Gaudichaud) 1826

First, Carb Moscov: *Oligocarpia brongniarti* Stur, Basal Pictou, New Brunswick, Canada, fertile leaf fragments. This sp. has also been recorded from Lancaster Fm, New Brunswick, which is possibly Carb Bashk. A total of nine spp. of *Oligocarpia* have been recorded, all Carb Moscov, Europe and N. America. The only other fossil genus assigned to this family, *Gleichenites* Goeppert, contains several spp. ranging from Trias to Quat Holo (Abbott 1954). **Extant.**

Spores: Associated spores described include species of *Oligocarpia* and *Gleichenites* (Potonié 1962).

Comment: Family most widely represented during Cret with few records from Trias-Jur and Eocene, but for many spp. of infertile fronds described under *Gleichenites* the implied affinity cannot always be substantiated (Andrews 1961, Arnold 1964). Present distribution of only genus (sometimes split into four) *Gleichenia* (c. 130 spp.) pan-tropical, extending as far as Japan, New Zealand, etc. (Sporne 1962, Copeland 1947).

Family MATONIACEAE Presl 1848

First, Trias Carn-Nor: *Phlebopteris muensteri* (Schenk) Hirmer & Hörhammer, M. Keuper, Lunz, Austria (Hirmer & Hörhammer 1936). Also U. Trias, *P. smithii* (Daugherty) Arnold, Chinle Fm, Arizona, U.S.A. (Arnold 1956). **Extant.**

Spores: Associated spores from numerous members including species of *Phlebopteris* described (Pontonié 1962).

Comment: Family's widest distribution during Mesozoic with records of *Phlebopteris* and *Matonidium* Schenk from Greenland to Australia (Hirmer & Hörhammer 1936). Present distribution of two genera *Matonia* (2 spp.) and *Phanerosorus* (2 spp.) restricted to Malaysia (Christensen 1938).

Family HYMENOPHYLLACEAE Gaudichaud 1826

First, Carb Bashk: *Hymenophyllites quadridactylites* Gutbier, middle U. Carb, France, Germany and U.K., fertile leaf fragments, may doubtfully be assigned to this family. Not all infertile specimens placed under this genus and under *Trichomanites* Geoppert, can be accepted as showing affinities with the Hymenophyllaceae (Hirmer 1927, Seward 1910, Andrews 1955). *Trichomanides laxum* Tenison-Woods, Jur, Queensland, Australia, fertile frond, of which the author says "this fossil cannot be distinguished from (the extant) *Trichomanes*" is probably more reliable (Tenison-Woods 1884). **Extant.**

Spores: Spores associated with a Tert Plioc species of *Trichomanes* described (Potonié 1962).

Comment: Family poorly represented in the fossil record. Present distribution of about 650 spp. variously placed in 2–34 genera mainly tropical but extends to moist habitats in temperate regions (Sporne 1962).

Family DIPTERIDACEAE Seward & Dale 1901

First, Trias Carn-Nor: *Camptopteris lunzensis* Stur, Lunz, Austria, leaf fragment, is not figured and consequently of uncertain value. Alternatively, Trias Nor: *Dictyophyllum serratum* (Kurr) Frentzen, Keuper, Sweden, Switzerland and Germany, and *Thaumatopteris lunzensis* Stur, Keuper, Lunz, Austria, fertile leaf fragment (Ôishi & Yamasita 1936). **Extant.** (See Comment below).

Spores: Spores associated with Trias Rhaet and Jur species of *Dictyophyllum*, *Thaumatopteris* etc. described (Potonié 1962).

Comment: The fossil Dipteridaceae reached its maximum development in Trias Rhaet to

Jur Bajoc and waned towards the end of the Mesozoic, except *Hausmannia* which flourished during the younger Mesozoic (Ôishi & Yamasita 1936, p. 175). Present distribution of the single genus *Dipteris* (c. 8 spp.) restricted to Indo-Malayan region (Sporne 1962). However, the genus is sometimes included with the Polypodiaceae (Holttum 1949).

Family PLAGIOGYRIACEAE Bower 1926

No known fossil record.

Comment: Present distribution of single genus Plagiogyra (c. 35 spp.) S.E. Asia, N. and S. America (Copeland 1947).

Family DICKSONIACEAE Presl 1836

First, Jur Hett-Bajoc: *Coniopteris hymenophylloides* (Brongniart), Seward, (as *Dicksonia heeri* Raciborski and *D. zareczyi* Rac.) Lias, Poland, fertile leaf fragments; also from L. and M. Jur of Spitsbergen, Greenland and England. *C. lunzensis* Stur, U. Trias, Lunz, Austria, has no affinities with the Dicksoniaceae (Hirmer 1927). Also *Dicksonites pluckeneti* (Schlotheim) Sterzel, U. Carb and Perm, Germany, has been shown to be a pteridosperm (Seward 1910). **Extant.**

Spores: Spores associated with *C. hymenophylloides* and other members of the family described (Potonié 1962).

Comment: Present distribution of four genera (c. 30 spp.) *Dicksonia, Cibotium, Cystodium* and *Thyrsopteris* mainly tropical and southern (Holttum 1949).

Family PROTOCYATHEACEAE (Bower) 1926

No known fossil record.

Comment: *Protocyathea trichinopoliensis* Ottokar Feistmantel, Cret Cenom, India, silicified stem, has no direct affinity with this family (Andrews 1955). Present distribution of two genera *Lophosoria* (1 sp.) and *Metaxya* (1 sp.) restricted to tropical America (Holttum 1949).

Family CYATHEACEAE Reichenbach 1828

First, Jur Oxf-'Tith': *Cyathocaulis naktongensis* Ogura, L. Kyong-sang Fm, N. Kyong-sang Do, Korea, silicified stem; also *Cibotiocaulis tateiwae* Ogura, from the same location (Arnold 1964, Andrews 1955). *Alsophilites polonica* (Raciborski) Hirmer, Jur, Poland, fertile foliage (Hirmer 1927). Palaeozoic infertile foliage described under such generic names as *Cyatheites* etc. cannot be accepted as evidence of the existence of the family at that time (Seward 1910). **Extant.**

Comment: Present distribution of three genera *Alsophila* (c. 300 spp.), *Hemitelia* (c. 100 spp.) and *Cyathea* (c. 300 spp.) pantropical and southern (Sporne 1962, Holttum 1949).

Family POLYPODIACEAE R. Brown 1810

First, Jur: *Polypodium oregonense* Fontaine, Jur, Oregon, U.S.A., infertile leaf fragments and consequently of uncertain value (Seward 1910). Plants resembling the extant *Drynaria ireoides* Lam. have been described from Tert Mioc, Switzerland (Hirmer 1927). **Extant.**

Spores: Reliable records of associated spores from the Polypodiaceae sensu stricto appear to be lacking.

Comment: The Polypodiaceae and the four remaining extant families Grammitidaceae, Thelypteridaceae, Dennstaedtiaceae and Adiantaceae all of which are included in the Polypodiaceae by some authors (Bower, Christensen etc.), have a very uncertain history reflecting the confused taxonomic status of many living members of the family. Many taxa included in these families are probably late products of evolution and some of the unclassified ferns of the Mesozoic probably belong here (Arnold 1964). The fossil record is further confused by determinations made on infertile foliage and often fragmentary remains. Thus most of the Palaeozoic forms assigned to such genera as *Adiantites* etc. must be regarded as having very doubtful affinities with these families. The twelve extant genera which Holttum lists for the Polypodiaceae sensu stricto, have a widespread present distribution (Holttum 1949).

Family GRAMMITIDACEAE Holttum 1947

No known fossil record.

Comment: Present distribution of this mainly epiphytic and highly specialized family of nine genera (c. 250 spp.) is pantropical (Holttum 1949). See also comment under Polypodiaceae.

Family THELYPTERIDACEAE (Ching) Holttum 1947

No known fossil record.

Comment: Present distribution of six genera mainly tropical (Holttum 1947, 1949). See also comment under Polypodiaceae.

Family DENNSTAEDTIACEAE (Ching) Holttum 1947

Comment: Holttum proposed eleven subfamilies for his family Dennstaedtiaceae and his arrangement is followed here although subsequent authors have suggested raising these to family rank (Pichi-Sermolli 1958, Sporne 1962). Fossil members of the Dennstaedtiaceae have been described mostly under Polypodiaceae sensu lato but an attempt has been made here to arrange them according to these more modern views. See also comment under Polypodiaceae.

Subfamily DENNSTAEDTIOIDEAE Holttum 1947

No certain fossil record.

Comment: Spores resembling those of *Leptolepia novae-zelandiae* (Col.) Kuhn have been described from U. Jur beds in New Zealand as *Leptolepidites verrucatus* Couper (Harris 1955). Nine extant genera are included in this subfamily (Holttum 1947).

Subfamily LINDSAYOIDEAE Holttum 1947

First, Jur: *Adiantum (Adiantides) lindsayoides* Seward, Jur, Victoria, Australia, fertile leaf fragments recorded as resembling extant species of *Lindsaya* may be included here (Seward 1910).
Extant.

Comment: Six extant genera of varying habits included (Holttum 1949).

Subfamily DAVALLIOIDEAE Holttum 1947

First, Jur Hett-Bajoc: *Davallia saportana* Raciborski, Lias, Krakau, Poland, is described as resembling the form of the genus *Davallia* (Hirmer 1927). **Extant.**
Comment: Six extant genera included (Holttum 1949).

Subfamily OLEANDROIDEAE Holttum 1947

No known fossil record.

Comment: Three highly specialized genera *Nephrolepis*, *Oleandra* and *Arthropteris* included (Holttum 1949).

Subfamily PTERIDOIDEAE Holttum 1947

First, Cret Berr-Barrem: *Acrostichopteris ruffordi* Seward, Wealden, England is of uncertain value (Seward 1910). *Pteris nitida* Hollick, U. Cret Chignick Fm, Alaska Peninsular, infertile leaf fragments (Hollick 1930). Species assigned to *Pteris* have been described from M. and U. Tert, Europe and N. America (Hirmer 1927). First definite record, Tert M. Eoc: *Acrostichum lanzeanum* (Gardner & Ettingshausen) Seward, Eoc, Bournemouth, England, infertile leaf fragments (Seward 1910). "The genus appears in the basal Eocene and has several European and American Species in Eocene and Oligocene deposits, the principal forms being *A. lanzeanum* (Gardner & Ettingshausen) of the European Lutetian and Bartonian, and *A. georgianum* Berry, and *A. hesperium* Newberry of the Claiborne, Jackson and Green River deposits". (Berry 1916).
Extant.

Comment: Nine extant genera are included (Holttum 1949).

Chapter 5: Pteridophyta—2

Subfamily ASPLENIOIDEAE Holttum 1947

First, Cret Barrem: *Asplenium dicksonianum* Heer, Kootenai Fm, British Columbia, Canada. Also recorded from L. Cret, Greenland, America and Argentina and U. Cret, Greenland and America, but Berry doubts that all the specimens represent the same species (Berry 1919). Specimens assigned to *Phyllitis* (as *Scolopendrium*) have been recorded from Tert Plioc, Thuringia, Germany (Hirmer 1927). **Extant.**

Comment: Seven extant genera are included (Holttum 1949). Dispersed spores attributed to either Asplenioideae or Blechnoideae have been recorded from L. Cret upwards under the genus *Peromonolites* (Couper 1958).

Subfamily BLECHNOIDEAE Holttum 1947

First, Tert Olig: *Woodwardites minor* Beck, Olig, Saxony, Germany (Hirmer 1927). *W. microlobus* Schenk, Rhaet-Lias, Germany, has been removed from this genus and transferred to the Dipteridaceae (Ôishi & Yamasita 1936). Specimens assigned to the extant genus *Blechnum* have been recorded from Tert Eoc, Sezanne, France, and Olig, Czechoslovakia and Yugoslavia (Hirmer 1927). **Extant.**

Spores: Spores associated with *W. muensterianus* Sternbg. & Presl have been described (Potonié 1962).

Comment: See also comment under Asplenioideae. Five extant genera included (Holttum 1949).

Subfamily LOMARIOPSIDOIDEAE Holttum 1947

No known fossil record.

Comment: Seven extant genera included (Holttum 1949).

Subfamily DRYOPTERIDOIDEAE Holttum 1947

First, Cret Valang: *Dryopterites macrocarpa* (Fontaine) Berry, Patuxent Fm, L. Cret, Dutch Gap, Virginia, U.S.A., foliage (Andrews 1955). Other species have been recorded from the Patapsco Fm, Albian, Maryland, U.S.A. (*ex* Read & Brown 1937). Specimens referred to the extant genus *Dryopteris* are recorded from Cret, N. America (Berry 1919, Read and Brown 1937.) **Extant.**

Comment: Fourteen extant genera are included (Holttum 1949).

Subfamily TECTARIOIDEAE Holttum 1947

No known fossil record.

Comment: Fourteen extant genera included (Holttum 1949).

Subfamily ATHYRIOIDEAE Holttum 1947

No known fossil record.

Comment: Two extant genera *Athyrium* and *Cystopteris* (Holttum 1949).

Subfamily ONOCHLEOIDEAE Sporne 1962

First, U. Cret: *Onoclea neomexicanum* Knowlton, Kirtland Sh, New Mexico, U.S.A., infertile leaf fragments (Knowlton 1916). The extant *O. sensibilis* L. (as *O. s. fossilis*) has been recorded as abundant and widely distributed in Fort Union Fm, (Eocene), Montana, U.S.A. by Newberry (Knowlton 1916). *O. hebraidica* Forbes, Eocene, Mull, Scotland, is reported as closely resembling *O. sensibilis* (Seward 1910). **Extant.**

Comment: Sporne tentatively places this group of two extant genera *Matteuccia* (2 spp.) and *Onoclea* (1 sp.) in Holttum's Dennstaedtiaceae as the latter leaves them unplaced (Sporne 1962).

Family ADIANTACEAE Presl 1836

First, Jur: *Onychiopsis elongata* (Geyler) Yokoyama, Jur, Tetorigawa, Japan, fertile leaf fragments (Andrews 1955), but interpreted as Wealden (L. Cret) (Seward 1910). *O. psilotoides* (Stokes & Webb) is also recorded from the Wealden and L. Cret, Europe, Japan, India, S. Africa and N. America (Hirmer 1927, Read & Brown 1937). Also Cret Apt: *Adiantum montanensis*, Kootenai Fm, Montana, U.S.A. (*ex* Read & Brown 1937). *Adiantum* (*Adiantides*) *lindsayoides* Seward, Jur, Victoria, Australia and possibly *A. sewardi* Yabe, Jur, Korea, show affinities with Dennstaedtiaceae Subfamily Lindsayoideae (Seward 1910), and is treated thereunder. *Adiantites antiquus* (Ett.) recorded from Carb and other Palaeozoic records are not considered to show any reliable affinity with this family (Seward 1910). **Extant.**

Comment: About 37 extant genera included (Holttum 1947).

Family TEMPSKYACEAE Read & Brown 1937

First, Cret Valang: *Tempskya erosa* Stokes, Webb & Mantell, Hastings Beds, Wealden, Sussex, England, also *T. schimperi* Corda, Wealden, France and Germany (Read & Brown 1937).

Last, Cret Coniac-Santon: *T. knowltoni* Seward, Colorado Sh, Montana, U.S.A., also *T. minor* Read & Brown, ?Senonian, Wyoming, U.S.A. (Reid & Brown 1937).

Comment: A specialised family containing one genus confined to the Cret although there is some evidence to indicate that it may have extended back into the U. Jur (Andrews 1961). The direct affinities of the group are uncertain, but they "lie with the Leptosporangiate ferns, and trends are seen that suggest relations with the Schizaeaceae and the Loxsomaceae on one hand, and the Gleicheniaceae on the other" (Read & Brown 1937). [F.R.G. & M.G.C.]

HYDROPTERID FERNS (HETEROSPORONS)—Incertae sedis

Some of the many late Mesozoic megaspores from all parts of the world, which are still unassigned, probably belong to these orders (e.g. spores described by Hughes 1955, Cookson and Dettmann 1958, Ellis & Tschudy 1963).

Order MARSILIALES

Genus MARSILIA L.

First, Tert Mioc: *Marsilia* sp. (Megaspore), Ukraine, U.S.S.R. (Dorofeev 1963). **Extant.**

Comment: *M. vera* Jarmolenko 1935, Cenom-Turon, Kazakhstan, U.S.S.R. is a leaf impression. Dorefeev has expressed the opinion (pers. comm. to Dijkstra) that *Arcellites lobatus* (Dijkstra 1949), Senon, Netherlands, closely resembles *M. turgaica* Dorofeev.

Order SALVINIALES

Genus SALVINIA (Mich.) Schreb.

First, Tert Paleoc-Eoc: *S. elliptica* Newberry *in* Hollick 1894, Carbonado Fm, Washington, U.S.A. **Extant.**

Comment: Numerous other Eocene records (Florin 1940), including *S. hantonensis*, Up. Eoc., Hordle, Hants (Chandler 1925).

Genus AZOLLA Section AZOLLA

First, Cret Maestr: *A. geneseana* Hills and Weiner 1965, Edmonton Fm, Alberta, Canada.
Extant.

Comment: Mädler (1954) suggested that the megaspore genus *Thomsonia*, L. Cret, Germany and England, belonged to this group.

Genus AZOLLA Section RHIZOSPERMA

First, Tert Olig: *A. Sibirica* Dorofeev 1959, M.Olig, Western Siberia (Dorofeev 1963).
[N.F.H.]
Extant.

REFERENCES

ABBOTT, M. L. 1954. Revision of the Palaeozoic fern genus *Oligocarpia*. *Palaeontographica*, **96B,** 39–65.

ANDREWS, H. N. 1955. Index of generic names of fossil plants, 1820–1950. *Bull. U.S. geol. Surv.*, **1013.**

—— 1961. *Studies in paleobotany*. New York & London.

ARNOLD, C. A. 1935. Some new forms and new occurrences of fossil plants from the Middle and Upper Devonian of New York State. *Bull. Buffalo Soc. nat. Sci.*, **17,** 1–11, pl. 1.

—— 1956. Fossil ferns of the Matoniaceae from North America. *J. palaeont. Soc. India*, **1,** 1, 118–121.

—— 1964. Mesozoic and Tertiary fern evolution and distribution. *Mem. Torrey bot. Club*, **21,** 5, 58–66.

BANKS, H. P. 1964. Putative Devonian Ferns. *Mem. Torrey bot. Club*, **21,** 10–25. pl. 1–2.

——, HUEBER, F. M. & WILCOX, M. S. 1959. Remarks on Devonian ferns. *9th Int. bot. Congr.*, Proc. II, 18.

BERRY, E. W. 1916. *In* MATSON, G. C. & BERRY, E. W., The Catahoula Sandstone and its flora. *Prof. Paper U.S. geol. Surv.*, **98-M,** 227–243.

—— 1919. Upper Cretaceous floras of the Eastern Gulf region in Tennessee, Mississippi, Alabama and Georgia. *Prof. Pap. U.S. geol. Surv.*, **112.**

BERTRAND, P. 1935. Contribution à l'étude des Cladoxylées de Saalfeld. *Palaeontographica*, **80B,** 101–170, pl. 16–38.

BHARDWAJ, D. C. R. & SINGH, H. P. 1956. *Asterotheca meriani* (Brongn.) Stur and its spores from the Upper Triassic of Lunz (Austria). *Palaeobotanist*, **5,** 51–55.

CHANDLER, M. E. J. 1925. The Upper Eocene flora of Hordle, Hants, I. *Palaeont. Soc.* [*Monogr.*].

CHRISTENSEN, C. 1938. *In* VERDOORN, F. *Manual of Pteridology;* Chapter 20, Filicinae. The Hague.

COOKSON, I. C. & DETTMANN, M. E. 1958. Cretaceous 'megaspores' and a closely related microspore from the Australian region. *Micropaleontology*, **4,** 39–49.

COPELAND, E. B. 1947. *Genera Filicum*. Waltham, Mass.

COUPER, R. A. 1958. British Mesozoic microspores and pollen grains. *Palaeontographica*, **103B,** 75–179.

CROFT, W. N. & LANG, W. H. 1952. The Lower Devonian of the Senni Beds of Monmouthshire and Breconshire. *Phil. Trans. R. Soc.*, **231B,** 131–163.

DIJKSTRA, S. J. 1949. Megaspores and some other fossils from the Aachenian (Senonian) in South Limburg, Netherlands. *Meded. Geol. Sticht.* N.S., **3,** 19–32, 2 pl;

DOROFEEV, P. I. 1963. *The Tertiary floras of Western Siberia*. Bot. Inst. Komarov. Acad. Nauk S.S.S.R., 346 pp., 50 pl.

DELEVORYAS, T. & MORGAN, J. 1954. Observations on petiolar branching and foliage of an American *Botryopteris*. *Am. Midl. Nat.*, **52,** 374–387.

EGGERT, D. A. 1959. Studies of Paleozoic Ferns: *Tubicaulis stewartii* sp. nov. and evolutionary trends in the genus. *Am. J. Bot.*, **46,** 594–602. Fig. 1–14.

—— 1963. Studies of Paleozoic ferns: The frond of *Ankyropteris glabra*. *Am. J. Bot.*, **50,** 379–387. Fig. 1–31.

—— & TAYLOR, T. N. 1966. Studies of Palaeozoic ferns: on the genus *Tedelea* gen. nov. *Palaeontographica*, **118B,** 52–73.

ELLIS, C. H. & TSCHUDY, R. H. 1963. The Cretaceous megaspore genus *Arcellites* Miner. *Micropaleontology*, **10,** 73–79.

FLORIN, R. 1940. Zur kenntnis einiger fossiler *Salvinia*-arten und der früheren geographischen verbreitung der gattung. *Svensk bot. Tidskr.*, **34,** 265–292, 2 pl.

HARRIS, W. F. 1955. A manual of the spores of New Zealand Pteridophyta. *Bull. N.Z. Dep. Scient. ind. Res.*, **116.**

HILLS, L. & WEINER, N. 1965. *Azolla geneseana* n. sp. and revision of *Azolla primaeva*. *Micropaleontology*, **11,** 255–61, 2 pl.

HIRMER, M. 1927. *Handbuch der Paläobotanik, I: Thallophyta–Bryophyta–Pteridophyta.* Munich and Berlin.

—— & HÖRHAMMER, L. 1936. Morphologie, Systematik und geographische Verbreitung der fossilen und rezenten Matoniaceen. *Palaeontographica,* **81B,** 1–70.

HOLDEN, H. S. & CROFT, W. N. 1962. The morphology of *Tubicaulis africanus. Bull. Br. Mus. (Nat. Hist.) Geol.,* **7,** 199–211, pls 33–36.

HOLLICK, A. 1894. Fossil Salvinias, including description of a new species. *Bull. Torrey bot. Club,* **21,** 253–7, 1 pl.

—— 1930. The Upper Cretaceous floras of Alaska. *Prof. Paper U.S. geol. Surv.,* **159.**

HOLTTUM, R. E. 1947. A revised classification of the Leptosporangiate ferns. *J. Linn. Soc. (Bot.),* **53,** 123–158.

—— 1949. The classification of ferns. *Biol. Rev.,* **24,** 267–296.

HOPPING, C. A. 1956. On a specimen of *"Psilophyton robustius"* Dawson, from the Lower Devonian of Canada. *Proc. R. Soc. Edinb.* B, **66,** 10–28, pl. 1–2.

HUEBER, F. M. 1964. The psilophytes and their relationship to the origin of ferns. *Mem. Torrey bot. Club,* **21,** 5–9, pl. 1.

HUGHES, N. F. 1955. Wealden plant microfossils. *Geol. Mag.,* **92,** 201–217.

JARMOLENKO, A. V. 1935. Upper Cretaceous flora of the north-west Kara Tau. *Trudy Sred.-aziat. gos. Univ.* series 8b (Botany), **28,** 1–36.

KNOWLTON, F. H. 1916. Contributions to the geology and palaeontology of San Juan County, New Mexico; 4. Flora of the Fruitland and Kirtland Formations. *Prof. Paper U.S. geol. Surv.,* **98-S,** 327–344.

LECLERCQ, S. 1951. Étude morphologique et anatomique d'une fougère du Dévonien supérieur. Le *Rhacophyton zygopteroides* nov. sp. *Annls. Soc. géol. Belg.,* **9,** 1–62, pl. 1–12.

—— & BANKS, H. P. 1962. *Pseudosporochnus nodosus* sp. nov. a Middle Devonian plant with cladoxylalean affinities. *Palaeontographica,* **110B,** 1–34, pl. 1–10.

MAMAY, S. H. 1950. Some American Carboniferous fern fructifications. *Ann. Mo. bot. Gdn.,* **37,** 409–459.

—— & ANDREWS, H. N. 1950. A contribution to our knowledge of the anatomy of *Botryopteris. Bull. Torrey bot. Club,* **77,** 462–494, pl. 1–7.

MÄDLER, K. 1954. *Azolla* aus dem Quartär und Tertiär. Sowie ihre bedeutung fur die taxonomie älterer sporen. *Geol. Jb.,* **70,** 143–158, 1 pl.

MORGAN, J. & DELEVORYAS, T. 1954. An anatomical study of a new coenopterid and its bearing on the morphology of certain coenopterid petioles. *Am. J. Bot.,* **41,** 198–203. Fig. 1–9.

ÔISHI, S. & YAMASITA, K. 1936. On the fossil Dipteridaceae. *J. Fac. Sci. Hokkaido Univ.,* series 4, **3,** 135–184.

PICHI-SERMOLLI, R. E. G. 1958. The higher taxa of the Pteridophyta and their classification. *Uppsala Univ. Arsskr.,* **6,** 70–90.

POTONIÉ, R. 1962. Synopsis der Sporae in situ. *Beih. geol. Jb.* 52.

RADFORTH, N. W. 1939. Further contributions to our knowledge of the fossil Schizaeaceae; genus *Senftenbergia. Trans. R. Soc. Edinb.,* **59,** 745–761.

READ, C. B. 1938. Some psilophytales from the Hamilton group of western New York. *Bull. Torrey bot. Club,* **65,** 599–606. pl. 30.

—— & BROWN, R. W. 1937. American Cretaceous ferns of the genus *Tempskya. Prof. Paper U.S. geol. Surv.,* **186-F,** 105–129.

SEWARD, A. C. 1910. *Fossil Plants, II.* Cambridge.

SPORNE, K. R. 1962. *The morphology of Pteridophytes.* London.

STOCKMANS, F. 1940. Végéteaux Eodevoniens de la Belgique. *Mém. Mus. r. Hist. nat. Belg.,* **93.**

SURANGE, K. R. 1952a. The morphology of *Stauropteris burntislandica* P. Bertrand and its megasporangium *Bensonites fusiformis* R. Scott. *Phil. Trans. R. Soc.,* **237B,** 73–91. pl. 1–4.

—— 1952b. The morphology of *Botryopteris antiqua* with some observations on *B. ramosa. Palaeobotanist,* **1,** 420–434. pl. 1–4.

TENISON-WOODS, J. E. 1884. On the fossil flora of the coal deposits of Australia. *Proc. Linn. Soc. N.S.W.,* **8,** 37–167.

[Professor] H. P. Banks
    Department of Botany, Cornell University, Ithaca, N.Y., U.S.A.
M. G. Collett, PH.D.
    Exploration Division, B.P. Research Centre, Chertsey Road, Sunbury-on-Thames, Middle-sex.
F. R. Gnauck, PH.D.
    Exploration Division, B.P. Research Centre, Chertsey Road, Sunbury-on-Thames, Middle-sex.
N. F. Hughes, M.A. F.G.S.
    Department of Geology, Sedgwick Museum, Downing Street, Cambridge.

CHAPTER 6

Gymnospermophyta

Contributors: K. L. ALVIN, P. D. W. BARNARD, T. M. HARRIS,
N. F. HUGHES, R. H. WAGNER & A. WESLEY

The classification of this division is still evolving from the traditional framework of extant higher taxa to one in which the many extinctions of the Mesozoic will be made clear by groupings based on the fossils alone. New discoveries have made the relationships of Upper Palaeozoic families both more interesting and much less certain; the order of their arrangement here is therefore of necessity arbitrary. Some fossils from some of the new groups of the Angara flora (Permian) are little known as yet and their inclusion has not been attempted. No attempt has been made to keep the level of taxa recorded consistent throughout this chapter.

Gymnosperm family names have been under consideration by the Section of Nomenclature of the Tenth International Botanical Congress (1964), and a provisional list with authorities and dates for the extant families has been published by (BUCHHEIM, G. 1966. Nomina Familiarum Conservanda Proposita: Gymnospermae. *Taxon,* **15,** 219–220). [N.F.H.]

Class PROGYMNOSPERMOPSIDA Beck 1960

First, Dev Givet: *Aneurophyton germanicum,* Honseler-schichten, Elbefeld, Germany (Kräusel & Weyland 1929); also *A. hallei* and *Eospermatopteris,* New York.

Last, Carb Tourn: *Callixylon arnoldii,* Falling Run member, Sanderson Fm, New Albany Sh, Kentucky. (Beck 1962).

Constituent orders: Aneurophytales Beck, Givet-Frasn; Callixylales (*Archaeopteris, Callixylon*), Frasn-Tourn; Protopityales Nemejc, Tourn. [P.D.W.B.]

Comment: The Order Archaeopteridales is recorded separately below.

REFERENCES

BECK, C. B. 1962. Plants of the New Albany Shale II *Callixylon arnoldii* sp. nov. *Brittonia,* **14,** 322–7.

KRÄUSEL, R. & WEYLAND, H. 1929. Beiträge zur Kenntnis der Devonflora, II. *Abh. senckenb. naturforsch. Ges.,* **41,** 315–60, pls. 1–15.

Class PTERIDOSPERMOPSIDA

The classification is that of Corsin (1960) with some modifications. Some leaf genera only known from Angaraland and some dispersed seeds have been omitted.

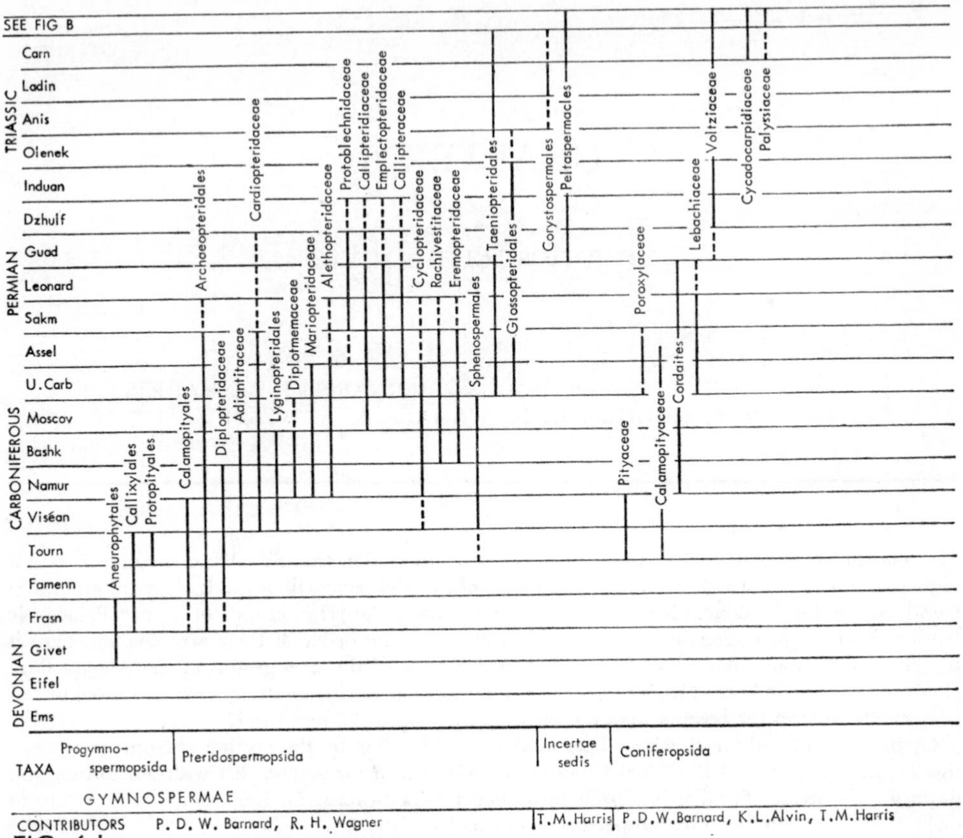

The figure is a stratigraphic range chart. Time periods (left axis, top to bottom): TRIASSIC (Carn, Ladin, Anis, Olenek, Induan), PERMIAN (Dzhulf, Guad, Leonard, Sakm, Assel), CARBONIFEROUS (U.Carb, Moscov, Bashk, Namur, Viséan, Tourn), DEVONIAN (Famenn, Frasn, Givet, Eifel, Ems). Top note: "SEE FIG B".

Taxon range-columns (left to right): Aneurophytales, Callixylales, Protopityales, Calamopityales, Diplopteridaceae, Adiantitaceae, Lyginopteridales, Diplolemeaceae, Mariopteridaceae, Archaeopteridales, Cardiopteridaceae, Protoblechnidaceae, Callipteridiaceae, Emplectopteridaceae, Calliperaceae, Alethopteridaceae, Cycliopteridaceae, Rachivestitaceae, Eremopteridaceae, Sphenospermales, Taeniopteridales, Glossopteridales, Corystospermales, Peltaspermales, Poroxylaceae, Calamopityaceae, Pityaceae, Cordaites, Lebachiaceae, Voltziaceae, Cycadocarpidiaceae, Palysiaceae.

TAXA row: Progymnospermopsida | Pteridospermopsida | Incertae sedis | Coniferopsida — GYMNOSPERMAE

CONTRIBUTORS P. D. W. Barnard, R. H. Wagner | T. M. Harris | P.D.W.Barnard, K.L.Alvin, T.M.Harris

FIG. 6.1 A

Order CALAMOPITYALES (petrifactions only)

First, Dev Frasn-Famenn: *Calamopitys americana* Scott and Jeffrey, *C. foersti* Read, *Stenomyelon muratum* Read, *Diichnia kentuckiensis* Read, upper part of New Albany Sh, Kentucky (Read 1937).

Last, Carb Viséan: *Calamopitys radiata* Scott, Calciferous Sandstone, Scotland (Scott 1924).

Comment: See also pycnoxylic Calamopityaceae under Cordaitales (below).

Order ARCHAEOPTERIDALES

First, Dev Frasn: *Archaeopteris* (fronds), several species in N. America, Bear Isl., Europe and Australia. Arnold (1947, p. 175) records rare occurrence in Mid Dev., and Beck (1962) mentions persistence into L.Carb. Also *Archaeopteridium*, Viséan, Germany, Scotland; *Anisopteris* (=*Rhacopteris* auct.), L.Carb, world-wide and ?Mosc, Australia (Gondwanaland only); *Rhacopteris* (pro parte), U.Carb-L.Perm, Europe, China; *Triphyllopteris*, L.Carb, Europe, America; *Aneimites*, L.Carb, Europe, America; *Spathulopteris*, L.Carb, Britain, Germany, Spitsbergen.

Last, L.Perm: *Rhacopteris bertrandi*, Chao-Ko-Chwang, Kaiping basin, China (Stockmans & Mathieu 1939), Hsuanmachung Beds, Tachingshan, China (Lee 1963).

Comment: *Callixylon* (wood) is recorded under Progymnospermopsida (above).

Order DIPLOPTERIDALES

Family DIPLOPTERIDACEAE

First, Dev Frasn-Famenn: *Sphenopteridium lebedevii* (Schmalhausen), Altai Mts, Asia (Ananiev 1959). Also *Diplopteridium* (frond) and *Telangium* (male fruct.), Viséan, Britain (Walton 1931). *Sphenopteridium* world-wide.

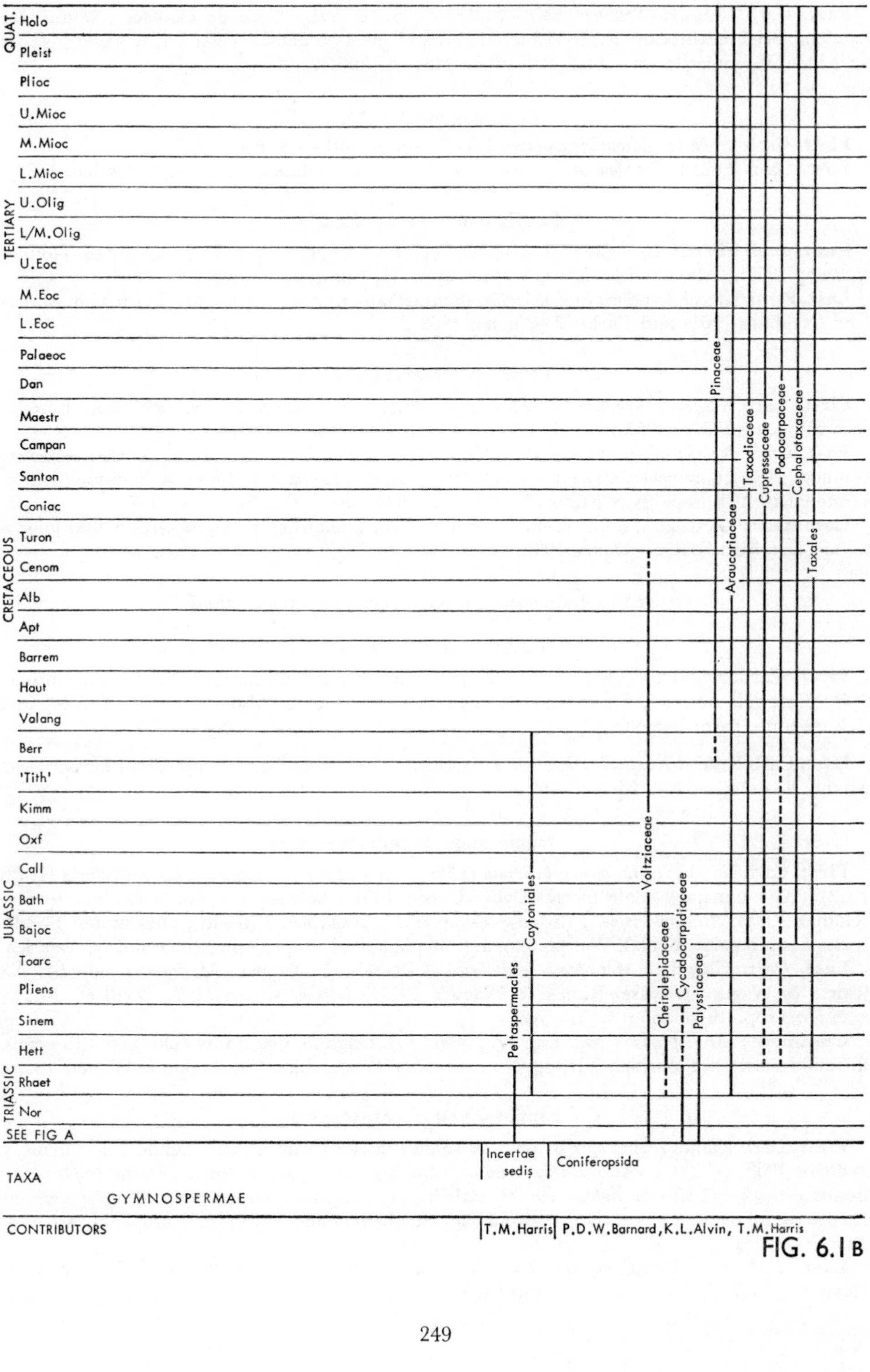
QUAT.
Holo
Pleist
Plioc
U.Mioc
M.Mioc
L.Mioc
TERTIARY
U.Olig
L/M.Olig
U.Eoc
M.Eoc
L.Eoc
Palaeoc
Dan
Maestr
Campan
Santon
Coniac
CRETACEOUS
Turon
Cenom
Alb
Apt
Barrem
Haut
Valang
Berr
'Tith'
Kimm
Oxf
Call
JURASSIC
Bath
Bajoc
Toarc
Pliens
Sinem
Hett
TRIASSIC
Rhaet
Nor
SEE FIG A
Peltaspermacles
Caytoniales
Voltziaceae
Cheirolepidaceae
Cycadocarpidiaceae
Palyssiaceae
Pinaceae
Araucariaceae
Taxodiaceae
Cupressaceae
Podocarpaceae
Cephalotaxaceae
Taxales
TAXA
Incertae sedis
Coniferopsida
GYMNOSPERMAE
CONTRIBUTORS
T.M.Harris
P.D.W.Barnard, K.L.Alvin, T.M.Harris

FIG. 6.1 B

Last, Carb Namur: *Sphenopteridium baldurnense* St. & Wi., Assise de Chokier (Namur A), Baudour, Belgium (Stockmans & Willière 1953) and *Sphenopteridium noeldeki* Daber, Petershofener Schichten, E_2 goniatite zone, Czechoslovakia (Havlena 1961).

Family ADIANTITACEAE

First, Carb Viséan: *Adiantites antiquus* Ett., Europe (Gothan & Remy 1957).
Last, Carb Bashk: *Pseudadiantites sessilis* (v. Roehl), Westphalian A, Europe (Gothan 1929).

Family CARDIOPTERIDACEAE

First, Carb Viséan: *Cardiopteris polymorpha* (Goepp.), Europe, S. America, Asia Minor (Gothan & Remy 1957). Also *Cardiopteridium*, Viséan-Nam. A?, Europe, America.
Last, Perm: *Angaropteridium cardiopteroides* (Schmalhausen) Zal., U.Carb and Perm, Gondwanaland (Neuburg 1961) and Turkey? (Wagner 1962).

Order LYGINOPTERIDALES

First, Carb Viséan: *Lyginopteris* (*Sphenopteris* auct.) *bermudensiformis* (v. Schloth.), Europe, Asia Minor (Patteisky 1957).
Last, Carb Bashk: *Lyginopteris* (*Sphenopteris*) *hoeninghausi* (Bgt.) (frond), *Lyginopteris oldhamia* (Binney) (stem), *Calymmatotheca hoeninghausi* (Bgt.) (cupule), *Lagenostoma lomaxi* Williamson (ovule), Westphalian A, Europe, Asia Minor, N. America (Jongmans 1952, Patteisky 1957).
Comment: *Crossotheca*, until recently considered the male fruct. of *Lyginopteris*, is now known to be a fern fructification (Danzé 1960).

Order PTERIDOSPERMALES (MEDULLOSALES—petrifactions)

Family DIPLOTMEMACEAE

First, Carb Namur: *Diplotmema* (*Sphenopteris*) *adiantoides* (v.Schloth.), Namur A, Europe, Asia Minor, N. America, Greenland (Gothan & Remy 1957). Also *Ovospermum* (ovule) and *Telangium* pro parte (male fruct.).

Last, Carb Bashk-Moscow: *Diplotmema* (*Sphenopteris*) *striata* Gothan, Westphalian, Europe, Asia Minor, N. America, N. Africa.

Family MARIOPTERIDACEAE

First, Carb Namur: *Mariopteris laciniata* H.Pot., Randgruppe, Namur A, Upper Silesia (Huth 1912). Also unnamed male fruct. (Danzé-Corsin 1957), *Calathiops bernhardti* Gothan (ovule) (Gothan 1935), *Pseudomariopteris* (frond), *Tetratmema* (*Palmatopteris*) (frond), Dicksonites (frond), *Samaropsis* pro parte (ovule), Westphalian and Stephanian, Europe, Asia Minor and N. America.
Last, Carb U.Carb: *Mariopteris cantabrica* A.-Ramis & Wagner, *Mariopteris melendezi* A.-Ramis & Wagner (Alvarez-Ramis & Wagner 1967), *Dicksonites leptophylla* (Zeiller), *Pseudomariopteris* spp., Stephanian C, Europe.
Comment: *Mariopteris renieri* St. & Wi., Namur A, Belgium, doubtfully belongs to this genus, the main occurrence of which is Upper Namurian and Westphalian (Stockmans & Willière 1953).

Family ALETHOPTERIDACEAE

First, Carb Namur: *Alethopteris* spp., Assise de Chokier (Namur A), Belgium (Stockmans & Willière 1953, p. 241). Also *Lonchopteridium, Lonchopteris, Neuralethopteris, ?Macralethopteris* (all fronds), *Whittleseya, Givesia, Aulacotheca* (all male fructs), *Pachytesta, Trigonocarpus, Hexapterospermum, Dictyotesta* (all ovules), Namurian, Westphalian, Stephanian and ?L. Perm, Europe, N. America, Asia, N. Africa.
Last, ?L.Perm: *Macralethopteris hallei* Jongmans & Gothan, L.Perm, Sumatra and China (Kaiping coalfield) (Stockmans & Mathieu 1939).

Chapter 6: Gymnospermophyta

Family PROTOBLECHNIDACEAE

First, L.Perm.: "*Alethopteris*" *norini* Halle, L. Shihhotse, N. China (with *Rhabdocarpus* ovule) (Halle 1929, Asama 1962). Also *Protoblechnum*, Perm, China, India (Halle 1927).

Last, U.Perm: "*Psygmophyllum*" *multipartitum* Halle, Upper Shihhotse, China (Asama 1962).

Comment: Fam. nov. Wagner 1967.

Family CALLIPTERIDIACEAE

First, Carb Moscov: *Callipteridium* (*Praecallipteridium*) *lerati* (Buisine) and *C. vermeleni* (Buisine), Assise de Bruay (Westphalian C), Northern France (Buisine 1961). Also *Emplectopteridium*, *Palaeoweichselia*, *Cathaysiopteris*, *Bicoemplectopteridium*, *Gigantopteris* (all fronds), *Konnoa* (ovule), Westphalian D, Stephanian and Perm, Europe, N. America and Asia (Asama 1959).

Last, U.Perm: *Gigantopteris nicotianaefolia* (Schenk), China (Asama 1959).

Family EMPLECTOPTERIDACEAE

First, Carb U.Carb: *Lescuropteris moorii* (Lesq.), Stephanian, N. America (Darrah 1937). Also *Emplectopteris triangularis* Halle, L. Perm, China and Korea, *Gigantonoclea*, *Bicoemplectopteris*, *Tricoemplectopteris*, Perm, China and Korea (Asama 1959).

Last, U.Perm: *Tricoemplectopteris taiyuanensis*, Upper Shihhotse, N. China (Asama 1959).

Comment: Fam. nov. Wagner 1967.

Family CALLIPTERACEAE

First, Carb U.Carb: *Callipteris bilharzi* (Frentzen), Stephanian B, Europe (Wagner 1958). Also *Callipteris* (frond), *Callipterianthus*, *?Thuringia* (both male fructs), Perm, Europe, N. America, Siberia, China (Roselt 1962).

Last, U.Perm: *Callipteris zeilleri* Zal., Siberia (Neuburg 1948) *?Callipteris martinsi* (Kurtze), Zechstein, Germany and England (Stoneley 1958).

Family CYCLOPTERIDACEAE (including ODONTOPTERIDACEAE Corsin)

First, Carb Viséan-Namur: *Neuropteris antecedens* Stur, Viséan-Namur A, Europe, N. America (Patteisky 1929). Also *Neuropteris* (*Imparipteris*), *Cyclopteris*, *Mixoneura*, *Reticulopteris*, *Odontopteris*, *Anastomopteris* (all fronds); *Goldenbergia*, *Codonotheca*, *Psaliangium* (all male fructs), and *Rhabdocarpus* pro parte), *Odontopterocarpus* (ovules), Namurian, Westphalian and Stephanian Europe, Asia Minor, Asia, N. America, N. Africa, persisting into L. Perm.

Last, L.Perm: *Neuropteris pseudovata* Gothan & Sze, Stephanian and Perm, China (Stockmans & Mathieu 1939).

Family RACHIVESTITACEAE

First, Carb Bashk: *Paripteris* (*Neuropteris* auct.) *gigantea* (Sternb.), Assise d'Andenne, Namur C, (Stockmans & Willière 1953). Also *Linopteris* sensu stricto (frond), *Potoniea* (male fruct.), *Hexagonocarpus* (ovule), Namurian, Westphalian and Stephanian (rarely L.Perm), Europe, Asia Minor, N. America, China, N. Africa.

Last, L.Perm: *Linopteris neuropteroides* (v. Gutb.), Autunian, Bussaco, Portugal (Teixeira 1944).

Family EREMOPTERIDACEAE

First, Carb Bashk: *Eremopteris lincolniana* D. White, Kanawha and Pottsville fms, (M. Westphalian), N. America (White 1943). Also *Pteridozamites* (male fruct.), *Samaropsis* pro parte (ovule) (Corsin 1928).

Last, L.Perm: *Eremopteris golondrinensis* Archangelski, La Golondrina Beds, Bajo de la Leona, Sta Cruz, Argentina (Archangelski 1958).

Order SPHENOSPERMALES

First, Carb Tourn-Viséan: *Rhodeopteridium (Rhodea* auct.) *goepperti* Ett., Europe and ?N. America (Kidston 1923). Also *Paracalathiops* (male fruct.) which, according to Remy (1953), may belong to *Rhodea stachei* Stur, and *Rhodeites* (frond).

Last, Carb Moscov: *Rhodeites (Rhodea* auct.) *subpetiolata* (H.Pot.), Westphalian C, Europe.

Order TAENIOPTERIDALES

First, Carb U.Carb: *Taeniopteris jejunata* Grand'Eury, Stephanian B, Europe. Also *Taeniopteris* (frond), *Ilfeldia* (male fruct.), *Spermopteris* (ovule), Stephanian and Perm, Europe, Asia, N. America (Remy 1953, Cridland & Morris 1960).

Last, Trias Carn: *Taeniopteris angustifolia* Schenk, Lettenkohle beds, Germany; this species has been selected arbitrarily to indicate that although by tradition the form-genus *Taeniopteris* has been used widely throughout the Mesozoic and Early Tertiary (Jongmans and Dijkstra 1965), most of the more important of these records from the Jurassic onwards have been placed in species of various other genera (e.g. *T. vittata* Brongn. to *Nilssoniopteris* in the Cycadophyta).

Order GLOSSOPTERIDALES

First, Carb U.Carb: *Gangamopteris cyclopteroides* Feistm., widespread on Gondwanaland. Also *Glossopteris, Palaeovittaria, ?Pursongia, ?Zamiopteris* (all leaves), *Scutum* (strobilus bearing tufted seeds), *Ottokaria* (fruct.), *Vertebraria* (rooting system), Perm and early Mesozoic, Gondwanaland and Angaraland (Plumstead 1958, Mukherjee *et al.* 1966).

Last, Trias Induan-Olenek: *Glossopteris indica, G. angustifolia,* Panchet beds, India (Jacob 1952).

[R.H.W.]

INCERTAE SEDIS

Order CORYSTOSPERMALES

First, Trias Anis-Ladin: *Pteruchus simmondsi* (Shirley) Thomas, Ipswich 'Series', Denmark Hill, Queensland, Australia (Townrow 1962).

Last, Trias, Ladin-Carn: *Pteruchus africanus* Thomas 1933, Molteno Fm, Burnera Waterfall, Upper Umkomaas, Natal, South Africa (Townrow 1962).

Comment: The Ipswich fossils may be just earlier.

Order PELTASPERMALES

First, Perm Guad: *Lepidopteris martinsi* (Kurtze) Townrow 1960, Kupferschiefer, Niederrheinische Zechstein, Germany (Gothan and Nagelhard 1923); also English material (Stoneley 1958).

Last, Trias Rhaet: *Lepidopteris ottonis* (Goepp.) Schimper, Mine Fm, Scania, Sweden (Lundblad 1950). [N.F.H.]

Order CAYTONIALES Thomas 1925

First, Trias Rhaet: *Sagenopter isundulata* Nathorst, Scania. Sweden, but *S. nilssoniana* possibly Trias Carn, Japan (Oishi 1940). Leaf (in isolation) *Sagenopteris* spp., male organ *Caytonanthus* spp., female organ *Caytonia* spp. found isolated but associated with *Sagenopteris* where suitably looked for (England, Poland, Sardinia, U.S.S.R.).

Last, Cret Berr: *Sagenopteris mantelli* (Dunker), Wealden fm, North-west Germany, but *S. suspecta* Hollick is from U. Cret, Alaska.

Comment: The detached leaf male and female organs are found associated and the 'Caytoniales' refers to the inference that they belong together (Thomas 1925). The fullest is the assemblage of *Sagenopteris phillipsi, Caytonanthus arberi, Caytonia sewardi,* with unnamed bud scales and stem fragment (Bajoe, see Harris 1964), but there are others with three organs in Hett and Bajoc; the assembled (imaginary) plant has no name. Dispersed pollen (*Alisporites, Vitreisporites* may belong to *Caytonanthus* but to other plants as well).

Sagenopteris leaves placed in many species, mostly ill-defined, are widespread in N. Hemisphere from Rhaet to L. Cret (Europe, Asia, America) but are rarer in S. Hemisphere and most of S. Hemisphere records are doubtful. However good specimens occur in Jur, Argentina (Frenguelli 1941, Menéndez 1956). Caytoniales consists at present of a single plant genus but a few rather similar isolated organs may be allied; the leaf *Scoresbya dentata* (Hett.) Harris 1932 also *Pseudosagenopteris* Potonié 1900, the male organ *Pramelreuthia,* Carn (see Kraüsel 1949) the seed *Amphorispermum,* Rhaet-Bajoc (see Harris 1964). [T.M.H.]

REFERENCES

ALVAREZ-RAMIS, C. & WAGNER, R. H. 1967. *Mariopteris* from the Stephanian of N.W. Spain. (in press).

ANANIEV, A. R. 1959. [*Die wichtigste Fundstellen von Devonfloren in Ssajan-Altaj-Berggebiete*]. Publication of Tomsk University, U.S.S.R., 89 pp., 25 pls. (in Russian).

ARCHANGELSKI, S. 1958. *"Eremopteris golondrinensis"* nueva especie de la Serie La Golondrina, Bajo de la Leona, Santa Cruz. *Acta geol. lilloana*, **2**, 285–289, 3 pls.

ARNOLD, C. A. 1947. *An introduction to Paleobotany*. New York & London, McGraw Hill, 433 pp.

ASAMA, K. 1959. Systematic Study of So-called *Gigantopteris*. *Sci. Rep. Tôhoku Univ.* (Geol. Ser.), **31**, 1–72, pls. I–XX.

—— 1962. Evolution of Shansi Flora and Origin of Simple Leaf. *Sci. Rep. Tohoku Univ.* (Geol. Ser.), Special Vol. **5** (Kon'no Mem. Vol.), 247–273, pls. 41–42.

BECK, C. B. 1962. Reconstructions of Archaeopteris, and further consideration of its phylogenetic position. *Am. J. Bot.*, **49**, 373–382.

BUISINE, M. 1961. Contribution à l'étude de la flore du terrain houiller. Les Aléthoptéridées du Nord de la France. *Et. géol. Atlas topogr. souterr. Serv. géol. H.B.N.P.C.*, I.Flore fossile, **4**, 1–317, pls. I–LXXIV.

CHALONER, W. G. & PETTITT, J. M. 1963. A Devonian seed megaspore. *Nature, Lond.*, **198**, 808–809.

CORSIN, P. 1928. Sur la fructification et la position systématique de *Sphenopteris zamioides* P. Bertrand. *Ann. Soc. géol. Nord*, **56**, 25–33.

—— 1960. Classification des Ptéridophytes et des Ptéridospermophytes du Carbonifére. *Bull. Soc. géol. Fr.*, (7), **2**, 566–572.

CRIDLAND, A. A. & MORRIS, J. E. 1960. Spermopteris, a new genus of Pteridosperms from the Upper Pennsylvanian Series of Kansas. *Am. J. Bot.*, **47**, 855–859, figs. 1–15.

DANZÉ, J. 1960. Remarques sur quelques fructifications de fougères carbonifères. *C.R. 4 Congrès Carbonifère, Heerlen 1958*, **1**, 93–99, figs. 1–6.

DANZÉ-CORSIN, P. 1957. Note préliminaire sur la découverte d'échantillons fructifiés appartenant au genre Mariopteris (Mariopteris latifolia Zeiller). *Ann. Soc. géol. Nord*, **67**, 181–183.

DARRAH, W. C. 1937. Recent studies of American Pteridosperms. *C.R.2e Congrès Carbonifère, Heerlen 1935*, **1**, 131–137, pls. 4–5.

FRENGUELLI, J. 1941. Sagenopteris y Linguifolium. *Notas Mus. La Plata*, **6** (Paleontología No. 34).

GOTHAN, W. 1929. Steinkohlenflora der westlichen paralischen Carbonreviere Deutschlands, 1. *Arb. Inst. Paläobot.*, **1**, 1–48, Tafn 1–16.

—— 1935. Steinkohlenflora der westlichen paralischen Steinkohlenreviere Deutschlands, 3. *Abh. preuss. geol. Landesanst.* (N.F.), **167**, 1–54, Tafn 29–48.

—— & NAGELHARD, K. 1923. Kupferschieferpflanzen aus dem rheinischen Zechstein. *Jb. preuss. geol. Landesanst. Berg Akad.*, **42**, 440–460, 3 pls.

—— & REMY, W. 1957. *Steinkohlenpflanzen*. Glückauf, Essen, 248 pp., 6 pls.

HALLE, T. G. 1927. Palaeozoic Plants from Central China. *Palaeont. sin.* (A), **2** (1), 1–316, 64 pls.

—— 1929. Some Seed-bearing Pteridosperms from the Permian of China. *K. svenska Vetensk-Akad. Handl.* (3), **6**, no. 8, 1–24, pls. 1–6.

HARRIS, T. M. 1932. The fossil flora of Scoresby Sound East Greenland Part 2. *Meddr. Grønl.*, **85**, no. 3.

—— 1964. *The Yorkshire Jurassic Flora, II*. British Museum (Natural History), London.

HAVLENA, V. 1961. Die flöznahe und flözfremde Flora des oberschlesischen Namurs A und B. *Palaeontographica*, **108B**, 22–38, 3 pls.

HUTH, W. 1912. *Die fossile Gattung Mariopteris in geologischer und botanischer Beziehung*. Inaug. Diss. Berlin, 88 pp., 41 figs.

JACOB, K. 1952. A brief summary of the stratigraphy and palaeontology of the Gondwana System. Symposium Sér Gondwana. *19th Int. geol. Congr.*, 153–174.

JONGMANS, W. J. 1952. The female fructification of *Sphenopteris hoeninghausi* and the (supposed) relation of this species with *Crossotheca*. *Palaeobotanist*, **1**, 267–276, pls. 1–21.

—— & DIJKSTRA, S. J. 1965. Fossilium Catalogus, II: Plantae. Pars 62, Filicales, Pteridospermae, Cycadales (35). Junk, 's-Gravenhage.

KIDSTON, R. 1923–25. Fossil Plants of the Carboniferous Rocks of Great Britain. *Mem. geol. Surv. U.K.*, Palaeont., **2**, pts. 1–6, 681 pp., 153 pls.

KRÄUSEL, R. 1949. Koniferen und anderer Gymnospermen aus der Trias von Lunz, Neider-Östereich. *Palaeontographica*, **89B**, 35–82.

LEE, H. H. 1963. Fossil plants of the Yuehmenkou Series, North China. *Palaeont. sinica*, (N.S./A.), **6**, 1–185, pls. 1–45.

LUNDBLAD, A. B. 1950. Studies in the Rhaeto-Liassic floras of Sweden, I. *K. svenska VetenskAkad. Handl.*, ser. 4, **1** (8).

MENÉNDEZ, C. A. 1956. Flórula Jurásica del Bajo de los Baguales. *Acta. geol. Lilloana*, **1**, 315–338.

MUKHERJEE, S., BANERJEE, M. & SEN, J. 1966. Further Glossopteridean Fructifications from India. *Palaeontographica*, **117B**, 99–113, Pls. 35–41.

NEUBURG, M. F. 1948. [*Upper Palaeozoic Flora from the Kusnetzk Basin*], in [*Palaeontologiya S.S.S.R.*], XII, 3, 2, p. 1–342, pls. I–LXXIII, Akademii Nauk SSSR (in Russian).

—— 1961. Present State of the question on the origin, stratigraphic significance and age of Paleozoic floras of Angaraland. *C.R. 4e Congrès Carbonifère, Heerlen 1958*, **2**, 443–452.

OISHI, S. 1940. Mesozoic Floras of Japan. *J. Fac. Sci. Hokkaido Univ.* (Ser. 4), **5**, nos. 2–4.

PATTEISKY, K. 1929. *Die Geologie und Fossilführung der mährisch-schlesischen Dachschiefer- und Grauwackenformation*. Troppau.

—— 1957. Die phylogenetische Entwicklung der Arten von *Lyginopteris* und ihre Bedeutung für die Stratigraphie. *Mitt. westf. Berggewerkschaftskasse*, **12**, 59–83, 5 pls.

PLUMSTEAD, E. P. 1958. Further Fructifications of the Glossopteridae and a Provisional Classification based on them. *Trans. geol. Soc. S. Africa*, **61**, 51–75, pls. VII–XXIII.

POTONIÉ, H. 1900. Über die fossilen Filicales in Allgemeinen und die Rests derselben zweifelhafter Verwandschaft *in* ENGLER, A. & PRANTL, K. *Die natürlichen Pflanzenfamilien*, **1**, part 4.

READ, C. B. 1937. The Flora of the New Albany Shale, pt. 2. The Calamopityeae and their relationships. *Prof. Paper U.S. geol. Surv.*, **186-E**, 81–91, pls. 16–26.

REMY, W. 1953. Untersuchungen über einige Fruktifikationen von Farnen und Pteridospermen aus dem mitteleuropäischen Karbon und Perm. *Abh. dt. Akad. Wiss., Berlin* for 1952, no. 2., 1–38, Tafn 1–7.

ROSELT, G. 1962. Untersuchungen zur Gattung *Callipteris*. *Freiberger ForschHft.*, Series C, **131**, 1–38, 21 pls.

SCOTT, D. H. 1924. Fossil Plants of the *Calamopitys* type from the Carboniferous Rocks of Scotland. *Trans. R. Soc. Edinb.*, **43**, 579.

STONELEY, H. 1958. The Upper Permian Flora of England. *Bull. Br. Mus. (nat. Hist.), Geol.*, **3**, 295–337, Pls. 36–40.

STOCKMANS, F. & MATHIEU, F. F. 1939. *La flore paléozoique du bassin houiller de Kaiping (Chine)*. Musée R. Hist. nat., Belgique, 49–165, 34 pls.

—— & WILLIÈRE, Y. 1953. Végétaux namuriens de la Belgique. *Publ. Ass. Étude Paléont. Stratigr. houill.*, **13**, 1–382, pls. I–LVII.

TEIXEIRA, C. 1944. O Antracolitico Continental Português. *Bol. Soc. geol. Portugal*, **5**, 1–139, figs. 1–64.

THOMAS, H. H. 1925. The Caytoniales, a new group of Angiospermous plants from the Jurassic rocks of Yorkshire. *Phil. Trans. R. Soc.*, **213B**, pp. 299–363.

—— 1933. On some pteridospermous plants from the Mesozoic rocks of South Africa. *Phil. Trans. R. Soc.*, **222B**, 193–265, 2 pl.

TOWNROW, J. A. 1960. The Peltaspermaceae, a pteridosperm family of Permian and Triassic age. *Palaeontology*, **3**, 333–361, 1 pl.

—— 1962. On *Pteruchus*, microsporophyll of the Corystos permaceae. *Bull. Br. Mus. (nat. Hist.), Geol.*, **6,** 289–320, 3 pl.

WAGNER, R. H. 1958. On the occurrence of Callipteris bilharzi (Frentzen) in the Stephanian of Northern Spain. *Estudios geol., Inst. Invest. geol. 'Lucas Mallada'*, **14,** 71–80, pls. VII–VIII.

—— 1962. On a mixed Cathaysia and Gondwana flora from SE Anatolia (Turkey). *C.R. 4e Congrès Carbonifère, Heerlen 1958*, **3,** 745–752, pls. 24–28.

—— 1967. Two new family names in the Class Pteridospermopsida. *Proc. geol. Soc. Lond.* no. 1640, pp. 150–1.

WALTON, J. 1931. Contributions to the knowledge of Lower Carboniferous Plants, Part III. *Phil. Trans. R. Soc.*, **219B,** 347–379, pls. 23–26.

WHITE, D. 1943. Lower Pennsylvanian Species of Mariopteris, Eremopteris, Diplothmema, and Aneimites from the Appalachian Region. *Prof. Paper U.S. geol. Surv.*, **197-C,** 85–103, pls. 8–39.

Class CONIFEROPSIDA

Order CORDAITALES

Family PITYACEAE Scott 1909

First, Carb Tourn: *Pitys antiqua*, Cementstone group, Scotland, and *Archaeopitys eastmani*, Waverley sh, Kentucky. (Gordon 1935, Scott & Jeffrey 1914).

Last, Carb Viséan: *Pitys dayi*, oil sh, Scotland.

Comment: Petrified stems. Should now be regarded as Lyginopterid Pteridosperms Long 1963. *Callixylon*, U. Dev now associated with *Archaeopteris* Beck 1960 and placed in Progymnospermopsida.

Family POROXYLACEAE Renault 1881

First, Carb UCarb: *Poroxylon stephanense*, Stephanian, Grand'Croix, France.

Last, L.Perm: *Poroxylon boysseti*, Autunian, Autun, France (Renault 1896).

Comment: Petrified stems and petioles, associated simple leaves. Stems very like the pteridosperm *Callistophyton*.

Pycnoxylic CALAMOPITYACEAE Read 1937

First, Carb Tourn: *Eristophyton waltoni*, Cementstone group, Scotland; also *Bilignea* and *Endoxylon*. (Lacey 1953).

Last, L Perm ?Assel: *Mesopitys tchihatcheffi*, P_2, Kuznetsk basin, Russia. (Neuburg 1948).

Comment: Petrified stems. Regarded by most recent workers as more closely related to the Cordaitales than *Calamopitys* and the Pteridosperms.

Family CORDAITACEAE Renault 1881

Genus CORDAITES Unger 1850

First, Carb Namur: *Cordaites palmaeformis, Cordaianthus pitcairniae*, Assise de Chokier, R_1Z, Belgium (Stockmans & Willière 1954); also R_2Z, Lancashire (Lacey 1951).

Last, Perm Leonard: *Cordaites principalis*, Rôdai Fm, Parafusulina Z., Honshû, Japan (Asama 1956); also Autunian, Autun, France and Bussaco, Portugal (Teixeira 1945).

Comment: The above range includes that of the petrified stems *Cordaites* S. str. and *Mesoxylon*, Westphalian, Lanarkshire, Scotland and Kansas. *Noeggerathiopsis* of Russian authors probably identical with *Cordaites;* range in Kuznetsk basin extended into U Perm, *N. aequalis* and *N. minima* (Neuburg 1948). *Noeggerathiopsis* of Gondwana floras said to be generically distinct by Indian authors (Lele & Maithy 1964).

The form genera (Organ genera sens, lat.) *Amyelon;* Tourn *A. bovius* Cementstone group, E. Lothian, Scotland and *Dadoxylon; D. (Cordaites) missouriensis*, U. Burlington Lst, Missouri; *D. chaneyi* U. Trias, Chinle Fm, Arizona, greatly extend the range of the family *sens. lat.*

Mesozoic genera incertae sedis associated with the Cordaitales by Russian authors. Perm-Trias *Yuceites* Schimper & Mugeot 1844; Trias *Uralophyllum* Kristofovich & Prynada 1933; Jur *Eretmophyllum* Thomas 1914, *Torellia* Heer 1870: Cret *Krannera* Corda 1866. [P.D.W.B.]

Order CONIFERALES

Family LEBACHIACEAE

First, Carb U. Carb: *Lebachia parvifolia* Florin, L. Ottweiler Schichten (L. Stephanian), Saarland, Germany. (Numerous records from U. Stephanian.)

Last, Perm ?Leonard: *Lebachia* spp., *Ernestiodendron filiciforme* Florin, etc., 'Ober Rotliegendes,' Ottendorf, Sudetengau, Germany; *Ernestiodendron filiciforme*, Waderner Schichten ('Ober Rotliegendes'), Rheinpfalz, Germany (Florin 1938–45).

Comment: The Lebachiaceae, as here interpreted, comprises the northern element of U. Carb and L. Perm conifers. A group of very imperfectly known presumed conifers also occurs in the Permo-Carb of the southern hemisphere (Florin 1963).

Family VOLTZIACEAE

First, Perm ?Guad: *Ulmannia bronni* Goeppert, *U. frumentaria* (Schloth.) Goeppert and *Pseudovoltzia liebeana* (Geinitz) Florin, Kupferschiefer, L. Zechstein, Germany and Marl Slate, L. Magnesian Lst, England (Stoneley 1958).

Last, Cret ?Cenom: *Protodammara speciosa* Hollick & Jeffrey, *Dactylolepsis cryptomerioides* Hollick & Jeffrey, etc., Raritan Fm, Staten I., N.Y. (Hollick & Jeffrey 1909).

Comment: The Voltziaceae, as here interpreted, comprises a diverse assemblage of mainly U. Perm-Jur conifers based on cones or cone-scales, or material including such organs, the organization of which is broadly intermediate between that of the Lebachiaceae and that of some of the extant families. It probably includes the stock from which most of the extant families evolved.

Family CHEIROLEPIDACEAE

First, Trias ?Rhaet: Cf. *Cheirolepis*, Siltstone in Keuper Conglomerate, near Cowbridge, Glamorgan, Wales.

Last, Jur Hett: *Cheirolepis muensteri* (Schenk) Schimper, Lias (?Lower), Lyme Regis, England (Wood 1961); Lias *alpha*, Franconia, Germany (see Gothan 1914) and other localities in northwest Europe.

Comment: The family is here interpreted as containing only the single genus *Cheirolepis*. The less well known genera *Hirmeriella* Hörhammer, *Takliostrobus* Sahni and *Indostrobus* Sahni were originally also included in it by Hirmer & Hörhammer (1934). Although *Cheirolepis* is known to have borne pollen of the *Classopollis* type, this pollen type cannot be assumed necessarily to represent the family. Pollen type *Classopollis* Pflug emend. Couper extends from about Trias Carn to Cret Apt (Taugourdeau-Lantz & Jekhowsky 1959).

Family CYCADOCARPIDIACEAE

First, Trias Carn: *Cycadocarpidium* spp., uppermost horizon in Hiramatsu Fm and Idenouwe Fm (both Tsubuta Group)(Ladino-Carnic), Yamaguchi, Japan (Kon'no 1961).

Last, L. Jur?: *Cycadocarpidium minor* Turutanova-Ketova, 'Jur', Lake Issyk-Kul, U.S.S.R. (Florin 1953) and '*C.* sp.', above Rhaeto-Liassic Bausandstein (Jur Hett?), Sassendorf, Bamberg, Germany (Kräusel 1958).

Comment: Foliage genus *Podozamites* Braun is of wider geological occurrence, but cannot be assumed to represent the family.

Family PALYSSIACEAE

First, Trias ?Carn: *Stachyotaxus lipoldi* (Stur) Kräusel, Lunzer Sandstein (Keuper), Lunz, Austria; *S. sahnii* Kräusel, Neuwelt-Schichten, Neuewelt, Basel, Switzerland (Kräusel 1952).

Last, Jur Hett: *Palyssia sphenolepis* (Braun) Nathorst, L. Helsingborg Stage, Scania, Sweden; also Nurenberg, Germany (Trias Rhaet or Jur Hett) (Florin 1958).

Comment: *Stachyotaxus sampathkumarani* Roa (1964) from Rajamahal Ser. (M. Jur?) cannot be accepted as a definite member of the family.

Family PROTOPINACEAE

Comment: A family based only on secondary woods having araucarioid pitting but other features similar to those found in extant families. Such woods are particularly abundant in Jur and L. Cret, but according to modern view the family is artificial and cannot be clearly delimited (Grambast 1952).

Family PINACEAE

First, Cret ?Berr: *Pityites solmsi* Seward (1919), Fairlight Clay, Sussex England. **Extant.**

Comment: Records based on pollen, vegetative remains and occasional cones and seeds indicate that the family probably existed in Jur (perhaps even Jur Hett) but there is no completely convincing record (Florin, 1958; Alvin, 1960). Oldest extant genera are *Pinus* L. [*P. belgica* Alvin (1960), L. Cret (Apt or older), Wealden, Belgium] and *Pseudolarix* Gordon [*Ps. dorofeevii* Samylina (1963), L. Cret, Aldan River, U.S.S.R.]. *Picea* Dietrich appears in U. Cret [*P. cliff-woodensis* Berry, Magothy Fm, U.S.A. (Penny 1947)]. Most other genera appear in Tert Eoc or Olig (Florin 1963).

Family ARAUCARIACEAE

First, Trias Rhaet: *Araucarites charcoti* Harris (1935), Lepidopteris Z., Scoresby Sound, E. Greenland. *Primaraucaria wielandi* Bock (1954), 'below Venita Sandstone', Richmond, Virginia, U.S.A. is probably Trias Rhaet. *Araucarites parsorensis* Lele (1955) and *A. indica* Lele (1962), Parsora beds, India are probably Trias. **Extant.**

Comment: Not all fossils named *Araucarites* can be accepted as Araucariaceae; records given are based on cone scales or material including cone remains, and are acceptable at least tentatively. There is no certain distinction between *Araucarites* Presl and the extant Araucaria Jussieu. Only other extant genus, *Agathis* Steudel, appears in Tert Olig (Florin 1963).

Family TAXODIACEAE

First, Jur Bajoc: *Elatides williamsonii* (Brongniart) Seward, M. Deltaic Series, Yorkshire, England. *Sewardiodendron laxum* (Phillips) Florin, L.-M. Deltaic, and *Farndalea fragilis* Bose, L.-U. Deltaic, Yorkshire, based only on vegetative specimens are almost certainly Taxodiaceae (Florin 1958). **Extant.**

Comment: Oldest extant genus is *Sciadopitys* Siebold & Zuccarini, probable remains of which occur in Jur Bajoc, Yorkshire and in U. Jur, Scotland and N. Norway (Florin 1958, 1963). *Sciadopitys siberica* Samylina (1963), L. Cret, Aldan River, U.S.S.R. Most of the other extant genera extend back to U. Cret or Tert Palaeoc (Florin 1963). Some of the younger Voltziaceae are not readily distinguished from the Taxodiaceae.

Family CUPRESSACEAE

First, L. or M. ?Jur: *Cupressinocladus ramonensis* Chaloner & Lorch (1960), 'Marly Cuesta', Makhtesh Ramon, Israel. *Cupressinocladus walkeri* Sahni and *C. burmensis* Sahni, Loian Ser., Kalaw Coalfield, Burma (Trias Rhaet or L. Jur) (Sahni 1928). **Extant.**

Comment: The Israeli record may be accepted as Cupressaceae on the basis of morphology and cuticle structure of vegetative specimens. The Burmese records are based only on morphology. The extant genera are difficult to distinguish as fossils. At least three distinct kinds of foliage, *Cupressinocladus* Seward, *Frenelopsis* Schenk and *Moriconia* Debey & Ettingshausen, are widespread in U. Cret, N. hemisphere. The extant genera *Chamaecyparis* Spach and *Juniperus* L. appear in Tert Palaeoc, *Tetraclinis* Masters in Eoc; *Callitris* Ventenat of S. hemisphere is recorded from Cret, S. Queensland (Florin 1963).

Family PODOCARPACEAE

First, Jur: *Nipaniostrobus* Rao, *Nipanioruha* Rao, *Mehtia* Vishnu-Mittre and *Sitholeya* Vishnu-Mittre, Rajmahal Series, Nipania, Bihar, India (Vishnu-Mittre 1959). **Extant.**

Comment: These records, based on fertile specimens, are acceptable as Podocarpaceae. The beds cannot be precisely dated. Probable Podocarpaceae (based on vegetative material) are widespread in Jur in S. hemisphere (Florin 1963). *Brachyphyllum angustum* Walkom, Narrabeen Group (Trias), N.S.W., Australia may be Podocarpaceae (Florin 1940). Extant *Podocarpus* Persoon (probably also *Dacrydium* Solander and *Microcachrys* Hooker fil) appears in Jur Florin 1963).

Family CEPHALOTAXACEAE

First, Jur Bajoc: *Thomasiocladus zamoides* (Leckenby) Florin, M. Deltaic Series, Gristhorpe, Yorkshire, England. **Extant.**

Comment: This record is based on vegetative material but is acceptable on evidence of cuticle structure and shoot morphology. *Elatocladus cephalotaxoides* Florin, L. Helsingborg Stage (Jur Hett), Scania, Sweden, and top of Thaumatopteris Z. (Jur Hett), Cape Stewart, Scoresby Sound, E. Greenland, is probably Cephalotaxaceae (Florin, 1958). The only extant genus, *Cephalotaxus* Siebold & Zuccarini, appears in L. Cret [*C. cretacea* Samylina (1963), Aldan River, U.S.S.R.]. [K.L.A.)

Order TAXALES

First, Jur Hett: *Palaeotaxus rediviva* Nathorst well authenticated Lias, South Sweden (see Florin 1944, 1958) but several leaves with more or less similar cuticles occur in Trias Rhaet, Greenland. **Extant.**

Comment: The Taxales are distinguished from the Coniferales by bearing terminal seeds on small shoots while in Conifers the seeds are always on some sort of lateral scale. Where these scales are large and numerous they form a 'cone' but where they are few (as in many Podocarps) or very minute (as in *Cephalotaxus*) the difference from the Taxales is not obvious and in the older classifications these and other Conifers with un-conelike fructifications were placed in the Taxales. No other organ differentiates the two classes securely but the foliage of the two best known Recent genera *Taxus* and *Torreya* has strongly marked characters in form and in cuticle and fossils agreeing closely with these are placed confidently in or near these genera. Fossils not quite so similar are grouped with the Taxales or Coniferales with varying confidence. Only two fossil Taxales are known fruiting, *Palaeotaxus* (see above) (rather like *Taxus*) and *Taxus jurassica* Florin (1944, 1958) but many fossil conifers have cones which clearly separate them from Taxales.

Taxus jurassica Florin Bajoc, Yorkshire, has a shoot and seed closely resembling *Taxus*, other species are known from Yorkshire and ?U. Lias, Bornholm with shoots alone. Other species in Tertiary of Europe and E. Asia. *Torreya gracilis* Florin (1958) Bajoc, Yorkshire is a shoot like Recent. *T. californica* and other species of *Torreya* from Bornholm Lias, Late Cretaceous of U.S.A. and Tertiary of Europe and U.S.A. (Florin 1963). *Amentotaxus* widespread in Tertiary, now confined to China. Other Recent genera unknown as fossil.

The following Jurassic fossils agreeing less perfectly with a single Recent Taxalean genus very possibly represent extinct genera of that family; *Storgaadia spectabilis* Harris (Lias Hett, E. Greenland; *Elatocladus amblus* Harris (Lias Hett, E. Greenland); *Tomharrisia ramosa* Florin Bajoc, Yorkshire; *Bartholinodendron punctulatum* Florin Lias (?Upper), Bornholm and Bajoc, Yorkshire; *Marskea Thomasiana* Florin, Bajoc, Yorkshire. There are in addition many Jur fossils which could equally well be Taxaleans or Conifers; See Florin 1958 and Harris 1935).

A considerable number of fossils have been described under the names *Taxites* and *Torreyites* but are useless as records of this family, some are more like Conifers, others are of diverse nature. Conifer-like wood showing tracheids with tertiary spirals has been named *Taxoxylon*, some of these are useless (the 'spirals' being cracks caused by decay) gut others have real tertiary spirals and other characters resembling *Taxus* e.g. *Taxoxylon rajmahalense* Bhardwaj (Jur, India). It must be remembered, however, that certain Recent Conifers also have tertiary spirals. The isolated seed *Vesquia* Alvin L. Cret, Belgium is like Recent *Torreya* seeds in most respects but like *Taxus* in others.

Pollen of Recent Taxales is poorly characterised and fossil Taxalean pollen is not as a rule recognised. [T.M.H.]

Order GINKGOALES

Although this group is of considerable importance in the Mesozoic, it has not yet been formally divided into families and the taxa are therefore shown as genera. The classification of Florin (1936) into non-petiolate and petiolate groups of genera is retained with a stratigraphical arrangement in each group. As indicated by Harris (1951) *Czekanowskia* and other genera may no longer be included with Ginkgophytes when their reproductive structures have been studied.

Chapter 6: Gymnospermophyta

Non-petiolate Group of Florin 1936

Genus TRICHOPITYS Saporta 1875

First and Last, Perm Assel-Sakm: *T. heteromorpha,* Autunian beds, Lodève, Hérault, Southern France (Florin 1949).

Genus SPHENOBAIERA Florin 1936

First, Trias Carn: *S. furcata* (Heer) Florin, Schilfsandstein, Neue Welt bei Basel, Switzerland (Kräusel 1943a).

Last, Cret Valang-Apt: *S. ikorfatensis* (Seward 1926) Florin, Kome fm, Ikorfat, Nûgssuaq Peninsula, W. Greenland (Koch 1964).

Comment: *S. raymondii,* Perm, Le Creusot, France (Florin 1936) may belong to this genus. Several other early Cret species, none accurately dated (see Lundblad 1959).

Genus CZEKANOWSKIA Heer 1876

First, Trias Rhaet: *C. nathorsti* Harris, Stabbarp, Scania, Sweden, and *Hartzia* Harris, Rhaet, E. Greenland (Harris 1935).

Last, Cret Valang-Barrem: *C. rigida* Heer, Franz-Josef-Land, Barents Sea, and other localities (Florin 1936).

Genus PHOENICOPSIS Heer 1876

First, Jur Bajoc-Bath: *P. angustifolia* Heer, Irkutsk basin, U.S.S.R. (see Florin 1936, p. 77).

Last, Cret Valang-Apt: *P. steenstrupi* Seward 1926, Kome fm, Angiarsuit (B), Nûgssuarq Peninsula, W. Greenland (Koch 1964); described by Florin (1936, p. 80) in the genus *Culgoweria* Florin.

Genus PSEUDOTORELLIA Florin 1936

First, Trias Rhaet: *P. minuta* Lundblad 1957, Bjuv, layer 1 of Nathorst (lower coal bed), Scania, Sweden.

Last, Cret Haut-Barrem: *P. nordenskioldii* Florin 1936 (p. 142), Advent Bay, Spitsbergen.

Genus FURCIFOLIUM Kräusel 1943b

First and Last, Jur Kimm: *F. longifolium* (Seward) Krausel 1943b; Solnhofener Plattenkalk, south-west Germany.

Genus WINDWARDIA Florin 1936

First and Last, Cret Valang-Apt: *W. crookallii* Florin, Kap Stephen, Franz-Josef-Land, Barents Sea.

Comment: Genera *Stephenophyllum* and *Arctobaiera,* same distribution (Florin 1936).

Genus TORELLIA Heer emend. Florin 1936

First and Last, Tert Eoc: *T. rigida* Heer, Cape Staratschin, Spitsbergen (Florin 1936; stratigraphical position, Manum 1962).

Petiolate Group of Florin 1936

Genus BAIERA F. Braun emend Florin 1936

First, Trias Rhaet: *B. minuta* Nathorst, Lepidopteris Z., Scoresby Sound, E. Greenland (Harris 1937); also Scania.

Last, Cret Berr: *B. brauniana* Dunker, Wealden fm, North-west Germany (see Michael 1936, for older refs.).

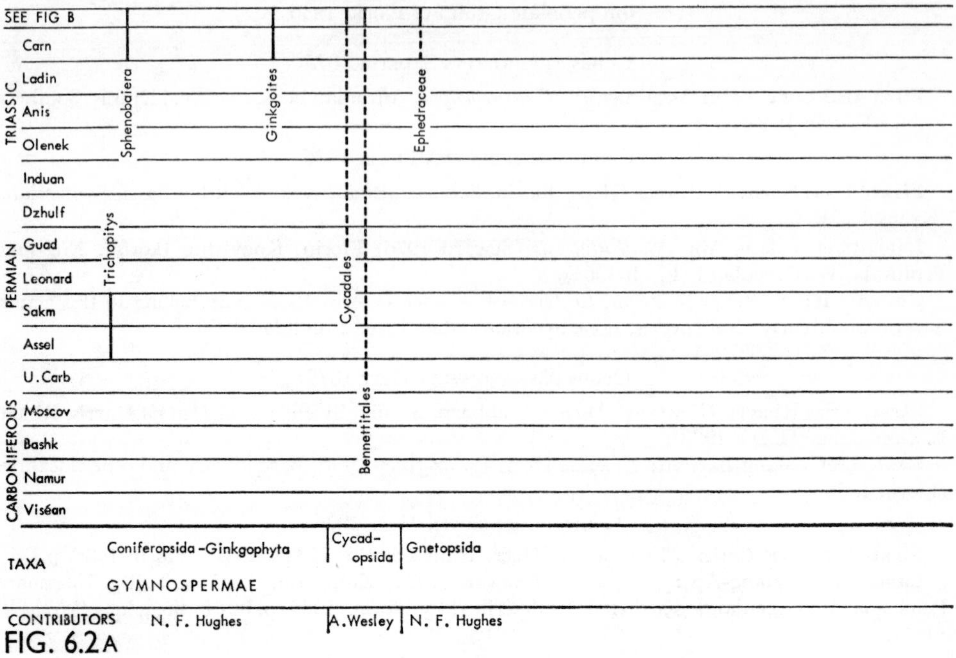

FIG. 6.2A

Genus GINKGOITES Seward emend Florin 1936

First, Trias Carn: *G. lunzensis* (Stur) Florin, Lunz beds, Lower Austria (Kräusel 1943a).

Last, Cret Cenom: *G. arcticus* (Heer) Florin, Upernivik Naes fm, W. Greenland (Seward 1936, Koch 1964); see also Florin (p. 34, 1936.)

Genus GINKGO L.

First, Jur Bajoc: *G. digitata* (Brongniart) Heer, Gristhorpe Bed, M. Deltaic Beds, Yorkshire, England (Harris 1948, p. 207). **Extant.**

Comment: First certain wood, *G. bonesii,* Up Eoc, Clarno fm, Oregon, U.S.A. (Scott *et al.* 1962).

Genus GINKGODIUM Yokoyama 1889

First and Last, Jur Bajoc: *G. nathorsti* Yokoyama, Japan, and Kamenka, Izium, Kharkov, U.S.S.R. (Thomas 1911). [N.F.H.]

REFERENCES

ALVIN, K. L. 1960. Further conifers of the Pinaceae from the Wealden formation of Belgium. *Mém Inst. r. Sci. nat. Belg.,* **146.**

ASAMA, K. 1956. Permian plants from Maiya in northern Honshû Japan. *Proc. Japan. Acad.,* **32,** 469–71.

BOCK, W. 1954. *Primaraucaria,* a new araucarian genus from the Virginia Triassic. *J. Paleont.,* **28,** 32–42.

CHALONER, W. G. & LORCH, J. 1960. An opposite-leaved conifer from the Jurassic of Israel. *Palaeontology,* **2,** 236–42.

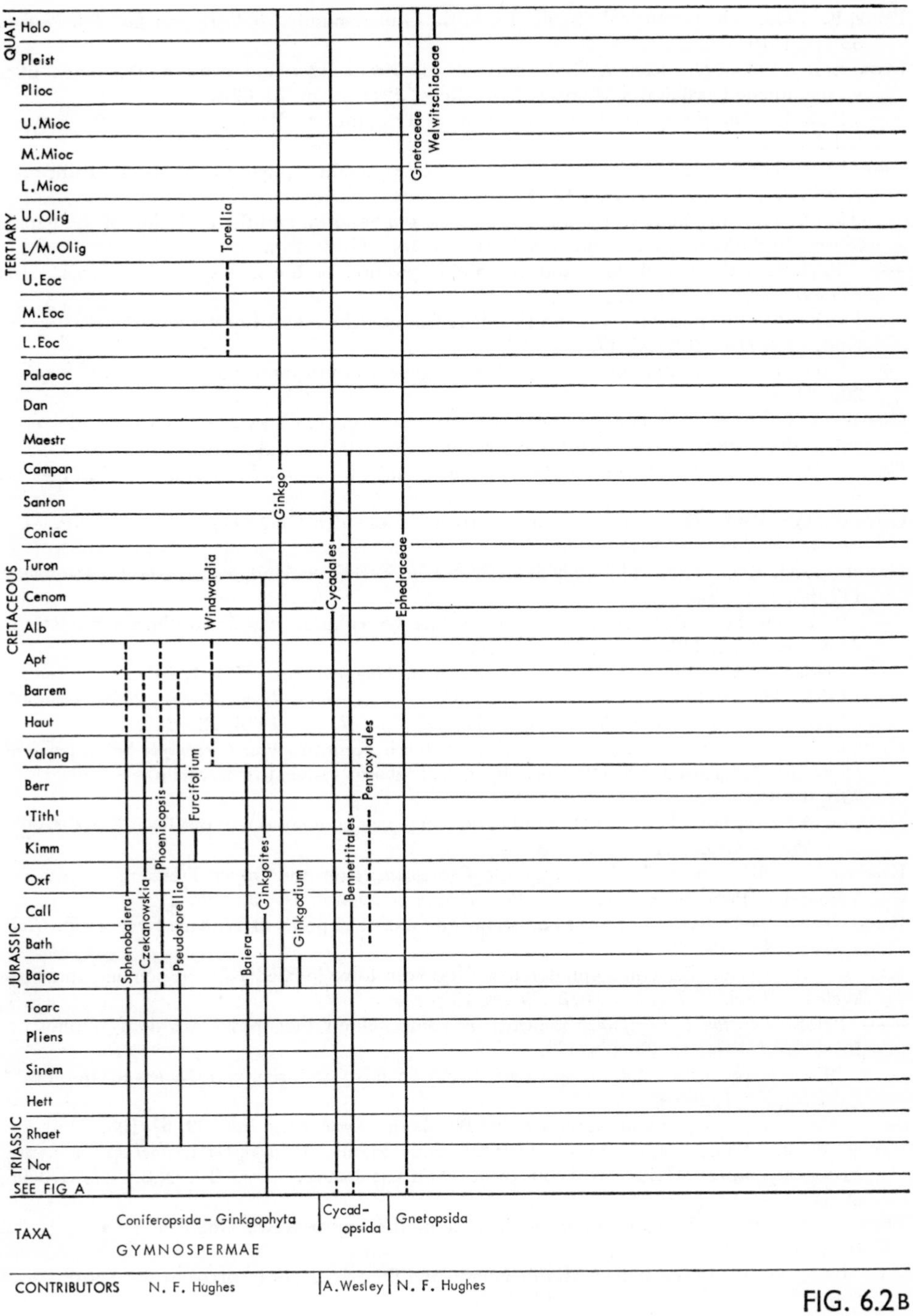
QUAT.
Holo
Pleist
Plioc
U.Mioc
M.Mioc
L.Mioc
TERTIARY
U.Olig
L/M.Olig
U.Eoc
M.Eoc
L.Eoc
Palaeoc
Dan
Maestr
Campan
Santon
Coniac
CRETACEOUS
Turon
Cenom
Alb
Apt
Barrem
Haut
Valang
Berr
'Tith'
Kimm
Oxf
Call
JURASSIC
Bath
Bajoc
Toarc
Pliens
Sinem
Hett
TRIASSIC
Rhaet
Nor
SEE FIG A
Gnetaceae
Welwitschiaceae
Torellia
Ginkgo
Cycadales
Ephedraceae
Windwardia
Pentoxylales
Furcifolium
Phoenicopsis
Bennettitales
Ginkgoites
Ginkgodium
Sphenobaiera
Czekanowskia
Pseudotorellia
Baiera
TAXA
Coniferopsida - Ginkgophyta
GYMNOSPERMAE
Cycad-opsida
Gnetopsida
CONTRIBUTORS
N. F. Hughes
A.Wesley
N. F. Hughes

FIG. 6.2B

Dorf, E. 1958. The Geological distribution of the Ginkgo family. *Bull. Wagner Inst. Sci. Philad.*, **33** (1), 1–10.

Florin, R. 1936. Die fossilen Ginkgophyten von Franz-Josef-land nebst erörterungen über vermeintliche Cordaitales Mesozoischen Alters. *Palaeontogr.*, **81–82B.**

—— 1938–45. Die Koniferen des Oberkarbons und des unteren Perms, (8 parts). *Palaeontogr.*, **85B.**

—— 1940. The Tertiary fossil conifers of South Chile and their phytogeographical significance. *K. svenska VetenskAkad. Handl.*, **19** (2).

—— 1949. The morphology of *Trichopitys heteromorpha* Saporta, and the evolution of the female flowers in the Ginkgoinae. *Acti Horti Bergiani*, **15**, 79–109, 4 pl.

—— 1953. On the morphology and taxonomic position of the genus *Cycadocarpidium*. *Acta Horti Bergiani*, **16**, 257–75.

—— 1958. On the Jurassic taxads and conifers from northwestern Europe and eastern Greenland. *Acta Horti Bergiani*, **17**, 257–402.

—— 1963. The distribution of conifer and taxad genera in time and space. *Acta Horti Bergiani*, **20**, 121–312.

Grambast, L. 1952. Sur la signification des structures généralisées chez les Coniferales et la valeur des Protopinacées en tant que groupe. *C.R. hebd. Séanc. Acad. Sci., Paris*, **235**, 1533–5.

Gordon, W. T. 1935. The genus *Pitys* Witham, emend. *Trans. R. Soc. Edinb.*, **58**, 279–311, pls. 1–8.

Gothan, W. 1914. Die unterliassische (rhätische) Flora der Umgegend von Nürnberg. *Abh. naturh. Ges. Nürnberg*, **19**, 91–186.

Harris, T. M. 1935. The fossil flora of Scoresby Sound East Greenland, part 4. *Medd. om Grønland*, **112**, no. 1, 176 pp.

—— 1937. The Fossil Flora of Scoresby Sound, East Greenland; part 5, Stratigraphic relations. *Medd. om Grønl.*, **112**, no. 2, 114 pp., 2 pl.

—— 1948. Notes on the Jurassic flora, 37–39. *Ann. Mag. nat. Hist.* (12), **1**, 181–213.

—— 1951. The fructification of *Czekanowskia* and its allies. *Phil. Trans. R. Soc.*, **235B**, 483–508.

—— 1957. A Liasso-Rhaetic flora in south Wales. *Proc. R. Soc.*, **147B**, 289–308.

Hirmer, M. & Hörhammer, L. 1934. Zur weiteren Kenntnis von *Cheirolepis* Schimper und *Hirmeriella* Hörhammer mit Bemerkungen über deren systematische Stellung. *Palaeontogr.*, **79B**, 67–84.

Hollick, A. & Jeffrey, E. C. 1909. Studies of Cretaceous coniferous remains from Kreisherville, New York. *Mem. N.Y. bot. Gdn.*, **3**, 1–76.

Kon'no, E. 1961. Some *Cycadocarpidium* and *Podozamites* from the Upper Triassic formations in Yamaguchi Prefecture, Japan. *Sci. Rep. Tohoku Univ. Geol. Ser.*, **32**, 195–212.

Koch, B. E. 1964. Review of fossil floras and nonmarine deposits of Western Greenland. *Bull. geol. Soc. Am.*, **75**, 535–48.

Kräusel, R. 1943a. Die Ginkgophyten der Trias vom Lunz in Nieder-Osterreich und von Neue Welt bei Basel. *Palaeontogr.*, **87B**, 59–93, 15 pls.

—— 1943b. *Furcifolium longifolium* (Seward) n. comb., eine Ginkgophyte aus dem Solnhofener Jura. *Senckenbergiana*, **26**, 426–433.

—— 1952. *Stachyotaxus sahnii* n. sp., eine Konifere aus der Trias von Neuewelt bei Basel. *Palaeobotanist*, **1**, 285–8.

—— 1958. Die Juraflora von Sassendorf bei Bamberg. *Senckenberg. leth.*, **39**, 67–103.

Lacey, W. S. 1953. Scottish Lower Carboniferous Plants. *Eristophyton waltoni* sp. nov. and *Endoxylon zonatum* (Kidston) Scott from Dumbartonshire. *Ann. Bot.* N.S., 17, 579–96, pl. 34.

Lele, K. M. 1955. Plant fossils from Parsora in the South Rewa Gondwana basin, India. *Palaeobotanist*, **4**, 23–34.

—— 1962. Studies in the Indian Middle Gondwana flora 2. Plant fossils from the South Rewa Gondwana basin. *Palaeobotanist*, **10**, 69–82.

—— & Maithy, P. K. 1964. Studies in the *Glossopteris* flora of India 15 Revision of the epidermal structure of *Noeggerathiopsis* Feistmantel. *Palaeobotanist*, **12**, 7–17, pls. 1–3.

Chapter 6: Gymnospermophyta

LUNDBLAD, A. B. 1957. On the presence of *Pseudotorellia* (Ginkgophyta) in the Rhaetic of N.W. Scania. *Geol. För. Stockh. Förh.*, **79**, 759–765.

—— 1959. Studies in the Rhaeto-Liassic Floras of Sweden, 2:1: Ginkgophyta from the Mining district of Scania. *K. svenska Vetensk Akad. Handl.*, Ser. 4, **6** (2), 38 pp, 6 pl.

MANUM, S. 1962. Studies in the Tertiary floras of Spitsbergen. *Skr. Norsk Polarinst.*, **125**, 127 pp., 20 pl.

MICHAEL, F. 1936. Paläobotanische und Kohlenpetrographische studien in der Nordwestdeutschen Wealdenformation. *Abh. preuss. geol. Landesamst* (N.F.), **166**, 79 pp., 4 pl.

NEUBURG, M. F. 1948. [Upper Palaeozoic flora of the Kuznetsk basin.] *in* [*Palaeontology of U.S.S.R.*] **12**, 1–342, pls. 1–73 Akademii Nauk SSSR (in Russian).

PENNY, J. S. 1947. Studies on the conifers of the Magothy flora. *Am. J. Bot.*, **34**, 281–96.

RAO, A. R. *Stachyotaxus sampathkumarani* sp. nov. from Onthea in the Rajmahal Hills, Bihar. *Palaeobotanist*, **12**, 217–19.

RENAULT, M. B. 1896. *Bassin Houiller et Permien d'Autun et d'Epinac. Fasc. IV. Flore Fossile. Etude des gîtes mineraux de la France.*

SAHNI, B. 1928. Revision of Indian fossil plants I. Coniferales. *Mem. geol. Surv. India Palaeont. indica* (N.S.), **11**, 1–49.

SAMYLINA, V. A. 1963. [The Mesozoic flora of the lower course of the Aldan River.] *Trudȳ bot. Inst. Akad. nauk SSSR*, for 1963, no. 4, 57–139 (in Russian).

SCOTT, D. H. & JEFFREY, E. C. 1914. On fossil plants showing structure from the base of the Waverley shale of Kentucky. *Phil. Trans. R. Soc.*, **205B**, 315–73, pls. 27–39.

SCOTT, R. A., BARGHOORN, E. S. & PRAKASH, U. 1962. Wood of Ginkgo in Tertiary of Western North America. *Am. J. Bot.*, **49**, 1095–1101.

SEWARD, A. C. 1919. *Fossil Plants, Vol.* 4. Cambridge.

—— 1926. The Cretaceous plant-bearing rocks of Western Greenland. *Phil. Trans. R. Soc.*, **215B**, 57–175, 9 pl.

STOCKMANS, F. & WILLIÈRE, Y. 1954. Flores Namuriennes de la Belgique: Incertitudes et Hypothères de Travail *in Vol. Victor Van Straelen*, Institut Royal Science Naturelle de Belgique, Bruxelles, 117–32, pls. 1–3.

STONELEY, H. M. M. 1958. The Upper Permian flora of England. *Bull. Br. Mus. (nat. Hist)*, *Geol.*, **3**, 295–337.

TAUGOURDEAU-LANTZ, J. & JEKHOWSKY, B. de. 1959. Spores et pollens du Keuper, Jurassique et Crétacé inférieur d'Aquitaine. *C. r. Somm. Soc. géol. France*, (7), **1**, 167–8.

TEIXEIRA, C. 1944. O Antracolitico Continental Português. *Bol. Soc. geol. Portugal*, **5**, 1–139, pls. 1–20.

THOMAS, H. H. 1911. The Jurassic flora of Kamenka. *Trudȳ geol. Kom.*, **71**, 95 pp., 8 pl.

VISHNU-MITTRE. 1959. Studies on the fossil flora of Nipania (Rajmahal Series), Bihar-Coniferales. *Palaeobotanist*, **6**, 82–112.

WOOD, C. J. 1961. *Cheirolepis muensteri* from the Lower Lias of Dorset. *Ann. Mag. nat. Hist.* (13), **4**, 505–10.

Class CYCADOPSIDA

Order CYCADALES Engler 1892

First, Trias Nor: megasporophylls, *Dioonitocarpidium pennaeforme* (Schenk) Lilienstern (leaf is probably *Danaeopsis angustifolia* Schenk), Lettenkohle, Estenfeld, Bavaria (Lilienstern 1928; Schuster 1932). Two other species of *Dioonitocarpidium* at same horizon at Lunz, Austria (Kräusel 1953). **Extant.**

Comment: Early records scarce. Additional Trias representatives include *Palaeocycas integer* (Nathorst) Florin (megasporophylls) with related leaves, *Bjuvia simplex* Florin (syn: *Taeniopteris* (*Macrotaeniopteris*) *gigantea* Nathorst), Rhaet, Bjuv, Sweden (Florin 1933). Attribution to Cycadales by Schuster 1932 of contemporaneous *Zamioidea keuperiana* Schuster, *Lepacyclotes triphyllus* (Heer) Schuster, *Androstrobilites triassicus* (Krasser) Schuster, *Moltenia dentata* Du Toit and *Walkomia feistmantelii* (Johnson) Schuster, from other localities, not strongly supported. Expansion in

Rhaet-Lias with greatest development in Jur. Last traces of older types (often classed separately as Nilssoniales) in U.Cret, Chignuk Fm, Alaska (Hollick 1930). Living types already in Tert, with widespread distribution (Hollick 1932), but present distribution of the nine existing genera very restricted in tropical and sub-tropical regions only. Detached organs include ovulate strobili, *Beania* Carruthers 1869, Trias Rhaet to Jur Bath, England (relatively complete specimens), Sweden, Greenland, Germany, Russia, France, ? Sardinia, ? India (mainly isolated seeds always in association with *Nilssonia* leaves); ? megasporophylls, *Cycadospadix* Schimper 1870, ? Trias Ladin to Jur Kimm, France, Italy, Scotland; staminate strobili, *Androstrobus* Schimper 1870, ? Trias Nor to Jur Bath, England, France, Germany, Russia; scale-leaves, *Deltolepis* Harris 1942, Jur Bajoc, England; foliage-leaves, *Nilssonia* Brongniart 1825, Trias Rhaet to U.Cret, widely distributed, *Ctenis* Lindley & Hutton 1834 (including *Anthrophyopsis* Nathorst 1878), Trias Rhaet to L.Cret, widespread in N. Hemisphere, *Pseudoctenis* Seward 1911 (including *Pseudopterophyllum* Florin 1933), Trias Rhaet to Cret Barrem, widespread, but not in America or Africa, *Paracycas* Harris 1964, Jur Bajoc, England, *Doratophyllum* Harris 1932, Trias Rhaet, Greenland, Sweden, *Quervainia* Harris 1932, Trias Rhaet, Greenland, *Almargemia* Florin 1933, Cret Apt, Portugal, *Apoldia* Wesley, Trias Nor, Hungary, *Aldania* Samylina 1956, L.Cret, Siberia (Andrews 1955; Florin 1933; Harris 1932, 1941, 1964; Hollick 1930; Orlov 1963; Schuster 1932; Wesley 1958). *Rhabdotaenia* Pant 1958, U.Perm, Tanganyika and India, may represent an early cycad leaf (Pant 1958, Pant & Verma 1963). In rare cases species of *Beania*, *Nilssonia*, *Androstrobus* and *Deltolepis* have been attributed to the same plant, and in one case *Androstrobus* has been correlated with *Pseudoctenis* (Harris 1964; Thomas & Harris 1960). Number of old generic identifications unreliable and suspect without support from cuticle structure (see comments under Bennettitales). *Androstrobus* also includes cones of lycopods in addition to genuine cycad staminate strobili. *Zamiostrobus* Endlicher 1836 refers to conifer shoots with cones. *Cycadites* is a *nomen confusum*.

Order BENNETTITALES Engler 1892

First, Trias Nor: bisexual "flowers", *Sturianthus* (*Sturiella*) *langeri* Kräusel; ovulate "flowers", *Westersheimia pramelreuthensis* Krasser; seed-bearing "fruit", *Bennetticarpus wettsteini* (Krasser) Kräusel; staminate organs, *Haitingeria krasseri* (Schuster) Krasser, *Lunzia austriaca* Krasser, "*Macrotaeniopteris*" *lunzensis* Krasser; leaves, *Pterophyllum filicoides* (Schlotheim) Thomas (syns: *P. longifolium* Brongniart, *P. jaegeri* Brongniart and *P. brevipenne* Kurr), *Taeniopteris* spp.; scale-leaves, *Cycadolepis wettsteini* Krasser, Lettenkohle, Lunz, Austria (Krasser 1916, 1918; Kräusel 1948, 1949, 1950; Thomas 1930). *Pterophyllum filicoides* and petrified wood, *Paradoxoxylon leuthardti* Kräusel, at same horizon at Neuewelt, Basel, Switzerland (Kräusel 1955; Thomas 1930).

Last, Cret Campan: trunks with bisexual "flowers", *Monanthesia magnifica* Wieland ex Delevoryas, Mesaverde Fm, Mew Mexico (Delevoryas 1959).

Comment: Great diversification of species and geographical expansion in Rhaet-Lias to world-wide distribution during Jur and early Cret, finally becoming extinct in U.Cret. Genera refer to complete plants, *Williamsonia* Carruthers 1870 (but name mostly used for detached unisexual "flowers", either ovulate or staminate; restriction of *Williamsonia* to ovulate "flowers" would be more correct, with revival of its earlier name, *Weltrichia* C. F. Braun 1847, for staminate "flowers"), Trias Rhaet to early Cret, England, Scotland, France, Germany, Italy, Sardinia, Sweden, Afghanistan, India, S. W. Russia, Siberia, Japan, N. America, Mexico; trunks with bisexual "flowers", *Cycadeoidea* Buckland 1828 (including *Bennettites* Carruthers 1870, *Raumeria* Goeppert 1853 and *Cycadella* Ward 1900), U.Trias to early Cret, N. America, England, France, Italy, Poland, Germany, Belgium, ? Russia, ? India; bisexual "flowers", *Williamsoniella* Thomas 1915, Jur Bajoc, England, Central Russia, *Wielandiella* Nathorst 1910, Trias Rhaet, Sweden, Greenland; seed-bearing "fruits", *Vardekloeftia* Harris 1932, Trias Rhaet, Greenland; scale-leaves, *Cycadolepis* Saporta 1874, Jur, widespread; leaves, *Anomozamites* Schimper 1870, Trias Rhaet to early Cret, widespread, *Zamites* Brongniart 1828, Trias Rhaet to early Cret, widespread, *Ptilophyllum* Morris 1840, Jur "Lias" to early Cret, widespread, *Otozamites* C. F. W. Braun 1842, Trias Rhaet to early Cret, *Nilssoniopteris* Nathorst 1909 (including *Taeniozamites* Harris 1932), Trias Rhaet to early Cret, widespread, *Pterophyllum* Brongniart 1828 (including *Leptopterophyllum* Thomas 1930), Trias Nor to late Cret, widespread, *Sphenozamites* Brongniart

1849, Jur Toarc, Italy, *Pseudocycas* Nathorst 1907, Jur "Lias" to early Cret, widespread, *Dictyoza-mites* Medlicott & Blanford 1879, Jur, widespread, *Tyrmia* Prynada 1955, Jur to early Cret, Russia, *Jacutiella* Samylina 1956, early Cret, Russia, *Neozamites* Vakhrameev 1962, early Cret, Russia (selected references, in which further bibliographies may be found, are Andrews 1955; Florin 1933; Harris 1932, 1937; Orlov 1963; Seward 1917, 1926, 1941; Sitholey 1963; Thomas 1930; Turutanova-Ketova 1963; Vakhrameev 1962, 1964; Wesley 1958; Wieland 1906, 1914–16, and 1916). In certain cases, detached organs have been correlated together as parts of an individual plant, e.g. *Wielandiella* with *Anomozamites; Williamsoniella* with *Nilssoniopteris; Williamsonia* variously with *Ptilophyllum, Zamites* and *Otozamites*. Number of generic identifications unreliable and suspect because of close superficial resemblance between some foliage of Bennetti-tales and that of other Orders. Without support from cuticle structure many leaves cannot be assigned to a systematic position. Thus, when cuticle is known, *Taeniopteris*-like leaves may be referred to Bennettitales (*Nilssoniopteris, Jacutiella*), Cycadales (*Bjuvia, Doratophyllum, Rhabdotaenia*) or Pentoxylales (*Nipaniophyllum*), and *Sphenozamites*-like leaves to Bennettitales (*Sphenozamites*) or Cycadales (*Apoldia*). Palaeozoic foliage records are not authenticated by cuticle structure. Thus, *Pterophyllum grand'euryi* Saporta & Marion, U.Carb "Stephanian", Blanzy, France and *P. fayoli* Renault, U.Carb, Commentary, France, are incorrectly identified and do not belong to Bennetti-tales (Thomas 1930). Further difficulties arise from innumerable name changes in the leaf genera, and identifications based on poor material or inadequate observations. *Pterophyllum lipoldi* Stur, *P.meriani* Brongniart and *P.pulchellum* Heer, Trias Nor, Lunz and Neuewelt, are conifer shoots now called *Stachyotaxus* and *Voltzia* (Kräusel 1955). *Wonnacottia* Harris 1942, Jur Bajoc, is only an *Anomozamites* leaf with insect galls, not a microsporophyll.

Constituent families: Williamsoniaceae Carruthers 1870 (including Wielandiellaceae auct.), Trias to early Cret, with great development during Jur. Cycadeoideaceae Buckland 1828, mainly early Cret.

Order PENTOXYLALES Pilger & Melchior 1954

First, M. or U. Jur: stems, *Pentoxylon sahnii* Srivastava and *Nipanioxylon guptai* Srivastava; leaves, *Nipaniophyllum raoi* Sahni; ovulate strobili, *Carnoconites compactum* Srivastava; staminate organs, *Sahnia nipaniensis* Vishnu-Mittre, Rajmahal Series, Upper Gondwana System, Nipania, Rajmahal Hills, Bihar, India (Pilger & Melchior *in* Melchior & Werdermann 1954; Sahni 1948; Srivastava 1944 and 1946; Vishnu-Mittre 1953, 1958).

Last, Jur 'Tith': *Carnoconites cranwelli* Harris, Waikato Heads, North Island, New Zealand (Harris 1962).

Comment: Order restricted to these localities. *Nipaniophyllum* originally referred to *Taenio-pteris spatulata* McClelland. Latter species associated with *Carnoconites cranwelli* in New Zealand. *Taeniopteris spatulata* is an aggregate species reported from Mesozoic in India, Australia, New Zealand, Ceylon, Tonkin and Korea, and may include unrecognised pentoxylalean foliage (Harris 1962). *Haitingeria rajmahalensis* (Wieland) Krasser (syn: *Strobilites pascoei* Sahni) is probably a compression of *Carnoconites* (Sahni 1948). [A.W.]

REFERENCES

ANDREWS, H. N. 1955. Index of Generic Names of Fossil Plants, 1820–1950. *Bull. U.S. geol. Surv.*, **1013**, 1–262.

DELEVORYAS, T. 1959. Investigations of North American cycadeoids: Monanthesia. *Am. J. Bot.*, **46**, 657–666.

FLORIN, R. 1933. Studien über die Cycadales des Mesozoikums. *K. svenska Vetensk Akad. Handl*, ser. 3, **12** (5), 1–134, pl. 1–16.

HARRIS, T. M. 1932. The fossil flora of Scoresby Sound, East Greenland, 3. *Medd. om Grønl.*, **85** (5), 1–133, pl. 1–19.

—— 1937. The fossil flora of Scoresby Sound, East Greenland, 5. *Medd. om Grønl.*, **112** (2), 1–114, pl. 1.

HARRIS, T. M. 1941. Cones of extinct Cycadales from the Jurassic rocks of Yorkshire. *Phil. Trans. R. Soc.*, **231B**, 75–98, pl. 5–6.

—— 1942. *Wonnacottia*, a new Bennettitalean microsporophyll. *Ann. Bot. (n.s.)*, **6**, 577–592.

—— 1962. The occurrence of the fructification *Carnoconites* in New Zealand. *Trans. R. Soc. N.Z.* (Geology), **1**, 17–27, pl. 1–3.

—— 1964. *The Yorkshire Jurassic Flora, II. Brit. Mus. (Nat. Hist.)*, London, 1–191, pl. 1–7.

HOLLICK, A. 1930. The Upper Cretaceous floras of Alaska. *Prof. Pap. U.S. geol. Surv.*, **159**, 1–123, pl. 1–186.

—— 1932. Descriptions of new species of Tertiary cycads, with a review of those previously recorded. *Bull. Torrey bot. Club*, **59**, 169–189, pl. 1–14.

KRASSER, F. 1916. Studien über die fertile Region der Cycadophyten aus den Lunzer Schichten: Mikrosporophylle und Männliche Zapfen. *Anz. Akad. Wiss. Wien*, **53**, 335–337.

—— 1918. Studien über die fertile Region der Cycadophyten aus den Lunzer Schichten. *Denkschr. Akad. Wiss, Wien*, **94**, 489–554, pl. 1–4.

KRÄUSEL, R. 1948. *Sturiella langeri* nov. gen. nov. sp., eine Bennettitee aus der Trias von Lunz (Nieder-Österreich). *Senckenbergiana*, **29**, 141–149.

—— 1949. Koniferen und andere Gymnospermen aus der Trias von Lunz in Nieder-Österreich. *Palaeontogr.*, **89B**.

—— 1950. *Versunkene Floren.* 1–152, pl. 1–64.

—— 1953. Ein neues *Dioonitocarpidium* aus der Trias von Lunz. *Senckenbergiana*, **34**, 105–108, pl. 1.

—— 1955. Die Keuperflora von Neuewelt bei Basel, 1. Koniferen und andere Gymnospermen. *Schweiz. paläont. Abh.*, **71**, 1–27, pl. 1–9.

LILIENSTERN, H. RÜHLE VON. 1928. *Dioonites pennaeformis* Schenk, eine fertile Cycadee aus der Lettenkohle. *Paläont. Z.*, **10**, 91–107, pl. 5–6.

MELCHIOR, H. & WERDERMANN, E. 1954. A. Engler's *Syllabus der Pflanzenfamilien*, 12th edn., 1, 1–323.

ORLOV, J. A. *et al.* 1963. *Osnovy paleontologii* (Handbook of the Palaeontology and Geology of the USSR), *XV: Gymnospermae, Angiospermae*, 1–743, pl. 1–40.

PANT, D. D. 1958. The structure of some leaves and fructifications of the Glossopteris flora of Tanganyika. *Bull. Br. Mus. (Nat. Hist.)*, *Geol.*, **3**, 127–175, pl. 18–21.

—— & VERMA, B. K. 1963. On the structure of leaves of *Rhabdotaenia* Pant from the Raniganj coalfield, India. *Palaeontology*, **6**, 301–314, pl. 49–50.

SAHNI, B. 1948. The Pentoxyleae: a new group of Jurassic gymnosperms from the Rajmahal Hills of India. *Bot. Gaz.*, **110**, 47–80.

SCHUSTER, J. 1932. Cycadaceae *in* ENGLER, A. *Das Pflanzenreich*, *IV: 1*, 1–168.

SEWARD, A. C. 1917. *Fossil Plants*, **3**, 1–656.

—— 1926. The Cretaceous Plant-bearing rocks of Western Greenland. *Phil. Trans. R. Soc.*, **215B**, 57–175, pl. 4–12.

—— 1941. *Plant Life through the Ages.* Cambridge, 1–607.

SITHOLEY, R. V. 1963. Gymnosperms of India, 1. Fossil forms. *Bull. natn. bot. Gdn. Lucknow*, **86**, 1–78, pl. 1–15.

SRIVASTAVA, B. P. 1944. Silicified plant remains from the Rajmahal Hills. *Proc. natn. Acad. Sci., India*, **14B**, 73–76.

—— 1946. Silicified plant remains from the Rajmahal Series of India. *Proc. natn. Acad. Sci., India*, **15**, 185–211.

THOMAS, H. H. 1930. Further observations on the cuticle structure of Mesozoic cycadean fronds. *J. Linn. Soc.*, Botany, **48**, 389–415, pl. 20–21.

—— & HARRIS, T. M. 1960. Cycadean Cones of the Yorkshire Jurassic. *Senckenberg. leth.*, **41**, 139–161, pl. 1–4.

TURUTANOVA-KETOVA, A. I. 1963. Williamsoniaceae Sovietskogo souza. (Williamsoniaceae of the USSR). *Trudy bot. Inst. Akad. nauk SSSR*, **4**, 5–55, pl. 1–7.

VAKHRAMEEV, V. A. 1962. Novie rannemelovie cycadofitie Jacutii. (New early Cretaceous Cycadophytes from Jacutia), *Paleont. Zh.*, **3**, 123–129, pl. 12–13.

Chapter 6: Gymnospermophyta

VAKHRAMEEV, V. A. 1964. Urskie i rannemelovie flori Evrazii i paleofloristicheskie provintsii etogo vremeni. (Jurassic and early Cretaceous floras of Eurasia and the palaeofloristic provinces of this period), *Trudy. geol. Inst., Moscow*, **102**, 1–263.

VISHNU-MITTRE. 1953. A male flower of the Pentoxyleae with remarks on the structure of the female cones of the group. *Palaeobotanist*, **2**, 78–84, pl. 1–5.

—— 1958. Studies on the fossil flora of Nipania (Rajmahal Series), India—Pentoxyleae. *Palaeobotanist*, **6**, 31–46, pl. 1–3.

WESLEY, A. 1958. Contributions to the knowledge of the flora of the Grey Limestones of Veneto, 1. *Memorie Ist. geol. miner. Univ. Padova*, **21**, 1–55, pl. 1–3.

WIELAND, G. R. 1906. *American Fossil Cycads, 1*. Carnegie Institute, 1–296, pl. 1–50.

—— 1914–16. La flora liásica de la Mixteca Alta. *Bol. Inst. geol. México*, **31,** pl. 1–50.

—— 1916. *American Fossil Cycads, 2*. Carnegie Institute, 1–277, pl. 1–58.

Class GNETOPSIDA

Family EPHEDRACEAE

First, Trias Carn-Nor: *Ephedra chinleana* (Daugherty) Scott (Pollen), Chinle fm, Arizona, U.S.A. (Scott 1960). **Extant.**

Comment: *Ephedripites* (pollen), Mid Perm, Oklahoma, U.S.A. (Wilson 1962) is as yet not fully described. *Ephedra*-like pollen becomes suddenly common in Cret Barrem (e.g. Couper and Hughes 1963). First macrofossil, *Ephedra miocenica*, Olig., Florissant, Colorado, U.S.A. (Wodehouse 1934).

Family GNETACEAE

First, Tert Plioc: *Gnetum scandens* var. *robustum* Reid and Reid 1915, Reuver, Eastern Netherlands. **Extant.**

Comment: *Gnetumites* sp. (pollen), Up. Eoc., U.S.S.R. (Zaklinskaya 1957) is inadequately illustrated. *Rogersia* Fontaine and other genera, Lr. Cret, Potomac fm, Eastern U.S.A. suggested as Gnetales (Berry 1911).

Family WELWITSCHIACEAE

First, Quat Holo: *Welwitschia mirabilis* Hooker, South-West Africa. **Extant.**

Comment: *Vittatina* sp. (pollen) and *Hamiapollenites*, Mid Permian, Flowerpot fm, Oklahoma, U.S.A. no longer attributed to this group (Wilson 1959, 1962). *Welwitschia* has a benettitalean-type leaf cuticle. [N.F.H].

REFERENCES

BERRY, E. W. 1911. *in The Lower Cretaceous deposits of Maryland*. Maryland Geol. Surv., Baltimore.

COUPER, R. A. & HUGHES, N. F. 1963. Jurassic and Lower Cretaceous palynology of the Netherlands and adjacent areas. *Verh. ned. geol.-mijnb. Genoot.* (Geol. Series), **21**, 105–8, 3 pl.

SCOTT, R. A. 1960. Pollen of *Ephedra* from the Chinle formation (Upper Triassic). *Micropaleontology*, **6**, 271–6, 1 pl.

WILSON, L. R. 1959. Geological History of the Gnetales, *Okla. Geol. Notes*, **19**, 2, 35–40.

—— 1962. Plant microfossils from the Flowerpot formation. *Circ. Okla. geol. Surv.*, **49**, 50 pp., 4 col. pl.

WODEHOUSE, R. P. 1934. A Tertiary Ephedra. *Torreya*, **34**, 1–4.

ZAKLINSKAYA, E. D. 1957. Stratigraphical importance of the pollen of the gymnospermous Cainozoic deposits of the Pavloda Irtvysk and the Northern Aral region. *Trud. geol. Inst. Acad. nauk SSSR*, no. **6,** 184 pp., 17 pl. [in Russian].

K. L. Alvin, PH.D.
Department of Botany, Imperial College of Science and Technology, Prince Consort Road, London S W 7.

P. D. W. Barnard, PH.D.
    Department of Botany, The University, Reading, Berkshire.
[Professor] T. M. Harris, F.R.S.
    Department of Botany, The University, Reading, Berkshire.
N. F. Hughes, M.A. F.G.S.
    Department of Geology, Sedgwick Museum, Downing Street, Cambridge.
R. H. Wagner, GEOL. DRS. F.G.S.
    Geology Department, The University, St. George's Square, Sheffield 1.
A. Wesley, B.SC. A.R.C.S. F.L.S. F.G.S.
    Department of Botany, The University, Leeds 2.

CHAPTER 7

Angiospermae

Contributors: K. I. M. CHESTERS, F. R. GNAUCK & N. F. HUGHES

The families have been arranged in alphabetical order with the Monocotyledons included; approximately 110 families have been omitted as no fossil record has been found (e.g. Orchidaceae, Orobanchaceae etc.).

The records are known to be of varying quality, and it is likely that some of the Cretaceous records will prove later to have been in error; re-assessment of all these is however beyond the scope of the present work.

In most cases the palynological records have been entered under "Comment". These have of necessity been drawn from those papers using extant taxa, rather than those using morphographic criteria; this was done purely from expediency and implies no judgement of methods. In order to keep the chapter within bounds, palynological records have been restricted to those supporting the macrofossils or the reverse, those showing possibility of recognition or preservation, and others of special interest; Pleistocene pollen records have not been given.

Family ACANTHACEAE

First, Tert Olig: *Acanthus rugatus* Reid and Chandler 1926, Bembridge Beds, Isle of Wight, England. **Extant.**

Family ACERACEAE

First, Cret Cenom: *Acer amboyense* Newberry 1895, Raritan Fm, Eastern U.S.A. **Extant.**
Comment: *Acer* cf. *platanoides* (pollen), Olig, U.S.S.R. (Pokrovskoi 1956b, p. 202).

Family ACTINIDIACEAE

First, Tert Eoc: *Actinidia poolensis* Chandler 1963a, Lower Bagshot Beds, Lake, Dorset. **Extant.**

Family AGAVACEAE

First, Tert Eoc: *Phormium reticulatus* (pollen) Couper 1960, Arnold Series, New Zealand. **Extant.**

Family ALANGIACEAE

First, Tert Eoc: *Alangium jenkinsi* Chandler 1961, London Clay, Herne Bay, Kent, England. **Extant.**

Family ALISMACEAE

First, Cret Cenom: *Alismaphyllum victor-masoni* (Ward) Berry 1912, White House Bluff, Patapsco Fm, Eastern U.S.A. **Extant.**

The Fossil Record, Part II

Family AMARYLLIDACEAE

First, Quat Pleist: *Agave utahensis* Engelmann, Gypsum Cave, Nevada, U.S.A. (Laudermilk & Munz 1934). **Extant.**
Comment: see also Agavaceae.

Family ANACARDIACEAE

First, Cret Cenom: *Rhus powelliana* Lesquereux 1891, Dakota Fm, U.S.A. **Extant.**
Comment: *Rhus* cf. *semialata* (pollen), Mioc, U.S.S.R. (Pokrovskoi 1956b, p. 201).

Family ANONACEAE

First, Cret Maestr: *Anonaspermum gilbediensis* Chesters 1955, Mosasaur Sh, Nigeria. **Extant.**

Family APOCYNACEAE

First, Cret Cenom: *Apocynophyllum sordidum* Lesquereux 1891, Dakota Fm, Ellesworth Co., Kansas, U.S.A. **Extant.**

Family AQUIFOLIACEAE

First, Cret Cenom: *Ilex scudderi* Lesquereux 1891, Dakota Fm, Ellesworth Co., Kansas, U.S.A. **Extant.**
Comment: *Ilex* cf. *cassine* (pollen), Olig, U.S.S.R. (Pokrovskoi 1956a, p. 127).

Family ARACEAE

First, Cret Cenom: *Aniscrema cretacea* Lesquereux 1891, Dakota Fm, U.S.A. **Extant.**

Family ARILIACEAE

First, Cret Cenom: *Araliaephyllum crassinerve* (Fontaine), Patapsco Fm, Eastern U.S.A. (Berry 1912). **Extant.**

Family ARISTOLOCHIACEAE

First, Cret Cenom: *Aristolochiaephyllum crassinerve* (Fontaine 1889), Patapsco Fm, Eastern U.S.A. **Extant.**

Family ASCLEPIADACEAE

First, Cret Cenom: *Accrates amboyensis* Berry 1911, Raritan Fm, Eastern U.S.A. **Extant.**

Family BALSAMINACEAE

First, Quat Pleist: *Impatiens capensis* Meerburgh, Pamlico, Maryland, U.S.A. (R. W. Brown 1935b). **Extant.**

Family BERBERIDACEAE

First, Tert Palaeoc: *Winchellia triphylla* Lesquereux 1893, Fort Union Fm, Montana, U.S.A. (Lamotte 1952). **Extant.**

Family BETULACEAE

First, Cret Cenom: *Alnites grandiflora* Newberry 1868, Blackbird Hill, Nebraska, U.S.A. (Lesquereux 1878). **Extant.**
Comment: *Betula* sp. (pollen), Olig, North-western U.S.A. (Gray 1964, p. 23).

Family BIGNONIACEAE

First, Tert Eoc: *Bignonicapaula formosa* Berry 1930, Holly Springs, Tennessee, U.S.A. **Extant.**

Family BOMBACACEAE

First, Cret Cenom: *Bombax virginiensis* Fontaine 1889, Patapsco Fm, Eastern U.S.A. **Extant.**
Comment: *Bombacidites bombaxoides* (pollen), L. Olig, North Island, New Zealand (Couper 1960, p. 53).

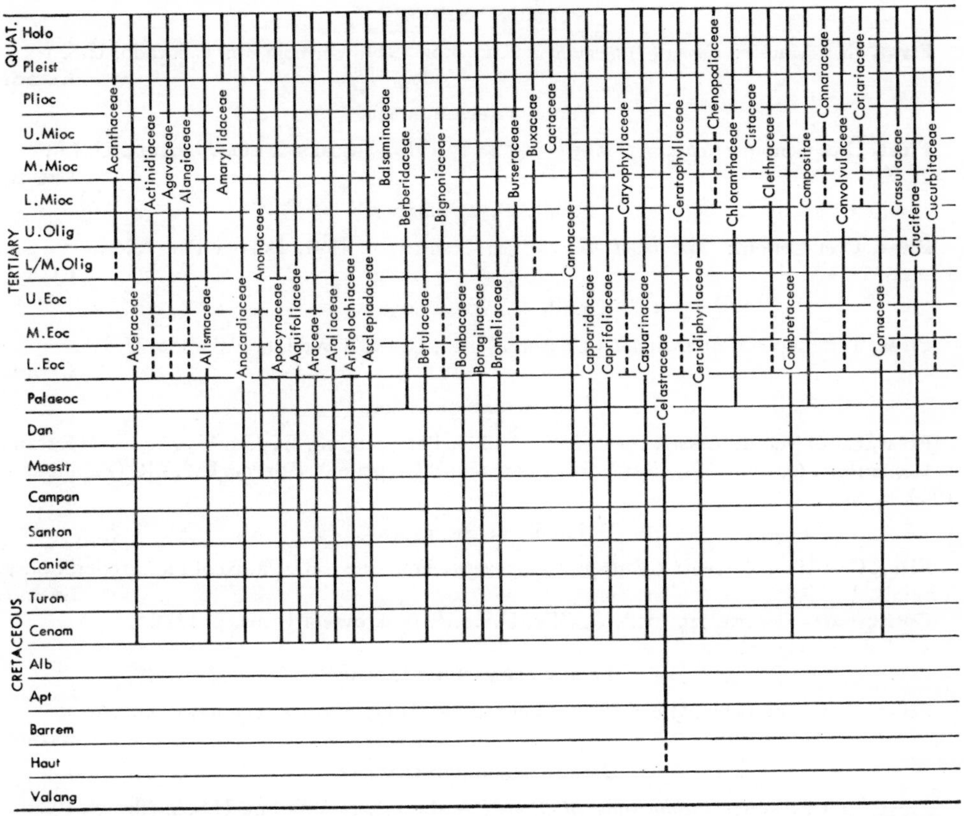

TAXA   ANGIOSPERMAE

CONTRIBUTORS   K. I. M. Chesters,   F. R. Gnauck,   N. F. Hughes

FIG. 7.1 B

Family BORAGINACEAE

First, Cret Cenom: *Cordia apiculata* (Hollick) Berry 1911, Raritan Fm, Eastern U.S.A.
Extant.

Family BROMELIACEAE

First, Cret Cenom: *Bromelia* (?) *tenuifolia* Lesquereux 1891, Dakota Fm, U.S.A.   **Extant.**

Family BURSERACEAE

First, Tert Eoc: *Phellodendron costatum* Chandler 1961, Reading Beds.   **Extant.**

Family BUXACEAE

First, Tert Olig: *Pachysandra* sp. (pollen), North-western U.S.A. (Gray 1964).   **Extant.**
Comment: *Buxus sempervivens* Mädler 1939, Plioc, Germany.

Family CACTACEAE

First, Quat Pleist: *Mamillaria tuberculosa* Engelmann, Shelter Cave, New Mexico, U.S.A. (Fosberg 1936).   **Extant.**
Comment: *Eopuntia* (Chaney 1944), Eoc, Green River Fm, not Cactaceae (Brown 1959).

271

Family CANNACEAE

First, Cret Maestr: *Canna* (?) *magnifolia* Knowlton 1917, Vermejo Fm, Colorado, U.S.A.
Extant.

Family CAPPARIDACEAE

First, Cret Cenom: *Capparites cynphylloides* Berry 1919, Tuscaloosa Fm, Alabama, U.S.A.
Extant.

Family CAPRIFOLIACEAE

First, Cret Cenom: *Virburnum grewiopsidum* Lesquereux 1891, Dakota Fm, Ellesworth Co.,
Kansas, U.S.A. **Extant.**

Family CARYOPHYLLACEAE

First, Tert Eoc: *Alsinites revelatus* Cockerell 1925, Green River Fm, Colorado, U.S.A.
Extant.

Family CASUARINACEAE

First, Cret Cenom: *Casurina covillei* Ward 1895, Patapsco Fm, Eastern U.S.A. **Extant.**
Comment: *Casuarinidites cainozoicus* Cookson and Pike (pollen), Palaeoc, U.S.S.R. (Zaklinskaya
1963, p. 235).

Family CELASTRACEAE

First, Cret Haut-Barrem: *Celastrophyllum circinerve* Fontaine 1889, Patuxent Fm, Frederiksburg,
Virginia, U.S.A. **Extant.**
Comment: *Euonymus* sp. (pollen), Olig, U.S.S.R. (Pokrovskoi 1956a, p. 127).

Family CERATOPHYLLACEAE

First, Tert Eoc: *Ceratophyllum incertum* Berry 1930, Holly Springs, Tennessee, U.S.A.
Extant.

Family CERCIDIPHYLLACEAE

First, Cret Cenom: *Cercidiphyllum ellipticum* (Newberry), Dakota Fm, U.S.A. (Brown 1939).
Extant.

Family CHENOPODIACEAE

First, Tert Mioc: cf. *Sarcobatus* (pollen), North-western U.S.A. (Gray 1964). **Extant.**

Family CHLORANTHACEAE

First, Tert Palaeoc: *Ascarina* sp. (pollen), Waipawan, New Zealand, (Couper 1960, p. 47).
Extant.

Family CISTACEAE

First, Quat Pleist: *Helianthemum* sp., Berry 1933, Pamlico, Washington D.C., U.S.A.
Extant.

Family CLETHRACEAE

First, Tert Eoc: *Clethra hantonensis* Chandler 1963b, Highcliffe Sands, Mudeford, Hants,
England. **Extant.**

Family COMBRETACEAE

First, Cret Cenom: *Terminaliphyllum rectinerve* Velenovsky 1889, Bohemia. **Extant.**

Family COMPOSITAE

First, Tert Palaeoc: *Bidentites groenlandicus* Heer 1883, Atanekerdluk, Greenland. **Extant.**
Comment: *Artemisia* sp. (pollen), Mioc, U.S.S.R. (Pokrovskoi 1956b, p. 213).

Chapter 7: Angiospermae

Family CONNARACEAE

First, Tert Mioc: *Cnestis rusingensis* (fruit) Chesters 1957, Lake Victoria, Kenya. *Connarus carmenensis* (leaf) Berry 1923, Mioc, Mexico. **Extant.**

Family CONVOLVULACEAE

First, Tert Eoc: *Porana speirii* Lesquereux, Green River Fm, Wyoming, U.S.A. (R. W. Brown 1937). **Extant.**

Family CORIARIACEAE

First, Tert Mioc: *Coriaria* sp. (pollen), New Zealand (Couper 1953, p. 44). **Extant.**
Comment: *C.* cf. *japonica* Gray, Plioc, Poland (Szafer 1943).

Family CORNACEAE

First, Cret Cenom: *Cornus praecox* Lesquereux 1891, Dakota Fm, U.S.A. **Extant.**
Comment: *Griselinia* sp. (pollen), L. Mioc, New Zealand (Couper 1953, p. 52).

Family CRASSULACEAE

First, Tert Eoc: *Sedum* (?) *hisperium* Knowlton 1923, Green River Fm, Colorado, U.S.A.
Extant.

Family CRUCIFERAE

First, Cret Maestr: "Cruciferae" (pollen), New Zealand (Couper 1960, p. 47). **Extant.**
Comment: *Draba fladnizensis* Wulfenius, Pleist, Fairbanks, Alaska (Chaney & Mason 1936).

Family CUCURBITACEAE

First, Tert Eoc: *Cucurbitospermum cooperi* Chandler 1961, London Clay, Herne Bay, Kent, England. **Extant.**

Family CUNONIACEAE

First, Tert Palaeoc: *Weinmannia europaeum* (Unger) Heer 1883, Greenland. **Extant.**

Family CYCLANTHACEAE

First, Tert Eoc: *Cyclanthodendron sahnii* (Rode), Intertrappean beds, Mohgaon Kalan, India (Sahni & Surange 1944). **Extant.**

Family CYPERACEAE

First, Cret Coniac: *Carex clarkii* Berry 1911, Magothy Fm, Eastern U.S.A. **Extant.**
Comment: "Cyperaceae" (pollen), Cret, New Zealand (Couper 1953, p. 60).

Family DATISCACEAE

First, Quat Pleist: *Datisca glomerata* Brewer and Watson, Tornales, Marin Co., Calif., U.S.A. (Mason 1934). **Extant.**

Family DILLENIACEAE

First, Tert Eoc: *Tetracera sheppeyensis* Reid and Chandler 1933, London Clay, Sheppey, Kent, England. **Extant.**
Comment: *Dillenites paucidentatus?* Cret Coniac-Campan, British Columbia, Canada (Bell 1957).

Family DIOSCOREACEAE

First, Cret Cenom: *Dioscorea* (?) *cretacea* Lesquereux 1874, Dakota Fm, U.S.A. **Extant.**

273

The Fossil Record, Part II

Family DIPTEROCARPACEAE

First, Tert Plioc: *Dipterocarpaceophyllum sumatrense* Kräusel 1929, Sungei Tjakon, Palembang, Sumatra. **Extant.**

Family DROSERACEAE

First, Tert Olig: *Aldrovanda ovata* (Chandler 1925) Reid and Chandler 1926, L. Headon Beds, Hordle, Hants, England. **Extant.**

Family EBENACEAE

First, Cret Cenom: *Diospyron amboyensis* Berry 1911, Raritan Fm, Eastern U.S.A., and *Diospyrophyllum provectum* Velenovsky 1889, Cenom, Bohemia. **Extant.**

Family ELAEAGNACEAE

First, Tert Eoc: *Shepherdia weaverii* Hollick 1936, Kachemak Bay, Alaska. **Extant.**

Family ELAEOCARPACEAE

First, Tert Eoc: *Echinocarpus priscus* Reid and Chandler 1933, London Clay, Sheppey, Kent, England. **Extant.**

Family EPACRIDACEAE

First, Tert Eoc: *Epacridicarpum headonense* Chandler 1963a, Bournemouth Freshwater Beds, Hants, England. **Extant.**
Comment: *Dracophyllum* sp. (pollen), U. Eoc, New Zealand (Couper 1960, p. 59).

Family ERICACEAE

First, Cret Cenom: *Andromeda* sp., Dakota Fm, U.S.A. (Knowlton 1917). **Extant.**
Comment: "Ericaceae" (pollen), Olig, U.S.S.R. (Pokrovskoi 1956a, p. 86).

Family ERIOCAULACEAE

First, Tert Palaeoc: *Eriocaulon porosum* Lesquereux, Denver Fm, Colorado, U.S.A. (Knowlton 1930). **Extant.**

Family ERYTHROXYLACEAE

First, Tert Mioc: *Erythroxylon leucinum* Massalongo 1858, Italy. **Extant.**

Family EUCOMMIACEAE

First, Tert Eoc: *Eucommia eocenica* (Berry) R. W. Brown 1940, Wilcox Fm, Tennessee, U.S.A. **Extant.**

Family EUPHORBIACEAE

First, Cret Coniac: *Crotonophyllum cretaceum* Velenovsky, Magothy Fm, Eastern U.S.A. (Berry 1916). **Extant.**

Family FAGACEAE

First, Cret Cenom: *Quercophyllum chinkapinense* Ward 1905, Patapsco Fm, Eastern U.S.A. **Extant.**

Comment: *Nothofagus* aff. *menziesii* (pollen), Cret Maestr, New Zealand (Couper 1960, p. 55).

Family FLACOURTIACEAE

First, Tert Eoc: *Oncoba variabilis* (Bowerbank) Reid and Chandler 1933, London Clay, Sheppey, Kent, England. **Extant.**
Comment: *Banarophyllum ovatum* Berry 1937, ? Palaeoc, Cerro Funes, Patagonia.

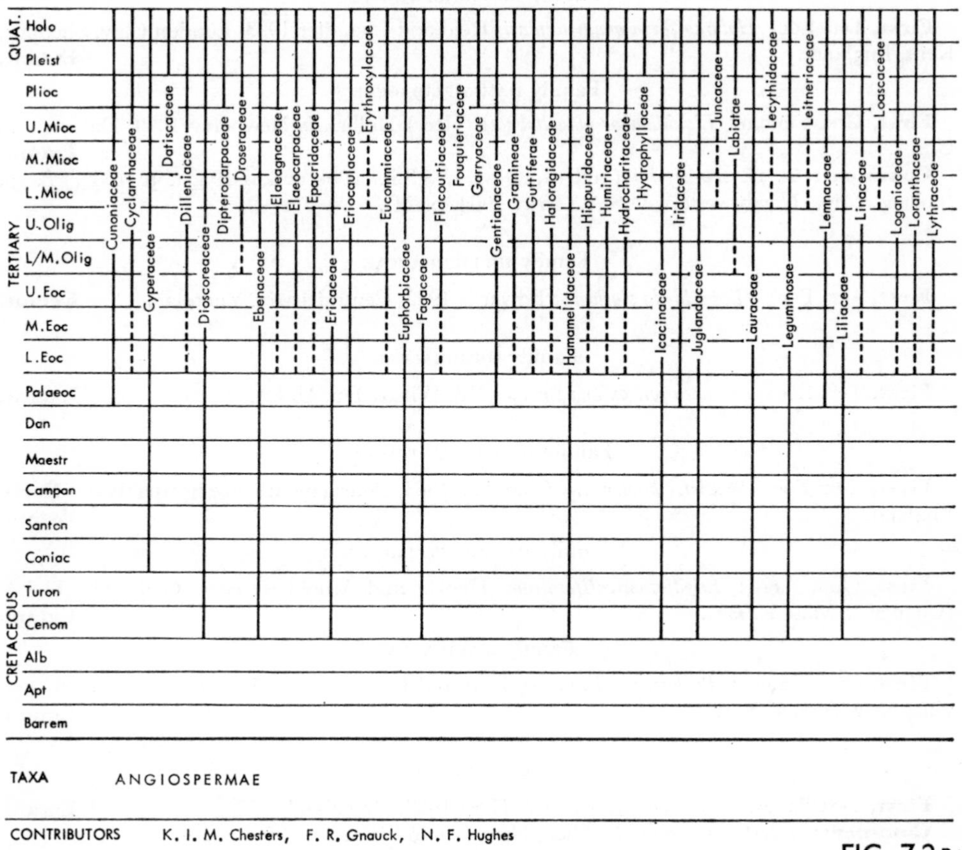

QUAT.	Holo
	Pleist
	Plioc
	U. Mioc
	M. Mioc
	L. Mioc
TERTIARY	U. Olig
	L/M. Olig
	U. Eoc
	M. Eoc
	L. Eoc
	Palaeoc
	Dan
	Maestr
	Campan
	Santon
	Coniac
CRETACEOUS	Turon
	Cenom
	Alb
	Apt
	Barrem

Families (columns, left to right): Cunoniaceae, Cyclanthaceae, Cyperaceae, Datiscaceae, Dilleniaceae, Dioscoreaceae, Dipterocarpaceae, Droseraceae, Ebenaceae, Elaeagnaceae, Elaeocarpaceae, Epacridaceae, Ericaceae, Eriocaulaceae, Erythroxylaceae, Eucommiaceae, Euphorbiaceae, Fagaceae, Flacourtiaceae, Fouquieriaceae, Garryaceae, Gentianaceae, Gramineae, Guttiferae, Haloragidaceae, Hamamelidaceae, Hippuridaceae, Humiriaceae, Hydrocharitaceae, Hydrophyllaceae, Icacinaceae, Iridaceae, Juglandaceae, Juncaceae, Labiatae, Lauraceae, Lecythidaceae, Leguminosae, Leitneriaceae, Lemnaceae, Liliaceae, Linaceae, Loasaceae, Loganiaceae, Loranthaceae, Lythraceae

TAXA   ANGIOSPERMAE

CONTRIBUTORS   K. I. M. Chesters, F. R. Gnauck, N. F. Hughes

FIG. 7.2 B

Family FOUQUIERIACEAE

First, Quat Pleist: *Fouquieria splendens* Engelmann, Shelter Cave, New Mexico, U.S.A. (Fosberg 1936).   **Extant.**

Family GARRYACEAE

First, Tert Plioc: *Garrya masoni* Dorf, California, U.S.A. (Axelrod 1944).   **Extant.**

Family GENTIANACEAE

First, Tert Palaeoc: *Menyanthes arctica* Heer 1883, Atanekerdluk, Greenland.   **Extant.**

Family GRAMINEAE

First, Tert Eoc: "Graminae"?, Chandler 1964, Woolwich Beds, Newhaven, Sussex, England; "Graminae" sp. (pollen), L. Olig, New Zealand (Couper 1960, p. 60), and Olig, North-western U.S.A. (Gray 1964, p. 23), and Olig, U.S.S.R. (Pokrovskoi 1956a, p. 83).   **Extant.**
Comment: Uncertain *Phragmites cliffwoodensis* Berry 1903, Cret Coniac, Magothy Fm, New Jersey, U.S.A.

Family GUTTIFERAE

First, Tert Eoc: *Clusiaphyllum eocenicum* Berry 1930, Arkansas, U.S.A.   **Extant.**

Family HALORAGIDACEAE

First, Tert Eoc: *Haloragicarya quadrilocularis* Reid and Chandler 1933, London Clay, Sheppey, Kent, England. **Extant.**

Family HAMAMELIDACEAE

First, Cret Cenom: *Liquidambar obtusilobatus* (Heer) Hollick *in* Newberry 1898, Dakota Fm, U.S.A. **Extant.**

Comment: *L.* cf. *styracifolia* (pollen), Olig. U.S.S.R. (Pokrovskoi 1956a, p. 103); *L.* sp. (pollen), Mioc, North-western U.S.A. (Gray 1964, p. 23).

Family HIPPURIDACEAE

First, Tert Eoc: *Hippuridella stacheana* Edwards 1932, Central Istria, Yugoslavia. **Extant.**

Family HUMIRIACEAE

First, Tert Eoc: *Vantanea wilcoxiana* Berry 1916, Wilcox Fm, U.S.A. **Extant.**

Family HYDROCHARITACEAE

First, Tert Eoc: *Stratiotes hantonensis* Chandler 1963, Bournemouth Freshwater Beds, Hants, England. **Extant.**

Family HYDROPHYLLACEAE

First, Quat Pleist: *Eriodictyon californicum* (Hooker and Arnold) Greene, California, U.S.A. (Chaney & Mason 1933). **Extant.**

Family ICACINACEAE

First, Cret Cenom: *Phytocrene microcarpa* Scott and Barghoorn 1957, Raritan Fm, Kreischerville, New York, U.S.A. **Extant.**

Family IRIDACEAE

First, Tert Palaeoc: *Iridium groenlandicum* Heer 1868, Greenland. **Extant.**

Comment: *Libertia* sp. (pollen), Plioc, New Zealand (Couper 1953, p. 58).

Family JUGLANDACEAE

First, Cret Cenom: *? Juglandites* spp., Dakota Fm; Kansas, U.S.A. (Lesquereux 1891) **Extant.**

Comment: *Carya* sp. (pollen), Olig, Northwestern U.S.A. (Gray 1964), *Juglans* sp. (pollen), *Carya* sp. (pollen), Olig, U.S.S.R. (Pokrovskoi 1956a, p. 83).

Family JUNCACEAE

First, Tert Mioc: *Juncus crassulus* Cockerell 1908, Florissant, Colorado, U.S.A. **Extant.**

Family LABIATAE

First, Tert Olig: *Ajuginucula smithi* Reid and Chandler 1926, Bembridge Beds, Isle of Wight, England. **Extant.**

Family LAURACEAE

First, Cret Cenom: *Sassafras potomacensis* Berry 1912, Patapsco Fm, Eastern U.S.A. **Extant.**

Family LECYTHIDACEAE

First, Tert Mioc: *Lecythidocinthus kuegleri* Berry 1924, West Indies. **Extant.**

Family LEGUMINOSAE

First, Cret Cenom: *Caesalpina raritanensis* Berry 1909, Raritan Fm, Eastern U.S.A.   **Extant.**
  Comment: *Astragalus* sp. (pollen-Papilionaceae), Olig, U.S.S.R. (Pokrovskoi 1956a, p. 228),
and *Acacia* sp. (pollen-Mimosaceae), Plioc, Australia (Cookson 1964, p. 84).

Family LEITNERIACEAE

First, Tert Mioc: *Leitneria pacifica* Chaney and Axelrod 1959, Mascall Fm, Oregon, U.S.A.
                                                                                         Extant.

Family LEMNACEAE

First, Tert Palaeoc: *Spirodela scutata* (Dawson) Berry, Fort Union Fm, Montana, U.S.A.
(Ward 1887).   **Extant.**

Family LILIACEAE

First, Cret Cenom: *Smilax kansana* Cockerell 1914, Dakota Fm, U.S.A.   **Extant.**
  Comment: *Liliacidites intermedius* (pollen), Cret Maestr, New Zealand (Couper 1960, p. 60).

Family LINACEAE

First, Tert Eoc: *Decaplatyspermum bowerbanki* Reid and Chandler 1933, London Clay, Sheppey,
Kent, England.   **Extant.**

Family LOASCACEAE

First, Tert Mioc: *Mentzelia occidentalis* (Berry) R. W. Brown 1935a, Latah Fm, Western
U.S.A.   **Extant.**

Family LOGANIACEAE

First, Tert Eoc: *Strychnos?* sp. Chaney and Sanborn 1933, Fisher Fm, Western U.S.A.
                                                                                       Extant.

Family LORANTHACEAE

First, Tert Eoc: *Elytranthe striatus* (pollen), U. Eoc, New Zealand (Couper 1960, p. 57).
                                                                                       Extant.

  Comment: *Loranthocites succineus* Conwentz 1886, Tert Olig, Baltic Amber.

Family LYTHRACEAE

First, Tert Eoc: *Minsterocarpum alatum* Reid and Chandler 1933, London Clay, Sheppey, Kent,
England.   **Extant.**

Family MAGNOLIACEAE

First, Cret Cenom: *Magnolia* spp., Dakota Fm, U.S.A. (Newberry 1898).   **Extant.**
  Comment: *Magnolia* spp. (pollen), Olig, U.S.S.R. (Pokrovskoi 1956a, p. 227).

Family MALPIGHIACEAE

First, Tert Eoc: *Banisteria wilcoxiana* Berry 1916, Lagrange, U.S.A.   **Extant.**

Family MALVACEAE

First, Tert Eoc: *Abutilon eakini* Hollick 1936, Alaska.   **Extant.**
  Comment: *Plagianthus* sp. (pollen), L. Eoc, New Zealand (Couper 1960, p. 53).

Family MARANTACEAE

First, Tert ?Olig: *Palaeothalia sanctaejustinae* Squinabol 1892, Italy.   **Extant.**

Family MELASTOMACEAE

First, Tert Eoc: *Melastomites verus* Duckworth 1941, Holly Springs, Tennessee, U.S.A.
                                                                                       Extant.

Family MELIACEAE

First, Tert Palaeoc: *Carapa eolignitica* Berry, Raton, Colorado, U.S.A. (Knowlton 1917).
Extant.
Comment: *Dysoxylum* aff. *spectabile* (pollen), U. Eoc, New Zealand (Couper 1960, p. 58).

Family MENISPERMACEAE

First, Cret Cenom: *Menispermites potomacensis* Berry 1912, Patapsco Fm, Eastern U.S.A.
Extant.

Family MONIMIACEAE

First, Tert Palaeoc: *Monimiopsis arboraefolia* Saporta, Fort Union Fm, Montana, U.S.A. (Ward 1884).
Extant.
Comment: *Laurelia* cf. *novae-zealandiae* (pollen), M. Olig, New Zealand (Couper 1960, p. 47).

Family MORACEAE

First, Cret Apt?: *Ficophyllum serratum* Fontaine, Arundel Fm, Maryland, U.S.A. (Berry 1912).
Extant.
Comment: *Morus* sp. (pollen), Olig, U.S.S.R. (Pokrovskoi 1956a, p. 103).

Family MUSACEAE

First, Tert Palaeoc: *Musophyllum complicatum* Lesquereux, Bridger Fm, Wyoming, U.S.A. (Berry 1930).
Extant.

Family MYRICACEAE

First, Tert Eoc: *Myrica boveyana* (Heer) pars, London Clay, Nursling, Hants, England. (Chandler 1961). Several doubtful species in Dakota Fm, U.S.A. (Cret Cenom). **Extant.**
Comment: *Myrica* sp. (pollen), Olig, U.S.S.R. (Polrovskoi 1956a, p. 83).

Family MYRISTICACEAE

First, Tert Eoc: *Myristica catahoulensis* Berry, Catahoula (Jackson) Fm, Texas, U.S.A. (Ball 1931).
Extant.

Family MYRSINACEAE

First, Cret Cenom: *Myrsine gaudini* (Lesquereux) Berry 1909, Raritan Fm, Eastern U.S.A.
Extant.
Comment: *Suttonia* sp. (pollen), L. Olig, New Zealand (Couper 1960, p. 59).

Family MYRTACEAE

First, Cret Alb: *Myrtophyllum boreale* Seward and Conway, British Columbia (Bell 1956).
Extant.
Comment: *Leptospermum* sp. (pollen), Tert Dan, New Zealand (Couper 1960, p. 52).

Family NAIADACEAE

First, Tert Eoc: *Cymodoceites parisiensis* Bureau 1886, France. **Extant.**
Comment: Macrofossil records, Olig of Bembridge, England and Florissant, U.S.A.

Family NYCTAGINACEAE

First, Cret Campan: *Pisonia cretacea* Berry 1910, Black Creek Fm, Carolinas, U.S.A.
Extant.

Family NYMPHAEACEAE

First, Cret Cenom: *Nelumbites tenuinervis* (Fontaine), Patapsco Fm, Eastern U.S.A. (Berry 1912).
Extant.
Comment: "Nymphaeaceae" (pollen), Mioc, Northwestern U.S.A. (Gray 1964, p. 23).

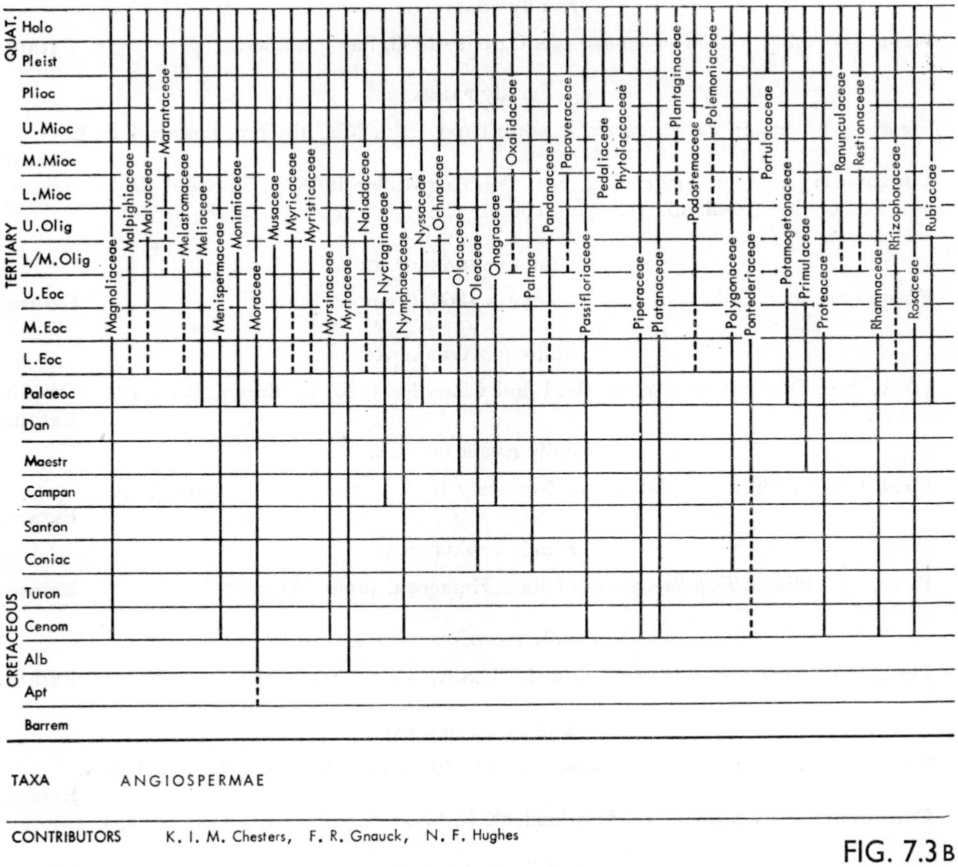

Time scale (left axis):

- **QUAT.**: Holo, Pleist
- **TERTIARY**: Plioc, U.Mioc, M.Mioc, L.Mioc, U.Olig, L/M.Olig, U.Eoc, M.Eoc, L.Eoc, Palaeoc, Dan
- **CRETACEOUS**: Maestr, Campan, Santon, Coniac, Turon, Cenom, Alb, Apt, Barrem

Family columns (left to right): Magnoliaceae, Malpighiaceae, Malvaceae, Marantaceae, Melastomaceae, Meliaceae, Menispermaceae, Monimiaceae, Moraceae, Musaceae, Myricaceae, Myristicaceae, Myrsinaceae, Myrtaceae, Naiadaceae, Nyctaginaceae, Nymphaeaceae, Nyssaceae, Ochnaceae, Olacaceae, Oleaceae, Onagraceae, Oxalidaceae, Palmae, Pandanaceae, Papaveraceae, Passifloriaceae, Pedaliaceae, Phytolaccaceae, Piperaceae, Platanaceae, Plantaginaceae, Podostemaceae, Polemoniaceae, Polygonaceae, Pontederiaceae, Portulacaceae, Potamogetonaceae, Primulaceae, Proteaceae, Ranunculaceae, Restionaceae, Rhamnaceae, Rhizophoraceae, Rosaceae, Rubiaceae

TAXA   ANGIOSPERMAE

CONTRIBUTORS   K. I. M. Chesters, F. R. Gnauck, N. F. Hughes

FIG. 7.3 B

Family NYSSACEAE

First, Tert Palaeoc: *Nyssa lanceolata* Lesquereux, Golden, Colorado, U.S.A. (Knowlton 1930). Also *N. bilocularis*, London Clay (Chandler 1961).   **Extant.**

Family OCHNACEAE

First, Tert Eoc: *Ouratea eocenica* Berry 1930, Holly Springs, Tennessee, U.S.A.   **Extant.**

Family OLACACEAE

First, Cret Maestr: *Anacolosidites acutullus* (pollen), New Zealand (Couper 1960, p. 57).   **Extant.**

Comment: *Heisteria sapindifolia* (Hollick) Berry 1938, Eoc, Wilcox Fm, U.S.A.

Family OLEACEAE

First, Cret Coniac: *Ligustrum subtile* Hollick 1912, Magothy Fm, Eastern U.S.A.   **Extant.**
Comment: *Fraxinus* sp. (pollen), Olig, U.S.S.R. (Pokrovskoi 1956, p. 202).

Family ONAGRACEAE

First, Cret Campan: *Trapa(?) microphylla* Lesquereux 1878, Mesa Verde Fm, Western U.S.A.   **Extant.**

Comment: *Epilobium* sp. (pollen), M. Olig, New Zealand (Couper 1960, p. 48). *Trapa* sp. (pollen), Mioc, U.S.S.R. (Pokrovskoi 1956b, p. 231).

279

Family OXALIDACEAE

First, Tert Olig: *Oxalidites brachysepalus* Caspary 1886, Baltic Amber. **Extant.**

Family PALMAE

First, Cret Coniac: *Palmoxylon cliffwoodensis* Berry 1916, Magothy Fm, Eastern U.S.A.
Extant.
Comment: *Nypa* sp. (pollen), L. Eoc, Borneo (Muller 1964, p. 35), and *Rhopalostylis* aff. *sapida*, U. Eoc, New Zealand. (Couper 1960, p. 62).

Family PANDANACEAE

First, Tert Eoc: *Ludoviopsis discerpta* Saporta 1868, Sézanne, France. **Extant.**

Family PAPAVERACEAE

First, Tert Olig: *Papaver pictum* Reid and Chandler 1926, Bembridge Beds, Isle of Wight, England. **Extant.**

Family PASSIFLORACEAE

First, Cret Cenom: *Passiflora antiqua* Newberry 1895, Raritan Fm, Eastern U.S.A.
Extant.

Family PEDALIACEAE

First, Tert Plioc: *Trapella antennifer* Glück, Hatagoya, Japan (Miki 1941). **Extant.**

Family PHYTOLACCACEAE

First, Quat Pleist: *Phytolacca americana* L., U.S.A. (C. A. Brown 1938). **Extant.**

Family PIPERACEAE

First, Cret Cenom: *Piperites tuscaloosensis* Berry 1919, Tuscaloosa Fm, Eastern U.S.A.
Extant.
Comment: *Macropiper* aff. *excelsum* (pollen), L. Mioc, New Zealand (Couper 1953, p. 40).

Family PLATANACEAE

First, Cret Cenom: *Platanus* spp., Dakota Fm, U.S.A. (Newberry 1898). **Extant.**
Comment: *Platanus* sp. (pollen), Olig, U.S.S.R. (Pokrovskoi 1956a, p. 280).

Family PLANTAGINACEAE

First, Tert Mioc: *Littonella baldassari* Massalonga, Italy (Meschinelli & Squinabol 1892).
Extant.
Comment: *Plantago* sp. (pollen), Plioc, New Zealand (Couper 1953, p. 55).

Family PODOSTEMACEAE

First, Tert Eoc: *Magleia ceratophylloides* Massalongo, Italy (Meschinelli & Squinabol 1892).
Extant.

Family POLEMONIACEAE

First, Tert Mioc: cf. *Gilia* (pollen), California (Gray 1964, p. 23). **Extant.**
Comment: *Phlox* cf. *siberica* L., Pleist, Fairbanks, Alaska (Chaney & Mason 1936).

Family POLYGONACEAE

First, Cret Coniac: *Coccolobites cretaceus* Berry 1916, Magothy Fm, Eastern U.S.A. **Extant.**
Comment: *Muehlenbeckia* sp. (pollen), L. Mioc, New Zealand (Couper 1953, p. 40).

Chapter 7: Angiospermae

Family PONTEDERIACEAE

First, Cret (U): *Heteranthera cretacea* Knowlton 1916, U.S.A..   **Extant.**

Family PORTULACACEAE

First, Quat Pleist: *Claytonia virginica* L., U.S.A. (R. W. Brown 1935b).   **Extant.**

Family POTAMOGETONACEAE

First, Tert Palaeoc: *Limnocarpus cooperi* Chandler 1961, Oldhaven Beds, Kent, England.   **Extant.**

Comment: *Potamogeton* sp. (pollen), Olig, U.S.S.R. (Pokrovskoi 1956a, p. 186), and L. Mioc, New Zealand (Couper 1953, p. 55).

Family PRIMULACEAE

First, Cret Maestr: *Lysimachia* sp., Lance Fm, Western U.S.A. (Knowlton 1909).   **Extant.**

Family PROTEACEAE

First, Cret Cenom: *Personia spatulata* Hollick, Raritan Fm, Eastern U.S.A. (Berry 1911).   **Extant.**

Comment: *Proteacidites palisadus* (pollen), Maestr., New Zealand (Couper 1960, p. 49).

Family RANUNCULACEAE

First, Tert Olig: *Clematis vectensis* Reid and Chandler 1926, and *Ranunculus ovaliformis* (R. & C.) Chandler 1963a, Bembridge Beds, Isle of Wight, England.   **Extant.**
Comment: "Ranunculaceae" (pollen), Olig, U.S.S.R. (Pokrovskoi 1956a, p. 103).

Family RESTIONACEAE

First, Tert Olig: "Restionaceae" (pollen), L. Olig, New Zealand (Couper 1960, p. 62).   **Extant.**

Family RHAMNACEAE

First, Cret Cenom: *Eorhamnidium platyphylloides* (Lesquereux) Berry 1919, Dakota Fm, U.S.A.   **Extant.**

Family RHIZOPHORACEAE

First, Tert Eoc: *Palaeobruguieria elongata* Chandler 1961, London Clay. Also *Rhizophora eocenica* Berry 1914, Georgia, U.S.A.   **Extant.**
Comment: *Rhizophora* sp. (pollen), lowest Olig, Borneo (Muller 1964, p. 38).

Family ROSACEAE

First, Cret Cenom: *Pyrus* spp., Dakota Fm, U.S.A. (Newberry 1898).   **Extant.**
Comment: "Rosaceae" and *Potentilla* sp. (pollen), Olig, U.S.S.R. (Pokrovskoi 1956a, p. 85).

Family RUBIACEAE

First, Tert Palaeoc: *Cinchonidium ovale* Lesquereux 1883, Fort Union Fm, N. Dakota, U.S.A.   **Extant.**

Comment: *Coprosina* sp. (pollen), M.Olig, New Zealand (Couper 1960, p. 59).

Family RUTACEAE

First, Cret Cenom: *Citrophyllum aligerum* (Lesquereux) Berry 1909, Raritan Fm, Eastern U.S.A.   **Extant.**

Comment: *Phellodendron* sp. (pollen), Olig, U.S.S.R. (Pokrovskoi 1956a, p. 280).

Family SABIACEAE

First, Tert Eoc: *Meliosma cantiensis* Reid and Chandler, London Clay, Basement Beds, Harefield, Middlesex, England (Chandler 1961).   **Extant.**

281

Family SALICACEAE

First, Cret Cenom: *Populus* spp., Dakota Fm, U.S.A. (Newberry 1898). **Extant.**
Comment: *Salix* sp. (pollen), Olig, U.S.S.R. (Pokrovskoi 1956a, p. 123).

Family SANTALACEAE

First, Cret Coniac: *Santalum novae-caesareae* Berry 1906, Magothy Fm, Eastern U.S.A.
Extant.
Comment: *Santalumidites* sp. (pollen), Eoc, Australia (Cookson 1964, p. 83).

Family SAPINDACEAE

First, Cret Cenom: *Sapindopsis brevifolia* Fontaine, Patapsco Fm, Eastern U.S.A. (Berry 1912).
Extant.
Comment: *Cardiospermum* sp., Cret Campan, U.S.S.R. (Zaklinskaya 1963, p. 243).

Family SAPOTACEAE

First, Cret Cenom: *Sapotacites haydenii* Heer, Dakota Fm, U.S.A. (Newberry 1898).
Extant.

Family SAXIFRAGACEAE

First, Cret Coniac-Campan: *Philadelphus normalis* Bell 1957, British Columbia, Canada.
Extant.

Family SCHEUCHZERIACEAE

First, Tert Plioc: *Scheuchzeria palustris* L., U. Plioc, Neudorf, Czechoslovakia (Rudolf 1935).
Extant.

Family SCROPHULARIACEAE

First, Tert Olig: *Mimulus saxorum* Cockerell 1908, Florissant, Colorado, U.S.A. **Extant.**

Family SIMARUBACEAE

First, Tert Eoc: *Ailanthus lesquereuxi* Cockerell 1927, Green River Fm, U.S.A. **Extant.**

Family SOLANACEAE

First, Tert Eoc: *Cantisolanum daturoides* Reid and Chandler 1933, London Clay, Sheppey,
Kent, England. **Extant.**

Family SONNERATIACEAE

First, Tert Mioc: *Sonneratia caseolaris* (pollen), lowest Mioc, Borneo (Muller 1964, p. 38).
Extant.

Family SPARGANIACEAE

First, Tert Palaeoc: *Sparganium stygium* Heer, Fort Union Fm, U.S.A. (Knowlton 1899).
Extant.
Comment: *Sparganium* sp. (pollen), Olig, U.S.S.R. (Pokrovskoi 1956a, p. 187).

Family STAPHYLEACEAE

First, Cret Coniac-Campan: *Staphylea usheri*, British Columbia, Canada (Bell 1957).
Extant.

Family STERCULIACEAE

First, Cret Cenom: *Sterculia elegans* Fontaine 1889, Patapsco Fm, Eastern U.S.A. **Extant.**
Comment: *Sterculia* spp. (pollen), Olig, U.S.S.R. (Pokrovskoi 1956a, p. 200).

Family STYRACACEAE

First, Tert Palaeoc: *Styrax larcuniense* Lesquereux, Denver Fm, Colorado, U.S.A. (Knowlton
1930). **Extant.**

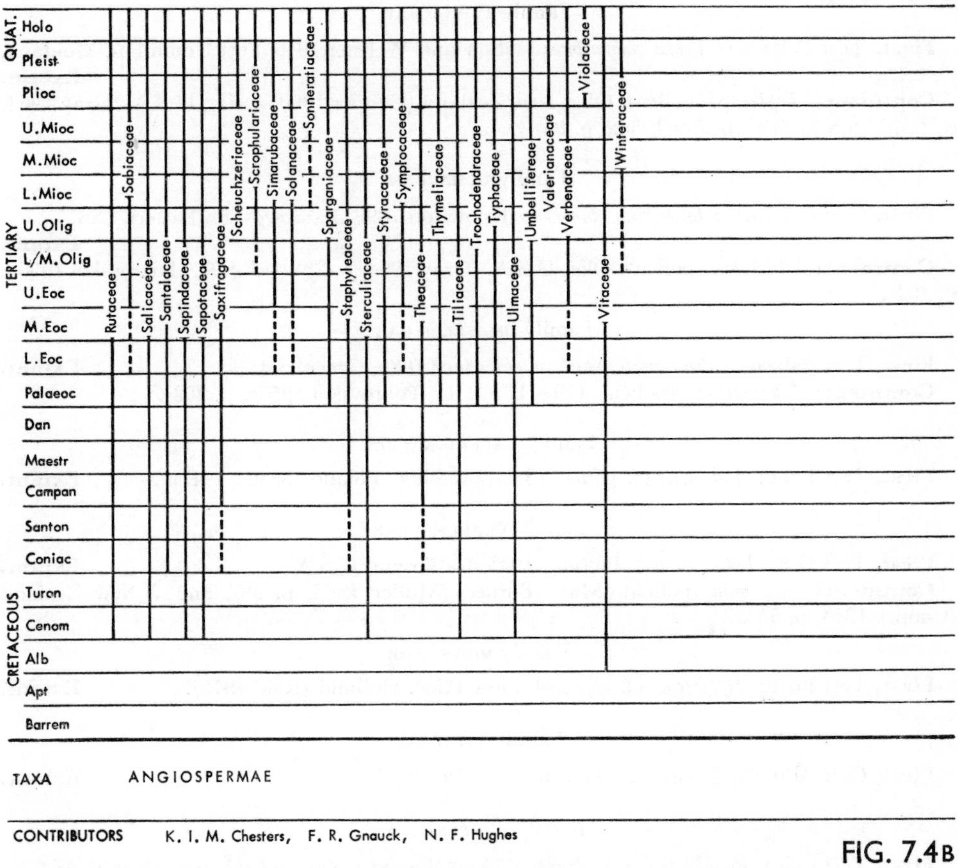
QUAT.
Holo
Pleist
Plioc
U.Mioc
M.Mioc
L.Mioc
U.Olig
L/M.Olig
U.Eoc
M.Eoc
L.Eoc
Palaeoc
Dan
Maestr
Campan
Santon
Coniac
Turon
Cenom
Alb
Apt
Barrem
TERTIARY
CRETACEOUS
Rutaceae
Sabiaceae
Salicaceae
Santalaceae
Sapindaceae
Sapotaceae
Saxifragaceae
Scheuchzeriaceae
Scrophulariaceae
Simarubaceae
Solanaceae
Sonneratiaceae
Sparganiaceae
Staphyleaceae
Sterculiaceae
Styracaceae
Symplocaceae
Theaceae
Thymeliaceae
Tiliaceae
Trochodendraceae
Typhaceae
Ulmaceae
Umbelliferae
Valerianaceae
Verbenaceae
Vitaceae
Violaceae
Winteraceae
TAXA ANGIOSPERMAE
CONTRIBUTORS K. I. M. Chesters, F. R. Gnauck, N. F. Hughes

FIG. 7.4B

Family SYMPLOCACEAE

First, Tert Eoc: *Symplocos curvata* Reid and Chandler 1933, London Clay, Sheppey, Kent, England, and *S. oregona* Chaney and Sanborn 1933, Goshen Fm, Oregon, U.S.A. **Extant.**

Comment: *Symplocos scabripollina* Traverse (pollen), Paleoc, U.S.S.R. (Zaklinskaya 1963, p. 249).

Family THEACEAE

First, Cret Coniac-Campan: *Ternstroemites harwoodensis* (Dawson) British Columbia, Canada (Bell 1956). **Extant.**

Comment: *Gordonia egregia* (Lesquereux) MacGinitie 1941, Eoc, Western U.S.A.

Family THYMELIACEAE

First, Tert Palaeoc: *Daphne persooniaeformis* Weber, Greenland (Heer 1883). **Extant.**

Family TILIACEAE

First, Cret Cenom: *Grewiopsis flabellata* (Lesquereux), Dakota Fm, U.S.A. (Knowlton 1898). **Extant.**

Comment: *Brownlownia* sp. (pollen), lowest Eoc, Borneo (Muller 1964, p. 37); *Tilia* sp. (pollen), Olig, U.S.A. (Gray 1964 p. 23) and Olig, U.S.S.R. (Pokrovskoi 1956a, p. 86).

Family TROCHODENDRACEAE

First, Tert Palaeoc: *Tetracentronites hartzi* Mathiesen 1932, East Greenland. **Extant.**

Family TYPHACEAE

First, Tert Palaeoc: *Typha ratifolipites* Wilson and Webster 1946, Fort Union Fm, Montana, U.S.A. **Extant.**
Comment: *Typha* sp. (pollen), Olig, New Zealand (Couper 1960, p. 61), U.S.A. (Gray 1964, p. 23), U.S.S.R. (Pokrovskoi 1956a, p. 83).

Family ULMACEAE

First, Cret Cenom: *Ulmophyllum brookense* Knowlton 1898, Patapsco Fm, Eastern U.S.A. **Extant.**
Comment: *Ulmus* sp. (pollen), Olig, U.S.A. (Gray 1964, p. 23), U.S.S.R. (Pokrovskoi 1956a, p. 102).

Family UMBELLIFERAE

First, Tert Palaeoc: *Peucedanites nordenskioldi* Heer 1880, Greenland. **Extant.**
Comment: *Libanotis* sp. (pollen), Olig, U.S.S.R. (Pokrovskoi 1956a, p. 202).

Family VALERIANACEAE

First, Tert Plioc: *Valeriana* cf. *officinalis* L., Low Plioc, Poland (Szafer 1947). **Extant.**

Family VERBENACEAE

First, Tert Eoc: *Petrea rotunda* Potbury 1935, California, U.S.A. **Extant.**
Comment: *Avicennia* (pollen), Mioc, Borneo (Muller 1964, p. 39), and ? New Zealand (Couper 1953, p. 55).

Family VIOLACEAE

First, Tert Plioc: *Hypericum* cf. *ascyron* L., low Plioc, Holland (Reid 1915). **Extant.**

Family VITACEAE

First, Cret Alb: *Cissites sinuosus* Saporta 1894, Portugal. **Extant.**

Family WINTERACEAE

First, Tert Olig: *Pseudowintera* sp. (pollen), M. Olig, New Zealand (Couper 1960, p. 46).
Extant.

REFERENCES

AXELROD, D. I. 1944. The Sonoma flora (California). *Publs Carnegie Instn*, **553,** 167–206, 6 pls.
BALL, O. M. 1931. A contribution to the paleobotany of the Eocene Texas. *Bull. Tex. Agric. Mech. Coll.*, series 4, **2,** no. 5, 173 pp.
BELL, W. A. 1956. Lower Cretaceous Floras of Western Canada. *Mem. Can. geol. Surv.*, **285,** 331 pp.
—— 1957. Flora of the Upper Cretaceous Nanaimo Group, Vancouver Island, British Columbia. *Mem. geol. Surv. Can.*, **293,** 89 pp., 57 plates.
BERRY, E. W. 1903. The flora of the Matawan formation (Crosswicks clays). *Bull. N.Y. bot. Gdn.*, **3,** 45–103.
—— 1906. Contributions to the Mesozoic flora of the Atlantic Coastal Plain. I. *Bull. Torrey bot. Club*, **33,** 163–182.
—— 1909. Contributions to the Mesozoic flora of the Atlantic Coastal Plain, III. *Bull. Torrey bot. Club*, **36,** 245–264.
—— 1910. Contributions to the Mesozoic flora of the Atlantic Coastal Plain, IV. *Bull. Torrey bot. Club*, **37,** 19–29.
—— 1911. The flora of the Raritan formation. *Bull. geol. Surv. New Jers.*, **3,** 233 pp.
—— 1912. *Lower Cretaceous*, Maryland Geological Survey, Baltimore.

Chapter 7: Angiospermae

BERRY, E. W. 1914. The Upper Cretaceous and Eocene flora of South Carolina and Georgia
Prof. Pap. U.S. geol. Surv., **84**, 200 pp.

—— 1916. The Upper Cretaceous floras of the World. *in Upper Cretaceous*, 183–213. Maryland
Geological Survey, Baltimore.

—— 1919. Upper Cretaceous floras of the eastern Gulf region in Tennessee, Mississippi,
Alabama, and Georgia. *Prof. pap. U.S. geol. Surv.*, **112**, 177 pp.

—— 1923. Miocene plants from Southern Mexico. *Proc. U.S. natn. Mus.*, **62**, art. 19, 27 pp.

—— 1924. The Middle and Upper Eocene floras of southeastern North America. *Prof. Pap.
U.S. geol. Surv.*, **92**, 206 pp.

—— 1930. Revision of the L.Eocene Wilcox flora of the Southeastern States; etc., *Prof. Pap.
U.S. geol. Surv.*, **156**, 196 pp.

—— 1933. New occurrences of Pleistocene plants in the District of Columbia. *J. Wash. Acad.
Sci.*, **23**, 1–25.

—— 1937. A late Tertiary flora from Trinidad, B.W.I. *John Hopkins Univ. Stud. Geol.*, **12**, 69–
79.

—— 1938. A representation of the Olacaceae in the Eocene of Southeastern North America.
Torreya, **38**, 5–7.

BROWN, C. A. 1938. The flora of Pleistocene deposits in the western Florida Parishes, West
Feliciana Parish and east Baton Rouge Parish, La. *Geol. Bull. La.*, **12**, 59–96.

BROWN, R. W. 1935a. Miocene leaves, fruits and seeds from Idaho, Oregon and Washington.
J. Paleont., **9**, 572–587.

—— 1935b. Some fossil conifers from Maryland and North Dakota. *J. Wash. Acad. Sci.*, **25**,
441–450.

—— 1937. Additions to some fossil floras of the western United States. *Prof. Pap. U.S. geol.
Surv.*, **186-J**, 163–206.

—— 1939. Fossil leaves, fruits, and seeds of *Cercidiphyllum*. *J. paleont.*, **13**, 485–99, pls. 51–56.

—— 1940. New species and changes of name in some America fossil floras. *J. Wash. Acad. Sci.*,
30, 344–356.

—— 1959. Some paleobotanical problematica. *J. Paleont.*, **33**, 120–4, pl. 23.

BUREAU, E. 1880. Étude sur une plante phanerogame (*Cymodoceites parisiensis*) de l'ordre des
Naiadées, que vivait dans les mers d'l'époque éocène. *C.r. hebd. Séanc. Acad. Sci., Paris*,
102, 191–193.

CASPARY, R. 1886. Einige neue Pflanzenreste ausdem samländischen Bernstein. *Scht. phys.-ökon.
Ges., Königsb.*, **27**, 1–9.

CHANDLER, M. E. J. 1925. The Upper Eocene flora of Hordle, Hants., Part 1. *Palaeontogr. Soc.*
[*Monogr.*].

—— 1961. *The Lower Tertiary floras of southern England, 1. Palaeocene floras. London Clay flora
(Supplement)*. xi + 354 pp., Atlas, 34 pls. Brit. Mus. (Nat. Hist.), London.

—— 1963a. Revision of the Oligocene floras of the Isle of Wight. *Bull. Brit. Mus. (Nat. Hist.)
Geol.*, **6**, 321–384, pls. 27–35.

—— 1963b. *The Lower Tertiary floras of southern England, 3. Flora of the Bournemouth Beds, the
Boscombe, and the Highcliff sands*. Brit. Mus. (Nat. Hist.), London.

—— 1964. *The Lower Tertiary floras of southern England, 4*. Brit. Mus. (Nat. Hist.), London.

CHANEY, R. W. 1944. A fossil cactus from the Eocene of Utah. *Am. J. Bot.*, **31**, 507–528.

—— & AXELROD, D. I. 1959. Miocene forests of the Columbia Plateau. *Publs Carnegie Instn*, **617**.

—— & SANBORN. 1933. The Goshen flora of west-central Oregon. *Publs Carnegie Instn*, **439**,
103 pp.

—— & MASON, H. L. 1933. A Pleistocene flora from the asphalt deposits of Carpinteria, Calif.
Publs Carnegie Instn, **415**, 45–80, 9 pls.

—— & —— 1936. A Pleistocene flora from Fairbanks, Alaska. *Am. Mus. Novit.*, **887**, 17 pp.

CHESTERS, K. I. M. 1955. Some plants remains from the Upper Cretaceous and Tertiary of west
Africa. *Ann. Mag. nat. Hist.* (12), **8**, 498–503.

—— 1957. The Miocene flora of Rusinga island, Lake Victoria, Kenya. *Palaeontogr.*, **101B**
30–67.

285

COCKERELL, T. D. A. 1908. The fossil flora of Florissant, Colorado. *Bull. Am. Mus. nat. Hist.*, **24,** 71–110.

—— 1914. Two new plants from the Tertiary rocks of the West. *Torreya*, 14, 135–137.

COCKERELL, T. D. A. 1925. Plant and insect fossils from the Green River Eocene of Colorado. *Proc. U.S. natn. Mus.*, **66,** art. 19, 13 pp.

—— 1927. A supposed fossil catmint [From Florissant, Colorado]. *Torreya*, **27,** 94–95.

CONWENTZ, H. W. 1886. *Die Flora des Bernsteins, etc., 2. Die Angiospermen des Bernsteins.*

COOKSON, I. C. 1964. Some early angiosperms from Australia: the pollen record *in* CRANWELL, L. M. (Editor), *Ancient Pacific Floras: the pollen story*, pp. 81–84. Honolulu (University of Hawaii Press).

COUPER, R. A. 1953. Upper Mesozoic and Cainozoic spores and pollen grains from New Zealand. *Palaeont. Bull., Wellington*, **22.**

—— 1960. New Zealand Mesozoic and Cainozoic plant microfossils. *N.Z. geol. Surv. Palaeont. Bull., Wellington*, **32.**

DUCKWORTH, A. S. 1941. Fossil leaves from southeast Missouri. *Proc. Mo. Acad. Sci.*, **6,** 84–86.

EDWARDS, W. N. 1932. Lower Eocene plants of Istria. *Ann. Mag. Nat. Hist.* (10), **10,** 213–216.

FONTAINE, W. M. 1889. The Potomac or younger Mesozoic Flora. *Monogr. U.S. geol. Surv.*, **15.**

FOSBERG, F. R. 1936. Plant remains in Shelter cave, New Mexico. *Bull. Sth. Calif. Acad. Sci.*, **35,** 154–5.

GRAY, J. 1964. Northwest American Tertiary palynology: the emerging picture *in* CRANWELL, L. M. (Editor), *Ancient Pacific Floras: the pollen story*, pp. 21–30. Honolulu (University of Hawaii Press).

HEER, O. 1868. *Flora fossilis Arctica, I. Die fossile Flora der Polarländer.* Zürich.

—— 1880. *Flora fossilis Arctica, VI, 1.2. Nachträge zur fossilen Flora Grönlands.* Zürich.

—— 1883. *Flora Fossilis Arctica, VII.2. Die Tertiare Flora von Grönland.* Zürich.

HOLLICK, C. A. 1912. Additions to the paleobotany of the Cretaceous formation on Long Island, III. *Bull. N.Y. bot. Gdn.*, **8,** 154–170.

—— 1936. The Tertiary floras of Alaska, with a chapter on the geology of the Tertiary deposits by P. S. Smith. *Prof. Pap. U.S. geol. Surv.*, **182,** 185 pp.

KNOWLTON, F. H. 1898. A catalogue of the Cretaceous and Tertiary plants of North America. *Bull. U.S. geol. Surv.*, **152,** 244 pp.

—— 1899. Fossil floras [of Yellowstone National Park]. *Monogr. U.S. geol. Surv.*, **32,** part 2. 651–882.

—— 1909. The stratigraphic relations and paleontology of the "Hell Creek beds", "Ceratops beds", and equivalents, and their reference to the fort Union formation. *Proc. Wash. Acad. Sci.*, **11,** 179–238.

—— 1916. The flora of the Fox Hill sandstone. *Prof. Pap. U.S. geol. Surv.*, **98,** 85–93.

—— 1917. Fossil flora of the Vermejo and Raton formation of Colorado and New Mexico. *Prof. Pap. U.S. geol. Surv.*, **101,** 223–435.

—— 1923. Revision of the flora of the Green River formation with descriptions of new species. *Prof. Pap. U.S. geol. Surv.*, **131,** 133–182.

—— 1930. The flora of the Denver and associated formations of Colorado (posthumous, edited by E. W Berry) *Prof. Pap. U.S. geol. Surv.*, **155,** 142 pp.

KRÄUSEL, R. 1929. Fossile Pflanzen aus dem Tertiär von Süd-Sumatra. *Verh. geol.-mijnb. Genoot. Ned.* (geol. ser.), **9,** 1–44.

LAMOTTE, R. S. 1952. Catalogue of the Cenozoic Plants of North America through 1950. *Mem. geol. Soc. Am.*, **51,** 381 pp.

LAUDERMILK, J. D. & MUNZ, P. A. 1934. Plants in the dung of Nothotherium from Gypsum Cave, Nevada. *Publs Carnegie Instn*, **453,** 29–37.

LESQUEREUX, L. 1874. Contribution to the fossil flora of the Western Territories; Part 1. The Cretaceous flora. *Rep. U.S. geol. Surv. Territ.*, **6,** 136 pp.

—— 1878. *Illustrations of Cretaceous and Tertiary plants of the Western territories of the United States.* U.S. geol. geogr. Surv. Terr., Hayden.

—— 1883. Contributions to the fossil flora of the Western territories; Part 3. The Cretaceous and Tertiary floras. *Rep. U.S. geol. Surv. Territ.*, **8**, 283 pp.

—— 1891. The Flora of the Dakota group. *Monogr. U.S. geol. Surv.*, **17**.

—— 1893. The genus *Winchellia*. *Am. Geol.*, **12**.

McGINITIE, H. D. 1941. A middle Eocene flora from the central Sierra Nevada. *Publs Carnegie Instn*, **534**, 178 pp.

MÄDLER, K. 1939. Die pliozäne flora von Frankfurt-am-Main. *Abh. senskenerg. naturfasch. Ges.*, **446**, 1–202.

MASON. 1934. Pleistocene flora of the Tomales formation. *Publs Carnegie Instn*, **415**, 81–180.

MASSALONGO, A. 1858. *Synopsis Florae fossilis senogalliensis*. Verona, 136 pp.

MATHIESEN, F. J. 1932. Notes on some fossil plants from East Greenland. *Meddr. Grønl.*, **85**, no. 4, 62 pp.

MESCHINELLI, A. & SQUINABOL, S. 1892. *Flora Tertianica Italica*. Patavii.

MIKI, S. 1941. On the change of Flora in E. Asia since Tertiary Period, (1). *Jap. J. Bot.*, **11**, 237–303.

MULLER, J. 1964. A palynological contribution to the history of the mangrove vegetation in Borneo *in* CRANWELL, L. M. (Editor) *Ancient Pacific Floras: the pollen story*, pp. 33–42. Honolulu (University of Hawaii Press).

NEWBERRY, J. S. 1868. Note on the later extinct floras of North America, with descriptions of some new species of fossil plants from the Cretaceous and Tertiary strata. *Ann. Lyc. N.Y. nat. Hist.*, **9**, 1–76.

—— 1895. The flora of the Amboy clays, edited by Arthur Hollick. *Monogr. U.S. geol. Surv.*, **26**, 260 pp.

—— 1898. The later extinct floras of North America, Edited by Arthur Hollick. *Monogr. U.S. geol. Surv.*, **35**, 295 pp.

POKROVSKOI, I. M. (Ed.) 1956a. [*Atlas of the spore and pollen complexes of the Oligocene of various parts of the U.S.S.R.*]. Moscow, State Scientific-technical Publishing House, 312 pp. (in Russian).

—— (Ed.) 1956b. [*Atlas of the Miocene spore and pollen complexes of various parts of the U.S.S.R.*]. Moscow, State Scientific-technical Publishing House, 461 pp. (in Russian).

POTBURY, S. S. 1935. The La Porte flora of Plumas County, California. *Publs Carnigie Instn*, **465**, 31–81.

REID, C. 1915. The Pliocene Floras of the Dutch-Prussian border. *Meded. Ryksopspor. Delfstoff.*, **6**.

REID, E. M. & CHANDLER, M. E. J. 1926. *The Bembridge Flora. Catalogue of Cainozoic Plants in the Department of Geology, I*. viii + 206 pp., 12 pls. Brit. Mus. (Nat. Hist.), London.

—— & —— 1933. *The Flora of the London Clay*. viii + 561 pp., 33 pls. Brit. Mus. (Nat. Hist.), London.

RUDOLPH, K. 1935. Mikroflorische Untersuchung der tertiäre Ablagerungen im nordlichem Böhm. *Beih. bot. Zenbralbl.*, **54** (B).

SAHNI, B. & SURANGE, K. R. 1944. On the structure and affinities of *Palmoxylon sahnii*. *Proc. natn. Acad. Sci. India*, **14** (B), 83–85.

SAPORTA, G. 1868. Prodrome d'une flore fossile des travertines anciens de Sézanne. *Mém. Soc. géol. Fr.* (2), **8**, 289–436.

—— 1894. *Flore fossile du Portugal*, 288 pp., 39 pls. Lisbon.

SCOTT, R. A. & BARGHOORN, E. 1957. *Phytocrene microcarpa*—a new species of Icacinaceae based on the Cretaceous fruits from Kreischerville, New York. *Palaeobotanist*, **6**, 25–28.

SQUINABOL, S. 1892. *Contributzioni alla flora fossile dei terreni della Liguria, IV, Moncatiledeni*. Genova.

SZAFER, W. 1946. Flora Plioceńska z Krościenka n/Dunajcem. I. cześć ogólna. *Rozpr. Wydz. mat.-przyr. pol. Akad. Umiejet.*, **72** (B), no. 1.

—— 1947. Flora Plioceńska z Krościenka n/Dunajcem. II. cześć opisowa. *Rozpr. Wydz. mat.-przyr. pol. Akad. Umiejet.*, **72** (B), no. 2, 213 pp., 15 pls.

VELENOWSKY, 1889. Května Českého Cenomanu. *Rozpr. mat.-přir. K. české Spob. Náuk*, (7), **3**.

WARD, L. F. 1884–85. Synopsis of the flora of the Laramie group. *A. Rep. U.S. geol. Surv.*, **6**, 399–557.

—— 1887. Types of the Laramie flora. *Bull. U.S. geol. Surv.*, **37,** 117 pp.

—— 1895. The Potomac formation. *A. Rep. U.S. geol. Surv.*, **15,** 307–397.

—— 1905. Status of the Mesozoic flora of the United States (second paper) (in collaboration with W. M. Fontaine, A. Bibbins and G. R. Weiland). *Monogr. U.S. geol. Surv.*, **48,** 616 pp.

WILSON, L. R. & WEBSTER, R. M. 1946. Plant microfossils in a Fort Union coal of Montana (abstract). *Am. J. Bot.*, **33,** 271–278.

ZAKLINSKAYA, E. D. 1963. *Angiosperm pollen and its significance for stratigraphical analysis: Upper Cretaceous and Paleogene.* Moscow, Academy of Science U.S.S.R., 258 pp. (in Russian).

K. I. M. Chesters, PH.D.
Department of Palaeontology, British Museum (Natural History), Cromwell Road, London SW 7.

F. R. Gnauck, PH.D.
Exploration Division, B.P. Research Centre, Chertsey Road, Sunbury-on-Thames, Middlesex.

N. F. Hughes, M.A. F.G.S.
Department of Geology, Sedgwick Museum, Downing Street, Cambridge.

The Fossil Record, Part II

INVERTEBRATA

INVERTEBRATA

Introduction. There is no agreed high-level classification of the Invertebrata. The following chapters are divided on fairly conventional lines, for the sake of convenience. Archaeocyatha are regarded as a phylum but are assigned to the same chapter (9) as Porifera, without implying that they are related. Some grouping such as Nautiloidea are retained for chapter headings, being familar to non-specialists although their validity is questioned or even rejected by some specialists. A special chapter (24) on Trace-Fossils is used for all traces of animal activity that cannot be referred with complete certainty to groups known in conventional ('body-fossil') preservation. Contributors were given discretion, within the limits of available space, whether or not to mention taxa that are not known in the fossil record. In general, where an entire phylum or other major taxon is completely unknown in the fossil state, it is omitted altogether from this volume; but where some taxa are known as fossils while closely related taxa have a good fossil record, this fact is noted and the taxa without a fossil record are mentioned as 'Extant' only. Attention is drawn to the remarks made in the Introduction to this volume on the relation between the documentation given here and that contained in the *Treatise on Invertebrate Palaeontology*.

The schemes of classification used in the volumes of the *Treatise* so far published have been adopted, with more or less modification, in some of the relevant chapters on Invertebrata in this volume, and some contributors to these chapters have used the Treatise as a source for other information. But these chapters have a purpose different from that of the Treatise: they aim to give much more detailed documentation, in both stratigraphical and taxonomic terms, of the first and last known records of taxa, with full supporting references and bibliography.

M. J. S. R.

CHAPTER 8

Protozoa

Contributors: F. T. BANNER, W. J. CLARKE, J. L. CUTBILL, F. E. EAMES, A. J. LLOYD, W. R. RIEDEL & A. H. SMOUT

Class ACTINOPODA Calkins 1909

Subclass HELIOZOA Haeckel 1866

Unimportant as fossils. Range Pleist—extant. (Treatise D).

Subclass RADIOLARIA Müller 1858

Introduction: Radiolarian literature is replete with unjustifiably precise identifications of poorly preserved specimens, resulting in taxa appearing to have longer time-ranges than they actually had. These very numerous doubtful records cannot all be included here because of considerations of space, and therefore only those based on well preserved specimens are mentioned. Also, some minor families of uncertain taxonomic position are omitted. The taxonomic system presented herein differs somewhat from that generally used in the past, and is believed to reflect natural relationships more closely.

Order TRIPYLEA Hertwig 1879

First, Tert M.Mioc: *Protocystis* Wallich spp., *Lithogromia* Haeckel sp. and *Challengeranium* Haeckel sp., upper Tortonian zone of diapiric folds, Ploiesti region, Romania (Dumitrica 1964, 1965). **Extant.**

Comment: Records few because of fragility and/or solubility of skeleton. Cret *Cannosphaeropsis* described by Wetzel 1933 is a hystrichosphaerid (Deflandre 1952a).

Order POLYCYSTINA Ehrenberg 1838 emend.

Comment: Emended definition of order—Radiolaria with skeleton of opaline silica without admixed organic compounds.

Suborder SPUMELLARIA Ehrenberg 1875

Family ENTACTINIIDAE Riedel 1967

First, Dev Frasn-Famenn: *Haplentactinia* Foreman spp., *Entactinia* Foreman spp., *Entactinosphaera* Foreman spp., *Polyentactinia* Foreman spp., *Tetrentactinia* Foreman spp., and *Cyrtentactinia* Foreman spp., Huron member, Ohio shale, northern Ohio (Foreman 1963).

Last, Carb Namur: *Entactinia*, *Entactinosphaera*, and *Polyentactinia*, Reticuloceras bilingue Z., Staffordshire and Derbyshire, England (Holdsworth 1966).

The Fossil Record, pp. 291–332. Geological Society of London, 1967. Printed in Northern Ireland.

SEE FIG B
TRIASSIC
Carn
Ladin
Anis
Olenek
Induan
PERMIAN
Dzhulf
Guad
Leonard
Sakm
Assel
CARBONIFEROUS
U. Carb
Moscov
Bashk
Namur
Viséan
Tourn
DEVONIAN
Famenn
Frasn
Givet
Eifel
Ems
Siegen
Gedinn
SILURIAN
Ludl
Wenl
Lldov
ORDOVICIAN
Ashg
Carad
Lldeil
Llvirn
Arenig
Tremad
CAMBRIAN
U. Camb
M. Camb
L. Camb
PRE-CAMB
Varang
Pre-Var
Entactiniidae
Actinommidae
Phacodiscidae
Spongodiscidae
Litheliidae
Theoperidae
Albaillellidae
Palaeoscenidiidae
Diffiugiidae
TAXA
Radiolaria
ACTINOPODA
RHIZOPODEA
CONTRIBUTORS
W. R. Riedel

FIG. 8.1A

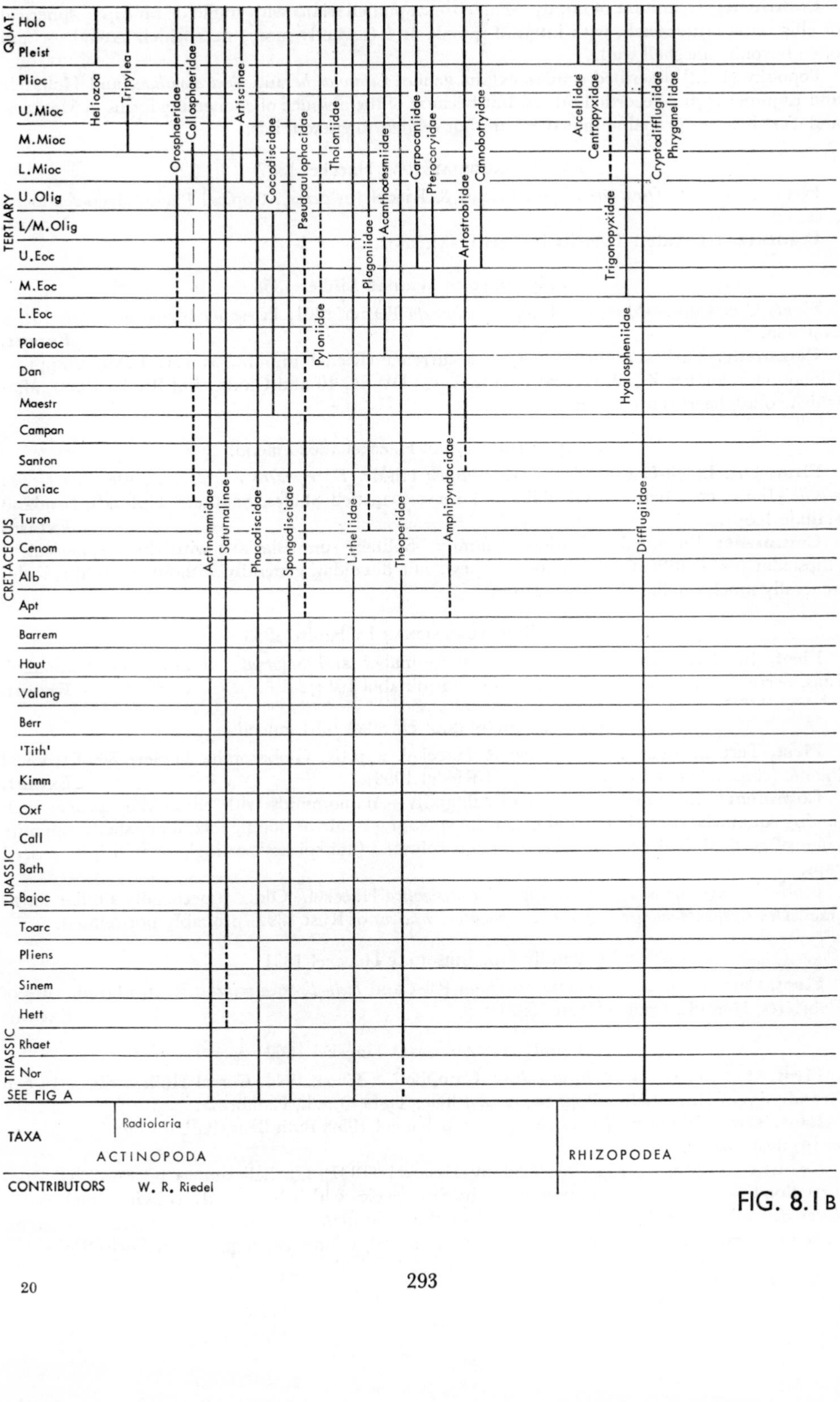
QUAT.
Holo
Pleist
Plioc
U.Mioc
M.Mioc
L.Mioc
TERTIARY
U.Olig
L/M.Olig
U.Eoc
M.Eoc
L.Eoc
Palaeoc
Dan
Maestr
CRETACEOUS
Campan
Santon
Coniac
Turon
Cenom
Alb
Apt
Barrem
Haut
Valang
Berr
'Tith'
Kimm
Oxf
JURASSIC
Call
Bath
Bajoc
Toarc
Pliens
Sinem
Hett
TRIASSIC
Rhaet
Nor
SEE FIG A
Heliozoa
Tripylea
Orosphaeridae
Collosphaeridae
Actinommidae
Saturnalinae
Artiscinae
Phacodiscidae
Coccodiscidae
Spongodiscidae
Pseudoaulophacidae
Pyloniidae
Tholoniidae
Litheliidae
Plagoniidae
Acanthodesmiidae
Theoperidae
Carpocaniidae
Pterocorydae
Amphipyndacidae
Artostrobiidae
Cannobotryidae
Arcellidae
Centropyxidae
Trigonopyxidae
Hyalospheniidae
Difflugiidae
Cryptodifflugiidae
Phryganellidae
TAXA
Radiolaria
ACTINOPODA
RHIZOPODEA
CONTRIBUTORS
W. R. Riedel

FIG. 8.1 B

Comment: Definition of family—Palaeozoic spumellarians with single or multiple, spherical or ellipsoidal lattice-shell, with internal spicule of 4–6 (rarely more) rays which extend to (and often beyond) the shell wall.

Popofsky (1912) described similar extant genera *Centrolonche* and *Centracontium*, and Hollande and Enjumet (1960) recorded others, but because of the absence of connecting forms in Mesozoic and Tert it seems probable that these are not related to entactiniids.

Family OROSPHAERIDAE Haeckel 1887

First, Tert Eoc: *Orostaurs simplex* Friend & Riedel (in press), tropical Pacific deep-sea localities. **Extant.**

Comment: Greatest diversity in Tert L.-M.Mioc.

Family COLLOSPHAERIDAE Müller 1858

First, Cret Coniac-Maestr: *Acrosphaera hirsuta* Perner 1891, Priesener Schichten, Postelberg, Bohemia. **Extant.**

Comment: Earliest known post-Cret occurrence (Riedel unpubl.) is Tert L.Mioc, approx. Globorotalia kugleri Z., of tropical Pacific (cores DWBG 10 and Chub 17 of Riedel 1959), after which collosphaerids are common.

Family ACTINOMMIDAE Haeckel 1862 emend.

First, Ord Lldeil-Carad: *Haliomma vetustum* Hinde, *Dorysphaera reticulata* Hinde, *Doryplegma gracile* Hinde, etc., between Glenkiln and Lower Hartfell Shales, Southern Uplands, Scotland (Hinde 1890). **Extant.**

Comment: Emended definition of family—Solitary spumellarians with shells spherical or ellipsoidal (or modifications of those shapes), not discoidal, generally without internal spicule; generally much smaller than orosphaerids.

Subfamily SATURNALINAE Deflandre 1953

First, Jur Hett-Toarc: *Saturnalis major* Squinabol and *Saturnalis dicranacanthos* Squinabol, Lias, Serra di St. Abbondio, Marche, Italy (Squinabol 1914). **Extant.**

Subfamily ARTISCINAE Haeckel 1881 emend.

First, Tert L.Mioc: *Pipettaria tubaria* Haeckel, approx. Globorotalia kugleri Z. of tropical Pacific (cores DWBG 10 and Chub 17 of Riedel 1959). **Extant.**

Comment: Emended definition of subfamily—Actinommids with ellipsoidal cortical shell having equatorial constriction and generally enclosing single or double medullary shell; opposite poles of cortical shell generally bear spongy columns (not spines) or single or multiple latticed caps.

Probable ancestor is Tert Olig *Pipettella prismatica* Haeckel. Older superficially similar forms (incl. Dev *Cyphanta quiniseriata* and *Peripanartus deficiens* of Rüst 1892) probably not related.

Family PHACODISCIDAE Haeckel 1881

First, Carb Viséan: *Sethostaurus exsculptus* Rüst and *Heliodiscus acucinctus* Rüst, phosphorites of Cabrières, Hérault, France (Rüst 1892). **Extant.**

Family COCCODISCIDAE Haeckel 1862

First, Cret Maestr: *Coccodiscus holmesi* Campbell & Clark 1944, Corral Hollow Sh, (Moreno Grande Fm of Huey 1948; Popenoe *et al.* 1960), Tesla Quad., California.

Last, Tert L/M.Olig: *Trigonactura? angusta* Riedel 1959, Bath Beds, Barbados and equivalent in tropical Pacific.

Comment: Many forms described by Haeckel (1887) are believed to be reworked from Tert Eoc-Olig into younger sediments. The few species which he records as living (incl. *Coccodiscus darwinii* Haeckel 1862, type species of the type genus) or cosmopolitan are anomalous, since no coccodiscids are known from uncontaminated sediments younger than Tert Olig.

Chapter 8: Protozoa

Family SPONGODISCIDAE Haeckel 1862 emend.

First, Dev Givet: *Spongodiscus* spp., tuffs and siliceous lsts, Tamworth, N.S.W., Australia (Hinde 1899). **Extant.**

Comment: Emended definition of family—Discoidal, spongy or finely-chambered skeleton, with or without surficial pore-plate, often with radiating arms or marginal spines, and without a large central phacoid shell.

Large, polyphyletic group for which no satisfactory classification has been proposed.

Family PSEUDOAULOPHACIDAE Riedel 1967

First, Cret Apt-Coniac: *Theodiscus superbus* Squinabol (1914), M. Cret, Novale, Vicentino, Italy.

Last, Cret Campan: *Pseudoaulophacus* spp. Pessagno (1963), Cariblanco Fm and Parguera lst, southern Puerto Rico.

Comment: Definition of family—Spongy discoidal spumellarians, with all or part of the surface covered by meshwork of equilateral triangular frames. *Spongotrochus ehrenbergi* Bütschli 1882, from probably U. Eoc Oceanic Fm, Barbados, may be a pseudoaulophacid and thus extend range.

Family PYLONIIDAE Haeckel 1881

First, Tert U. Mioc: *Tetrapyle quadriloba* (Ehrenberg), Tripoli of Grotte, Girgenti Province, Sicily (Stöhr 1880). **Extant.**

Comment: An unidentified genus probably belonging to this family, in tropical Pacific M. Eoc core DWBG 23B of Riedel & Funnell (1964), extends the range. Well developed and common only in Tert Mioc and later.

Family THOLONIIDAE Haeckel 1887

First, Quat Holo-Pleist: *Tholonium bicubicum* Haeckel, etc., many localities in Pacific, Atlantic and Indian Oceans (Haeckel 1887). **Extant.**

Comment: An unidentified genus probably belonging to this family, from tropical Pacific Tert Plioc core CAP 42 BP, 757–803 cm (7°19′S, 118°40′W; water depth 4200 m), extends the range.

Family LITHELIIDAE Haeckel 1862

First, Carb Tourn-Bashk: *Spironium haeckelii* Rüst (1892), L. Carb Kieselschiefer, Harz Mts. **Extant.**

Suborder NASSELLARIA Ehrenberg 1875

Family PLAGONIIDAE Haeckel 1881 emend.

First, Cret Turon-Santon: *Tripocalpis ellyae* Tan and perhaps *Dictyophimus gracilis* Tan (1927), radiolarian-coccolith chalks, west of Bebalain, Rotti Is. **Extant.**

Comment: Emended definition of family—Skeleton consisting entirely of spicule with median bar, apical and dorsal spines, vertical spine, primary lateral spines and sometimes other spines; or having a lattice skeleton including large cephalis within which this spicule is well developed.

Synon. with Plectida Haeckel 1881, = Plagoniicae (incl. Plectaniidae) of Campbell (1954 *in* Treatise D). Large, probably polyphyletic taxon. Earlier superficially similar forms omitted because of uncertainty of spicular structure. Spicule in Dev *Cyrtentactinia* Foreman 1963 appears not to have spines homologous with those listed above. Age of Tan's samples based on calcareous nannoplankton (M. N. Bramlette, pers. comm.).

295

The Fossil Record, Part II

Family ACANTHODESMIIDAE Hertwig 1879

First, Tert Palaeoc: *Brachiospyris martini* Middour, Porters Creek Fm, Missouri (Frizzell & Middour 1951). **Extant.**

Comment: Family equivalent to Stephoidea + Spyroidea of Haeckel 1887, or Stephaniicae + Triospyridicae of Campbell (1954 *in* Treatise D).

Family THEOPERIDAE Haeckel 1881 emend.

First: Trias Anis-Rhaet: *Dictyomitra* Zittel and approx. fourteen other genera, associated with Halobia and Daonella Lsts, Rotti and Savu Is. (Hinde 1908). **Extant.**

Comment: Emended definition of family—Cephalis relatively small, approximately spherical, often poreless or sparsely perforate, the internal spicule, homologous with that of plagoniids, reduced to a less conspicuous structural element than in the latter group.

Large taxon, probably polyphyletic, including the majority of cyrtoids.

Family CARPOCANIIDAE Haeckel 1881 emend.

First, Tert U.Eoc: *Carpocanium coronatum* and *Cryptoprora ornata* Ehrenberg (1873), Oceanic Fm, Barbados. **Extant.**

Comment: Emended definition of family—Cephalis small, not sharply distinguished in contour from thorax, and tending to be reduced to a few bars within top of thorax.

Family PTEROCORYIDAE Haeckel 1881 emend.

First, Tert M.Eoc: *Podocyrtis papalis* Ehrenberg, possibly Hantkenina aragonensis Z. or Globigerapsis kugleri Z., tropical Pacific (core DWBG of Riedel & Funnell 1964). **Extant.**

Comment: Emended definition of family—Cephalis subdivided into three lobes by two obliquely downwardly directed lateral furrows arising from the apical spine, in the manner described for *Anthocytidium cineraria* Haeckel and *Calocyclas virginis* Haeckel by Riedel (1957).

Family AMPHIPYNDACIDAE Riedel 1967

First, Cret Apt?: *Amphipyndax* Foreman sp., Thirindine Fm, Murchison River area, W. Australia (Foreman 1966).

Last, Cret Maestr: *Amphipyndax* sp., Moreno Fm, Fresno County, California (Foreman 1966).

Comment: Definition of family—Cephalis, generally with poreless wall, divided into two chambers by a transverse internal ledge.

Family ARTOSTROBIIDAE Riedel 1967

First, Cret Santon-Campan: *Artostrobium* Haeckel sp., Pre-Habana Fm (Bermudez 1963). Jibacoa, Habana prov., Cuba (Foreman 1966). **Extant.**

Comment: Definition of family—Cephalis bears a lateral tubule, its relation to the internal spicular structure being generally similar to that described by Riedel (1958) for *Siphocampe* sp. and *Dictyocephalus papillosus* (Ehrenberg).

Family CANNOBOTRYIDAE Haeckel 1881 emend.

First, Tert U.Eoc: *Lithobotrys* Ehrenberg spp., Oceanic Fm, Barbados (Ehrenberg 1873). **Extant.**

Comment: Emended definition of family—Cephalis consisting of two or more unpaired lobes, only one of which is homologous with the cephalis of theoperids (Petrushevskaya 1964, Clark 1965).

Synon. with Cannobotrydicae Haeckel of Campbell (1954 *in* Treatise D).

RADIOLARIA INCERTAE SEDIS

Family ALBAILLELLIDAE Deflandre 1952b

First, Carb Viséan: *Albaillella* Deflandre spp., "lydiennes" of Cabrières, Montagne Noire, France (Deflandre 1952b).

Chapter 8: Protozoa

Last, Carb Namur: *Albaillella pennata* Holdsworth, Reticuloceras paucicrenulatum, R. circumplicatile Z., SW Derbyshire, England (Holdsworth 1966).

Comment: *Ceratoikiscum* Deflandre and *Holoeciscus* Foreman, which range from Dev Frasn-Famenn (Foreman 1963) may also belong in this family.

Family PALAEOSCENIDIIDAE Riedel 1967

First, Dev Frasn-Famenn: *Palaeoscenidium cladophorum* Deflandre, Huron member, Ohio shale, northern Ohio (Foreman 1963).

Last, Carb Viséan: *Palaeoscenidium cladophorum*, *P. bicorne* Deflandre, "lydiennes" of Cabrières, Montagne Noire, France (Deflandre 1953, 1960).

Comment: Definition of family—Four divergent basal spines connected proximally by flat lamellae, and 2–4 shorter apical spines, no additional regular structures at junction of these spines.

REFERENCES

BERMÚDEZ, P. J. 1963. *Las formaciones geológicas de Cuba*, ed. 2. La Havana (Inst. Cubano Rec. Mineral).

BÜTSCHLI, O. 1882. Radiolazia. *In* H. G. BRONN (Editor) *Klassen und Ordnungen des Thier Reichs* **1** (1), 332–478, pls. 17–32.

CAMPBELL, A. S. & CLARK, B. L. 1944. Radiolaria from Upper Cretaceous of Middle California. *Spec. Pap. geol. Soc. Am.*, **57**, 61 pp., 8 pl.

CLARK, C. A. 1965. *Radiolaria in Recent pelagic sediments from the Indian and Atlantic Oceans.* Dissertation, Cambridge.

DEFLANDRE, G. 1952a. Groupes incertae sedis, in *Traité de Paléontologie* (ed. J. Piveteau), 1. Paris.

—— 1952b. Albaillella nov. gen., Radiolaire fossile du Carbonifère inférieur, type d'une lignée aberrante énteinte. *C.r. hebd. Séanc. Acad. Sci., Paris*, **234**, 872–874.

—— 1953. Radiolaires fossiles *in* P.-P. GRASSÉ (Editor) *Traité de Zoologie* **1** (2). Paris, Masson.

—— 1960. A propos du développement des recherches sur les radiolaires fossiles. *Revue Micropaléont.*, **2**, 212–218.

DUMITRICA, P. 1964. Aspura prezentei unor radiolari din familia Challengeridae (Ord. Phaeodaria) in Tortonianul din Subcarpati. *Studii Cerc. Geogr. Geof. Geol.*, Bucarest, **9**, 217–222.

—— 1965. Sur la présence de Phéodaires dans le Tortonien des Subcarpathes roumaines. *C.r. hebd. Séanc. Acad. Sci., Paris*, **260**, 250–253.

EHRENBERG, C. G. 1873. Grössere Felsproben des Polycystinen-Mergels von Barbados mit weiteren Erläuterungen. *Monatsber. k. preuss. Akad. Wiss.* for 1873, 213–263.

FOREMAN, H. P. 1963. Upper Devonian Radiolaria from the Huron member of the Ohio shale. *Micropaleontology*, **9**, 267–304, pl. 1–9.

—— 1966. Two Cretaceous radiolarian genera. *Micropaleontology*, **12**, 355–359.

FRIEND, J. K. & RIEDEL, W. R. in press. Cenozoic orosphaerid radiolarians in tropical Pacific sediments. *Micropaleontology* (in press).

FRIZZELL, D. L. & MIDDOUR, E. S. 1951. Paleocene Radiolaria from Southeastern Missouri. *Tech. Ser. Sch. Mines Metall. Univ. Mo.*, **77**, 1–41, pl. 1–3.

HAECKEL, E. 1862. *Die Radiolarien*. Berlin.

—— 1887. Report on the Radiolaria collected by H.M.S. *Challenger* during the years 1873–1876. *Challenger Rep.*, Zool., **18**, clxxxviii + 1803 pp., 140 pls.

HINDE, G. J. 1890. Notes on Radiolaria from the Lower Palaeozoic rocks (Llandeilo-Caradoc) of the South of Scotland. *Ann. Mag. nat. Hist.* (6), **6**, 40–59, pl. 3–4.

—— 1899. On the Radiolaria in the Devonian rocks of New South Wales. *Q.Jl geol. Soc. Lond.*, **55**, 38–64, pl. 8–9.

—— 1908. Radiolaria from Triassic and other rocks of the Dutch East Indian Archipelago. *Jaarb. Mijnw. Ned.-Ost-Indië.*, **37** (French edition), 709–751, pl. 5–10.

HOLDSWORTH, B. K. 1966. Radiolaria from the Namurian Series of Derbyshire. *Palaeontology*, **9**, 319–329, pl. 54.

HOLLANDE, A. & ENJUMET, M. 1960. Cytologie, évolution et systématique des Sphaeroidés (Radiolaires). *Archs Mus. natn Hist. nat., Paris* (7), **7**, 1–134, pl. 1–64.

HUEY, A. S. 1948. Geology of the Tesla Quadrangle, California. *Bull. Div. Mines Calif.* **140**, 1–75.

PERNER, J. 1891. O radiolariich z ceskeho utvaru kridoveho. *Sber. K. böhm. Ges. Wiss.* for 1891, 255–269.

PESSAGNO, E. A. 1963. Upper Cretaceous Radiolaria from Puerto Rico. *Micropaleontology,* **9**, 197–214.

PETRUSHEVSKAYA, M. G. 1964. [On homologies in the elements of the inner skeleton of some Nassellaria] *Zool. Zh.,* **43** (8), 1121–1128 (Russian).

POPENOE, W. P., IMLAY, R. W. & MURPHY, M. A. 1960. Correlation of the Cretaceous formations of the Pacific Coast (United States and Northwestern Mexico). *Bull. geol. Soc. Am.* **71**, 1491–1540, 1 pl.

POPOFSKY, A. 1912. Die Sphaerellarien des Warmwassergebietes. *Dt. Südpol.-Exped.,* **13** (Zool. 5) (2), 73–159, pl. 1–8.

RIEDEL, W. R. 1957. Radiolaria: a preliminary stratigraphy. *Rep. Swed. Deep Sea Exped.,* **6** (3), 61–96, pl. 1–4.

—— 1958. Radiolaria in Antarctic sediments. *Rep. B.A.N.Z. antarct. Res. Exped.* Series B, **6** (10), 217–255.

—— 1959. Oligocene and Lower Miocene Radiolaria in tropical Pacific sediments. *Micropaleontology,* **5**, 285–302.

—— 1967. Some new families of Radiolaria. *Proc. geol. Soc. Lond.* no. 1640, 148–9.

—— & FUNNELL, B. M. 1964. Tertiary sediment cores and microfossils from the Pacific Ocean floor. *Q. Jl. geol. Soc. Lond.,* **120**, 305–368, pl. 14–32.

RÜST, D. 1892. Beiträge zur Kenntniss der fossilen Radiolarien aus Gesteinen der Trias und palaeozoischen Schichten. *Palaeontographica,* **38**, 107–192, pl. 6–30.

SQUINABOL, S. 1914. Contributo alla conoscenza dei Radiolarii fossili del Veneto. *Mem. Ist. geol. miner. Univ. Padova,* **2** (7), 249–306, pl. 20–24.

STÖHR, E. 1880. Die Radiolarienfauna der Tripol: von Grotte. *Palaeontographica,* **26**, 69–124, pls. 17–23.

TAN SIN HOK, 1927. Over de samensteling en het ontstaan van krijt- en mergelgesteenten van de Molukken. *Jaarb. Mijnw. Ned.-Oost-Indië* for 1926, 1–165, pl. 1–16.

TREATISE D 1954. CAMPBELL, A. S. & MOORE, R. C. Protista 3: Chiefly Radiolarians and Tintinnines *in* MOORE, R. C. (Editor) *Treatise on Invertebrate Paleontology* Part D. University of Kansas Press.

WETZEL, O. 1933. Die in organischer Substanz erhaltenen Mikrofossilien des baltischen Kreide-Feuersteins. *Palaeontographica,* **77A**, 141–186 & **78A**, 1–110, pl. 1–7.   [W.R.R.]

Class RHIZOPODEA von Siebold 1845

Order ARCELLINIDA Kent 1880

Superfamily ARCELLACEA Ehrenberg 1832

Family ARCELLIDAE Ehrenberg 1832

First, Quat Pleist: *Arcella* Ehrenberg 1832, monotypic, cosmop.   **Extant.**

Family CENTROPYXIDAE Jung 1942

First, Quat Pleist: *Centropyxis* Stein 1859, monotypic, cosmop.   **Extant.**

Family TRIGONOPYXIDAE Loeblich and Tappan 1964

First, Tert Mioc: *Cyclopyxis* Deflandre 1929.   **Extant.**

Chapter 8: Protozoa

Family HYALOSPHENIIDAE Schulze 1877

First, Tert M. Eoc: *Quadrulella* Cockerell 1909.   **Extant.**

Family DIFFLUGIIDAE Wallich 1864

First, Carb Namur: *Prantlitina* Vašíček and Růžička 1957, Czechoslovakia.   **Extant.**

Superfamily CRYPTODIFFLUGIACEA Jung 1942

Family CRYPTODIFFLUGIIDAE Jung 1942

First, Quat Pleist: *Cryptodifflugia* Penard 1890, Europe.   **Exta nt**

Family PHRYGANELLIDAE Jung 1942

First, Quat Pleist: *Phryganella* Penard 1902, monotypic.   **Extant.**

Class RETICULAREA Lankester 1885

Subclass FILOSIA Leidy 1879

Order GROMIDA Claparède & Lachmann 1959

Superfamily GROMIACEA Reuss 1862

Family GROMIIDAE Reuss 1862

First, Quat Pleist: *Pseudodifflugia* Schlumberger 1845, Europe.   **Extant.**

Family AMPHITREMATIDAE Poche 1913

First, Quat Pleist: *Amphitrema* Archer 1867, Europe and *Archerella* Loeblich and Tappan
1961, Europe and N. America.   **Extant.**

Superfamily EUGLYPHACEA Wallich 1864

Family EUGLYPHIDAE Wallich 1864

First, Tert M. Eoc: *Euglypha* Dujardin 1840.   **Extant.**

[Data from Treatise C, Compiled by Editor]

Subclass GRANULORETICULOSIA de Saedeleer 1934

Order FORAMINIFERIDA Eichwald 1830

Introduction: Apart from the contribution by J. L. Cutbill on Endothyracea and Fusulinacea, documentation of the bulk of the foraminifera has been arbitrarily divided between A. J. Lloyd, who has taken the small benthonic forms, and F. E. Eames and his associates, who have given documentation to the generic level for the larger foraminifera. This latter contribution is retained as a separate section at the end of this chapter but cross-references to it are given in the section which follows upon this introduction. In this following section the order of classification is as in Treatise C. Dr. Lloyd provides this introduction to his contribution:

For the purpose of this survey the small benthonic foraminifera are those that do not fall within (a) the Superfamily Globigerinaceae, (b) the Suborder Fusulinina and (c) certain familes in which "larger" foraminifera predominate. Following the Treatise C classification fossil members comprise 758 genera grouped into 55 families and 12 superfamilies.

In preparing the entries for this section a search was made for the first and last species in each family but, according to an estimate now some six years old (Rainwater 1960) the number of species and sub-species recognized as belonging to the Foraminiferida is in excess of 20,000. Of these 70% or more fall within the category of small benthonic foraminifera and are the concern of this section. In the time available it was not possible to review 15,000 species and verify their

299

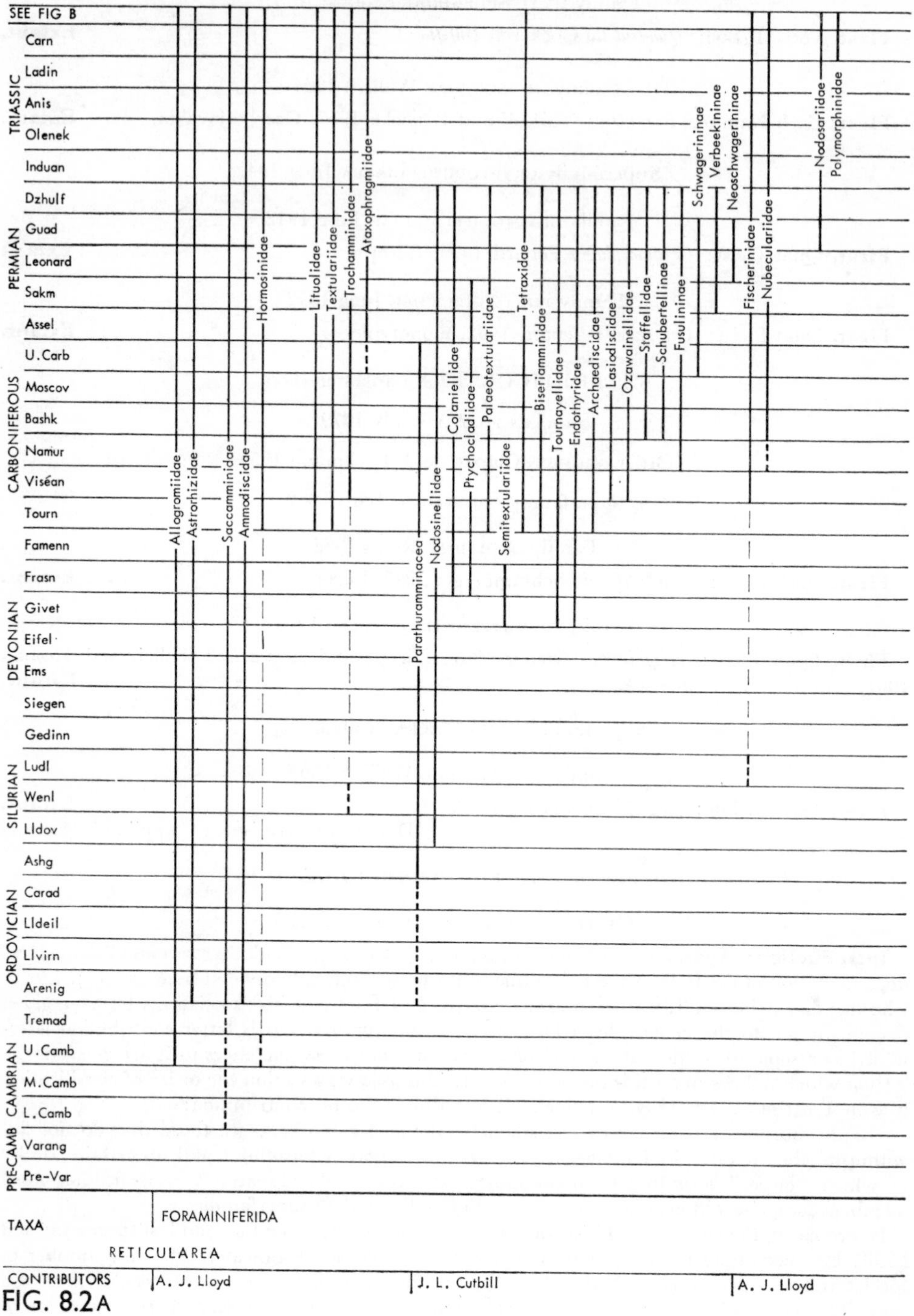
SEE FIG B
TRIASSIC
Carn
Ladin
Anis
Olenek
Induan
PERMIAN
Dzhulf
Guad
Leonard
Sakm
Assel
CARBONIFEROUS
U.Carb
Moscov
Bashk
Namur
Viséan
Tourn
DEVONIAN
Famenn
Frasn
Givet
Eifel
Ems
Siegen
Gedinn
SILURIAN
Ludl
Wenl
Lldov
ORDOVICIAN
Ashg
Carad
Lldeil
Llvirn
Arenig
Tremad
CAMBRIAN
U.Camb
M.Camb
L.Camb
PRE-CAMB
Varang
Pre-Var
Allogromiidae
Astrorhizidae
Saccamminidae
Ammodiscidae
Hormosinidae
Lituolidae
Textulariidae
Trochamminidae
Ataxophragmiidae
Parathuramminacea
Nodosinellidae
Colaniellidae
Ptychocladiidae
Polaeotextulariidae
Semitextulariidae
Tetraxidae
Biseriamminidae
Tournayellidae
Endothyridae
Archaediscidae
Lasiodiscidae
Ozawainellidae
Staffellidae
Schubertellinae
Fusulininae
Schwagerininae
Verbeekininae
Neoschwagerininae
Fischerinidae
Nubeculariidae
Nodosariidae
Polymorphinidae
TAXA
FORAMINIFERIDA
RETICULAREA
CONTRIBUTORS
A. J. Lloyd
J. L. Cutbill
A. J. Lloyd

FIG. 8.2A

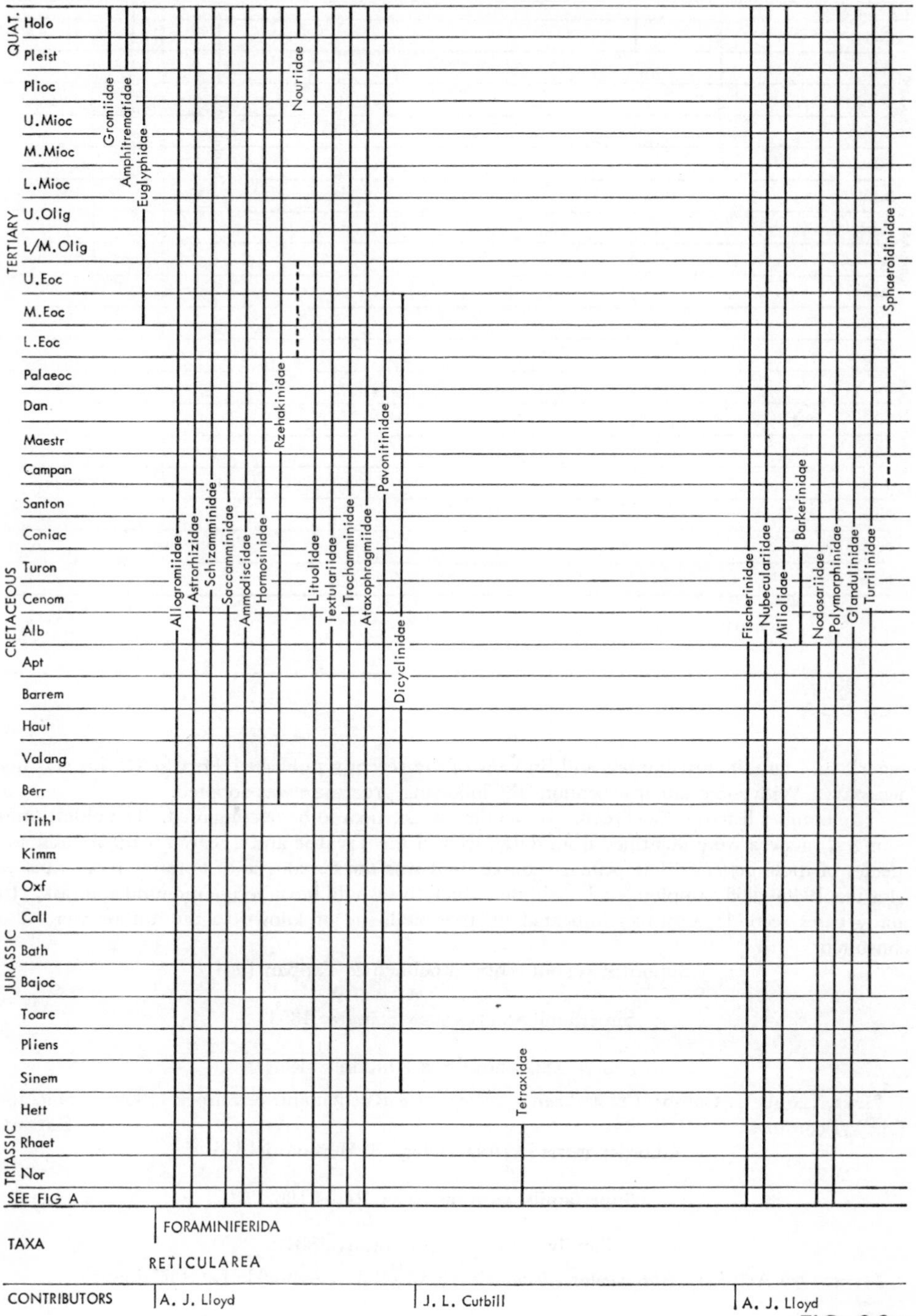
QUAT.
Holo
Pleist
Plioc
U.Mioc
M.Mioc
L.Mioc
TERTIARY
U.Olig
L/M.Olig
U.Eoc
M.Eoc
L.Eoc
Palaeoc
Dan
Maestr
Campan
Santon
Coniac
CRETACEOUS
Turon
Cenom
Alb
Apt
Barrem
Haut
Valang
Berr
'Tith'
Kimm
Oxf
JURASSIC
Call
Bath
Bajoc
Toarc
Pliens
Sinem
Hett
TRIASSIC
Rhaet
Nor
SEE FIG A
Gromiidae
Amphitrematidae
Euglyphidae
Nouriidae
Allogromiidae
Astrorhizidae
Schizamminidae
Saccamminidae
Ammodiscidae
Hormosinidae
Rzehakinidae
Lituolidae
Textulariidae
Trochamminidae
Ataxophragmiidae
Pavonitinidae
Dicyclinidae
Tetraxidae
Fischerinidae
Nubeculariidae
Miliolidae
Barkerinidae
Nodosariidae
Polymorphinidae
Glandulinidae
Turrilinidae
Sphaeroidinidae
TAXA
FORAMINIFERIDA
RETICULAREA
CONTRIBUTORS
A. J. Lloyd
J. L. Cutbill
A. J. Lloyd

FIG. 8.2B

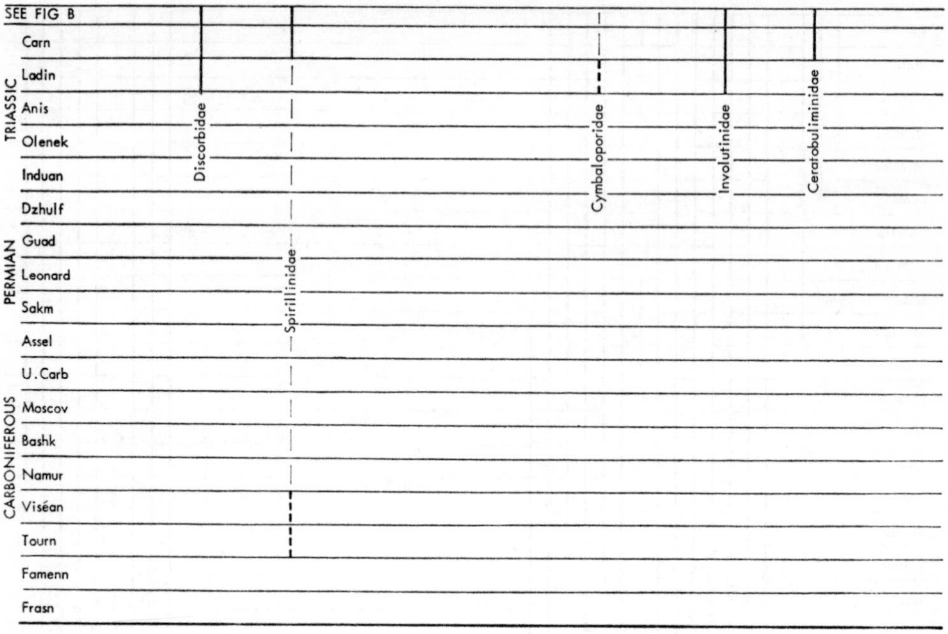

	SEE FIG B					
TRIASSIC	Carn					
	Ladin					Ceratobuliminidae
	Anis	Discorbidae			Involutinidae	
	Olenek			Cymbaloporidae		
	Induan					
	Dzhulf					
PERMIAN	Guad		Spirillinidae			
	Leonard					
	Sakm					
	Assel					
CARBONIFEROUS	U.Carb					
	Moscov					
	Bashk					
	Namur					
	Viséan					
	Tourn					
	Famenn					
	Frasn					

TAXA FORAMINIFERIDA

CONTRIBUTORS A. J. Lloyd

FIG. 8.3 A

generic and familial attributions and, in view of the recently published Treatise C, this was not necessary. With some minor exceptions the following procedure was adopted.

The families listed in the Treatise were taken as the taxa to be documented. The oldest (and youngest) genera were identified from data given in the Treatise and a search made among *new* species of these genera. The primary source used was the Catalogue of Foraminifera (Ellis & Messina 1940–1966, supplement 1), without which this would have been a monumental task. In many cases secondary sources indicated by the catalogue or known to the author were also consulted.

Suborder ALLOGROMIINA Loeblich & Tappan 1961

Superfamily LAGYNACEA Schultze 1854

Family ALLOGROMIIDAE Rhumbler 1904

First, Camb U. Camb: *Chitinodendron franconianum* Ruedemann & Shrock (1939), Franconia Fm, Wisconsin.   **Extant.**

Suborder TEXTULARIINA Delage & Hérouard 1896

Superfamily AMMODISCACEA Reuss 1862

Family ASTRORHIZIDAE Brady 1881

First, Ord Arenig: *Hyperammina minuta* Moreman (1930), Arbuckle Lst, Oklahoma.

Extant.

Comment: Treatise C records *Bathysiphon* from L. Camb. Earliest record found was *B. exiguus* Moreman (1930) from Viola Lst, Oklahoma (Ord M. Carad).

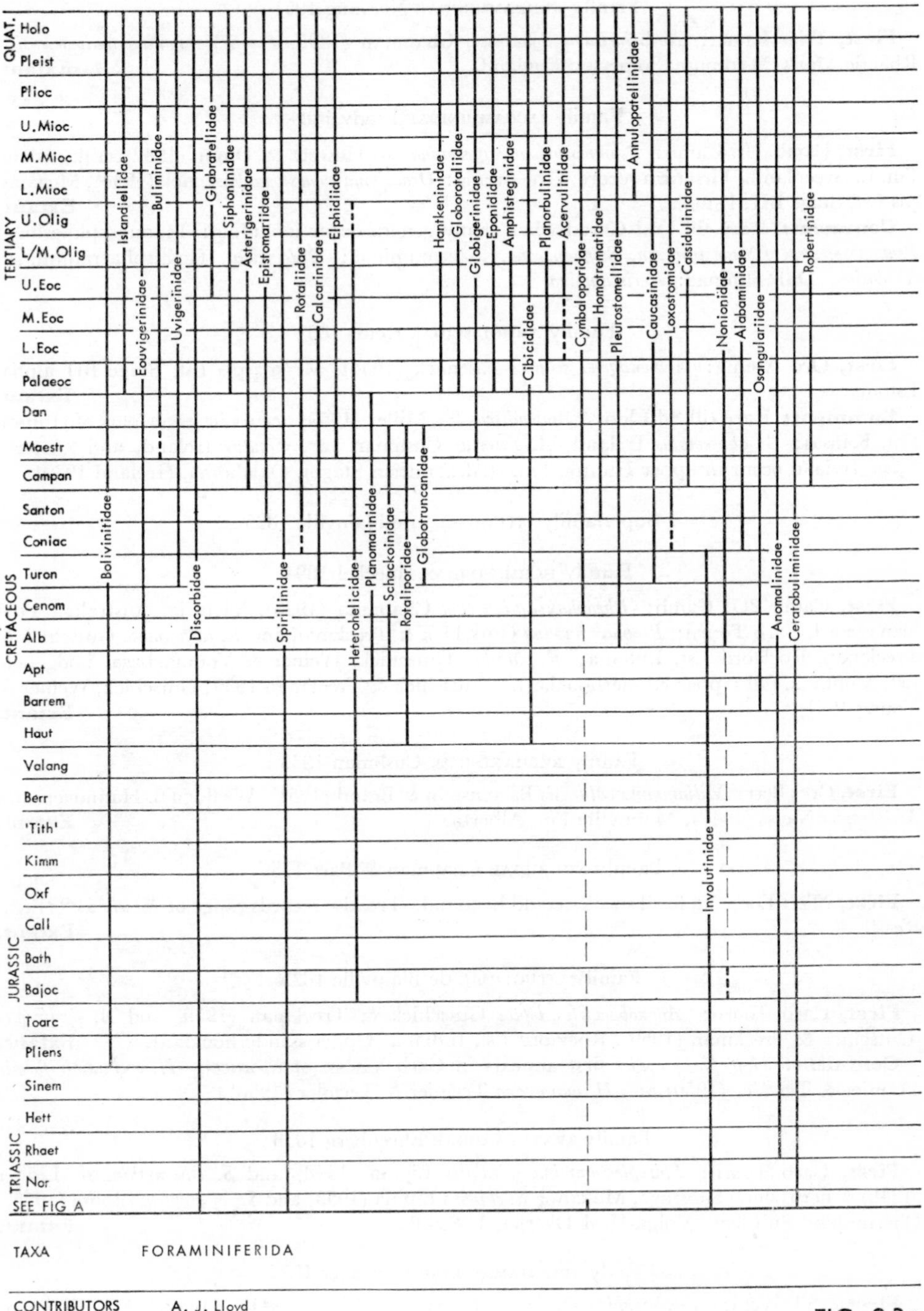
QUAT.
Holo
Pleist
Plioc
TERTIARY
U.Mioc
M.Mioc
L.Mioc
U.Olig
L/M.Olig
U.Eoc
M.Eoc
L.Eoc
Palaeoc
Dan
Maestr
Campan
Santon
Coniac
CRETACEOUS
Turon
Cenom
Alb
Apt
Barrem
Haut
Valang
Berr
'Tith'
Kimm
Oxf
JURASSIC
Call
Bath
Bajoc
Toarc
Pliens
Sinem
Hett
TRIASSIC
Rhaet
Nor
SEE FIG A
Bolivinitidae
Islandiellidae
Eouvigerinidae
Buliminidae
Uvigerinidae
Discorbidae
Glabratellidae
Siphoninidae
Asterigerinidae
Epistomariidae
Spirillinidae
Rotaliidae
Calcarinidae
Elphidiidae
Heterohelicidae
Planomalinidae
Schackoinidae
Rotaliporidae
Globotruncanidae
Hantkeninidae
Globorotaliidae
Globigerinidae
Eponididae
Amphisteginidae
Cibicididae
Planorbulinidae
Acervulinidae
Cymbaloporidae
Homotrematidae
Pleurostomellidae
Annulopatellinidae
Caucasinidae
Loxostomidae
Cassidulinidae
Involutinidae
Nonionidae
Alabaminidae
Osangulariidae
Anomalinidae
Ceratobuliminidae
Robertinidae
TAXA
FORAMINIFERIDA
CONTRIBUTORS
A. J. Lloyd

FIG. 8.3B

Family SCHIZAMMINIDAE Nørvang 1961

First, Trias Rhaet: *Nodosinella wedmoriensis* Chapman (1895) (= *Schizammina wedmoriensis*), Rhaetic Marls, Wedmore, Somerset, England. **Extant.**

Family SACCAMMINIDAE Brady 1884

First, Camb ?L. Camb: *Psammosphaera? greenlandensis* Howell & Dunn (1942), Ella Island Fm, E. Greenland. First firm record, Ord Arenig: *Ordovicina monostoma* Eisenack (1954), Megalaspis Lst, Stage BII, Estonia. **Extant.**

Comment: Rare till Ord Carad when many genera occur including: Psammosphaerinae: *Psammosphaera, Pseudastrorhiza, Stegnammina.* Saccamminae: *Ordovicina.* Hemisphaeramminae: *Tholosina.* Diffusilininae: *Kerinammina.*

Family AMMODISCIDAE Reuss 1862

First, Ord Arenig: *Ammolagena silurica* Eisenack (1954), Megalaspis Lst, Stage BII alpha, Estonia. **Extant.**

Comment: Rare till Sil Lldov. *Ammodiscus leei* Miller (1956) occurs in lower part of Hunton Fm, Kansas; *A. abbreviatus* Ireland, *A. exsertus* Cushman var. *minutus* Ireland, and *Lituotuba inflata* Ireland occur in upper Hunton Fm. (Alexandrian Stage), Oklahoma, (Ireland 1939).

Superfamily LITUOLACEA de Blainville 1825

Family HORMOSINIDAE Haeckel 1894

First, Camb ?U. Camb: *Rheophax antiquorum* Chapman (1923), Victoria, Australia. First firm record, Carb Tourn: *Reophax buccina* Gutschick & Treckman and *R. lachrymosa* Gutschick & Treckman, Rockford Lst, Indiana; *R. calathus* Gutschick, Weiner & Young, basal Lodgepole Lst, Montana, (all Upper Kinderhookian). (Gutschick & Treckman 1959; Gutschick, Weiner & Young 1961). **Extant.**

Family RZEHAKINIDAE Cushman 1933

First, Cret Berr: *Miliammina valdensis* Bartenstein & Brand (1951), Wealden 6, Hannover, and *M. sproulei* Nauss (1947), Mannville Fm, Alberta. **Extant.**

Family NOURIIDAE Chapman & Parr 1936

First, ?Tert Eoc: No fossil species could be found. Treatise records range of *Nouria* as " ?Eoc., Rec." **Extant.**

Family LITUOLIDAE de Blainville 1825

First, Carb Tourn: *Ammobaculites leptos* Gutschick & Treckman (1959) and *A. pyriformis* Gutschick & Treckman (1959), Rockford Lst, Indiana (Upper Kinderhookian). **Extant.**

Comment: *Haplophragmoides* first appears in Carb Viséan of Morocco—*H. cyclamminiformis* Termier & Termier (1950) and *H. maroccana* Termier & Termier (1950).

Family TEXTULARIIDAE Ehrenberg 1838

First, Carb Tourn: *Spiroplectammina mirabilis* Lipina (1948) and *S. tchernyshinensis* Lipina (1948), Chernyshino Substage, Moscow; *S. spinosa* Lipina (1955) and *S.*(?) *angusta* Lipina (1955), Chernyshino Substage, Volga-Ural District, U.S.S.R. **Extant.**

Family TROCHAMMINIDAE Schwager 1877

First, Sil Wenl: *Trochammina ?prima* Stewart & Priddy (1941), Osgood Fm, Indiana. (Niagaran). Next record, Carb Viséan: *Trochammina anceps* Brady, *T. annularis* Brady and *T robertsoni* Brady, Yoredales, N. England and Scotland. (Brady 1876). **Extant.**

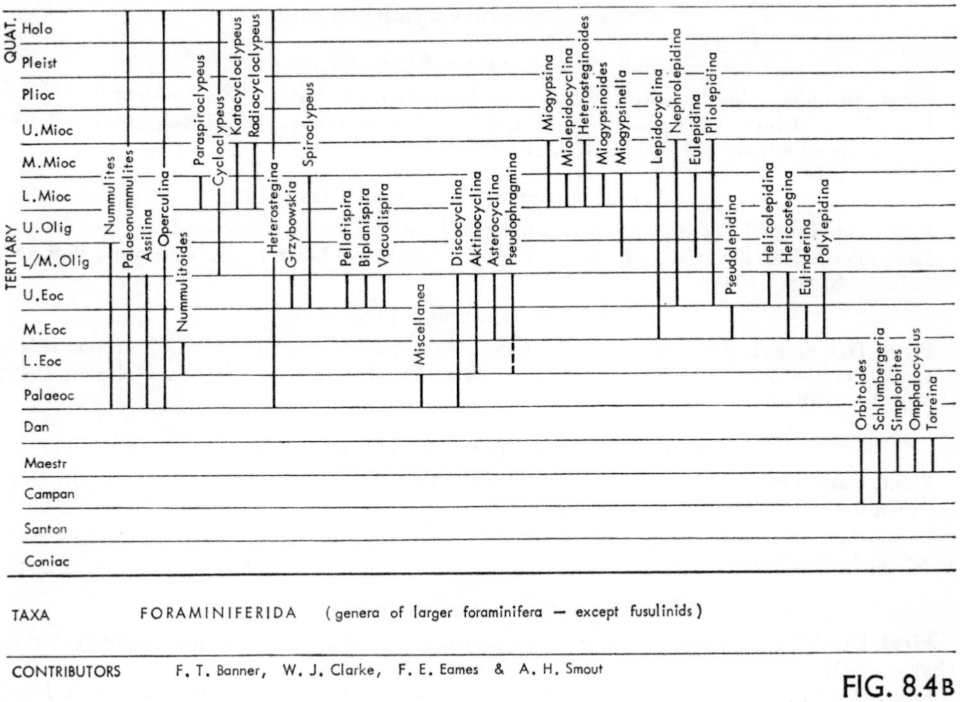

QUAT.	Holo
	Pleist
	Plioc
	U.Mioc
TERTIARY	M.Mioc
	L.Mioc
	U.Olig
	L/M.Olig
	U.Eoc
	M.Eoc
	L.Eoc
	Palaeoc
	Dan
	Maestr
	Campan
	Santon
	Coniac

Genera labels (left group): Nummulites, Palaeonummulites, Assilina, Operculina, Nummulitoides, Paraspiroclypeus, Cycloclypeus, Katacycloclypeus, Radiocycloclypeus, Spiroclypeus, Heterostegina, Grzybowskia, Pellatispira, Biplanispira, Vacuolispira, Miscellanea, Discocyclina, Aktinocyclina, Asterocyclina, Pseudophragmina

Genera labels (right group): Miogypsina, Miolepidocyclina, Heterosteginoides, Miogypsinoides, Miogypsinella, Lepidocyclina, Nephrolepidina, Eulepidina, Pliolepidina, Pseudolepidina, Helicolepidina, Helicostegina, Eulinderina, Polylepidina, Orbitoides, Schlumbergeria, Simplorbites, Omphalocyclus, Torreina

TAXA   FORAMINIFERIDA   (genera of larger foraminifera — except fusulinids)

CONTRIBUTORS   F. T. Banner, W. J. Clarke, F. E. Eames & A. H. Smout

FIG. 8.4B

Family ATAXOPHRAGMIIDAE Schwager 1877

First, Carb ?U. Carb: *Mooreinella biserialis* Cushman & Waters (1928), Strawn Fm, Texas. **Extant.** [A. J. L.]

Family PAVONITINIDAE Loeblich & Tappan 1961

First, Jur Bath: *Pfenderina* Henson 1948, *Kilianina* Pfender 1933, Arabia; *Meyendorffina* Aurouze and Bizon 1958, France (Treatise C). **Extant.** [Editor]

Family DICYCLINIDAE Loeblich & Tappan 1964

First, Jur Sinem: *Orbitulites circumvulvata* Gümbel (1872) (= *Orbitopsella praecursor*), Lower Lias, S. Tyrol.

Last, Tert M. Eoc: *Saudia discoidea* Henson (1948a), Saudi Arabia. Quoted by Henson as "Lower Eocene"; given in Treatise C as Lutetian. [A. J. L.]

Family ORBITOLINIDAE Martin 1890
(see page 320)

Suborder FUSULININA Wedekind 1937

Superfamily PARATHURAMMINACEA E. V. Bykova 1955

First, Ord: *Saccamminopsis* Sollas 1921, British Isles.

Last, Carb (U.): *Earlandia* Plummer 1930, Texas and U.S.S.R.; *Earlandinita* Cummings 1955, Penn., Texas; and *Turrispiroides* Reytlinger *in* Rauzer-Chernousova & Fursenko 1959, L. Moscov, Russian Platform.

Constituent families: Parathuramminidae E. V. Bykova 1955, Dev—Carb Tourn; Caligellidae Reytlinger 1959, Dev Frasn—Carb Tourn; and Moravamminidae Pokorný 1951, Ord—Carb (U.). (Treatise C). [Editor]

Superfamily ENDOTHYRACEA Brady 1884

Family NODOSINELLIDAE Rhumbler 1895

First, Sil Lldov: *Illigata annae* Bykova, near Zezmariai, Lithuanian SSR (Bykova 1956).
Last, Perm Dzhulf: *Pachyphloia pediculus* Lange and several other species, basin of river Laba, N. Caucasus, U.S.S.R. (Miklukho-Maklay 1954).

Family COLANIELLIDAE Fursenko 1959

First, Dev Frasn: *Multiseptida corallina* Bykova, Russian Platform (Bykova 1952).
Last, Perm Dzhulf: *Colaniella parva* (Colani), Urushton horizon, N. Caucasus, U.S.S.R. (Miklukho-Maklay 1954).

Family PTYCHOCLADIIDAE Elias 1950

First, Dev Frasn: *Tscherdyncevella acervulinoides* Antropov, Russian Platform (Antropov 1950).
Last, Perm Sakm: *Palaeonubecularia* sp. Fort Riley Lst, Kansas, U.S.A. (Johnson 1947; Reitlinger 1950).

Family PALAEOTEXTULARIIDAE Galloway 1933

First, Carb Tourn: *Palaeotextularia* sp., horizon Tn3, Campine, Belgium (Conil 1963). Also reported from late Dev (Cummings 1956).
Last, Perm Dzhulf: *Palaeotextularia sumatrensis* (Lange), Urushton horizon, N. Caucasus, U.S.S.R. (Miklukho-Maklay 1954).

Family SEMITEXTULARIIDAE Pokorný 1956

First, Dev Givet: *Semitextularia oscoliensis* Bykova, Stary Oskol beds, Voronetz region, U.S.S.R. (Bykova 1952).
Last, Dev Frasn: *Pseudopalmula palmuloides* Cushman & Stainbrook, Independence Sh, Iowa, U.S.A. (Cushman & Stainbrook 1943).

Family TETRAXIDAE Galloway 1933

First, Carb Tourn: *Tetraxis* aff. *paraminimus* Vissarionova, Assise de Celles, horizon Tn3a, Basin de Dinant, Belgium (Conil & Lys 1964).
Last, Trias Rhaet: *Tetraxis humilis* Kristan, Lower Hallstatt Nappe, Austria (Kristan 1957).

Family BISERIAMMINIDAE Chernysheva 1941

First, Carb Tourn: *Biseriammina uralica* Chernysheva, Makarov district, S. Ural, U.S.S.R. (Chernysheva 1942).
Last, Perm Dzhulf: *Globivalvulina kantharensis* Reichel, Urushten horizon, N. Caucasus, U.S.S.R. (Miklukho-Maklay 1954).

Family TOURNAYELLIDAE Dain 1953

First, Dev Givet: *Glomospiranella* sp., Russian Platform (Lipina 1963).
Last, Perm Dzhulf: *Gourisina rossica* Miklukho-Makay, Urushten horizon, N. Caucasus, U.S.S.R. (Miklukho-Maklay 1954).

Family ENDOTHYRIDAE Brady 1884

First, Dev Givet: *Rhenothyra refrathiensis* Beckmann, near Baden, Germany (Beckmann 1950).
Last, Perm Dzhulf: *Robuloides lens* Reichel, Urushten horizon, N. Caucasus, U.S.S.R. (Miklukho-Maklay 1954).

Family ARCHAEDISCIDAE Cushman 1928

First, Carb Tourn: *Brunsia* sp., Donets basin, U.S.S.R. (Aizenberg et al. 1963).
Last, Perm Dzhulf: *Permodiscus mililoides* (Miklukho-Maklay), Urushten horizon, N. Caucasus, U.S.S.R. (Miklukho-Maklay 1954).

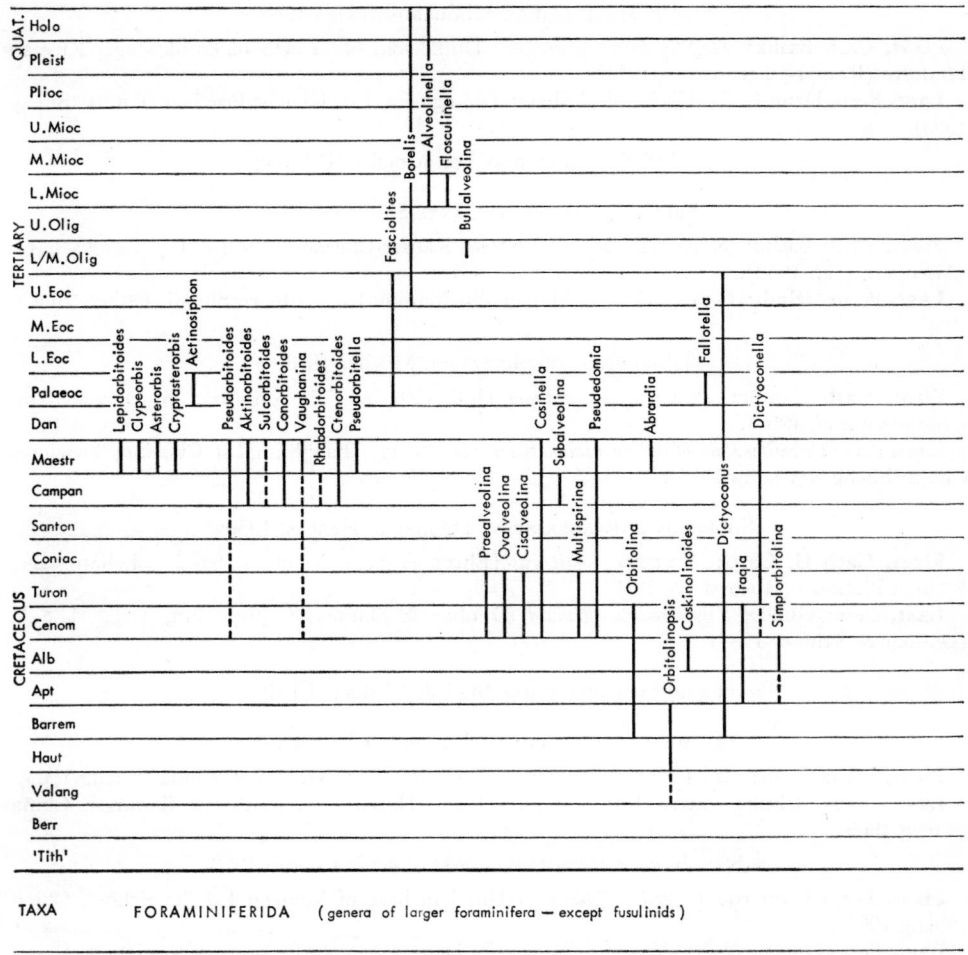

TAXA FORAMINIFERIDA (genera of larger foraminifera — except fusulinids)

CONTRIBUTORS F. T. Banner, W. J. Clarke, F. E. Eames & A. H. Smout

FIG. 8.5B

Family LASIODISCIDAE Reitlinger 1956

First, Carb Viséan: *Howchinia bradyana* (Howchin), D Z., Northumberland, England (Davis 1951).

Last, Perm Dzhulf: *Lasiodiscus minor* Reichel, Urushten horizon, N. Caucasus, U.S.S.R. (Miklukho-Maklay 1954).

Superfamily FUSULINACEA von Moeller 1878

Family OZAWAINELLIDAE Thompson & Foster 1937

First, Carb Viséan: *Eostaffella parastruvei* var. *parastruvei* Rauser-Chernousova, horizon VIb, Assise de Dinant, Belgium (Conil & Lys 1964).

Last, Perm Dzhulf: *Reichelina changhsingensis* Sheng & Chang, Changhsing Lst, Chekiang province, China (Sheng & Chang 1958).

307

Family STAFFELLIDAE Miklukho-Maklay 1949

First, Carb Bashk: *Staffella pseudosphaeroidea* Dutkevich, basal beds of Bashk stage, Russian Platform (Rauser-Chernousova 1951).

Last, Perm Dzhulf: *Nankinella minor* Sheng, Changhsing Lst, Kiangsi Province, China (Sheng 1955).

Family FUSULINIDAE von Moeller 1878

Subfamily SCHUBERTELLINAE Skinner 1931

First, Carb Bashk: *Schubertella* aff. *pauciseptata* Rauser-Chernousova, Lst H_4, Donets basin (Aisenberg *et al.* 1963).

Last, Perm Dzhulf: *Codonofusiella lui* Sheng, Wuchiaping Lst, southern Shensi, China (Sheng 1956).

Subfamily FUSULININAE von Moeller 1878

First, Carb Namur: *Pseudostaffella antiqua* Dutkevich, Lst, E_5 Namurian B, Donets basin (Aisenberg *et al.* 1963).

Last, Perm Dzhulf: *Palaeofusulina minima* Sheng & Chang, Changhsing Lst, Chekiang Province, China (Sheng & Chang 1958).

Subfamily SCHWAGERININAE Dunbar & Henbest 1930

First, Carb U. Carb: *Triticites montiparus* (Ehrenberg em. Moeller), basal Gshelian stage, Russian Platform (Rozovskaya 1958).

Last, Perm Guad: *Polydiexodina shumardi* Dunbar & Skinner, Capitan Fm, Texas, U.S.A. (Dunbar & Skinner 1937).

Family VERBEEKINIDAE Staff & Wedekind 1910

Subfamily VERBEEKININAE Staff & Wedekind 1910

First, Perm Sakm: *Misellina claudiae* (Deprat), Chihsia Lst, Kueichow, China (Sheng 1963).

Last, Perm Dzhulf: *Eoverbeekina fusuiensis* Sheng, Hoshan fm, southwest Kwangsi, China (Sheng 1963).

Subfamily NEOSCHWAGERININAE Dunbar & Condra 1928

First, Perm Leonard: *Cancellina primigena* Hayden, base of Maokou Lst, Kueichow, China (Sheng 1963).

Last, Perm Guad: *Neoschwagerina megasphaerica* Deprat, top of Maokou Lst, Kueichow, China (Sheng 1963). [J. L. C.]

Suborder MILIOLINA Delage and Hérouard 1896

Superfamily MILIOLACEA Ehrenberg 1839

Family FISCHERINIDAE Millett 1898

First, Sil Ludl: *Hemigordius lilydalensis* Chapman (1933), Yeringian Fm, Victoria, Australia. Next record, Carb Viséan: *Hemigordius morillensis* Conklin (1961) and *Agathammina mississipiana* Conklin (1961), Glen Dean Fm, Kentucky (Chesteran). **Extant.**

Family NUBECULARIIDAE Jones 1875

First, Carb Namur: *Eosigmoilina explicata* Ganelina (*in* Kiparisova *et al.* 1956), M. Carb,. Dnieper-Donetz region, U.S.S.R. **Extant.**

Family MILIOLIDAE Ehrenberg 1839

First, Jur Hett: *Spiroloculina antillarum* d'Orbigny. Bartenstein & Brand (1937), Lias alpha, N.W. Germany. **Extant.**

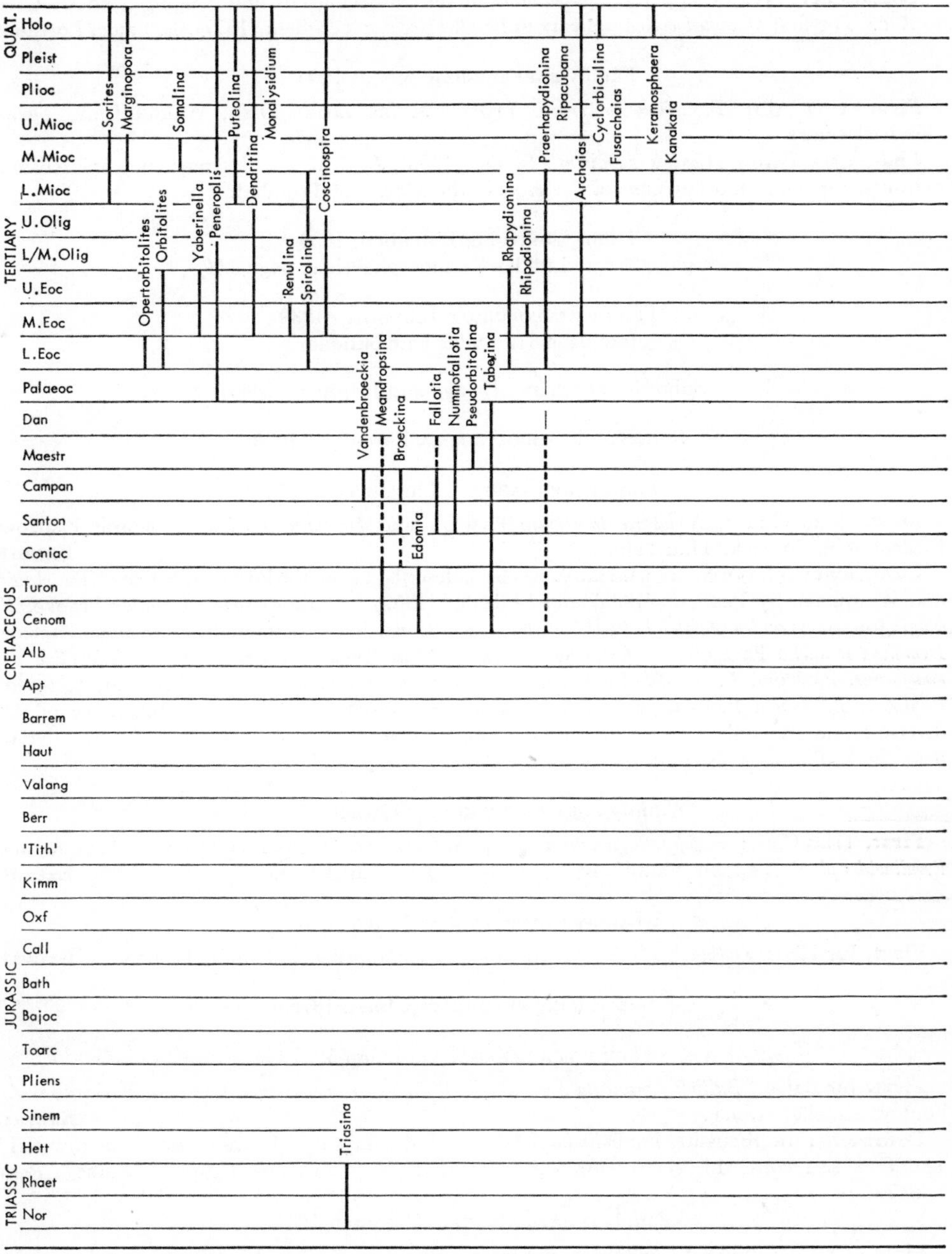

TAXA   FORAMINIFERIDA   (genera of larger foraminifera — except. fusulinids)

CONTRIBUTORS   F.T.Banner,   W.J.Clarke,   F.E.Eames & A.H.Smout

FIG. 8.6B

Comment: Treatise C places *Spiroloculina* in the Nubecularids and ranging from U. Cret. to Rec. The first *Quinqueloculina* appears to be *Q. bajociana* Terquem (1877), L. Bajoc, Lorraine.

Family BARKERINIDAE Smout 1956

First, Cret Alb: *Barkerina barkerensis* Frizzell & Schwartz (1950), Walnut Clay, Texas, (Fredricksburg).

Last, Cret Turon: *Coxites zubairensis* Smout (1956), Mishrif Lst, S. Iraq; but Frizzell and Schwartz mention an occurrence of *Barkerina* in the Maestr of Trinidad.

Family SORITIDAE Ehrenberg 1839
(see page 321 and under Keramosphaeridae page 324)

Family ALVEOLINIDAE Ehrenberg 1839
(see page 319 under Fasciolitidae)

Suborder ROTALIINA Delage and Hérouard 1896

Superfamily NODOSARIACEA Ehrenberg 1838

Family NODOSARIIDAE Ehrenberg 1838

First, Perm Guad: *Nodosaria thuringica* Paalzow and *Dentalina farcimen* (Soldani) Paalzow, L. Zechstein, Pösneck, Thuringia.   **Extant.**

Comment: A large Nodosariid fauna has been described from the lower Zechstein of Thuringia and Westphalia by Paalzow (1935) and Malzahn (1957) including *Nodosaria fallax* Franke, *N. kingi* (Jones), *N. conicodensistriata* Paalzow, *N. acicula* Reuss, *N. ovalis* Schmidt, *N. cushmani* Paalzow *Dentalina striatella* Paalzow, *D. permiana* (Jones), *D. lilli* Reuss, *D. speyeri* Geinitz, *Lingulina linguaeformis*, Paalzow, *L. spandeli* Paalzow, *L. permo-striata* Paalzow, *L. ovalis* Schmidt, *L. pulchra* Paalzow, *L. clavata* Paalzow, and *Frondicularia fischeri* Spandel. The first appearance of this diverse fauna can only be due to immigration. Treatise C records *Lingulonodosaria* Silvestri from the L. Perm. This could not be verified.

Family POLYMORPHINIDAE d'Orbigny 1839

First, Trias Carn: *Sagoplecta goniata* Tappan, *S. himatioides* Tappan, *S. incrassata* Tappan, and *Pyrulinoides plagia* Tappan, Shublik Fm, N. Alaska. (Tappan 1951).   **Extant.**

Family GLANDULINIDAE Reuss 1860

First, Jur Hett: *Oolina fusiformis* Terquem (1864), Planorbis Z., Semur, France.   **Extant.**

Superfamily BULIMINACEA Jones 1875

Family TURRILINIDAE Cushman 1927

First, Jur Bajoc: *Bulimina muricata* Terquem (1883) (= *Praebulimina muricata*), Parkinsoni Z., Fontoy, Moselle, France.   **Extant.**

Comment: In discussing *Praebulimina*, Hofker (1951a) says that Jurassic forms are "dubious" The Treatise records this genus from Bathonian and Terquem's type figure looks like a *Praebulimina*.

Family SPHAEROIDINIDAE Cushman 1927

First, Cret ?Campan: *Pullenoides senoniensis* Hofker (1951b), U. Senonian, Maastricht.
Extant.

Family BOLIVINITIDAE Cushman 1927

First, Jur Pliens: *Bolivina rhumbleri* Franke (1936), Lias gamma (L. Pliensbachian), N. Germany.   **Extant.**

Comment: The Treatise records *Brizalina* Costa from U. Trias. No record could be found.

Chapter 8: Protozoa

Family ISLANDIELLIDAE Loeblich & Tappan 1964

First, Tert Palaeoc: *Cassidulina caucasica* Subbotina (1952) (? = *Islandiella caucasica*), Velascoensis Z., N. Caucasus.   **Extant**

Comment: *Islandiella* is an external isomorph of *Cassidulina*, differing in wall structure and the presence of a tooth-plate. These characters were not mentioned in Subbotina's description.

Family EOUVIGERINIDAE Cushman 1927

First, Cret Alb: *Eouvigerina laxistoma* Loeblich & Tappan (1946), Grayson Fm, Washita, Texas.   **Extant.**

Family BULIMINIDAE Jones 1875

First, Cret ?Maestr: *Globobulimina sobrina* Galloway & Morrey (1931), "Late Cretaceous", Tabasco, Mexico.   **Extant,**

Comment: The Treatise records the oldest *Globobulimina* as Danian.

Family UVIGERINIDAE Haeckel 1894

First, Cret Turon: *Orthocerina ewaldi* Karsten (1858) (= *Orthokarsteniaewaldi*), L. Turon, New Granada, Colombia.   **Extant.**

Superfamily DISCORBACEA Ehrenberg 1838

Family DISCORBIDAE Ehrenberg 1838

First, Trias Ladin: *Diplotremina astrofimbriata* Kristan-Tollman (1960), St. Cassian Beds, South Tirol.   **Extant**

Family GLABRATELLIDAE Loeblich & Tappan 1964

First, Tert U.Eoc: *Glabratella crassa* Dorreen (1948), Omotumotu Fm, Kaiatan Stage, New Zealand.   **Extant.**

Family SIPHONINIDAE Cushman 1927

First, Tert Palaeoc: *Siphonina* (*Pulsisiphonina*) *elegans* Brotzen (1948), Zealandian, Sweden & Denmark.   **Extant.**

Family ASTERIGERINIDAE d'Orbigny 1839

First, Cret Campan: *Asterigerina* sp. Schifsma (1946), L. Hervian, Limburg, Netherlands.   **Extant.**

Comment: Indicated as first by Brotzen (1948).

Family EPISTOMARIIDAE Hofker 1954

First, Cret Santon: *Nuttallina coronula* Belford (1958), Toolonga calcilutite, U. Santon, W. Australia.   **Extant.**

Superfamily SPIRILLINACEA Reuss 1862

Family SPIRILLINIDAE Reuss 1862

First, Carb ?Viséan: *Spirillina plana* Möller (1879), "Lower Carboniferous Limestone", Province of Perm; *S. subangulata* Möller (1879), "Lower Carboniferous Limestone", Province of Tula, U.S.S.R.   **Extant.**

Comment: First occurence is at least late Viséan—*S. obduxa* Coryell & Rozanski (1942), upper Mid. Chesteran, Illnois. Next record is U. Trias—*S. gurgitata* Tappan (1951), Shublik Fm, Alaska.

Superfamily ROTALIACEA Ehrenberg 1839

Family ROTALIIDAE Ehrenberg 1839

First, Cret ?Coniac: *Rotalia* [vel *Biapertorbis*] *algeriana* Magné & Sigal (1954), L. Senonian, Algiers Province.   **Extant.**

Family CALCARINIDAE Schwager 1876

First, Cret Turon: *Siderolites heracleae* Arni (1932), U. Turon., Paphlagonia, Turkey.

Extant.

Family ELPHIDIIDAE Galloway 1933

First, Cret Maestr: *Elphidiella multiscissurata* Smout (1955), Iraq & Arabia. **Extant.**

Family NUMMULITIDAE de Blainville 1825
(see page 314 and under Pellatispiridae and Miscellaneidae page 315)

Family MIOGYPSINIDAE Vaughan 1928
(see page 316)

Superfamily GLOBIGERINACEA Carpenter, Parker & Jones 1862

First, Jur Bajoc: *Gubkinella gaurdakensis* (Balkhmatova and Morozova 1961), U. Bajoc, beds with Garantia sp., Gaurdak, Turkmenistan, U.S.S.R., (Morozova & Moskalenko 1961).

Extant.

Constituent familes: Heterohelicidae Cushman 1927, Jur Bajoc—Tert Olig; Planomalinidae Bolli, Loeblich and Tappan 1957, Cret Apt—Tert Dan; Schackoinidae Pokorný 1958, Cret Apt—Maestr; Rotaliporidae Sigal 1958, Cret Haut—Maestr; Globotruncanidae Brotzen 1942, Cret Turon—Maestr; Hantkeninidae Cushman 1927, Tert Palaeoc—extant; Globorotaliidae Cushman 1927, Tert Palaeoc—extant; and Globigerinidae Carpenter, Parker and Jones, Cret Maestr—extant (Treatise C).

Superfamily ORBITOIDACEA Schwager 1876

Family EPONIDIDAE Hofker 1951

First, Tert Palaeoc: *Pseudogloborotalia ranikotensis* Haque (1956), L. Ranikot, Salt Range, Pakistan. **Extant.**

Family AMPHISTEGINIDAE Cushman 1927

First, Tert Palaeoc: *Amphistegina schoeffleri* de Cizancourt (1951), M. Palaeoc., Barbados.

Extant.

Family CIBICIDIDAE Cushman 1927

First, Cret Haut: *Cibicides djaffaensis* Sigal (1952), Algeria. **Extant.**

Family PLANORBULINIDAE Schwager 1877

First, Tert Palaeoc: *Planorbulinella khairabadensis* Haque (1956), Ranikot, Salt Range, Pakistan.

Extant.
[A.J.L.]

Family ACERVULINIDAE Schultze 1854

First, Tert Eoc: *Gypsina* Carter 1877, cosmop. (Treatise C). **Extant.**
[Editor]

Family CYMBALOPORIDAE Cushman 1927

First, Trias Ladin: *Cymbalopora hungarica* Vadász and *C. oblonga* Vadász, Bakony, Hungary (Vadász 1911). First firm record, Cret Cenom: *Archaecyclus cenomaniana* Seguenza (1882), "Middle Cretaceous", Reggio, Italy. **Extant.**

Family HOMOTREMATIDAE Cushman 1927

First, Cret Santon: *Carpenteria conica* Belford (1960) and *C. globosa* Belford (1960), Toolonga calcilutite, W. Australia. **Extant.**

Chapter 8: Protozoa

Family ORBITOIDIDAE Schwager 1876
(see page 318 and under Lepidorbitoididae page 318)

Family DISCOCYCLINIDAE Galloway 1928
(see page 316)

Family LEPIDOCYCLINIDAE Scheffen 1932
(see page 317 and under Helicolepidinidae page 317)

Family PSEUDORBITOIDIDAE M. G. Rutten 1935
(see page 318)

Superfamily CASSIDULINACEA d'Orbigny 1839

Family PLEUROSTOMELLIDAE Reuss 1860

First, Cret Alb: *Pleurostomella obtusa* Berthelin (1880), Alb, Montcley, Doubs, France, and L. Alb, N.W. Germany (Simon & Bartenstein, 1962).   **Extant.**

Family ANNULOPATELLINIDAE Loeblich & Tappan 1964

First, Tert L. Mioc: *Annulopatellina advena* Cushman & Stainforth (1945), Fohsi Z., Cipero Fm, Trinidad.   **Extant.**

Family CAUCASINIDAE Bykova 1959

First, Cret Turon: *Virgulina tegulata* Reuss (1845) (= *Cassidella tegulata*), Plänermergel, Bohemia.   **Extant.**

Family LOXOSTOMIDAE Loeblich & Tappan 1962

First, Cret Coniac: *Loxostomum curvatum* Ehrenberg (1854) and *L. vorax* Ehrenberg (1854), Senonian, Gravesend, Kent, England.

Last, Quat Holo: *Loxostomum abruptum* Phleger & Parker (1952), Late Pleist or early Holo submarine sediments, N.W. Gulf of Mexico.

Family CASSIDULINIDAE d'Orbigny 1839

First, Cret Campan: *Cassidulina cretacea* Cushman (1931), Taylor-Navarro contact, Gulf Series, Tennessee.   **Extant.**
Comment: Wall structure unknown, may be an Islandiellid.

Family INVOLUTINIDAE Bütschli 1880

First, Trias Ladin: *Trocholina biconvexa* Oberhauser, *T. cordevolica* Oberhauser and *T. granosa* Frentzen, U. Ladin, Seelandalpe, Tirol, Austria (Oberhauser 1964).

Last, Cret Turon: *Trocholina* (*Paratrocholina*) *oscillens* Oberhauser (1956), E. Turkey, but Oberhauser (1964) states that the last representative was *Trocholina lenticularis* Henson (1948b), type from U. Cenom, Qatar.

Family NONIONIDAE Schultze 1854

First, Jur Bajoc: *Allomorphina prima* Terquem (1886), "Inferior Oolite", Warsaw. Next record, Cret Alb: *Quadrimorphina albertensis* Mellon & Wall (1956), Clearwater Fm, Alberta (M. Albian).   **Extant.**

Family ALABAMINIDAE Hofker 1951

First, Cret Coniac: *Alabamina jimrothi* Trujillo (1960), Popenoe Fm, California.   **Extant.**

Family OSANGULARIIDAE Loeblich & Tappan 1964

First, Cret Barrem: *Globorotalites bartensteini* Bettenstaedt (1952) (= *Conorotalites bartensteini*), L. Barrem, N.W. Germany.   **Extant.**

Family ANOMALINIDAE Cushman 1927

First, Trias Rhaet: *Asymmetrina biomphala* Kristan-Tollman (1960), Zlambach Beds, Hallstadt, Austria. **Extant.**

Comment: Occurs with *Involvina obliqua* Kristan-Tollmann and *Plagiostomella inflata* Kristan-Tollmann.

Superfamily ROBERTINACEA Reuss 1850

Family CERATOBULIMINIDAE Cushman 1927

First, Trias Carn: *Reinholdella helenentalensis* (Oberhauser), Reingraben Shs, Hohe Wand, Austria (Grill *et al.* 1963). **Extant.**

Family ROBERTINIDAE Reuss 1850

First, Cret Campan: *Colomia californica* Bandy (1951), Panoche Group, California. **Extant.**

[A.J.L.]

LARGER FORAMINIFERA (EXCEPT THE FUSULINIDS)

Family NUMMULITIDAE

Genus NUMMULITES
(*Ranikothalia* is regarded as a synonym)

First, Tert Palaeoc: *N. globulus*, U. Ranikot (mid-Palaeoc), Pakistan (Davies 1937).
Last, Tert L/M. Olig: *N. fichteli*, L. Nari, M. Olig, Pakistan (Nuttall 1925).

Genus PALAEONUMMULITES
(*Operculinella* and *Operculinoides* are regarded as synonyms).

First, Tert Palaeoc: *P. deserti*, L. Libyan, Egypt (Harpe 1883).

Extant: *P. cumingii*, (Carpenter 1860).

Genus ASSILINA

First, Tert Palaeoc: *A. dandotica*, U. Ranikot (mid-Palaeoc), Pakistan (Davies 1937).
Last, Tert U. Eoc: *A. exponens*, "Auversian" strata (L. Ledian), France (Boussac 1911).
Comment: Azzaroli (1958) acknowledged that *A. tudensis*, previously described by him from the U. Eoc of Somaliland, is really a *Pellatispira*.

Genus OPERCULINA

First, Tert Palaeoc: *O. canalifera*, U. Ranikot (mid-Palaeoc), Pakistan & India (Davies 1937).

Extant: *O. gaymardi*, (Cushman 1933).

Comment: Cret forms referred to the genus belong to other genera; e.g., *O. cretacea*, *O. fleuriausi* auctt., and *O. labanae* have been shown by Hofker (1962) not to belong to *Operculina*.

Genus NUMMULITOIDES

First and Last, Tert L. Eoc: *N. tessieri*, Fresco beds, Ivory Coast (Abrard 1956).

Comment: *N. torifera* from the Scotland beds of Barbados could be of L. Eoc age. *Operculina sindensis*, Palaeoc, Middle East, Pakistan and India, belongs to the same broad group, but is completely involute and probably requires a new generic name.

Genus PARASPIROCLYPEUS

First and Last, Tert L. Mioc: *P. chawneri*, Cojimar fm (fohsi fohsi Zone), Lower Burdigalian, Cuba (Palmer 1934).

Genus CYCLOCLYPEUS

First, Tert L/M. Olig: *C. koolhoveni*, "Lattorfian" marl, L. Olig, Java (Tan Sin Hok 1930).

Extant. *C. guembeliana*, (Brady 1884).

Comment: *C. mammillatus* Carter 1861, recorded as from the "Eocene" of Arabia, occurs with lepidocyclines, and is of L. Mioc age. *C. papillatus* Hadley 1934, U. Eoc, Cuba, is, from the original description, not a *Cycloclypeus*.

Genus KATACYCLOCLYPEUS

First, Tert L. Mioc: *K. annulatus*, Taurian stage, (U. Burdigalian), Papua (Australasian Petroleum Co. Prop. Ltd 1961). (*K. transiens*, uppermost 'e' Stage, Sumatra; unpublished).

Last, Tert Mioc (M. Mioc): *K. annulatus*, ?basal Ivorian stage, (?basal Vindobonian) Papua (Australasian Petroleum Prop. Co. Ltd 1961).

Genus RADIOCYCLOCLYPEUS

First, Tert L. Mioc: *R. stellatus*, "Burdigalian" strata, Borneo (Tan Sin Hok 1930).
Last, Tert M. Mioc: *R. stellatus*, "Vindobonian" strata, Java (Tan Sin Hok 1930).

Genus HETEROSTEGINA

First, Tert Palaeoc: *H.* sp., "Palaeocene" strata, U. Palaeoc, (velascoensis Zone) Somalia (Eames MS). *H. ruida* U. Libyan stage, L. Eoc, Egypt. **Extant.** *H. depressa*, (d'Orbigny 1826).

Genus GRZYBOWSKIA

First and **Last,** Tert U. Eoc: *G. multifida*, "U. Eocene" flysch, (Bartonian), Poland (Bieda 1950).

Comment: Some Aquitanian species of *Heterostegina* (e.g., *blanckenhorni*) have been suggested to belong to this genus, but they do not conform to the generic diagnosis.

Genus SPIROCLYPEUS

First, Tert U. Eoc: *S. vermicularis*, "Eocene" strata, Borneo (Tan Sin Hok 1937).
Last, Tert L. Mioc: *S. orbitoideus*, "U. Aquitanian" strata, Borneo (Douvillé 1905).

Genus SULCOPERCULINA

Comment: This genus is here tentatively referred to the Amphisteginidae. It is not regarded as properly placed in the Nummulitidae.

Family PELLATISPIRIDAE

Genus PELLATISPIRA

First and **Last,** Tert U. Eoc: *P. madarászi*, "U. Eocene" strata, Borneo (Umbgrove 1928). Also in the lower part of the *Clavulina szabói* beds of Hungary (Hantken 1875).

Genus BIPLANISPIRA

First and **Last,** Tert U. Eoc: *B. mirabilis*, Eocene? lst, Borneo (Umbgrove 1936).

Genus VACUOLISPIRA

First and **Last,** Tert U. Eoc: *V. inflata*, "Eocene" strata, Borneo (Umbgrove 1928).

Family MISCELLANEIDAE

Genus MISCELLANEA

First and **Last,** Tert Palaeoc: *M. miscella*, U. Ranikot, U. Paleoc, Pakistan & India (Davies 1937).

Comment: U. Eoc, L. Olig and middle Aquitanian records of *M.* cf. *miscella* from the Moluccas by Bursch (1947) are elphiliids belonging to some such genus as *Parrellina*.

315

The Fossil Record, Part II

Family DISCOCYCLINIDAE

Genus DISCOCYCLINA

First, Tert Palaeoc: *D. ranikotensis*, U. Ranikot, mid-Palaeoc, Pakistan (Davies 1937).
Last, Tert U. Eoc: Numerous records, e.g., *D. omphalus*, Yaw Stage (Bartonian), Burma (Cotter 1912).

Genus AKTINOCYCLINA

First, Tert L. Eoc: *A. praeradians*, "L. Eocene" strata, France (Douvillé 1922).
Last, Tert U. Eoc: *A. crassicostata*, "U. Priabonian" strata (Bartonian), Italy (Douvillé 1922).

Genus ASTEROCYCLINA

First, Tert M. Eoc: *A. stellata* (d'Archiac *non* Férussac), "Lutetian" beds, France (Treatise C, Schlumberger 1904).
Last, Tert U. Eoc: *A. georgiana*, Ocala lst, Georgia, U.S.A. (Cushman 1917).

Genus PSEUDOPHRAGMINA (s.s.)

First, Tert Eoc: *P. zaragosensis*, Claiborne/Willcox group, M./L. Eocene, Mexico (Vaughan 1929a).
Last, Tert U. Eoc: *P. floridana*, Ocala lst, Florida (Cushman 1917).

Subgenus PSEUDOPHRAGMINA (ASTEROPHRAGMINA)

First and Last, Tert U. Eoc: *P.(A). pagoda*, Yaw stage, Bartonian, Burma (Rao 1942).

Subgenus PSEUDOPHRAGMINA (ATHECOCYCLINA)

First, Tert Palaeoc: *P.(A.) macglameriae*, Midway group, Alabama (Vaughan 1945).
Last, Tert M. Eoc: *P.(A.) jukes-browni*, U. Scotland formation, Barbados (Vaughan 1945).

Subgenus PSEUDOPHRAGMINA (PROPOROCYCLINA)

First, Tert Palaeoc: *P.(P.) cedarkeysensis*, Salt Mountain lst, Florida (Cole 1944).
Last, Tert U. Eoc: *P.(P.) flintensis*, Ocala limestone, Georgia, U.S.A. (Cushman 1917).

Family MIOGYPSINIDAE

Genus MIOGYPSINA (s.s.)

First, Tert L. Mioc: *M. septentrionalis*, Lower Doberg beds (upper part of C), low Mioc ("Eochattian"), Germany (Drooger 1960).
Last, Tert M. Mioc: *M. subtilis*, Bentang series, Java (Tan Sin Hok 1937).

Subgenus MIOGYPSINA (MIOGYPSINOPSIS)

First, Tert L. Mioc: *M. (M.) gunteri*, Suwannee lst, (Aquitanian), Florida (Cole 1938).
Last, Tert L. Mioc: *M.(M.) cupulaeformis*, "L. Miocene" strata (Burdigalian), Borneo (Zuffardi-Comerci 1929).

Genus MIOLEPIDOCYCLINA

First, Tert L. Mioc: *M. mexicana*, Suwannee lst (Aquitanian), Florida (Eames *et al.* 1962).
Last, Tert L. Mioc: *M. negrii*, "Burdigalian" strata, Italy (Ferrero 1909).

Genus HETEROSTEGINOIDES

First, Tert L. Mioc: *H. panamensis*, Lower Tuffs (upper part), Aquitanian (opima Zone), Carriacou (Eames *et al.* 1962).
Last, Tert M. Mioc: *H. panamensis*, Panama fm (mayeri Zone), Panama fm (Eames *et al.* 1962).

316

Chapter 8: Protozoa

Genus MIOGYPSINOIDES

First, Tert L. Mioc: *M. dehaarti,* "L. Miocene" strata (Aquitanian), Moluccas (van der Vlerk 1924).

Last, Tert L. Mioc: *M. formosensis,* Arisan fm (Burdigalian), Japan (Yabe & Hanzawa 1928).

Genus MIOGYPSINELLA

First, Tert L/M. Olig: *M. complanata,* "M. Oligocene" strata, France (Szöts, Malmoustier & Magné 1962).

Last, Tert L. Mioc: *M. complanata,* M. Asmari lst (near top), (high Aquitanian), Persia (Eames *et al.* 1962).

Family LEPIDOCYCLINIDAE (*sensu* Hanzawa 1962)

Genus LEPIDOCYCLINA

First, Tert M. Eoc: *L. claibornensis,* Cook Mountain fm, Mississippi (Gravell & Hanna 1940).

Last, Tert L. Mioc: Numerous records, Aquitanian, e.g. *L. colei,* Heterostegina Zone, Texas (Gravell & Hanna 1937).

Comment: Records such as that of *L. epigona,* U. Mioc/Plioc, New Guinea, are to be disregarded; in this example the specimens are either derived or an f_3 limestone has been referred to the U. Mioc (cf. Leupold & van der Vlerk 1931).

Genus NEPHROLEPIDINA

First, Tert U. Eoc: *N. mauretanica minor,* "Ledian" lst, Morocco (Brönnimann 1940).

Last, Tert M. Mioc: *N. makiyamai,* Saigo mudstone (f_3 stage) (L. Vindobonian), Japan (Morishima 1949).

Genus EULEPIDINA

First, Tert L/M. Olig: *E. dilatata,* "M. Oligocene" strata, France (Douvillé 1924).

Last, Tert L. Mioc: *E. favosa,* Moneague lst member of White Lst, high Aquitanian (insueta/barisanensis Zone), Jamaica (Eames *et al.* 1962).

Genus PLIOLEPIDINA

First, Tert U. Eoc: *P. tobleri,* uppermost Eocene, Trinidad (Hanzawa 1962).

Last, Tert M. Mioc: *P. luxurians,* low "f_3" strata, low Vindobonian, Fiji Islands (personal observation).

Genus PSEUDOLEPIDINA

First and **Last,** Tert M. Eoc: *P. trimera,* "Middle Eocene" strata, low M. Eocene, Mexico (Barker & Grimsdale 1937).

Family HELICOLEPIDINIDAE (*sensu* Hanzawa, 1962)

Genus HELICOLEPIDINA

First and **Last,** Tert U. Eoc: *H. spiralis,* Pauji shs, Venezuela (Tobler 1922).

Genus HELICOSTEGINA

First, Tert M. Eoc: *H. dimorpha,* "M. Eocene (lower part)" strata, Mexico (Hanzawa 1962).
Last, Tert U. Eoc: *H. dimorpha,* "U. Eocene (upper part)" strata, Mexico (Hanzawa 1962).

Genus EULINDERINA

First and **Last,** Tert M. Eoc: *E. guayabalensis,* Guayabal fm, Mexico (Hanzawa 1962).

317

Genus POLYLEPIDINA

First, Tert M. Eoc: *P. chiapasensis subplana,* "lower M. Eocene" strata, Mexico (Barker & Grimsdale 1936).
Last, Tert U. Eoc: *P. birmanica,* Yaw stage (Bartonian), Burma (Rao 1942).

Family ORBITOIDIDAE (*sensu* Hanzawa 1962)

Genus ORBITOIDES

First, Cret Campan: *O. vredenburgi,* base of Rudist lst, Senonian (L. Campanian (?vel Maestrichtian, ed.)), Tibet (Douvillé 1916).
Last, Cret Maestr: *O. faujasi* (= *media*), "Cretaceous" strata, France (Schlumberger 1901).

Genus SCHLUMBERGERIA
(MONOLEPIDORBIS is a synonym)

First, Cret Campan: *S. douvillei,* Alveolina lst, France (Silvestri 1910).
Last, Cret Maestr: *S. beotica,* "U. Cretaceous" lst, Greece (Reichel 1949).

Genus SIMPLORBITES

First and **Last,** Cret Maestr: *S. gensacicus,* "Cretaceous" lst, France (Schlumberger 1902).

Genus OMPHALOCYCLUS

First and **Last,** Cret Maestr: *O. macropora,* "Maestrichtian" strata, France (Neumann 1958).

Genus TORREINA

First and **Last,** Cret (U.): *T. torrei,* "U. Cretaceous" strata (Hanzawa (1962) says Maestrichtian), Cuba (Palmer 1934).

Family LEPIDORBITOIDIDAE

Genus LEPIDORBITOIDES (*s.s.*)

First and **Last,** Cret Maestr: *L. socialis,* "Maestrichtian" strata, France (Schlumberger 1902).
Comment: *L. minima pembergeri,* recorded as being from Campan, Austria, may really be Maestr.

Subgenus LEPIDORBITOIDES (ORBITOCYCLINA)

First and **Last,** Cret Maestr: *L.(O.) minima,* "Cretaceous" strata, Mexico (Hanzawa 1962).

Genus CLYPEORBIS

First and **Last,** Cret Maestr: *C. mamillata,* "Cretaceous" strata, France (Schlumberger 1902).

Genus ASTERORBIS

First and **Last,** Cret Maestr: *A. rooki,* "U. Cretaceous" strata, Mississippi (Hanzawa 1962).

Genus CRYPTASTERORBIS

First and **Last,** Cret Maestr: *C. cubensis,* "U. Cretaceous" strata, Cuba (Hanzawa 1962).

Genus ACTINOSIPHON

First and **Last,** Tert Palaeoc: *A. semmesi,* Chicontepec fm, Mexico (Vaughan 1929b).

Family PSEUDORBITOIDIDAE

Genus PSEUDORBITOIDES

First, Cret Cenom-Campan: *P. trechmanni, Barrettia* beds, Jamaica (Brönnimann 1955a).
Last, Cret Maestr: *P. kozaryi,* "Maestrichtian" lst, Cuba (Brönnimann 1956).

Chapter 8: Protozoa

Genus AKTINORBITOIDES

First and **Last,** Cret Campan-Maestr: *A. browni,* "Campanian/Maestrichtian" lst, Cuba Brönnimann 1958).

Genus SULCORBITOIDES

First, Cret ?Campan: *S. pardoi,* Anacacho lst, Cuba (Brönnimann 1954a).
Last, Cret ?Maestr: *S. pardoi,* "U. Cretaceous" lst, Cuba (Brönnimann 1954a).

Genus CONORBITOIDES

First and **Last,** Cret Campan-Maestr: *C. cristalensis,* "U. Cretaceous" lst, Cuba (Brönnimann 1958).

Genus VAUGHANINA

First, Cret (U.): *V. cubensis,* "U. Cretaceous" strata, Cuba (Palmer 1934).
Last, Cret Maestr: *V. barkeri,* Mendez sh, Mexico (Brönnimann 1954b).

Genus RHABDORBITOIDES

First and **Last,** Cret ?Campan: *R. hedbergi,* Tinajita fm, Cuba (Brönnimann 1955b).

Genus CTENORBITOIDES

First and **Last,** Cret Campan-Maestr: *C. cardwelli,* "U. Cretaceous" lst, Cuba (Brönnimann 1958).

Genus PSEUDORBITELLA

First and **Last,** Cret Maestr: *P. americana,* "Maestrichtian" strata, Florida (Hanzawa 1962).

Family: FASCIOLITIDAE (= ALVEOLINIDAE)

Genus FASCIOLITES (*s.s.*)
(*Alveolina* is a synonym)

First, Tert Palaeoc: *F. vredenburgi,* Patala shs, (U. Palaeoc), W. Pakistan (Davies 1937).
Last, Tert U. Eoc: *F. elongata,* "Eocene" beds (L. Ledian), France (Hottinger 1960).

Subgenus FASCIOLITES (EOALVEOLINELLA)

First, Tert M. Eoc: *F.(E.) violae,* "M. Eocene" strata, Italy (Checchia-Rispoli 1905).
Last, Tert U. Eoc: *F. (E.) fusiformis,* "Eocene" Beloptera bed (L. Ledian), England (Adams 1962).

Subgenus FASCIOLITES (GLOMALVEOLINA)

First, Tert Palaeoc: *F.(G.) primaeva,* Miliolid lst (U. Palaeocene), Pyrenees (Reichel 1937).
Last, Tert Eoc: *F.(G.) minutula,* "L. Lutetian" strata, Europe (Hottinger 1960).

Genus BORELIS

First, Tert U. Eoc: *B. vonderschmitti,* "U. Eocene" lst (L. Ledian), Italy (Schweighauser 1952). **Extant:** *B. pygmaea schlumbergeri* (Reichel 1937).

Genus ALVEOLINELLA

First, Tert L. Mioc: *A. fennemai,* "L. Miocene" lst (f$_1$) (Burdigalian), Java (Checchia-Rispoli 1909). **Extant:** *A. quoyi* (Treatise C).

Genus FLOSCULINELLA

First, Tert L. Mioc: *F. reicheli,* e$_5$ stage (high Aquitanian). Borneo (Mohler 1949).
Last, Tert L. Mioc: *F. bontangensis,* "Burdigalian" strata, Borneo (Rutten 1913).

319

Genus BULLALVEOLINA

First and **Last,** Tert L/M. Olig: *B. bulloides,* Gaas beds (M. Olig), France (Reichel 1937).

Genus PRAEALVEOLINA (*s.s.*)

First, Cret Cenom: *P. cretacea,* "Cenomanian" strata, France (Reichel 1937).
Last, Cret Turon: *P. cretacea brevis,* "Turonian" strata, France, (Reichel 1937).
Comment: The record of *P.* sp. by Owen & Nasr (1958), Senonian, Iraq, is not believed to be authentic. The U. Alb age given by Reichel, in Treatise C, is dependent upon opinion as to where to place the Alb/Cenom boundary.

Subgenus PRAEALVEOLINA (SIMPLALVEOLINA)

First and **Last,** Cret Cenom: *P.(S.) simplex,* "Cenomanian" strata, France (Reichel 1937).

Genus OVALVEOLINA

First, Cret Cenom: *O. ovum,* "Cenomanian" strata, France (Reichel 1937).
Last, Cret Turon: *O. ovum,* "Turonian" strata, France (Reichel 1937).
Comment: The U. Alb age given by Reichel, in Treatise C, is dependent upon opinion as to where to place the Alb/Cenom boundary.

Genus CISALVEOLINA

First, Cret Cenom: *C. fallax,* "Cenomanian" lst, (U. Cenom), Iran (Reichel 1941).
Last, Cret Turon: *C. fallax,* Mishrif fm (L. Turonian), Iraq (Owen & Nasr 1958).

Genus COSINELLA

First, Cret Cenom: *C. viallii,* "Cenomanian" strata, Italy (Colalongo 1963).
Last, Cret Maestr: *C. cardenasensis,* Cardenas beds, Mexico (Colalongo 1963).

Genus SUBALVEOLINA

First and **Last,** Cret Campan: *S. dordonica,* "Campanian" lst, France (Reichel 1937).

Genus MULTISPIRINA

First, Cret Cenom: *M. iranensis,* "Cenomanian" lst, Iran (Reichel 1947).
Last, Cret Turon: *M. iranensis,* Mishrif fm, Iraq (Owen & Nasr 1958).

Genus PSEUDEDOMIA

First, Cret Cenom: *P. drorimensis,* Drorim fm, Israel (Reiss, Hamaoui & Ecker 1964).
Last, Cret Maestr: *P. multistriata,* Aruma group, Qatar (Henson 1948a).

Family ORBITOLINIDAE

Genus ORBITOLINA

(The use of this generic name for a foraminifer is not strictly in accord with the Rules—see Treatise F).
First, Cret Barrem: *O. conulus,* "U. Barremian" strata, France (Douvillé 1912).
Last, Cret Cenom: *O. concava,* "Cenomanian" strata, Middle East (Henson 1948a).
Comment: The record of *Orbitolina* by Marie & Fadre (1960), U. Jur, Spain, is very doubtful; they could be *Orbitolinopsis* of Valanginian age. The overlying beds called "Purbeckian" contain *Natica* cf. *vilanovae,* which is an Apt species.

Genus ABRARDIA

First and **Last,** Cret Maestr: *A. mosae,* Maestricht chalk, Holland (Hofker 1955).

Genus [ORBITOLINOPSIS]

(cf. Henson 1948, Moullade 1960, *non* Cushman 1940).
First, Cret ?Valang: [*O.*] *kiliani,* ?"Valanginian" strata, France (Moullade 1960).
Last, Cret Barrem: [*O.*] *kiliani,* "M. Barremian" strata, France (Moullade 1960).

Genus COSKINOLINOIDES

First and **Last,** Cret Alb: *C. adkinsi,* Walnut clay, Texas (Barker 1944).

Genus FALLOTELLA

First and **Last,** Tert Palaeoc: *F. alavensis,* 1st with *Alveolina ovulum,* Spain (Mangin 1954).

Genus DICTYOCONUS

First, Cret Barrem: *D. reicheli,* "U. Barremian" strata, Switzerland (Guillaume 1956).
Last, Tert U. Eoc: *D. puilboreauensis nannoides,* "U. Eocene" 1st, Haiti (Woodring 1924).
Comment: The L. Olig forms from Borneo being referred to this genus by Adams (MS) seem to be atypical.

Genus IRAQIA

First, Cret Apt: *I. simplex,* "L. Cretaceous" 1st, Iraq (Henson 1948a).
Last, Cret Cenom: *I. simplex,* "M. Cretaceous" 1st, Iran-Iraq (Henson 1948a).

Genus DICTYOCONELLA

First, Cret Cenom-Turon: *D. minima,* "Cretaceous" 1st (U. Cenomanian/Turonian), Qatra (Henson 1948a).
Last, Cret Maestr: *C. complanata,* "Maestrichtian" 1st, Qatar (Henson 1948a).

Genus SIMPLORBITOLINA

First, Cret Apt-Alb: *S. manasi,* "L. Cretaceous" 1st, (U. Aptian/L. Albian), Spain (Ciry & Rat 1953).
Last, Cret Alb: *S. manasi,* "L. Cretaceous" 1st (L. Albian), Spain (Ciry & Rat 1953).

Family SORITIDAE

Genus SORITES
(includes *Amphisorus*)

First, Tert L. Mioc: *S. martini,* "L. Miocene" 1st, Java (Verbeek & Fennema 1896).
Extant: *S. marginalis,* (Treatise C).

Genus MARGINOPORA

First, Tert M. Mioc: *M. vertebralis,* f$_3$ 1sts, Papua (Australasian Petroleum Co. Prop. Ltd 1961).
Extant: *M. vertebralis* Treatise C).

Genus OPERTORBITOLITES

First and **Last,** Tert L. Eoc: *O. douvillei,* Laki series, W. Pakistan (Nuttall 1925).
Comment: Lehman's (1961) record of *"Orbitolites* cf. *douvillei"* from the "Ilerdian" should be regarded as of L. Eoc, not Palaeoc, age. Henson's (1950) record of *O. douvillei* from limestones of supposed Lutetian age in S.W. Iraq may be disregarded.

Genus ORBITOLITES

First, Tert L. Eoc: *O. complanata,* Meting 1st, lower L. Eoc, W. Pakistan (Nuttall 1925).
Last, Tert U. Eoc: *O. complanata,* "U. Eocene" 1st (L. Ledian), Iraq (Henson 1950).
Comment: Supposed Palaeoc records of the genus are really of L. Eoc age.

321

Genus SOMALINA

First and **Last,** Tert M. Mioc: *S. stefaninii,* "Eocene" lst, Somalia (Silvestri 1939).
Comment: Although originally recorded as "lower Eocene", the species is really of M. Mioc age.

Genus YABERINELLA

First, Tert M. Eoc: *Y. jamaicensis,* Yellow lst, Jamaica (Vaughan 1928).
Last, Tert U. Eoc: *Y. jamaicensis,* Catadupa fm, Jamaica (Schuchert 1935).

Genus PENEROPLIS

First, Tert Palaeoc: *P.* sp. (MS). "Palaeocene" strata, E. Africa.
Extant: *P. planatus* (Treatise C).
Comment: *P. dusenburyi* is from the "?L./M. Eocene" limestone of S.W. Iraq (Henson 1950). *P. turonicus* from the Turonian of Egypt seems likely to be a *Stomatostoecha*.

Genus PUTEOLINA

First, Tert L. Mioc: *P. anahensis,* M. Asmari lst (Aquitanian), Iran (Henson 1950).
Extant: *P. protea* (Hofker 1950).

Genus DENDRITINA

First, Tert M. Eoc: *D. depressa,* "Lutetian" strata, France (Le Calvez 1952).
Extant: *D. rangi* (Fornasini 1904).

Genus MONALYSIDIUM (*sensu* Moore 1964—Treatise C)

No fossil record.
Extant: *M. sollasi* (Treatise C).

Genus RENULINA

First and **Last,** Tert M. Eoc: *R. opercularia,* "M. Eocene" strata, Grignon (Treatise C).

Genus SPIROLINA

First, Tert L. Eoc: *S. pusilla,* Libyan stage, Egypt (Schwager 1883).
Last, Tert L. Mioc: *S. arrecta,* Byram marl, Aquitanian (high ampliapertura Zone), Mississippi (Cushman 1935).
Comment: The genus, with a single aperture, may extend up to Recent.

Genus COSCINOSPIRA

First, Tert M. Eoc: *C. coryensis,* Dictyoconus cookei Zone, Florida (Cole 1941).
Extant: *C. hemprichii* (Ehrenberg 1840).

Genus TRIASINA

First and **Last,** Trias Nor-Rhaet: *T. hantkeni,* Dachstein lst, Hungary (Majzon 1954).

Genus VANDENBROECKIA

First and **Last,** Cret Campan: *V. munieri,* "Campanian" strata, France (Marie 1958a).

Genus MEANDROPSINA

First, Cret Cenom: *M. vidali,* "Cenomanian" lst, Palestine (Henson 1948a).
Last, Cret Turon-Maestr: *M. vidali,* "Senonian" strata, Spain (Schlumberger 1898).
Comment: The *anahensis* group is placed in *Puteolina*.

Genus BROECKINA

First and **Last,** Cret Campan: *B. moureti,* "Campanian" strata, France (Douvillé 1902).
Comment: *B. dufresnoyi* is given merely as "Senonian".

Chapter 8: Protozoa

Genus EDOMIA

First, Cret Cenom: *E. reicheli,* "Cenomanian" lst, Palestine (Henson 1948a).
Last, Cret Turon: *E. reicheli,* "Turonian" lst, Palestine (Henson 1948a).

Genus FALLOTIA

First, Cret Santon: *F. colomi,* "Santonian" strata, Spain (Silvestri 1940).
Last, Cret ?Maestr: *F. colomi,* "?Maestrichtian" strata, Spain (Silvestri 1940).

Genus NUMMOFALLOTIA

First, Cret Santon: *N. cretacea,* "Santonian" strata, Spain (Schlumberger 1900).
Last, Cret Maestr: *N. (?) sanctipetri,* Maestrichtian Md, Holland (Marie 1958b).

Genus PSEUDORBITOLINA

First and **Last,** Cret Maestr: *P. marthae,* "Dordonian" chalk, France (Douvillé 1910).
Comment: *P. cubensis,* Eoc, Cuba, is the type of *Eodictyoconus* which is a synonym of *Fabiania.*

Genus TABERINA

First, Cret Cenom: *T. bingistani,* "Cenomanian" lst, Palestine (Henson 1948a).
Last, Tert Dan: *T. cubana,* Cobre fm, Cuba (Keijzer 1945).

Genus [TABERINA *auctt. pars non* Keijzer]

First and **Last,** Tert Palaeoc: [*T.*] *daviesi,* "Palaeocene" strata, Iraq (Henson 1950).

Genus [TABERINA *auctt. pars non* Keijzer]

First and **Last,** Tert L. Mioc: [*T.*] *malabarica,* U. Gaj series (Burdigalian), India (Eames *et al.* 1962).
Comment: M. Mioc records of this species are really of Burdigalian age.

Genus RHAPYDIONINA

First, Tert L. Eoc: *R. limbata,* "L. Eocene" strata, Guatemala (van den Bold 1946).
Last, Tert U. Eoc: *R. urensis minima,* "Eocene" lst (Ledian), Iraq (Henson 1948a).
Comments: (1) *Haurania* we regard as a lituolid (cf. Moore *in* Treatise C). (2) *R. liburnica,* the type species, comes from the Liburnian stage of Istria, sometimes called Palaeocene, referred to the L. Eocene by Moore (Treatise C) but now believed to be M. Eocene.

Genus RHIPIDIONINA

First and **Last,** Tert M. Eoc: *R. liburnica,* Liburnian stage, Istria (Stache 1913).
Comment: See Note 2 under *Rhapydionina.*

Genus PRAERHAPYDIONINA

First, Cret (U.): *P. cubana,* Habana fm, Cuba (van Wessem 1943).
Comment: Some Eocene beds have evidently, from time to time, been included in the Habana formation; should *P. cubana* not be Cretaceous, the oldest species may be *P. huberi* from the L? Eocene of Iraq (Henson 1950).
Last, Tert L. Mioc: *P. delicata,* M. Asmari lst (Aquitanian), Iran (Eames *et al.* 1962).

Genus RIPACUBANA

No fossil record.   **Extant:** *R. conica* (Treatise C).

Genus ARCHAIAS

First, Tert M. Eoc: *A. columbiensis,* Lake City lst (early M. Eocene), Florida (Applin & Applin 1944).   **Extant:** *A. angulatus* (Treatise C).

Genus CYCLORBICULINA

No fossil record. **Extant:** *C. compressa* (Treatise C).
Comment: The L. Mioc "*Orbitolites americana*" has no coiled and reniform early stage.

Genus FUSARCHAIAS

First and **Last,** Tert L. Mioc: *F. bermudezi*, "Oligo-Miocene" strata. Cuba (Treatise C).
Comment: The genus *Praepeneroplis* is regarded as a lituolid. The genus *Craterites* does not seem to be a peneroplid.

Family KERAMOSPHAERIDAE

Genus KERAMOSPHAERA

No fossil record **Extant:** *K. murrayi* (Treatise C).
Comment: *K. irregularis*, from the L. Tongrian of Poland, is arenaceous, so cannot be a *Keramosphaera*.

Genus KANAKAIA

First and **Last,** Tert L. Mioc: *K. marianensis*, "Aquitanian" strata, Saipan (Treatise C).
[F.E.E., F.T.B., W.J.C. & A.H.S.]

REFERENCES

ABRARD, R. 1956. Une Operculine cordelée de l'Eocène inférieur de la Cote-d'Ivoire, *Operculina* (*Nummulitoides*) *tessieri* n. subgen. n.sp. *Bull. Soc. géol. Fr.* (6), **5**, 489–493.

ADAMS, C. G. 1962. *Alveolina* from the Eocene of England. *Micropaleontology*, **8**, 45–54, pls 1–3.

AISENBERG, D. E., *et al.* 1963. Stratigrafiya kamennougol'nikh otlozheniy Donetskogo Basseyna. *Trudy Inst. geol. nauk, Kiev*, ser. strat. paleont., **37.**

ANTROPOV, I. A. 1950. Novye vidy Foraminifer Verkhnego Devona nekotorykh rayonov vostoko Russkoy Platformy. *Izv. kazan. Fil. Akad. nauk SSSR* (geological sciences series) **1**, 21–33.

APPLIN, E. R. & APPLIN, E. R. 1944. Regional subsurface stratigraphy and structure of Florida and southern Georgia. *Bull. Am. Ass. Petrol. Geol.*, **28,** .

ARNI, P. 1932. Eine neue Siderolites Spezies (S. Heraclaea) (aus dem Senon von Eregli an der kleinasiatischen Schwarzmeerküste) und Versuch einer Bereinigung der Gattung. *Eclog. geol. Helv.*, **25**, 199–221, pl. 8–10.

Australian Petroleum Prop. Co. Ltd. 1961. *Geological results of petroleum exploration in Western Papua* 1937–1961.

AZZAROLI, A. 1958. L'Oligocene e il Miocene della Somalia. *Palaeontogr. ital.*, **52**, (new series **22**), 1–142, Pls 1–36.

BANDY, O. L. 1951. Upper Cretaceous foraminifera from the Carlsbad area, San Diego County, California. *J. Paleont.*, **25**, 488–513, pl. 72–75.

BARKER, R. W. 1944. Some larger foraminifera from the Lower Cretaceous of Texas. *J. Paleont.*, **18**, 204–209 & 416.

—— & GRIMSDALE, T. 1936. A contribution to the phylogeny of the orbitoidal foraminifera, with descriptions of new forms from the Eocene of Mexico. *J. Paleont.*, **10**, 231–247.

—— & —— 1937. Studies of Mexican fossil foraminifera. *Ann. Mag. nat. Hist.* (10), **19**, 161–178.

BARTENSTEIN, H. & BRAND, E. 1937. Mikropaläontologische Untersuchungen zur Stratigraphie des nordwest-deutschen Lias und Doggers. *Abh. senckenb. naturforsch. Ges.*, **439**, 1–224, pl. 1–20.

—— & —— 1951. Mikropaläontologische Untersuchungen zur Stratigraphie des nordwestdeutschen Valendis. *Abh. senckenb. naturforsch. Ges.*, **485**, 339–336, pl. 1–25.

BECKMANN, H. 1950. *Rhenothyra*, eine neue Foraminiferengattung aus dem rheinischen Mitteldevon. *Neues Jb. Geol. Paläont. Mh.*, **6**, 183–187.

Chapter 8: Protozoa

BELFORD, D. J. 1958. The genera Nuttallides Finlay 1939 and Nuttallina, n. gen., *Contr. Cushman Fdn foramin. Res.*, **9**, 93–98, pl. 18–19.

—— 1960. Upper Cretaceous foraminifera from the Toolonga Calcilutite and Gingin Chalk, Western Australia. *Bull. Bur. Miner. Resour Geol. Geophys. Aust.*, **57**, 1–198, pl. 1–35.

BERTHELIN, G. 1880. Mémoire sur les Foraminiféres de l'ètage Albien de Montcley (Doubs). *Mém. Soc. géol. Fr.* (3), **1**, 1–84, pl. 24–27.

BETTENSTAEDT, F. 1952. Stratigraphisch wichtige Foraminiferen-Arten aus dem Barrême vorwiegend nordwest-Deutschlands. *Senckenbergiana*, **33**, 263–295, pl. 1–4.

BIEDA, F. 1950. Sur quelques foraminiféres nouveaux ou peu connus du Flysch des Karpates polonaises. *Roczn. pol. Tow. geol.*, **18**, 167–179.

BOLD, W. A. VAN DEN. 1946. *Contribution to the study of ostracoda, with special reference to the Tertiary and Cretaceous microfaunas of the Caribbean region.* (Thesis of the University of Utrecht). Amsterdam.

BOUSSAC, J. 1911. Étude paléontologique sur le Nummilitique Alpin. *Mém. Serv. carte géol. dét. Fr.*, Paris.

BRADY, H. B. 1876. A monograph of Carboniferous and Permian foraminifera (the genus Fusulina excepted). *Palaeontogr. Soc.* [*Monogr.*]

—— 1884. Report on the foraminifera dredged by H.M.S. Challenger during the years 1873–76. *Challenger Expedition 1873–76, Rep., London, Zool.*, **9** (22), 1–814, pls 1–115.

BRÖNNIMANN, P. 1940. Über die tertiären Orbitoididen und Miogypsiniden von Nordwest-Marokko. *Schweiz. paläont. Abh.*, **63**, art. 1, 3–113.

—— 1954a. Upper Cretaceous orbitoidal foraminifera from Cuba Part 1—*Sulcorbitoides* n. gen., *Contr. Cushman Fdn foramin. Res.*, **5**, 55–61.

—— 1954b. Upper Cretaceous orbitoidal foraminifera from Cuba, Part II—*Vaughanina* Palmer 1934. *Contr. Cushman Fdn foramin. Res.*, **5**, 91–105.

—— 1955a. Upper Cretaceous orbitoidal foraminifera from Cuba, Part III—*Pseudorbitoides* H. Douvillé. *Contr. Cushman Fdn foramin. Res.*, **6**, 57–76.

—— 1955b. Upper Cretaceous orbitoidal foraminifera from Cuba, Part IV—*Rhaborbitoides* n. gen., *Contr. Cushman Fdn foramin. Res.*, **6**, 97–104.

—— 1956. Upper Cretaceous orbitoidal foraminifera from Cuba. Part V—*Historbitoides* n. gen., *Contr. Cushman Fdn foramin. Res.*, **7**, 60–66.

—— 1958. New Pseudorbitoididae from the Upper Cretaceous of Cuba, with remarks on encrusting foraminifera. *Micropaleontology*, **4**, 165–185, pls 1–7.

BROTZEN, F. 1934. Foraminiferen aus dem Senon Palästinas. *Z. dt. Paläst Ver.*, **57**, 28–72.

—— 1948. The Swedish Paleocene and its foraminiferal fauna. *Årsb. Sver. geol. Unders.* Series C, **42**, 1–140, pl. 1–19.

BURSCH, J. G. 1947. Mikropaläontologische Untersuchungen des Tertiär von Gross Kei (Mulukken). *Schweiz. paläont. Abh.*, **65**, art. 3, 1–69.

BYKOVA, E. V. 1952. Foraminifery Devona Russkoy Platformy i Priural'ya. *Trudy vses. nauchno-issled. geol.-razv. neft. Inst.*, **60**, 5–64.

—— 1956. [Foraminifera of the Ordovician and Silurian of the Soviet pre-Baltic]. *Trudy vses. nauchno-issled. geol.-razv. neft. Inst.*, **98**, 6–27 (Russian).

CARPENTER, W. B. 1860. Researches on the foraminifera, Part III. *Phil. Trans. R. Soc.*, **149**, 1–41.

CHAPMAN, F. 1895. On Rhaetic Foraminifera from Wedmore, in Somerset. *Ann. Mag. nat. Hist.* (6), **16**, 305–329, pl. 11–12.

—— 1923. See HOWITT, A. M. 1923.

—— 1933. Some Palaeozoic fossils from Victoria. *Proc. R. S. Vict.* (n.s.), **45**, 245–248, pl. 11.

CHECCHIA-RISPOLI, G. 1905. Sopra alcune Alveoline eoceniche della Sicilia. *Palaeontogr. ital.*, **11**, 147–167.

—— 1909. Nuova contribuzione alla conocenza delle Alveoline eoceniche della Sicilia. *Palaeontogr. ital.*, **15**, 57–70.

CHERNYSHEVA, N. E. 1941. A new genus of foraminifera from the Tournaisian deposits of the Urals. *Dokl. Akad. nauk SSSR*, **32**, 69–70.

CIRY, R. & RAT, P. 1953. Description d'un nouveau genre de foraminifère: *Simplorbitolina manasi* nov. gen., nov. sp., *Bull. Scient. Bourgogne*, **14,** 85–100.

CIZANCOURT DE, M. 1951. Grands foraminifères du Paléocène, de l'Eocène inférieur et de l'Eocène moyen du Venezuela. *Mêm. Soc. géol. Fr.* (n.s.), **30,** 1–68.

COLALONGO, M. L. 1963. *Sellialveolina vialli* n. gen., n. sp., di Alveolinide Cenomaniano dell' Appennino Meridionale. *Anali Mus. geol. Bologna* (2), **30,** 1–10, pl. 1.

COLE, W. S. 1938. Stratigraphy and micropaleontology of two deep wells in Florida. *Bull. Fla St. geol. Surv.*, **16,** 1–73, pls 1–12.

—— 1941. Stratigraphic and paleontologic studies of wells in Florida. *Bull. Fla St. geol. Surv.*, **19,** 91 pp.

—— 1944. Stratigraphic and paleontologic studies of wells in Florida, No. 3. *Bull. Fla St. geol. Surv.*, **20,** 89 pp.

CONIL, R. 1963. Interpretation micropaleontologique de quelques sondages de Campine. *Bull. Soc. belge Géol. Paléont. Hydrol.*, **72,** 123–135.

—— & LYS, M. 1964. Materiaux pour l'Etude Micropaleontologique du Dinantien de la Belgique et de la France (Avesnois). Première partie: Algues et Foraminiferes. *Mém. Inst. géol. Univ. Louvain*, **23.**

CONKLIN, J. E. 1961. Mississippian smaller foraminifera of Kentucky, southern Indiana, northern Tennessee and south-central Ohio. *Bull. Am. paleont.*, **43,** no. 196.

CORYELL, H. N. & ROZANSKI, G. 1942. Microfauna of the Glen Dean Limestone. *J. Paleont.*, **16,** 137–151, pl. 23–24.

COTTER, G. DEP. 1912. The Pegu-Eocene Succession in the Minbu District. *Rec. geol. Suv. India*, **41** (4), 221–239, pls 17–21.

CUMMINGS, R. H. 1955. Nodosinella Brady, 1876, and associated Upper Palaeozoic genera. *Micropaleontology*, **1,** 221–238, pl. 1.

—— 1956. Revision of the Upper Palaeozoic textulariid foraminifera. *Micropaleontology*, **2,** 201–242.

CUSHMAN, J. A. 1917. Orbitoid foraminifera of the genus *Orthophragmina* from Georgia and Florida. *Prof. Pap. U.S. geol. Surv.*, **108-G,** 115–118.

—— 1931. A preliminary report on the foraminifera of Tennessee. *Bull. Tenn. Div. Geol.*, **41.**

—— 1933. The foraminifera of the tropical Pacific collections of the "Albatross" 1899–1900, Part 2. *Bull. U.S. natn. Mus.*, **161,** 1–79.

—— 1935. New species of foraminifera from the Lower Oligocene of Mississippi. *Contr. Cushman Lab. foramin. Res.*, **11** (2), 25–39.

—— & STAINBROOK, M. A. 1943. Some foraminifera from the Devonian of Iowa. *Contr. Cushman Lab. foramin. Res.*, **19,** 73–79.

—— & STAINFORTH, R. M. 1945. The foraminifera of the Cipero marl formation of Trinidad, British West Indies. *Spec. Publs Cushman Lab.*, **14,** 1–74, pl. 1–16.

—— & WATERS, J. A. 1928. Some foraminifera from the Pennsylvanian and Permian of Texas. *Contr. Cushman Lab. foramin. Res.*, **4,** 31–55, pl. 4–7.

DAM, A. ten & REINHOLD, Th. 1942. Some foraminifera from the lower Liassic and lower Oolitic of the eastern Netherlands. *Geologie Mijnb.*, **4,** 8–11.

DAVIES, L. M. 1937. The Eocene Beds of the Punjab Salt Range. II. Palaeontology. *Mem. geol. Surv. India.*, *Palaeont. indica* (N.S.) **24**(1), 14–79, pls 3–7.

DAVIS, A. G. 1951. *Howchinia bradyana* (Howchin) and its distribution in the lower Carboniferous of England. *Proc. Geol. Ass.*, **62,** 248–253.

DORREEN, J. M. 1948. A foraminiferal fauna from the Kaiatan Stage (Upper Eocene) of New Zealand. *J. Paleont.*, **22,** 281–300, pl. 36–41.

DOUVILLÉ, H. 1902. Essai d'une révision des Orbitolites *Bull. Soc. géol. Fr.* (4), **2,** 239–306, pls 9–10.

—— 1905. Les foraminiféres dans le Tertiare de Bornéo. *Bull. Soc. géol. Fr.* (4), **5,** 435–464, pl. 14.

—— 1910. La Craie et le Tertiaire des environs de Royan. *Bull. Soc. géol. Fr.* (4), **10,** 51–61.

—— 1912. Les Orbitolines et leur enchaînements. *C. r. hebd. Séanc. Acad. Sci., Paris*, **155,** 567–571.

DOUVILLÉ 1916. Le Crétace et l'Eocène du Tibet Central. *Mem. geol. Surv. India, Palaeont. indica* (n.s.), **5**, 1–84, pls 1–16.

—— 1922. Revision des Orbitoides: Deuxiéme partie. Orbitoides du Danien et l'Eocene. *Bull. Soc. géol. Fr.* (4), **22**, 55–100.

—— 1924. Revision des Lépidocyclines. *Mém. Soc. géol. Fr.* (n.s.), **2**, 1–49.

DROOGER, C. W. 1960. *Miogypsina* in northwestern Germany. *Proc. K. ned. Akad. Vet.* (B), **63** (1), 38–50.

DUNBAR, C. O. and SKINNER, J. W. 1937. Permian Fusulinidae of Texas. *Bull. Univ. Texas*, **3701**, 517–825.

EAMES, F. E. *et al.* 1962. *Fundamentals of mid-Tertiary Stratigraphical Correlation*, Cambridge University Press.

EHRENBERG, C. G. 1840. Eine weiter Erlauterung des Orgamismus mehrerer in Berlin lebend beobachteter Polythalamien der Nordsee. *Abh. preuss. Akad. Wiss. Berlin*, for 1838, 18–23.

—— 1854. *Mikrogeologie*. Leipzig.

EISENACK, A. 1954. Foraminiferen aus dem baltischen Silur. *Senckenberg. leth.* **35**, 51–72, pl. 1–5.

ELLIS, B. F. & MESSINA, A. R. 1940–1966. Catalogue of Foraminifera, *Supplement* 1. American Museum of Natural History, New York.

FERRERO, L. 1909. Osservazioni sul Miocene medio nei dintorno di S. Mauro Torinese. *Boll. Soc. geol. ital.*, **28**, 131–144.

FORNASINI, C. 1904. Illustrazione di especie orbignyne di foraminifere istituite nel 1826. *Memorie R. Acead. Sci. Ist. Bologna* (6), **1**, 3–17.

FRANKE, A. 1936. Die Foraminiferen des deutschen Lias. *Abh. preuss. geol. Landesanst.*, (N.F.), **169**, 1–138, pl. 1–12.

FRIZZELL, D. L. & SCHWARTZ, E. 1950. A new lituolid foraminiferal genus from the Cretaceous with an emendation of Cribrostomoides, Cushman. *Bull. Mo. Sch. Mines. tech. ser.*, **76**, 1–12, pl. 1.

GALLOWAY, J. J. & MORREY, M. 1931. Late Cretaceous foraminifera from Tabasco, Mexico. *J. Paleont.*, **5**, 329–354, pl. 37–40.

GRAVELL, D. W. & HANNA, M. A. 1937. The *Lepidocyclina texana* horizon in the *Heterostigina* zone, Upper Oligocene of Texas and Louisiana. *J. Paleont.*, **11**, 517–529.

—— & —— 1940. New larger foraminifera from the Claibourne of Mississippi. *J. Paleont.*, **14**, 412–416.

GRILL, R., KOLIMANN, K. KÜPPER, H. & OBERHAUSER, R. 1963. Excursions-führer für das Achte Europäische Mikropaläontologische Kolloquium im Osterreich. *Verh. geol. Bundesanst.*, *Wien*, Sonderheft **F**, 1–92.

GUILLAUME, H. 1956. Une nouvelle espèce crètacée du genre *Dictyoconus* Blanckenhorn. *Eclog. geol. Helv.*, **49**, 141–147.

GÜMBEL, C. W. 1872. Ueber zwei jurassische Vorläufer des Foraminiferen-Geschlechtes Nummulina und Orbitulites. *Neues Jb. Miner. Geol. Paläont.* for 1872, pp. 241–260, pl. 6–7.

GUTSCHICK, R. C. & TRECKMAN, J. F. 1959. Arenaceous foraminifera from the Rockford limestone of northern Indiana. *J. Paleont.*, **33**, 229–250, pl. 33–37.

——, WEINER, J. L. & YOUNG, L. 1961. Lower Mississippian arenaceous foraminifera from Oklahoma, Texas and Montana. *J. Paleont.*, **35**, 1193–1221, pl. 147–150.

HANTKEN, M. VON 1875. Die Fauna der Clavulina Szaboi—Schichten; Theil 1—Foraminifera. *Mitt. Jb. K. ung. geol. Anst.*, **4**, 1–93.

HANZAWA, S. 1962. Upper Cretaceous and Tertiary three-layered larger foraminifera and their allied forms. *Micropaleontology*, **8**, 129–186, pls 1–8.

HAQUE, A. F. M. M. 1956. The smaller foraminifera of the Ranikot and the Laki of the Nammal Gorge, Salt Range. *Mem. geol. Surv., Pakist.* **1**, 1–300, pl. 1–34.

HARPE, P. DE LA 1883. Monographie der in Aegypten und der Libyschen Wüste vorkommenden Nummuliten. *Palaeontographica*, **30**, 155–218.

HENSON, F. R. S. 1948a. *Larger imperforate foraminifera from south-western Asia*, 127 pp., London, British Museum (Natural History).

HENSON, F. R. S. 1948b. Foraminifera of the genus Trocholina in the Middle East. *Ann. Mag. nat. Hist.* (11), **14**, 445–459, pl. 11–13.

—— 1950. *Middle Eastern Tertiary Peneroplidae (foraminifera), with remarks on the phylogeny and taxonomy of the family*, 70 pp. (Doctoral dissertation, Univ. Leiden). Wakefield, England, West Yorkshire Printing Co.

HOFKER, J. 1950. Recent Peneroplidae, Part I. *J. R. microsc. Soc. Lond.* (3), **70**, 388–396.

—— 1951a. The foraminifera of the Siboga Expedition; Part III. *Siboga Exped.*, Monograph 4b.

—— 1951b. On foraminifera from the Dutch Cretaceous. *Natuurh. Genoot. Limburg.* **4**, 1–40.

—— 1955. Foraminifera from the Cretaceous of southern Limburg, Netherlands, IX—*Dictyoconus mosae* nov. spec., *Natuurh. Maandbl.*, **44** (11–12), 115–117.

—— 1962. Foraminifera from the Cretaceous of south-Limburg, LX. *Natuurh. Maandbl.*, **51**(6), 79–82.

HOTTINGER, L. 1960. Über paläocene und eocäne Alveolinen. *Eclog. geol. Helv.*, **53**, 265–284, pls 1–21.

HOWELL, B. F. & DUNN, P. H. 1942. Early Cambrian "foraminifera". *J. Paleont.*, **16**, 638–639, pl. 91.

HOWITT, A. M. 1923. Phosphate deposits in the Mansfield district: Appendix 1; Report on fossils from an Upper Cambrian horizon at Loyola, near Mansfield. *Bull. geol. Surv. Vict.*, **46**, 1–46, pl. 1–14.

IRELAND, H. A. 1939. Devonian and Silurian foraminifera from Oklahoma. *J. Paleont.*, **13**, 190–202.

JOHNSON, J. H. 1947. *Nubecularia* from the Pennsylvanian and Permian of Kansas. *J. Paleont.*, **21**, 41–45.

KARSTEN, H. 1858. Über die geognostischen Verhältnisse des westlichen Colombien, der heutigen Republiken Neu-Granada und Equador. *Amtl. Ber. Versamml. dt. Naturf. Ärzte*, **32**, 80–117, pl. 1–6.

KEIJZER, F. G. 1945. Outline of the geology of the eastern part of the Province of Oriente, Cuba (E of 76° W.L.), with notes on the geology of other parts of the island. *Geogr. geol. Meded.* (2), No. 6, 238 pp.

KIPARISOVA, L. D., MARKOVSKY, B. P. & RADCHENKO, G. P. 1956. Materially po paleontologii, novye semeystva i rody. *Mater. vses. nauchno-issled. geol. Inst.* (n.s.), **12**, Paleont., 1–354, pl. 1–43.

KRISTAN, E. 1957. Opthalmidiidae und Tetraxinae (Foraminifera) aus dem Rhät der Hohen Wand in Nieder-Osterreich. *Jb. geol. Bundesanst.*, *Wien*, **100**, 269–298.

KRISTAN-TOLIMANN, E. 1960. Rotaliidea (Foraminifera) aus der Trias der Ostalpen. *Jb. geol. Bundesanst*, *Wien*, Sonderband **5**, 47–78, pl. 7–21.

LE CALVEZ, Y. 1952. Revision des foraminifères lutétiens du Bassin de Paris. IV. Valvulinidae, Peneroplidae, Ophthalmidiidae, Lagenidae. *Mém. Serv. carte géol. dét. Fr.*, IV, 9–64, pls 1–4.

LEHMAN, R. 1961. Strukturanalyse einiger Gattungen der Subfamilie Orbitolitinae. *Eclog. geol. Helv.*, **54**, 597–667.

LEUPOLD, W. & VELRK, I. M. VAN DER. 1931. Stratigraphie van Nederlandsch Oost-Indië. *Leid. geol. Meded.*, **5**, 611–648.

LIPINA, O. A. 1948. [Foraminifera of the Chernyshino series of the Tournaisian stage of the Lower Carboniferous near Moscow] in Rausser-Chernoussova *et al.*, *Trudy Inst. geol. Nauk. Mosk.*, **62**, 251–259, pl. 19–20 (Russian).

—— 1955. [Foraminifera of the Tournaisian and Upper Devonian of the Volga-Ural region and the Western slopes of the Middle Urals] *Trudy Akad. nauk SSSR*, **163**, 1–96, pl. 1–13 (Russian).

—— 1963. Ob etapnosti razvitiya Tourneyskikh foraminifer. *Vop. Mikropaleont.*, **7**, 13–21.

LOEBLICH, A. R. JUN. & TAPPAN, H. 1946. New Washita foraminifera. *J. Paleont.*, **20**, 238–258, pl. 35–36.

MAGNÉ, J. & SIGAL, J. 1954. Description des espèces nouvelles; 1—Foraminiferes *in* CHEYLAN, G., MAGNÉ, J., SIGAL, J. & GREKOFF, N. Resultats géologiques et micropaleontologiques du sondage d'El Krachem (Hauts Plateaux algérois). *Bull. Soc. géol. Fr.* (6), **3**, 471–491.

Chapter 8: Protozoa

MAJZON, L. 1954. Contributions to the stratigraphy of the Dachstein limestone. *Acta geol. hung.*, **2**, 243–249, pl. 1–3.

MALZAHN, E. 1957. Neue Fossilfunde und vertikale Verbreitung der niederrheinischen Zechsteinfauna in der Bohrungen Kamp 4 und Friedrich Heinrich 57, bei Kamp-Lintfort. *Geol. Jb.*, **76**, 91–126.

MANGIN, J. P. 1954. Description d'un nouveau genre de foraminifere: *Fallotella alavensis*. *Bull. scient. Bourgogne*, **14**, 209–219.

MARIE, P. 1958a. Peneroplidae du Cretace superieur a facies recifal; 1—A propos des genres *Broe[c]kina* et *Praesorites et* sur le nouveau genre *Vanderbroe[c]kia*. *Revue Micropaléont.*, **1**, 125–139.

—— 1958b. *Goupillaudina*, nouveau genre de Foraminifere du Crétacé superieur. *Bull. Soc. géol. Fr.* (6), **7**, 861–876.

—— & FABRE, J.-C. 1963. Presence of true Orbitolines in the Upper Jurassic of the Cantavieja region (Teruel Province, Spain). *C.r. hebd. Séanc. Acad. Sci., Paris*, **257**, 3006–3007.

MARTIN, K. 1880. *Die Tertiärschichten auf Java*, **3**, Pal. Theil.

MELLON, G. B. & WALL, J. H. 1956. Geology on the McMurray formation; Part 1—Foraminifera of the upper McMurray and basal Clearwater formations. *Rep. Res. Coun. Alberta*, **72**.

MIKLUKHO-MAKLAY, K. V. 1954. *Foraminifery verkhnepermskikh otlozheniy Severogo Kavkaza.* Vses. naucho-issled. geol. Inst. (VSEGEI), Moscow.

MILLER, H. W. JR. 1956. The index value of Silurian foraminifera and some new forms from wells in Kansas. *J. Paleont.*, **30**, 1350–1359.

MOHLER, W. A. 1949. *Flosculinella reicheli* n.sp. aus dem Tertiär e₅ von Borneo. *Verh. schweiz. naturf. Ges.*, **129**, 151.

MÖLLER, V. VON. 1879. Die Foraminiferen des Russisches Kohlenkalks. *Zap. imp. Akad. nauk* (7), **27**, 1–131, pl. 1–7.

MOREMAN, W. L. 1930. Arenaceous foraminifera from Ordovician and Silurian limestones of Oklahoma. *J. Paleont.*, **4**, 42–59, pl. 5–7.

MORISHIMA, M. 1949. A new Miocene Lepidocyclina from Shizuoka Prefecture, Japan. *J. Paleont*, **23**, 210–213.

MOROZOVA, V. G. & MOSKALENKO, T. A. 1961. Planktonye foraminifery pogranichnykh otlozhenyi bayosskogo i batskogo yarusov tsentralnogo Dagestana (severo-vostochnyy Karkaz). *Vop. Mikropaleont.*, no. 5, 3–30.

MOULLADE, M. 1960. Les Orbitolinidae des Microfaciès Barrémiens de la Drôme. *Revue Micropaléont.*, **3**, 188–198, pls 1–3.

NAUSS, A. W. 1947. Cretaceous microfossils of the Vermilion area, Alberta. *J. Paleont.*, **21**, 329–343, pl. 48–49.

NEUMANN, N. 1958. Révision des *Orbitoides* du Crétacè et l'Écoene en Aquitaine occidentale. *Mém. Soc. géol. Fr.* (N.S.), **37** (2–3), mem. 83, 174 pp, 36 pls.

NUTTALL, W. L. F. 1925. Indian reticulate Nummulites. *Ann Mag. nat. Hist.* (9), **15**, 661–667.

OBERHAUSER, R. 1956. Neue mesozoische Foraminiferen aus der Türkei. *Mitt. geol. Ges., Wien*, **48**, 193–200, pl. 1.

—— 1957. Ein Vorkommen von Trocholina und Paratrocholina in der Trias des Helenentales bei Baden. *Jb. Geol. Bundesanst., Wien*, **100**, 257–267.

—— 1964. Zur Kenntnis der Foraminiferengattungen Permodiscus, Trocholina und Triasina in der alpinen Trias und ihrer Einordnung zu den Archaediscien. *Verh. geol. Bundesanst., Wien*, **2**, 196–210, pl. 1–4.

——, KRISTAN-TOLIMANN, E., KOLLMANN, K. & KLAUS, W. 1960. Beiträge zur Mikropaläontologie der alpinen Trias. *Jb. geol. Bundesanst., Wien*, Sonderband **5**.

ORBIGNY, A. D. 1826. Tableau méthodique de la class de Céphalopodes. *Annls Sci. nat.* (1), **7**, 96–314.

OWEN, R. M. S. & NASR, S. N. 1958. *Habitat of Oil.* American Association of Petroleum Geologists.

PAALZOW, R. 1935. Die Foraminiferen im Zechstein des östlichen Thüringen. *Jb. preuss. geol. Landesanst.*, **56**, 26–45, pl. 4–5.

329

PALMER, D. K. 1934. Some large fossil foraminifera from Cuba. *Memorias Soc. Cubana Hist. nat.*, **8**, 235–264, pls 12–16.

PHLEGER, F. B. & PARKER, F. L. 1951. Ecology of foraminifera, northwest Gulf of Mexico; Part II—Foraminifera species. *Mem. geol. Soc. Am.*, **46**, 1–64 pp., 20 pls.

RAINWATER, 1960. Stratigraphy and its role in the future exploration for oil and gas in the Gulf Coast. *Tr. Gulf Coast Geol. Soc.*, **10**, 33–75.

RAO, S. R. N. 1942. On *Lepidocyclina (Polylepidina) birmanica* sp. nov. and *Pseudophragmina (Asterophragmina) pagoda* s. gen. nov. et sp. nov., from the Yaw stage (Priabonian) of Burma. *Rec. geol. Surv. India*, **77**, no. 12, 1–16.

RAUSER-CHERNOUSOVA, D. M. *et al.* 1951. *Srednekamennougol'nikh fuzulinidi Russkoy platformi i sopredel'nikh oblastey.* Akademii Nauk, SSSR, Moskva.

REICHEL, M. 1937. Étude sur les Alvéolines; Second fascicule. *Abh. schweiz. paläont. Ges.*, **59**, 95–147.

—— 1941. Sur un nouveau genre d'alvéolines du Crétacé supérieur. *Eclog. geol Helv.*, **34**, 254–260.

—— 1947. *Multispirina iranensis* n. gen. n. sp., foraminifere nouveau du Cretace superieur de l'Iran. *Abh. schweiz. paläont. Ges.*, **65**, no. 6, 1–13.

—— 1949. Sur un nouvel orbitoidé du Crétacé supérieur hellénique. *Verh. schweiz. naturf. Ges.*, **129**, 140.

REISS, Z., HAMAOUI, M. & ECKER, A. 1964. *Pseudedomia* from Israel. *Micropaleontology*, **10**, 431–437, pls 1–2.

REITLINGER, E. A. 1950. Foraminifery srednekamennougol'nikh otlozheniy tsentralnoy chasti Russkoy Platformy (isklyuchaya semeystvo Fusulinidae). *Trudȳ geol. Inst. Akad. Nauk SSSR*, **126**.

ROZOVSKAYA, S. E. 1958. Fusulinidi i biostratigraficheskoi raschlenie verkhnekamennougol'nikh otlozheniy Samarskoy Luki. *Trudȳ geol. inst.*, Leningr., **13**, 57–120.

REUSS, A. E. 1845. *Die Versteinerungen der böhmischen Kreideformation.* Stuttgart.

RUEDEMANN, R. & SCHROCK, R. R. 1939. A new Wisconsin Upper Cambrian foraminifer. *Am. J. Sci.*, 237, 66–71.

RUTTEN, L. 1913. Studien über Foraminiferen aus Öst-Asien: Zweiter Theil. *Samml. geol. Reichsmus. Leiden.* (1), **9**, 219–224.

SCHIFSMA, E. 1946. The Foraminifera from the Hervian (Campanian) of southern Limburg, Netherlands. *Medes. geol. Sticht.* C, **5**, 1–174.

SCHLUMBERGER, C. 1898. Note sur le genre *Meandropsina*. Mun.-Chalm., n.g., *Bull. Soc. géol. Fr.* (3), **26**, 336–339.

—— 1900. Note sur quelque foraminifères nouveaux ou peu connus du Crétacé d'Espagne. *Bull. Soc. géol. Fr.* (3), **27**, 456–465.

—— 1901. Premiere note sur les Orbitoides. *Bull. Soc. géol. Fr.* (4), **1**, 459–467.

—— 1902. Deuxieme note sur les Orbitoides. *Bull. Soc. géol. Fr.* (4), **2**, 255–261.

—— 1904. Quatrieme note sur les Orbitoides. *Bull. Soc. géol. Fr.* (4) **4**, 119–135.

SCHUCHERT, C. 1935. *Historical Geology of the Antillean-Caribbean Region.*

SCHWAGER, C. 1883. Die Foraminiferen aus den Eocaenablagerungen der libyschen Wüste und Aegyptens. *Palaeontographica*, **30**, 79–153.

SCHWEIGHAUSER, J. 1962. Ein Vorkommen von Neoalveolina aus dem vicentinischen Obereocäen. *Eclog. geol. Helv.*, **44**, 465–469.

SEGUENZA, G. 1882. Studi geologici e paleontologici sul Cretaceo medio dell'Italia meridionale. *Atti Accad. naz. Lincei Memoire* (3), **12**, 65–214, pl. 1–21.

SHENG, J. 1955. Some fusulinids from the Changhsing Limestone. *Acta palaeont. sin.*, **3**, 287–308.

—— 1956. Permian Fusulinids from Liangshan, Hanchung, southern Shensi. *Acta palaeont. sin.*, **4**, 175–227.

—— 1963. Permian fusulinids from Kwangsi, Kueichow and Szechuan. *Palaeont. sin.* (n.s.), **10**, no. 149.

—— & CHANG, L. H. 1958. Fusulinids from the type locality of the Changhsing Limestone. *Acta Palaeont. sin.*, **6**, 205–214.

SIGAL, J. 1952. Aperçu stratigraphique sur la micropaléontologique du Crétacé. *19th Int. geol. Congr.*, Reg. Monograph. Ser. 1, no. 26, 1–47.

SILVESTRI, A. 1910. Lepidocicline sannoisiane di Antonimina in Calabria. *Memorie Accad. pont. Nouvi Lincei.*, **28**, 103–163.

—— 1939. Foraminiferi dell'Eocene della Somalia; Parte II. *in* Paleontologia della Somalia; IV—Fossil dell'Eocene. *Paleontogr. ital.*, **32**, suppl. 4, 1–102.

—— 1940. Illustrazione di specie caratteristica del Cretaceo superior. *Boll. Soc. geol. ital.*, **58**, 225–234, pl. 12.

SIMON, W. & BARTENSTEIN, H. 1962. *Leitfossilien der Mikropaläontologie.* Berlin-Nikolassee.

SMOUT, A. H. 1955. Reclassification of the Rotaliidae (foraminifera) and two new Cretaceous forms resembling Elphidium. *J. Wash. Acad. Sci.*, **45**, 201–210.

—— 1956. Three new Cretaceous genera of foraminifera related to the Ceratobuliminids. *Micropaleontology*, **2**, 335–348, pl. 1–2.

STACHE, G. 1913. Ueber *Rhipidionina* St. und *Rhapydionina* St., *Jb. geol. Reichsanst., Wein*, **62**, 659–680.

STEWART, G. A. & PRIDDY, R. R. 1941. Arenaceous foraminifera from the Niagaran rocks of Ohio and Indiana. *J. Paleont.*, **15**, 366–375, pl. 54.

SUBBOTINA, N. N. 1952. in: VOLOSHINOVA, N. A. *et al.*, Fossil foraminifera of the U.S.S.R. (Cassidulinidae). *Vsesoyuz. Nauch.-Issled. Geol.-Razved. Inst.*, vyp. 63.

SZÖTS, E., MALMOUSTIER, G. & MAGNÉ, J. 1962. *Colloque sur le Paléogène*, Bordeaux, September 1962.

TAN SIN HOK. 1930. Over *Cycloclypeus;* vooloopige resultaten einer biostratigraphische studie. *Mijningenieur* (Java), **11**, 180–184.

—— 1937. On the genus *Spiroclypeus* H. Douvillé with a description of the Eocene *Spiroclypeus vermicularis* nov. sp. from Koetai in east Borneo. *Ing. Ned.-Indie*, **4**(10), part 4, 177–193.

TAPPAN, H. 1951. Foraminifera from the Arctic slope of Alaska; General introduction and Part 1, Triassic foraminifera. *Prof. Pap. U.S. geol. Surv.*, **236-A**, 1–20, pl. 1–5.

TERQUEM, O. 1864. Troisième mémoire sur les foraminifères du Lias des départments de la Moselle, de la Côte-d'Or, du Rhône, de la Vienne et du Calvados. *Mém. Acad. Imp. Metz.* (2), **44**, 361–438, pl. 7–10.

—— 1877. Récherches sur les foraminifères du Bajocien de la Moselle. *Bull. Soc. géol. Fr.* (3), **4**, 477–500.

—— 1883. *Cinquième mémoire sur les foraminifères du système Oolithique de la zone à* Ammonites parkinsoni *de Fontoy (Moselle)*. Metz.

—— 1886. Les foraminifères et les ostracodes du Fuller's Earth des environs de Varsovie. *Mém. Soc. géol. Fr.* (3), **4**, no. 2.

TOBLER, A. 1922. *Helicolepidina*, ein neues subgenus von *Lepidocyclina. Eclog. geol. Helv.*, **17**, 380–384.

TREATISE, C. 1964. LOEBLICH, A. R. & TAPPAN, H. Protista 2: Sarcondina Chiefly "Thecamoebians" and Foraminiferida (2 volumes) *in* MOORE, R. C. (Editor) *Treatise on Invertebrate Paleontology*, Part C. University of Kansas Press.

TREATISE, F. 1956. BAYER, F. M. *et al.* Coelenterata *in* MOORE, R. C. (Editor) *Treatise on Invertebrate Paleontology*, Part F. University of Kansas Press.

TRUJILLO, E. F. 1960. Upper Cretaceous foraminifera from near Redding, Shasta County, California. *J. Paleont.*, **34**, 290–346, pl. 43–50.

UMBGROVE, J. H. F. 1928. Het genus *Pellatispira* in het indo-pacifische gebied. *Wet. Meded. Dienst. Mijnb. Ned. Oost-Indië*, **10**, 43–71.

—— 1936. *Heterospira*, a new foraminiferal genus from the Tertiary of Borneo. *Leid. geol. Meded.*, **8**, 155–157, pl. 1.

VADÁSZ, M. E. 1911. Triasforaminiferen aus dem Bakony. *Result. wiss. Erforsch. Balatonsees Paläont.*, **1** (1), 1–44, pl. 1–2.

VAUGHAN, T. W. 1928. *Yaberinella jamaiconsis*, a new genus and species of arenaceous foraminifera. *J. Paleont.*, **2**, 7–12, pls 4–5.

—— 1929a. Description of new species of foraminifera of the genus *Discocyclina* from the Eocene of Mexico. *Proc. U.S. natn. Mus.*, **76**, art. 3, 1–18, pls 1–7.

—— 1929b. *Actinosiphon semmesi*, a new genus and species of orbitoidal foraminifera, and *Pseudorbitoides trechmanni* H. Douvillé.—*J. Paleont.* **3,** 163–169, pl. 21.

—— 1945. American Paleocene and Eocene larger foraminifera. *Mem. geol. Soc. Amer.*, **9** (1), 1–175.

VERBEEK, R. D. M. & FENNEMA, R. 1896. *Description geologique de Java et Madoura*, Volume 2. Amsterdam, Stemler.

VLERK, I. M. VAN DER. 1924. *Miogypsina dehaartii* nov. species de Larat (Moluques). *Eclog. geol. Helv.*, **18,** 429–432.

WESSEM, A. VAN. 1943. Geology and paleontology of central Camaguey, Cuba. *Geogr. geol. Meded.* (2), no. 5, 1–91.

WOODRING, W. P. 1924. Some new Eocene foraminifera of the genus *Dictyoconus*. in WOODRING, W. P., BROWN, J. S. & BURBANK W. S. *Geology of the Republic of Haiti.* Port-au-Prince, Geological Survey, Republic of Haiti.

YABE, H. & HANZAWA, S. 1928. Tertiary foraminiferous rock of Taiwan (Formosa). *Proc. imp. Acad. Japan*, **4,** 533–536.

ZUFFARDI-COMERCI, R. 1929. Di alcuni foraminiferi tertiari dell'Isola de Borneo. *Boll. Soc. geol. ital.*, **47,** 127–148.

F. T. BANNER, PH.D.
   Department of Geology, University College of Swansea, Singleton Park, Swansea.
W. J. CLARKE, PH.D.
   B.P. Research Centre, Chertsey Road, Sunbury-on-Thames, Middlesex.
J. L. CUTBILL, M.A. PH.D F.G.S.
   Department of Geology, Sedgwick Museum, Downing Street, Cambridge.
F. E. EAMES, D.SC. A.R.C.S. F.G.S.
   B.P. Research Centre, Chertsey Road, Sunbury-on-Thames, Middlesex.
A. J. LLOYD, PH.D. F.G.S.
   Department of Geology, University College, Gower Street, London W C 1.
W. R. RIEDEL, M.SC.
   Scripps Institution of Oceanography, La Jolla, California 92037, U.S.A.
A. H. SMOUT, PH.D. F.G.S.
   B.P. Research Centre, Chertsey Road, Sunbury-on-Thames, Middlesex.

CHAPTER 9

Porifera and Archaeocyatha

Contributors: R. M. FINKS & D. HILL

Phylum PORIFERA Grant 1836

Introduction. The first fossil remains definitely referable to sponges are hexactinellid stauractin spicules and heteractinid octactin spicules, both known from L.Camb strata. Spicules, or spicule-like objects, have been reported from Precambrian rocks (viz., Treatise E, 33 and Doubinger and Eller, 1963) but they cannot be referred with certainty to sponges, to the exclusion of some other spicule-producing organism. The Camb sponge fauna is not very diversified. Beginning in the middle Camb (Burgess shale) the record of the demosponges commences with sponges bearing simple monaxons. They are followed probably in the upper Camb and certainly in the Arenigian by the first lithistids, namely orchocladines, whose dendroclones are derivable from simple monaxons. The earliest rhizomorine lithistids, whose spicules are also monaxonic, may be present at this time. The orchocladine lithistids expand rather suddenly in Ord Llvirn to Ord Carad, totalling some 30 genera, and constituting the first major expansion of the sponges. Reefs in the Chazy beds of North America were built partly by sponges during this time, along with the bryozoans, corals and stromatoporoids which subsequently tended to exclude the sponges from middle Palaeozoic reefs. The lithistids undergo a contraction following Silurian times, whilst the hexactinellids (some 40 genera) tend to dominate in the late Dev and early Carb. During the Carb most of the lithistid demosponge orders that will dominate the Mesozoic and Cenozoic have appeared.

The Class Heteractinida attain a modest climax of some 10 genera in Carb time, concluding their career shortly thereafter in Perm Leonard. The Class Calcarea is the last of the sponge classes to appear. The first of the modern calcareous sponges, the pharetrones, appear in Perm Sakm, but they are preceded by the aberrant sphinctozoans which enter the record in mid-Carb, possibly stemming from the Camb Archaeocyatha through the Sil Aphrosalpingoidea. It is the Sphinctozoa which dominate the sponge faunas of the Perm and Trias and indeed form reefs during this time, a time which coincides with the decline and extinction of the Palaeozoic corals and precedes the rise of the Mesozoic and later scleractinians.

The Perm extinction affected the Porifera. The dominant taxa of Palaeozoic sponges (dictyospongid hexactinellids, orchocladine and eutaxicladine lithistids and heteractinids) became extinct by the close of the Perm. However, most of the sponges which dominate the Mesozoic had originated during Carb or Perm times. The only exceptions to this statement are the hexactinosa and lychniscosa among the Class Hexactinellida, which do not appear until the middle Triassic, although hexactinosan structure is foreshadowed in Palaeozoic hexactinellids.

The all-time heyday of sponges was undoubtedly during the Cret. This is not an artifact of preservation, for it is shown by several groups which are readily preserved owing to their coherent

The Fossil Record, pp. 333–345. Geological Society of London, 1967. Printed in Northern Ireland.

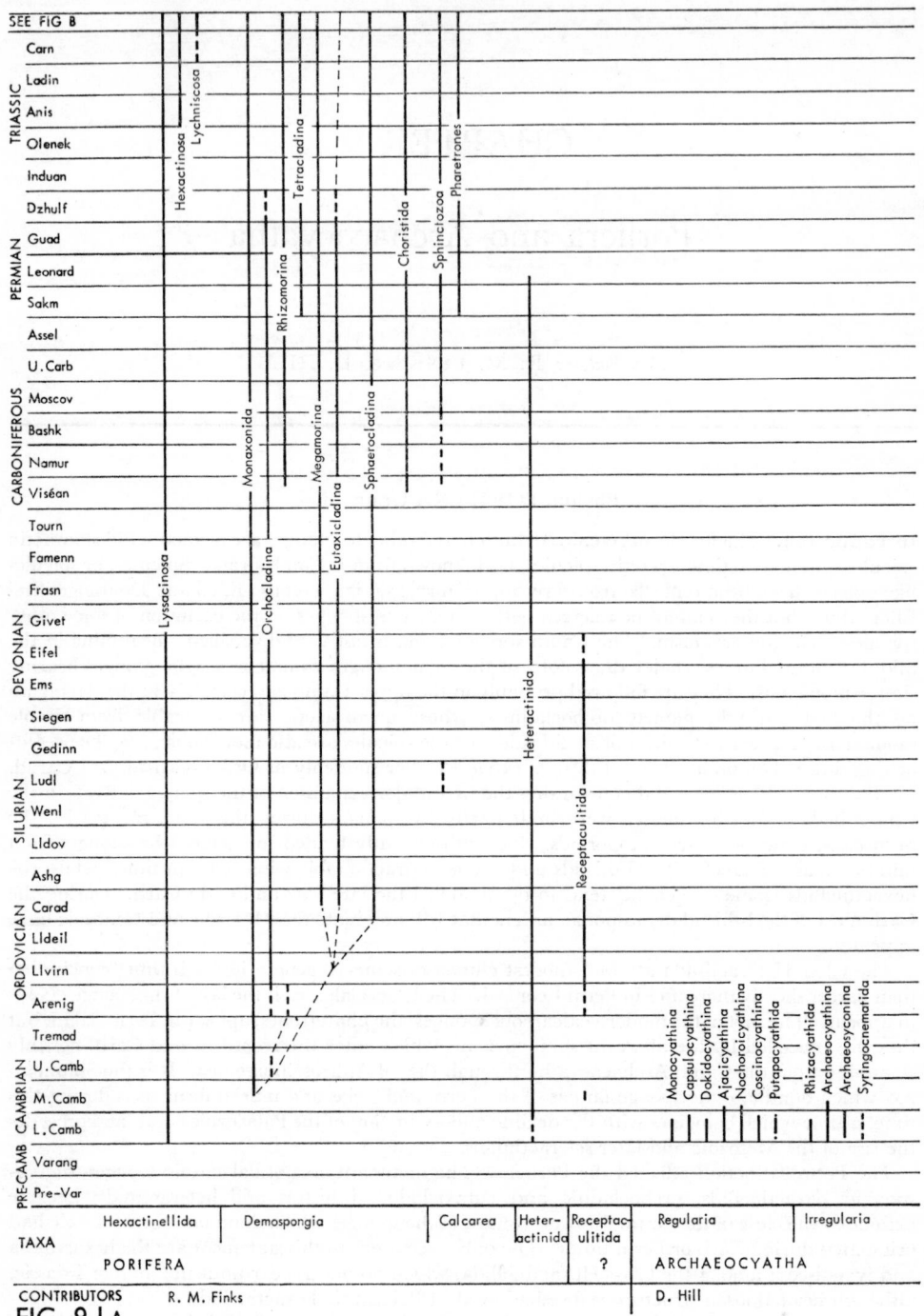

FIG. 9.1 A

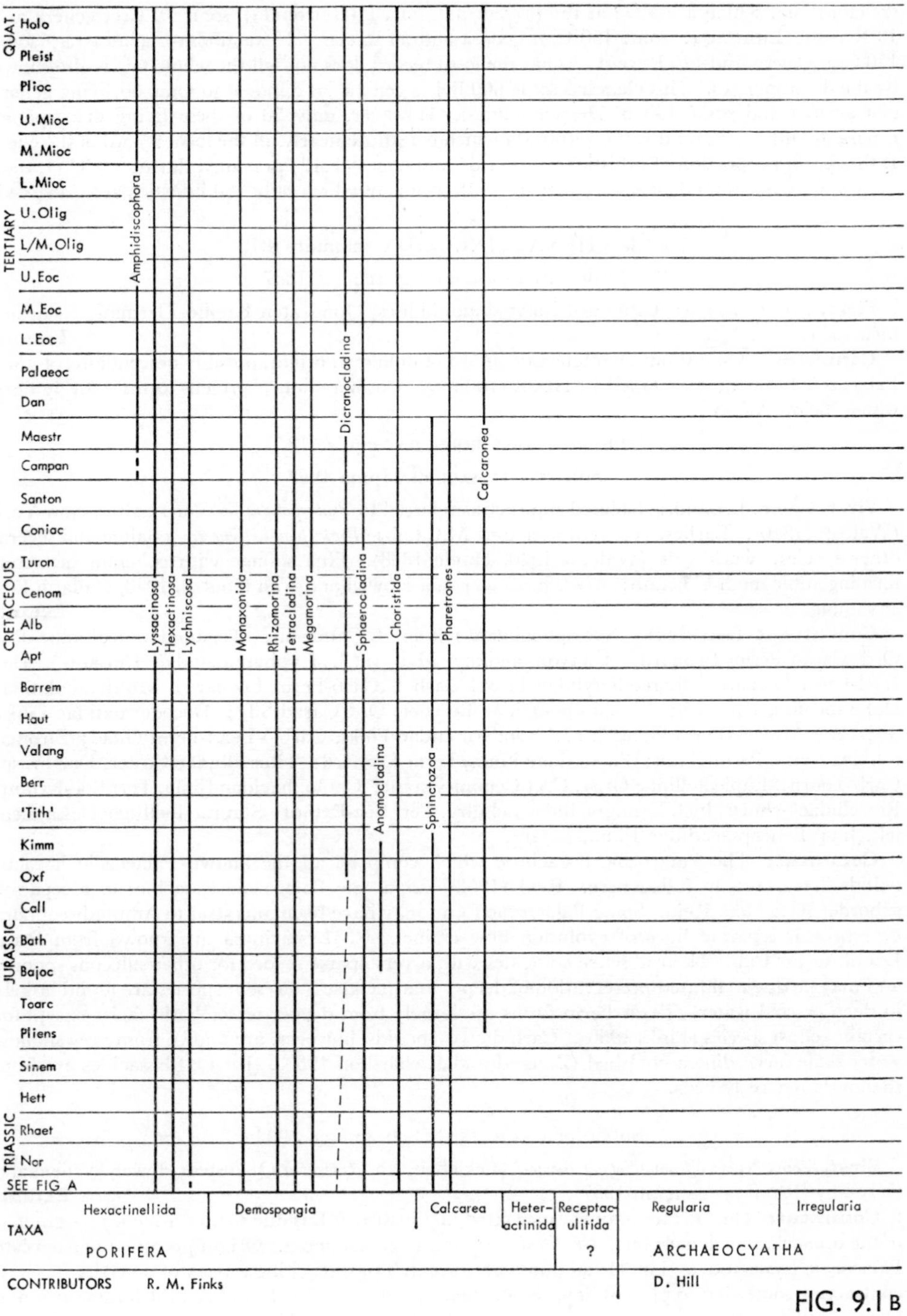
QUAT.
Holo
Pleist
Plioc
U.Mioc
M.Mioc
L.Mioc
TERTIARY
U.Olig
L/M.Olig
U.Eoc
M.Eoc
L.Eoc
Palaeoc
Dan
Maestr
Campan
Santon
Coniac
CRETACEOUS
Turon
Cenom
Alb
Apt
Barrem
Haut
Valang
Berr
'Tith'
Kimm
Oxf
Call
JURASSIC
Bath
Bajoc
Toarc
Pliens
Sinem
Hett
TRIASSIC
Rhaet
Nor
SEE FIG A
Amphidiscophora
Lyssacinosa
Hexactinosa
Lychniscosa
Monaxonida
Rhizomorina
Tetracladina
Megamorina
Dicranocladina
Sphaerocladina
Anomocladina
Choristida
Sphinctozoa
Pharetrones
Calcaronea
TAXA
Hexactinellida
Demospongia
Calcarea
Heter-actinida
Receptac-ulitida
Regularia
Irregularia
PORIFERA
?
ARCHAEOCYATHA
CONTRIBUTORS
R. M. Finks
D. Hill

FIG. 9.1 B

skeletons, and which are alive at the present day (viz. Pharetronida: some 70 Cret genera and 10 Recent; Lithistida: some 150 Cret genera and 50 Recent; Hexactinosa-Lychniscosa: some 170 Cret genera and 120 Recent). That the fossil record does not tell the whole tale is also shown by the demosponges. This class has some 600 living genera (as opposed to some 60 living genera of Calcarea and some 130 of Hexactinellida). However, only 50 of these living demosponge genera are lithistids and it is the Lithistida which constitute nearly all the fossil record of the class. If the recent proportion of lithistids to other demosponges (1:12) prevailed during the Cret, then there were some 1800 demosponge genera at that time of which only 150 lithistids are preserved.

Class HEXACTINELLIDA Schmidt, 1870

Order AMPHIDISCOPHORA Schulze 1887

First, Cret Campan: Unnamed isolated amphidiscs, Quadraten Kreide, Germany (Schrammen 1924). **Extant.**

Comment: A small but characteristic group of unknown origin, possibly descendants of some Palaeozoic forms here included in Hexasterophora. Cosmopolitan; present forms entirely deep water (below 200 m.).

Order HEXASTEROPHORA Schulze 1870

Suborder LYSSACINOSA Ijima 1987

First, Camb. L.Camb: Isolated stauractins referred to *Protospongia fenestrata* Salter, New York (Walcott, 1920). Earliest coherent skeletons M.Camb: *Protospongia fenestrata* Salter and several other species; worldwide (Walcott 1920, Hinde 1888). First sponge with coherent hexactins forming cubic mesh U.Camb: *Multivasculatus ovatus* Howell and Van Houten, 1940, Gallatin Fm, Wyoming. **Extant.**

Constituent families: Protospongiidae Hinde, L.Camb-Sil; Teganiidae DeLaubenfels, Ord Carad-Perm Leonard; Dictyospongiidae Hall (incl. Hyphantaeniidae DeLaub.), Dev Eifel-Perm Leonard; Stereodictyiidae Finks, Carb U.Carb-Perm Leonard; Multivasculatidae DeLaubenfels, U.Camb; Brachiospongiidae Beecher, Ord Carad-Sil?; Docodermatidae Finks, Sil?-Carb Moscov-Perm Guad-Jur?; Stiodermatidae Finks, Carb Viséan-Perm Guad; Stromatidiidae Finks, Perm Guad; Pileolitidae Finks, Perm Leonard; Titusvilliidae Caster, Dev Frasn-Carb Tourn; Euplectellidae Gray, Cret Cenom-Extant; Caulophacidae Ijima, Tert Eoc-Extant; Rossellidae Schulze, incl. Lanuginellidae Schulze, Tert Eoc-Extant; Stauractinellidae DeLaubenfels, Jur; Leucopsacadidae Ijima, Extant.

Comment: The Palaeozoic lyssacines, which comprise all the known Palaeozoic hexactinellids, have been included here. Reid (1958) assigns the Palaeozoic lyssacines to a separate suborder Reticulosa Reid. Some Palaeozoic forms may have been ancestral to Amphidiscophora or represent separate lines of evolution now extinct. No Lyssacinosa are known from Perm Dzhulf to Jur Call. Their absence coincides with a very sparse record for other siliceous sponges and may be due to limited preservation of deeper marine facies. Present species are found largely in deep or cold water. Texas Perm forms are largely from deeper water basin facies except for certain robust species (Finks 1960). Carb dictyospongids, however, are known from very shallow water shale succeeding a coal bed (Zangerl and Richardson 1963). Jur Oxf lyssacines are from shallow water reefy beds.

Suborder HEXACTINOSA Schrammen 1903

First, Trias Anis: *Tremadictyon roemeri* (Eckleben) and *Caesaria* Quenstedt, lower Wellenkalk, Germany (Rauff *in* Assmann 1937). **Extant.**

Comment: The Ord first-appearance cited in Treatise pt E is due to an erroneous assignment of the orchocladine demosponge *Okulitchina* Wilson to Hexactinosa. Origin presumably from late Palaeozoic Lyssacinosa. The Hexactinosa are rare in Trias, reaching a peak of diversity in Cret, contracting somewhat to present day. Since their appearance they have been the largest group of Hexactinellida. Present species have wide bathymetric range but are less common in water shallower than 100 m. They occur in oolitic and reefy facies in Jur of Europe. Worldwide.

Suborder LYCHNISCOSA Schrammen 1903

First, Trias Carn: *Triadocoelia magyara* Vinassa, Veszprém Fm, Bakony, Hungary. (Vinassa 1901) **Extant.**

Comment: Origin either from early Hexactinosa, (suggested by incomplete development of lychnisc nodes in *Triadocoelia*) or independently from Lyssacinosa. Most diversified and abundant in Cret. Distribution worldwide. Found today in moderately deep tropical waters (80–600 m.), but occur in reefy and oolitic facies in Jur of Europe.

Class DEMOSPONGIA Sollas 1885
Order KERATOSA Grant 1861

No known fossil record. **Extant.**

Order MONAXONIDA Sollas 1883

First, Camb M.Camb: *Hazelia palmata* Walcott, *Wapkia grandis* Walcott, *Hamptonia bowerbanki* Walcott, and possibly others, Burgess shale, British Columbia (Walcott 1920). **Extant.**

Comment: Comprising all non-lithistid demosponges having exclusively monaxonic spicules, this group almost certainly includes many lines of descent, but as a grade of organization it may represent the earliest stock of demosponges. Its priority in time, as well as the fact that the earliest lithistid desmas are monaxonic, lends support to this idea. *Leptomitus zitteli* Walcott 1886 (L.Camb) is more likely a hexactinellid root-tuft than a monaxonid sponge.

Order LITHISTIDA Schmidt 1870
Suborder ORCHOCLADINA Rauff 1893

First, Ord Arenig: *Archaeoscyphia minganensis* Billings, Romaine Fm, Quebec (Billings 1865). *Wilbernicyathus donegani* Wilson 1950, U.Camb, Morgan Creek member, Wilberns Fm, Texas, may be an earlier member of the group, as may be *Gallatinospongia conica* Okulitch and Bell, 1955, U.Camb, Gallatin Fm, Wyoming, but both are poorly preserved.

Last, Perm Dzhulf: *Aulacospongia? parvula* Gerth and probably *Timorella permica* Gerth, Amarassi Fm, Timor (Gerth 1927).

Constituent families: Anthaspidellidae Miller (includes Archaeoscyphiidae Rauff, Aulocopiidae Rauff, Eospongiidae DeLaubenfels in part), Ord Arenig-Perm Dzhulf; Chiastoclonellidae Rauff, Sil Wenl-Perm Guad; possibly Anomoclonellidae Rauff, Sil Wenl.

Comment: Probably originated from non-lithistid sponges with monaxonic spicules. Greatest diversity from Ord Llvirn to Ord Carad when they were reef-builders. Locally abundant in Sil Wenl (Tennessee and Gotland, Rauff 1893, 1894) but unrecorded from Dev, they occur sparsely in Carb and expand slightly in Perm (Timor, Gerth 1927; Texas, Finks 1960). Distribution worldwide; most abundant in shelly and reef facies of Ord; in Perm of Texas occur in both shelf and marginal basin facies.

Suborder RHIZOMORINA Zittel 1878

First, Carb Viséan: *Hapliston armstrongi* Young and Young, and another species, D_1 Z., L. Carboniferous Lst series, Scotland. Also *Cnemidiastrum priscum* Hinde, U. Carboniferous Lst, Ireland. (Hinde 1888). *Nipterella paradoxica* (Billings) from the Ord Arenig, Romaine Fm, Quebec, was considered a rhizomorine by Hinde (1889) but it may be an orchocladine allied to *Archaeoscyphia*. **Extant.**

Comment: Origin probably from non-lithistid monaxonida. Become more complex and diversified in U.Carb and Perm, Trias records apparently wanting, greatest diversity in Cret. Distribution worldwide in both shallow and deep water. Possibly polyphyletic. As understood here, includes all forms in which rhizoclones form the principal coherent skeletal net.

Suborder TETRACLADINA Zittel 1878

First, Perm Sakm: *Dactylites micropora* Finks, base of Bone Spring Fm, Texas (Finks 1960). **Extant.**

Comment: Pre-Perm records in the literature refer to the Orchocladina, here treated as a separate suborder.

Suborder MEGAMORINA Zittel 1878 (incl. Helomorina Schrammen 1924)

First, Ord Carad: *Saccospongia danvillensis* Ulrich, Perryville Fm, Kentucky; *S. massalis* Bassler and *S. laxata* Bassler, Cannon Fm, Tennessee. Both Fms are middle Trentonian. (Ulrich 1889, Bassler 1932). **Extant.**

Comment: Origin probably from non-lithistid Monaxonida. Pre-Jur records sparse, greatest diversity in Cret.

Suborder EUTAXICLADINA Rauff 1894

First, Ord Carad: *Hindia parva* Ulrich, Decorah Fm, Minnesota (Ulrich 1889).

Last, Perm Dzhulf: *Scheiia permica* (Gerth), Amarassi Fm, Timor (Gerth 1927).

Comment: The order is restricted here to the family Microspongiidae Miller 1889 (= Hindiidae Rauff 1893). Origin unknown, but external spicule form as well as arrangement of spicules in skeleton, suggest relationship to Megamorina Zittel and to Dicranocladina Schrammen.

Suborder DICRANOCLADINA Schrammen 1924

First, Jur Oxf: *Dicranoclonella praecursor* Schrammen, Weisse Jura *alpha*, Germany (Schrammen 1936). **Extant.**

Comment: May be related to Megamorina and Eutaxicladina. A small group.

Suborder SPHAEROCLADINA Schrammen 1910

First, Ord Carad: *Astylospongia parvula* Billings, Trenton (Ottawa) Fm, Ontario (Billings 1861). If the Palaeozoic Astylospongiidae are not related to later forms then first is Jur Oxf: *Mastosia wetzleri* Zittel, Weisse Jura *eta*, Germany (Schrammen 1936). **Extant.**

Comment: No certain record of this group is known between Sil Wenl and Jur Oxf. The Perm forms from Timor (Gerth 1927) included in the Astylospongiidae in Treatise pt. E are Orchocladina.

Suborder ANOMOCLADINA Zittel 1878
(=Didymmorina Rauff 1893)

First, Jur Bajoc: *Melonella ovata* (Sollas), Humphresianus Z., Inferior Oolite, England (Hinde 1893).

Last, Jur Kimm: *Cylindrophyma milleporata* (Goldfuss), Weisse Jura *zeta*, Germany (Kolb 1910, Schrammen 1936).

Constituent families: Cylindrophymatidae Schrammen, Coscinodiscidae Schrammen (?) Lecanellidae Schrammen.

Comment: The Sil Wenl genera *Anomoclonella* Rauff 1894 and *Pycnopegma* Rauff 1894, are here considered to belong to the Orchocladina. A relation between Anomocladina and Sphaerocladina was suggested by Hinde (1887) but rejected by Schrammen (1936) and Reid (1963).

Order CHORISTIDA Sollas 1880

First, Carb Viséan: *Geodites antiquus* (Hinde) and *G. hastatus* Hinde, isolated protriaene spicules, D_1 Z., L. Carboniferous Lst series, Scotland (Hinde 1888). **Extant.**

Comment: This group includes all non-lithistid sponges with tetraxonic spicules. Although an artificial category, its late appearance in the fossil record suggests that the tetraxon may have evolved during Palaeozoic time.

Class CALCAREA Bowerbank 1864
Order SPHINCTOZOA Steinmann 1882
(=Thalamida DeLaubenfels 1955)

First, Carb Viséan to Moscov: *Sollasia ostiolata* Steinmann, *Amblysiphonella barroisi* Steinmann and *Sebargasia carbonaria* Steinmann, Carboniferous Lst of Sebargas, Asturias, Spain (Steinmann

1882). The contributor has not been able to ascertain the precise age of the beds from which the sponges came, but the marine limestones in the area range from upper Viséan to Moscovian (Gignoux 1955). They are probably from the U. Bashk, Lena beds. The first securely dated record is *Fissispongia spinosa* R. H. King, Carb Moscov (= basal Westphalian C), Dickerson Fm (base of Des Moines series), Texas (King 1938). If *Aphrosalpinx textilis* Myagkova, Sil Ludl, N. Urals (Myagkova 1955), should prove to be a guadalupiid sphinctozoan then this would be an earlier record.

Last, Cret Maestr: *Verticillites cretaceus* Defrance, Calcaire à Baculites, Northern France and Maastricht (Steinmann 1882). Steinmann calls this Dan but the cited localities and formations indicate Maestr.

Comment: Origin uncertain, perhaps from Archaeocyatha (Camb) through *Aphrosalpinx* Miagkova (Sil Ludl) (Zhuravleva and Rezvoi 1956). Worldwide distribution but absent from present high latitudes (except in Jur to Cret); may have been chiefly circumtropical during time of greatest diversity and abundance in Perm and Trias. Reef-builders in Perm of Texas (Finks 1960) and Trias of Alps (Sieber 1937). Most families established by U. Carb, diversity reduced in Jur and Cret, all but one species extinct by end of Cret Cenom (Seilacher 1961). Confined to shallow water deposits in general.

Order PHARETRONES Zittel 1878

First, Perm Sakm: Two undescribed genera probably related to *Corynella* Zittel or *Stellispongia* D'Orbigny ("Pharetronid genera A, B"), Lenox Hills Fm, Texas (Finks 1960). First described forms are *Corynella chrysanthemum* Parona, *Stellispongia permica* Parona and other species, Perm Guad, Sosio Fm, Sicily (Parona 1933) and Djébel Tébaga Fm, Tunisia (Termier and Termier 1955).   **Extant.**

Comment: Expand gradually from first appearance to acme of some 70 genera in Cret, thereafter contracting to some 10 extant genera. Distribution worldwide. Probably confined to shallow water since their origin.

Order CALCINEA Bidder 1898

Comment: No certain fossil record. *Camarocladia dichotoma* Miller 1889, Ord Carad: Trenton group, Illinois, is not clearly a calcareous sponge.

Order CALCARONEA Bidder 1898

First, Jur Pliens: *Leuconia walfordi* Hinde, M. Lias, England (Hinde 1893).   **Extant.**

Class HETERACTINIDA Hinde 1888, emend.
Reid 1963 (=Wewokellida Croneis and Toomey 1965)

First, Camb L.Camb: *Allonnia tripodophora* Doré and Reid, Carteret group, Grès à nodules calcaires, Northern France, and spp. of *Chancelloria* Walcott, Siberia (Zhuravleva and Korde 1955) and England (Reid 1959). (Doré and Reid 1965).

Last, Perm Leonard: *Talpaspongia clavata* R. H. King, Talpa Fm, Texas (King 1943). In the well-collected and sponge-rich beds of West Texas, both *Talpaspongia* King and *Wewokella* Girty disappear at the tops of the Perm Assel, Neal Ranch and Hueco Fms (Finks 1960).

Constituent families: Chancelloriidae Walcott, L.Camb.-U.Camb; Astraeospongiidae Miller, M. Camb-Dev Givet; Wewokellidae R. H. King (= Asteractinellidae DeLaubenfels), Carb Tourn-Perm Leonard. Families as in Treatise pt E, except *Hyalostelia* Zittel, and possibly *Tholiasterella* Hinde, should be removed to Class Hexactinellida.

Comment: Chancelloriidae, with articulated spicule rays, may possibly not belong with the rest.

? Class RECEPTACULITIDA Hinde 1888

First, Ord Arenig: *Receptaculites calciferus* Billings, and one other species, Romaine Fm, Quebec (Billings 1865). If *Pirania muricata* Walcott 1920 belongs here, then first is Camb M.Camb, Stephen Fm, Ogygopsis Z., British Columbia.

Last, Dev Eifel: *Sphaerospongia tesselata* (Phillips) and *Receptaculites neptuni* Defrance, Newton Bushell and Mudstone Bay, Devonshire, respectively, also in type Eifelian, Germany and elsewhere in Europe and N. America (Hinde 1888).

Comment: These objects may not be sponges. Kesling and Graham (1962) analyze the structure of *Ischadites iowensis* (Owen) in terms of a dasycladacean alga. If their interpretation is correct, the other members of this group may also be algae, as well as *Calathium* Billings (Ord), *Amphispongia* Salter (Sil Ludl) and *Pirania* Walcott (M.Camb) which have been placed in other groups of sponges but which resemble the receptaculitids in structure.

REFERENCES

BASSLER, R. S. 1932. The stratigraphy of the central basin of Tennessee. *Bull. Tenn. Div. Geol.*, **38,** 183 pp., 49 pls.

BILLINGS, E. 1861. I. On some new or little known species of lower Silurian fossils from the Potsdam group (primordial zone). II. On some new species of fossils from the Calciferous, Chazy, Black River and Trenton formations., *in* E. Hitchcock, and others, *Report on the geology of Vermont*, vol. II, pp. 942–960. (Also as preprint of *Palaeozoic Fossils*, vol. 1, fasc. 1, pp. 1–24, Geol. Surv. Canada, Montreal, 1863).

—— 1865. *Palaeozoic fossils.* Vol. 1, fasc. 4, 5, Geological Survey of Canada, Montreal.

DORE, F. & REID, R. E. H., 1965. *Allonnia tripodophora* nov. gen., nov. sp., nouvelle Eponge du Cambrien inférieur de Carteret (Manche). *C.r. somm. Séanc. Soc. géol. Fr.*, fasc. 1, p. 20.

DOUBINGER, J. & ELLER, J.-P. von, 1963. Présence de spongiaires dans les schistes précambriens métamorphiques des Vosges. *Bull. Serv. Carte géol. Als. Lor.*, **16** (3), 111–123, 3 plates, 3 text-figs.

FINKS, R. M. 1960. Late Paleozoic sponge faunas of the Texas region: The siliceous sponges. *Bull. Am. Mus. nat. Hist.*, **120,** art. 1, 1–160, pls. 1–50, figs. 1–77.

GERTH, H. 1927. Die Spongien aus dem Perm von Timor. *Jaarb. Mijnw. Ned.-Oost-Indië*, for 1926, 99–132, 6 pls.

GIGNOUX, M. 1955. *Stratigraphic Geology.* Transl. by Gwendolyn G. Woodford from 4th French ed., 1950. Freeman, San Francisco, 682 pp.

HINDE, G. J. 1887. A monograph of the British fossil sponges. London, *Paleontogr. Soc. [Monogr.]*, pt. 1, 1–92, pl. 1–8.

—— 1888. *ibid.*, pt. 2, 93–188, pl. 9.

—— 1889. On Archaeocyathus, Billings, and on other genera, allied to or associated with it, from the Cambrian strata of North America, Spain, Sardinia, and Scotland. *Q. Jl geol. Soc. Lond.*, **45,** 125–148, pl. 5.

—— 1893. A monograph of the British fossil sponges. *Paleontogr. Soc. [Monogr.]*, pt. 3, 189–254, pl. 10–19.

HOWELL, B. F. & VAN HOUTEN, F. B. 1940. A new sponge from the Cambrian of Wyoming. *Bull. Wagner Inst. Sci. Philad.*, **15,** 1–8, pl. 1–3.

KESLING, R. V. & GRAHAM, A. 1962. *Ischadites* is a dasycladacean alga. *J. Paleont.*, **36,** 943–952, pl. 135–136, 2 figs.

KING, R. H. 1938. Pennsylvanian sponges of north-central Texas. *J. Paleont.*, **12,** 498–504, fig. 1–14.

—— 1943. New Carboniferous and Permian sponges. *Bull. Kansas Univ. geol. Surv.*, **47,** 1–36, pl. 1–3, fig. 1, 2.

KOLB, R. 1910. Die Kieselspongien des schwäbischen Weissen Jura. *Palaeontographica*, **57,** 141–246, pl. 11–21, fig. 1–27.

MILLER, S. A. 1889. *North American Geology and Paleontology.* Cincinnati, 664 pp., 1194 figs.

MYAGKOVA, E. I. 1955. Novye predstaviteli tipa Archaeocyatha. *Dokl. Akad. nauk SSSR*, **104,** 638–641, fig. 1, 2.

OKULITCH, V. J. & BELL, W. G. 1955. *Gallatinospongia*, a new siliceous sponge from the upper Cambrian of Wyoming. *J. Paleont.*, **29,** 460–461, pl. 48–49.

PARONA, C. F. 1933. Le spugne della fauna permiana di Palazzo Adriano (Bacino di Sosio) in Sicilia. *Mem. Soc. geol. ital.*, **1**, 1–58, pl. 1–12, fig. 1–7.

RAUFF, H. 1893. Palaeospongiologie. *Palaeontgraphica*, **40**, 1–232, fig. 1–48.

—— 1894. *ibid.*, **40**, 233–346, pl. 1–17, fig. 49–75.

—— 1937. *In* ASSMANN, P., Revision der fauna der Wirbellosen der oberschlesischen Trias, mit einem Beitrag über die Spongien von H. Rauff. *Abh. preuss. geol. Landesanst.*, **170**, 7–14, pls. 1, 2.

REID, R. E. H. 1958. A monograph of the upper Cretaceous Hexactinellida of Great Britain and Northern Ireland. *Palaeontogr. Soc.* [*Monogr.*], pt. 1, i-xlvi; pt. 2, xlvii-xlviii, 1–26, pl. 1–4.

—— 1959. Occurrence of *Chancelloria* Walc. in the Comley limestone. *Geol. Mag.*, **96**, 261.

—— 1963. A classification of the Demospongia. *Neues Jb. Geol. Paläont. Mh.* for 1963, 196–207.

SCHRAMMEN, A. 1924. Kieselspongien der oberen Kreide von Nordwestdeutschland. *Monogrn. Geol. Paläont.* ser. 1, **2**, 1–159.

—— 1936. Die Kieselspongien des oberen Jura von Süddeutschland. *Palaeontographica*, **84A**, 149–197, pl. 1–10; **85A**, 1–114, pl. 1–27.

SEILACHER, A. 1961. Die Sphinctozoa, eine Gruppe fossiler Kalkschwämme. *Abh. Math.-naturw. Kl. Akad. Wiss. Mainz* for 1961, 10, 726–790, pl. 1–9, fig. 1–8.

SIEBER, R. 1937. Neue Untersuchungen über die Stratigraphie und Ökologie der Alpinen Triasfaunen. I. Die Faunen der Nordalpinen Rhätriffkalke. *Neues Jb. Miner. Geol. Paläont. BeilBd.*, **78B**, 123–188, pl. 1–4, fig. 1–5.

STEINMANN, G. 1882. Pharetronen-Studien. *Neues Jb. Miner. Geol. Paläont.* for 1882, 139–191, pl. 6–9.

TERMIER, H. & TERMIER, G. 1955. Contribution à l'étude des spongiaires du Djébel Tébaga (extrême sud Tunisien). *Bull. Soc. géol. Fr.* (6), **5**, 613–630, fig. 1–10.

TREATISE, E. 1955. MOORE, R. C. (editor). *Treatise on Invertebrate Paleontology, Part E:* De LAUBENFELS, M. W., Porifera, pp. 21–112. University of Kansas Press.

ULRICH, E. O. 1889. Preliminary description of new lower Silurian Sponges. *Am. Geol.*, **3**, 233–248, figs. 1–10.

VINASSA, DE REGNY, P. E. 1901. Trias-spongien aus dem Bakony. *Resultate wiss. Erforschung Balaton-Sees, Paläont.*, **1**, no. 2.

WALCOTT, C. D. 1886. Second contribution to the studies on the Cambrian faunas of North America. *Bull. U.S. geol. Surv.*, **30**, 1–369, pls. 1–33.

—— 1920. Middle Cambrian Spongiae. *Smithson. misc. Collns*, **67**, no. 6, 261–364, pl. 60–90.

WILSON, J. L. 1950. An upper Cambrian Pleospongid (?). *J. Paleont.*, **24**, 591–593, pl. 80, fig. 1.

ZANGERL, R. & RICHARDSON, E. S., JR. 1963. The Paleoecological History of Two Pennsylvanian Black Shales. *Fieldiana, Geol. Mem.* **4**, 1–352, pl. 1–55.

ZHURAVLEVA, I. T. & KORDE, K. B. 1955. Nakhodka gubki *Chancelloria* Walcott v otlozheniyakh nizhnevo kembriya sibiri. *Dokl. Akad. nauk SSSR*, **104**, 474–477, fig. 1.

—— & REZVOI, P. D. 1956. K sistematike iskopaemykh gubok i arkheotsiat. *Dokl. Akad. nauk SSSR*, **111**, 449–451, fig. 1–2. [R.M.F.]

Phylum ARCHAEOCYATHA Vologdin 1937

Introduction. Archaeocyatha are characteristic of the calcareous facies of the Lower Cambrian and are known in all continents except South America. A few species extended into the early Middle Cambrian. Pre-Cambrian records and records of occurrences later than early Middle Cambrian are all discounted (Hill, 1965). [Documentation is here given for orders and suborders, with briefer details of constituent families—Ed.]

Only in Siberia[1] is the biostratigraphy of the L. Cambrian sufficiently advanced for ranges of

---

[1] The important work by Mme F. Debrenne (1964) "Archaeocyatha Contribution a l'etude des faunes cambriennes du Maroc de Sardaigne et de France. *Notes Mem. Serv. Mines Carte geol.* Maroc, **179** (2 vols)" unfortunately came to hand too late for its conclusions to be incorporated in the text.

archaeocyathan taxa to be established, so that the ranges given herein are the Russian ranges as given by Zhuravleva, 1960b, Zhuravleva, Repina and Khomentovskiy, 1962; Repina, Khomentovskiy, Zhuravleva and Rozanov (1964), Zhuravleva (1963) and Zhuravleva, Konyushkov and Rozanov (1964). In their latest (1963 and 1964) works, these authors divide the Siberian L. Cambrian into 3 stages, Aldanian, Botomian and Lenian, herein referred to as L. Cambrian (L.), L. Cambrian (M.) and L. Cambrian (U.) respectively. The Botomian covers the Lower Lena stage (Botomian substage) and the uppermost portion of the Zhurian substage of the Aldanian as used by Hill (1965); it includes the Kameshki and Sanashtykgol faunal horizons (f.h.) of the Altai-Sayan fold-belt. Transliteration from the Russian names for faunal horizons is as in Hill (1965).

Families are as in Hill (1965), Zhuravleva (1963) or Zhuravleva, Konyushkov & Zhuravleva (1964) unless otherwise noted.

Precamb records, not authentic, are as follows. *Atikokania lawsoni* Walcott, Steeprock Series, L. Superior, Canada (Hill, 1965). *Misracyathus vindhianus* Vologdin (1959d), Vindhyan, India, is not archaeocyathan (Zhuravleva 1960b). Archaeocyathids (Haughton, 1959) Kuibis beds, Nama System, S.W. Africa are filled-in tracks of burrowing animals, not archaeocyathan (Glaessner, 1962). *Rhabdocyathella karpinskii* Vologdin (1956a) considered by him L. Camb, is probably Precamb and not *Rhabdocyathella* (Zhuravleva 1960b, 1963).

Archaeocyatha from localities in the U.S.S.R. referred to M. Camb by Vologdin in many papers from 1931 to 1963 (especially Vologdin 1937b, 1940b, 1957a, 1962d) are L. Camb (Zhuravleva 1960b, 1963; Zhuravleva, Konyushkov and Rozanov, 1964). Thus Torgashino is L. Camb (M.), Kameshki-Sanashtykgol f.h. Mt. Dolgiy Mys (Obruchev's horizon) is L. Camb (U.). River Lebed is L. Camb (M.). Sanashtykgol spring is L. Cambrian (M.), Sanashtykgol f.h. Vologdin's 1939 South Urals and 1940a Tuva and Mongolian M. Camb references are to L. Camb genera (Zhuravleva, 1960b). Some Spanish archaeocyatha, thought by Simon (1939) and others to be M. Camb, are more likely to be L. Camb (Hill, 1965).

Matthewcyathus pavonoides (Matthew), M. Camb, New Brunswick, Canada, is too imperfectly known for taxonomic placement (Hill 1965). *Orlinocyathus algae* Krasnopeeva, M. Camb, Mt. Orlinaya, Siberia, is a sponge (Zhuravleva 1960b). Microfossils described by Vologdin (1963) from late M. Camb Tankhai Suite, R. Amga, Siberia, are only doubtfully referable to the Archaeocyatha. *Archaeoscyphia minganensis* (Billings), Ord, Canada, is a sponge (Hinde, 1889). The sponge nature of *Archaeoscyphia chihliensis* Grabau, Ord., China, is doubted by Chi (1940). Kobayashi (1944) considered that reports of *Archaeocyathus* in Manchuria refer to the sponge *Archaeoscyphia* common in the Ord, Wolungian limestone. Kahr (1951) and Schouppé (1950) described from the Austrian Ord Carad, fossils that seem to me best regarded as Problematica. The U.Sil Ludl Class Aphrosalpingoida Myagkova (1955) was treated as a class of Archaeocyatha by Vologdin and Myagkova (1962) but is herein regarded as *incertae sedis*, as is Dev Eifel, *Miassocyathus* Fomin (1963) from the S. Urals. The Carb to Cret Sphinctozoa Steinmann are a class of uncertain position, near the Porifera (Zhuravleva, 1962).

The Class Cribrocyathida Vologdin (1964) including the order Pterocyathida Yankauscas (1965) are L. and ?M. Camb microfossils herein regarded as not archaeocyathan.

Class REGULARIA Vologdin 1937

Order MONOCYATHIDA Okulitch 1935

Suborder MONOCYATHINA Okulitch 1935

First, Camb L.Camb (L.): *Monocyathus polaris* (Vologdin) and *Cryptoporocyathus junicanensis* Zhuravleva, Sunnagin f.h., Siberian Platform (Zhuravleva, 1960b). Record from "L.Camb Byk f-h" (Vologdin 1956a) is ?Precamb and *incertae sedis*.

Last, Camb L.Camb (U.): *Monocyathus nalivkini* (Vologdin) and *Rhabdocyathella baileyi* Vologdin, Solontsov f.h., Siberia. *Monocyathus partibus* Vologdin, Camb M.Camb, Amga or Maya, Tankhai suite, R. Amga, Siberian Platform, probably not archaeocyathan.

Constituent families. Monocyathidae Bedford and Bedford, L.Camb (L.-U.), Sunnagin-Solontsov f.h.; Rhabdocyathellidae Zhuravleva, L.Camb (M.-U.), Sanashtykgol-Solontsov f.h.; Cryptoporocyathidae Zhuravleva, L.Camb (L.), Sunnagin-Kenyada f.h..

Suborder CAPSULOCYATHINA Zhuravleva, in Zhuravleva, Konyushkov and Rozanov 1964

First, Camb L.Camb (L.): *Capsulocyathus subcallosus* Zhuravleva, Kundat f.h., Altai-Sayan fold belt, Siberia (Zhuravleva, Konyushkov and Rozanov, 1964).

Last, Camb L.Camb (U.): *Capsulocyathus subcallosus* Zhuravleva, Solontsov f.h., Altai-Sayan fold belt, Siberia (Zhuravleva, Konyushkov and Rozanov, 1964).

Constituent families: Capsulocyathidae Zhuravleva, L.Camb (L.), Kundat-Solontsov f.h.; Uralocyathellidae Zhuravleva, L.Camb (M.), Sanashtykgol f.h.; Uralocyathidae Zhuravleva, L.Camb (L.-M.), late Atdaban-Kameshki f.h., also France, N. Africa.

Order AJACICYATHIDA Bedford and Bedford 1939

Suborder DOKIDOCYATHINA Vologdin 1957

First, Camb L.Camb (L.): *Dokidocyathus* sp., Sunnagin f.h., Siberian Platform (Zhuravleva, 1960b).

Last, Camb L.Camb (M.): *Dokidocyathus* Taylor and four other genera, Sanashtykgol f.h., Siberian Platform and Altai-Sayan fold belt, Siberia (Zhuravleva, Konyushkov and Rozanov, 1964).

Constituent families: Dokidocyathidae Bedford and Bedford, L.Camb (L.-M.), Sunnagin-Sanashtykgol f.h.; Kaltatocyathidae Rozanov, L.Camb (L.-M.), Bazaikha-Kameshki f.h.; Kidrjasocyathidae Rozanov, L.Camb (M.), Kameshki-Sanashtykgol f.h.; Soanicyathidae Rozanov, L.Camb (M.), Sanashtykgol f.h.; Acanthinocyathidae Bedford and Bedford, 1934, L.Camb, S. Australia.

Suborder AJACICYATHINA Bedford and Bedford 1939

First, Camb L.Camb (L.): *Ajacicyathus* Bedford and Bedford and two other genera, Sunnagin f.h., Siberian Platform and Altai-Sayan fold belt of Siberia (Zhuravleva, 1960b).

Last, Camb, M.Camb (L.): *Tegerocyathus* Krasnopeeva and *Ethmophyllum* aff. *ratum* Vologdin, Kaimskaya Suite, Katun Anticline, Altai-Sayan fold belt, Siberia (Khomentovskiy, Zhuravleva, Repina and Rozanov (1962). *Ajacicyathus, Orbicyathus* Vologdin, and *Syringocyathus* Vologdin, M.Camb, Paradoxides oelandicus Z., Poland, not archaeocyathan but cystid (Palmer and Rozanov *in* Hill, 1965). *Binatocyathus obliquoseptatus* Vologdin, M.Camb, Tankhai Suite, Siberian Platform (Vologdin 1963) possibly not archaeocyathan. *Serligocyathus* Vologdin and *Leiocyathus* Vologdin, considered U.Camb by Vologdin (1959b), are L.Camb (Menner, Pokrovskaya and Rozanov 1960).

Constituent families: Ajacicyathidae Bedford and Bedford, L.Camb, Sunnagin-Solontsov f.h.; Cyclocyathellidae Zhuravleva, L.Camb (L.-M.), Sunnagin-Sanashtykgol f.h.; Ethmophyllidae Okulitch, L.Camb-M.Camb (L.), Kenyada-basal Amga f.h.; Annulocyathidae Krasnopeeva, L.Camb (M.), Kameshki-Sanashtykgol f.h.; Tumulocyathidae Krasnopeeva, L.Camb (L.-M.), Bazaikha-Sanashtykgol f.h.; Vologdinocyathidae Yaroshevich, L.Camb (M.-U.) Sanashtykgol-Obruchev f.h.; Porocyathidae Zhuravleva, L.Camb (L.-M.) Bazaikha-Sanashtykgol f.h.; Sigmocyathidae Krasnopeeva, L.Camb, S. Australia; Tercyathidae Vologdin, L.Camb (M.), Sanashtykgol f.h.; Botomocyathidae Zhuravleva, L.Camb (M.), U. Atdaban-Sanashtykgol f.h.; Erbocyathidae Vologdin and Zhuravleva, L.-M.Camb (L.), Bazaikha-Amga f.h.

Suborder NOCHOROICYATHINA Zhuravleva 1956

First, Camb L.Camb (L.): *Nochoroicyathus vulgaris* Zhuravleva, Sunnagin f.h., Siberian Platform (Zhuravleva, 1960b).

Last, Camb M.Camb (L.): *Nochoroicyathus* sp, Kaimskaya Suite, Katun Anticline, Altai-Sayan fold-belt, Siberia (Khomentovskiy, Zhuravleva, Repina and Rozanov, 1962).

Constituent families: Nochoroicyathidae Zhuravleva, L.Camb-M.Camb (L.), Sunnagin-basal Amga f.h.; Bronchocyathidae Bedford and Bedford, L.Camb (L.-U.), Kenyada-Solontsov f.h.; Formosocyathidae Rozanov, L.Camb (L.-M.), Kenyada-Sanashtykgol f.h.; Lenocyathidae Zhuravleva, L.Camb (L.-M.), Kenyada-Kameshki f.h.; Carinacyathidae Krasnopeeva, L.Camb (?L.-M.), ?Bazaikha-Sanashtykgol f.h.; Piamaecyathidae Zhuravleva, L.Camb (M.), Sanashtykgol f.h.; Kordecyathidae Missarzhevskiy (1961), L.Camb, Shangan Suite, Tuva.

Suborder COSCINOCYATHINA Zhuravleva 1955

First, Camb L.Camb (L.): *Coscinocyathus* sp., "La Sèrie des calcaires superieurs", Assadasian substage (Hupé, 1960), Morocco (Debrenne 1960).

Last, Camb L.Camb (U.): *Coscinocyathus* spp. and *Clathricoscinus* sp., Solontsov and Ketema f.h. (Zhuravleva, 1960b). *Coscinocyathus* cf. *corbicula* Bornemann, doubtful record (Reed, 1910) M. Camb, M. Parahio Series, Salt Range. *Coscinocyathus elvira* Walcott (1906, 1913), unconfirmed, M.Camb, near base of Kichou Fm, Shansi, N. China.

Constituent families: Coscinocyathidae Taylor, L.Camb (L.-U.), Sunnagin-Solontsov f.h. and Assadasian substage, Morocco; Salairocyathidae Zuravleva, L.Camb (L.-M.), Bazaikha and Sanashtykgol f.h.; Coscinocyathellidae Zhuravleva, L.Camb (L.-M.), Bazaikha and Sanashtykgol f.h., and Amouslekian substage, Morocco; Alataucyathidae Zhuravleva, L.Camb (L.-M.), Bazaikha-Sanashtykgol f.h.; Sigmocoscinidae Bedford and Bedford, L.Camb, S. Australia.

Order PUTAPACYATHIDA Vologdin 1962

First, Camb L.Camb (L.), *Galinaecyathus* sp., Atdaban f.h., Siberian Platform (Zhuravleva, Konyushkov and Rozanov 1964) or *Putapacyathus regularis* Bedford and Bedford, Ajax lst, S. Australia.

Last, L.Camb (M.), four genera from the Sanashtykgol faunal horizon, Siberian Platform and Altai-Sayan fold belt, or *Putapacyathus regularis*, Ajax lst, S. Australia.

Constituent families: Putapacyathidae Bedford and Bedford, L.Camb, Ajax lst, S. Australia; Aptocyathidae Konyushkov, L.Camb (L.-M.), Atdaban-Sanashtykgol f.h., Siberian Platform and Altai-Sayan fold belt.

Class IRREGULARIA Vologdin 1937

Order RHIZACYATHIDA Zhuravleva 1955

First, Camb L.Camb (L.). *Bacatocyathus tunicatus* (Zhuravleva), Kenyada f.h., Siberian Platform.

Last, Camb L.Camb (M.), *Bacatocyathus kazakevitchi* Vologdin and *Rhizacyathus compositus* (Vologdin), Sanashtykgol f.h., Siberia.

Constituent families: Rhizacyathidae Bedford and Bedford, L.Camb (L.-M.), Sunnagin-Sanashtykgol f.h.; Bacatocyathidae Zhuravleva, L.Camb (L.-M.), Kenyada-Sanashtykgol f.h.

Order ARCHAEOCYATHIDA Okulitch 1935

Suborder ARCHAEOCYATHINA Okulitch 1935

First, Camb L.Camb (L.) *Dictyocyathus* sp. and *Okulitchicyathus discoformis* Zhuravleva, Sunnagin f.h., Siberian Platform (Zhuravleva, 1960b).

Last, Camb M.Camb (L.) *Archaeocyathus* sp., *Paradoxides oelandicus* Z., Alexandra Beds and Ranken lst, Northern Territory, Australia (Öpik 1956, 1961).

?Archaeocyathina (Zhuravleva 1960b), *Tanchocyathus amgaensis* Vologdin and *Archaeocyathus kordeae* Vologdin (1963), M.Camb, Tankhai Suite, R. Amga, Siberian Platform, are only doubtfully archaeocyathan.

Constituent families: Dictyocyathidae Taylor, L.Camb (L.-U.), Kenyada-Ketema f.h.; Metacyathidae Bedford and Bedford, L.Camb (L.-U.), Sunnagin-Solontsov f.h.; Archaeocyathidae Hinde, L.-M.Camb (L.), Kenyada f.h.- *Paradoxides oelandicus* Z.; Prismocyathidae Fonin, L.Camb, Shangan Suite, Tuva, Mongolia; Protocyclocyathidae Vologdin, L.Camb;

Tabellaecyathidae Fonin, L.Camb (M.), Sanashtykgol f.h. (Fonin, 1963); Bicyathidae Vologdin, L.Camb (L.-M.), early Atdaban-Sanashtykgol f.h.

Suborder ARCHAEOSYCONINA Zhuravleva 1955

First, Camb L.Camb (L.): *Sphinctocyathus (Dictyosycon) gravis* Zhuravleva, Kenyada f.h., Siberian Platform (Zhuravleva, 1960b).

Last, Camb L.Camb (U.): *Archaeosycon okulitchi* Zhuravleva, Elanka f.h., Siberian Platform (Zhuravleva, 1960b).

Constituent families: Archaeosyconidae Zhuravleva, L.Camb (L.-U.), Kenyada-Elanka f.h.; Tabulacyathidae Vologdin, L.Camb (M), Sanashtykgol f.h.; Dictycoscinidae Bedford and Bedford, L.Camb, S. Australia; Metacoscinidae Bedford and Bedford, L.Camb (M.-U.), Olekma-Elanka f.h.

Order SYRINGOCNEMATIDA Okulitch 1935

First, Camb L.Camb: possibly *Syringocnema favus* Taylor, Ajax lst, S. Australia (Hill, 1965).

Last, Camb L.Camb: possibly *Syringocnema gracilis* Gordon, Antarctica. *Syringocnema* sp, M.Camb, Paradoxides Z., Poland (Orlowski 1959, 1960, 1962) not archaeocyathan but cystid (Palmer & Rozanov *in* Hill, 1965).

Constituent family: Syringocnematidae Taylor, L.Camb.

REFERENCES

Of the works cited above, only those not listed in Hill 1965 are given below.

HILL, D. 1965. Archaeocyatha from Antarctica and a review of the phylum. *Scient. Rep. trans-antarct. Exped.*, No. 10, Geology 3, 151 pp. 12 plates.

FOMIN, Y. M. 1963. O nakhodke arkheotsiatopodobnykh organizmov v srednedevoniskikh otlozheniyakh vostochnogo sklona yuzhnogo Urala. *Paleont. Zh.* for 1963, no. 2, 17–19.

FONIN, V. D. 1963. K poznaniya tenial'nykh arkeotsiat Altai-Sayanskoy skladchatoy oblasti. *Paleont. Zh.* for 1963, no. 4, 14–29.

MISSARZHEVSKIY, V. V. 1961. Rannekembriyskie Arkheotsiaty basseÿna reki Shivelig-Khem. *Paleont. Zh.* for 1961, no. 4, 19–23.

REPINA, L. N., KHOMENTOVSKIY, V. V., ZHURALEVA, I. T., & ROZANOV, A. Y. 1964. *Biostratigrafiya nizhnego kembriya Sayano-Altayskoy skladchatoy oblasti.* Akadamii Nauk SSSR, Sibir. Otdel. Inst. Geol. Geofiz., Moscow.

VOLOGDIN, A. G. 1964. Kribritsiaty-noviy klass arkheotsiat. *Dokl. Akad. nauk SSSR*, **157**, 1391–1394.

—— & MYAGKOVA, E. I. 1962. Klass Aphrosalpingidae *in* ORLOV, Y. A. *Osnovy Paleontologii: Gubki, Arkheotsiati, Kishechnopolostnye, Chervi.* Akademii Nauk SSSR, Moscow.

YANKAUSKAS, T. V. 1965. Pterotsiatidy-Noviyotryad Kribritsiat. *Dokl. Akad. nauk SSSR*, **162**, 438–440.

ZHURALEVA, I. T. 1962. Klass Sphinctozoa *in* ORLOV, Y. A. (Editor) *Osnovy Paleontologii: Gubki Arkheotsiati, Kishechnopolostnye, Chervi.* Akademii Nauk SSSR, Moscow.

—— 1963. *Arkheotsiaty Sibiri, Odnotennye arkeheotsiaty (otryady Monocyathida i Rhizocyathida).* Akademii Nauk SSSR, Sibir. otdel. Inst. Geol. Geofiz., Moscow.

—— KONYUSHKOV, K. N. & ROZANOV, A. Y. 1964. *Archeotsiaty Sibiri. Dvustennye Arkheotsiaty.* Akademii Nauk SSSR, Sibir, Otdel. Inst. Geol. Geofiz., Moscow. [D.H.]

R. M. Finks, PH.D.
Department of Geology and Geography, Queen's College, Flushing 67, N.Y., U.S.A.
[Professor] D. Hill, PH.D. D.SC. F.R.S. F.A.A.
Department of Geology, University of Queensland, St Lucia, Brisbane, Australia.

CHAPTER 10

Coelenterata

Contributors: G. A. L. JOHNSON, I. D. SUTTON,
F. M. TAYLOR & G. THOMAS

Class PROTOMEDUSAE Caster 1945

Order BROOKSELLIDA Harrington & Moore 1956

First, Pre-Camb Varang: *Brooksella canyonensis* Bassler, Nankoweap group, Algonkian, Grand Canyon, Arizona (Bassler 1941, Van Gundy 1951). Allegedly older medusoid fossils from Grand Canyon described by Alf 1959 probably inorganic and/or algal in origin (see Glaessner 1962, pp. 479, 493).

Last, Ord Arenig: *Brooksella silurica* (von Huene), "oberen rothen Orthocerenkalk", Kärgarde, Dalarna, Sweden (von Huene 1904), and ?*Brooksella cambria* (? = *Staurophyton bagnolensis* Meunier 1891), "Grès Armoricains" (of uncertain L. Ord age), Bagnoles (Orne), France (Meunier 1891). Reference to *Laotira* sp. [now *Brooksella*] from Penn of Sinai, Egypt (Couyat & Fritel 1912) not substantiated by figs. or descriptions; Avnimelech (1966) suggests it is *Duodecimedusina*, describes *D. aegyptiaca* Avnimelech from Carb ?Namur, Um Bogma fm., Eastern Desert, Egypt, and places genus *Duodecimedusina* in Protomedusae.

Comment: Classification here follows Treatise F, but designations are subjective and uncertain. One family, Brooksellidae Walcott. Only other records: "Star cobbles", *B. cambria* and *B. alternata*, M. Camb, Conasauga sh, Olenoides—Marumia Z., Coosa Valley, Alabama (Walcott 1898); *B. cambria*, U. Camb, Grove Creek member, Boysen fm, Wind River Canyon, Wyoming (Caster 1942b).

Class SCYPHOZOA Götte 1887

General Comment: Taxa as in Treatise pt F, but classification of fossil medusae subjective and uncertain, as emphasized by Glaessner & Wade (1966).

Subclass SCYPHOMEDUSAE Lankester 1881

Order STAUROMEDUSIDA Haeckel 1880

Extant only; comprises Tesseranthidae Haeckel, Eleutherocarpidae Clark, Cleistocarpidae Clark; No known fossil representatives; Present distribution, cold seas.

Order CARYBDEIDA Claus 1886

First, Jur 'Tith': *Quadrimedusina quadrata* (Haeckel), Solnhofen Lst (M. Kimm), Germany (Harrington & Moore 1955) may belong to this Order. **Extant.**

The Fossil Record, pp. 347–378. Geological Society of London, 1967. Printed in Northern Ireland.

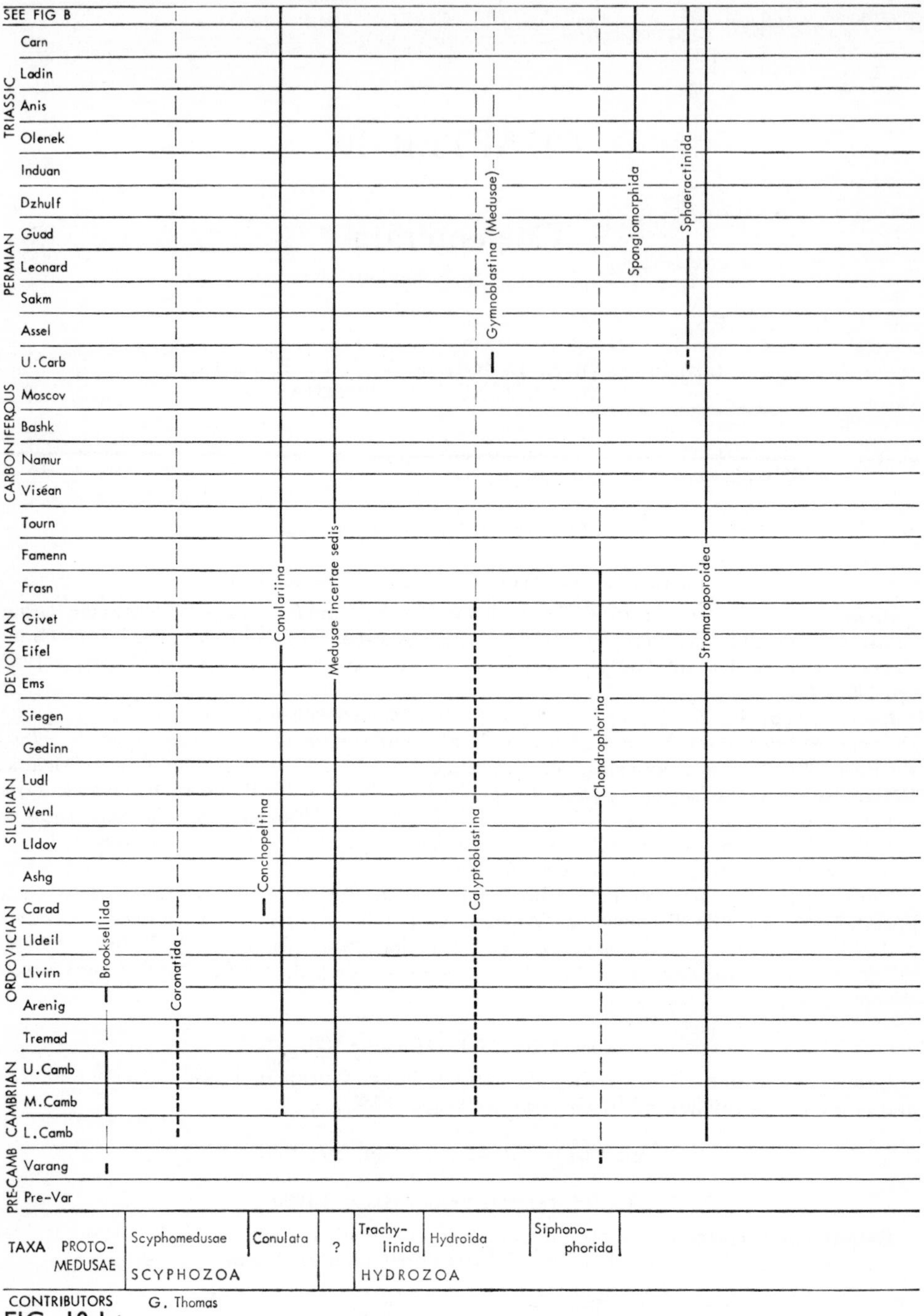

SEE FIG B

	Stage									
TRIASSIC	Carn									
	Ladin									
	Anis									
	Olenek								Sphaeractinida	
PERMIAN	Induan					Gymnoblastina (Medusae)				
	Dzhulf									
	Guad						Spongiomorphida			
	Leonard									
	Sakm									
	Assel									
CARBONIFEROUS	U.Carb									
	Moscov									
	Bashk									
	Namur									
	Viséan									
	Tourn									
DEVONIAN	Famenn		Conulariina	Medusae incertae sedis					Stromatoporoidea	
	Frasn									
	Givet									
	Eifel									
	Ems									
SILURIAN	Siegen					Chondrophorina				
	Gedinn									
	Ludl									
	Wenl			Conchopeltina						
	Lldov									
	Ashg									
ORDOVICIAN	Carad	Brooksellida			Calyptoblastina					
	Lldeil		Coronatida							
	Llvirn									
	Arenig									
	Tremad									
CAMBRIAN	U.Camb									
	M.Camb									
	L.Camb									
PRE-CAMB	Varang									
	Pre-Var									

TAXA	PROTO-MEDUSAE	Scyphomedusae	Conulata	?	Trachy-linida	Hydroida	Siphono-phorida			
		SCYPHOZOA			HYDROZOA					

CONTRIBUTORS   G. Thomas

FIG. 10.1 A

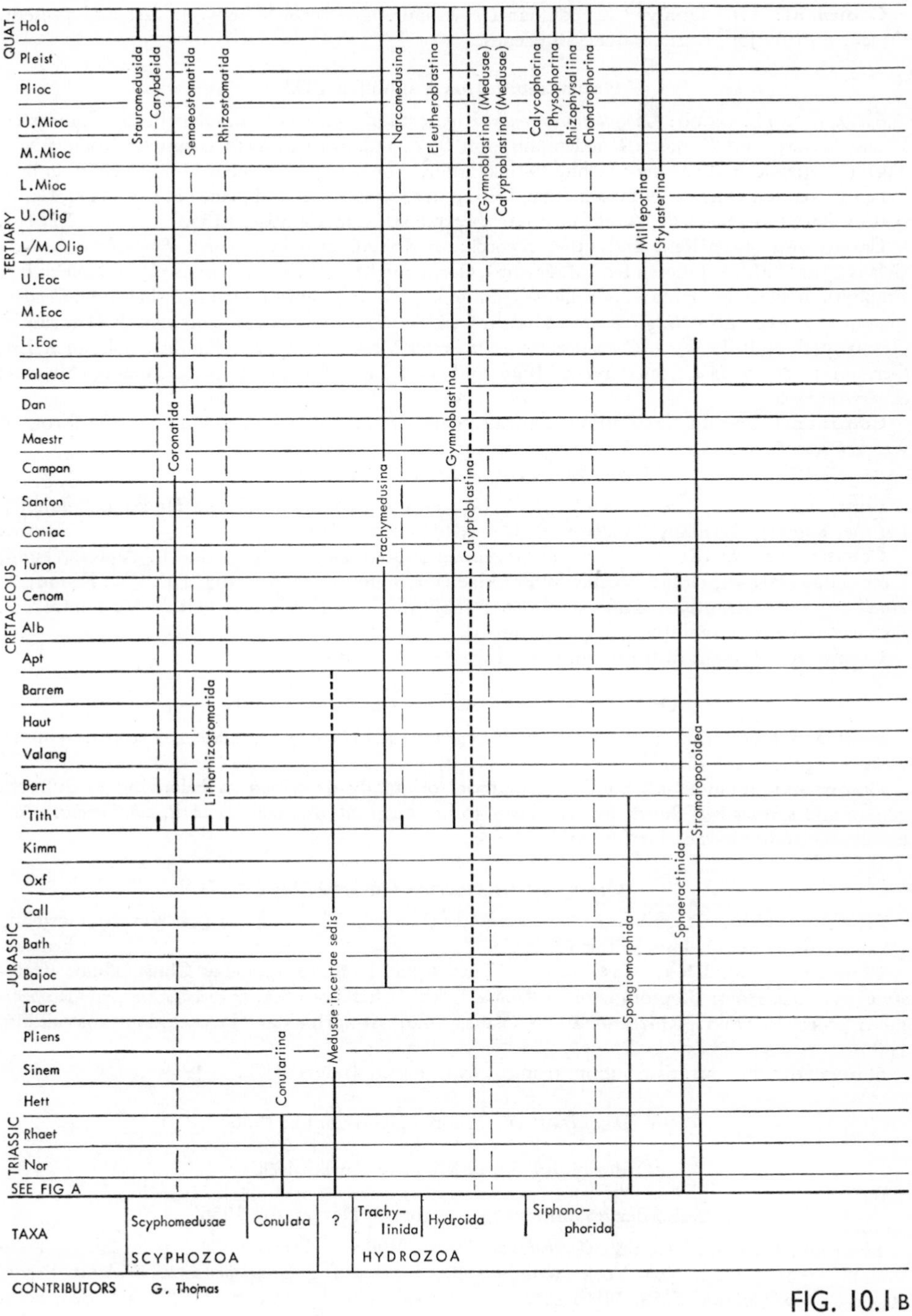
QUAT.
Holo
Pleist
Plioc
U.Mioc
M.Mioc
L.Mioc
TERTIARY
U.Olig
L/M.Olig
U.Eoc
M.Eoc
L.Eoc
Palaeoc
Dan
Maestr
Campan
Santon
Coniac
CRETACEOUS
Turon
Cenom
Alb
Apt
Barrem
Haut
Valang
Berr
'Tith'
Kimm
Oxf
Call
JURASSIC
Bath
Bajoc
Toarc
Pliens
Sinem
Hett
TRIASSIC
Rhaet
Nor
SEE FIG A
Stauromedusida
Carybdeida
Semaeostomatida
Rhizostomatida
Coronatida
Lithorhizostomatida
Conulariina
Medusae incertae sedis
Trachymedusina
Narcomedusina
Eleutheroblastina
Gymnoblastina
Gymnoblastina (Medusae)
Calyptoblastina (Medusae)
Calyptoblastina
Calycophorina
Physophorina
Rhizophysaliina
Chondrophorina
Milleporina
Stylasterina
Spongiomorphida
Sphaeractinida
Stromatoporoidea
TAXA
Scyphomedusae
Conulata
?
Trachylinida
Hydroida
Siphonophorida
SCYPHOZOA
HYDROZOA
CONTRIBUTORS
G. Thomas

FIG. 10.1 B

Comment: One family, Carybdeidae Gegenbaur. No records between first and present. Present distribution, warm waters, all oceans.

Order CORONATIDA Vanhöffen 1892

First, Camb L. Camb: *Camptostroma roddyi* Ruedemann, Kinzers Fm., Olenellus Z., Lancaster, Pennsylvania; and *C. resseri* Ruedemann (fm. & Z. unknown), North Granville Bridge, New York (Ruedemann 1933) may belong to this Order. Former species believed by Durham to be a helicoplacoid (cf. Durham & Caster 1966, U131), not scyphozoan, and placed in new class. Latter species placed in *Protolyella* Torell, medusae incertae sedis, in Treatise, F155.   **Extant.**

Constituent families, and other records: Periphyllidae Claus, (first, *Epiphyllina distincta* (Maas), Jur 'Tith', Solnhofen Lst (M. Kimm), Germany (Maas 1906); otherwise Quat Holo only); Epiphyridae Haeckel, Holo; Atorellidae Vanhöffen, Holo; Collaspididae Haeckel (first, *Camptostroma*, see above; also ?*C. germanicum* Hundt, Ord Trem (U), Phycodes-Schichten, E. Thuringia, Germany (Hundt 1939): ?*Cannostomites multicirratus* Maas, 'Tith' (M. Kimm), Solnhofen Lst, Germany; ?*Lorenzinia* from Cret of Italy and Tert Eoc of Italy, Cyprus, Poland, Albania; otherwise Holo).

Comment: Present distribution, typically deep waters, all oceans; some surface forms in warmer waters.

Order SEMAEOSTOMATIDA L. Agassiz 1862

First, Jur 'Tith': *Semaeostomites zitteli* Haeckel and *Eulithota fasciculata* Haeckel, Solnhofen Lst (M. Kimm), Germany (Walcott 1898) may belong to this Order.   **Extant.**

Constituent families: Pelagiidae Gegenbaur, Quat Holo; Cyaneidae L. Agassiz, Holo; Ulmariidae Haeckel, Holo: ?Semaeostomitidae Harrington & Moore, Jur 'Tith' (M. Kimm), *S. zitteli* only representative (single specimen); ?Eulithotidae Kieslinger, 'Tith' (M. Kimm), *E. fasciculata* only representative (single specimen).

Comment: Present distribution, coastal waters, all oceans.

Order LITHORHIZOSTOMATIDA von Ammon 1886

First and Last, Jur 'Tith': *Rhizostomites admirandus* Haeckel, Solnhofen Lst (M. Kimm), Germany (Treatise F46).

Comment: Includes all Solnhofen material originally described as belonging to different genera and species but shown by Kieslinger to be preservational aspects of *R. admirandus*. One family, Rhizostomitidae Harrington & Moore.

Order RHIZOSTOMATIDA Cuvier 1799

First, Jur 'Tith': ?*Leptobrachites trigonobrachius* Haeckel, Solnhofen Lst (M. Kimm), Germany (Walcott 1898) may belong to this Order.   **Extant.**

Constituent families: Cassiopeidae Claus, Quat Holo; Cepheidae Claus, Holo; Catostylidae Claus, Holo; Leptobrachiidae Claus, 'Tith' (M. Kimm), *L. trigonobrachius*, single specimen; otherwise Holo; Rhizostomatidae Claus, Holo; Archirhizidae Haeckel, doubtful validity, Holo.

Comment: Present distribution, tropical seas, mainly Indo-Pacific.

Subclass CONULATA Moore & Harrington 1956

Order CONULARIIDA Miller & Gurley 1896

Suborder CONCHOPELTINA Moore & Harrington 1956

First and Last, Ord Carad: *Conchopeltis alternata* Walcott, Trenton Lst (upper third), Trentonian, Trenton Falls, New York (Knight 1937, Treatise F). *C. minnesotensis* Walcott, Stones River Group, Cannon Falls, Minnesota, is gastropod (Ulrich & Scofield 1897, pp. 823, 839). *Conchopeltis*-like form (not yet figured or described) reported by Glaessner & Wade (1966, p. 628) from Pre-Camb Varang, Pound Quartzite fm., Upper Adelaide Series, Ediacara, S. Australia.

Chapter 10: Coelenterata

Comment: One family, Conchopeltidae Moore & Harrington. Originally described as gastropod.

Suborder CONULARIINA Miller & Gurley 1896

First, Camb M. Camb: *Conulariella* ("*Conularia* sp. b", Wurm 1925), Paradoxides-Schichten, Galgenberg, Wildenstein, Frankenwald, Germany (Kiderlen 1937).

Last, Trias Rhaet: *Conularia stromeri* Osswald, oberen Kössener Mergel, Tegernsee, Bavaria, W. Germany (Osswald 1918). Existence of *Conularia* in Jur Hett not substantiated.

Constituent families: Conulariellidae Kiderlen, M. Camb—Ord Arenig (*Conulariella* only genus); Conulariidae Walcott, U. Camb—Trias Rhaet (17 genera in 3 subfamilies, some world-wide in distribution); Conulariopsidae Sugiyama, Trias Olenek (*Conulariopsis* only genus).

Class HYDROZOA Owen 1843

Introduction: Taxa mainly as in Treatise F, but classification of fossil medusae subjective and uncertain, as emphasized by Glaessner & Wade 1966, whose views on Pre-Camb medusae from Ediacara, S. Australia, are incorporated here. Order Sphaeractinida as in Sokolov 1962.

Order TRACHYLINIDA Haeckel 1877

General comment: Open ocean, world-wide distribution, more frequent in warmer seas than in cold waters; exceptions are 2 freshwater genera. Forms considered as Trachylinida Incertae Sedis in Treatise F now all treated under broader category of Medusae Incertae Sedis (*q.v.*).

Suborder TRACHYMEDUSINA Haeckel 1866

First, Jur Bajoc: *Kirklandia* sp., L. Dogger ß, Opalinusschichten, Talheim, Württemberg, Germany (Lörcher 1931). Other records: *Kirklandia texana* Caster, Cret Alb, Pawpaw fm., Washita series, Comanchian, Roanoke, Denton County, Texas (Caster 1945); medusa similar to modern *Gonionemus murbachi* Mayer recorded by Grauvogel 1951 from L. Trias of Saverne, Vosges; figs. and substantiation required. **Extant.**

Constituent families: Olindiadidae Haeckel, Quat Holo; Petasidae Haeckel, Holo; Limnocnididae Mayer, Holo; Pectyllididae Haeckel, Holo; Kirklandiidae Caster (*Kirklandia* only genus, see above); Geryoniidae Eschscholtz, Holo; Trachynematidae Gegenbaur, Holo, (*Beltanella gilesi* Sprigg, Pre-Camb Varang, Pound Quartzite fm., Upper Adelaide Series, Ediacara, S. Australia (Sprigg 1947), placed here in Treatise F, but taxon regarded as doubtful by Glaessner & Wade (1966) and possible synonym of *Ediacaria*, itself in "medusae incertae sedis").

Suborder NARCOMEDUSINA Haeckel 1879

First, Jur 'Tith': *Acalepha deperdita* (Beyrich), Solnhofen Lst (M. Kimm), Germany (Walcott 1898) may belong to this Suborder. **Extant.**

Constituent families: Cuninidae Broch (*Acalepha*, see above); otherwise Quat Halo; Aeginidae Haeckel, Holo.

Order HYDROIDA Johnston 1836

General comment: Typically littoral and shallow offshore; some in deeper waters. Most abundant in temperate and cold zones.

Suborder ELEUTHEROBLASTINA Allman 1871

Extant only.

Suborder GYMNOBLASTINA Allman 1871

First, Jur 'Tith': *Hydractinia* sp. Mainly L. Cret, L. Eoc-Quat Holo, but tentative records in Jur, earliest uncertain. One family, Hydractiniidae Agassiz. **Extant.**

Suborder CALYPTOBLASTINA Allman 1871

First, Camb M. Camb: *Archaeocryptolaria skeatsi* Chapman and 2 other spp, *Archaeolafoea longicornis* Chapman and 3 other spp, *Protohalecium hallianum* Chapman & Thomas, *Sphenoecium filicoides* (Chapman) and 1 other sp, all from Dinesus-Hydroid beds and equivalents, "low in M. Camb", Victoria, S. Australia (Chapman & Skeats 1919; Chapman & Thomas 1936), may all belong to this Suborder. Also *Archaeolafoea terranovaensis* Howell, M. Camb., Kelligrew Brook fm., Paradoxides davidis Z, Murphy's Cove, Little Lawn Harbor, Burin Peninsula, southern Newfoundland (Howell 1963). Many extant families.   **Extant.**

Medusae of Order HYDROIDA Johnston 1836

General comment: Coastal waters, rarely open ocean.

Suborder GYMNOBLASTINA (Anthomedusina) Haeckel 1879

First, Carb U. Carb: *Crucimedusina walcotti* (Barbour), "U. Penn.", zone unknown, Burlington quarries, South Bend, Nebraska (Barbour 1914, Harrington & Moore 1955) may belong to this Suborder.   **Extant.**
Constituent families: Sarsiidae Forbes, Quat Holo; Cladonematidae Gegenbaur, Holo; Oceaniidae Eschscholtz (*Crucimedusina*, see above; otherwise Holo).

Suborder CALYPTOBLASTINA (Leptomedusina) Haeckel 1879

Extant only. *Protodipleurosoma wardi* Sprigg, Pre-Camb Varang, Pound Quartzite fm., Upper Adelaide Series, Ediacara, S. Australia (Sprigg 1949; Glaessner & Daily 1959, pp. 380–1), placed in Thaumantiadidae in Treatise F, but in synonymy of *Ediacaria flindersi* (medusae incertae sedis, *q.v.*) by Glaessner & Wade 1966.
Constituent families: Thaumantiadidae Gegenbaur, Quat Holo (see above); Eucopidae Gegenbaur, Holo; Aequoreidae Eschscholtz, Holo.

Order SIPHONOPHORIDA Eschscholtz 1829

General comment: Typically pelagic, world-wide, more abundant in warm waters. A few forms live in moderate depths.

Suborder CALYCOPHORINA Leuckart 1854

Extant only. 4 families, no known fossil representatives.

Suborder PHYSOPHORINA Eschscholtz 1829

Extant only. 5 families, no known fossil representatives.

Suborder RHIZOPHYSALIINA Chun 1882

Extant only. 2 families, no known fossil representatives.

Suborder CHONDROPHORINA Chamisso & Eysenhardt 1821

First, Pre-Camb Varang: *Ovatoscutum concentricum* Glaessner & Wade, Pound Quartzite fm., Upper Adelaide Series, Ediacara, S. Australia (Glaessner & Wade 1966) may belong to this Suborder.   **Extant.**
Constituent families: Velellidae Brandt [fossil forms include *Plectodiscus molestus* Ruedemann, and *P. cortlandensis* Caster, Dev Frasn, Ithaca Beds, New York (Caster 1942a); also *Palaeonectris discoidea* Rauff, Dev Gedinn, Bundenbacher Schiefer, Kirn, Germany (Rauff 1939)]; Porpitidae Brandt [fossil forms include *O. concentricum*, see above; *Discophyllum peltatum* Hall, Ord Carad, Hudson river gp, Snake Hill sh, South Troy, New York (Ruedemann 1916); *Palaeoscia floweri* Caster, Ord Carad, Corryville member, McMillan fm., Cincinnatian Ser., Stonelick Creek, Clermont County, Ohio (Caster 1942a); *Paropsonema mirabile* (Chapman), Sil, "Melbournian series", Brunswick, N. of Melbourne, S. Australia (Chapman 1926); *P. cryptophya* (Clarke), Dev Frasn, Naples bed, New York (Clarke 1902, Ruedemann 1916)].

Chapter 10: Coelenterata

Order SPONGIOMORPHIDA Alloiteau 1952

First, Trias Olenek: *Spongiomorpha* Frech, *Heptastylis* Frech and *Stromatomorpha* Frech; characteristic of Trias and widely distributed in warm waters of Tethys. Actual first record uncertain. (Frech 1890, LeMaitre 1935).

Last, Jur 'Tith': *Heptastylis stromatoporoides* Frech and *Stromatomorpha stylifera* Frech occur in Jur of Asia and N. Africa. Actual last record uncertain (Refs. as above).

Order MILLEPORINA Hickson 1901

First, Tert Dan: *Millepora parva* Nielsen, Danian chalk, Faxe quarry, Denmark (Nielsen 1919) may belong to this Order. **Extant.**

Constituent families: Milleporidae Fleming (Tert Dan—Quat Holo); Axoporidae Boschma (Tert Eoc-Olig). Commonly found on coral reefs. Classification here follows Treatise F (Sokolov (1962) has Order Hydrocorallina, with families Milleporidae, Axoporidae and Stylasteridae).

Order STYLASTERINA Hickson & England 1905

First, Tert Dan: *Sporadopora faxensis* Nielsen, *Pliobothrus dispergens* Nielsen, *P. laevis* Nielsen, *Errina* (*Inferiolabiata*) *irregularis* (Nielsen), *Errina* (*Errina*) *lobata* (Nielsen), *Congregopora nasiformis* Nielsen, *Astya crassus* (Nielsen), *Conopora arborescens* Nielsen, Danian chalk, Faxe quarry, Denmark (Nielsen 1919). **Extant.**

Constituent family: Stylasteridae Gray. Shallow-water, especially tropical, but also in deeper seas; world-wide distribution.

Order SPHAERACTINIDA Yavorsky 1962 (as in Sokolov 1962)

First, Carb U. Carb: *Palaeoaplysina* sp. Krotov 1888, Urals and Timan, U.S.S.R. (Sokolov 1962 pp. 151–2) may belong to this Order.

Last, Cret Cenom: *Cycloporidium tuberiforme*, Parona, *Ellipsactinia* cf. *micropora* Canavari, and *Sphaeractinia* sp. cf. *dicotoma* Canavari, Calcari di Scogliera, Monti di Bagno, Italy (Parona 1909) may belong to this Order.

Constituent families: Heterastridiidae Frech, Trias; Sphaeractinidae Waagen & Wentzel, ?U. Carb—Cret ?Cenom.

Comment: Kühn (1927, 1939) placed sphaeractinoids in separate order. Tentatively assigned to Suborder Gymnoblastina by Hill and Wells in Treatise F. Partly excluded from stromatoporoids and partly included in stromatoporoid family Actinostromatidae by Lecompte in Treatise F. Excluded from stromatoporoids by Stearn (1966).

Order STROMATOPOROIDEA Nicholson & Murie 1878

First, Camb: *Actinostroma* Nicholson and *Clathrodictyon* Nicholson & Murie, cosmopolitan (Nicholson 1886–92, Nicholson & Murie 1878).

Last, Tert L. Eoc: *Milleporella adriatica* (Chalmas), Italy (Lecompte, Treatise F138).

Comment: Classification into families not universally agreed; 10 listed by Lecompte in Treatise F. First and last records of families not included owing to death of original contributor, Prof. R. G. S. Hudson. For recent references see Stearn 1966. [G.T.]

MEDUSAE INCERTAE SEDIS

First, Pre-Camb Varang: Special mention must be made of the Late Pre-Camb medusae from the Pound Quartzite Fm., Upper Adelaide Series, Ediacara, S. Australia, described by Glaessner & Wade (1966), who believe it premature to attempt suprageneric classification. Taxa: *Ediacaria flindersi* Sprigg [*Protodipleurosoma wardi* Sprigg in synonymy]; *Beltanella gilesi* Sprigg [Possible synonym of *Ediacaria*]; *Medusinites asteroides* (Sprigg) [*Protolyella asteroides* (Sprigg) in synonymy]; *Cyclomedusa davidi* Sprigg, *C. radiata* Sprigg, *C. plana* Glaessner & Wade [*Madigania* Sprigg, *Tateana* Sprigg, *Ediacaria* Sprigg (partim), *Spriggia* Southcott in synonymy]; *Mawsonites spriggi* Glaessner & Wade ["approaches Stauromedusae"]; *Conomedusites lobatus* Glaessner & Wade ["resemblance to Ordovician *Conchopeltis alternata* Walcott," see Order Conulariida];

353

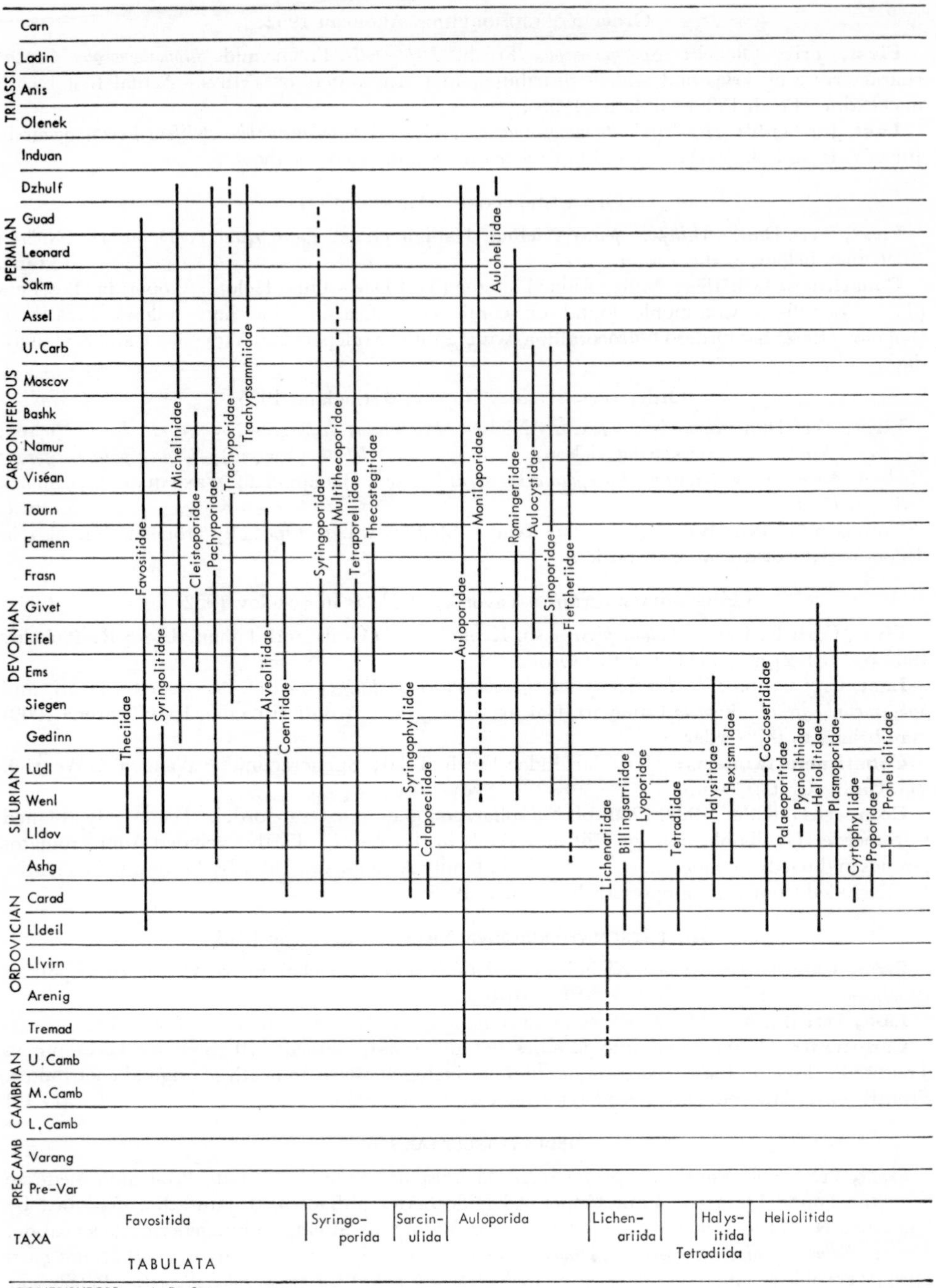

FIG. 10.2A

CONTRIBUTORS   I. D. Sutton

Lorenzinites rarus Glaessner & Wade ["resembles *Palaeosemaeostoma* Rüger from German M. Jur", classified as Trachylinida incertae sedis in Treatise F76]; *Pseudorhizostomites howchini* Sprigg [*Pseudorhopilema* Sprigg, *Protolyella* Torell (partim) in synonymy]; *Rugoconites enigmaticus* Glaessner & Wade; *Kimberia* quadrata Glaessner & Wade ["May belong to Leptomedusae, Trachymedusina or Carybdeida"]; [*Ovatoscutum concentricum* Glaessner & Wade—see under Suborder Chondrophorina].

Last, Cret Valang-Barrem: *Atollites zitteli* Maas, Warnsdorfer Schichten (Moravia and Silesia), Carpathia, Germany (Maas 1902).

Comment: Various Medusae Incertae Sedis occur between the above records. [G.T.]

Class ANTHOZOA

Sub-class TABULATA

Introduction: The classification in this section is based on that of Sokolov *in* Orlov (1962). The genera in the families of Sokolov are closely adhered to, the one major difference in this present work being that the Heliolitids are here regarded as an Order of the Sub-Class Tabulata rather than as a separate sub-class. [In addition to Sokolov (1962), the following references are also given: Bassler (1950), Buchler (1955), Edwards & Haime (1855), Hill & Strumm (*in* Treatise F,) Lang, Smith & Thomas (1940), and Nicholson (1879).—Ed.]

Order FAVOSITIDA Sokolov 1962

Family THECIIDAE Edwards and Haime 1850

First, Sil Lldov: *Thecia swinderniana* (Goldfuss) 1829, U. Lldov, numerous localities, Great Britain; and *Romingerella major* Rominger 1876, U. Clintonian, Indiana.

Last, Sil Ludl: *Thecia swinderniana* (Goldfuss) 1829, Kamentz Podolski, bank of Smotryez R., Ukraine; and Aymestry Lst, England.

Family FAVOSITIDAE Dana 1846

First, Ord Lldeil: *Favosites ramulosus* Phillips 1848, Abberley, England.
Last, Perm Guad: *Favosites relictus* Gerth 1924, Yugoslavia and Timor.

Family SYRINGOLITIDAE Waagen and Wentzel, 1886

First, Sil Lldov: *Syringolites huronensis* Hind 1879, Brassfield-Sexton Creek Lst, nr. Hamburg and Custer Park, W. Illinois.

Last, Carb Tourn: *Roemeripora arctica, R. fenitima* and *R. golovanovi* Smirnova 1957, L. Carb, Russian Arctic.

Family MICHELINIDAE Waagen and Wentzel 1886

First, Dev Gedinn: *Pleurodictyum* Goldfuss 1829, numerous species, cosmopolitan.
Last, Perm Dzhulf. *Michelinia* Konnick 1841, numerous species, Europe and Asia.

Family CLEISTOPORIDAE Easton 1944

First, Dev Ems: *Cleistopora geometrica* Nicholson 1888, Vire and Loue, N.W. France.
Last, Carb Bashk: *Palaeacis testata* and *P. walcotti* Moore and Jeffords 1945, Smithwick Fm, Llano region, Texas.

Family PACHYPORIDAE Gerth 1921

First, Ord Ashg: *Thamnopora lonsdalei* (D'Orbigny) 1850, Kegel Fm, Dalarne, Sweden.
Last, Perm Dzhulf: *Thamnopora jabiensis* (Waagen and Wentzel) 1886, Djoulfa on the Arexes R., Iran. Also *T. jabiensis, T. lobata* (Gerth) 1922, and *T. monstrosa* (Gerth) 1922 and *T. curvata* (Waagen and Wentzel) 1886, Timor.

Family TRACHYPORIDAE Waagen and Wentzel 1886

First, Dev Siegen: *Trachypora oriskania* Weller 1903, Orbiculoidea Jervensis Z, Oriskany Fm, Wallpack Ridge, 5 mls. S. of New York Line, New Jersey.

Last, Perm Sakm-Dzjulf: *Gertholites curvata* Sokolov 1955, Salt Range, Pakistan.

The Fossil Record, Part II

Family TRACHYPSAMMIIDAE Gerth 1921

First, Perm Assel: *Oculinella gerthi* Yakovlev 1939, Oufimskoe Plateau, Urals, U.S.S.R.
Last, Perm Dzhulf: *Trachypsammia dendroides* Gerth 1922, Basleo Lst, Timor. E. Indies.

Family ALVEOLITIDAE Duncan 1872

First, Sil Lldov: *Alveolites labechi* Edwards and Haime 1851, Shallock Mill Beds, Girvan, Ayrshire, Scotland.
Last, Carb Tourn: *Alveolites depressus* (Eichwald) 1865, Kaluga, Kaluga Province, U.S.S.R.

Family COENITIDAE Sardeson 1896

First, Ord Carad: *Coenites fruticosus* Steiniger 1831, *C. juniperinus* Eichwald 1829 and *C. repens* (Fougt in Lamarck) 1749, Bala Lst, Presteign, Radnorshire, Wales.
Last, Dev Famenn: *Scoliopora denticulata* (Edwards and Haime) 1851, U. Dev beds of Europe.

Order SYRINGOPORIDA

Family SYRINGOPORIDAE Nicholson 1879

First, Ord Carad: *Syringopora lonsdaleiana* (McCoy) 1846, Carad Lst, Scotland.
Last, Perm Leonard-Guad: *Syringopora fischeri* Geinitz 1863, Zechstein, Pössneck, Germany.

Family MULTITHECOPORIDAE Sokolov 1950

First, Dev Givet: *Syringoporella moravica* Roemer 1883, Klein—Latein, nr. Olmütz, Czechoslovakia.
Last, Carb U. Carb-Perm Assel: *Multithecopora grandis* Grabau 1936, Maping Lst, Kwangsi and Kweichow, China.

Family TETRAPORELLIDAE Sokolov 1950

First, Ord Ashg: *Tetraporella monticulipoioides* Sokolov 1947, Cape Calhoun Fm, N.E. side of Kane Basin, N.W. Greenland.
Last, Perm Dzhulf: *Hayasakaia aequitabulata* (Huang) 1932, *H. elegantula* (Yabe and Hayasaka) 1915, and *H. lanchugensis* (Huang) 1932, Wushan Lst, Hupei and N. Szechuan, China.

Family THECOSTEGITIDAE Sokolov 1950

First, Dev Ems: *Chonostegites clappi* Edwards and Haime 1851, Onondaga Lst, Williamsville, New York and Ontario.
Last, Dev Famenn: *Thecostegites bouchardi* (Michelin) 1846, N.E. of Arrondisement of Avesnes, N. France.

Order SARCINULIDA Sokolov 1962

Family SYRINGOPHYLLIDAE Pocta 1902

First, Ord Carad: *Sarcinula organum* (Linnaeus) 1758, from many N. European localities.
Last, Sil Wenl: *Sarcinula organum* (Linnaeus) 1758, from many N. European localities.

Family CALAPOECIIDAE Radugin 1938

First, Ord Carad: *Calapoecia canadensis* Billings 1865, Kimmswick Lst, nr. Batchtown, Illinois.
Last, Ord Ashg: *Calapoecia anticostiensis* Billings 1865, Ellis Bay Fm, Ellis Bay and Prinsta Bay, Anticosti Island, Canada.

Chapter 10: Coelenterata

Order AULOPORIDA Sokolov 1962

Family AULOPORIDAE Edwards and Haime 1851

First, Camb U. Camb: *Protoaulopora ramosa* Sokolov 1950 (*Syringopora ramosa*, Vologdin 1931) U. Camb, Kazakhstan.

Last, Perm Dzhulf: *Aulopora timorica* Gerth 1922, Basleo Lst, Timor, E. Indies.

Family MONILOPORIDAE Grabau 1899

First, Dev Ems: *Cladochonus intraspinosus* Wohburg, Oppershofen, Germany. *Cladochonus? siluriensis,* Ball and Grove 1940, Sil Wenl., Bainbridge Lst, S.E. Missouri, may belong to this family.

Last, Perm Dzhulf: *Cladochonus dendroidea* (Yoh) 1932, Likodra, Yugoslavia and *C. beecheri* Gerth 1922, *C. crassus* (?McCoy) 1844 and *C. magnus* Gerth 1922, Basleo Lst, Timor, E. Indies.

Family AULOHELIIDAE Sokolov 1950

First and Last, Perm Dzhulf: *Aulohelia irregularis* Gerth 1921 and *A. laevis* Gerth 1921, Basleo Lst, Timor, E. Indies.

Family ROMINGERIIDAE Sokolov 1950

First, Sil Wenl: *Romingeria vannula* Davis 1887, Louisville Lst, Louisville, Kentucky.

Last, Perm Leonard: *Romingeria kotoi* Yabe and Hayasaka 1915 (*Pseudoromingeria* Yabe and Sugiyama 1941), Kinshozan, Akasaka, Province of Mino, Japan.

Family AULOCYSTIDAE Sokolov 1950

First, Dev Eifel: *Aulocystis entalophoroides* Schlüter 1885, Gerolstein, Germany.

Last, Carb U. Carb: *Aulocystella syringoporoides* Kuzina in Sokolov 1955, U. Carb, Donetz Basin.

Family SINOPORIDAE Sokolov 1955

First, Sil Wenl: *Cylindrostylus turcmensaica* (Rukhin) 1937, Sil, Kazakhstan.

Last, Carb U. Carb: *Rossopora alta* Sokolov 1955 and *Sinopora dendroides* (Yoh) 1932, U. Carb, Russia.

Family FLETCHERIIDAE Zittel 1876

First, Ord Ashg: *Fletcheriella evenkiana* Sokolov 1955, U. Ord, Siberian Platform.

Last, Perm Assel: *Seleucites tschernyschevi* (Stuckenberg) 1898, Artinskian, W. Urals.

Order LICHENARIIDA Sokolov 1962

Family LICHENARIIDAE Okulitch 1936

First, Camb U. Camb: *Bija sibirica* Vologdin 1932, U. Camb, Altai Mts., U.S.S.R. Possibly not a tabulate coral but appears to be ancestral to *Lichenaria*. If not, then **first,** Ord Arenig: *Lichenaria cloudi* Bassler 1950, Tanyard Fm, San Saba, Texas and *L. simplex* (Bassler) 1919, Nittany dolomite, Virginia.

Last, Ord Carad: *Lichenaria minor* Ulrich 1875, Minnesota, Ontario and Tennessee.

Family BILLINGSARIIDAE Okulitch 1936

First, Ord Lldeil: *Billingsaria parva* (Billings) 1859, Valcour Lst, Lake Champlain Region New York and Vermont; Mingan Fm, Quebec, and Lenoir Lst, Tennessee. Also *Nyctopora, vantuyli* Bassler 1950, Valcour Lst, Middleburg, Vermont.

Last, Ord Ashg: *Nyctopora* Nicholson 1879, *Saffordophyllum* Bassler 1950 and *Foerstephyllum* Bassler 1941. Numerous species of these three genera in N. America and two species of *Nyctopora* in Norway.

Family LYOPORIDAE Kiaer 1930

First, Ord Lldeil: *Eofletcheria incerta* (Billings) 1859, Valcour Lst, Sloop Island, New York; Minegan Fm, Quebec, and Aylmer Lst, Ontario. Also *E. laxa* Bassler 1950, Lenoir Lst, Friendsville, Tennessee.

Last, Sil Lldov: *Reuschia aperta* Kiaer 1930, Island of Strand, Bergen area, Norway.

The Fossil Record, Part II

Order TETRADIIDA Sokolov 1962

Family TETRADIIDAE Nicholson 1879

First, Ord Lldeil: *Tetradium syringoporoides* Ulrich 1910, Aymler Lst, Ottawa Valley, Ontario.
Last, Ord Ashg: *Tetradium* Dana 1848, five species, N. America.

Order HALYSITIDA Sokolov 1962

Family HALYSITIDAE Edwards and Haime 1850

First, Ord Carad: *Catenipora quebecensis* (Lambe) 1899, Blackriveran, Chaumont Lst, 2 mls.
S. of Blue Point, Lake St. John, Quebec.
Last, Dev Ems: *Halysites catenularia longicatena* Weissermel 1939, Agrelopus Lst, Kambia-Tal,
Chios, Aegaean Sea.

Family HEXISMIIDAE Sokolov 1950

First, Ord Ashg: *Labyrinthites childensis* Lambe 1906. Richmondian, Cape Chidley, Hudson
Strait, N. America.
Last, Sil Wenl: *Hexismia compactus* (Rominger) 1876. Lockport Dolomite, Guelph division,
Guelph, Elora and Hespeler, Ontario.

Order HELIOLITIDA Sokolov 1962

Sub-Order PROTARAEINA Leith 1952

Family COCCOSERIDIDAE Kiaer 1899

First, Ord Lldeil: *Protarea confluens* (Eichwald) 1856 and *P. diffluens* (Eichwald) 1856, Orthoceras Lst, Wesenberg, Estonia.
Last, Sil Ludl: *Cosmiolithus ornatus* Lindström 1899, L. Ludl, Mulde Shales, Fröjel, Gotland.

Family PALAEOPORITIDAE Kiaer 1899

First, Ord Carad: *Trochiscolithus micraster* (Lindström) 1899, U. Ord, Norway, Sweden and
Estonia.
Last, Ord Ashg: *Palaeoporites estonicus* Kiaer 1899, Borkholm Beds, Borkholm, Estonia and
U. Chasmops Beds, Norway.

Family PYCNOLITHIDAE Lindström 1899

First and **Last,** Sil Lldov. *Pycnolithus bifidus* Lindström 1899, L. Wisby Sh, Gotland.

Sub-Order HELIOLITINA

Family HELIOLITIDAE Lindström 1873

First, Ord Lldeil: *Heliolites inordinatus* (Lonsdale) 1839, Robeston Walthen, Pembrokeshire.
Wales.
Last, Dev Frasn: *Heliolites porosus* Goldfuss 1826, Torquay and Plymouth, England, and Ron,
Annam, Indo-China.

Family PLASMOPORIDAE Wentzel 1895

First, Ord Carad: *Plasmopora petalliformis* Lonsdale 1839, Coniston Lst, Coniston, England,
and Carmarthenshire, Wales.
Last, Dev Eifel: *Plasmopora carnica* Vinassa 1918, M. Dev Carinthia, Austria. Also *P. micropora* Edwards and Haime 1851, M. Dev, Eifel, Germany.

Family CYRTOPHYLLIDAE Sokolov 1950

First and **Last,** Ord Carad: *Cyrtophyllum densum* Lindström 1882, M. Tunguska R., Siberia
and *Karagemia altaica* Dzubo 1960, Altai mountains, Russia.

Chapter 10: Coelenterata

Sub-Order PROPORINA Sokolov 1962

Family PROPORIDAE Sokolov 1950

First, Ord Carad: *Propora tubulata* (Lonsdale) 1839, L. Carad, Bala Lst, Merionethshire, Wales.

Last, Sil Ludl: *Propora conferta* Edwards and Haime 1851, *P. magnifica* Pocta 1902 and *P. tubulata* (Lonsdale) 1839, Tachlowitz, Bohemia.

Family PROHELIOLITIDAE

First, Ord Ashg: *Proheliolites dubius* (Schmidt) 1858, Keisley Lst, Cross Fell Inlier, N.W. England.

Last, Sil Lldov: *Proheliolites dubius* (Schmidt) 1858, Ojle myr, Gotland. Possibly from Ord drift. If so, last member of this family is *P. dubius* (Schmidt) 1858, U. Ashg, from many European localities.   [I.D.S.]

Sub-Class RUGOSA E. and H. 1850

Introduction: Two recent revisions of this group of corals (Treatise F; Sokolov 1962) have illustrated the profound disagreement which exists between specialists, in preparing a classification of the Rugosa. As space is not available to consider 600 or more genera in detail, the broad outlines of the classification proposed in Treatise F are used, with certain minor amendments, realizing that the inclusion or exclusion of certain disputed genera in the various families will have a serious effect on the stratigraphical range of these families. Wherever possible the limits of the range are marked by species certainly included in the listed family. Families marked by a (*) contain many disputed genera which could seriously effect the stratigraphical ranges. Three families not used by the Treatise F but which were used by either Formichev (1953) or by Sokolov (1962) are included here; otherwise the revisions and new families proposed by the two works have not been followed. [In addition to references used in this section, the following have been given: Bassler (1950), Easton (1960), Hill (1951, 1960), and Schouppe & Stacul (1955).—Ed.]

Order STREPTELASMATIDA Wedekind 1927

Sub-Order CYATHAXONIINA E. and H. 1850

General comment: First record of sub-order is *Lambeophyllum*, see below. Last is Perm Leonard and Guad, at least 18 genera from N. America, Europe and Asia, including the Polycoelidae fauna of Timor (Guad and ?Dzhulf) probably the last of all.

Family METRIOPHYLLIDAE Hill 1939

First, Ord Carad: *Lambeophyllum profundium* (Conrad) 1843, Blackriver Fm, N. gracilis Z., N. America.

Last, Carb Bashk; *Stereocorypha* Moore and Jeffords 1945, Morrow Fm, U.S.A. All Perm records of this family are doubtful.

Family LACCOPHYLLIDAE Grabau 1928

First, Sil Lldov: *Syringaxon* Lindström 1882.

Last, Dev Famenn: *Barrandeophyllum* Počta 1902, or possibly *Amplexocarinia* Soshkina 1928, Perm Leonard.

359

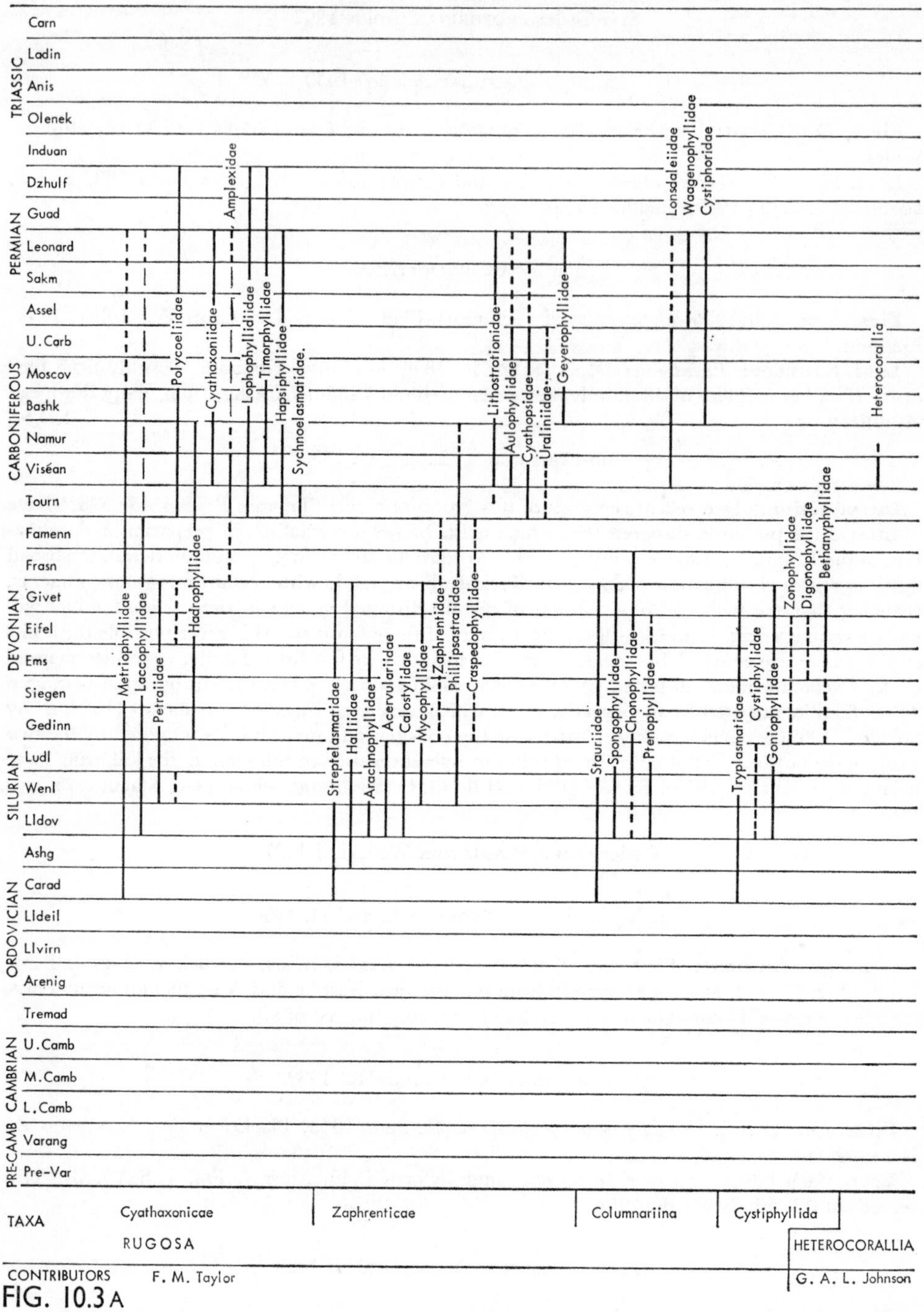
TRIASSIC
Carn
Ladin
Anis
Olenek
PERMIAN
Induan
Dzhulf
Guad
Leonard
Sakm
Assel
CARBONIFEROUS
U. Carb
Moscov
Bashk
Namur
Viséan
Tourn
DEVONIAN
Famenn
Frasn
Givet
Eifel
Ems
Siegen
Gedinn
SILURIAN
Ludl
Wenl
Lldov
ORDOVICIAN
Ashg
Carad
Lldeil
Llvirn
Arenig
Tremad
CAMBRIAN
U. Camb
M. Camb
L. Camb
PRE-CAMB
Varang
Pre-Var
Metriophyllidae
Laccophyllidae
Petraiidae
Hadrophyllidae
Polycoeliidae
Cyathaxoniidae
Amplexidae
Lophophyllidiidae
Timorphyllidae
Hapsiphyllidae
Sychnoelasmatidae.
Streptelasmatidae
Halliidae
Arachnophyllidae
Acervulariidae
Calostylidae
Mycophyllidae
Zaphrentidae
Phillipsastraiidae
Craspedophyllidae
Lithostrotionidae
Aulophyllidae
Cyathopsidae
Uraliniidae
Geyerophyllidae
Lonsdaleiidae
Waagenophyllidae
Cystiphoridae
Stauriidae
Spongophyllidae
Chonophyllidae
Prenophyllidae
Tryplasmatidae
Cystiphyllidae
Goniophyllidae
Zonophyllidae
Digonophyllidae
Bethanyphyllidae
Heterocorallia
TAXA
Cyathaxonicae
Zaphrenticae
Columnariina
Cystiphyllida
RUGOSA
HETEROCORALLIA
CONTRIBUTORS
F. M. Taylor
G. A. L. Johnson

FIG. 10.3 A

Chapter 10: Coelenterata

Family PETRAIIDAE de Koninck 1872

First, Sil Wenl: *Petraia decussata* (Münster), Europe only; all other stratigraphical records of this genus should be verified; they are probably species of other families, particularly Streptelasmatidae.

Last, Dev Eifel-Givet: *Orthophyllum* Počta 1902.

Comment, Only two or three genera in this family.

Family POLYCOELIIDAE Roemer 1883

First: Carb Tourn, e.g. *Claviphyllum* Hudson 1942. Early genera, said to be of this family, can only doubtfully be included, e.g., Sil Wenl, *Anisophyllum* E. and H. 1850, and M. Dev *Oligophyllum* Počta 1902.

Last, Perm Guad-Dzhulf: Polycoelidae fauna of Timor.

Comment: Family here includes Plerophyllidae Koker 1924 and Tachylasmatidae Grabau 1928. Most genera belong to Carb or Perm, and at least 8 genera from Perm Leonard. This family could provide an ancestor for Scleractinia.

Family HADROPHYLLIDAE Nicholson, in N. and Lydekker 1889

First, Dev Gedinn: *Cambophyllum osismorun* E. and H. 1850, France, or various species of *Hadrophyllum* E. and H. 1850, N. America.

Last, Carb Bashk: *Cumminsia* Moore and Jeffords 1945.

Family CYATHAXONIIDAE E. and H. 1850

First, Carb Viséan: *Cyathaxonia* Michelin 1847, Europe, N. America, Asia, Australia.

Last, Perm Leonard: *Cyathocarinia* Soshkina 1928, U.S.S.R.

Comment: 2 genera only.

Family AMPLEXIDAE Chapman 1893

First and **Last,** Carb Tourn Viséan: *Amplexus*, Europe.

Comment: One genus only. The inclusion of *Nalivkinella* Soshkina 1939 in this family would extend range down to U. Dev, whilst *Amplexocarinia* Soshkina 1928 would extend range up to Perm Leonard.

Family LOPHOPHYLLIDIIDAE Moore and Jeffords 1945

First, Carb Tourn: *Lophophyllum konincki* E. and H., but this species is not well documented, otherwise *Lophocarinophyllum* Grabau 1922, China.

Last, Perm Leonard: *Stereostylus* Jeffords 1947.

Comment: Most genera are from U. Carb of Europe, Asia, N. America and ?New Zealand.

Family TIMORPHYLLIDAE Soshkina in S. Dobrolyubova and Porfriev 1941

First, Carb Viséan: *Cravenia* Hudson, England.

Last, Perm Dzjulf: e.g., *Verbeckiella* Gerth 1921, Timor. Most genera are U. Perm.

Family HAPSIPHYLLIDAE Grabau 1928

First, Carb Tourn: *Zaphrentites* Hudson 1941.

Last, Perm Leonard: *Allotropiophyllum* Grabau or *Euryphyllum* Hill 1937.

Comment: The family is recorded from Europe, Australia, New Zealand, Asia and N. America.

Family SYCHNOELASMATIDAE Kabakovitsch 1962

First, Carb Tourn: *Menophyllum* E. and H. 1850 France.

Last, Carb Tourn: *Sychnoelasma* L. and S. 1940, U.S.S.R.

Comment: Two genera only.

Sub-Order ZAPHRENTINA E. and H. 1850

General comment: First record of sub-order is *Streptelasma*, see below. Last is Perm Leonard, at least two genera from the Amygdalophyllinae, and one each from Lithostrotionidae and Cyathopsidae. Others are questionably allocated to families within this order, such as *Endamplexus dentatus* Koker 1924. None of the species are considered to possess morphological characters which would suggest ancestry for the Scleractinia.

Family STREPTELASMATIDAE Nicholson in N. and Lydekker 1889

First, Ord Carad: *Streptelasma corniculum* (Hall) 1847, Blackriver Fm, N. gracilis Z, N. America; closely followed by *Coelostylis toernquisti* Lindstrom 1873, N. America.

Last, Dev Ems-Eifel: at least four genera, e.g. *Siphonophrentis* O'Connell 1914.

Comment: From Ashg, family becomes widespread in N. America, Europe, Asia and Australia; the Acrophyllinae Stumm 1949, are restricted to N. America.

Family HALLIIDAE Chapman 1893

First, Ord Ashg: *Holophragma* Lindström 1896, N. America.

Last, Dev Gedinn-Eifel: Four genera in the Hallinae Chapman, of N. America, and *Aulocophyllum* E. and H. 1850 from New South Wales, Australia.

Comment: Most genera are from Sil, e.g. *Phaulactis* Ryder, Wenl and Ludl. Earlier records of this genus are doubtful and should be verified. The family is recorded from Europe, N. America and Australia. *Pseudocystiphyllum* Wang 1947 China, would extend the geographical range.

*Family ARACHNOPHYLLIDAE Dybowski 1873

First, Sil Lldov: various species of the Arachnophyllinae from Europe, N. America, Australia and Asia.

Last, Dev Gedinn-Siegen: Arachnophyllinae.

Comment: The Kyphophyllinae Wedekind 1927 are restricted to Sil of Gotland, and the Ptychophyllinae Dybowski 1873 to Sil of N. America.

*Family ACERVULARIIDAE Lecompte 1952

First and **Last,** Sil: all genera Europe, N. America, U.S.S.R. *Acervularia adjunctus* White 1880, L. Carb, N. America, probably not *Acervularia* Schweigger 1819.

Family CALOSTYLIDAE Roemer 1883

First and **Last,** Sil: at least three genera. The family may not belong to the Zaphrentina.

*Family MYCOPHYLLIDAE Hill 1940

First, Sil Wenl: *Mucophyllum* Etheridge 1894.

Last, Dev Ems-Eifel: *Aspasmophyllum* Roemer 1880.

Comment: The family is recorded from Europe and Australia.

*Family ZAPHRENTIDAE E. and H. 1850

First and **Last,** Dev: all genera, N. America, Europe, Australia, S. America.

Family PHILLIPSASTRAIIDAE Roemer 1883

First, Sil Wenl: *Disphyllum* de Fromental 1861, New South Wales: elsewhere this genus is Dev.

Last, Carb Viséan-Namur: *Hexagonaria* Gurich 1896 from China; this genus is normally Dev.

Comment: Most genera in the family are Dev in age, including the Phacelliphyllinae. The family is cosmopolitan.

Family CRASPEDOPHYLLIDAE Dybowski 1873

First and **Last,** Dev: one genus only, from N. America and Morocco.

Chapter 10: Coelenterata

Family LITHOSTROTIONIDAE D'Orbigny 1851

First, Carb Tourn-Viséan: *Lithostrotion* Fleming 1828, e.g. *L. sociale* (Phillips) 1826, ?C_1 Z., Tourn, certainly Viséan, C_2 Z.

Last, Perm Leonard: *Tschussovkenia capitosa* Dobrolyubova 1936, also *Diphyphyllum connorsessis* Easton 1960, L. Perm (?Assel) of Nevada. Two other Perm genera doubtfully included in this family are *Lithostrotionella*, Yabe and Hayasaka 1915 and *Thysanophyllum* Nicholson and Thomson 1876 (Easton 1960).

Comment: A cosmopolitan family. Most genera belong to Viséan and Namur, E Z.

Family AULOPHYLLIDAE Dybowski 1873 (or
CLISIOPHYLLIDAE Nicholson and Thomson 1883)

First, Carb Viséan: a large number of genera from Europe, N. America, Asia and N. Africa, incl. *Clisiophyllum*, Dana 1846, *Aulophyllum* E. and H. 1850 *Dibunophyllum* Thomson and Nicholson 1876 and *Amygdalophyllum* Dun and Benson 1920.

Last, Carb U. Carb: *Amandophyllum* Heritsch 1941, Tricites Z., Carnic Alps. *Yatsengia* Haung 1932, Perm Leonard probably belongs to another family.

*Family CYATHOPSIDAE Dybowski 1873

First, Carb Tourn: *Caninia* Michelin, in Gervais 1840, e.g. *C. cornucopiae*, Zaphrentis Z, England and Belgium.

Last, Carb U. Carb: *Timania* Stuckenburg 1895, U.S.S.R. and Spitsbergen. Other genera could extend the range of the family into Perm Leonard if they are included in the right family, e.g. *Endamplexus* Koker 1924, Australia, and *Paracaninia* Chi 1937, China. *Caninia hanseni* Wilson & Langenheim 1962 is recorded from L. Perm (?Assel) of Nevada.

Family URALINIDAE Dobrolyubova 1962

First and Last, Carb: all genera, U.S.S.R., China and Canada.

Family GEYEROPHYLLIDAE Minato 1955

First, Carb ?Bashk: *Kionophyllum* Chi, China.
Last, Perm Leonard: *Lonsdaleiodes* Heritsch 1936, Carnic Alps.

Order COLUMNARIIDA Rominger 1876

General comment: First record of order is Ord Carad *Favositella*, see below; last are Perm Leonard, at least seven are genera from the Waagenophyllinae, China and Japan.

Family STAURIDAE E. and H. 1850

First, Ord Carad: *Favisitella alveolata* (Goldfuss), Trenton Fm, D. Clingani Z, N. America, possibly also from the Blackriver Fm, N. Gracilis Z. usually recorded as *Columnaria* sp.

Last, Dev Ems-Eifel: *Columnaria sulcata* M'Coy.

Comment: Initially distributed in N. America, the family is cosmopolitan in U. Ord and Sil. *Kwangsiphyllum* Grabau and Yoh, in Yoh, 1931, L. Carb of China, probably not Columnariida.

Family SPONGOPHYLLIDAE Dybowski 1873

First, Sil Lldov: *Taimyrophyllum* Tchernychev 1941, U.S.S.R., or Wenl; *Spongophyllum* E. and H. 1851 Australia.

Last, Dev: Most species of this family are from the L.-M. Dev. *Tabellaeaphyllum* Stumm 1948, U. Dev, N. America, may extend the range of this family.

Family CHONOPHYLLIDAE Homes 1887

First, Sil Wenl: *Chonophyllum* E. and H. 1850, Gotland, or *Ketophyllum* 1927, Europe and China. Many genera of the Endophyllinae, Torley 1937, L. and M. Dev. *Strombodes* Schweigger 1819, if included in the family, would extend range down to Sil. Lldov.

Last, Dev Frasn: *Smithiphyllum* Berenheim 1962, N. America and Timor.

Family PTENOPHYLLIDAE Wedekind 1923

First, Sil Lldov: *Cymatelasma* Hill and Butler 1936, England.

Last, Dev Ems-Eifel: *Acanthophyllum* spp., e.g. *A. (Grypophyllum) denckmanni*, Germany and *Neostringophyllum* Wedekind 1922.

Comment: Most genera are from M. Dev, e.g. *Acanthophyllum* Dybowski 1873, and are cosmopolitan. This family may be closer to the Zaphrentina than the Columnariina. It could also include Stringophyllidae Wedekind 1921, containing only one genus from L.-M. Dev of Europe and Australia.

Family LONSDALEIIDAE Chapman 1893

First, Carb Viséan: *Londsdaleia* McCoy 1849 e.g. *L. duplicata.* Most of Europe and Asia, Viséan or Namur.

Last, Perm Leonard: *Lonsdaleia illipahensis* Easton 1960. Another species, *L. cordillerensis,* has since been allocated to *Durhamina,* Wilson & Langenheim 1962 and placed in Lithostrotionidae.

Family WAAGENOPHYLLIDAE Wang 1950

First and **Last,** Perm Assel-Leonard: all species, mainly from Asia but *Heritschia* Moore and Jeffords 1941 is also found in Europe and N. America.

Family CYSTOPHORIDAE Formitchev 1953

First, Carb Bashk: all genera, Asia.
Last, Perm Leonard: all genera, Asia.

Order CYSTIPHYLLIDA Nicholson in N. and Lydekker 1889

General comment: Early records of this order are represented by spinose members of the Tryplasmatidae, usually considered on other morphological grounds to be "*Columnaria*", from Ord Carad, Blackriver and Trenton Fms, N. Gracilis and D. Clingani Zs, N. America. Also M. Ord, *primitophyllum primum* Kalgo 1956, U.S.S.R. Last records of order are M. Dev Digonophyllidae Wedekind 1923, from Europe, Asia, N. America, Australia.

Family TRYPLASMATIDAE Etheridge 1907

First, Ord ?Carad: *Primitophyllum,* or spinose "*Columnaria*" (see above). These are quickly followed throughout the N. Hemisphere and Australia by U. Ord, *Tryplasma* Lonsdale 1845 and *Rhabdocyclus* Land and Smith 1939.

Last, Dev Ems-Eifel: *Tryplasma* continues into the M. Dev. *Bojocyclus* Prantl 1939, M. Dev of Czechoslovakia, questionably included in this family.

Family CYSTIPHYLLIDAE E. and H. 1850

First and **Last,** Sil: at least six genera, all from Sil of Europe, Asia, N. America and Australia.

Family GONIOPHYLLIDAE Dybowski 1873

First, Sil Lldov: *Goniophyllum pyramidiale* (Hisinger) 1831, Europe.
Last, Dev Ems-Eifel: *Calceola sandalina* Linnaeus 1799, Europe, Asia, N. America, Africa, Australia.

*Family ZONOPHYLLIDAE Wedekind 1924

First and **Last,** Dev Gedinn-Eifel: all genera from Europe, Asia and N. America.

Family DIGONOPHYLLIDAE Wedekind 1923

First and **Last,** Dev Ems-Eifel: all genera, from Europe, Asia, Australia. *Cystiphylloides* Chapman 1893 from N. America.

Chapter 10: Coelenterata

Family BETHANYPHYLLIDAE Stumm 1949

First, Dev Ems: *Glossophyllum* Wedekind 1924, Germany and U.S.S.R. Early genera in L. Dev can only tentatively be included in the family, e.g. *Helliophylloides* Stumm 1937 or *Nevadaphyllum* Stumm 1937.

Last, Dev Givet-Frasn: various species of *Charactophyllum*, Simpson, e.g. *C. nanum* from N. America. [F.M.T.]

Subclass HETEROCORALLIA Schindewolf, 1941

General comment: The heterocorals are a small subclass of very elongate, narrow diameter, cylindrical solitary corals. They possess septa and tabulae but may lack an epitheca, the external wall being formed of thickened steeply sloping edges of tabulae. The method of insertion of the septa is characteristic. Distribution restricted to Carb, Viséan and possibly L. Namur, of Europe and Asia. Only two described genera, *Hexaphyllia* and *Heterophyllia*.

First, Carb Viséan (L.): *Hexaphyllia*? Stuckenberg 1904, C_2S_1 Z., Scotland. This early record is a gregarious form and is probably a new genus; it may well be a member of the ancestral stock of the group (Wilson, 1961).

Last, Carb Viséan (U.): *Hexaphyllia* Stuckenberg 1904 and *Heterophyllia* McCoy 1849, P_{2b} Z., England and Scotland. Namurian records, in *Treatise* F, probably refer to Scottish material now known to be of U Viséan age. [G.A.L.J.]

Subclass SCLERACTINIA Bourne 1900

General comment: The two classifications of this group which have appeared recently are those by Alloiteau (1952) and Wells (In Treatise F). Russian authors (*in* Sokolov 1962) have accepted Alloiteau's classification with only minor amendments. The grouping of genera into families by these authors shows some similarity, so that the main taxon used in this section is the family. Those marked with an (*) contain certain disputed genera which could affect the stratigraphical range of the family. Families proposed by Alloiteau (1952) have caused difficulties in that many of them are based on genera invalid at the time of publication of the 1952 work. Some of these were redescribed in 1957; others still require description and figures. Where invalid genera may affect the range of the family, this is noted in the text. Where numerous species of the same genus appear together, only the genus is listed. As little agreement is apparent above family level, families are listed in the text according to the first appearance of the family in the geological record, rather than on a postulated relationship; in the table accompanying this section, the families are arranged alphabetically. [In addition to references cited specifically in this section, the following have been used: Eguchi 1951; Felix 1914, 1925, 1927, 1929; Squires 1958; and Vaughan & Wells 1943—Ed.]

Family PINACOPHYLLIDAE Vaughan & Wells 1943

First, Trias Anis: *Koilocoenia* Duncan 1884, Germany, Alps, Corsica and Sicily.
Last, Trias Rhaet: *Koilocoenia* and *Pinacophyllum* Frech 1890, Europe.

Family STYLOPHYLLIDAE Volz 1896

First, Trias Anis: *Protoheterastrea leonardi* (Volz) Europe. Numerous species occur in U Trias and those of *Oppelismilia* Duncan 1867 are more widespread, occurring throughout the northern hemisphere and in S. America.

Last, Jur Bajoc: *Lepidophyllia* Duncan 1868, British Isles and S. America, and *Heterastrea* Tomes 1888, Europe. Alloiteau's inclusion of *Trochosmilia* E. & H. 1848 in this family would extend its range into Tert Eoc. Doubtful records of *Trochosmilia* E. & H. 1848 continue into Tert U. Mioc of Spain.

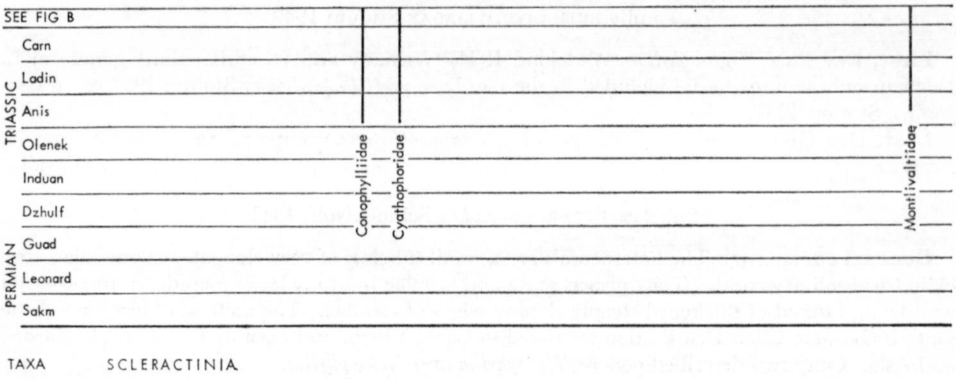

SEE FIG B

Carn				
Ladin				
Anis				
Olenek		Conophylliidae	Cyathophoridae	Montlivaltiidae
Induan				
Dzhulf				
Guad				
Leonard				
Sakm				

TRIASSIC: Carn, Ladin, Anis, Olenek, Induan, Dzhulf
PERMIAN: Guad, Leonard, Sakm

TAXA   SCLERACTINIA

CONTRIBUTORS   F. M. Taylor and I. D. Sutton

FIG. 10.4A

Family CYATHOPHORIDAE Vaughan & Wells 1943

First, Trias Anis: *Procyathophora furstenbergensis* (Eck) 1880 Germany.

Last, Cret Apt: *Cyathophora* Michelin 1843, Europe, N. & S. America; two spp. from Apt of Mexico. *C. monticularia* d'Orbigny 1850 has been doubtfully recorded from Greensand (Alb) of Haldon, England, and from Senonian of France. *Ewaldocoenia hawelkai* Oppenheim 1921, Europe, if a member of this family, extends its range into Tert U. Eoc.

Family MONTLIVALTIIDAE Dietrich 1926

First, Trias Anis: *Montlivaltia* Lamouroux 1821, *Thecosmilia* E. & H. 1848, *Palaeastraea* Kuhn 1936 and *Elyastraea* Laube 1864; Germany, S. Alps, Corsica and Sicily. Later, in Trias Carn, cosmopolitan.

Last, Cret Turon: *Mycetophyllopsis* Oppenheim 1930, Austria; and *Lasmosmilia* d'Orbigny 1949, Europe. The genera *Montlivaltia* and *Thecosmilia* are here restricted in the sense suggested by Wells (1956) and Alloiteau (1952). In other literature *Montlivaltia* spp. have been recorded in beds up to Quat Pleist and *Thecosmilia* spp. from beds as high as Tert Mioc.

Family CONOPHYLLIIDAE Alloiteau 1952

First, Trias Anis: *Triadophyllum posthumum* Weissermel 1925, Austria; in Ladin, *Margarosmilia septanectens* (Loretz) and *Conophyllia boletiformis* (Münster), also Austria.

Last, Trias Rhaet: *Margophyllia crenata* (Münster) Carnic Alps, and *Craspedophyllia* Volz 1896, Europe.

Family THAMNASTERIIDAE Vaughan & Wells 1943

First, Trias Anis: *Thamnasteria* Lesauvage 1823, Europe.

Last, Cret Cenom: *Ahrdorffia stellulata* (Reuss) 1854, Austria. It is possible that two untraced spp. of *Thamnasteria* from Cret Maestr of Maestricht, Netherlands, may well be the youngest representatives of this family. There are many records of *Thamnasteria* from younger rocks, e.g. two spp. from Tert Mioc of Tasmania, but certain authorities (Wells 1956, Alloiteau 1952) consider that *Thamnasteria* should be restricted to Mesozoic rocks at least until Tertiary species have been re-examined. The inclusion of *Psammocora* Dana 1846 in this family would extend its range to the present, in the West Indies, Indian and Pacific Oceans.

*Family ACTINASTRAEIDAE Alloiteau 1952

First, Trias Nor-Rhaet: *Actinastraea* D'Orbigny 1849. This record should be verified as most species of this genus are Cret. *Isastrocoenia kachensis* Gregory 1900, Jur Bath, is possibly the first record.   **Extant:** *Actinastraea* spp., Cosmopolitan.

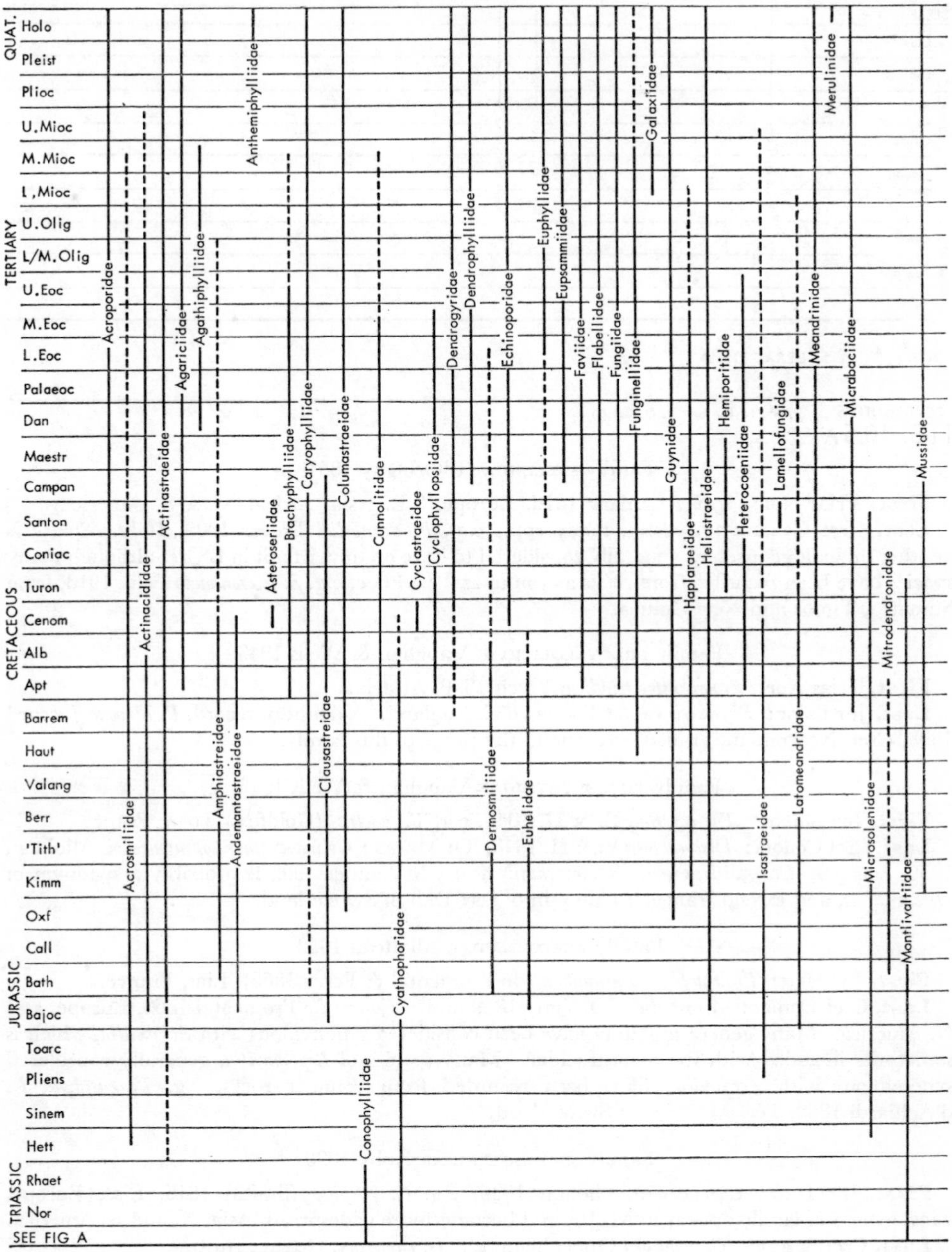

TAXA   SCLERACTINIA

CONTRIBUTORS   F. M. Taylor and I. D. Sutton

FIG. 10.4B

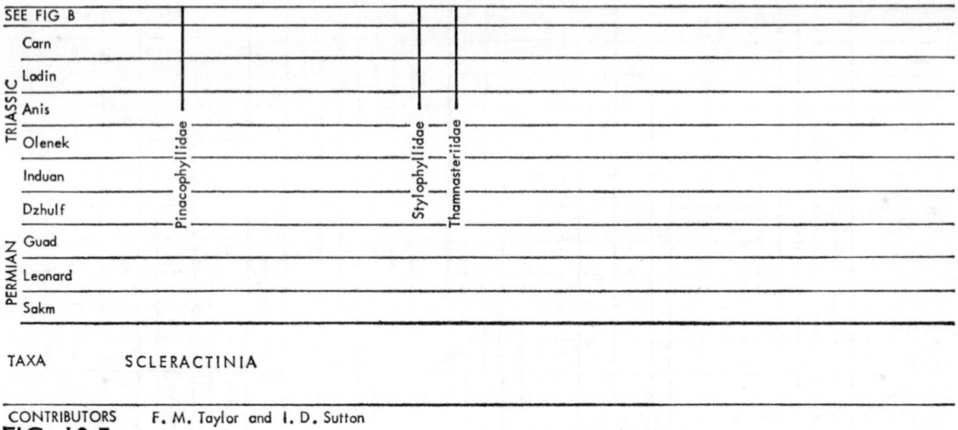

		Pinacophyllidae	Stylophyllidae	Thamnasteriidae
	SEE FIG B			
	Carn			
TRIASSIC	Ladin			
	Anis			
	Olenek			
	Induan			
	Dzhulf			
PERMIAN	Guad			
	Leonard			
	Sakm			

TAXA   SCLERACTINIA

CONTRIBUTORS   F. M. Taylor and I. D. Sutton

FIG. 10.5A

Family STYLINIDAE d'Orbigny 1851

First, Trias Nor: *Stylina* Lamark 1816, Europe, S.E. Asia, Africa, N. & S. America.

Last, Cret Cenom: *Felixigyra*, many spp., e.g., *F. deangelisi* Prever 1909, Italy. *Stylina* is another difficult genus, now generally considered to have an upper limit in L Cret although many species have been recorded from rocks as young as Tert Plioc, e.g. *S. micrommata* Felix 1913, from Sumatra, Timor and New Guinea.

Family PROCYCLOLITIDAE Vaughan & Wells 1943

First, Trias Nor: *Procyclolites triadicus* Frech 1890, Austria.

Last, Jur Bajoc: *Phyloseris rugosa* Tomes 1882, England. A doubtful record, *P. convexa* Jaccord 1893, Cret, Neocomian, France may extend the range of this family.

Family THECOCYATHIDAE Vaughan & Wells 1943

First, Jur Sinem: *Thecocyathus* E. & H. 1848, e.g. *T. mactrus* (Goldfuss) Toarc France.

Last, Cret Cenom: *Discocyathus* E. & H. 1848. Or Maestr: *Cylindocyathus popenguirensis* Alloiteau 1950, Senegal, if a valid genus. *Brachycyathus daniensis* Wanner 1902 is probably a synonym of *Discocyathus*, and extends range of family into Tert Dan of Switzerland.

Family ACROSMILIIDAE Alloiteau 1952

First, Jur Hett: *Proleptophyllia granulum* (de Fromental & Ferry 1866), Lias, France.

Last, Cret Coniac: *Acrosmilia* d'Orbigny 1849 and *Placoseris* de Fromental 1863, Europe, and N. America. Many genera in family have been considered synonymous with *Acrosmilia*, which is sometimes included with the Synastraeidae. Many species of *Leptophyllia*, generally considered synonymous with *Acrosmilia*, have been recorded from younger rocks, e.g. *L. eurphylloides* d'Achiardi 1868, Tert M. Mioc of Switzerland.

Family MICROSOLENIDAE Koby 1890

First, Jur Hett: *Chomatoseris* Thomas 1936, e.g. *C. porpites* (Smith) 1816, Lias, Europe. Most genera of family appear in M. Jur and become more widespread, Asia, N. and S. America.

Last, Cret Santon: *Gosaviaraea* Oppenheim, e.g. *G. camerina*, Gossau, Austria.

Family EUHELIDAE de Fromental 1861

First, Jur Bajoc: *Euhelia* E. & H. 1850, Europe.

Last, Cret Apt-Alb: *Stylangia* de Fromental 1857, e.g. *S. neocomiensis*, Neocomian, France, and *S. anomalus*, Mexico. *S. panamensis* Vaughan 1919, from Tert Olig, Emperador Lst, is possibly youngest record.

368

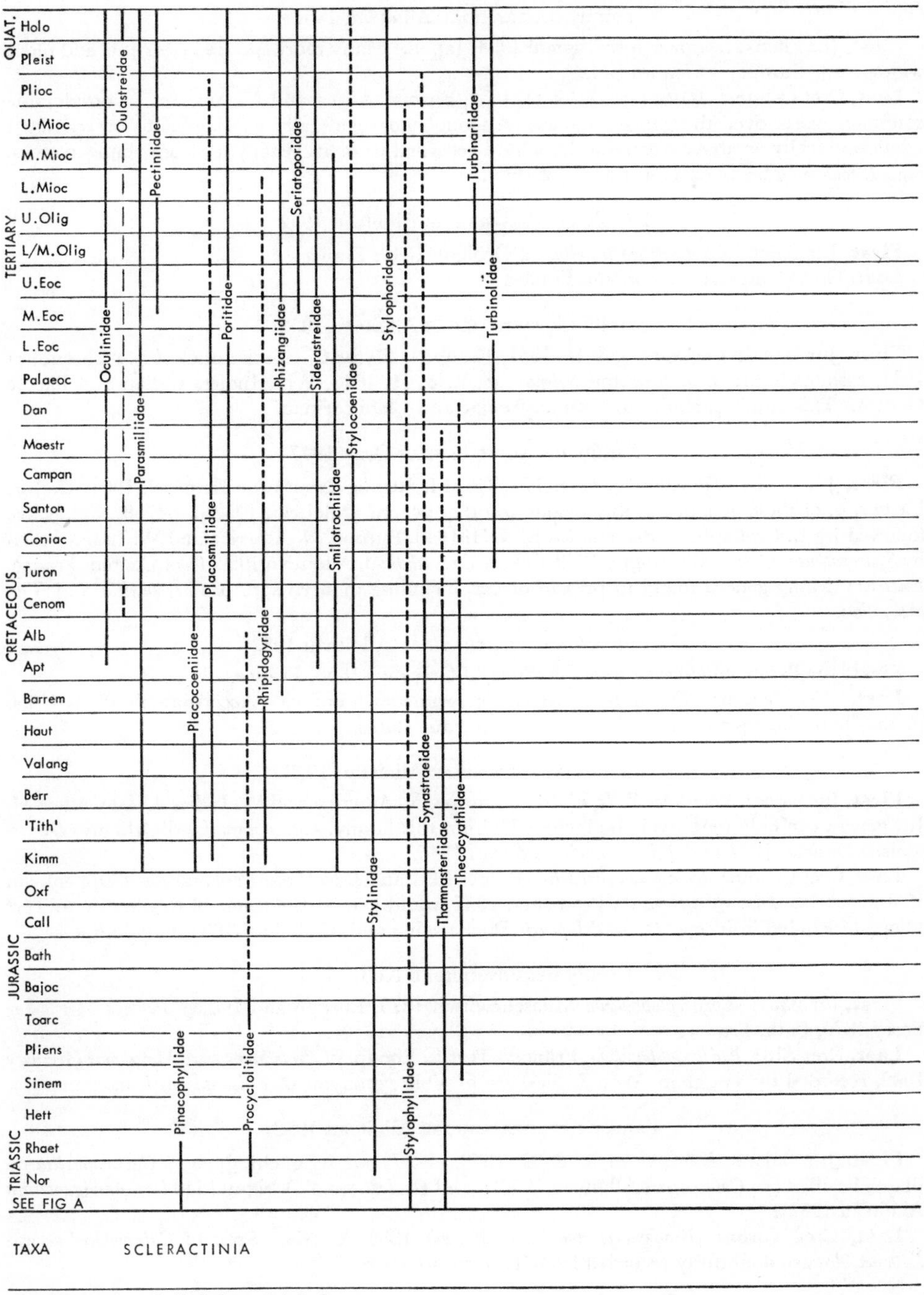

QUAT.
Holo
Pleist
Plioc
U.Mioc
M.Mioc
L.Mioc
TERTIARY
U.Olig
L/M.Olig
U.Eoc
M.Eoc
L.Eoc
Palaeoc
Dan
Maestr
Campan
Santon
Coniac
CRETACEOUS
Turon
Cenom
Alb
Apt
Barrem
Haut
Valang
Berr
'Tith'
Kimm
Oxf
Call
JURASSIC
Bath
Bajoc
Toarc
Pliens
Sinem
Hett
TRIASSIC
Rhaet
Nor
SEE FIG A
Oculinidae
Oulastreidae
Parasmiliidae
Pectiniidae
Pinacophyllidae
Placocoeniidae
Placosmiliidae
Poritidae
Procyclolitidae
Rhipidogyridae
Rhizangiidae
Seriatoporidae
Siderastreidae
Smilotrochiidae
Stylocoenidae
Stylinidae
Stylophoridae
Stylophyllidae
Synastraeidae
Thamnasteriidae
Thecocyathidae
Turbinariidae
Turbinolidae
TAXA
SCLERACTINIA
CONTRIBUTORS
F. M. Taylor and I. D. Sutton

FIG. 10.5B

Family ISASTRAEIDAE Alloiteau 1952

First, Jur Pliens: *Isastraea yabei* Eguchi 1934, Japan. Many more species in M. Jur, and more widespread, Europe, Africa and N. America.

Last, Cret Cenom: *Isastrea* sp., E. & H. 1851, Europe, Africa and N. America. Considerable confusion exists over the genus *Isastraea*. Although now generally considered to be restricted stratigraphically as above, many authors have recorded it, or its synonyms, from younger rocks, e.g., *I. miocoenia* Seguenza, Tert Mioc of Italy.

Family CLAUSASTREIDAE Alloiteau 1952

First, Jur Bajoc: *Clausastraea tessellata* d'Orbigny 1849, France.
Last, Cret Campan: *C. tessellata*, France.

Family HELIASTRAEIDAE Alloiteau 1952

First, Jur Bajoc: *Goniocora* E. & H. 1951, Europe. **Extant:** Species of *Cladocora* Ehrenburg 1934, cosmopolitan; *Leptastrea* and *Solenastraea* E. & H. 1848, West Indies, Indian and Pacific Oceans. This family includes the Montastreinae and Cladocorinae.

Family CARYOPHYLLIIDAE Gray 1847

First, Jur Bath: *Trochocyathus* E. & H. 1848, M. Jur, or *Caryophyllia* Lamarck 1801, U. Jur. Early spp. of these genera possibly belong to other genera (Alloiteau 1952 p. 647–8). They are followed by L. Cret spp. of *Bathycyathus* E. & H. 1848, Europe, N. America and W. Indies; then by *Stylocyathus dentalinus* d'Orbigny 1849 and *Dendrocyathus* sp. Alloiteau 1952, Cret Cenom, France. **Extant:** Many genera found in present oceans including modern spp. of *Caryophyllia* and *Trochocyathus*.

Family ANDEMANTASTRAEIDAE Alloiteau 1952

First, Jur Bajoc: *Andemantastraea consobrina* (d'Orbigny) 1850, France.
Last, Cret Cenom: *Trigerastraea trigeri* (de Fromental) France. According to Wells (1956 p. 436) both these genera are of uncertain systematic status.

Family SYNASTRAEIDAE Alloiteau 1952

First, Jur Bajoc: *Synastraea* E. & H. 1848, Europe, N. America and W. Indies. Many other M. Jur genera can only tentatively be included within this family. e.g. *Acrosmilia* d'Orbigny, *Dimorphoseris* Duncan 1872 and *Edwardoseris* Alloiteau 1946.

Last, Cret Cenom: *Synastraea raristella* (Reuss) 1854 and *Leptophyllastraea irregularis* Oppenheim 1930, Austria. *Dimorphastraea* de Fromental 1857 would extend the range of this family to Tert Plioc, if included in it, e.g. *D. guadalupensis* Duchassaing and Michelotti 1864, Guadalupe.

Family DERMOSMILIIDAE Koby 1887

First, Jur Bath: *Epistreptophyllum* Milaschewitsch 1875, Europe and India; *Ferraya burgundiae* Ferry 1870, Bath, France.

Last, Cret Alb: *Epistreptophyllum*, France. Tert L. Eoc sp. of *Protethmos* and *Metethmos* Gregory 1900, recorded by Vaughan, West Indies, are possible synonyms of *Epistreptophyllum*.

Family LATOMEANDRIDAE Alloiteau 1952

First, Jur Bajoc: *Latomeandra* E. & H. 1849, e.g. *L. yabei* Eguchi, Japan; *Calamophyllia* de Blainville 1830 (= *Calamoseris* Alloiteau 1952); and *Ovalastraea* d'Orbigny 1849 (= *Ambiguastraea* Alloiteau 1952).

Last, Cret Turon: *Brachyseris morchella* (Reuss) 1859 Austria. Spp. of *Calamophyllia* and *Latomeandra* are doubtfully recorded from Tert, up to Mioc.

Family ACTINACIDIDAE Vaughan & Wells 1943

First, Jur Bajoc-Bath: *Dendraraea* d'Orbigny 1849, e.g. *D. racemosa* (Michelin) 1843, Sequan, France.

Last, Tert M. Olig: At least 7 spp. of *Actinacis* d'Orbigny 1849, Eurasia, N. & S. America, W. Indies and Africa. 2 spp. are recorded from U. Mioc at Tortona, and *Thamnarea polymorpha* (synonym of *Dendraraea*) from U. Mioc of Armenia.

Family AMPHIASTREIDAE Ogilvie 1896

First, Jur Bath: *Ceratocoenia elongata* Tomes 1884, France, *Amphiastrea* Étallon 1859, Europe and *Axosmilia* E. & H. 1848.

Last, Cret Cenom: Spp. of *Amphiastrea* and *Axosmilia*, Italy. Tert M. Olig: *Amphiastrea monitor* (Duncan) 1867, West Indies, may be the last record.

Family MITRODENDRONIDAE Alloiteau 1952

First, Jur Bath: *Polymorphastraea* Koby 1888.

Last, Jur Kimm: At least 6 genera, including *Schizosmilia* Koby 1888, Switzerland, and *Mitrodendron* Quenstedt 1880, Portlandian, Czechoslovakia. *M. bassani* (d'Angelis) 1905 is recorded from L Cret of Italy.

Family PLACOSMILIIDAE Alloiteau 1952

First, Jur Kimm: *Peplosmilia* E. & H. 1850, Europe.

Last, Tert M Eoc: At least 12 spp. of *Placosmilia* E. & H. 1848, Europe and Alabama, and *Elasmophyllia* d'Achiardi 1875, Europe and S. America, e.g. *E. gigantea*. Younger records have not been confirmed, e.g. L. Mioc: *P. panovani* Gerth 1920, and Plioc: *P. bipartita* Felix 1913, both from Java.

Family COLUMASTRAEIDAE Alloiteau 1952

First, Jur Oxf: *Stephanocoenia* E. & H. 1848, Europe. **Extant:** *S. intersepta* (Esper) 1797, Caribbean and Australia; *Plesiastraea versipora* (Lamarck) 1816 Torres Str., Australia.

Family MUSSIDAE Ortmann 1890

First, Jur Kimm: *Palaeomussa* Alloiteau 1952, Rauracian, Europe. **Extant:** Many genera including *Mussismilia* Ortmann 1890, Brazil; *Homophyllia* Brueggemann 1877, Australia; *Lobophyllia* Blainville 1830 and *Symphyllia* E. & H. 1848, Indian and Pacific Oceans; *Mussa* Oken 1815, and *Mycetophyllia* E. & H. 1848, W. Indies.

Family SMILOTROCHIIDAE Alloiteau 1952

First, Jur Kimm: *Paramontlivaltia charcennensis* (de Fromental) 1862, Rauriacian, France.
Last, Tert M Mioc: *Phyllocoenia radiata* E. & H. 1848, Stampian, France.

Family RHIPIDOGYRIDAE Koby 1904

First, Jur Kimm: At least 8 genera mainly from Europe, including *Cymosmilia* Koby 1894 and *Rhipidogyra* E. & H. 1848. *Codonosmilia* Koby 1888, if included in this family, extends its range down to the Jur Bath.

Last, Cret Santon: *Aplosmilia* d'Orbigny 1849, Austria and France; *Fromentelligyra* Alloiteau 1952, France. The latter is a possible synonym of *Rhipidogyra* which has doubtfully been recorded from Tert Mioc of Turin and Sardinia, e.g. *R. michelotti* d'Archiardi 1868.

Family GUYNIDAE Hickson 1910

First, Jur Oxf: *Microsmilia erguelense* (Thurmann) 1851, Switzerland. **Extant:** At least three genera, e.g. *Guynia* Duncan 1873, W. Indies, Mediterranean, Persian Gulf and Australia; *Stenocyathus* Poutales 1871, Atlantic, West Indies, and Australia.

Family PARASMILIIDAE Alloiteau 1952

First, Jur Kimm: *Dungulia milneri* (Gregory) 1898. Most genera are from the U. Cret: *Parasmilia* E. & H. 1848, e.g. *P. centralis*, Senonian, England. **Extant:** Many genera including

Asterosmilia Duncan 1867; *Gemmulatrochus* Duncan 1878. Mediterranean, English Channel, and North Sea.

Family HAPLARAEIDAE Vaughan & Wells 1943

First, Jur Kimm: *Diplaraea arbuscula* Milaschevitsch 1876, Europe, Japan and S. America. Most species are found in Cret.
Last, Tert Eoc-Mioc: *Confusastraea obsoleta* Gerth 1823, E. Indies.

*Family PLACOCOENIIDAE Alloiteau 1952

First, Jur Kimm: *Columnocoenia* Alloiteau 1951, Santorian, France.
Last, Cret Santon: *Columnocoenia* and *Placocoenia* d'Orbigny 1849, Europe.

*Family HETEROCOENIIDAE Oppenheim 1930

First, Cret Barrem: *Heterocoenia* E. & H. 1848, Neocomian, e.g. *H. verrucsa* Reuss 1854, Europe. Other species in N. America and Japan.
Last, Tert U. Eoc: *Ewaldocoenia hawelkai* Oppenheim 1921, Switzerland.

Family RHIZANGIIDAE d'Orbigny 1851

First, Cret Barrem: *Arctangia nathorsti* (Lindstrom) 1900, Neocomian, King Charles Is, Arctic
Extant: Most genera of this family are cosmopolitan, living in present seas and include *Culicia* Dana 1846, *Oulangia* and *Astrangia* E. & H. 1848.

Family OCULINIDAE Gray 1847

First, Cret Apt: *Pseudogatheria hiraigensis* Eguchi 1951, Miyako Gp., Japan. **Extant:** Most genera including *Schizoculina* Wells 1937, W. Africa; *Bathelia* Moseley 1881, S. Atlantic; *Cyathelia* E. & H. 1849, Indian and Pacific Oceans; *Madrepora* Linné 1758, Galapagos Isles; *Oculina* Lamarck 1816, West Indies, Florida, Antilles and Australia.

Family FLABELLIDAE Milne-Edwards 1857
Bourne 1905

First, Cret Alb: *Adkinsella edwardsensis* Wells 1933, Texas. **Extant:** *Flabellum* Lesson 1831, cosmopolitan, and other genera including *Gardineria* Vaughan 1907, West Indies, S. Atlantic and Pacific Oceans.

Family CYCLOPHYLLOPSIIDAE Alloiteau 1952

First, Cret Apt: *Cyclophyllopsis aptiensis* (de Fromental) 1870, France. The genus (Alloiteau 1951) is probably invalid.
Last, Tert M Eoc: *Anisoria vidali* Mallada, Spain. This genus is possibly a synonym of *Leptoria*.

Family FUNGINELLIDAE Alloiteau 1952

First, Cret Haut: *Funginella* d'Orbigny 1850, e.g. *F. neocomiensis*, France.
Last, Tert M Mioc: *Pachyseris* E. & H. 1849. Two spp. from Indian and Pacific Oceans and Great Barrier Reef, Australia, are possibly extant.

Family SIDERASTREIDAE Vaughan & Wells 1943

First, Cret Apt: *Siderastrea* de Blainville 1830, Europe; and *Thalamocoeniopsis* Alloiteau 1954, from possible L. Cret rocks of N. America. **Extant:** *Siderastrea radians* (Pallas) 1766, Caribbean, *S. siderea* (Ellis & Solander) 1786, Caribbean and Brazil, and *Coscinaraea monile* (Forskål) 1775, E. Africa.

*Family ECHINOPORIDAE Milne-Edwards 1857

First, Cret Cenom: *Agathelia* Reuss 1854, Europe and Texas. **Extant:** *Echinopora* Lamarck 1816, Indian and Pacific Oceans; *Cyphastrea* E. & H. 1848, West Indies, Pacific and Indian Oceans.

Chapter 10: Coelenterata

Family DENDROGYRIDAE Alloiteau 1952

First, Cret Barrem: *Dendogyra* Ehrenburg 1834, Neocomian. Doubtful records from Mexico, Spain and Italy; Cret Cenom: *Cenomania* Alloiteau 1951, France, possibly the first record. **Extant:** *Dendrogyra cylindrus* Ehrenburg 1834, Antilles.

*Family MEANDRINIDAE Gray 1847

First, Cret Cenom: *Aulosmilia* Alloiteau 1952, Europe, N. America, W. Indies. **Extant:** *Meandrina braziliensis* E. & H. 1848, Brazil and *M. meandrites* (Linné) 1758, Bahamas.

Family AGARICIIDAE Gray 1847

First, Cret Apt: At least three spp. of *Trochoseris* E. & H. 1849 from Haldon and Atherfield, England. Very common in Cenom of Europe and Asia. **Extant:** *Agaricia agaricites* (Pallas), W. Indies and Florida; *Pavona frondifera* (Lamarck) 1801, Marshal Isles, Pacific; and *Leptoseris* E. & H. 1849, Hawaii, Fiji, Maldive Isles, Indian Ocean, Cocos-Keeling Isles.

Family FUNGIIDAE Dana 1846

First, Cret Apt: *Cycloseris escosurae* Mallada 1887, Spain; becomes common in the Cret Cenom of Europe, Asia, Indian and Pacific Ocean regions. **Extant:** At least 9 genera, cosmopolitan, including *Fungia* Lamarck 1801, *Halomitra pileus* (Linné) 1758 and *Fungiacyathus* Sars 1872.

Family MICRABACIIDAE Vaughan 1905

First, Cret Barrem: *Micrabacia beaumonti* E. & H. 1851, Neocomian, France; Alb: *M. fittoni* Duncan 1870, Folkestone, England; widespread in Cenom, e.g. *M. coronula* Goldfuss 1827, Germany, Austria and France; later cosmopolitan. **Extant:** *Leptopenus* Moseley 1881, S. Atlantic, Indian and Pacific Oceans, and *Micrabacia* E. & H. 1849, cosmopolitan.

Family PORITIDAE Gray 1842

First, Cret Cenom: *Goniopora* Blainville 1830, e.g. *G. cretacea* (Sokle) 1897 Austria. *G. taurica* (Eichwald) 1865 is possibly of Neocomian (Barrem) age. **Extant:** All genera including *Porites* Link 1807 and *Goniopora*, Cosmopolitan.

*Family CYCLASTRAEIDAE Alloiteau 1952

First and **Last,** Cret Cenom: *Cyclastraea spinosa* (de Fromental) 1864, France. The genus possibly belongs to the Calamophyllidae, Vaughan & Wells 1943 (Wells 1952).

*Family ASTEROSERIIDAE Alloiteau 1952

First and **Last,** Cret Cenom: *Asteroseris* and *Microseris* de Fromental 1870, France. Both genera are possibly synonymous with *Cycloseris* E. & H. 1849 (Wells 1952).

Family STYLOPHORIDAE Milne-Edwards 1857

First, Cret Turon: *Madracis* E. & H. 1849, Europe, N. America, Indian and Pacific Oceans, W. Indies. **Extant:** *Madracis* and *Stylophora* Schweigger 1819, Indian and Pacific Oceans, W. Indies and Mediterranean.

Family ACROPORIDAE Verrill 1902

First, Cret Turon: *Astreopora* Blainville 1830, Europe. **Extant:** at least 4 genera, including *Astreopora*, in Indian and Pacific Oceans and Caribbean.

Family FAVIIDAE Gregory 1900

First, Cret Apt: *Diploria conferticostata* Vaughan 1899, Jamaica. Many genera occur in Turon, including *Ogilviastraea* Oppenheim 1930, *Leptoria* E. & H. 1848, *Dictnophyllia* Blainville 1830 and *Hydnophora* Fischer 1807. All Cret spp. of *Favia* Oken are probably other genera

373

according to Alloiteau 1952 p. 616. **Extant:** *Manicinia* and *Platygyra* Ehrenburg 1834, *Oulophyllia* E. & H. 1848, *Favites* Link 1807, *Favia* and *Caulastraea* Dana 1846. Family is cosmopolitan.

*Family EUPHYLLIDAE Alloiteau 1952
(*nom. transl.* EUPHYLLINAE *Alloiteau* 1952)

First, Cret ?Santon: *Rennensismilia* and *Meandrosmilia* Alloiteau 1951. Both these genera may belong to other families. Tert L. Eoc: *Euphyllia* Dana 1846, Spain is the first certain record. **Extant:** Most genera of family, including *Plerogyra* E. & H. 1848, Indian and Pacific Oceans; *Gyrosmilia* E. & H. 1851, Red Sea; and *Eusmilia* E. & H. 1848, Florida and W. Indies.

Family STYLOCOENIDAE Alloiteau 1952

First, Cret Apt; *Astrocoenia japonica* Eguchi 1951, Morhi Sst, Japan, and *Stylocoenia solomkoi* Karatasc 1907, Neocomian, Crimea. Family is found frequently up to Tert M. Mioc: *Astrocoenia* E. &. H. 1848, Czechoslovakia, Italy, Egypt and Java, also *Stylocoenia* E. &. H. 1849. *A. almerai* d'Angelis 1895 has been recorded from the L. Plioc of Spain. *Glyphastraea* Duncan 1887 (? synonym of *Septastraea* d'Orbigny 1849) would represent the family in the Plioc of N. America. **Extant:** *Astrocoenia* recorded by Wells 1935 in the West Indies and Indian Ocean.

Family HEMIPORITIDAE Alloiteau 1952

First, Cret Turon: *Hemiporites jacobi* Alloiteau 1950, France.
Last, Cret Maestr: *Placocoeniopsis arnaudi* Alloiteau 1951, France.
Both these genera are probably invalid.

Family TURBINOLIDAE Edwards & Haime 1848
Milne-Edwards 1857

First, Cret Turon: *Bothriophoria*, e.g. *B. ornata* Felix 1909, Snow Hill Island, Antarctica and *Platytrochus* e.g. *P. speciosus* Gubb & Horn 1860, Tennesey. **Extant:** Many genera including *Conocyathus* d'Orbigny 1849, *Batotrochus* Wells 1937, *Notocyathus* T.-Woods 1880 and *Kiolotrochus* T.-Woods 1878. Family is cosmopolitan.

Family LAMELLOFUNGIDAE Alloiteau 1952

First and **Last,** Cret Santon: *Lamellofungia rennensis* Alloiteau 1951, France. This genus is probably invalid.

Family CUNNOLITIDAE Alloiteau 1952. (CYCLOLITIDAE d'Orbigny 1851)

First, Cret Barrem: *Cyclolites* Lamarck 1801, e.g. *C. eturbensis* De Fromental 1857, or *C. japonica*, L. Cret, Japan. There are many Turon spp. of *Cyclolites*.
Last, Tert M. Eoc: *Cyclolitopsis patera* Meneghins 1867, Italy. Three unconfirmed spp. of *Cyclolites* have been recorded from Mioc of W. Indies.

*Family BRACHYPHYLLIIDAE Alloiteau 1952

First, Cret Apt: *Brachyphyllia*, e.g. *B. haueri* (Reuss) 1854, Spain; or Turon: *B. depressa* (Reuss) 1854, Austria.
Last, Tert U. Eoc: *Antilloseris* Vaughan 1905, Europe, N. & S. America, and W. Indies. Two unconfirmed spp. of *Brachyphyllia* have been recorded from Mioc of Italy and W. Indies.

Family DENDROPHYLLIIDAE Gray 1847. (Eupsammiidae Milne-Edwards 1857)

First, Cret Campan: *Wadeopsammia nodosa* (Wade) 1926, Navarro, Texas. An unverified sp. of *Eupsammia* E. & H. 1848, Europe, may be earlier. **Extant:** Many genera in present seas including *Dendrophyllia* Blainville 1930, cosmopolitan, and *Balanophyllia* Wood, 1884, Mediterranean.

Chapter 10: Coelenterata

Family SERIATOPORIDAE Edwards & Haime 1849

First, Tert M Eoc: *Pocillopora* Lamarck 1818, e.g. *P. infundibuliformis*, M Eoc, Italy, Fiji. Other species from W. Indies, Indian and Pacific Oceans. **Extant:** *Seriatopora* Lamarck 1816, e.g. *S. hystrix*, Dana 1846, and *Pocillopora*, at least three spp., Indian and Pacific Oceans and Torres Strait, Australia.

Family AGATHIPHYLLIIDAE Vaughan & Wells 1943

First, Tert Dan: *Pattalophyllia aegyptiaca* Wanner; many spp. in the M. Eoc of Europe.
Last, Tert M Mioc: *Cricocyathus* Quenstedt 1881, Europe.

Family GALAXEIDAE Vaughan & Wells 1943

First, Tert L Mioc: *Galaxea* Oken 1815, e.g. *G. fascicularis* (Linné) 1767, Borneo & Java, Maldive and Phillipine Is, Singapore, Fiji and Ceylon; other spp. in N. America. **Extant:** *Galaxea*, Torres Strait, Australia; *Simplastraea* Umbgrove 1939, E. Indies, and *Acrhelia* E. & H. 1849, Pacific.

Family PECTINIIDAE Vaughan & Wells 1943

First, Tert M. Eoc: *Pectinia pseudomeandrites* d'Archiardi, Italy, followed in Olig by *Fungophyllia* Gerth 1923, E. Indies, W. Pacific and West Indies. **Extant:** All other genera including *Oxypora* Saville-Kent 1871, Pacific and *Pectinia* Oken 1815, Indian and Pacific Oceans.

Family TURBINARIIDAE M.-Edwards 1857

First, Tert L/M Olig: *Turbinaria* Oken 1815 at least 5 European spp. **Extant:** *Turbinaria*, in Indian and Pacific Oceans, e.g. *T. peltata* (Esper), E. Indies.

Family OULASTREIDAE Vaughan 1907

Extant: *Oulastrea crispata* (Lamarck) 1816, Indian Ocean. Six spp. have been recorded from Cret Cenom of Monti d'Ocre, Italy as the genus *Ulastraea*.

Family ANTHEMIPHYLLIIDAE Vaughan 1907

Extant: *Anthemiphyllia* Pourtales 1878, Hawaii, and *Bathytrochus* Gravier 1915, Atlantic.

Family MERULINIDAE Verrill 1866

Extant: 4 genera in the Pacific Ocean. *Montlivaltiopsis* Alloiteau 1952, M. Jur (Rauracian), France, has been included in this family.   [F.M.T. & I.D.S.]

REFERENCES

ALLOITEAU, J. 1952. *In* PIVETEAU, J. (Editor) *Traité de Paleontologie*, **1,** 539–684. Paris, Masson.
AVNIMELECH, M. A. 1966. A new medusoid fossil from the Lower Carboniferous of Egypt. *J. Paleont*, **40,** 742–745.
BARBOUR, E. H. 1914. *Medusina walcotti*, a Carboniferous jellyfish. *Am. J. Sci.*, **38,** no. 228, 505–6.
BASSLER, R. S. 1941. A supposed jellyfish from the Precambrian of the Grand Canyon. *Proc. U.S. natn. Mus.*, **89,** no. 310H, 519–22, 1 pl.
—— 1950. Faunal lists and descriptions of Palaeozoic corals. *Mem. geol. Soc. Am.*, **44.**
BUEHLER, E. J. 1955. The morphology and taxonomy of the *Halysitidae*. *Bull. Peabody Mus. nat. Hist.*, **8,** 1–79.

CASTER, K. E. 1942a. Two siphonophores from the Paleozoic. *Palaeont. Am.*, **3,** 57–90, pl. 1, 2.
—— 1942b. A laotirid from the Upper Cambrian of Wyoming. *Am. J. Sci.*, **240,** 104–12, pl. 1.
—— 1945. A new jellyfish (*Kirklandia texana* Caster) from the Lower Cretaceous of Texas. *Palaeont. Am.*, **3,** 169–220, pl. 1–5.
CHAPMAN, F. 1926. New or little-known fossils in the National Museum. Part XXX, A, Silurian jellyfish. *Proc. R. Soc. Vict.*, **39,** 13–17, pl. 1, 2.
—— & SKEATS, E. W. 1919. Fossil hydroid remains in the Palaeozoic of Victoria. *Geol. Mag.* **6,** 550.
—— & THOMAS, D. E. 1936. The Cambrian Hydroida of the Heathcote and Monegeeta Districts. *Proc. R. Soc. Vict.*, **48,** 193–212, pl. 14–17.
CLARKE, J. M. 1900. *Paropsonema cryptophya*, a peculiar echinoderm from the intumescens zone (Portage beds) of western New York. *Bull. N.Y. St. Mus.*, **39,** vol. 8, 172–178, pl. 5–9.
COUYAT, J. & FRITEL, P. 1912. Sur des empreintes (Méduses, Algues) recueillies dans le Carbonifère des environs de Suez. *C.r. hebd. Séanc. Acad. Sci., Paris*, **155,** 795–6.
DURHAM, J. WYATT, & CASTER, K. E. 1966. Helicoplacoidea. *In* MOORE R. C. (Editor), *Treatise on Invertebrate Paleontology*, Part U. University of Kanas Press.
EASTON, W. H. 1960. Permian Corals from Nevada and California. *J. Palaeont.*, **34,** 583–590.
EDWARDS, H. M. & HAIME, J. 1855. Corals from the Silurian Formation: *in* A monograph of the British Fossil Corals: 245–299, *Palaeontogr. Soc.* [*Mongr.*]
EGUCHI, M. 1951. Mesozoic Hexacorals from Japan. *Sci. Rep. Tohoku Univ.* (2), **24.**
FELIX, J. 1914–1929. Parts on Anthozoa *in Fossilium Catalogus* (*Animalia*), **5–7** (1914), **28** (1925), **35** (1927) and **44** (1929).
FORMICHEV, V. D. 1953. Koralli Rugosa i stratigrafya Sredne i Verkhnekennougolnikh i Permskikh oblochenii Donetzkogo Basseina. *Trudý vses. nauchno-issled. geol. Inst.* (VSEGEI), Miner. Geol., Moscow, 622 pp., 44 pls.
FRECH, F. 1890. Die Korallenfauna der Trias, I. Die Korallen der juvavischen Triasprovinz. *Palaeontographica*, **37,** 116 pp., 21 pl.
GLAESSNER, M. F. 1962. Pre-Cambrian fossils. *Biol. Rev.*, **37,** 467–94, pl. l.
—— & DAILY, B. 1959. The geology and Late Precambrian fauna of the Ediacara fossil reserve. *Rec. S. Aust. Mus.*, **13,** 369–401, pls. 42–47.
—— & WADE, M. 1966. The Late Precambrian fossils from Ediacara, South Australia. *Palaeontology*, **9,** 599–628, pls. 97–103.
GRAUVOGEL, L. 1951. Découverte de Méduses dans le Grès à *Voltzia* (Trias inf.) des Vosges. *C.r. Somm. Soc. géol. Fr.*, **1,** 139–41.
HARRINGTON, H. J. & MOORE, R. C. 1955. Fossil jellyfishes from Kansas Pennsylvanian rocks and elsewhere. *Bull. Kansas Univ. geol. Surv.*, **114,** 153–164, pls. 1 & 2.
HILL, D. 1951. The Ordovician Corals. *Proc. R. Soc. Qd*, **62,** 1–27.
—— 1960. Possible intermediates between Alcyonaria and Tabulata, Tabulata and Rugosa, and Rugosa and Hexacoralla. *21st. Int. geol. Congr.*, **22,** 51–58.
HOWELL, B. F. 1963. New Cambrian conchostracans from Wyoming and Newfoundland, Brachiopods from Vermont, and Worm, Hydrozoan and problematicum from Newfoundland. *J. Paleont.*, **37,** 264–7.
HUENE, F. VON. 1904. Geologische Notizen aus Oeland und Dalarne, sowie über eine Meduse aus dem Untersilur. *Zentbl. Miner. Geol. Paläont.*, **1904,** 450–61.
HUNDT, R. 1939. *Camptostroma* aus den Phycodens-schichten Ostthüringens. *Zentbl. Miner. Geol. Paläont.* (B). **1939,** 477–79.
KIDERLEN, H. 1937. Die Conularien, über Bau und Leben der ersten Scyphozoa. *Neues Jb. Miner. Geol. Paläont. Beil. Bd* (B), **77,** 113–69.
KNIGHT, J. B. 1937. *Conchopeltis* Walcott, an Ordovician genus of Conulariida. *J. Paleont.*, **11,** 186–8, pl. 29.
KÜHN, O. 1927. Zur Systematik und Nomenklatur der Stromatoporen. *Neues Jb. Miner. Paläont. Geol.*, *Abt. B, Centralbl.* 546–51.

—— 1939. Hydrozoa. *In* Schindewolf, O. H. *Handbuch der Paläozoologie*, **2A.**

Lang, W. D., Smith, S. & Thomas, H. D., 1940. *Index of Palaeozoic Coral Genera*, 231 pp. London, British Museum (Natural History).

LeMaitre, D. 1935. Études paléontologiques sur le Lias du Maroc, Description des spongio-morphides et des algues. *Notes Mém., Serv. Min. Carte géol. Maroc*, **34,** 58 pp, 12 pl.

Lörcher, E. 1931. Eine neue fossile Qualle aus dem Opalinusschichten und ihre paläogeo-graphische Bedeutung. *Jber. Mitt. oberrhein. geol. Ver.* (N.F.), **20,** 44–46, pl. 1.

Mass, O. 1902. Über Medusen aus dem Solnhofen Schiefer und der unteren Kreide der Karpathen. *Palaeontographica*, **48,** 297–321, pl. 22, 23.

—— 1906. Über eine neue Medusengattung aus dem lithographischen Schiefer. *Neues Jb. Miner. Geol. Paläont.*, Jahrg. 1906 (2), 90–99.

Meunier, S. 1891. *Staurophyton bagnolensis* Stan. Meun. Nouveau fossile des Grès armoricains de Bagnoles (Orne). *Naturaliste* (2) **13,** 134.

Nicholson, H. A., 1879, *On the structure and affinities of the tabulate corals of the Palaeozoic period*, 342 pp. London & Edinburgh.

—— 1886–1892. A monograph of the British stromatoporoids. *Palaeontogr. Soc. [Monogr.]*

—— & Murie 1878. On the minute structure of *Stromatopora* and its allies, *J. Linn. Soc. Lond.*, **14,** 187–246, pl. 1–4.

Nielsen, K. B., 1919. En hydrocoralfauna fra Faxe og bemaerkninger om Danien'ets geologiske stilling. *Danm. geol. Unders.* (4), **1** (10), 66 pp, 2 pl.

Osswald, K. 1918. Mesozoische Conulariiden. *Zentbl. Miner. Geol. Paläont.* For 1918, 337–344.

Parona, C. F. 1909. La fauna coralligena del Cretaceo dei Monti d'Ocre nell'Abruzzo Aquilano. *Mem., Carta geol. Ital.*, **5,** 148–64.

Rauff, H. 1939. *Palaeonectris discoidea* Rauff, eine siphonophoroide Meduse aus dem rheinischen Unterdevon nebst Bemerkungen zur umstrittnen *Brooksella rhenana* Kinkelin. *Paläont. Z.*, **21,** 194–213, pl. 8–11.

Ruedemann, R. 1916. Note on *Paropsonema cryptophya* Clarke and *Discophyllum peltatum* Hall. *Bull. N.Y. St. Mus.*, **189,** 22–27.

—— 1933. *Camptostroma*, a Lower Cambrian floating hydrozoan. *Proc. U.S. natn. Mus.*, **82,** 1–8, pls 1–4.

Schouppe, A. & Stacul, P. 1955. Die genera *Verbeekiella* Penecke, *Timorphophyllum* Gerth, *Wanner-ophyllum* Gen. Nov., *Lophophyllidium* Grabau aus dem Perm von Timor. *Palaeontographica*, Suppl. **4,** (5), 95–196.

Sokolov, B. S. (Editor) 1962. [Fossil Coelenterates of the U.S.S.R.] *in* Orlov, Yu. A. (General Editor) *Osnovy Palaeontologii*, volume 2. Akademii Nauk S.S.S.R., Moscow [in Russian].

Sprigg, R. C. 1947. Early Cambrian (?) jellyfishes from the Flinders Ranges, South Australia. *Trans. R. Soc. S. Aust.*, **71,** 212–24, pl. 5–8.

—— 1949. Early Cambrian 'jellyfishes' of Ediacara, South Australia, and Mt. John, Kimberley District, Western Australia. *Trans. R. Soc. S. Aust.*, **73,** 72–99, pl. 9–21.

Squires, D. F. 1958. The Cretaceous and Tertiary corals of New Zealand. *Palaeont. Bull.*, Wellington, **29.**

Stearn, C. W. 1966. The microstructure of stromatoporoids. *Palaeontology*, **9,** 74–124, 14–19.

Steinmann, G. 1878. Über fossile Hydrozoan aus den Familie der Corynidae. *Palaeontographica*, **25,** 101–24, pl. 12–14.

Treatise F. 1956. Bayer, F. M. *et al.* Coelenterata. *In* Moore, R. C. (Editor), *Treatise on Invertebrate Paleontology*, Part F. University of Kansas Press.

Ulrich, E. O. & Scofield, W. H. 1897. The Lower Silurian Gastropoda of Minnesota. *Rep. Minn. geol. nat. Hist. Surv.*, **3,** (2), 813–1081.

Van Gundy, C. E. 1951. Nankoweap group of the Grand Canyon Algonkian of Arizona. *Bull. geol. Soc. Am.*, **62,** 953–60, pl. 1.

Vaughan, T. W. & Wells, J. W. 1943. Revision of the suborders, families and genera of the Scleractinea. *Spec. Pap. geol. Soc. Am.*, **44.**

Walcott, C. D. 1898. Fossil Medusae. *Monogr. U.S. geol. Surv.*, **30,** 201 pp., 47 pls.

WILSON, R. B. 1961. Palaeontology of the Archerbeck Borehole, Canonbie, Dumfriesshire. *Bull. geol. Surv. Gt. Br.*, **18**, 90–106.

WURM, A. 1925. Über ein Vorkommen von Mittelcambrium (*Paradoxides*-Schichten) im bayrischen Frankenwald bei Wildstein südlich Preßeck. *Neues Jb. Miner. Geol. Paläont.* (B), **52**, 71–93.

G. A. L. Johnson, PH.D. F.G.S.
    Department of Geology, University Science Laboratories, South Road, Durham.
I. D. Sutton, PH.D.
    Department of Geology, The University, Nottingham.
F. M. Taylor, PH.D. F.G.S.
    Department of Geology, The University, Nottingham.
G. Thomas, PH.D. D.I.C. F.G.S.
    Department of Geology, Imperial College of Science & Technology, Prince Consort Road, London S W 7.

CHAPTER 11

Bryozoa

Contributors: G. P. LARWOOD, A. W. MEDD, D. E. OWEN
& R. TAVENER-SMITH

Introduction. The arrangement of the documentation and the sequence in which family or subordinal ranges is shown on the range charts follows that of the Treatise, Pt.G (Bassler 1953). Departures from this arrangement are given in the general comment on each Order.

Although a general revision of the Treatise Pt G, is contemplated, and much taxonomic study of fossil Bryozoa is still necessary, the distributions plotted on the accompanying stratigraphic range charts appear to reflect real phases of diversification in the *Trepostomata, Cystoporata, Crypto-stomata* and *Cheilostomata*. Details of diversification in the *Ctenostomata* are likely always to be obscure, but extensive revision of the *Cyclostomata* should reveal their true pattern of development in geological time   [G.P.L.]

Class PHYLACTOLAEMATA Allman 1856

First, Cret Cenom: *?Plumatella proliferus* Fric, Bohemia. **Extant,** *Cristatella mucedo* Cuvier, cosmopolitan.

Comment: The Phylactolaemata are freshwater Ectoprocta lacking a mineralised skeleton. They may be presumed to have a long geological history; a single imperfectly preserved specimen has been assigned to *Plumatella*.

Order CTENOSTOMATA Busk 1852

General Comments: The Ctenostomata are Bryozoa in which the skeleton is membranous or only imperfectly mineralised. In life they are able, by chemical secretion, to excavate hollows in the surfaces of the substrata which they encrust. Such excavations are found fossil and their form is used to diagnose zoarial characters. On this basis, three long-ranging extinct families are recognised, greatest diversification being in the Palaeozoic. Several extant families occur, but only one of these has a recognised fossil occurrence from Tert Mioc onward.

Suborder STOLONIFERA Ehlers 1876

Family ROPALONARIIDAE Bassler 1953

First, Ord Ashg: *Ropalonaria venosa* Ulrich, Richmond fm., Ohio, U.S.A.
Last, Perm: *Ropalonaria sp.*
Comment: *Ropalonaria* is the only genus.

Family VINELLIDAE Ulrich & Bassler 1904

First, Ord Arenig: *Marcusodictyon priscum* (Bassler), Jegelecht Falls sst., Estonia.
Last, Cret Campan: *Vinella sp.*, Germany.

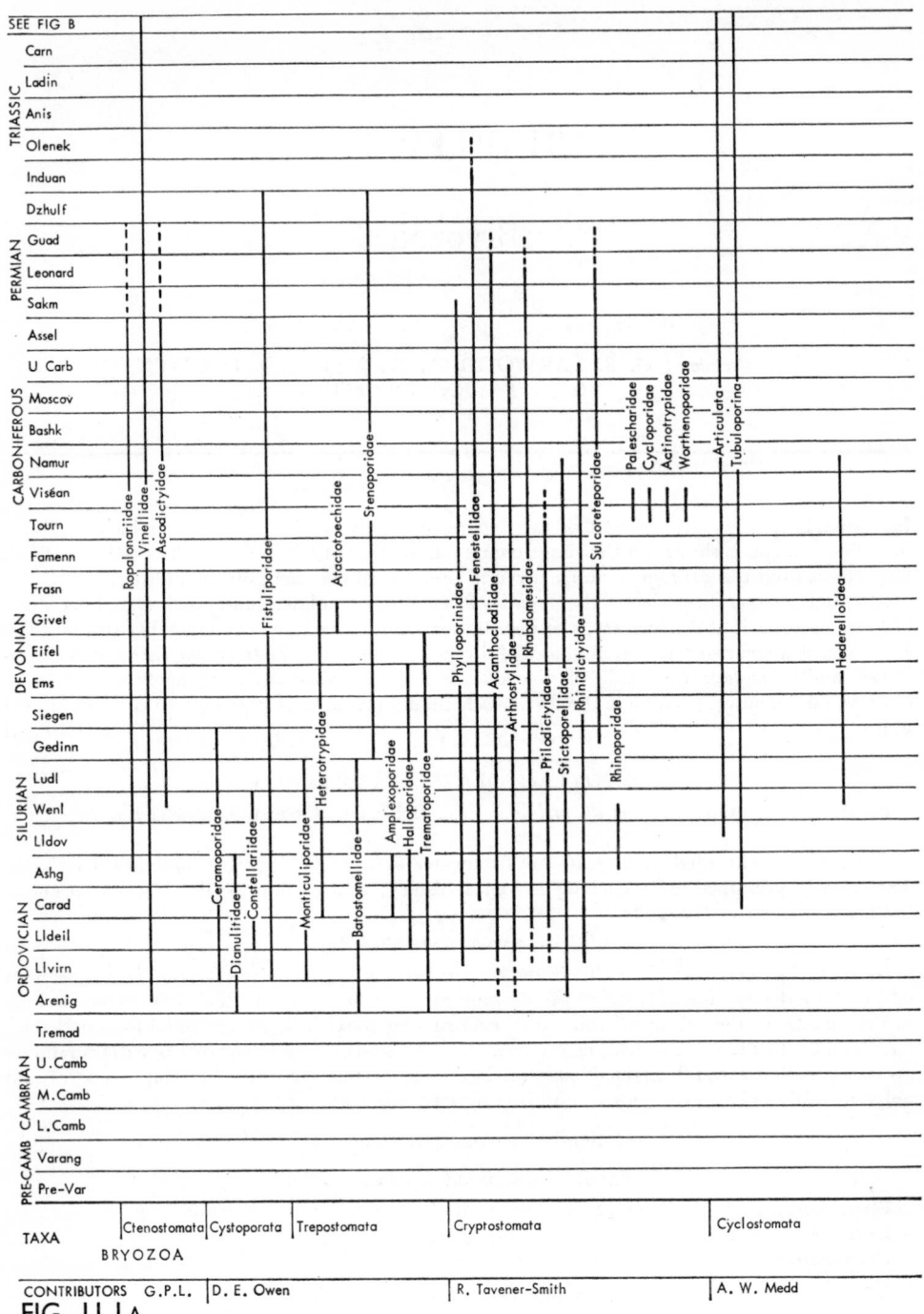

FIG. 11.1A

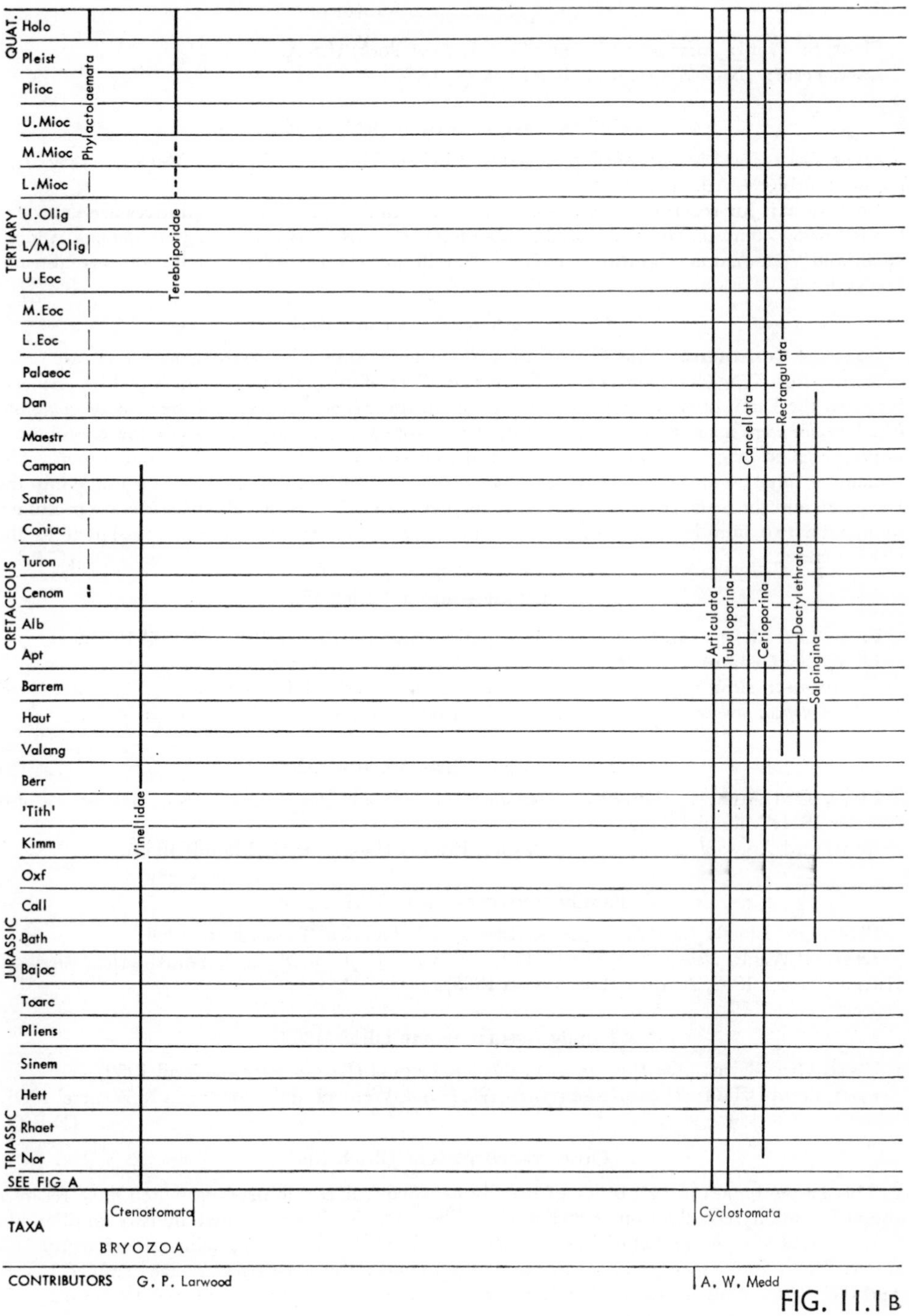
QUAT.
Holo
Pleist
Plioc
U.Mioc
M.Mioc
L.Mioc
TERTIARY
U.Olig
L/M.Olig
U.Eoc
M.Eoc
L.Eoc
Palaeoc
Dan
Maestr
Campan
Santon
Coniac
Turon
CRETACEOUS
Cenom
Alb
Apt
Barrem
Haut
Valang
Berr
'Tith'
Kimm
Oxf
Call
JURASSIC
Bath
Bajoc
Toarc
Pliens
Sinem
Hett
TRIASSIC
Rhaet
Nor
SEE FIG A
Phylactolaemata
Terebriporidae
Vinellidae
Articulata
Tubuloporina
Cancellata
Cerioporina
Rectangulata
Dactylethrata
Salpingina
TAXA
Ctenostomata
Cyclostomata
BRYOZOA
CONTRIBUTORS
G. P. Larwood
A. W. Medd

FIG. 11.1B

The Fossil Record, Part II

Family ASCODICTYIDAE Miller 1889

First, Sil Wenl: *Eliasopora siluriensis* (Vine), New York, U.S.A.
Last, Perm: *Bascomella sp.* and *Ascodictyon sp.*, U.S.A.

Family TEREBRIPORIDAE d'Orbigny 1847

First, Tert L–M.Mioc: *Spathipora sertum* Fischer, Helvetian, France. **Extant,** *Terebripora ramosa* d'Orbigny, Atlantic.

Comment: Jur records of *Terebripora* very uncertain. No fossil representatives are known of the following ctenostomatous bryozoan suborders: CARNOSA Gray 1841, PALUDICELLEA Allman 1856, and VESICULARINA Johnston 1847. Six families of the suborder STOLONIFERA are also not known fossil.   [G.P.L.]

Order CYSTOPORATA Astrova 1964

General Comment: The Cystoporata is newly proposed by Astrova as a separate order of the Bryozoa. The Cystoporata includes four families; of these, the *Constellariidae*, which formerly included the Dianulitids, were placed previously in the Trepostomata, and the *Ceramoporidae* and *Fistuliporidae* were assigned previously to the Cyclostomata. All four families of the Cystoporata are represented by genera in the Ordovician, the *Dianulitidae* being confined to that system. The remaining three families also occur in the Silurian and, of these, the *Ceramoporidae* range into the Devonian and the *Fistuliporidae* to the end of the Permian. The revised *Fistuliporidae* are presumed to include two families, the *Hexagonellidae* and the *Goniocladiidae*, previously assigned to the Cyclostomata.   [G.P.L.]

Family CERAMOPORIDAE Ulrich 1882

First, Ord Llvirn: *Analotichia revalensis* Bassler, Estonia (Bassler 1911, Männil 1959).
Last, Dev Gedinn: *Ceramopora* spp., North America (Hall & Simpson 1887).
Comment: *Archaeotrypa prima* Fritz doubtful but described U.Camb North America (Fritz 1947). *Bolopora undosa* Lewis doubtful but described Ord Arenig, Britain (Lewis 1926).

Family DIANULITIDAE Vinassa 1920

First, Ord Arenig: *Dianulites glauconiticus* Männil and *Revalotrypa gibbosa* Bassler, Estonia (Bassler 1911, Männil 1959).
Last, Ord Ashg: *Dianulites grandis* Bassler, Estonia (Bassler 1911, Männil 1959).

Family CONSTELLARIIDAE Ulrich 1890

First, Ord Lldeil: *Constellaria islensis* Ross, North America (Ross 1963b, 1964).
Last, Sil Wenl: *Hennigopora florida* (Hall). *Nicholsonella parva* Owen, North America, England, Russia (Bassler 1952, Astrova 1965, Owen 1965).

Family FISTULIPORIDAE Ulrich 1882

First, Ord Llvirn: *Xenotrypa primaeva* Bassler, Estonia (Bassler 1911, Männil 1959).
Last, Perm Dzhulf: *Dybowskiella grandis* Waagen & Wentzel, India (Waagen & Wentzel 1886).
                                                                                      [D.E.O.]

Order TREPOSTOMATA Ulrich 1882

The Trepostomata are an order of heavily calcified Palaeozoic Bryozoa which have received much attention recently from systematists. These studies have resulted in two families, the *Constellariidae* and the *Phylloporinidae* (*vide* Treatise, Pt.G, Bassler 1953), being excluded from the order. Eight families are retained in the Trepostomata: the *Amplexoporidae* are confined to Ord and the *Atactotoechidae* to Dev. The *Monticuliporidae* and the *Batostomellidae* range from Ord to Sil and the *Stenoporidae* from Dev to Per. The remaining three families range from Ord to Dev.
                                                                                      [G.P.L.]

Chapter 11: Bryozoa

Family MONTICULIPORIDAE Nicholson 1881

First, Ord Llvirn: *Mesotrypa volchovensis* Modzalevskaja, Estonia (Männil 1959).
Last, Sil Ludl: *Orbignyella fibrosa* (Lonsdale), England (Owen 1961).

Family HETEROTRYPIDAE Ulrich 1890

First, Ord Carad: *Heterotrypa taffi* Loeblich, North America (Loeblich 1942).
Last, Dev Givet: *Leptotrypella* spp. and *Eridotrypella* spp., North America (Duncan 1939).
Comment: *Dannunzioporina inflecta* Bassler is recrystallised and is very doubtful Heterotrypid, Ord Llvirn, Estonia (Bassler 1911, Männil 1959).

Family ATACTOTOECHIDAE Duncan 1939

First and Last, Dev Givet: *Atactotoechus* spp., North America (Duncan 1939).
Comment: *Atactotoechus chazyensis* Ross, North America (Ross 1964) may be *Amplexopora*.

Family BATOSTOMELLIDAE Miller 1880

First, Ord Arenig: *Esthoniopora communis* Bassler and *E. lessnikowae* Modzalevskaja, Estonia (Bassler 1911, Männil 1959).
Last, Sil Ludl: *Batostomella* spp., *Bythopora parallela* Owen, England (Owen 1961).
Comment: Thomas (1931) described a doubtful polyzoan as possibly near this family from L.Camb, Shropshire, England. Duncan (1949) considered "Batostomellidae" from Carb and later to be Stenoporidae. Lazutkina (1963) described *Batostomella jakutica* from L.Trias but it may belong to Heteroporid Cyclostomata.

Family STENOPORIDAE Waagen & Wentzel 1886

First, Dev Gedinn: *Diplostenopora siluriana* (Weller), N. America (Ulrich and Bassler 1913).
Last, Perm Dzhulf: *Stenopora* spp., *Stenopora hardmani* Crockford, India and Australia (Waagen and Wentzel 1886, Crockford 1957).
Comment: In Treatise (Bassler 1953) *Leioclema* and *Lioclemella* are placed in this family though relationships of pre mid-Dev species are extremely doubtful. If accepted, first is Ord Llvirn, *Lioclemella spinea* (Bassler), Estonia (Bassler 1911, Männil 1959). *Dyscritella agischevi* Nekhoroshev 1949 Trias Nor, and *Arcticopora christiei* Fritz 1961 Trias Scyth. are Trepostomata and probably Stenoporidae. *Zlambachia alpina* Flügel 1961 Trias Rhaet is doubtful.

Family AMPLEXOPORIDAE Miller 1889

First and Last, Ord Carad and Ashg: *Amplexopora* spp, North America (Boardman 1960).
Comment: It is doubtful if remaining genera placed in the family by Bassler (1953) really belong to it.

Family HALLOPORIDAE Bassler 1911

First, Ord Lldeil: *Hallopora dumalis* (Ulrich), Estonia and North America (Bassler 1911 and Männil 1959).
Last, Dev Ems: *Hallopora perelegans* (Hall), North America (Hall and Simpson 1887).

Family TREMATOPORIDAE Miller 1889

First, Ord Arenig: *Dittopora clavaeformis* Dybowski, Estonia (Bassler 1911 and Männil 1959).
Last, Dev Eifel: *Monotrypa nannigensis* Hu, China (Hu Zhao-Xun 1965).
Comment: *Diatrypella baconica* Vinassa, Trias Italy, has been described as being related to *Monotrypa* (Vinassa 1901) but further work is needed. Species of *Monotrypa* have also been described from Trias of Bakony (Papp 1900) but their place in the Trepostomata is doubtful. The coral *Chaetetes* may account for similar identifications in various parts of the world (Duncan, pers. comm.). [D.E.O].

The Fossil Record, Part II

Order CRYPTOSTOMATA Vine 1883

General Comment: The cryptostomata constitute an order of well calcified Palaeozoic Bryozoa in which nine families, including the *Phylloporinidae*, are generally long-ranging from the Ordovician to the Carboniferous or Permian and one family is restricted to the highest Ordovician and lower half of the Silurian. Four other families of uncertain status and affinity have a restricted occurrence in the Lower Carboniferous. Families as in *Treatise* pt. G (Bassler 1953), with addition of Phylloporinidae, now generally agreed to belong here.   [G.P.L.]

Family PHYLLOPORINIDAE Ulrich 1890

First, Ord Llvirn: *"Phylloporina"* sp., Chazy Fm, New York and Vermont (Ross 1963a).
Last, Perm Sakm: *Chainodictyon kasayakensis* Nikiforova 1939, Pseudofusulina moelleri Z., Kasmarka Fm, Urals, U.S.S.R.

Family FENESTELLIDAE King 1850

First, Ord Carad: *Polypora quadrata* Bekker, Kuckers Sh, Estonia (Männil 1959).
Last, Trias ?Induan/Olenek: *Polypora* sp., Veszprém, Bakony, Hungary (Vinassa de Regny 1911). Also *P. darashamensis* Nikiforova, Trans-Caucasus, U.S.S.R. (Morozova 1965).

Family ACANTHOCLADIIDAE Zittel 1880

First, Ord Arenig-Llvirn: *Pteropora pennula* Eichwald 1860 and *P. exilis* Eichwald 1860, Orthoceras (Vaginaten) lst, Spitham and Erras, Estonia. These records are doubtful (Bassler 1911); if rejected, first is Ord Ashg: *P. pennula*, Lyckholm lst, Estonia (Männil 1959).
Last, Perm ?Guad: *Acanthocladia anceps* (Schlotheim) 1820; *Synocladia virgulacea* (Phillips) 1829, Magnesian Lst, NE. England (King 1850).

Family ARTHROSTYLIDAE Ulrich 1888

First, Ord Arenig-Llvirn: *Arthroclema armatum* Ulrich 1890, Glauconite Lst, Reval, Estonia (Bassler 1911). Also *?Helopora* sp. A (certainly an arthrostylid), Chazy Fm, Vermont (Ross 1963a).
Last, Carb U. Carb: *Nematopora ivanovi* Shulga-Nesterenko 1955, Triticites jigulensis Z., Gzhel, Moscow Province, U.S.S.R.

Family RHABDOMESIDAE Vine 1883

First, Ord Llvirn-Lldeil: *Nematotrypa gracilis* Bassler 1911, Echinospherites lst, Reval, Estonia.
Last, Perm Leonard-Guad: *Streblascopora delicatula* Sakagami 1961 and *Hayasakopora matsudae* Sakagami 1961, Parafusulina Z., Iwaizaki lst, N. Hônshu, Japan. Also *Streblascopora germana* (Bassler) 1929, Basleo and Amarassi Fm, Timor.

Family PTILODICTYIDAE Zittel 1880

First, Ord Llvirn-Lldeil: *Chazydictya chazyensis* Ross 1963a, Chazy Fm, New York and Vermont,
Last, Carb Viséan: *Stictoporina altaica* Nekhoroshev 1956 and *S. bifurcata* Nekhoroshev 1956. Tarkhansky Fm, Altai Mts, Siberia.

Family STICTOPORELLIDAE Nickles & Bassler 1900

First, Ord Arenig: *Stictoporellina gracilis gracilis* (Eichwald) 1860, Glauconite lst, Estonia (Männil 1959).
Last, Carb Namur: *Heliotrypa bifolia* Ulrich 1883, Glen Dean lst, Kentucky.

Family RHINIDICTYIDAE Ulrich 1895

First, Ord Llvirn: *Phyllodictya flabellaris* Bassler 1911, Orthoceras lst, Reval, Estonia (Männil 1959). Also *Sibiredictya usitata* Nekhoroshev 1961, Krivolutsky Fm, Kaluga, Siberia.
Last, Carb U. Carb: *Timanodictya dichotoma* (Stuckenberg) 1887, Indiga R., Timan, U.S.S.R. (Nikiforova 1938).

Chapter 11: Bryozoa

Family SULCORETEPORIDAE Bassler 1935

First, Dev Gedinn: *Sulcoretepora gilberti* (Meek) 1871 and five other spp. Also *Thamnotrypa divaricata* (Hall) 1883, U. Helderberg Fm, Buffalo, New York (Hall & Simpson 1887).

Last, Perm Leonard-Guad: *Sulcoretepora nipponica* Sakagami 1961, Parafusulina Z., Kamiyatsuse, N. Hônshu, Japan.

Family RHINOPORIDAE Miller 1889

First, Ord Ashg: *Lichenalia concentrica* Hall 1852, Borkholm lst, Borkholm, Estonia (Bassler 1911).

Last, Sil Wenl: *Diamesopora* Hall (four spp.) and *Stictotrypa* Ulrich (three spp.), Niagaran Series, Lockport, New York and Waldron, Indiana (Nickles & Bassler 1900).

General Comment: The following families are also included by Bassler (1953, *Treatise* pt G) in the Cryptostomata: *Palescharidae* Miller 1889, *Cycloporidae* Ulrich 1890, *Actinotrypidae* Ulrich 1890, *Worthenoporidae* Ulrich 1893. They include a total of only six genera recorded from the Keokuk and Warsaw Fms (Tourn-Viséan), Iowa, Illinois and Missouri. The genera are doubtfully assigned to the Cryptostomata: some appear to have stronger affinities with the Cheilostomata, others with the Cyclostomata. [R.T.-S.]

Order CYCLOSTOMATA Busk 1852

General Comment: The Cyclostomata are an order of strongly calcified Bryozoa occurring in all geological systems from Ord onward and possibly also represented in U. Camb. The relationship of the Cyclostomata to other bryozoan orders is not clear and there are many uncertainties concerning the status of the recognised families in the Cyclostomata. Excluding the four families assigned to other orders, 30 families are recognised in the Treatise, Pt.G (Bassler 1953), of these, four are not known fossil. Among the remaining 26 families, two are confined to the Palaeozoic, ranging from Sil to Carb. Two families, one appearing in Ord and one in Dev, are still extant. Of the other extant families, one ranges from Trias, seven from Jur, four from Cret and two from Tert Eoc. One family is confined to Jur and four to Cret, two range throughout Jur and Cret and one ranges from Jur to Tert Eoc. It is clear that Jur and Cret Cyclostomata have received more attention from taxonomists than have those from other geological systems. The order is much in need of general revision, which, if accomplished, would almost certainly substantially change the taxonomic content and stratigraphic range of its constituent families. At present there are so many uncertainties that it seemed advisable to represent the occurrence of the Cyclostomata at subordinal level. [G.P.L.]

Suborder ARTICULATA Busk 1859

First, Sil Lldov: *Phacelopora pertenuis* Ulrich, U.S.A. (Ulrich 1890). **Extant.**

Suborder TUBULOPORINA Milne-Edwards 1838

First, Ord Carad: *Mitoclema cinctosum* Ulrich, Tennessee (Ulrich 1882), and *Osburnostylus typicalis* Bassler, Virginia (Bassler 1952). **Extant.**

Constituent families: (except for the Multisparsidae, all extant), Diastoporidae Gregory, Carad; Tubuliporidae Johnston, Eifel; Multisparsidae Bassler, Bath; Oncousoeciidae Canu, Pliens; Terviidae Canu and Bassler, M. Eoc; Entalophoridae Reuss, Pliens; Diaperoeciidae Canu, Bath; Plagioeciidae Canu, Bath; Frondiporidae Busk, Bath; Theonoidae Busk, Bajoc; etc. Familes as in Treatise pt G (Bassler 1953).

Suborder CANCELLATA Gregory 1896

First, Jur Kimm: *Tetrapora suevica* Quenstedt, Mutabilis Z., Germany (Quenstedt 1858). **Extant.**

Constituent families: (all extant), Horneridae Gregory U. Eoc; Cytididae d'Orbigny Kimm; Petaloporidae Gregory Haut; etc. Families as in Treatise pt G (Bassler 1953).

Suborder CERIOPORINA von Hagenow 1851

First, Trias Nor: *Ceriopora cnemidium* von Klipst and *Ceriopora flabellum* Vinassa, Sicily (Vinassa 1901). **Extant.**

Constituent families: Heteroporidae Waters Nor–extant; Corymboporidae Smith Cenom–extant; Tretocycloeciidae Canu Cenom–extant; Cavidae d'Orbigny Bath to Maestr; Leiosoeciidae Canu and Bassler Bath to L. Eoc. Families as in Treatise pt G (Bassler 1953).

Suborder RECTANGULATA Waters 1887

First, Cret Valang: *Semimulticavea landrioti* (Michelin), France and Switzerland (Michelin 1841 and d'Orbigny 1853). **Extant.**
Constituent family: Lichenoporidae Smitt.

Suborder DACTYLETHRATA Gregory 1896

First, Cret Valang: *Reptoclausa neocomiensis* d'Orbigny, Switzerland (d'Orbigny 1853).
Last, Cret Maestr: *Cryptoglena adspersa* Marsson, Germany (Marsson 1887).
Constituent family: Clausidae d'Orbigny.

Suborder SALPINGINA von Hagenow 1851

First, Jur Bath: *Cyclocites primogenitum* Canu and Bassler, France (Canu and Bassler 1922).
Last, Tert Dan: *Meliceritella steenstrupi* (Pergens and Meunier), Denmark (Levinsen 1925).
Constituent families: Eleidae d'Orbigny Bath to Dan; Semiceidae Buge Coniac to Maestr; Lobosoeciidae Canu and Bassler Cenom. Families as in Treatise pt G (Bassler 1953).
Comment: *Cinctopora* Hutton 1873, appearing in Tert, Australia and New Zealand, is possibly an extant sample of this suborder (Buge 1952).

Suborder HEDERELLOIDEA Bassler 1939

First, Sil Wenl: *Hederella siluriana* Bassler, Sweden (Bassler 1939).
Last, Carb Namur: *Hederella chesterensis* Bassler, Illinois, U.S.A. (Bassler 1939).
Constituent family: Reptariidae Simpson. [A.W.M.]

Order CHEILOSTOMATA Busk 1852

General Comment: The Cheilostomata are the largest and most varied order of Bryozoa. In general the skeleton is well calcified and often very well preserved in Cret and younger strata. Among the 81 families assigned to this order in the Treatise pt G (Bassler 1953) 13 are not known fossil. The order is first represented by two families in Cret Alb and there is a marked increase with the appearance of seven new families in Cret Cenom. This rate of increase is sustained until Cret Coniac times and achieved again in Cret Camp and Maestr. In Tert the rate of appearance of new families is less with the notable exception of Tert L. Eoc, with six new families, and Tert M. Eoc, with eight new families. After Tert L. Mioc times only one new family appears, in the Quart Pleist. Recently published works on Cretaceous and later Cheilostomata include those of Berthelsen (1962), Brown (1952), Lagaaij (1952), Larwood (1962) and Voigt (1962). These contain assessments of terminology, morphology and stratigraphical distributions together with extensive taxonomic studies.

Suborder ANASCA Levinsen 1909

Family AETEIDAE Smitt 1867

First, Tert U.Eoc: *Aetea* cf. *truncata* Landsborough, Bartonian, Jackson fm., N. Carolina, U.S.A. **Extant,** *A. anguina* (Linnaeus), Atlantic.

Family SCRUPARIIDAE Busk 1852

First, Tert L.Eoc: *Eucratea wetherelli* (Busk), Ypresian, Europe. **Extant,** *Scruparia chelata* (Linnaeus), E. Atlantic.
Comment: *Eucratea labiata* Novak from the Cret Cenom is a *Pyripora*.

Family MEMBRANIPORIDAE Busk 1854

First, Cret Cenom: *?Cellarinidra clavata* (d'Orbigny), Europe. **Extant,** *Membranipora membranacea* (Linnaeus), Atlantic.

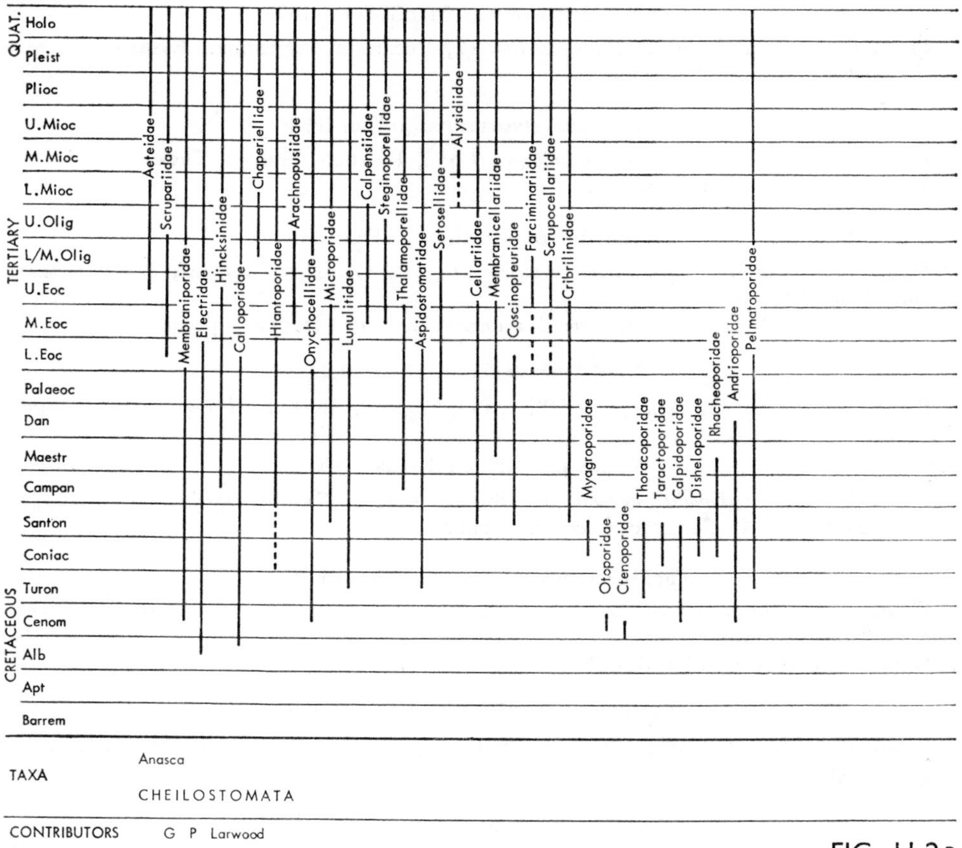
QUAT.
Holo
Pleist
Plioc
U.Mioc
M.Mioc
L.Mioc
U.Olig
L/M.Olig
U.Eoc
M.Eoc
L.Eoc
Palaeoc
Dan
Maestr
Campan
Santon
Coniac
Turon
Cenom
Alb
Apt
Barrem
TERTIARY
CRETACEOUS
Aeteidae
Scrupariidae
Membraniporidae
Electridae
Hincksinidae
Calloporidae
Chaperiellidae
Hiantoporidae
Arachnopusiidae
Onychocellidae
Microporidae
Lunulitidae
Calpensiidae
Steginoporellidae
Thalamoporellidae
Aspidostomatidae
Setosellidae
Alysidiidae
Cellariidae
Membranicellariidae
Coscinopleuridae
Farciminariidae
Scrupocellariidae
Cribrilinidae
Myagroporidae
Otoporidae
Ctenoporidae
Thoracoporidae
Taractoporidae
Calpidoporidae
Disheloporidae
Rhacheoporidae
Andrioporidae
Pelmatoporidae
TAXA
Anasca
CHEILOSTOMATA
CONTRIBUTORS
G P Larwood

FIG. 11.2B

Family ELECTRIDAE Lagaaij 1952

First, Cret Alb: *Pyripora texana* Thomas & Larwood, Comanchean, Fort Worth fm, Texas; and *Rhammatopora gaultina* (Vine), U.Gault, England. **Extant,** *Electra verticellata* (Ellis & Solander), N. Atlantic.

Family HINCKSINIDAE Canu & Bassler 1927

First, Cret Campan: *Cranosina alumensis* (Brydone), lower part of B. mucronata Z., England. **Extant,** *Hincksina flustroides* (Hincks), NE. Atlantic.

Family CALLOPORIDAE Norman 1903

First, Cret Alb: *Wilbertopora mutabilis* Cheetham, Comanchean, Fort Worth fm, Texas. **Extant,** *Callopora lineata* (Linnaeus), N. Atlantic.

Family CHAPERIELLIDAE Harmer 1957

First, Tert M.Olig: *Patsyella dentata* (Waters), Pareora Ser., Otaian Stg., Rupelian, New Zealand. **Extant,** *Chaperiella acanthina* (Lamouroux), S. Atlantic.

Family HIANTOPORIDAE MacGillivray 1895

First, Cret Coniac-Santon: *Tremogasterina sp.*, Rocanean, Argentina. **Extant,** *Tremopora dendracantha* Ortmann, NW. Pacific.

Family ARACHNOPUSIIDAE Jullien 1888

First, Tert M.Eoc: *Exechonella magniporosa* Canu, Lutetian, France. **Extant,** *Arachnopusia monoceras* (Busk), Straits of Magellan.

Family ONYCHOCELLIDAE Jullien 1881

First, Cret Cenom: *Hoplocheilina osculifera* (Reuss), Germany. **Extant,** *Floridina antiqua* (Smitt), Gulf of Mexico.
Comment: M.Jur record of *Onychocella* an error, refers to a late Cret specimen.

Family MICROPORIDAE Hincks 1880

First, Cret Santon: *Aechmella proteus* (Brydone), England. **Extant,** *Micropora coriacea* (Esper), N. Atlantic.

Family LUNULITIDAE Lagaaij 1952

First, Cret Turon: *Lunulites angulosa* (d'Orbigny), France. **Extant,** *Lunulites spp.*
Comment: Cret Cenom record very uncertain.

Family CALPENSIIDAE Canu & Bassler 1923

First, Tert M.Eoc: *Poricellaria alata* d'Orbigny, Lutetian, France. **Extant,** *Microporina elongata* (Hincks), Atlantic.
Comment: Cret record of *Microporina sp.* uncertain.

Family STEGINOPORELLIDAE Bassler 1953

First, Tert M.Eoc: *Gaudryanella variabilis* Canu, Lutetian, France. **Extant,** *Steginoporella magnilabris* (Busk), Gulf of Mexico.

Family THALAMOPORELLIDAE Levinsen 1902

First, Cret Campan: *Woodipora rhomboidalis* (Hennig), Sweden. **Extant,** *Thalamoporella rozieri* (Audouin), Mediterranean.

Family ASPIDOSTOMATIDAE Jullien 1888

First, Cret Turon: *?Euritina eurita* (d'Orbigny), France. **Extant,** *Aspidostoma giganteum* (Busk), SW. Atlantic, Antarctic.

Family SETOSELLIDAE Levinsen 1909

First, Tert Palaeoc: *Setosinella prolifica* Canu & Bassler, Vincentown Limesand, New Jersey, U.S.A. **Extant,** *Setosella vulnerata* (Busk), NE. Atlantic.

Family ALYSIDIIDAE Levinsen 1909

First, Tert L.-M.Mioc: *Catenariopsis morningtoniensis* Maplestone, Balcombian, Australia. **Extant,** *Alysidium parasiticum* Busk, SE. Atlantic.

Family CELLARIIDAE Hincks 1880

First, Cret Santon: *Escharicellaria polymorpha* Voigt, U.Emscherian, Germany. **Extant,** *Cellaria fistulosa* (Linnaeus), N. Atlantic.

Family MEMBRANICELLARIIDAE Levinsen 1909

First, Cret Maestr: *Dictuonia aceste* (d'Orbigny), Europe. **Extant,** *Membranicellaria dubia* (Busk), SE. Atlantic.

Chapter 11: Bryozoa

Family COSCINOPLEURIDAE Canu 1913

First, Cret Santon: *Escharifora argus* d'Orbigny, France.
Last, Tert L.Eoc: *Coscinopleura digitata* (Morton), Ypresian-Cuisian, Wilcox fm, New Jersey, U.S.A.

Family FARCIMINARIIDAE Busk 1884

First, Tert Eoc: *Nellia sp.*, England. **Extant,** *Farciminaria aculeata* Busk, SW. Pacific.

Family SCRUPOCELLARIIDAE Levinsen 1909

First, Tert Eoc: *Canda sp.*, France. **Extant,** *Scrupocellaria scruposa* (Linnaeus), N. Atlantic.
Comment: *Plicopora daedala* MacGillivray is recorded from the Tert, Australia—horizon uncertain.

Family CRIBRILINIDAE Hincks 1880

First, Cret Santon: *?Mumiella mumia* (d'Orbigny), France. **Extant,** *Cribrilina punctata* (Hassall), Ireland.

Family MYAGROPORIDAE Lang 1916

First, Cret Coniac: *Myagropora cavea* Lang and *M. muscipula* Lang, M. cortestudinarium Z., England.
Last, Cret Santon: *M. muscipula* Lang, M. coranguinum Z., England.
Comment: *M. cavea* and *M. muscipula* are the only species.

Family OTOPORIDAE Lang 1916

First and **Last,** Cret Cenom: *Anaptopora disjuncta* Lang and *Otopora auricula* Lang, Chalk Marl, England.
Comment: *Anaptopora* is the more primative genus of the two which comprise the family which is confined to the Cenomanian (Lang 1921).

Family CTENOPORIDAE Lang 1916

First and **Last,** Cret Cenom: *Ctenopora pecten* Lang, throughout Chalk Marl, England.
Comment: *C. pecten* is the only species.

Family THORACOPORIDAE Lang 1916

First, Cret Turon: *Thoracopora costata* Lang, H. planus Z., England.
Last, Cret Santon: *T. pontifera* (Brydone), M. coranguinum Z., England.
Comment: *Thoracopora* is the only genus.

Family TARACTOPORIDAE Lang 1916

First, Cret Coniac: *Taractopora confusa* Lang, low in M. cortestudinarium Z., England.
Last, Cret Santon: *T. obscurata* (Brydone), M. coranguinum Z., England.
Comment: *Taractopora* is the only genus.

Family CALPIDOPORIDAE Lang 1916

First, Cret Cenom: *Calpidopora diota* Lang, Czechoslovakia.
Last, Cret Santon: *Graptoporella scripta* Lang, France.

Family DISHELOPORIDAE Lang 1916

First, Cret Coniac: *Hystricopora horrida* Lang, France.
Last, Cret Santon: *Dishelopora claviceps* (Brydone), Marsupites Z., England.

Family RHACHEOPORIDAE Lang 1916

First, Cret Coniac: *Rhacheopora lavalis* Lang, France.
Last, Cret Maestr: *Geisopora protecta* Lang, Rügen, Germany.

Family ANDRIOPORIDAE Lang 1916

First, Cret Cenom: *Kankopora kankensis* Lang, Czechoslovakia.
Last, Tert Dan: *Auchenopora guttur* Lang, Denmark.

Family PELMATOPORIDAE Lang 1916

First, Cret Turon: *Sandalopora gallica* Lang, France. **Extant,** *Gephyrotes figularis nitidopunctata* (Smitt), N. Atlantic.

General Comment: No fossil representatives are known of the following families: Beaniidae Canu & Bassler 1927, bicellariellidae Levinsen 1909, Bugulidae Gray 1848, cothurnicellidae Bassler 1935, epistomiidae Gregory 1903, flustridae Smitt 1867 and labiostomellidae Silen 1942.

Suborder ASCOPHORA Levinsen 1909

Family PORINIDAE d'Orbigny 1852

First, Cret Turon: *Rotiporina culveriana* (Brydone), H. planus Z., England. **Extant,** *Porina spp.*

Family CYCLICOPORIDAE Hincks 1884

First, Cret Maestr: *?Taenioporina arachnoidea* (Goldfuss), Holland. **Extant,** *Cyclicopora longipora* (MacGillivray), SW. Pacific.

Family HIPPOTHOIDAE Levinsen 1909

First, Cret Cenom: *Dacryoporella reussi* (Lang), L. Plänerkalk, Bohemia. **Extant,** *Hippothoa divaricatar* Lamouroux, Mediterranean.

Family UMBONULIDAE Canu 1904

First, Tert M.Eoc: *Umbonula sp.*, Lutetian, France. **Extant,** *U. verrucosa* (Esper), NE. Atlantic.

Family PETRALIIDAE Levinsen 1909

First, Tert U.Eoc: *Hippopodina vibraculifera* Canu & Bassler, Bartonian, M. Jackson fm., N. Carolina, U.S.A. **Extant,** *Petralia undata* MacGillivray, SW. Pacific.

Family GIGANTOPORIDAE Bassler 1935

First, Cret ?Maestr: *Gigantopora sp.*, Europe. **Extant,** *G. lynchoides* Ridley, SW. Atlantic.

Family STOMACHETOSELLIDAE Canu & Bassler 1917

First, Tert M.Eoc: *Ochetosella jacksonica* Canu & Bassler, Lutetian-Auversian, N. Carolina, U.S.A. **Extant,** *Diastosula marionense* (Busk), NW. Atlantic.

Family SCHIZOPORELLIDAE Jullien 1903

First, Cret Maestr: *Systenostoma asperulum* (Marsson), Rügen, Germany. **Extant,** *Schizoporella unicornis* (Johnston), NE. Atlantic.

Comment: "*Schizoporella*" *carinata* Hennig 1892 (see also Voigt, 1930) is recorded from the Cret L.Campan, Sweden, but its systematic position is uncertain.

Family HIPPOPORINIDAE Bassler 1935

First, Cret Campan: *Balantiostoma marsupium* (Hagenow), Germany. **Extant,** *Hippoporidra edax* (Busk), NE. Atlantic.

Family EXOCHELLIDAE Bassler 1935

First, Cret Coniac-Santon: *Exochella sp.*, Rocanean, Argentina. **Extant,** *Didymosella larvalis* MacGillivray, SW. Pacific.

Comment: *Lepralia (Mucronella) neumayri* Pergens, Cret Maestr, Limbourg, Holland, appears to be an *Exochella*—the first occurrence in Europe.

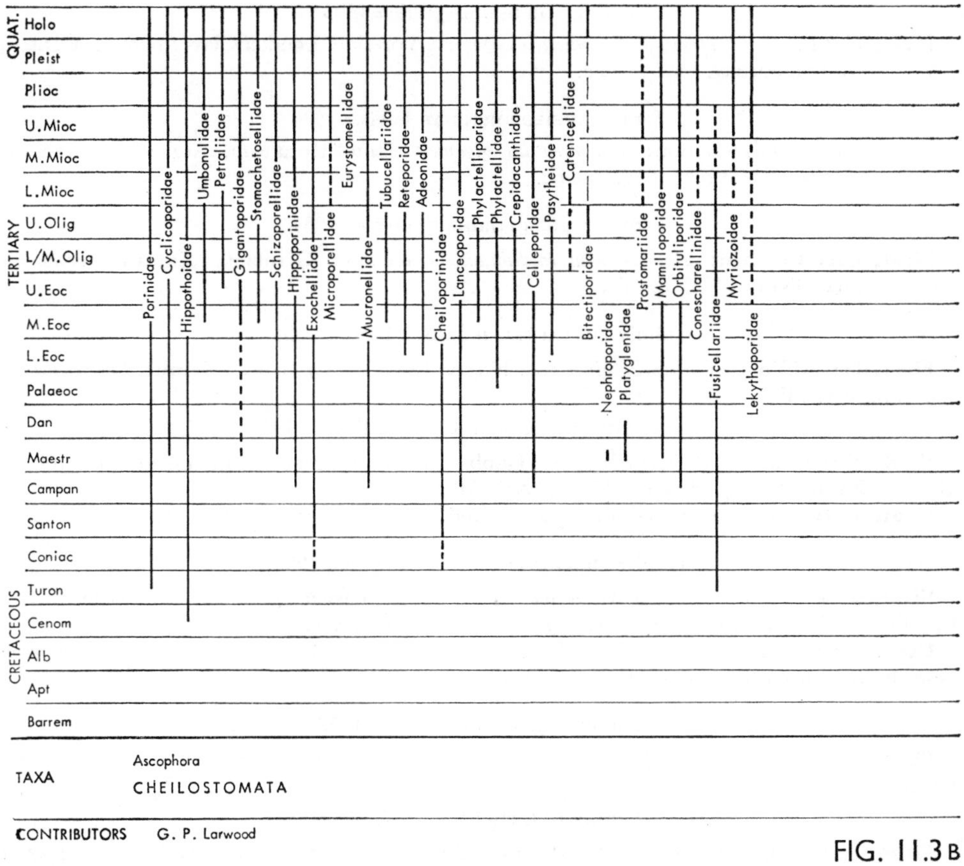

FIG. 11.3 B

TAXA — Ascophora / CHEILOSTOMATA

CONTRIBUTORS — G. P. Larwood

Family MICROPORELLIDAE Hincks 1880

First, Tert Mioc: *Calloporina decorata* (Reuss), Austria. **Extant,** *Microporella (Diporula) verrucosa* (Peach), Atlantic.

Family EURYSTOMELLIDAE Levinsen 1909

First, Quat Pleist: *Eurystomella bilabiata* Hincks, California, U.S.A. **Extant,** *E. foraminigera* (Hincks), S. Pacific, and *E. bilabiata* Hincks.

Family MUCRONELLIDAE Levinsen 1902

First, Cret Campan: *Cryptostomella gastroporum* (Marsson), Germany. **Extant,** *Mucronella peachi* (Johnston), E. Atlantic.

Family TUBUCELLARIIDAE Busk 1884

First, Tert M.Eoc: *Tubucellaria fragilis* (Michelin), Lutetian, France. **Extant,** *Tubiporella magnirostris* (MacGillivray), SW. Pacific.

Family RETEPORIDAE Smitt 1867

First, Tert L.Eoc: *Psilosecos muralis* (Gabb & Horn), Ypresian-Cuisian, Wilcox fm., New Jersey, U.S.A. **Extant,** *Retepora cellulosa* (Linnaeus), N. Atlantic.

The Fossil Record, Part II

Family ADEONIDAE Jullien 1903

First, Tert L.Eoc: *?Adeonellopsis wetherelli* Gregory, Ypresian, London Clay, London. **Extant,** *Adeona grisea* Lamouroux, SW. Pacific.

Family CHEILOPORINIDAE Bassler 1936

First, Cret Coniac-Santon: *Cianotremella gigantea* Canu, Rocanean, Argentina. **Extant,** *Cheiloporina haddoni* (Harmer), SW. Pacific.

Family LANCEOPORIDAE Harmer 1957

First, Cret Campan: *Bathystomella cordiformis* (Hagenow), Germany. **Extant,** *Parmularia obliqua* (MacGillivray), SW. Pacific.

Family PHYLACTELLIPORIDAE Bassler 1953

First, Tert M.Eoc: *?Cheilonella gigas* Koschinsky, Lutetian, Germany. **Extant,** *Phylactellipora hincksi* Bassler, Atlantic.

Family PHYLACTELLIDAE Canu & Bassler 1917

First, Tert Palaeoc: *Perigastrella exserta* Gabb & Horn, Vincentown Limesand, New Jersey, U.S.A. **Extant,** *Lagenipora socialis* Hincks, NE. Atlantic.
Comment: Cret occurrences of *Perigastrella* and *Lagenipora* very uncertain.

Family CREPIDACANTHIDAE Levinsen 1909

First, Tert M.Eoc: *Schizobathysella saccifera* Canu & Bassler, Lutetian, Claiborne gp, N. Carolina, U.S.A. **Extant,** *Crepidacantha crinispina* (Levinsen), SW. Pacific.
Comment: Cret occurrence of *Crepidacantha* very uncertain. *Mastigophorella* and *Pachycraspedon* both recorded from the Eoc—horizon uncertain.

Family CELLEPORIDAE Busk 1852

First, Cret Campan: *Acanthionella angustidens* (Levinsen), Germany. **Extant,** *Cellepora pumicosa* Hincks, Atlantic.

Family PASYTHEIDAE Davis 1934

First, Tert L.Eoc: *Dittosaria wetherelli* Busk, Ypresian, England. **Extant,** *Pasythea tulipifera* (Ellis & Solander), W. Indies.

Family CATENICELLIDAE Busk 1852

First, Tert Olig: *Pterocella alata* (W. Thomson), ?Mt. Gambier Lst, SW. Victoria, Australia. **Extant,** *Calpidium ornatum* Busk, SW. Pacific.
Comment: The locality given for *Pterocella alata* is Mt. Gambier—if the material is from the Mt. Gambier Lst. the age is Olig unspecified. Three other genera appear in Tert L.Mioc— *Claviporella*, *Strophipora* and *Vittaticella* all of Janjukian or Balcombian age, Victoria, Australia.

Family BITECTIPORIDAE MacGillivray 1895

First, Tert U.Olig: *Bitectipora lineata* MacGillivray, Gellibrand (U.Olig) and Bairnsdale stg., Tortonian, S. Australia (only species). **?Extant.**

Family NEPHROPORIDAE Marsson 1887

First and **Last:** Cret Maestr: *Nephropora elegans* Marsson, Rügen, Germany (only species).

Family PLATYGLENIDAE Marsson 1887

First, Cret Maestr: *Platyglena clava* Marsson, *P. ocellata* Marsson and *P. affinis* Marsson, all from Rügen.
Last, Tert Dan: *P. ocellata* Marsson, Germany.
Comment: *Platyglena* is the only genus.

Chapter 11: Bryozoa

Family PROSTOMARIIDAE MacGillivray 1895

First, Tert Mioc: *Prostomaria gibbericollis* MacGillivray, Balcomian, Victoria, Australia.
Comment: *Prostomaria* is the only genus, *P. gibbericollis* may occur in Pleist of Schnapper Pt, Victoria (? derived).

Family MAMILLOPORIDAE Canu & Bassler 1927

First, Cret Maestr: *Discoflustrellaria clypeiformis* d'Orbigny, France. **Extant,** *Mamillopora cupula* Smitt, Gulf of Mexico.

Family ORBITULIPORIDAE Canu & Bassler 1923

First, Cret Campan: *Stichopora pentasticha* (von Hagenow), Germany. **Extant,** *Sphaeropora fossa* Haswell, SW. Pacific.
Comment: Main early development—Cret Maestr: *Stichopora seriata* Marsson and *S. crassa* Marsson, Europe.

Family CONESCHARELLINIDAE Levinsen 1909

First, Tert ?Mioc: *Conescarellina sp.*, France. **Extant,** *Bipora umbonata* (Haswell), SW. Pacific.

Family FUSICELLARIIDAE d'Orbigny 1851

First, Cret Turon: *Fusicellaria pulchella* d'Orbigny, France.
Last, Tert Mioc: *Fusicanna dohmi* Sandberg, Dominican Republic.

Family MYRIOZOIDAE Smitt 1867

First, Tert Mioc: *Myriozoum sp.*, Europe. **Extant,** *Myriozoella crustacea* (Smitt), N. Atlantic.

Family LEKYTHOPORIDAE Levinsen 1909

First, Tert ?U.Eoc: *Lekythopora hystrix* MacGillivray, Victoria, Australia. **Extant,** *Actisecos regularis* Canu & Bassler, SW. Pacific.
Comment: *Lekythopora* is recorded from Aldinga (section U.Eoc-Plioc) and from River Murray Cliffs (Mioc—unspecified).
General Comment: No fossil representatives are known of the following families: Bifaxariidae Busk 1884, Euthyrisellidae Bassler 1953, Euthyroididae Levinsen 1909, Onchoporidae Levinsen 1909, Savignyellidae Levinsen 1909 and Sclerodomidae Levinsen 1909.   [G.P.L.]

REFERENCES

ASTROVA, G. G. 1965. [Morphology and history of the development and classification of the Ordovician and Silurian Bryozoa.] *Trudy Paleont. Inst.*, **106**, 1–432, pls. 1–84. 52 figs.
BASSLER, R. S. 1911. The early Palaeozoic Bryozoa of the Baltic Provinces. *Bull. U.S. natn. Mus.*, **77**, 1–382, pls. 1–13, 226 figs.
—— 1929. The Permian Bryozoa of Timor. *Paläeont. Timor*, **16** (28), 37–90.
—— 1939. The Hederelloidea, a suborder of Palaeozoic Cyclostomatous Bryozoa. *Proc. U.S. natn. Mus.*, **87** (3068), 25–91.
—— 1952. Taxonomic notes on fossil and Recent Bryozoa. *J. Wash. Acad. Sci.*, **42** (12), 381–385.
—— 1953. *In* MOORE, R. C. *Treatise on Invertebrate Palaeontology*, Part G. Bryozoa. Kansas.
BERTHELSEN, O. 1962. Cheilostome Bryozoa in the Danian Deposits of East Denmark. *Danm. geol. Unders.*, **83**, II Ser., 1–290, pls. 1–28.
BOARDMAN, R. S. 1960. Trepostomatous Bryozoa of the Hamilton Group of New York State. *Prof. Pap. U.S. geol. Surv.*, **340**, 1–87, pls. 1–22, 27 figs.
BROWN, D. A. 1952. *The Tertiary Cheilostomatous Polyzoa of New Zealand*, i–xii, 1–405. Br. Mus. (Nat. Hist.), London.

BUGE, E. 1952. Classe des Bryozoaires (Bryozoa Ehrenberg 1831) *in* PIVETEAU, J. *Traité de Paléontologie, 1.* Paris.

CANU, F. & BASSLER, R. S. 1922. Studies on the cyclostomatous Bryozoa. *Bull. U.S. natn Mus.,* **61** (22), 1–160.

CROCKFORD, J. 1957. Permian Bryozoa from the Fitzroy Basin, Western Australia. *Bull. Bureau Miner. Resour Geol. Geophys. Aust.,* **34,** 1–91.

DUNCAN, H. 1939. Trepostomatous Bryozoa from the Traverse Group of Michigan. *Contr. Mus. Paleont. Univ. Mich.,* **5** (10), 171–270, pls. 1–16.

—— 1949. Genotypes of some Paleozoic Bryozoa. *J. Wash. Acad. Sci.,* **39,** 122–136.

FLÜGEL, H. 1961. Bryozoa of the Zlambach-Schichten (Rhaetic), from Salskammergutes, Austria. *Sber. öst. Akad. Wiss.,* **171,** 1–13, 3 pls.

FRITZ, M. A. 1947. Cambrian Bryozoa. *J. Paleont.,* **21,** 434–435, pl. 60.

—— 1961. A New bryozoan genus from Lake Hazen, Northeastern Ellesmere Land. *Proc. geol. Ass. Can.,* **13,** 53–56, pls. 1–3.

HALL, J. & SIMPSON, G. B. 1887. Palaeontology Vol. 6., Corals and Bryozoa. *Geol. Surv. New York,* 1–297, pls. 1–116.

HU, ZHAO-XUN. 1965. Additional material of Bryozoa from the Yukiang Formation of early middle Devonian in Henghsien, Kwangsi. *Acta paleont. sin.,* **13,** 218–240, pls. 1–4.

KING, W. 1850. The Permian fossils of England. *Palaeontogr. Soc. (Monogr.),* **38,** 1–258, 28 plates.

LAGAAIJ, R. 1952. The Pliocene Bryozoa of the Low Countries and their bearing on the Marine Stratigraphy of the North Sea Region. *Meded. geol. Sticht.,* C, **5,** (5), 1–233, pls. 1–25.

LARWOOD, G. P. 1962. The Morphology and Systematics of some Cretaceous Cribrimorph Polyzoa (Pelmatoporinae). *Bull. Br. Mus. (Nat. Hist.) geol.,* **6** (1), 1–285, pls. 1–23.

LAZUTKINA, O. F. 1963. [Discovery in the Triassic of a Bryozoa belonging to the Palaeozoic genus *Batostomella.*] *Paleont. Zh.,* **4,** 126–128. [In Russian]

LEVINSEN, G. M. R. 1925. Bryozoer Danske Kridtform. *Overs. K. danske Vidensk. Selsk. Forh.,* **7,** 283–445.

LEWIS, H. P. 1926. On *Bolopora undoza* gen. et sp. nov.: a rock-building bryozoan with phosphatized skeleton, from the basal Arenig rocks of Ffestiniog (N. Wales). *Q. Jl geol. Soc. Lond.,* **82,** 411–426.

LOEBLICH, A. R. 1942. Bryozoa from the Ordovician Bromide Formation, Oklahoma. *J. Paleont.,* **16,** 413–436, pls. 61–64.

MÄNNIL, R. M. 1959. Problems in the Stratigraphy and Bryozoa of the Ordovician of Estonia. *Akad. Nauk. Estonian S.S.R.: Otdel Techni in Physical Mathematical Sci.* (Dissertation for degree of Candidate of the Geological-Mineralogical Sciences, Tallinn), 40 pp.

MARSSON, T. F. 1887. Die Bryozoen der weissen Schreibkreide der Insel Rügen. *Paläont. Abh.,* **4,** 1–112.

MICHELIN, H. 1841. *Iconographie zoophytologique.* Paris.

MOROZOVA, I. P. 1965. Development and change of marine organisms from Palaeozoic to Mesozoic times: Bryozoa. *Trans. Pal. Inst.,* **108,** 60–62.

NEKHOROSHEV, V. P. 1949. [First discovery of Triassic Bryozoa in the U.S.S.R.] *Dokl. Akad. Nauk. S.S.R. Geol.,* **66,** 459–461. [In Russian]

—— 1956. [Lower Carboniferous Bryozoa of the Altai and Siberian]. *Trudӱ vses. nauchno-issled. geol. Inst.,* new series 1, **13,** 1–418 [In Russian]

—— 1961. [Ordovician and Silurian Bryozoa from the Siberian Platform.] *Trudӱ vses. nauchno-issled. geol. Inst.,* **41,** 1–246, pls. 1–37. [In Russian]

NICKLES, J. M. & BASSLER, R. S. 1900. A synopsis of American fossil Bryozoa. *Bull. U.S. geol. Surv.,* **173,** 1–663.

NIKIFOROVA, A. I. 1938. [*Types of Carboniferous Bryozoa in the European part of the U.S.S.R. xx*]; *Paleontology of U.S.S.R.,* 4, part 5, fasc. 1. U.S.S.R. Academy of Sciences, Moscow and Leningrad [In Russian].

—— 1939. [New species of Upper Palaeozoic Bryozoa from the Bashkirian Urals.] *Trudӱ neft. geol.-razv. Inst.* series A, gasc. 45, 70–102 [In Russian].

Chapter 11: Bryozoa

ORBIGNY, A. d'. 1851–54. *Paléontologie Française. Description des Animaux Invertébrés: Terrain Crétacé*, **5**, *Bryozoaires*. Paris.

OWEN, D. E. 1961. On the species *Orbignyella fibrosa* (Lonsdale). *Geol. Mag.*, **98**, 230–234, pl. 14.

—— 1965. Silurian Polyzoa from Benthall Edge, Shropshire. *Bull. Br. Mus. (Nat. Hist.) geol.*, **10**, 93–117, pls. 1–6.

PAPP, C. 1900. *Trias-Korallen aus dem Bakony*. Resultate der wissenschaftlichen Erforschung des Balatonsees, Band I., Teil I. Anhang: Paläontologie der Umgebung des Balatonsees, **1** (5), 1–23, pl. 1.

QUENSTEDT, F. A. 1858. *Der Jura*. Tübingen.

ROSS, J. R. P. 1963a. Ordovician Cryptostome Bryozoa, Standard Chazyan Series, New York and Vermont. *Bull. geol. Soc. Am.*, **74**, 577–608.

—— 1963b. *Constellaria* from the Chazyan (Ordovician), Isle La Motte Vermont. *J. Paleont.*, **37**, 51–56, pls. 5–6.

—— 1964. Morphology and Phylology of early Ectoprocta (Bryozoa). *Bull. geol. Soc. Am.*, **75**, 927–948, 10 figs.

SAKAGAMI, S. 1961. Japanese Permian Bryozoa. *Spec. Pap. palaeont. Soc. Japan*, **7**, 1–58, pls. 1–30.

SARYTCHEVA, T. G. (editor) 1960. *Osnovi Palaontology Spravochnik: Mshansky, Brachiopody, Prologeny-Phoronidy*, Akad. Nauk S.S.S.R., Moskva. [Russian Treatise.]

SHULGA-NESTERENKO, M. I. 1955. [Carboniferous Bryozoa of the Russian Platform.] *Trudȳ paleont. Inst.*, **57**, 1–207, pls. 1–32 [in Russian].

THOMAS, H. D. in COBBOLD, E. S. 1931. Additional Fossils from the Cambrian rocks of Comley, Shropshire. *Q. Jl geol. Soc. Lond.*, **87**, 498, pl. 41.

ULRICH, E. O. 1882. American Paleozoic Bryozoa. *J. Cincinn. Soc. nat. Hist.*, **5**, 121–175, pls. 6–8.

—— 1890. Palaeozoic Bryozoa in *Geological Survey of Illinois, Volume* 8, pp. 285–728, pls. 1–78, Springfield, Ill.

—— & BASSLER, R. S. 1913. *Lower Devonian*, 259–290, pls. 41–52; Maryland Geological Survey, Baltimore.

VINASSA DE REGNY, P. E. 1911. *Trias-tabulaten Bryozoen und Hydrozoen aus dem Bakony*. Resultate der wissenschaftlichen Erforschung des Balatonsees, Band I, Teil I. Anhang: Paläontologie der Umgebung des Balatonsees, **1** (4), 1–22.

VOIGT, E. 1962. *Oberkreide-Bryozoen des Europäischen Teils der U.S.S.R. und einiger anliegender Gebiete*. 1–125, pls. 1–28, Moscow University.

WAAGEN, W. & WENTZEL, J. 1886. Salt Range Fossils, 1. Productus Limestone Fossils, 6, Coelenterata, *Mem. geol. Surv. India. Palaeont. indica. Ser.* **13**, 835–924, pls. 97–116.

G. P. Larwood, PH.D.
Hatfield College, Durham.

A. W. Medd,
Department of Palaeontology, Institute of Geological Sciences, Exhibition Road, London S W 7.

D. E. Owen, PH.D. F.G.S.
Manchester Museum, The University, Oxford Road, Manchester 13.

R. Tavener-Smith, M.SC. F.G.S.
Department of Geology, Queen's University, Belfast, Northern Ireland.

CHAPTER 12

Brachiopoda

Contributors: D. V. AGER, P. COPPER, G. M. DUNLOP, G. F. ELLIOTT,
F. A. MIDDLEMISS, A. J. ROWELL, A. WILLIAMS & A. D. WRIGHT

Class INARTICULATA

Order LINGULIDA Waagen 1885

Superfamily LINGULACEA Menke 1828

First, Camb L. Camb: *Lingulella* Salter, several sps., precise relative ages unknown, cosmopolitan, (e.g. *Lingulella viridis* Cobbold, Strenuella Lst. Comley, England) (Cobbold 1921, p. 341).
Extant.

Comment: Represented by several spp. of *Lingula* and *Glottidia* in present day oceans. Maximum number of genera in Ord.

Constituent families: Lingulidae Menke, ?Ord, Sil.-Rec; Obolidae King, L. Camb-Ashg; Elkaniidae Walcott and Schuchert, U. Camb-Arenig; Lingulasmatidae Winchell and Schuchert, Carad-Ashg; Andobolidae Kozłowski, Ord (known only from Bolivia); Paterulidae Cooper, Arenig-Wenl; Craniopsidae Williams, Carad-Tourn.

Superfamily TRIMERELLACEA Davidson & King 1872

First, Ord Carad: *Eodinobolus dixonensis* (Cooper), Platteville Fm, Illinois (Cooper 1956, p. 230).

Last, Sil Ludl: *Dinobolus davidsoni transversus* (Salter), Lower Llanbadoc Beds, Usk, England (Walmsley 1959, p. 513)

Constituent family: Trimerellidae Davidson and King, Carad-Ludl.

Order ACROTRETIDA Kahn 1949

Suborder ACROTRETIDINA Kahn 1949

Superfamily ACROTRETACEA Schuchert 1893

First, Camb L. Camb: *Botsfordia granulata* (Redlich), *Schizopholis rugosa* Waagen, and *Neobolus warthi* Waagen, Neobolus Beds, east Salt Range, Pakistan (Schindewolf 1955, p. 540; Waagen 1885, p. 752); also *Botsfordia caelata* (Hall) from various localities in eastern North America (Walcott 1912, p. 603), Bastion Fm., E. Greenland (Cowie and Adams 1957, p. 25; Poulson 1932, p. 15), Wulff River Fm, northwest Greenland (Poulson 1927, p. 249).

The Fossil Record, pp. 397–421. Geological Society of London, 1967. Printed in Northern Ireland.

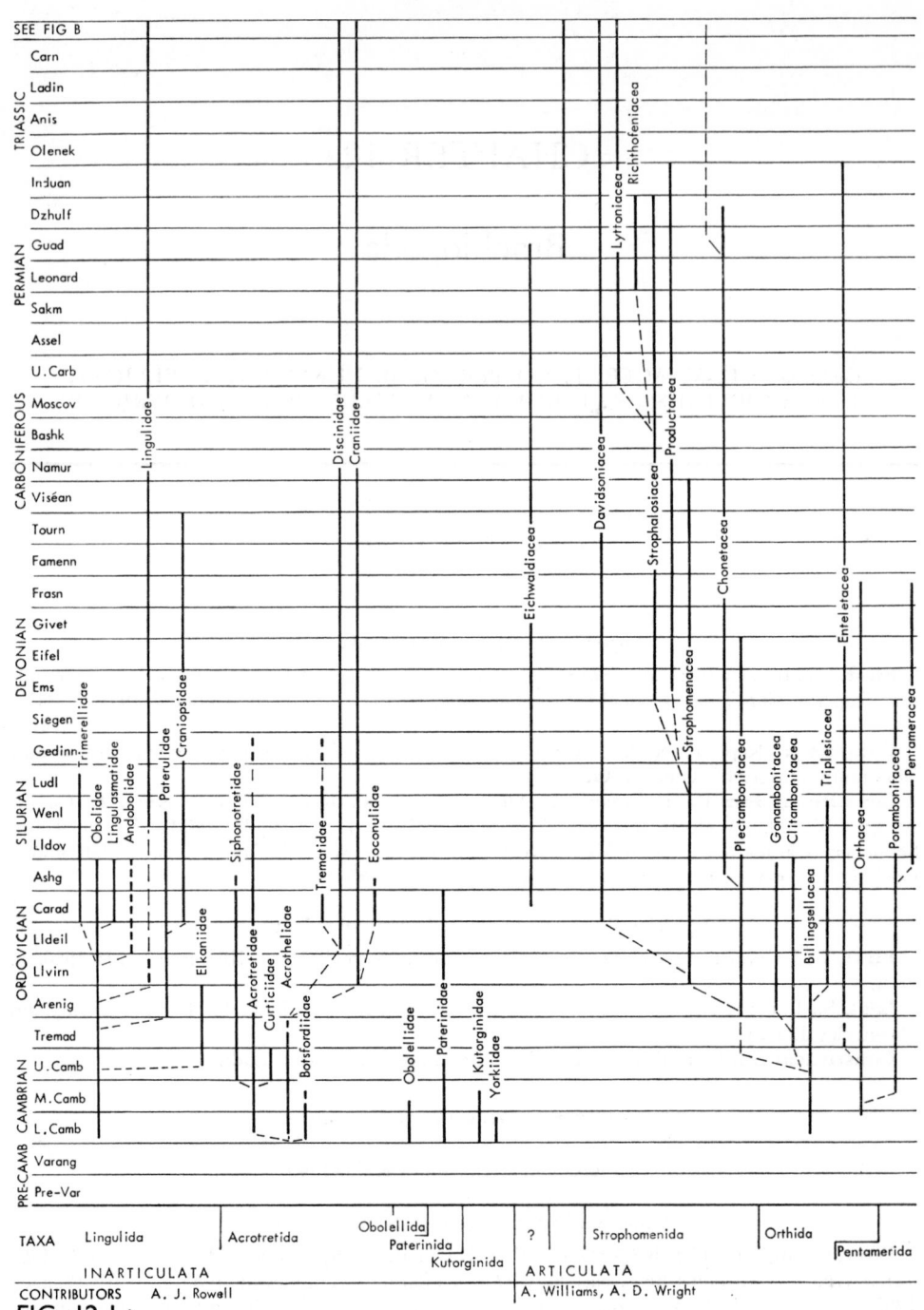

FIG. 12.1 A

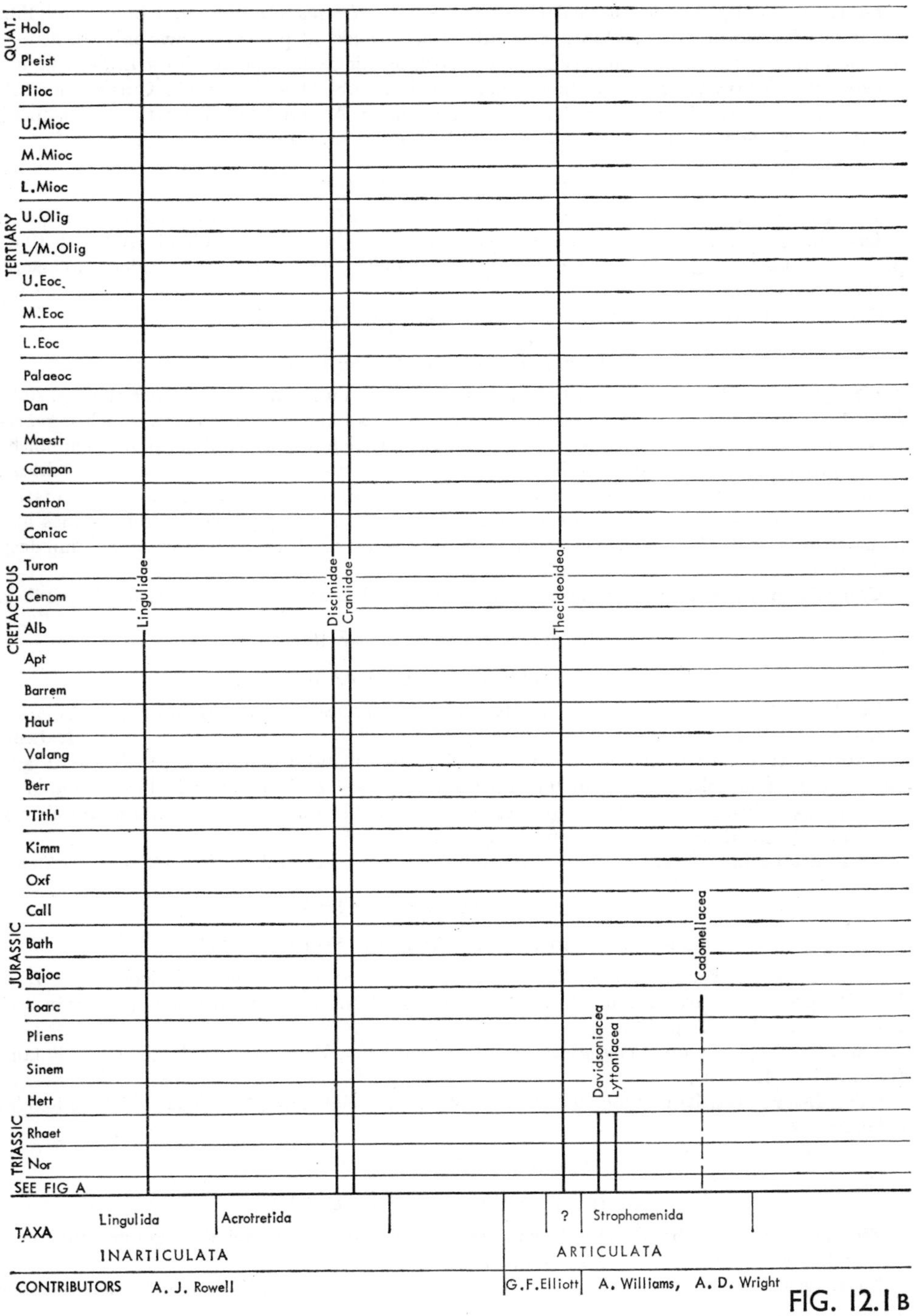

QUAT.
Holo
Pleist
Plioc

U.Mioc
M.Mioc
L.Mioc

TERTIARY
U.Olig
L/M.Olig
U.Eoc.
M.Eoc
L.Eoc
Palaeoc
Dan

Maestr
Campan
Santan
Coniac

CRETACEOUS
Turon
Cenom
Alb
Apt
Barrem
Haut
Valang
Berr

'Tith'
Kimm
Oxf
Call

JURASSIC
Bath
Bajoc
Toarc
Pliens
Sinem
Hett

TRIASSIC
Rhaet
Nor

SEE FIG A

Lingulidae

Discinidae
Craniidae

Thecideoidea

Cadomellacea

Davidsoniacea
Lyttoniacea

TAXA	Lingulida	Acrotretida		?	Strophomenida	
	INARTICULATA				ARTICULATA	

CONTRIBUTORS	A. J. Rowell		G.F.Elliott	A. Williams, A. D. Wright

FIG. 12.1 B

Last, Sil Wenl: *Artiotetra parva* Ireland and *Acrotretella siluriana* Ireland, Chimneyhill Fm, Oklahoma (Ireland 1961, p. 1138). Undoubted acrotretids, at present known only from their pedicle valves, occur in float material in New York seemingly associated with a L. Dev. fauna.

Constituent families: Acrotretidae Schuchert, L. Camb-Wenl (?Gedinn); Curticiidae Walcott and Schuchert, U. Camb (Dresbachian-Frankonian); Acrothelidae Walcott and Schuchert, L. Camb–Tremad; Botsfordiidae Schindewolf. L. Camb-?M. Camb.

Superfamily SIPHONOTRETACEA Kutorga 1848

First, Camb U. Camb: *Dysoristus lochmanae* Bell, Cedaria Z., Montana (Bell 1944, p. 147).

Last, Ord Carad: *Multispinula scotica* (Davidson), Craighead Lsts, Scotland (Williams 1962, p. 92). *Siphonotreta anglica* Morris, Wenlock Lst(Sil), Dudley, England, is not considered to belong to the superfamily.

Constituent family: Siphonotretidae Kutorga, U. Camb-Carad.

Superfamily DISCINACEA Gray 1840

First, Ord Lldeil: *Schizotreta* sp. 1 Cooper, Lincolnshire Fm, Tennessee (Cooper 1956, p. 282). *Discina pileolus* Davidson, M. Camb, Wales, is probably an acrothelid; *Oxlosia*, which is represented by several spp. in L. Ord, eastern N. America (Ulrich & Cooper 1938, p. 69), cannot be confidently referred to the superfamily. **Extant.**

Comment: During the Mesozoic and Tertiary, *Discinisca* was virtually the only representative of the superfamily; this genus is extant and known from several species. Recent faunas also include *Discina striata* (Schumacher), restricted to the seas off S. Africa, and the cosmopolitan, deep water species *Pelagodiscus atlanticus* (King).

Constituent families: Trematidae Schuchert, Carad-L. Dev; Discinidae Gray, Lldeil-Rec.

Suborder CRANIIDINA Waagen 1885

Superfamily CRANIACEA Menke 1828

First, Ord Llvirn: *Philhedra pustulosa* (Kutorga) and *Philhedra rivulosa* (Kutorga), Vaginatum Lst, U.S.S.R. (Huene 1899, p. 298). **Extant.**

Comment: *Philhedra columbiana* (Walcott), M. Camb, British Columbia, is poorly known and can only be doubtfully referred to the superfamily. The Craniacea are widely distributed in present oceans, being represented by species of three, possibly four genera. Maximum number of genera in Ord, with secondary maximum in Cret.

Constituent families: Craniidae Menke, Llvirn-Rec; Eoconulidae Rowell, Carad-?Ashg.

Order OBOLELLIDA Rowell 1965

Superfamily OBOLELLACEA Walcott & Schuchert 1908

First, Camb L. Camb: Spp. of *Obolella* Billings, *Alisina* Rowell, *Magnicanalis* Rowell and *Bicia* Walcott, precise relative ages unknown, "Obolella Z.," N. America, Greenland, Scandinavia, England (Rowell 1962, p. 138).

Last, Camb M. Camb: *Trematobolus pristinus* (Mathew), Paradoxides oelandicus Z., Poland (Orlowski 1964, p. 64).

Constituent family: Obolellidae Walcott and Schuchert, 'Obolella Z.'-Paradoxides oelandicus Z.

Order PATERINIDA Rowell 1965

Superfamily PATERINACEA Schuchert 1893

First, Camb L. Camb: *Paterina* Beecher, several spp. whose exact relative ages are unknown, L. Camb, cosmopolitan (Walcott 1912, p. 343).

Last, Ord Carad: *Dictyonites perforata* Cooper, Pratt Ferry Fm., Alabama, U.S.A. (Cooper 1956, p. 188).

Constituent family: Paterinidae Schuchert, L. Camb-Carad.

Chapter 12: Brachiopoda

Class UNCERTAIN

Order KUTORGINIDA Kahn 1949

Superfamily KUTORGINACEA Schuchert 1913

First, Camb L. Camb: Several species of *Kutorgina* Billings and *Yorkia* Walcott, precise relative ages unknown, N. America, Greenland, Europe, Asia (Walcott 1912, p. 579, Cowie & Adams 1957, p. 25).

Last, Camb M. Camb: *Schuchertina cambria* Walcott, Meagher Lst, Montana, U.S.A. (Bell 1941, p. 215). Taxonomic position of this species not well established.

Constituent families: Kutorginidae Schuchert, L. Camb-M. Camb; Yorkiidae Rowell, L. Camb.

[A.J.R.]

Class ARTICULATA

Documentation is here given for superfamilies or families. Classification as in Treatise H, unless otherwise stated.

Order ORTHIDA Schuchert & Cooper 1931

Suborder ORTHIDINA Schuchert & Cooper 1931

Superfamily BILLINGSELLACEA Schuchert 1893

(nom. transl. Williams 1965)

First, Camb. L. Camb: *Eoconcha austini* Cooper, *Matutella clarki* Cooper, *Nisusia* sp., Shady Fm, Virginia (Cooper 1951).

Last, Ord Arenig: *Eosotrematorthis sinensis* Wang, Liangchiashan Fm, Liaoning, China (Wang 1955).

Comment: The superfamily includes 8 genera (1964) with the highest proportion (50%) occurring in the L. Camb but excluding the Billingsellidae, the last recorded billingsellaceans. Stratigraphical occurrence and morphology indicate that they are the most primitive articulate brachiopods.

Superfamily ORTHACEA Woodward 1852

First, Camb L. Camb: *Wimanella shelbyensis* Walcott, Rome Fm, Alabama (Walcott 1908). Prof. C. Bell (University of Texas) is not entirely convinced about the generic identity of this fossil; should *shelbyensis* be a nisusiid, first is *W. catulus* Walcott, lower M. Camb. Articulate brachiopods of uncertain identity, which are more likely to be billingsellaceans than orthaceans, have been recorded from L. Camb *Archaeocyatha*-bearing lsts, S. Australia (Daily, *in* Öpik 1957).

Last, Dev Frasn: *Skenidium asellatum* Veevers, Sadler Fm, Fitzroy Basin, W. Australia. (Veevers 1959).

Comment: The superfamily consists of 81 genera (1964) with the highest proportion (42%) occurring in the U. Llvirn-L. Carad and including representatives of all families (among them, the Skenidiidae, the last recorded orthaceans) except the older Eoorthidae, Finkelnburgiidae, Hesperonomiidae, Orthidiellidae and Protorthidae and the younger Tuvaellidae. They were descended from the billingsellaceans.

Superfamily ENTELETACEA Waagen 1884

(nom. transl. Alichova 1960; *emend.* Wright 1965)

First, Ord Arenig: *Paurorthis resima* (Rubel), *Angusticardinia recta* (Pander), and *A. striata* (Pander), Leetse Stage ($B_1\beta$), Estonia (Rubel 1961). Generic placing of *Angusticardinia zelenkai* (Prantl & Ruzička 1941), L. Tremad. ($d\alpha_1$), Bohemia (Havlíček 1950), is uncertain.

Last, Trias Induan: *Orthotichia parva* Sokolskaja, and *Enteletes dzhagrensis* Sokolskaja, Transcaucasia (Sokolskaja, 1965).

Comment: The superfamily consists of 66 genera (1964) with the highest proportion (39%) occurring in the U. Llvirn-L. Carad and including representatives of all families (among them, the Enteletidae, the last recorded enteletaceans) except the Dicoelosiidae, Rhipidomellidae and *Hypsomyonia, Kayserella, Mystrophora, Tropidoleptus* and their allies which contribute to a secondary maximum (24%) of occurrence in the Eifel-Givet. They were descended, probably polyphyletically, from the orthaceans.

Suborder CLITAMBONITIDINA Öpik 1934

Superfamily CLITAMBONITACEA Winchell & Schuchert 1893

First, Ord Tremad: *Tritoechia kodymi* Havlíček, and *T. kolihai* Havlíček, Třenice Beds ($d\alpha_1$), Bohemia (Havlíček, 1949).

Last, Ord Ashg: *Vellamo diversus* (Shaler), Ellis Bay Fm, Anticosti, Canada (Twenhofel 1928), *Ilmarinia ponderosa* Öpik and *Vellamo silurica* Öpik, Porkuni Stage (F_2), Estonia (Öpik 1934).

Comment: The superfamily consists of 13 genera (1964) with the highest proportion (61%) occurring in the Tremad-L. Llvirn and including representatives of the Clitambonitinae, the last recorded clitambonitaceans. They were descended from the billingsellaceans.

Superfamily GONAMBONITACEA Schuchert & Cooper 1931

(*nom. transl.* Williams 1965)

First, Ord Arenig: *Antigonambonites planus* (Pander), Leetse Stage ($B_1\beta$), Estonia (Öpik 1934).

Last, Ord Ashg: *Kullervo complectens* (Wiman), Boda Lst, Dalarna, Sweden (Wiman 1907; Wright 1964).

Comment: The superfamily consists of 10 genera (1964) with the highest proportion (80%) occurring in the Tremad-L. Llvirn but excluding the Kullervoidae, the last recorded gonambonitaceans. They were descended from either the clitambonitaceans or the strophomenides.

Suborder TRIPLESIIDINA Moore 1952

Superfamily TRIPLESIACEA Schuchert 1913

First, Ord Llvirn: *Onychoplecia kindlei* Cooper, Table Head Fm, Newfoundland (Cooper 1956).

Last, Sil Wenl: *Plectotreta lindströmi* Ulrich & Cooper, Bara oolite, Gotland (Hede 1960) and Wenlock Lst, England; *Streptis grayii* (Davidson) and *Triplesia wenlockiensis* Davidson, Wenlock Lst, England (Hall & Clarke 1892).

Comment: The superfamily consists of one family of 10 genera (1964) with the highest proportion (60%) occurring in the Ashg-Lldov, but 40% persist into the Wenl. They were probably descended from the billingsellaceans.

Order PENTAMERIDA Schuchert & Cooper 1931

Suborder SYNTROPHIIDINA Ulrich & Cooper 1936

Superfamily PORAMBONITACEA Davison 1853

First, Camb M. Camb: *Cambrotrophia cambria* (Walcott), Ute Fm, Utah (Walcott 1908).

Last, Dev Siegen: *Anastrophia verneuili* Hall, Oriskany Fm, Glenerie, New York (Ingen & Clark 1903).

Constituent families: as in *Treatise* pt H except for the transfer of the Parallelelasmatidae from the Pentameracea to the Porambonitacea, to which group they are more closely related (Williams 1962).

Comment: The superfamily consists of 44 genera (1964) with the highest proportion (66%) occurring in the Tremad-L. Llvirn and including representatives of all families except the younger

Parallelelasmatidae and the Parastrophinidae, the last recorded porambonitaceans. They were descended from the orthaceans.

Suborder PENTAMERIDINA Schuchert & Cooper 1931

Superfamily PENTAMERACEA M'Coy 1844

First, Ord Ashg: *Holorhynchus giganteus* Kiaer and *Conchidium munsteri* St. Joseph, 5b, Norway (St. Joseph 1938).

Last, Dev Frasn: *Gypidula nucleolata* Belanski, Hackberry Fm, Iowa (Belanski 1928). This species appears to be a later form than species of *Ivdelinia, Levigatella* and *Procerulina* recorded from the Frasn of U.S.S.R. (Andronov 1961).

Constituent families: as in *Treatise* pt H except for the exclusion of the Parallelelasmatidae which are more closely related to the Porambonitacea.

Comment: The superfamily consists of 40 genera (1964) with the highest proportion (42%) occurring in the Wenl and including representatives of all families (among them, the Gypidulinae, the last recorded pentameraceans) except the older Virgianidae and the younger Enantiosphenidae. They were descended from the porambonitaceans.

Order UNCERTAIN

Suborder DICTYONELLIDINA Cooper 1956

Superfamily EICHWALDIACEA Schuchert 1893

First, Ord Carad: *Eichwaldia subtrigonalis* Billings, Leray-Rockland Fm, Allumette Is., Quebec and Paquette Rapids, Ontario, Canada (Wilson 1946).

Last, Perm Guad: *Megap euronia fabianii* Greco and *Megapleuronia grecoi* Cooper, Sosio Lst, Palermo, Sicily (Cooper 1952).

Comment: The superfamily consists of 4 genera (1964) with neither the older Eichwaldiidae nor the younger Isogrammidae yet recorded in Dev although they appear to be related to each other. There are no decisive morphological clues to their ancestry but they are probably closer to the articulates than the inarticulates.

Order STROPHOMENIDA Moore 1952

Suborder STROPHOMENIDINA Öpik 1934

Superfamily PLECTAMBONITACEA Jones 1928

First, Ord. Arenig: *Plectella uncinata* (Pander) and 6 other Spp., Leetse Stage ($B_1\beta$), Estonia (Öpik 1932); these may be older than *Taffia westgatei* Ulrich & Cooper, Yellow Hill Fm, Nevada (Ulrich & Cooper 1936).

Last, Dev Eifel: *Plectadontella redunca* Havlíček, Choteč Limestome, Hlubočepy Fm, Prague, Bohemia (Havlíček 1953).

Comment: The superfamily consists of 53 genera (1964) with the highest proportion (58%) occurring in the U. Llvirn-L. Carad and including representatives of all families (among them, the Sowerbyellinae, the last recorded plectambonitaceans) except for the older Taffidae. They were descended from the billingsellaceans.

Superfamily STROPHOMENACEA King 1846

First, Ord Llvirn: *Kirkina millardensis* Salmon, U. Pogonip Fm, Nevada, Utah, U.S.A. (Hintze 1952).

Last, Carb Viséan: *Leptagonia analoga* (Phillips), D_{2-3} Z., Carboniferous Lst, N. England (Garwood 1912; Trotter & Hollingworth 1932).

Comment: The superfamily consists of 68 genera (1964) with the highest proportion (38%) occurring in the U. Llvirn-L. Carad and including representatives of all families (among them, the

Leptaenidae, the last recorded strophomenaceans) except for the younger *Foliomena* group and the Stropheodontidae which together with the Leptaenidae constitute a secondary maximum (28%) of occurrence in the Eifel-Givet. They were descended from the plectambonitaceans.

Superfamily DAVIDSONIACEA King 1850

First, Ord Carad: *Gacella ponderosa* Williams, Confinis Flags, Ayrshire, Scotland (Williams 1962).

Last, Trias Rhaet: *Thecospira haidingeri* (Suess), Kössen and Starhemberg Fms, Austria (Zugmayer 1882).

Comment: The superfamily consists of 28 genera (1964) with the highest proportion (50%) occurring in the Assel-Sakm and including representatives of all families except the older Davidsoniidae and the younger Thecospiridae, the last recorded davidsoniaceans. They were descended from the strophomenaceans.

Suborder CHONETIDINA Muir-Wood 1955

Superfamily CHONETACEA Bronn 1862

First, Ord Ashg: *Strophochonetes primigenius* (Twenhofel), Vauréal Fm, Anticosti, Canada (Twenhofel 1928).

Last, Perm Dzhulf: *Lissochonetes laevis* (Davidson), Zewan Beds, Kashmir; *Waagenites aequicostus* (Waagen) and 3 other spp., U. Productus Lst, Salt Range, Pakistan (Muir-Wood 1962).

Comment: The superfamily consists of 34 genera (1964) with the highest proportion (41%) occurring in the Tourn-Viséan and including representatives of all families (among them, the Chonetidae, the last recorded chonetaceans) except the older Eodevonariidae which contribute to a secondary maximum (38%) of occurrence in the Gedinn-Givet. They were descended from the plectambonitaceans except, possibly, the chonostrophiidae which have stronger morphological affinities with the strophomenaceans.

Superfamily CADOMELLACEA Schuchert 1893

First, Jur Pliens: *Cadomella davidsoni* (E. Eudes-Deslongchamps) and *C. moorei* (Davidson), Margaritatus Z., Somerset, England (Davidson 1876).

Last, Jur Toarc: *Cadomella davidsoni* (E. Eudes-Deslongchamps), Bifrons Z. Normandy, France (Davidson 1876).

Comment: The superfamily is monotypic with one genus known only from the Pliens-Toarc, but despite the stratigraphical gap, the stock was undoubtedly descended from the chonetaceans.

Suborder PRODUCTIDINA Maillieux 1940

Superfamily PRODUCTACEA Gray 1840

First, Dev Ems: *Spinulicosta spinulicosta* (Hall), U. Columbus Lst, Ohio (Bassett 1935).

Last, Trias Induan: *Spinomarginifera pygmaea* Sarytcheva, *Haydenella minuta* Sarytcheva and *H. kiangsiensis* (Kayser), Transcaucasia (Sarytcheva, 1965).

Comment: The superfamily consists of 142 genera (mid-1965) with the highest proportion (45%) occurring in the Tourn-Visean and including representatives of all families with a secondary maximum (25%) of occurrence in the Leonard-Guad also including representatives of all families except the older Gigantoproductidae, Institinidae, Leiproductidae, Productellidae and Productidae. They were descended from the strophalosiaceans or, less likely, independently from the strophomenaceans.

Superfamily STROPHALOSIACEA Schuchert 1913

First, Dev Ems: *Truncalosia truncata* (Hall) var., Four Mile Brook Fm, Gaspé Peninsula, Quebec, Canada. This identification is given by Kindle (1938) in his assessment of the age of the Four Mile Brook Fm. The species is also known from the M. Dev (Eifel) Marcellus Fm, New York (Imbrie 1959).

Chapter 12: Brachiopoda

Last, Perm Dzhulf: *Tschernyschewia typica* Stoyanow and *T. yakowlewi* Stoyanow, Dzhulfa, Armenia (Stoyanow 1915, Muir-Wood & Cooper 1960).

Comment: The superfamily consists of 42 genera (1964) with the highest proportion (69%) occurring in the Leonard-Guad and including all families except the older Sinuatellidae. They were descended from the strophomenaceans.

Superfamily RICHTHOFENIACEA Waagen 1885

First, Perm Leonard: *Prorichthofenia licharewi* R. E. King, Hess Fm, Glass Mts and Sierra Diablo, Texas (King 1930).

Last, Perm Dzhulf: *Richthofenia lawrenciana* (de Koninck), U. Productus Lst, Salt Range, Pakistan (Waagen 1885).

Comment: The superfamily consists of 6 genera (1964) all of which are present in the Leonard-Guad. They were descended from the strophalosiaceans.

Suborder OLDHAMINIDINA Williams 1953

Superfamily LYTTONIACEA Waagen 1883

First, Carb U. Carb: *Poikilosakos petaloides* Watson, Cisco Beds, U. Coal Measures, Texas (Watson 1917).

Last, Trias Rhaet: *Bactrynium bicarinatum* Emmrich, Kössen and Starhemberg Fms, Austria (Zugmayer 1882).

Comment: The superfamily consists of 15 genera (1964) with the highest proportion (87%) occurring in the Leonard-Guad and including all families, but not *Bactrynium* the last recorded lyttoniacean. They were possibly descended together with the richthofeniaceans from the strophalosiaceans. [A.W. & A.D.W.]

Order UNCERTAIN

Suborder THECIDEIDINA Elliott 1958

("Treatise", H, *pro* Thecideoidea Elliott 1958).

Family THECIDELLINIDAE Elliott 1958

First, Trias Rhaet: *Moorellina prima* Elliott, Hirtenberg, Austria (Elliott 1953) **Extant.**
Thecidellina blochmanni (Dall)

Family THECIDEIDAE Gray 1840

First, Perm Guad: *Cooperina inexpectata* Termier, Termier and Pajaud (1966), Word Fm, Texas, U.S.A. **Extant.**

Comment: Present distribution, warm seas, Atlantic-Indian-Pacific oceans. [G.F.E.]

Order RHYNCHONELLIDA Moore 1952

General comment: No suborders are recognized within Rhynchonellida in Treatise H, but there is strong evidence of close affinities between rhynchonellids and atrypids, which were probably derived from them. Both D.V.A. and P.C. think that the atrypids are closer to the Rhynchonellida than to the Spiriferida.

Superfamily RHYNCHONELLACEA Gray 1848

First, Ord Llvirn (?): *Rostricellula* Ulrich & Cooper 1942, nine spp., Mosheim Fm or equivalent, U.S.A. and E. Canada (Cooper 1956); accurate correlation with British scale not possible. Seven other genera recorded from "M. Ord": *Ancistrorhyncha* Ulrich & Cooper 1942, *Drepanorhyncha* Cooper 1956, *Rhynchotrema* Hall 1860, *Oligorhynchia* Cooper 1935, *Sphenotreta* Cooper 1956, *Dorytreta* Cooper 1956, *Orthorhynchula* Hall & Clarke 1893. *Protorhyncha* Hall & Clarke 1893, commonly regarded as earliest member of order, unrecognizable and not certainly a rhynchonellacean. **Extant.**

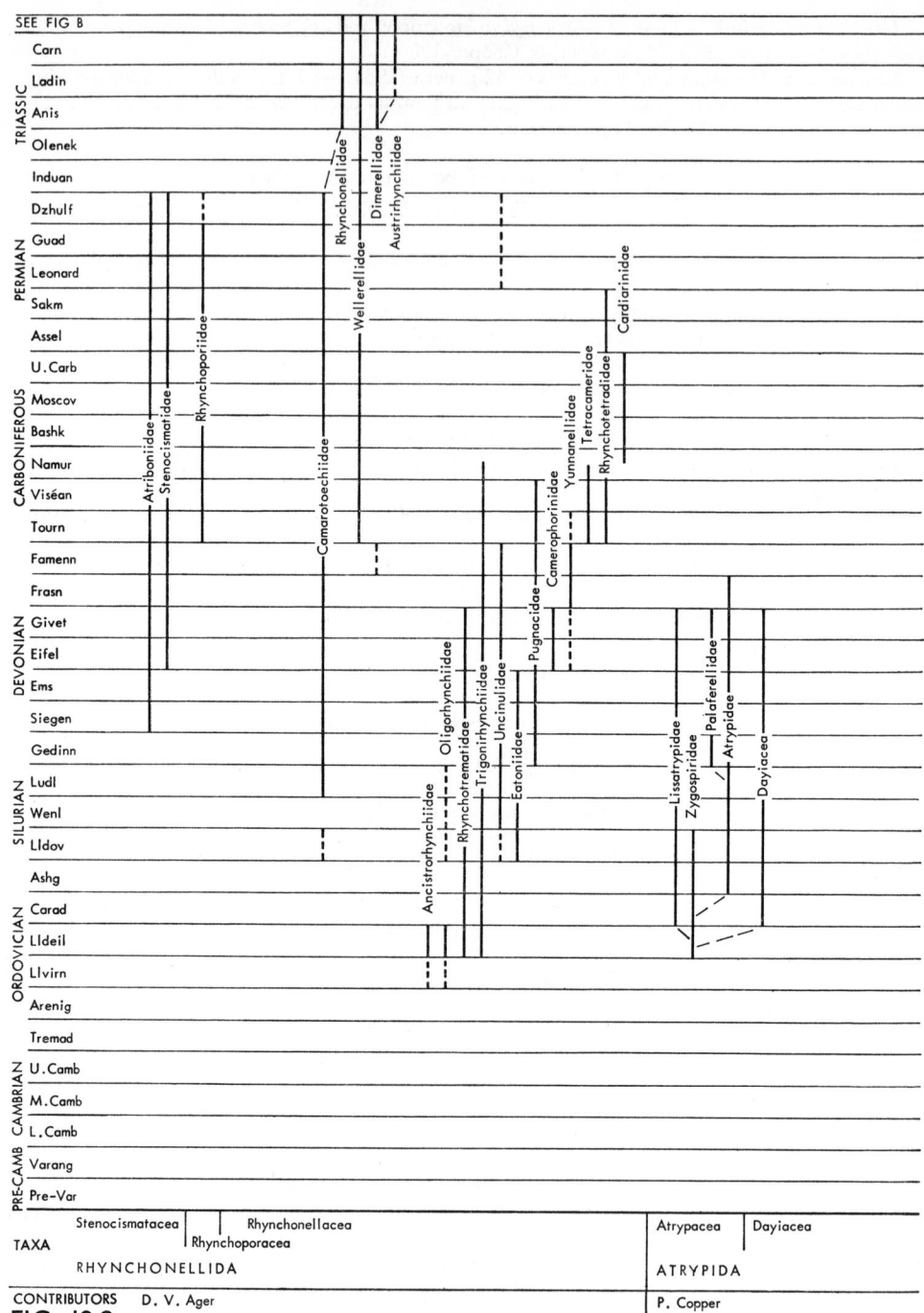

FIG. 12.2 A

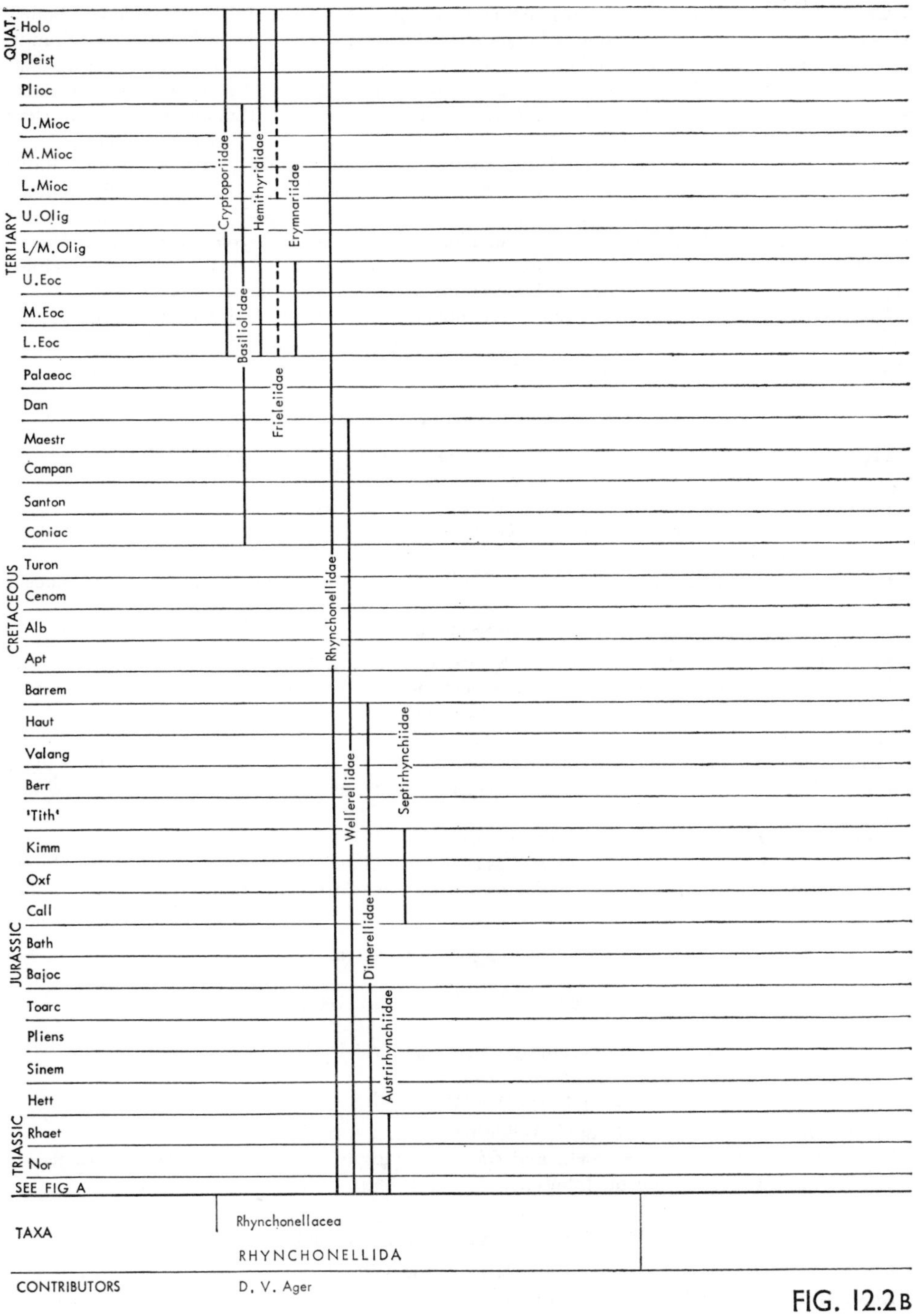
QUAT.
Holo
Pleist
Plioc
U.Mioc
M.Mioc
L.Mioc
U.Olig
L/M.Olig
U.Eoc
M.Eoc
L.Eoc
TERTIARY
Palaeoc
Dan
Maestr
Campan
Santon
Coniac
Turon
Cenom
Alb
Apt
CRETACEOUS
Barrem
Haut
Valang
Berr
'Tith'
Kimm
Oxf
Call
Bath
Bajoc
JURASSIC
Toarc
Pliens
Sinem
Hett
Rhaet
Nor
TRIASSIC
SEE FIG A
Cryptoporidae
Hemithyrididae
Erymnariidae
Basiliolidae
Frieleiidae
Rhynchonellidae
Wellerellidae
Septirhynchiidae
Dimerellidae
Austrirhynchiidae
TAXA
Rhynchonellacea
RHYNCHONELLIDA
CONTRIBUTORS
D. V. Ager

FIG. 12.2B

Constituent families: Ancistrorhynchiidae Cooper, M. Ord; Oligorhynchiidae Cooper, M. Ord, ?Sil; Rhynchotrematidae Schuchert, M. Ord-M. Dev; Trigonirhynchiidae Schmidt, M. Ord-L. Carb (Missis); Uncinulidae Rzhonitskaya, L. (?), M. Sil-U. Dev, Perm (?); Eatoniidae Schmidt, Sil-L. Dev; Pugnacidae Rzhonsnitzkaya, L. Dev-L. Carb; Camarotoechiidae Schuchert & LeVene, L.Sil, U. Sil-U. Perm; Camerophorinidae Rzhonsnitzkaya, M. Dev; Yunnanellidae Rzhonsnitzkaya, M. (?), U. Dev-L. Carb (?); Tetracameridae Rzhonsnitzkaya, L. Carb (Missis); Rhynchotetradidae Rzhonsnitzkaya, L. Carb-L. Perm; Wellerellidae Rzhonsnitzkaya, L. Carb-U. Cret; ?Cardiarinidae Cooper, U. Carb (Penn); Dimerellidae Buckman, U. Dev, M. Trias-L. Cret; Rhynchonellidae Gray, M. Trias-U. Cret; Septirhynchiidae Muir-Wood & Cooper, U. Jur; Austrirhynchiidae M.-U. Trias; Cryptoporiidae Muir-Wood, Eoc-Holo; Basiliolidae Cooper, U. Cret-Holo; Hemithyrididae Rzhonsnitzkaya Eoc-Holo; Frieleiidae Cooper, Eoc (?), Mioc (?), Plioc-Holo; Erymnariidae Cooper, Eoc.

Comment: Apparent burst of "first" rhynchonellids in "M. Ord" (i.e. Chazyan) essentially monographic. Earlier forms to be expected in L. Ord; derivation almost certainly from Orthida. Several of above families are regarded as of doubtful validity.

Superfamily STENOCISMATACEA Oehlert 1887

First, Dev Ems: *Atribonium subtransuralica* (Khodalevitch) and *A. transuralica* (Tchernyschev), U.S.S.R. (Grant 1963).

Last, Perm (U.): *Stenocisma* Conrad, world-wide and *Cyrolexis* Grant, Asia.

Constituent families: Atriboniidae Grant, L. Dev-U. Perm; Stenocismatidae Oehlert, M. Dev-U. Perm.

Comment: Probably derived from the family Camarotoechiidae of the Rhynchonellacea.

Superfamily RHYNCHOPORACEA Muir-Wood 1955

First, L. Carb Tourn: *Rhynchopora cooperensis* (Shumard), Chouteau Lst. (Kinderhookian) Missouri, U.S.A. (Branson 1938). Probably several other species at about this level. Muir-Wood (1955) suggested that *Rhynchopora* probably also occurs in the Devonian, but this has not been confirmed.

Last, Perm Guad-Dzhulf: *Rhynchopora relegata* Reed, U. Productus Lst, Salt Range, Pakistan (Reed 1944). Records above M. Perm seem to be few and mostly in strata of unproven age.

Constituent family: Rhynchoporiidae Muir-Wood 1955.

Comment: Rhynchoporacea (proposed as a subordinal name by Moore 1952, but introduced at the family level by Muir-Wood 1955) probably derived from the family Camarotoechiidae of the Rhynchonellacea. [D.V.A.]

Order ATRYPIDA Rzhonsnitskaya 1960

[Suborder ATRYPIDINA Moore 1952, in Treatise H. Ed.]

Superfamily ATRYPACEA Gill 1871

Family LISSATRYPIDAE Twenhofel 1914

First, Ord Carad: *Idiospira* Cooper, Wilderness St., N. America (Cooper 1956).

Last, Dev Givet: *Cryptatrypa* Siehl and *Glassia* Davidson, Massenkalk, Germany, England.

Constituent genera: Boucot, Johnson & Staton 1964 p. 812.

Family ZYGOSPIRIDAE Waagen 1883

First, Ord Lldeil: *Protozyga* Hall & Clarke, Crown Point Fm, N. America (Cooper 1956).

Last, Sil Lldov: *Pentlandella* Boucot, U. Lldov, Britain, Estonia and *Clintonella* Hall & Clarke, N. America.

Constituent genera: Boucot, Johnson & Staton 1964 p. 810.

Chapter 12: Brachiopoda

Family PALAFERELLIDAE Spriestersbach 1942

First, Dev Gedinn: *Carinatina* Nalivkin, Urals, Kutznetsk, U.S.S.R. (Rzhonsnitskaya 1964).
Last, Dev Givet: *Mimatrypa* Struve, Massenkalk, Germany, England.
Constituent genera: *Carinatina* Nalivkin; *Kwangsia* Grabau?; *Vagrania* Alekseeva; *Gruenewaldtia* Chernyshev; *Mimatrypa* Struve; *Karpinskia* Chernyshev. *Kerpina* Struve unrelated to *Carinatina. Anatrypa* Nalivkin (partim) a palaferellid?

Family ATRYPIDAE Gill 1871

First, Ord Ashg: *Plectatrypa* Schuchert & Cooper, N. America.
Last, Dev Frasn: *Atrypa* Dalman, *Anatrypa* Nalivkin, *Pseudogruenewaldtia* Rzhonsnitskaya, *Spinatrypa* Stainbrook, *Spinatrypina* Rzhonsnitskaya. Two doubtful Dev Famenn records (Mansuy 1912, Veevers 1959).
Constituent genera: also *Protatrypa* Boucot, Johnson & Staton; *Kerpina* Struve; *Desquamatia* Alekseeva; *Falsatrypa* Havlicek?; *Nalivkinia* Bublitschenko; *Punctatrypa* Havlicek; *Atrypinella* Khodalevich; *Atrypina* Hall & Clarke. Mass extinction at end of Dev Frasn.

Superfamily DAYIACEA Waagen 1883

First, Ord Carad: *Cyclospira* Schuchert & Cooper, Wilderness St., N. America (Cooper 1956).
Last, Dev Givet: *Anoplotheca* Sandberger, Flinzkalk, Iserlohn, Germany (Schmidt 1951).
Constituent families: Boucot, Johnson & Staton 1964 p. 806.   [P.C.]

Order SPIRIFERIDA Waagen 1883

Suborder RETZIIDINA Boucot, Johnson & Staton 1964

Superfamily RETZIACEA Waagen 1883

Family RETZIIDAE Waagen 1883

First, Sil Wenl ?Ludl: *Trematospira camura* Hall, M. Chaleur Series, Gaspé, U.S.A. (Northrop 1939).
Last, Trias Carn: *Retzia reticulata* Wilchens and *R. morganiana* Wilckens, Hokonui System, New Zealand (Marwick 1953). *Neoretzia* Dagis is from U. Trias of Southern U.S.S.R. and may be later than Carnian (Dagis 1963, not seen).

Family RHYNCHOSPIRINIDAE Schuchert & Le Vene 1929

First, Sil Lldov: *Rhynchospirina dispar* Reed, Mulloch Hill Group, Girvan, Scotland (Reed 1935).
Last, Dev Eifel: *Rhynhospirina of haidingeri* Barrande, Hlubočepy Limestone, Bohemia (Havliček 1956).

Superfamily ATHYRISINACEA Grabau 1931

Family ATHYRISINIDAE Grabau 1931

First, Dev M. Dev: *Athyrisina* 6 spp., Yunnan, Szechwan and Kansu, China (Grabau 1931).
Last, Trias Nor: *Misolia noetlingii* (Bittner), Sumra Fm, Arabia (Hudson and Jeffries 1961).

Suborder ATHYRIDIDINA Boucot, Johnson & Staton 1964

Superfamily ATHYRIDACEA McCoy 1844

Family MERISTELLIDAE Waagen 1883

First, Ord Carad: *Hyattidina ? sulcata* Williams, Kiln Mudstones, Ardmillan Series, Craighead, Scotland (Williams 1962).
Last, Carb Tourn: *Camarophorella mutabilis* Hyde, Logan Fm, Ohio (Hyde 1953).

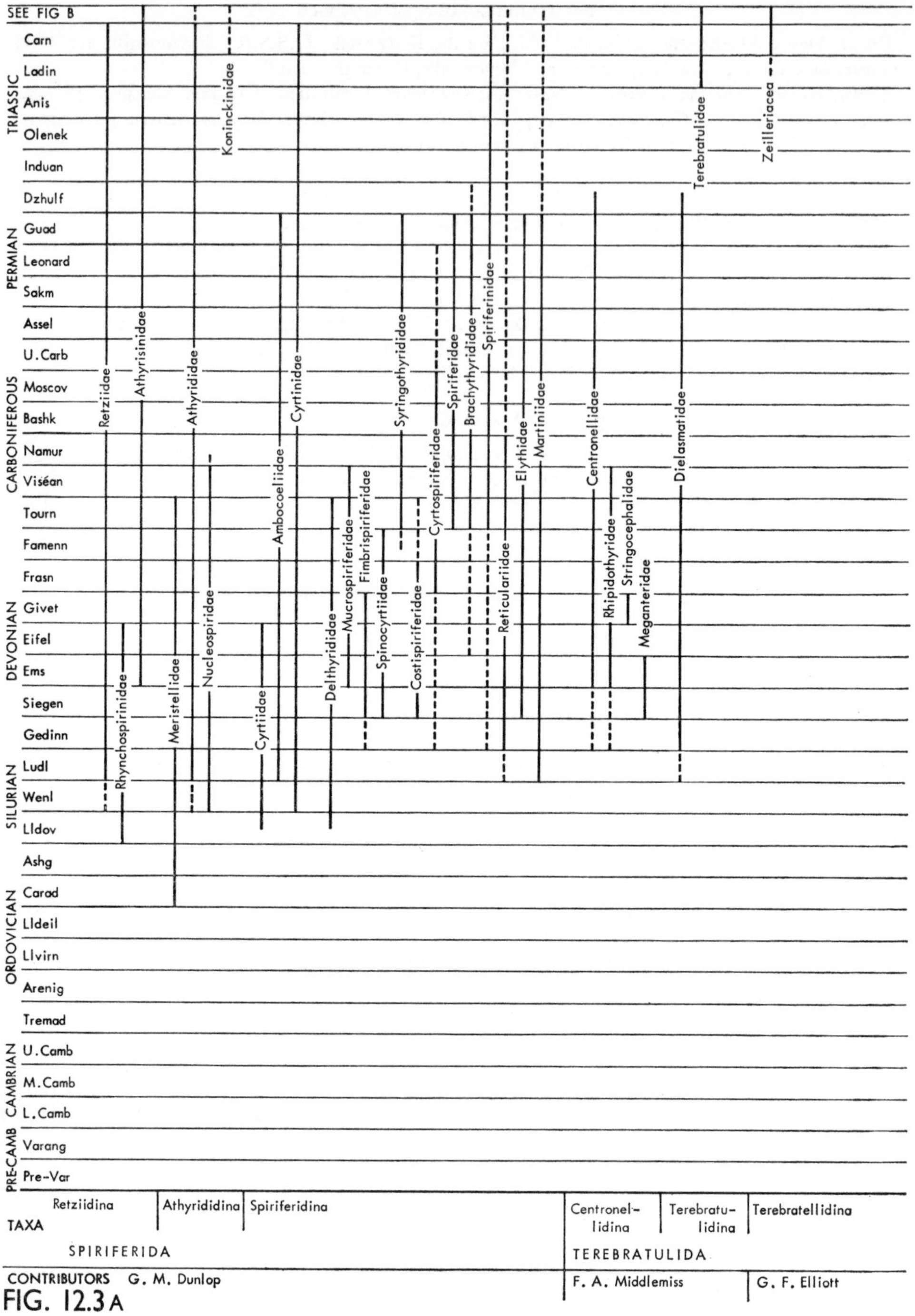
SEE FIG B
TRIASSIC
Carn
Ladin
Anis
Olenek
Induan
PERMIAN
Dzhulf
Guad
Leonard
Sakm
Assel
CARBONIFEROUS
U. Carb
Moscov
Bashk
Namur
Viséan
Tourn
DEVONIAN
Famenn
Frasn
Givet
Eifel
Ems
Siegen
Gedinn
SILURIAN
Ludl
Wenl
Lldov
ORDOVICIAN
Ashg
Carad
Lldeil
Llvirn
Arenig
Tremad
CAMBRIAN
U. Camb
M. Camb
L. Camb
PRE-CAMB
Varang
Pre-Var
Retziidae
Rhynchospirinidae
Athyrisinidae
Meristellidae
Athyrididae
Nucleospiridae
Koninckinidae
Cyrtiidae
Ambocoeliidae
Cyrtinidae
Delthyrididae
Mucrospiriferidae
Fimbrispiriferidae
Spinocyrtiidae
Syringothyrididae
Costispiriferidae
Cyrtospiriferidae
Spiriferidae
Brachythyrididae
Spiriferinidae
Reticulariidae
Elythidae
Martiniidae
Centronellidae
Rhipidothyridae
Stringocephalidae
Meganteridae
Dielasmatidae
Terebratulidae
Zeilleriacea
TAXA
Retziidina
Athyrididina
Spiriferidina
SPIRIFERIDA
Centronel-lidina
Terebratu-lidina
Terebratellidina
TEREBRATULIDA
CONTRIBUTORS G. M. Dunlop
F. A. Middlemiss
G. F. Elliott

FIG. 12.3A

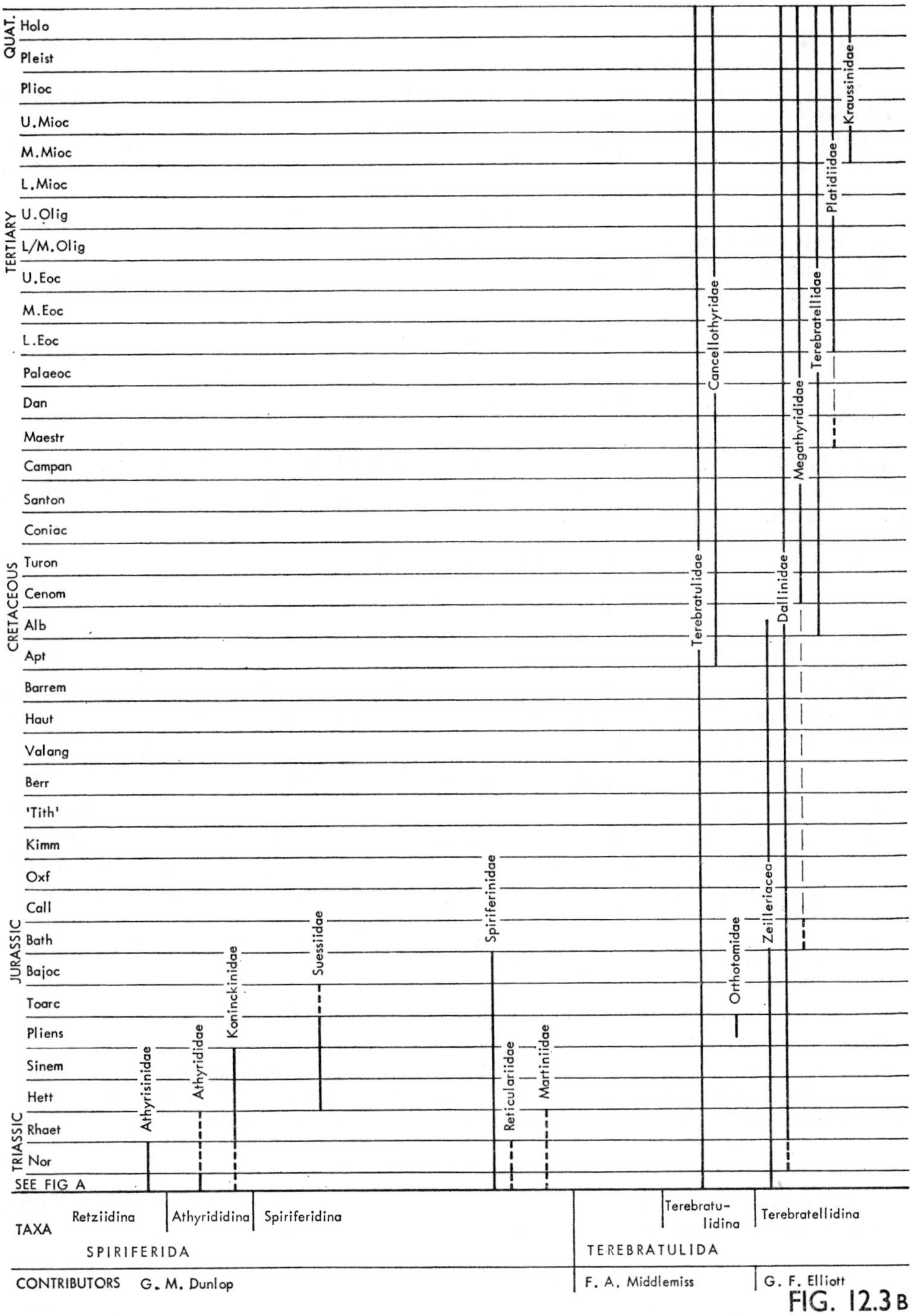

QUAT. — Holo, Pleist
Plioc
U.Mioc
M.Mioc
L.Mioc
TERTIARY — U.Olig, L/M.Olig, U.Eoc, M.Eoc, L.Eoc, Palaeoc, Dan
Maestr
Campan
Santon
Coniac
CRETACEOUS — Turon, Cenom, Alb, Apt, Barrem, Haut, Valang, Berr, 'Tith', Kimm, Oxf, Call
JURASSIC — Bath, Bajoc, Toarc, Pliens, Sinem, Hett
TRIASSIC — Rhaet, Nor
SEE FIG A

Ranges (vertical lines, labelled):
Athyrisinidae
Athyrididae
Koninckinidae
Suessiidae
Spiriferinidae
Reticulariidae
Martinidae
Orthotomidae
Zeilleriacea
Terebratulidae
Cancellothyridae
Dallinidae
Megathyrididae
Terebratellidae
Platidiidae
Kraussinidae

TAXA	Retziidina	Athyridiidina	Spiriferidina			Terebratulidina	Terebratellidina
	SPIRIFERIDA					TEREBRATULIDA	
CONTRIBUTORS	G. M. Dunlop					F. A. Middlemiss	G. F. Elliott

FIG. 12.3 B

411

Family ATHYRIDIDAE McCoy 1844

First, Sil Wenl?: *Protathyris didyma* (Dalman), Favosites Beds, Central Asiatic U.S.S.R. (Nikiforova 1937). Also Ludl: *Protathyris didyma* (Dalman), Podolia (Kozlowski 1929) and Kuznetsk (Lazutkin 1936) and Sil U. Sil: *Protathyris hesperalis* Waite, Laketown Dolomite, Utah and Neveda (Waite 1956).

Last, Trias U. Trias: *Majkopella worobieri* (Moisseiev), *M. manjavini* (Bittner), *M. slavini* Dagis, *Oxycolpella robinsoni* Dagis, *O. guseriplica* Dagis, *O. oxycolpos* (Emmrich), Lithuania (Dagis 1962).

Family NUCLEOSPIRIDAE Davidson 1881

First, Sil Wenl: *Nucleospira pisiformis* Hall, Upper Clinton Group, New York (Dale 1953).

Last, Carb Viséan or Namur: *Nucleospira superata* Easton, Cameron Creek Fm, Big Snowy Grp. Montana (Easton 1962).

Superfamily KONINCKINACEA Davidson 1853

Family KONINCKINIDAE Davidson 1853

First, Trias U. Trias: *Koninckina telleri* Bittner, *K. expansa* Bittner, *Amphiclina speciosa* Bittner, Yugoslavia (Veselinović 1951).

Last, Jur Sinem: *Koninckina alfurica* Wanner, *K.* (*Koninckodonta ?*)*eberhardi* Bittner, *K.* (*Koninckodonta*) *geyeri* Bittner, *K.* (*Koninckella*) *fornicata* Canavari, *K.* (*Koninckella ?*) *sicula* Gemmellaro, M. Lias, Corfu, Greece (Renz 1932).

Suborder SPIRIFERIDINA Waagen 1883

Family CYRTIIDAE Fredericks 1919 (1924)

First, Sil Lldov: *Eospirifer radiatus* (Sowerby) and other spp., Upper Llandoverian C_3, N. Greenland (Poulsen 1934).

Last, Dev Eifel: *Macropleura sibiricus* (Tschernychev) Chumishsk Beds, *M. cf rollandi* (Barrois) Salairkin Beds, Kuznetsk Basin, U.S.S.R. (Rzhonsnitskaya 1952). For discussion of sub-family Eospiriferinae see Boucot 1963.

Family AMBOCOELIIDAE George 1931

First, Sil U.Sil: *Ambothyris praecox* Kozlowski, Sil, Ukraine, stated by Havliček (1959 p. 337) to be earliest. *Alaskospira dunbari* Kirk and Amsden, Sil, Kosciusko Island, Alaska (Kirk and Amsden 1951) may belong to family. Otherwise, Dev Gedinn: *Ambocoelia praecox* Kozlowski, Etage de Borszczow, Podolia, U.S.S.R. (Kozlowski 1929) also *A. operculifera* Havliček, basal Sil, Bohemia, Czechoslovakia (Havliček 1959).

Last, Perm Guad: *Crurithyris clannyani* (King), Zechstein 1, Germany (Malzahn 1958); also *Ambocoelia telleri* (Schellwein), Anhui, China (Zhang and Ching 1961).

Family CYRTINIDAE Fredericks 1912

First, Sil Wenl: *Cyrtina extensa* Bolton, Amabel Fm, Ontario, Canada (Bolton 1957).

Last, Trias Carn: *Psioidea australis* (Trechman), *P. nelsonensis* (Trechman) and P. conjucta (Hector), Hokonui System, New Zealand (Marwick 1953). Dagis (1965) places spp. of *Thecocyrtella* Bittner and *Zugmayerella* Dagis, from Trias Nor of Siberia, in a new family, the Laballidae.

Family SUESSIIDAE Waagen 1883

First, and last, Jur L.Jur: *Suessia costata* Deslongchamps, Lias (Dacqué 1933): and Jur Pliens, *Suessia liasiana* Deslongchamps, Domerian, Morocco (Dubar 1948).

Family DELTHYRIDIDAE Waagen 1883

First, Sil Lldov: *Howellella anglicus* (Lamont and Gilbert) U. Llandovery Pentamerus Beds, Worcestershire, England (Lamont and Gilbert 1945).

Chapter 12: Brachiopoda

Last, Carv Tourn: *Delthyris clarksvillensis* (Winchel), Hikoroiti Series, Japan (Minato 1952), also *D. novamexicana* Weller and *D. farmeri* Branson, Chouteau Lst, Missouri (Branson 1938).

Family MUCROSPIRIFERIDAE Pitrat 1965

First, Dev Ems: *Mucrospirifer mucronatus* (Conrad), Romney Fm, Maryland (Vokes 1957).
Last, Carb Vis: *Tylothyris carlopsensis* Reed, North Greens Lst, Lower Limestone Group, Scotland (Reed 1954).

Family FIMBRISPIRIFERIDAE Pitrat 1965

First, Dev L.Dev ?Gedinn: *Fimbrispirifer charybdis* (Barrande), Bohemia, Czechoslovakia (Havliček 1959).
Last, Dev. Givet: *Fimbrispirifer venustus* (Hall), Hamilton Fm, New York (Cooper 1944, also Hall 1857).

Family SPINOCYRTIIDAE Ivanova 1959

First, Dev Sieg: *Spinocyrtia affinis* (Fuchs), Sg 2, Belgium (Vandercammen 1963).
Last, Dev Famenn: *Spinocyrtia struniana* (Gosselet) Couches d'Etroeungt, France (Vandercammen 1956).

Family SYRINGOTHYRIDIDAE Fredericks 1926

First, Dev Famenn or Carb Tourn: *Syringothyris spissus* Glenister, Moogooree Lst, W. Australia (Glenister 1955).
Last, Perm Guad: *Licharewia stuckenbergi* (Netschajew), *L. rugulata* (Kutorga), *L. grewingki* (Netschajew), *L. schrenckii* (Keyserling), *L. latiareata* (Netschajew), Kazan Beds, Russian Platform (Sluisareva 1960). Also *Pterospirifer alatus* (Schlotheim), Nathorsts Fjord, E. Greenland (Dunbar 1955).

Family COSTISPIRIFERIDAE Termier & Termier 1949

First, Dev Siegen: *Costispirifer arenosus* (Conrad), Oriskany Group, Maryland (Vokes 1957).
Last, Dev Frasn: *Theodossia keenei* (Crickmay), *T. scopulorum* (Crickmay), Kakisa Fm, Upper Mackenzie region, W. Canada (McLaren & Norris 1962). If *Eudoxina* belongs to family, last is Carb Tourn: *Eudoxina media* (Labedev), *E. inflata*, *E. danaica E. kynensis*, Kyn Lst, Urals, U.S.S.R. (Fredericks 1929).

Family CYRTOSPIRIFERIDAE Termier & Termier 1949

First, Dev Frasn: *Cyrtospirifer* 16 spp., Belgium (Vandercammen 1959); also *Cyrtospirifer* sp and *C. thalattodoxa* Crickmay, Canada (Warren and Stelck 1956). If *Indispirifer* belongs in family, first is Dev L.Dev: *Indispirifer chui* (Grabau), *I. kwangsiensis* Hou, Guansi, China (Hou 1959).
Last, Carb Moscov or Perm Leonard: *Cyrtospiriferl eoncitensis* Harrington, U. Tepuel System, Argentina (Amos 1958); or *Cyrtospirifer* (?) *kharaulakhensis* Fredericks, E. of Lena, U.S.S.R. (Kashirtzev 1959).

Family SPIRIFERIDAE King 1846

First, Carb Tourn: *Spirifer* 8 spp., *Fusella* 10 spp., *Neospirifer* 6 spp. C,^{1} to C,$^{2-3}$ Kuznetz Basin, U.S.S.R. (Besnosova 1959).
Last, Perm Guad: *Spirifer striato-paradoxus* Toula, Svalbardian, Svalbard, Arctic (Gobbett 1963).

Family BRACHYTHYRIDIDAE Fredericks 1919 (1924)

First, Dev Eifel: *Brachythyris* (?) *talicensis* Khodalevich, Bauxite-producing deposits, Urals (Khodalevich 1959), otherwise ? Dev Famenn: *Brachythyris bisbeensis* Stainbrook and *B. putilla* Stainbrook, Percha Sh, N. Mexico and Arizona (Stainbrook 1947).
Last, Perm Guad: *Spiriferella keilhavii* (von Buch) and *S. saranae* (de Verneuil). Assistance Fm., Grinnell Peninsula, Canadian Arctic (Harker and Thorsteinsson 1960). Or Perm Dzhulf?: *Purdonella limitaris* Reed, and *P. conformis* Reed, U. Productus Lst, Salt Range, Pakistan (Reed 1944).

Family SPIRIFERINIDAE Davidson 1884

First, Dev L.Dev: *Eospiriferina nakaolingensis* Hou, *E. wangi* Hou, pre-Eifelian, Guansi, China (Hou 1959). If, however, *Eospiriferina* does not belong to the Spiriferinidae but to the Delthyrididae, then first is Carb Tourn: *Spiriferina paratransversa* Minato, base of Tourn, Japan (Minato 1952).

Last, Jur Bajoc: *Spiriferina gryphaeoidea* Uhlig, L. Dogger and 5 spp. from Lias, Moluccas (Wanner and Knipscheer 1951) and 5 spp. from Toarcian of Spain (Batalier 1948).

Family RETICULARIIDAE Waagen 1883

First, Dev L.Dev: *Najadospirifer najadum* (Barrande), Koněprusy Lsts, and *Xenomartinia monosepta* Havliček, Bohemia, Czechoslovakia (Havliček 1957, 1959). *Proreticularia carens* (Barrande) Sil Ludl, Kopanina Lsts, Bohemia (Havliček 1957), may belong to family.

Last, Carb Namur: *Reticularia setigera* (Hall) Pitkin Lst, Arkansas (Easton 1942). Several other later genera are tentatively placed in this family e.g. U.Carb? *Ambikella fructiformis* Sahni & Srivastava, E. Himalayas (Sahni and Srivastava 1956), and Trias Nor *Triadispira caucasis* Dagis, Caucasus, U.S.S.R. (Dagis 1961).

Family ELYTHIDAE Fredericks 1924

First, Dev Siegen: *Elita [Elytha] saffordi* Hall, Oriskany Group, Pennsylvania (Cleaves 1939).

Last, Perm Guad: *Neophricodothyris asiatica* (Chao), Jingxian, S. Anhui, China (Zhang and Ching 1961).

Family MARTINIIDAE Waagen 1883

First, Sil Ludl: *Eomartiniopsis tenella* (Barrande), Bohemia, Czechoslovakia (Havliček 1959 p. 193)

Last, Perm Guadl: *Martinia orbicularis* Gemmellaro, *M. semiplana* Waagen, *M. lopingensis* Chao, *M. squamularioides* Huang, Jingxian, S. Anhui, China (Zhang and Ching 1961); or Perm Dzhulf?: *Martiniopsis inflata* Waagen, U. Productus Lst, Salt Range, Pakistan (Waagen 1883, Campbell 1959) or, if *Mentzelia* belongs to the family, last is Trias Rhaet: *Mentzelia kawhiana* Trechman, *M. cf. ampla* Bittner, Hokonui System, New Zealand (Marwick 1953).

[G.M.D.]

Order TEREBRATULIDA Waagen 1883

Suborder CENTRONELLIDINA Stehli 1965

Family CENTRONELLIDAE Waagen 1882

First, Dev Gedinn(?): *Nanothyris reesidei* Cloud, Keyser Fm, U.S.A. (Cloud 1942). Boucot (1957) regards *Nanothyris* as diagnostic of L. Dev.

Last, Perm Dzhulf: *Notothyris warthi* Waagen, U. Productus Lst, Pakistan, and *Cryptacanthia compacta* White & St. John, Perm, Caucasus (Waagen 1882, Licharew 1936).

Family RHIPIDOTHYRIDAE Cloud 1942

First, L. Dev: *Prorensselaeria nylanderi* Raymond, Helderberg Fm, Maine, U.S.A. (Cloud 1942). '*Waldheimia*' *mawii* Davidson, Sil Wenl, England, is a spiriferid (Cloud 1942). There are no known terebratulids in the British succession below the Ludlow Bone Bed.

Last, Carb Viséan: *Girtyella intermedia* Weller, Chester Fm, Illinois (Weller 1911, Cooper 1944).

Family STRINGOCEPHALIDAE King 1850

First, M.Dev: *Subrensselandia claypolii* (Hall), Hamilton Fm, Pennsylvania, U.S.A.

Last, Dev Givet: *Stringocephalus burtini* Defrance, Europe and N. America. Several other genera and species extend to the top of the Givet. (Cloud 1942, Cooper 1944.)

Chapter 12: Brachiopoda

Family MEGANTERIDAE Schuchert & Le Vene 1929

First and **Last,** Dev Siegen-Ems: *Meganteris suessi* Drevermann (Cloud 1942). Family confined to Siegen-Ems of Europe.

Suborder TEREBRATULIDINA Waagen 1883

Family DIELASMATIDAE Schuchert & Le Vene 1929

First, Sil Ludl or Dev Gedinn: *Brachyzyga pentameroides* Kozlowski and *Podolella rensselaeroides* Kozłowski, Borszczow Fm, Poland. Earliest of *Cryptonella* series (Cryptonellinae and Cranaeninae) is *Cryptonella melonica* (Barrande), U. Koněprusy Lst, Bohemia. (Weller 1911, Cloud 1942.) *Brachyzyga* and *Podolella* would probably be better included in the Centronellidae or a new family. The *Cryptonella* series should probably be separated from the Dielasmatidae. The Dielasmatinae proper are ubiquitous in the Carb and Perm.

Last, Perm Dzhulf: *Dielasma breviplicatum* Waagen and *Hemiptychina himalayensis* Davidson, U. Productus Lst, Pakistan (Waagen 1882) and *Dielasma elongatum* (Schlotheim), Magnesian Lst, and U. Zechstein, Western Europe; these are all late members of the Dielasmatinae. Of the *Cryptonella* series last is *Heterelasma shumardianum* Girty, Perm, W. Texas (Cooper 1944).

Family TEREBRATULIDAE Gray 1840

First, Trias Ladin: '*Terebratula*' *suborbicularis* Münster, '*T*'. *cassiana* Bittner and '*T*'. *capsella* Bittner, St. Cassian Beds, E. Alps, Europe (Bittner 1890). Also *Plectoconcha aequiplicata* (Gabb), Trias, Nevada (Cooper 1944). **Extant.**

Comment: '*Terebratula*' *laricimontana* Bittner, Muschelkalk, Central Europe, is earlier but is inadequately known (Bittner 1890).

Family CANCELLOTHYRIDAE Muir-Wood 1955

First, Cret Apt: *Terebratulina elongata* Davidson, Lower Greensand, England is one of several L.Cret. species. **Extant.**

Comment: *Terebratulina* is said to occur in the U.Jur but no clear evidence known. (Davidson 1851–86).

Family ORTHOTOMIDAE Muir-Wood 1936

First, Jur Pliens: *Orthotoma liasina* (Friren), Margaritatus Z., W. Europe (Muir-Wood 1936).
Last, Jur Pliens: *Orthotoma spinati* Rau, Spinatum Z., W. Europe.

Suborder TEREBRATELLIDINA Muir-Wood 1955

Superfamily ZEILLERIACEA Allan 1940

First, Trias Carn: '*Terebratula*' *julica* Bittner and '*T*'. *paronica* Tommasi, Raiblerschichten, '*T*'. *woehrmanniana* Bittner, Carditaschichten, and *Camerothyris ramsaurri* Suess, Trias, Alps, are all probable members of superfamily (Bittner 1890). '*Waldheimia*' *sulcifera* Schauroth, Muschelkalk, Alps, Europe, and *Cruratula eudora* (Laube), St. Cassian Beds, Eastern Alps, Europe, are earlier but doubtful members of the family.

Last, Cret Alb: *Modestella modesta* Owen, Tardefurcata Z., England. (Owen 1963.)

[F.A.M.]

Superfamily TEREBRATELLACEA King 1850

Family DALLINIDAE Beecher 1895

First, Trias ?Nor-Rhaet: *Eodallina peruviana* Elliott, Cerro de Pasco, Peru (Stehli 1956, Elliott 1959). **Extant.**

Family MEGATHYRIDIDAE Dall 1870

First, Cret Cenom: *Argyrotheca megatrema* (J. de C. Sow.), S. England. *A. oolitica* (Dav.), Jur Bath of S. England, is doubtful. **Extant.**

[G.F.E.]

The Fossil Record, Part II

Family TEREBRATELLIDAE King 1850
First, Cret Alb: *Australiarcula artesiana* Elliott, Oodnadatta, S. Australia.   **Extant.**

Family PLATIDIIDAE Thomson 1927
First, Tert L.Eoc: *Platidia cretacea* Weller, New Jersey, U.S.A. *P. heteroclyta* (Defr.), Cret
Maestr of France, is doubtful.   **Extant.**

Family KRAUSSINIDAE Allan 1940
First, Tert M. Mioc: *Megerlia oblita* (Michelotti), N. Italy.   **Extant.**

REFERENCES

AMOS, A. J. 1958. Algunos Spiriferacea y Terebratulacea (Brach.) del carbonífero superior del "Sistema del Tepuel". (Provincia de Chubut). *Contrns cient. Fac. Cienc. exact. fis. nat. Univ. B. Aires.* Ser Geol 2, 95–108.

ANDRONOV, S. M. 1961. Nekotorye predstaviteli semeystva Pentameridae iz devonskikh otlozheniy okrestnostey seberouralvska. *Trudy Inst. geol. Nauk, Mosk.*, **55**, 1–136, pl. A,B & 1–32.

BATALIER, J. R. 1948. Enameración de las Spiriferina del liásico español. *Ciencias*, **13** (1), 130–142.

BASSETT, C. F. 1935. Stratigraphy and Paleontology of the Dundee Limestone of Southeastern Michigan. *Bull. geol. Soc. Am.*, **46**, 425–462, pl. 33–39.

BELANSKI, C. H. 1928. Pentameracea of the Devonian of northern Iowa. *Stud. nat. Hist. Univ. Iowa*, new ser., 12, no. 7, 1–34, pl. 1–4.

BELL, W. C. 1941. Cambrian Brachiopoda from Montana. *J. Paleont.*, **15**, 193–255.

—— 1944. In LOCHMAN, C. and DUNCAN, D. Early Upper Cambrian Faunas of Central Montana. *Spec. Pap. geol. Soc. Am.*, **54**, 144–153.

BESNOSOVA, G. A. 1959. [Lower Carboniferous Brachiopods of the Kuznetz Basin]. *Trudy palèont. Inst.*, **75**, 1–136 (in Russian).

BITTNER, A. 1890. Brachiopoden der alpinen Trias. *Abh. geol. Reichsanst., Wien*, **14**, 1–325.

BOLTON, T. E. 1957. The Silurian stratigraphy and palaeontology of the Niagra Escarpment in Ontario. *Mem. geol. Surv. Can.*, **289**.

BOUCOT, A. J. 1957. Position of the North Atlantic Siluro-Devonian boundary. *Bull. geol. Soc. Am.*, **68**, 170–2.

—— 1963. The Eospiriferidae. *Palaeontology*, **5**, 682–711.

——, JOHNSON, J. G. & STATON, R. D. 1964. On some atrypoid, retzioid and athyridoid Brachiopoda. *J. Paleont.*, **38** (5), 805–22, pl. 125–28.

BRANSON, E. B. 1938. Stratigraphy and paleontology of the Lower Mississippian of Missouri. Pt. 1. *Univ. Mo. Stud.*, **13**, No. 3, 1–208, pls. 1–20.

CAMPBELL, K. S. W. 1959. The Martiniopsis-like Spiriferids of the Queensland Permian. *Palaeontology*, **1**, 333–350.

CLEAVES, A. B. 1939. In WILLARD, B. The Devonian of Pennsylvania. *Bull. Pa. geol. Surv.*, G19, 92–130.

CLOUD, P. 1942. Terebratuloid Brachiopoda of the Silurian and Devonian. *Spec. Pap. geol. Soc. Am.*, **38**.

COBBOLD, E. S. 1921. The Cambrian Horizons of Comley (Shropshire) and their Brachiopoda, Pteropoda, Gastropoda etc. *Q. Jl geol. Soc. Lond.*, **76**, 325–386.

COOPER, G. A. 1944. Phylum Brachiopoda *in* SHIMER, H. W. & SHROCK, R. R. *Index Fossils of North America*, 277–365, New York.

—— 1951. New brachiopods from the Lower Cambrian of Virginia. *J. Wash. Acad. Sci.*, **41**, 4–8.

—— 1952. Unusual specimens of the brachiopod family Isogrammidae. *J. Paleont.*, **26**, 113–119, pl. 21–23.

—— 1956. Chazyan and related Brachiopods. *Smithson. Misc. Collns.*, **127**.

COWIE, J. W. & ADAMS, P. J. 1957. The Geology of the Cambro Ordovician Rocks of central East Greenland. *Meddr. Grønl.*, **153**, No. 1, 3–193.

DACQUÉ, E. 1933. Wirbellose des Jura. I. *Leitfossilien*, 7, 147–172.

DAGIS, A. S. 1961. [New spiriferid genus Triadispira gen. nov.] *Dokl. Akad. nauk SSSR*, **141** (2), 457–460 (in Russian).

—— 1962. [Some new and little known Upper Triassic Athyrids]. *Nauchnye soobshcheniya Inst. geol. geogr., Lit. SSR*, **14** (1), 59–78 (in Russian).

—— 1963. [*Upper Triassic brachiopods of the southern U.S.S.R.*] Akademii Nauk SSSR, Sibir. Otdel, 248 pp. (in Russian).

—— 1965. [*Triassic brachiopods of Siberia.*] Akademii Nauk SSSR, Moscow (in Russian).

DAILY, B. 1957. The Cambrian in South Australia. *In* A. A. ÖPIK *et al.*, The Cambrian Geology of Australia. *Bull. Bur. Miner. Resour. Geol. Geophys. Aust.*, **49**, 1–284.

DALE, N. C. 1953. Geology and mineral Resources of the Orïskany Quadrangle (Rome Quadrangle). *Bull. N.Y. St. Mus.*, **345**, 1–197.

DAVIDSON, T. 1851–86. *British Fossil Brachiopoda. Palaeontogr. Soc.* [*Monogr.*]

DUBAR, G. 1948. La faune domerienne du Jebel Bou-Dahar près de Beni-Taggite. *Notes Mem. Serv. geol. Maroc.*, **68**, 1–248.

DUNBAR, C. O. 1955. Permian brachiopod faunas of central East Greenland. *Meddr. Grønland*, **110**, no. 3.

EASTON, W. H. 1942. Pitkin Limestone of northern Arkansas. *Bull. geol. Surv. Ark.*, **8**.

—— 1962. Carboniferous formations and faunas of Central Montana. *Prof. Pap. U.S. geol. Surv.*, **348** (I–IV), 1–126.

ELLIOTT, G. F. 1951. On the geographical distribution of terebratelloid brachiopods. *Ann. Mag. nat. Hist.* (12), **4**, 305–34.

—— 1958. Classification of thecidean brachiopods. *J. Paleont.*, **32**, 373.

—— 1959. Six new genera of Mesozoic brachiopoda. *Geol. Mag.*, **96**, 146–48.

FREDERICKS, G. 1929. The Fauna of the Kyn Limestone in the Urals. *Izv. geol. Kom.*, **48** (3), 87–136.

GARWOOD, E. J. 1912. The Lower Carboniferous Succession in the North-West of England. *Q. Jl geol. Soc. Lond.*, **68**, 449–572, pl. 44–56.

GLENISTER, B. F. 1955. Devonian and Carboniferous Spiriferids from the North-West Basin, Western Australia. *J. Proc. R. Soc. W. Aust.*, **39** (2), 46–71.

GOBBETT, D. J. 1963. Carboniferous and Permian Brachiopods of Svalbard. *Skr. Norsk Polarinst.*, **127**.

GRABAU, A. W. 1931. Devonian Brachiopoda of China. I. Devonian Brachiopoda from Yunnan and other districts in South China. *Palaeont. sin.*, B III, 3, 1–545.

GRANT, R. E. 1965. The brachiopod superfamily Stenocismatacea. *Smithson. Misc. Collns.*, **148**, 1–192, pls. 1–24.

HALL, J. 1857. Descriptions of Palaeozoic fossils. 10*th Annual Rep. N.Y. St. Cab. nat. Hist.*, 41–186.

—— & CLARKE, J. M. 1892. An introduction to the study of the genera of Palaeozoic Brachiopoda, pt. 1. *in* HALL, J. *Natural History of New York, Paleontology, Volume* 8, pp. 1–367, pl. 1–20, Albany, N.Y.

HARKER, P. & THORSTEINSSON, R. 1960. Permian rocks and faunas of Grinnell Peninsula, Arctic Archipelago. *Mem. geol. Surv. Can.*, **309**, 1–89.

HAVLÍČEK, V. 1949. Orthoidea a Clitambonoidea z Českého Tremadoku. *Sb. ústřed. Úst. geol.*, **16**, 93–144, pl. 1–5.

—— 1950. The Ordovician Brachiopoda from Bohemia. *Rozpr. ústřed. Úst. geol.*, **13**, 1–135, pl. 1–13.

—— 1953. O několika nových ramenonožcích českého a moravského středního devonu. *Věst. ústřed. Úst. geol.*, **28**, 4–9, pl. 1–2.

—— 1956. [The brachiopods of the Branik and Hlubočepy limestones in the immediate vicinity of Prague]. *Sb. ústřed. Úst. geol.*, **22**, 1–116 (535–650) (in Czech).

—— 1957. On new genera of spiriferidae of Bohemia (Brachiopoda). *Vest. ústřed. Úst. geol.*, **32** (4), 245–248.

—— 1959. The Spiriferidae of the Silurian and Devonian of Bohemia. *Rozpr. ústřed. Úst. geol.*, **25**, 1–275.

HEDE, J. E. 1960. The Silurian of Gotland. *21st Int. geol. Congr.*, Guide to excursions nos. A22 and C17, 44–87.

HINTZE, L. H. 1952. Lower Ordovician Trilobites from Western Utah and Eastern Nevada. *Bull. Utah geol. miner. Surv.*, **48**, 1–249, pl. 1–28.

HOU, KH. F. 1959. Spiriferids of Lower Devonian and Eifelian beds of the Southern part of Guansi. *Acta palaeont. sin.*, **7**, 450–476.

HUDSON, R. G. S. & JEFFRIES, R. P. S. 1961. Upper Triassic brachiopods and lamellibranchs from the Oman Peninsula, Arabia. *Palaeontology*, **4**, 1–41.

HUENE, F. VON. 1899. Die silurischen Craniaden der Ostseelander mit Ausschluss Gotlands. *Zap. imp. miner. Obshch.*, ser. 2, **36**, 181–359.

HYDE, J. E. 1953. Mississippian Formations of Central and Southern Ohio. *Bull. geol. Surv., Ohio*, **51**, 1–355.

IMBRIE, J. 1959. Brachiopods of the Traverse Group (Devonian) of Michigan. *Bull. Am. Mus. nat. Hist.*, **116**, 345–410, pl. 48–67.

INGEN, G. VAN & CLARK, P. E. 1903. Disturbed fossiliferous Rocks in the Vicinity of Rondout N.Y. *Bull. N.Y. St. Mus.*, **69**, 1176–1227, pl. 1–13.

IRELAND, H. A. 1961. New phosphatic brachiopods from the Silurian of Oklahoma. *J. Paleont.*, **35**, 1137–1142.

KASHIRTZEV, A. S. 1959. [*Field-atlas of the fauna of the Permian deposits of the north-east of the U.S.S.R.*]. 85 pp. Akademii Nauk SSSR, Moscow & Leningrad (in Russian).

KHODALEVICH, A. N. & BREIVEL, M. G. 1959. [*Brachiopods and corals from the Eifelian bauxite-producing deposits of the eastern slope of the Central and Northern Urals.*] Urals Geological Administration, 282 pp. (in Russian).

KINDLE, E. M. 1938. The correlation of certain Devonian faunas of east and west Gaspé. *Bull. Am. Paleont.*, **24.**

KING, R. E. 1930. The Geology of the Glass Mountains, Texas. *Bull. Univ. Texas*, **3042**, pt. 2, 1–245, pl. 1–44.

KIRK, E. & AMSDEN, T. W. 1952. Upper Silurian Brachiopods from S.E. Alaska. Descriptions and illustrations of a fauna from the Islands of Kosciusko and Hecta. *Prof. Pap. U.S. geol. Surv.*, **233C**, 53–66.

KOZLOWSKI, R. 1929. Les Brachiopodes gothlandiens de la Podolie polonaise. *Palaeont. pol.*, **1**, 1–254.

LAMONT, A. & GILBERT, D. L. F. 1945. Upper Llandovery Brachiopoda from Coneygore Coppice and Old Storridge Common, near Alfrick, Worcestershire. *Ann. Mag. nat. Hist.* (11), **12**, 641–682.

LAZUTKIN, P. S. 1936. [Upper Silurian Brachiopoda from the Ostracod Beds of the south western part of the Kuznetsk Basin.] *Trudy tsent. nauchno-issled. geologo-ravz. Inst.*, **80**, 1–72 (in Russian).

LICHAREW, B. 1936. Über einige paläozoische Gattungen der Terebratulacea aus Eurasien. *Problemy Paleont.*, Moscow, **1**, 263–73.

McLAREN, D. J. & NORRIS, A. W. 1962. Illustrations of Canadian fossils. Devonian of Western Canada. *Geol. Surv. Pap. Can.*, **62** (4), 1–35.

MALZAHN, E. 1958. Neue Fossilfunde und vertikale Verbreitung der niederrheinischen Zechsteine in den Bohrungen Kamp 4 und Frifaunadrich Heinrich 57 bei Kamp-Luitfort. *Geol. Jb.*, **73**, 91–126.

MAHSUY, H. 1912. Étude geologique du Yun-nan oriental. *Mem. Serv. geol. Indoch.*, **1**, (2), 1–46, 25 pl.

MARWICK, J. 1953. Divisions and faunas of the Hokonui System (Triassic and Jurassic). *Palaeont. Bull., Wellington*, **21**, 5–141.

MINATO, M. 1952. A Further Note on the Lower Carboniferous Fossils of the Kitakami Mountainland, N.E. Japan. *J. Fac. Sci. Hokkaido Univ.* (4), **8**, 2.

MUIR-WOOD, H. M. 1936. On the Liassic brachiopod genera *Orthoidea* and *Orthotoma*. *Ann. Mag. nat. Hist.* (10), **17**, 221–42.

—— 1962. *On the Morphology and Classification of the Brachiopod Suborder Chonetoidea.* 132 pp. pl. 1–16, British Museum (Natural History), London.

—— & Cooper, G. A. 1960. Morphology, Classification and Life Habits of the Productoidea (Brachiopoda). *Mem. geol. Soc. Am.*, **81**, 1–447, pl. 1–135.

Nikiforova, D. I. 1937. [Brachiopoda of the Cambrian and Silurian Systems of the U.S.S.R. Fasc. 1. Upper Silurian Brachiopoda of the central Asiatic part of U.S.S.R.]. *Central Geol. & Prospect. Inst. Pal. U.S.S.R. Monogr.*, **35** (1), 1–94 (in Russian).

Northrop, S. A. 1939. Palaeontology and Stratigraphy of the Silurian rocks of Port Daniel—Black Cape region, Gaspé. *Spec. Pap. geol. Soc. Am.*, **21**, 1–302.

Öpik, A. 1932. Über die Plectellinen. *Tatu Ülik. Geol.-Inst. Toim.*, **28**, 1–85, pl. 1–12.

—— 1934. Über Klitamboniten. *Tartu Ülik. Geol.-Inst. Toim.*, **39**, 1–239, pl. 1–48.

Orlowski, S. 1964. Kambr Srodkowy i jego Fauna we Wschodniej Czesci gor Swietokrzyskich. *Studia geol. pol.*, **16**, 7–94.

Owen, E. F. 1963. The brachiopod genus *Modestella* in the Lower Cretaceous of Great Britain. *Ann. Mag. nat. Hist.* (13), **6**, 199–203.

Poulson, C. 1927. The Cambrian, Ozarkian and Canadian Faunas of Northwest Greenland. *Meddr Grønl.*, 70, no. 2, 233–243.

—— 1932. The lower Cambrian Faunas of East Greenland. *Meddr Grønland*, **87**, No. 6, 5–67.

—— 1934. The Silurian faunas of North Greenland II. *Meddr Grønland*, **72**, no. 3, 1–59.

Reed, F. R. C. 1935. Some new brachiopods from Girvan. *Ann. Mag. nat. Hist.*, **16**, 1–12.

—— 1944. Brachiopoda and Mollusca from the Productus Limestones of the Salt Range. *Mem. geol. Surv. India Palaeont. Indica* (N.S.), **23** (2), 678 pp.

—— 1954. Lower Carboniferous Brachiopods from Scotland. *Proc. Leeds phil. lit. Soc.* (sci. sect.), **6** (3), 180–190.

Renz, C. 1932. Brachiopoden des südschweizerischen und west griechischen Lias. *Abh. schweiz. paläont. Ges.*, **52**, 1–61.

Rowell, A. J. 1962. The genera of the brachiopod superfamilies Obolellacea and Siphonotretacea. *J. Paleont.*, **36**, 136–152.

Rubel, M. P. 1961. Brakhiopody nadsemeystv Orthacea, Dalmanellacea i Syntrophiacea iz nizhnego Ordovika pribaltiki. *Geoloogia-Inst. Uurim.*, **6**, 141–226, pl. 1–27.

Rzhonsnitskaya, M. A. 1952. [Spiriferidae of the Devonian series of the margins of the Kuznetsk Basin.] *Trudy vses. nauchno-issled. geol. Inst.*, 3–232 (in Russian).

—— 1964. [On Devonian atrypids from the Kutznetsk Basin.] *Trudy vses. nauchno-issled. geol. Inst.*, **93**, 91–112, pl. 1–2 (in Russian).

St Joseph, J. K. S. 1938. The Pentameracea of the Oslo Region. *Norsk geol. Tidsskr.*, **17**, 225–336, pl. 1–8.

Sahni, M. R. & Srivastava, J. P. 1956. Discovery of Eurydesma and Conularia in the eastern Himalaya and description of associated faunas. *J. palaeont. Soc. India*, **1**, 202–214.

Sarytcheva, T. G. 1965. [Suborder Productoidea] *in* Razvitie i Smena morskikh Organizmov na Rybezhe Paleozoya i Mezozoya. *Trudy paleont. Inst.*, **108**, 1–431, pl. 1–58.

Schindewolf, O. H. 1955. Über einige Kambrische Gattungen inarticulater Brachiopoden. *Neues J. Geol. Paläont. Mh.*, **12**, 538–557.

Schmidt, H. 1951. Zur Brachiopoden-Fauna des mitteldevonischen Flinzkalk von Iserlohn-Letmathe. *Senckenberiana*, 32, 87–94.

Sluisareva, A. D. 1960. [Spiriferidae from the Kazan beds of the Russian Platform and the conditions of their existence. (Genera Licharewia Einor and Permospirifer Kulikov).] *Trudy paleont. Inst.*, **80**, 1–120 (in Russian).

Sokolskaja, A. N. 1965. Orders Orthida and Strophomenida *in* Razvitie i Smena morskikh Organizmov na Rybezhe Paleozoya i Mezozoya. *Trudy paleont. Inst.*, **108**, 1–431, pl. 1–58.

Stainbrook, M. A. 1947. Brachiopoda of the Percha Shale of New Mexico and Arizona. *J. Paleont.*, **21**, 297–328.

Stehli, F. G. 1956. A late Triassic terebratellacean from Peru. *J. Wash. Acad. Sci.*, **46**, 101–103.

Stoyanow, A. 1915. On some Permian Brachiopoda of Armenia. *Mém. Com. géol. St. Péters-bourg. n.s.*, **111**, 1–95, pl. 1–6.

TERMIER, G., TERMIER, H. & PAJAUD, D. 1966. Découverte d'une Thécidée dans le Permien de Texas. *C. R. Acad. Sci. Paris*, **263,** 332–335.

TREATISE, H. 1965. WILLIAMS, A. *et al.* Brachiopoda in MOORE, R. C. (Editor) *Treatise on Invertebrate Paleontology*, Part H. University of Kansas Press.

TROTTER, F. M. & HOLLINGWORTH, S. E. 1932. The Geology of the Brampton District. *Mem. Geol. Surv. U.K.*, 1–223, pl. 1–9.

TWENHOFEL, W. H. 1928. Geology of Anticosti Island. *Mem. geol. Surv. Can.*, **154,** 1–481, 1–60.

ULRICH, E. O. & COOPER, G. A. 1936. New genera and species of Ozarkian and Canadian Brachiopods. *J. Paleont.*, **10,** 616–631.

—— & —— 1938. Ozarkian and Canadian Brachiopoda. *Spec. Pap. geol. Soc. Am.*, **13.**

VANDERCAMMEN, A. 1956. Revision de *Spinocyrtia struniana. Bull. Inst. Sci. nat. Belg.*, 32 (59), 1–9.

—— 1959. Essai d'étude statistique des Cyrtospirifer du Frasnien de la Belgique. *Mem. Inst. r. Sci. nat. Belg.*, **145,** 1–175.

—— 1963. Spiriferidae du Dévonian de la Belgique. *Mem. Inst. r. Sci. nat. Belg.*, **150,** 1–177.

VEEVERS, J. J. 1959. Devonian Brachiopods from the Fitzroy Basin, Western Australia. *Bull. Bur. Miner. Resour. Geol. Geophys. Aust.*, 45, 220 pp.

VESELINOVIĆ, D. 1951. [The Triassic fauna from Bujkov and Bonin Potok (Vrška Čuka) telling precedently about its stratigraphical position]. *Zborn. Radova geol. Inst.*, **2,** 109–124 (in Yugoslav).

VOKES, H. E. 1957. Geography and geology of Maryland. *Bull. Md. Dep. Geol. Mines*, **19,** XIV, 1–243.

WAAGEN, W. 1882–5. Salt Range Fossils; Brachiopoda. *Mem. geol. Surv. India, Palaeont. indica*, **1,** 329–770.

WAITE, R. H. 1956. Upper Silurian Brachiopoda from the Great Basin. *J. Paleont.*, **30,** 19–28.

WALCOTT, C. D. 1908. Cambrian Brachiopoda. *Smithson. Misc. Collns.*, **53,** 53–137, pl. 7–10.

—— 1912. Cambrian Brachiopoda. *Monogr. U.S. geol. Surv.*, **51,** parts 1 and 2.

WALMSLEY, V. G. 1959. The geology of the Usk inlier (Monmouthshire). *Q. Jl geol. Soc. Lond.*, **114,** 483–521.

WANG, Y. 1955. New genera of Brachiopods. *Scientia sin.*, **4,** 327–357, pl. 1–6.

WANNER, J. & KNIPSCHEER, H. C. G. 1951. Der Lias der Niefschlucht in Ost Seran (Molukken). *Eclog. geol. Helv.*, **44** (1), 1–28.

WARREN, P. S. & STELCK, C. R. 1956. Reference fossils of Canada Part 1. Devonian faunas of western Canada. *Spec. Pap. geol. Ass. Can.*, **1,** 15 pp.

WATSON, D. M. S. 1917. *Poikilosakos*, a remarkable new genus of brachiopod from the Upper Coal-measures of Texas. *Geol. Mag.*, **54,** 212–219, pl. 14.

WELLER, S. 1911. Genera of Mississippian loop-bearing Brachiopoda. *J. Geol.*, **19,** 439–48.

WILLIAMS, A. 1962. The Barr and Lower Ardmillan Series (Caradoc) of the Girvan District, south-west Ayrshire, with descriptions of the Brachiopoda. *Mem. geol. Soc. Lond.*, **3,** 1–267, pl. 1–25.

WILSON, A. E. 1946. Brachiopoda of the Ottawa Formation of the Ottawa–St. Lawrence Lowland. *Bull. geol. Surv. Can.*, **8,** 1–149, pl. 1–11.

WIMAN, C. 1907. Über die Fauna des Westbaltischen Leptaenakalks. *Ark. Zool.*, **3,** no. 24, 1–20, pl. 1–2.

WRIGHT, A. D. 1964. The fauna of the Portrane Limestone, II. *Bull. Brit. Mus. (nat. Hist.) Geol.*, **9,** no. 6, 157–256, pl. 1–11.

ZHANG, Y. & CHING, Y. K. 1961. An Upper Permian Brachiopod fauna from Jingxian, Anhui Province. *Acta palaeont. sin.*, **9,** 401–425.

ZUGMAYER, H. 1882. Untersuchungen über Rhätische Brachiopoden. *Beitr. Paläont. Geol. Öst.-Ung.* **1,** 1–42, pl. 1–4.

D. V. Ager, PH.D. D.I.C. F.G.S.
Department of Geology, Imperial College, Prince Consort Road, London S W 7.

P. Copper
Department of Geology, Queen's University, Kingston, Ontario, Canada.

Chapter 12: Brachiopoda

G. M. Dunlop, PH.D. F.G.S.
   Bedford College, Regent's Park, London N W 1.
G. F. Elliott, F.G.S.
   Iraq Petroleum Co., 33 Cavendish Square, London W 1.
F. A. Middlemiss, PH.D. F.G.S.
   Department of Geology, Queen Mary College, Mile End Road, London E 1.
A. J. Rowell, PH.D. F.G.S.
   Department of Geology, The University, Nottingham.
[Professor] A. Williams, PH.D. F.R.S.E. M.R.I.A. F.G.S.
   Department of Geology, Queen's University, Belfast, Northern Ireland.
A. D. Wright, PH.D. F.G.S.
   Department of Geology, Queen's University, Belfast, Northern Ireland.

CHAPTER 13

Mollusca: Amphineura, Monoplacophora and Gastropoda

Contributors: D. CURRY & N. J. MORRIS

The classification used in this chapter follows that of the authors of the *Treatise* pt. I, and Wenz, Gastropoda in *Handbuch der Paläozoologie* Band 6, 1938–1944.

We would like to thank Mr. R. J. Cleevely of the Palaeontological Department of the British Museum (Natural History) for his help in the work associated with this chapter.

Class AMPHINEURA

Order PALAEOLORICATA Bergenhayn 1955

First, U.Camb.: *Preacanthochiton cooperi & P. productus* Bergenhayn, Eminence Fm, Missouri (Bergenhayn 1960, p. 169).

Last: Cret M. Campan: *Scanochiton* and *Olingechiton* Bergenhayn 1943, Mammillatus Z., Locality Sweden (Bergenhayn 1943 & 1960).

Constituent taxa: Chelodina Bergenhayn (Families as in *Treatise* pt. I) and *Septemchiton* Bergenhayn = *Solenocaris* (Information from Dr. W. D. I. Rolfe) plus Preacanthochitonidae Bergenhayn and Eochelodidae Marek.

Order NEOLORICATA Bergenhayn 1955

First, Ord Ashg: *Helminthochiton thraivensis* Reed, Starfish Bed, Drummock Gp. Ayrshire, Scotland. (Reed 1911). **Extant.**

Constituent taxa as in *Treatise* pt. I.

Note: *Helminthochiton aequivoca* (Robson 1913) L. Ord Aren, Bohemia, appears to more likely belong to the Palaeoloricata.

Class MONOPLACOPHORA

Order TRYBLIDIOIDEA Lemche 1957

First, L. Camb: *Scenella discinoides*, H. kjerulfi Beds, 1bα, Estonia (Opik 1956, p. 114). **Extant.**

Constituent taxa: as in *Treatise* pt. I.

Comment: Unknown in Mesozoic & Tertiary rocks

Order ARCHINACELLOIDEA Knight & Yochelson 1958

First, U. Camb: *Hypseloconus elongatus* Berkey, U. Dresbachian, Taylor Falls Conglomerate, Wisconsin, U.S.A. (Berkey 1898, p. 282).

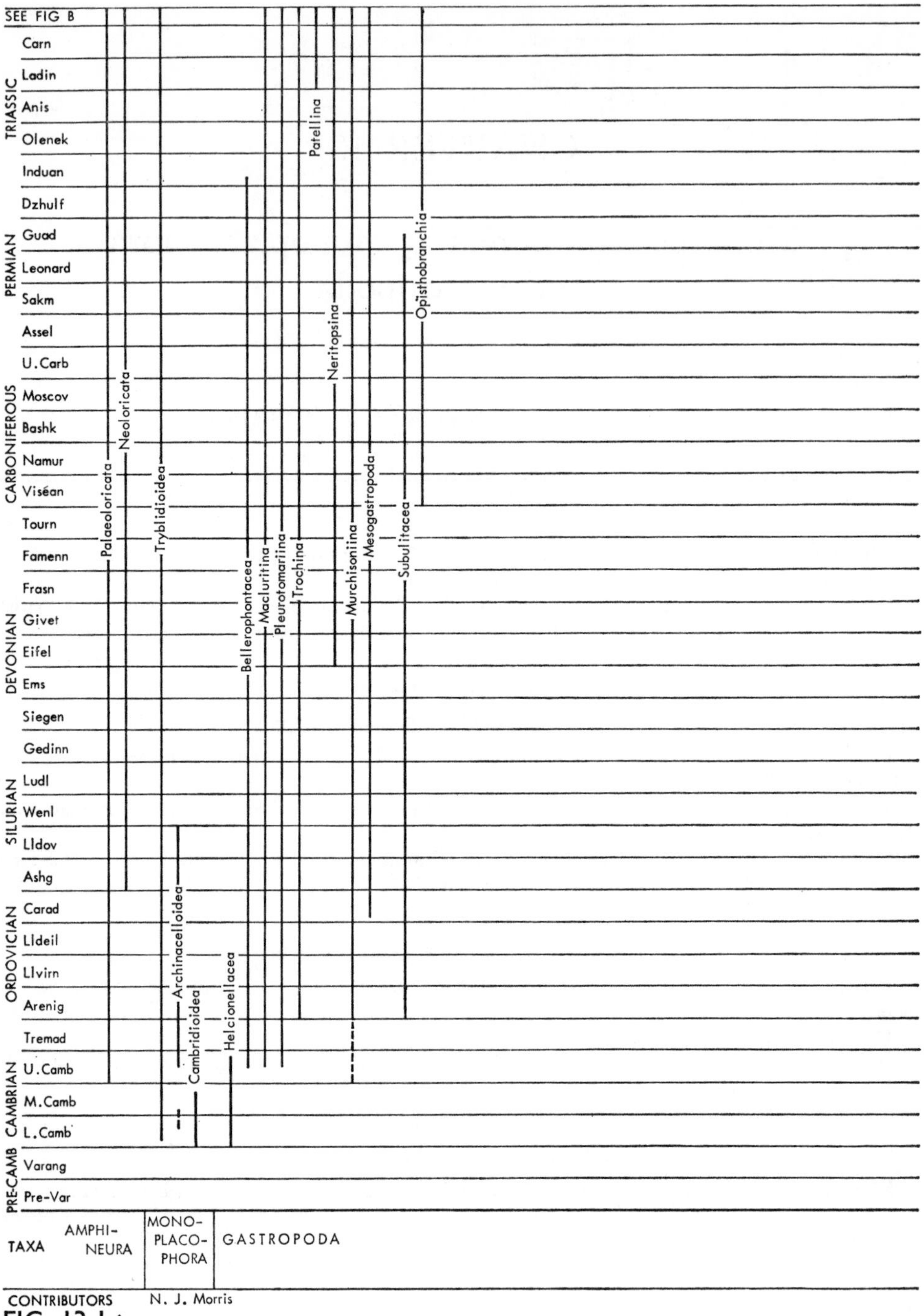
SEE FIG B
Carn
Ladin
TRIASSIC
Anis
Olenek
Induan
Dzhulf
Guad
PERMIAN
Leonard
Sakm
Assel
U.Carb
Moscov
CARBONIFEROUS
Bashk
Namur
Viséan
Tourn
Famenn
Frasn
Givet
DEVONIAN
Eifel
Ems
Siegen
Gedinn
Ludl
SILURIAN
Wenl
Lldov
Ashg
Carad
ORDOVICIAN
Lldeil
Llvirn
Arenig
Tremad
U.Camb
CAMBRIAN
M.Camb
L.Camb
PRE-CAMB
Varang
Pre-Var
Palaeoloricata
Neoloricata
Tryblidioidea
Archinacelloidea
Cambridioidea
Helcionellacea
Bellerophontacea
Macluritina
Pleurotomariina
Trochina
Patellina
Neritopsina
Murchisoniina
Mesogastropoda
Subulitacea
Opisthobranchia
TAXA
AMPHI-NEURA
MONO-PLACO-PHORA
GASTROPODA
CONTRIBUTORS
N. J. Morris

FIG. 13.1 A

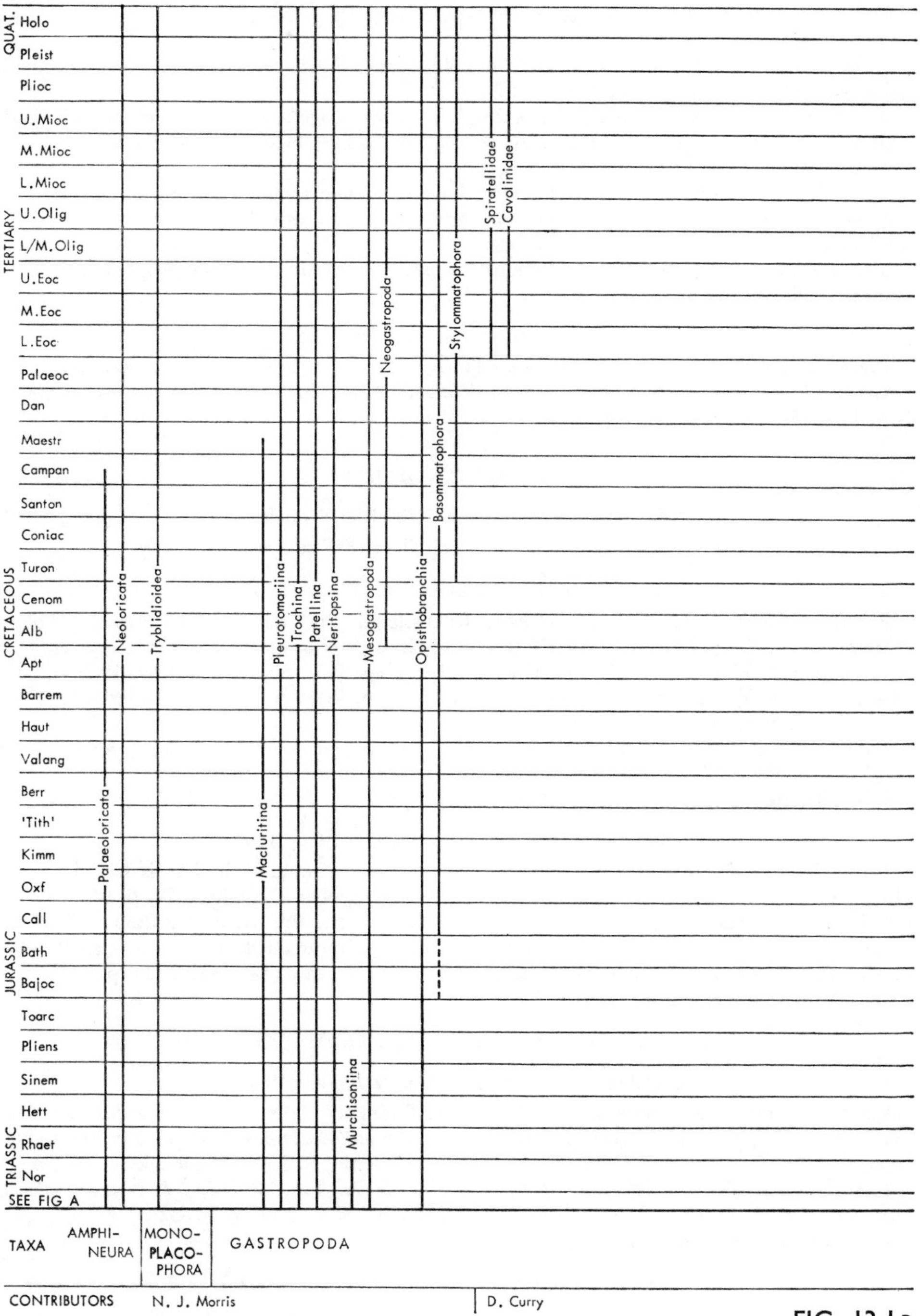
QUAT.
Holo
Pleist
Plioc
U.Mioc
M.Mioc
L.Mioc
TERTIARY
U.Olig
L/M.Olig
U.Eoc
M.Eoc
L.Eoc
Palaeoc
Dan
Maestr
Campan
Santon
Coniac
CRETACEOUS
Turon
Cenom
Alb
Apt
Barrem
Haut
Valang
Berr
'Tith'
Kimm
Oxf
Call
JURASSIC
Bath
Bajoc
Toarc
Pliens
Sinem
Hett
TRIASSIC
Rhaet
Nor
SEE FIG A
Palaeoloricata
Neoloricata
Tryblidioidea
Macluritina
Pleurotomariina
Trochina
Patellina
Neritopsina
Murchisontina
Mesogastropoda
Neogastropoda
Opisthobranchia
Basommatophora
Stylommatophora
Spiratellidae
Cavolinidae
TAXA
AMPHI-NEURA
MONO-PLACO-PHORA
GASTROPODA
CONTRIBUTORS
N. J. Morris
D. Curry

FIG. 13.1 B

Last, Sil Lldov: *Archinacella canadensis* (Whiteaves) 1884, Niagara Fm, Ontario, Canada (Bassler 1915).

Comments: *Stenothecopsis heraultensis* Cobbold, Upper L.Camb, Hérault, France, probably belongs to this group (Cobbold, 1935, p. 27).

The Metoptomatidae (*Treatise* pt. I, p. 231) and *Archaeopraga pinnaeformis* (Perner) Sil. Ludl., Přídolí Beds, Bohemia (Horny 1963) may belong here or may belong to the Patellina (i.e. it is uncertain whether or not they have undergone torsion).

The tall shells of the Hypseloconidae must have contained a very different animal from the limpet-like Archinacellidae. The association of the two families following the Treatise pt. I is retained for lack of evidence to the contrary.

The ancestor of the Cephalopoda might be expected to be a Monoplacophoran with an elongate shell resembling *Hypseloconus*.

Order CAMBRIDIOIDEA Horny 1957

First, L. Camb: *Cambridium nikiforovae* Horny, Obruchev horizon, Siberia (Horny 1957).
Last, M. Camb: *Stenothecoides elongata* Walcot, Eldorado Lst, Bathyuriscus-Elrathia Z, Nevada, U.S.A. (Rasetti 1954, p. 63).

Class GASTROPODA

Order BELLEROPHONTOIDEA Ulrich & Scofield 1897
(ex Bellerophontacea Ulrich & Schofield 1897 sub-ordinal name)

Superfamily HELCIONELLACEA Wenz 1938

First, L. Camb: *Helcionella cf. subrugosa* (d'Orbigny), 2nd horizon with *Kjerulfia*, Poland (Samsonovicz 1956, p. 136); *Helcionella* also occurs in beds of approximately the same age in S. Australia (Daily 1956 p. 138), Korea (Kobayashi 1956, p. 345), Shansi (Strakhov 1962, p. 207), England (Cobbold 1921, p. 365), Norway (Kiaer 1916, p. 19), Anti-Atlas (Termier 1950, p. 6), New York State (Fisher 1956, p. 342).
Last, U. Camb: *Cycloholcus nummus* Knight, Lst. intercalated with Nolichucky Shales, Dresbachian (Knight 1947, p. 5).
Constituent taxa: as in *Treatise* pt. I.

Superfamily BELLEROPHONTACEA M'Coy 1851

First, U. Camb: *Chalarostrepsis praecursor* Knight 1947, boulders in Laevis Conglomerate, Hungaia Z, ? Y. Dikocephalus Z., Trempealeauian of Quebec (Knight 1947, p. 6). Ruscion (1956, p. 755) records ? *Tropidodiscus* sp. (as *Oxydiscus*) from the M. or U. Camb of Bolivia.
Last, Trias Induan: *B. (Bellerophon) borealis* Spath, Vishnuites Beds, Greenland (Spath 1930, p. 43); *Bellerophon vaceki* Bittner, Strati di Suisi, Induan, N. Italy (Leonardi 1935, p. 83)
Constituent taxa: as in *Treatise* pt. I.

Order ARCHAEOGASTROPODA Thiele 1925

Suborder MACLURITINA Cox & Knight 1960

First, U. Camb: *Scaevogyra* sp., *Matherella* sp., Eminence Dolomite, Trempealeauian, Missouri; *Macluritina* sp., from the same formation, Oklahoma (Lochman 1956, p. 455; Fredrickson 1956, p. 497; Fisher 1956, p. 333). *Kobayashiella*, U. Camb, S. Korea (Kobayashi 1962, p. 1).
Last, U. Cret, Maastr.: *Weeksia amplificata* (Wade), Ripley Fm, Mississippi & *Weeksia deplanata* (Johnson), Prairie Bluff Chalk of Mississippi & Alabama (Sohl, 1960, p. 51–52).
Constituent taxa: as in *Treatise* pt. I.

Suborder PLEUROTOMARIINA Cox & Knight 1960

First, U. Camb: *Sinuopea sweeti* (Whitfield), Trempealeauian, Wisconsin & *Dirhachopea* sp., Eminence Dolomite, Trempealeauian, Missouri (Ulrich 1911 & 1931). **Extant.**
Constituent taxa: as in *Treatise* pt. I.

Chapter 13: Mollusca: Amphineura, Monoplacophora and Gastropoda

Suborder TROCHINA Cox & Knight 1960

First, L. Ord: The following species are described from E. North America *Straparollina pelagica* Billings, *S. minima* Whitfield, *Holopea dilicula* Hall, *H. ovalis* Billings, *H. obscura* Hall, *H. proserpula* Billings, ? *H. raymondea* Cleland & *Platyceras columbianum* Weller (Bassler 1915).
Extant.

Straparollina primaeva Billings from the L. Camb, Schodack Fm., New York (Bassler 1915) may be a *Pelagiella*
Constituent taxa: as in *Treatise* pt. I.

Suborder PATELLINA von Ihering 1876

First, Trias Ladin: ? *Acmaea cf. lineata* (Klipstein), Tommasi, Southern Alps (Diener & Kutassy 1926–40, p. 111). **Extant.**
Comments: The family Metoptomatidae, doubtfully included in this suborder by the *Treatise* authors, may be linked to the Monoplacophora. *Archaeopraga* (Horny 1963) is a likely intermediate. Several species of *Phryx* which may be related to either the Capulidae or the Patellacae are listed by Diener & Kutassy (1926–40, p. 122).

Suborder NERITOPSINA Cox & Knight 1960

First, Dev Eifel: *Naticopsis antiqua* & *N. efossa* Goldfuss, Eifel, Germany. (Goldfuss 1844).
Extant.
Constituent taxa: as in *Treatise* pt. I.

Suborder MURCHISONIINA Cox & Knight 1960

First, U. Camb or L. Ord.: *"Murchisonia" putilla* Sardeson, Ozark, Minnesota and *Seelya cassandra* (Billings) & *"Murchisonia" sylvia* Billings, Ozark, Laevis erratics, Quebec. The authors of the Treatise pt. I apparently consider these species to be L. Ord.
Last, Trias Nor.: *Vistilia klipsteini* (Koken), Austria (*Treatise* p. I1295)
Comment: *Protospira minuta* Ruedemann 1916, U. Camb. Hoyt Lst., New York, is too poorly preserved to be confidently placed in this suborder (*Treatise* p. I291)
Constituent taxa: as in *Treatise* pt. I.

Order MESOGASTROPODA Wenz 1938

First, Ord Carad: *Loxonema murrayana* Salter, Black River Fm, Canada (Salter 1859, p. 31).
Extant.
Constituent taxa: Superfamilies: Loxonematacea, Rissoacea, Viviparacea, Valvatacea, Littorinacea, Architectonicacea, Cerithiacea, Epitoniacea, Eulimacea, Calyptreacea, Naticacea, Strombacea, Cypraeacea, Tonnacea and ? Atlantacea.

Order NEOGASTROPODA Wenz 1938

Constituent taxa: Superfamilies: Buccinacea, Muricacea, Volutacea & Conacea.
Comment: Early Neogastropoda are in great need of revision. It seems unlikely that Thiele's separation of these superfamilies based upon the reduction in number of the radular teeth has produced a valid monophyletic order.
Lists of early members of these superfamilies (Pictet 1861–64, p. 642 & thereabouts) include Neocomian & Aptian species of which many may be attributed to the Strombacea. Definite Muricacea & Buccinacae first occur in the Albian (Pictet 1861–64, p. 643; d'Orbigny 1842). Information is not available to suggest which of these Albian forms might constitute the first record. **Extant.**

Order Uncertain

Superfamily SUBULITACEA Lindstrom 1884

First, Ord Arenig: *Fusirpira calcifera* (Billings), *F. psyche* (Billings) & *F. obeza* Whitfield from the Canadian of N. E. America (Bassler 1915).

Last, Perm Guad: *Labridens shupei* Yochelson, Wood Fm., Glass Mts., Texas (Yochelson 1956).

Comment: *"Fusispira"* sp. from the L.Ord, Peilintze Lst, of N. China (Grabau 1922, p. 36) is not sufficiently well preserved to be certain of its correct identification.

Order OPISTHOBRANCHIA Milne Edwards 1848

First, L.Carb Viséan: *Actaeonina carbonaria* de Koninck, Calc. de Visé, Belgium (de Koninck 1844, p. 469). **Extant.**

Comment: *Donaldina* spp. occur in the Viséan, Calciferous Sandstone Series of Scotland they are attributed to the Pyramidellacea which are also probably Opisthobranchs (Knight 1941, p. 104).

Order BASOMMATOPHORA Keferstein 1864

First, M.Jur: *Anisopsis calculus* (Sandberger) 1875, "Dogger", Cajac nr. Strasbourg, France (Zilch 1959–60). **Extant.**

Comment: The Basommatophora are the aquatic Pulmonates.

Order STYLOMMATOPHORA A. Schmidt 1856

First, Cret Turon: *Juvavina juvavensis* (Tausch) & *Conobulimisus fuggeri* (Tausch) Aigen nr. Salzburg, Austria. (Wenz 1940, p. 138). **Extant.**

Comments: The genera *Mesodon, Paravitrea & Euconulus* occur in the U. Cret. of North America.

The Stylommatophora are the land Pulmonates.

Information regarding the Opisthobranchs and following groups may be obtained in Zilch 1959–60, Ghiselin 1966 and Wenz 1940. (N.J.M.)

Order PTEROPODA Cuvier 1804

(*nom. correct.* Duméril 1806, *pro* "ptéropodes" Cuvier 1804)

Suborder THECOSOMATA de Blainville 1824

Comment: Blanckenhorn's Cret records now known to be Eoc or Mioc (Avnimelech 1945): all other pre-Tertiary records doubtful. Peraclidae, Cymbuliidae and Desmopteridae not known fossil; present distribution, all warm oceans. Of these three families only Peraclidae have calcareous shells.

Family SPIRATELLIDAE Dall 1921

First, Tert L.Eoc: *Spiratella mercinensis* (Watelet & Lefèvre) and other spp. London Clay Fm, England (Curry 1965); *S. elongatoidea, choctavensis* (Aldrich), Bashi Fm Wilcox Group, Alabama, U.S.A. (Collins 1934). **Extant.**

Comment: Present distribution, all oceans.

Family CAVOLINIDAE Gray 1850

First, Tert L.Eoc: *Camptoceratops prisca* (Godwin-Austen), London Clay Fm, England (Curry 1965). **Extant.**

Comment: Earlier forms simple, basically conical. *Cavolina* and *Diacria* not known before the Mioc. Present distribution, all oceans, mostly in warm waters.

Suborder GYMNOSOMATA de Blainville 1824

No hard parts, not known fossil: present distribution, all oceans. (D.C.)

REFERENCES

AVNIMELECH, M. 1945. Revision of fossil pteropoda from southern Anatolia, Syria and Palestine. *J. Paleont.*, **19,** 637–647.

Chapter 13: Mollusca: Amphineura, Monoplacophora and Gastropoda

BASSLER, R. S. 1915. Bibliographic index of American Ordovician and Silurian fossils (2 vols.). *Bull. U.S. natn. Mus.*, **92**, 1521.

BERGENHAYN, J. R. M. 1943. Preliminary notes on fossil Polyplacophora from Sweden. *Geol. För. Stockh. Förh.*, **65**, 297–303.

—— 1960. Cambrian and Ordovician Loricates from North America. *J. Paleont.*, **34**, 168–178.

BERKEY, C. P. 1898. Geology of the St. Croix Dalles. Pt. 3, Paleontology. *Am. Geol.*, **21**, 270–294.

BILLINGS, E. 1861–65. *Palaeozoic fossils*, Volume 1. Geological Survey of Canada, Montreal.

COBBOLD, E. S. 1921. The Cambrian horizons of Comley (Shropshire) and their Brachiopoda, Pteropoda, Gasteropoda etc. *Quart. Jl geol. Soc. Lond.*, **76**, 325–386.

—— 1935. Lower Cambrian faunas from Hérault, France. *Ann. Mag. nat. Hist.*, 10th Ser., **16**, 25–48.

COLLINS, R. L. 1934. A monograph of the American Tertiary pteropod mollusks. *Johns Hopkins Univ. Stud. Geol.*, **11**, 137–234.

CURRY, D. 1965. The English Palaeogene pteropods. *Proc. malac. Soc. Lond.* **36**, 357–371.

DAILY, B. 1956. The Cambrian in South Australia. *In* "El sistema Cambrico su paleogeografia . . . ." Pt. 2 *XXth Int. Geol. Congr. Mexico*, pp. 91–147.

DIENER, C. & KUTASSY, A. 1926–40. *Fossilium Catalogus 1: Animalia, Pars 34 & 81. Glossophora triadica.* Junk, Berlin.

FISHER, D. W. 1956. The Cambrian system of New York State. In "El sistema Cambrico . . . ." Part 2. *XXth Int. Geol. Congr. Mexico*, pp. 321–351.

FREDRICKSON, E. A. 1956. Cambrian of Oklahoma. In "El sistema Cambrico . . . ." Part 2. *XXth Int. Geol. Congr. Mexico*, pp. 483–508.

GHISELIN, M. T. 1966. Reproductive function and the phylogeny of opisthobranch gastropods. *Malacologia*, **3**, 327–378.

GOLDFUSS, G. A. 1826–44. Petrefacta Germaniae. *Petrefacten Deutschlands und der angrenzenden Lander* (in 3 parts). Düsseldorf.

GRABAU, A. W. 1922. Ordovician fossils of N. China. *Palaeont. sin.*, B, **1**, 127.

HORNY, R. 1957. Problematic molluscs (? Amphineura) from the Lower Cambrian of south & east Siberia (USSR). *Sb. ústřed. Úst. geol.*, **23**, 397–432.

—— 1963. *Archaeopraga*, a new problematic genus of monoplacophoran molluscs from the Silurian of Bohemia. *J. Paleont.*, **37**, 1071–1073.

KIAER, J. 1916. The Lower Cambrian *Holmia* fauna at Tömten in Norway. *Skr. Vidensk Selsk. Christiania*, No. **10**, 1–140.

KNIGHT, J. B. 1941. Paleozoic gastropod genotypes. *Spec. Pap. geol. Soc. Am.*, **32**, 510.

—— 1947. Some new Cambrian Bellerophont gastropods. *Smithson. misc. Collns.*, **106**, 1–11.

—— 1948. Further new Cambrian Bellerophont gastropods. *Smithson. misc. Collns*, **111**, 1–6.

KOBAYASHI, T. 1956. The Cambrian of Korea and its relation to the other Cambrian territories. In "El sistema Cambrico . . ." Part 1. *XXth Int. Geol. Congr. Mexico*, pp. 343–362.

—— 1962. The Cambro-Ordovician formations and faunas of South Korea—Part IX. Palaeontolgy, viii: The Machari formation. *J. Fac. Sci. Tokyo Univ.*, **14**, 1–152.

KOKEN, E. 1897. Die Gastropoden der Trias um Hallstadt. *Abh. geol. Bundesanst., Wien*, **17**, 112.

KONINCK, L. G. de 1841–44. *Description des animaux fossiles qui se trouvent dans le terrain carbonifère de Belgique*. Liege.

LEONARDI, P. 1935. Il Trias inferiore delle Venezie. *Memorie Ist geol Miner. Univ. Padova*, **XI**, 136.

LOCHMAN, C. 1956. The Cambrian of the Middle Central Interior States of the United States. In "El sistema Cambrico . . ." Part 2. *XXth Int. Geol. Congr. Mexico*, pp. 447–481.

MAREK, L. 1962. New polyplacophorid family Eochelididae n. fam. in the Ordovician of Bohemia. *Věst. st. geol., Úst. čsl. Repub.*, **37**, 373–375.

MOORE, R. C. (Ed.) 1960. *Treatise on Invertebrate Paleontology Part I: Mollusca.* Lawrence.

OPIK, A. A. 1956. Cambrian (Lower Cambrian) of Estonia. In "El sistema Cambrico . . . ." Part 1. *XXth Int. Geol. Congr. Mexico*, pp. 97–126.

ORBIGNY, A. D. 1842–43. *Paléontologie Francaise. Terrains Crétacés—2. Gastéropodes.* Paris.

—— 1845. Terrain Secondaire—Mollusques. In *The geology of Russia in Europe and the Ural*

Mountains, Vol. 2, *Paleontologie* by Murchison, R. I., Verneuil, E. de & Keyserling, A. de. London & Paris.

Pictet, F. J. & Campiche, G. 1861–64. Descriptions des fossiles du terrain crétacé des environs de Sante-Croix. *Pal. Suisse*, 3 Ser., **2**, 1861–64:752,51pls.

Rasetti, F. 1954. Internal shell structures in the Middle Cambrian gastropod *Scenella* and the problematic genus *Stenothecoides*. *J. Paleont.*, **28**, 59–66.

Reed, F. R. C. 1911. 1. Sedgwick Museum Notes. A new fossil from Girvan. *Geol. Mag.*, **8**, 337–339.

Robson, G. C. 1913. *Helminthochiton sequivoca*, n. sp. Lower Ordovician, Bohemia. *Geol. Mag.*, **10**, 302–304.

Rodgers, J. (Ed.) 1956. *El Cámbrico su paleogeografia y el problema de su base*. XXth Int. Geol. Conrg., Mexico 1956. Part 1: Europe, Africa, Asia; Part 2: Australia, America.

Ruedemann, R. 1916. Paleontologic contributions from the New York State Museum. *Bull. N.Y. St. Mus.*, **189**, 1–120.

Rusconi, C. 1956. Correlaciones Cambra—Ordovicicas entre Mendoza y Norte America. In "El sistema Cambrico . . . ." Part 2. XXth Int. Geol. Congr. Mexico. pp. 751–762.

Salter, J. W. 1859. *Figures and descriptions of Canadian organic remains* Dec. 1. Geological Survey Canada, Montreal.

Samsonowicz, J. 1956. Cambrian paleogeography and the base of the Cambrian system in Poland. In "El sistema Cambrico . . . ." Part 1. XXth Int. Geol. Congr. Mexico. pp. 127–160.

Sandberger, F. von. 1875. *Die Land—und Süsswasserconchylien der Vorwelt*. Wiesbaden.

Sardeson, F. W. 1896. The fauna of the Magnesian series. *Bull. Minn. Acad. nat. Sci.*, **4**, 92–105.

Sohl, N. F. 1960. Archaeogastropoda, Mesogastropoda and stratigraphy of the Ripley, Owl Creek, and Prairie Bluff Formations. *Prof. Pap. U.S. geol. Surv.* **331A**, 151.

Spath, L. F. 1930. The Eotriassic invertebrate fauna of East Greenland. *Meddr. Grønland*, **83**, 5–87.

Strakhov, N. M. 1962. *Principles of historical geology*, Part 1. (Transl'd from Russian, 3rd Ed. by J. Kolodny, 1948), p. 207. Israel Program for Scientific Translations, Jerusalem.

Termier, G. & H. 1950. Paleontologie Marocaine 11 Invertébres de L'Ere Primaire—3. Mollusques. *Notes Mém. Serv. Mines Carte géol Maroc*, **78**, 247.

Thiele, J. 1929–31. *Handbuch der systematischen Weichtierkunde*, Vol. 1, *Loricata & Gastropoda*. Gustav Fischer, Jena.

Ulrich, E. O. 1911. Revision of the Paleozoic systems. *Bull. geol. Soc. Am.*, **22**, 281–680.

—— & Bridge, J. 1930. Geology of the Eminence and Cardareva Quadrangles. Gastropoda, Chapter 6, Systematic paleontology. *Missouri Bur. Geol. Mines*, 2nd Ser., 186–227.

Wenz, W. 1940. Die ältesten Stylommatophora des europäischen Raumes. *Arch. Molluskenk*, **72**, 129–144.

Yochelson, E. L. 1956. Permian Gastropoda of the southwestern United States—1. Euomphalacea, Trochonematacea, Pseudophoracea, Anomphalacea, Craspedostomatacea and Platyceratacea. *Bull. Am. Mus. nat. Hist.*, **110**, 173–276.

Zilch, A. 1959–60. *Gastropoda*, Teil 2: *Euthyneura*. Gebrüder Bornträger, Berlin.

D. Curry, M.A. F.G.S.
    Eastbury Grange, Watford Road, Northwood, Middlesex.
N. J. Morris, B.A. F.G.S.
    Department of Palaeontology, British Museum (Natural History), Cromwell Road, London S W 7.

CHAPTER 14

Mollusca: Cephalopoda (Nautiloidea)

Contributor: C. H. HOLLAND

Introduction. The old, zoologically based, arrangement of classification of the cephalopods into two major divisions dependent upon the number of gill pairs has been generally superseded by the use of three equal categories representing the nautiloids, ammonoids and coleoids. Subsequent dissatisfaction with this latter widely used scheme has stemmed particularly from the now probably generally accepted notion that the diversity among the nautiloid cephalopods is such as to make their lumping as one taxon equivalent to the relatively uniform Ammonoidea an evident artificiality. To a lesser extent there has been dissatisfaction on the grounds that the loss of the external shell in the coleoids is so significant as to justify their former separation as a group equivalent to the remainder of the cephalopods. Recent reviews of the problem are provided by Donovan (1964), Flower (1961) and Sweet (*in* Treatise pt K).

The arrangement of two major divisions (Endocochlia and Ectocochlia) for the coleoids and all other cephalopods, respectively, employed in the Russian Osnovy (Ruzhentsev 1962), was not followed in the Treatise on Invertebrate Palaeontology. Sweet (*in* Treatise pt K), like Flower (1961, 1964a), referred to the difficulty that some Palaeozoic nautiloids display coleoid characteristics.

On the other hand, the Treatise classification follows the pattern in the Osnovy of various subdivisions of the nautiloids regarded as equivalent in status to the ammonoids. That this arrangement is premature is suggested by various lines of reasoning. First, it is by no means clear that the ammonoids should be accorded such high taxonomic status. Their stratigraphical importance, the long history of their detailed study in evolutionary palaeontology, and their vast numbers are presumably not in themselves sufficient justification for this. But it may be argued that their very success is the result of some highly appropriate modification (mutation) not recorded in the preserved fossils, but requiring recognition in an ideal phylogenetic classification. Again the proper subdivision of the nautiloid cephalopods themselves is as yet by no means clear. Flower (1964a) mentions the doubts still surrounding the content of the Endoceratoidea and Actinoceratoidea. He also deplores the inclusion of the Discosorida in a sub-class containing all the other coiled nautiloids, when these former seem to have a unique derivation directly from the Plectronoceratina, and not through the Ellesmeroceratina. Donovan (1964) suggests that the ammonoids and the clymeniids respectively may be closer to certain nautiloid groups than some of the latter are to each other. Donovan's own plan appears to involve the separation at sub-class level of the plectronoceratids from the ellesmeroceratids, grouped by Flower (1964a) in one order, the Ellesmeroceratida. Donovan recognizes the ammonoids and coleoids for the present as orders equivalent to the fairly well established nautiloid orders, and eventually to be fitted to a superposed sub-class structure. It seems likely, he suggests, that the coleoids will comprise one such sub-class; but that uncertainty is as yet such that the others cannot usefully

The Fossil Record, pp. 431–443. Geological Society of London, 1967. Printed in Northern Ireland.

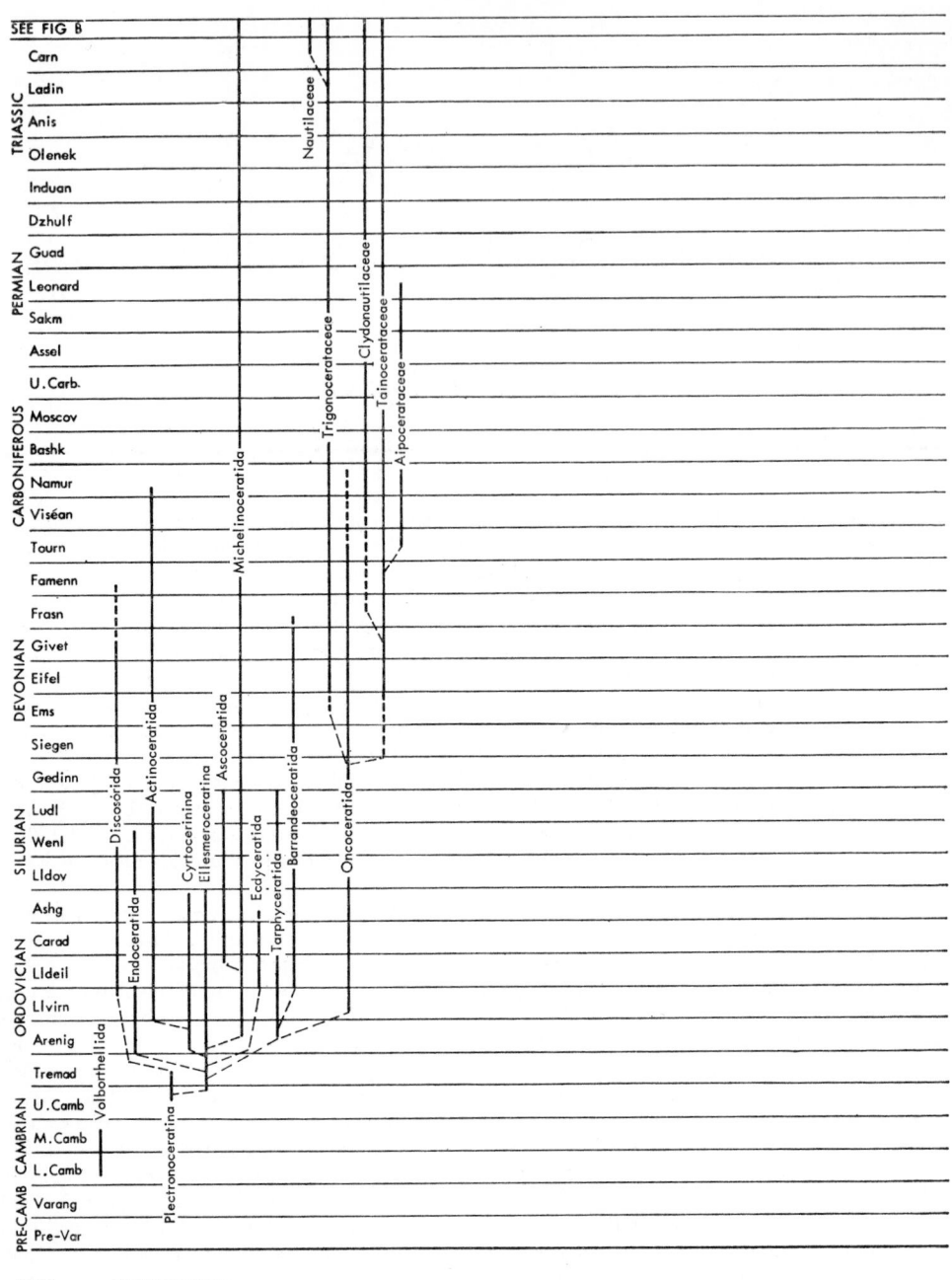

TAXA   NAUTILOIDEA

CONTRIBUTORS   C. H. Holland

FIG. 14.1 A

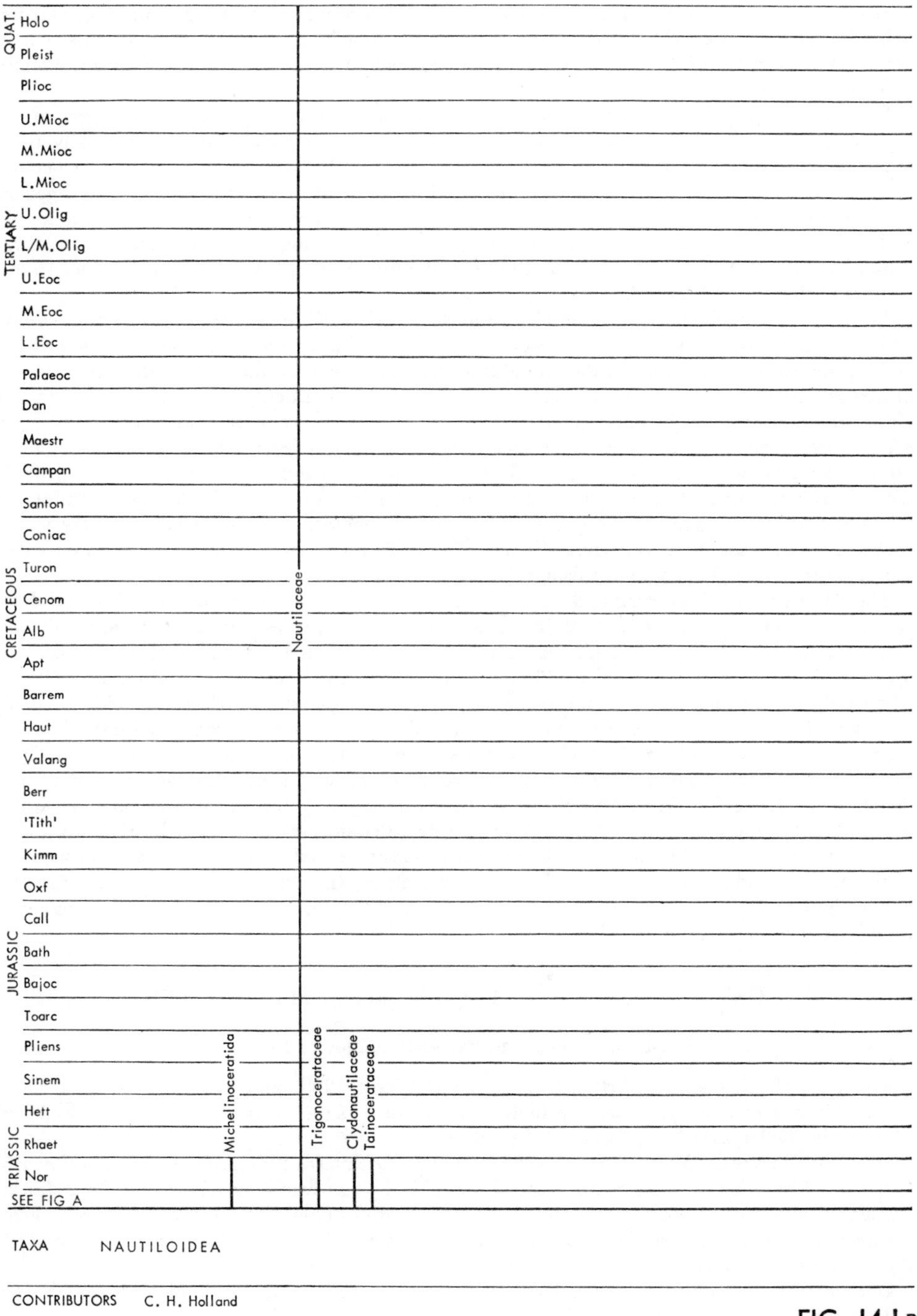

Chapter 14: Mollusca: Cephalopoda (Nautiloidea)

QUAT.	Holo						
	Pleist						
TERTIARY	Plioc						
	U.Mioc						
	M.Mioc						
	L.Mioc						
	U.Olig						
	L/M.Olig						
	U.Eoc						
	M.Eoc						
	L.Eoc						
	Palaeoc						
	Dan						
CRETACEOUS	Maestr						
	Campan						
	Santon						
	Coniac						
	Turon			Nautilaceae				
	Cenom						
	Alb						
	Apt						
	Barrem						
	Haut						
	Valang						
	Berr						
JURASSIC	'Tith'						
	Kimm						
	Oxf						
	Call						
	Bath						
	Bajoc						
	Toarc						
	Pliens		Michelinoceratida	Trigonocerataceae	Clydonautilaceae	Tainocerataceae		
	Sinem						
	Hett						
TRIASSIC	Rhaet						
	Nor						
	SEE FIG A						

TAXA   NAUTILOIDEA

CONTRIBUTORS   C. H. Holland

FIG. 14.1 B

433

be named. However his provisional approach to a sub-class arrangement is a stimulating starting point for further discussion. In the meantime the nautiloids, ammonoids, and coleoids remain useful informal categories, though probably not coincident with, and even tending to obscure, a detailed phylogenetic scheme.

In this chapter documentation is given of orders of nautiloid cephalopods as being of the highest taxa contained within the Class Cephalopoda. The orders used are essentially those of the Treatise with the addition of the Ecdyceratida Flower 1962 and omission of the Intejocerida Balashov 1960. Differences of scope are indicated in the text. The numerous nautiloid genera are in most cases relatively easily grouped into families, but accepted taxa between the family and order are few. Flower (1964a) makes a subdivision of the Ellesmeroceratida into three sub-orders, which are accepted here. Similarly Kummel (*in* Treatise pt K) provides super-families of the Order Nautilida.

There remains the question of the Cambrian forms *Volborthella*, *Vologdinella*, and *Salterella*, of which the first two are assigned to the Order Volborthellida in Osnovy. Teichert (*in* Treatise pt K) provides a short review of these doubtful forms and includes them all in this order, which he regards as a taxon 'doubtfully classifiable' within the nautiloids. Flower (1954) discusses *Volborthella* and *Salterella* in some detail and concludes that they cannot confidently be assigned even to the Cephalopoda. This wide spectrum of opinion reflects a long discussion of these rather poorly known genera, to which references are given in the works already mentioned. It is considered here that at the very most they should be assigned to a sub-class of the Cephalopoda different from those including the nautiloids and ammonoids, and equivalent in status to the coleoids. In the absence as yet, as mentioned, of a satisfactory sub-class structure they are treated as a separate order at the end of this chapter.

The Bactritida are here excluded from the nautiloid cephalopods on the grounds detailed by Erben (*in* Treatise pt K) i.e. that they are poised indeterminately between the nautiloids and ammonoids, but in the light of diagnostic requirements should be placed with the latter. An opposite view has been presented by Flower (1961, 1962b) and by Flower and Gordon (1959), who would regard these forms as not being involved in the ancestry of the ammonoids. Erben's evidence of a phylogenetic succession from bactritids to ammonoids remains impressive. In spite of their diametrically opposed views on the systematic position of the bactritids these authors would agree that the taxonomic status of the group is relatively low. However, according to a footnote by Moore (*in* Treatise pt K, p. K491) Erben agreed to a promotion from sub-order status to that of the Order Bactritida. Subsequently a decision (presumably editorial) was made to recognize the Bactritoidea as one of the sub-classes of the Cephalopoda. Even if an arrangement of the Cephalopoda into sub-classes were not premature, the creation of such a high-ranking buffer division at the already scarcely sensible boundary between the nautiloids and ammonoids would appear to be taxonomically unsound.

Order ELLESMEROCERATIDA Flower in Flower and Kummel 1950

Suborder PLECTRONOCERATINA Flower 1964

First, Camb U. Camb: *Plectronoceras cambria* (Walcott 1905) and *P. liaotungense* Kobayashi 1935, Tsinania canens Z. (probably high Franconian), former China (Shantung) and latter Manchuria (Kobayashi 1935, Flower 1954, 1964a).

Last, Ord Tremad: *Multicameroceras multicameratum* (Kobayashi 1931), *M. cylindricum* Kobayashi 1933, and *Sinoeremoceras wanwanense* (Kobayashi 1931), Wan-wan-kow Limestone, Manchuria. *Wanwanoceras peculiare* from the same horizon is of doubtful taxonomic position. *Multicameroceras siberiense*, Ord (L.), is recorded from the River Chunya, Kuznetsk, Siberia. (Flower 1954, 1964a, Balashov 1959.)

Comment: neglecting *Salterella*, *Volborthella*, and *Vologdinella* as nautiloid cephalopods (see p. 431), the Plectronoceratina comprise the root stock of the nautiloids and hence the Cephalopoda. Origin unknown. Very rare: U. Camb China and U.S.A., Ord Tremad Manchuria and Siberia. Flower (1964a) gives 2 families and 7 genera.

Chapter 14: Mollusca: Cephalopoda (Nautiloidea)

Suborder ELLESMEROCERATINA Flower 1964

First, Camb U.Camb: *Ectenolites primus* Flower 1964, cephalopod bed in San Saba Lst (Trempealeauan), central Texas, represented by single specimen and one other recorded as *E.*sp. aff. *primus* (Flower 1964a). *Ruthenoceras* Korde 1949 is an inadequately known ellesmeroceratid from Siberia, whose supposed U. Camb horizon has been questioned (Flower 1954, 1964a, Furnish & Glenister *in* Treatise pt K).

Last, Ord Ashg: *Shideleroceras sinuatum* Flower 1946 and *S. simplex* Flower 1946, cephalopod bed, L. Whitewater Fm, Cincinnati arch; *S. gracile* Flower 1946, Saluda Formation, Cincinnati arch. All upper Richmond. *Shideleroceras* is isolated morphologically and stratigraphically from the remaining Ellesmeroceratina and Flower (1964a) implies reservation in his assignment of the genus. Otherwise last records are Ord Carad: *Cartersoceras noveboracensis* (Flower 1952), Amsterdam Lst, New York; *C.* cf. *ottawaense* (Billings *vide* Wilson 1961), Leray-Rockland Beds, Quebec; and *C. shideleri* Flower 1964, Carters Lst, Tennesse. The first two are represented by single fragments and the third by several fragments (Flower 1964a).

Comment: Origin from Plectronoceratina (Flower 1964a). A diverse group of early nautiloids giving rise either directly or indirectly to all other orders except the Discosorida. Isolated U. Camb occurrence as above. Widespread and common in early Ord (Tremad-Arenig), N. America, China, Siberia, Australia, and Scandinavia. Subsequent rapid decline. Flower (1964a) gives 6 families and 61 genera.

Suborder CYRTOCERININA Flower 1964

First, Ord Arenig: *Eothinoceras americanum* Ulrich, Foerste, Miller, and Unklesbay 1944, Rochdale Lst, New York; *E. maitlandicum* Teichert and Glenister 1954, Emanuel Lst, Kimberley Division, Western Australia; and *E. marchense* Balashov 1960, 'Chun' Stage, Siberian Platform (Flower 1964a).

Last, Ord Ashg: *Cyrtocerina madisonensis* (Miller 1894), *C. patella* Flower 1943, and *C. modesta* Flower 1943, Hitz Bed, U. Whitewater, Madison, Indiana. *C.* (?) *carinifera* Flower 1946, Saluda beds, near Oxford, Ohio is represented by one specimen only, but Flower has little doubt of the validity of the assignment. (Flower 1964a.)

Comment: Three genera only placed by Flower (1964a) in three families and showing a discontinuous stratigraphical and geographical distribution in Europe, N. America, Australia, and Siberia.

Order DISCOSORIDA Flower in Flower and Kummel 1950

First, Ord Llvirn/Lldeil: *Ruedemannoceras boycii* (Whitfield 1886) and *Franklinoceras elongatum* Flower in Flower and Teichert 1957, Crown Point Lst, Champlain Valley, New York (Flower *in* Flower & Teichert 1957). One small fragment of *Ruedemannoceras* or an allied undescribed genus recorded from beds of probable Whiterock age (Flower 1964a). This "possible but too fragmentary form" here regarded as doubtful early Llvirn record. *Madiganella* (several species) Ord, Australia, probably derived from *Ruedemannoceras* and probably post-Lldeil (Flower & Teichert 1957).

Last, Dev Givet: *Alpenoceras ulrichi* Foerste 1927, Alpena Lst, Michigan and *A. eifelense* (Schindewolf 1942), Stringocephalus Lst, Sötenich, Eifel, Germany. *Alpenoceras? robustum* (Schindewolf 1942) is inadequately known from two specimens, Dev Famenn, Kellerwald, Germany, though an assignment to a larger species of *Alpenoceras* is likely. (Flower *in* Flower & Teichert 1957.)

Comment: Origin from Plectronoceratina and taxonomically isolated as the only order thus directly derived (Flower & Teichert 1957, Flower 1964a, Teichert *in* Treatise pt K). Rare. Early Ord genera N. America boreal, later Ord, N. America, Europe, Australia, Sil N. America, Europe. No L. Dev. Few M. Dev, N. America, Germany. Flower and Teichert (1957) list 8 families and 42 genera. Teichert (*in* Treatise pt K) gives 7 to 9 families and 46 genera.

Order ENDOCERATIDA Flower in Flower and Kummel 1950

First, Ord Arenig: *Proendoceras* Flower 1955, Lecanospira beds, eastern N. America (approximately Roubidoux age). Also, Flower (1964a) records "a host of straight endoceroid siphuncles,

435

probably *Proendoceras*" from the first endoceroid zone, El Paso Lst, Texas, again approximately basal M. Canadian and approximately basal Arenig. In addition to its stratigraphical position, *Proendoceras* has morphological and evolutionary characters appropriate to an ancestral form. (Flower 1955a, 1958, 1964a.) Stumbur (1962) records *Endoceras*, B_1 (Leetse) Stage (basal Arenig), Estonia, but the genus *Endoceras* Hall 1847 is poorly known and no illustration is provided here.

Last, Sil Wenl: *Humeoceras* Foerste 1925, Lockport Dolomite, Lake Timiskaming area, Ontaria, Canada, represented by three specimens only (Foerste 1925a). According to Flower (1964a) this belongs to the Piloceratidae, otherwise unknown post-Arenig. Because of the long time interval, Teichert (*in* Treatise pt K) regards the resemblance as homoemorphic and assigns the genus to a separate family. He also refers to a few Silurian specimens from the Endoceratida at several localities in northern Canada, but "none of them has been well described and all records are in need of further scrutiny".

Comment: Common in early Ordovician of Australia, E. Asia, Siberia, and eastern N. America. M. Ord all continents except Africa. Slight and partially doubtful N. American Sil. Flower (1958) erects two suborders and subsequently (1964a) presents evidence modifying their ranges: Protocameroceratina (Arenig-Lldeil) and Endoceratina (Arenig-Ashg-M. Sil), but Teichert (*in* Treatise pt K) finds this subdivision "probably taxonomically sound" but "difficult to implement in practice, and many genera cannot be assigned with certainty to either suborder". Balashov (1960) recognizes the suborder Intejoceratina. Flower (1964a) gives range equivalent to Arenig-Llvirn, but precise relationships of the group are not established.

Teichert (*in* Treatise pt K) lists 12–14 families and 63 genera within the Endoceratida.

Order ACTINOCERATIDA Flower in Flower and Kummel 1950

First, Ord Llvirn: *Polydesma* Lorenz 1906; Maruyama bed, Shantung and Korea; Ssuyen Lst, near Niu-hsin-tai, Manchuria (Flower 1957, Teichert *in* Treatise pt K). Teichert regards *Ormoceras* Stokes 1840 as derived, but an Estonian record, B_{iii} Stage (Kunda), is also Ord Llvirn (*Didymograptus bifidus* Z.) and cannot be separated stratigraphically (Stumbur 1962).

Last, Carb Namur: *Rayonnoceras* Croneis 1926; Mississippian/Pennsylvanian, Arkansas, California, Colorado, Indiana, Oklahoma and Texas (Gordon 1964a, 1964b; Flower 1943; Miller, Dunbar, and Condra 1933; etc.); L. Carboniferous (? Namur), Moscow Basin (Shimansky 1961b); Namur (E_2 Z.), Scotland (Turner 1951); and other N. American and European occurrences.

Comment: Origin from *Bathmoceras* of the Cyrtocerinina according to Flower (1957), but unknown according to Teichert (*in* Treatise pt K). Origin in American arctic and hence to circumpolar distribution. Abundant in Ord, Greenland, N. America, and E. Asia. Also Ord, Tasmania. Sil, N. America, Europe, and Siberia. Rare in Dev, N. America. Carb, N. America and Europe (Foerste & Teichert 1930, Teichert *in* Treatise pt K). Teichert (in Treatise) gives 7 families and 35 genera.

Order MICHELINOCERATIDA Flower in Flower and Kummel 1950

First, Ord Arenig: *Michelinoceras primum* Flower 1962, low in Cassinian portion of El Paso Fm, El Paso, Texas (Flower 1962b). Chinese occurrences recorded by Lai (1965) of *Palaeocycloceras*, Shihlianssu Sh, Shensi and of several species of *Michelinoceras* from the equivalent upper part of Dawan Fm, W. Hupeh are said to be upper Arenig and lower Llvirn on graptolite evidence and (by implication) Llvirn on cephalopod evidence. They are therefore probably to be regarded as stratigraphically slightly higher.

Last, Trias Nor: "*Orthoceras*" spp., Tethyan region e.g. "Zone of Trachyceras archelaus", Italian Alps (Mojsisovics 1882); Halorites Lst, Himalayas (Mojsisovics 1899); and "Karnisch-Norische Trias", Timor (Bülow 1915). Several species are recorded from the Alps and Timor, but the Himalayan records are said to be of rare fragmental material capable only of "generic" assignment.

Until modern studies of Trias material have been made it is not possible to improve upon the broad designation of "*Orthoceras*". Sweet (*in* Treatise pt K) employs *Michelinoceras* s.l. for such forms. He replaces the restricted genus *Orthoceros* by *Orthoceras* in apparent anticipation of action by the International Commission of Zoological Nomenclature to suppress the former in answer to an application by Melville (1959). This anticipation seems to be unjustified and a sound case has been made by Flower (1962b) for a different procedure. The latter attempts to refine the genus *Michelinoceras* for a group of species whose internal as well as external characters are becoming increasingly known, while leaving the name *Orthoceras* (admittedly invalid) as a convenient general designation for those orthocones whose internal structures remain unknown, and may, in some cases, always so remain. To quote Flower "As the genus [*Orthoceras*] is not properly used for cephalopods, but will not be used properly for anything else either (no student intends to use it for a rudistid); the retention of this old designation will at least indicate that the species is inadequately known." An even safer procedure may be to use *Orthoceras* in inverted commas as has been done above.

Finally it should be noted that the change in the Treatise from the Order Michelinoceratida of Flower, in Flower and Kummel 1950, to Orthoceratida, though it follows the Russian practice, appears to imply the same unwarranted assumption that Melville's application will be accepted.

Comment: World wide in distribution. Abundant in Lower Palaeozoic and Devonian, less so in Carboniferous to Trias, though individuals may be numerous in places. The large order of "generalized" orthocones described by Flower (1962b) as "perhaps the greatest remaining unexplored wilderness in the Cephalopoda".

Order ASCOCERATIDA Flower in Flower and Kummel 1950

First, Ord Lldeil: *Montyoceras* Flower 1941 and *Hebetoceras* Flower 1941, Valcour Lst, Champlain Valley, New York (Flower 1941, 1963). Furnish & Glenister (*in* Treatise pt K) regard these genera as of uncertain morphology and uncertain ascocerid affinities, yet include them under this order "for convenience". Flower (1963) describes an additional genus *Redpathoceras*, based upon a single specimen from the Black River (Carad), Quebec, which provides an intermediate form between *Montyoceras* or *Hebetoceras* and the late Trenton (later Carad) *Probillingsites* Foerste 1928, which last, according to Furnish and Glenister, "conforms in every respect to the concept of a primitive ascocerid".

Last, Sil Ludl: *Ascoceras* Barrande 1847, "Stage e2" (Budňanian) of Bohemia and Whitcliffian of the Welsh Borderland. The Budňanian is equivalent to the whole of the Ludlovian in the sense used in this volume, and thus it remains uncertain whether there may be Bohemian occurrences slightly later than the British ones. Also: *Aphragmites* Barrande 1865 and *Glossoceras* Barrande 1865, both "Stage e2" of Bohemia. (Miller 1932, Blake 1882).

Ascoceras, Glossoceras, Choanoceras Lindstrom 1890, and *Parascoceras* Miller 1932 are all known from Lindström's "Stratum h" (Wenl to Ludl), Gotland and one species at least—*Ascoceras* cf *gradatum* Lindström—is recorded from the Sundre Lst, which is the highest Sil of the island (probably middle Ludl). (Lindström 1890, Miller 1932, Hede 1921). N. American species of *Ascoceras* are probably confined to Wenl (Miller 1932).

Comment: Origin probably from *Clinoceras* of the Michelinoceratida according to Flower (1963). Schindewolf (1942) agrees on origin from this order but rejects the Hebetoceratidae (originally containing *Montyoceras, Hebetoceras,* and *Ecdyceras*) as the first group of ascocerids because they resemble the Michelinoceratida so strongly. Flower replies "If primitive members of the Ascoceratida are not expected to resemble their ancestors, it is not clear what we should expect them to look like."

Rare in Ord and Sil, N. America. European Sil, particularly Ludl of Gotland and Bohemia, provides richest faunas. Furnish & Glenister (*in* Treatise pt K) give 3 families and 13 genera.

Order ECDYCERATIDA Flower 1962

First, Ord Llvirn/Lldeil: *Ecdyceras sinuiferum* Flower 1941, U. Crown Point and L. Valcour lsts, S.W. of Chazy, New York (Flower 1962a).

Last, Ord Carad/Ashg: *Ecdyceras foerstei* Flower 1962, one specimen only from Arnheim Beds, Labanon, Kentucky (Flower 1962a).

Comment: Apart from the above, this anomalous genus occurs only in the Viola Lst (Ord Carad), Oklahoma. Flower (1962a) suggests likely derivation from Ellesmeroceratida. Its morphology appears to justify Flower's assignment to a separate order, though Furnish and Glenister (*in* Treatise pt K) include it in the Ascoceratida.

Order TARPHYCERATIDA Flower in Flower and Kummel 1950

First, Ord Arenig: *Tarphyceras* Hyatt 1894 and at least twenty five other genera of the families Tarphyceratidae, Estonioceratidae, Trocholitidae, and Lituitidae; widespread in Upper Canadian of N. America and to a lesser extent U. Canadian of Australia and Arenig of Baltic-Scandinavian region (Furnish & Glenister *in* Treatise pt K).

This implies exclusion of the Bassleroceratidae from the Tarphyceratida as in Treatise and Osnovy (Ruzhentsev 1962). Flower (1964a) sees some justification for this but finds, nevertheless, that "definitions are simplified" by the retention of the Bassleroceratidae in the Tarphyceratida. If this latter course were followed the first records of the latter would be earlier: Ord Tremad: *Anguloceras* Unklesbay and Young 1956, Chepultepec-Stonehenge (L. Canadian), Virginia (Unklesbay & Young 1956). *Bassleroceras* Ulrich and Foerste 1936 and *Dyscritoceras* Ulrich and Foerste 1936 are both recorded from limestone boulders, believed to be of Upper Ozarkian age, in the Levis Sh, Quebec. These therefore possibly constitute further L. Canadian (Tremad/Arenig) occurrences of the family (Ulrich, Foerste, Miller & Unklesbay 1944).

Last, Sil Ludl: *Ophioceras* Barrande 1865, Ludl, Europe (Furnish & Glenister *in* Treatise pt K). Two of Barrande's species are present in "Stage e2" (Budňanian), Bohemia (Barrande 1865, 1867). The Budňanian extends from the Monograptus vulgaris Z. to the base of the M. uniformis Zone (i.e. to the top of the Silurian as taken in the present volume). Tarphyceratida are said to be present in the "Upper Ludlow" of Podolia, U.S.S.R. (Astrova & Zhuravleva 1959). According to Blake (1882) British species do not occur above the "Lower Ludlow". In Gotland Lindström (1890) records two species both of which appear to be represented in the highest beds in the south east of the island. Hede (1960) regards the highest Silurian of Gotland as probably middle Ludl. Martinsson (1964) states that "we do not know how far above the *Pristograptus nilssoni* zone the Silurian sequence of Gotland reaches".

Comment: Representatives of the Tarphyceratida, comparatively rare though widespread in the lower part of Ord, become rarer still higher in that system, and remain so in Sil.

Furnish and Glenister give 5 families and 38 genera (*in* Treatise).

Order BARRANDEOCERATIDA Flower in Flower and Kummel 1950

First, Ord Llvirn/Lldeil: *Avilionella multicameratum* (Ruedemann 1906), middle Chazyan, Champlain Valley, New York; *Barrandeoceras natator* (Billings 1859), Chazy Lst, New York and Canada; and *Plectroceras jason* (Billings 1859), Chazy Lst, New York and Canada. In the case of the first genus at least, other undescribed species are involved. (Hyatt 1884, Ruedemann 1906, Flower 1952a). All three genera appear to be confined to N. America except that *Plectroceras* reaches Greenland in Ord Carad (Troedesson 1926).

Last, Dev Givet/Frasn: *Baeopleuroceras* Williams in Cooper and Williams 1935, Tully Lst, New York and Pennsylvania; *Triploceras* Hyatt 1884, Tully Limestone (Flower 1945). The M. or U. Devonian age of the Tully remains uncertain but House (1962, 1965) considers that Frasn may be the correct assignment.

Comment: Origin from Tarphyceratida (Sweet *in* Treatise pt K, Flower 1964a). Barrandeoceratida are rare and largely from N. America, though there are European and Australian occurrences.

Sweet (*in* Treatise) gives 6 families and 37 genera.

Order ONCOCERATIDA Flower in Flower and Kummel 1950

First, Ord Llvirn: four families, Graciloceratidae, Oncoceratidae, Tripteroceratidae, and Valcouroceratidae "appear simultaneously in early M. Ord rocks in N. America, and a few representatives of the latter three families are known from virtually contemporaneous strata in northern Europe" (Sweet *in* Treatise pt K). To these should perhaps be added the Diestoceratidae, though there is no evidence of close connection with other members of the Oncoceratida and the assignment is made only upon the presence of their actinosiphonate deposits. On the other hand the Diestoceratidae do show some affinities with the Discosorida, where they may eventually be placed. (Flower & Teichert 1957; Flower 1964a, 1964b). Flower (1964a) shows all four families as appearing at the base of the "Chazyan".

Last, Carb Tourn/Namur: *Antonoceras* Shimansky 1957, L. Carb, U.S.S.R.; *Argochilus* Shimansky 1961a, L. Carb, China; *Poterioceras* McCoy 1844, L. Carb, Western Europe and U.S.S.R., Mississippian, N. America (Northview Sst, Kinderhookian, Missouri and Redwall Lst, Kinderhookian-Osagean, Arizona); *Psiaoceras* Shimansky 1957, L. Carb, Russian Platform. (Shimansky 1957b, 1961a; Miller & Furnish 1938; Miller, Downs, & Youngquist 1949).

Comment: Origin from Basslerocerated of the Ellesmeroceratida (or possibly Tarphycera- tida, see p. 438) (Flower 1964a, Sweet *in* Treatise pt K). Oncoceratida become more abundant in Sil and Dev and are known also from Australia and Asia. They are much rarer in the L. Carb. Sweet (*in* Treatise pt K) gives 16 families and 143 genera.

<h3 style="text-align:center">Order NAUTILIDA Agassiz 1847</h3>

<h3 style="text-align:center">Superfamily TAINOCERATACEAE Hyatt 1883</h3>

First, Dev Siegen/Ems: *Ptenoceras* Hyatt 1894 and *Trochoceras* Barrande in von Hauer 1848, Upper Koněprusy Lst, Pragian, Bohemia (Hyatt 1894, Foerste 1926, Chlupáč 1955). Evidence from various sources now suggests that the Lochkovian of Bohemia extends into Siegen (Holland 1965), hence the Pragian must begin in the Siegen and not the Gedinn as previously supposed. *Trochoceras* is also recorded from the L. Dev, Turkestan, Asiatic Russia (Balashov 1959). *Rous-sanoffoceras* Foerste 1925 was originally described from strata of uncertain L. Dev age in Novaya Zemlya (Foerste 1925b). The first and last of the three genera appear to have reached N. America in Dev Eifel (Onondaga Limestone, New York) (Flower 1945).

Last, Trias Nor: *Enoploceras ausseeanus* Diener 1919 and *E. lepsiusiformis* Diener 1919, "Karnisch-Norische misch-fauna", Hallstätter Kalke, Eastern Alps; *E. lepsiusi* Mojsisovics 1902, "Karnisch-Norische misch-fauna", Hallstätter Kalke, Eastern Alps and Norian, Timor; *Phloioceras welteri* Kieslinger 1924, Nor, Timor; and *Germanonautilus kyotanii* Nakazawa 1959, Nariwa Group, Okayama Prefecture, Japan. (Kummel 1953a, Nakazawa 1959, Diener 1919, Kieslinger 1924).

Comment: Flower & Kummel (1950) allowed derivation from coiled Sil Barrandeoceratida, but with no real evidence. More recently Flower (1952b, 1955b, 1964a, 1964b) has suggested an origin in the Oncoceratida and is supported by Kummel (*in* Treatise pt K).

Kummel (*in* Treatise) gives 5 families and 64 genera.

<h3 style="text-align:center">Superfamily TRIGONOCERATACEAE Hyatt 1884</h3>

First, Dev Eifel (? Ems): *Centroceras* Hyatt 1884, M. Dev, N. America and Germany. Earliest records are of undescribed species from Pine Point Lst, Great Slave Lake region, Canada; Columbus Lst, Ohio; and Jeffersonville Lst, Indiana (Flower 1952b, 1945). House (1962) suggests that the goniatites of the Columbus Lst imply an Eifel age rather than the uppermost Ems assignment of Cooper *et al.* (1942). The Jeffersonville Lst is the equivalent of the Onondaga Lst of New York, which according to House (1962) contains some Eifel goniatites. However, its age remains in doubt and the alternative Ems (L. Dev) assignment would make the Jefferson-ville species the earliest *Centroceras*. *C. marcellensis* (Vanuxem 1842), the type species, is from the Cherry Valley Lst, New York, which House (1962) regards as Givet. The German *C. tetragonum* (D'Archiac and de Verneuil 1842) is probably also Givet (Flower 1952b).

Last, Trias Nor: Grypoceratidae: *Grypoceras* Hyatt 1883 and *Gryponautilus* Mojsisovics 1902; Syringonautilidae: *Syringonautilus* Mojsisovics 1902, *Clymenonautilus* Hyatt in Zittel 1900, *Juvavio-nautilus* Mojsisovics 1902, *Oxynautilus* Mojsisovics 1902, and *Syringoceras* Hyatt 1894. Nor records particularly from Alps, but also Timor and California (Kummel 1953a). Relative levels of extinction within Nor unknown (Kummel 1953b).

Comment: Kummel lists 5 families and 42 genera (*in* Treatise pt K).

Superfamily AIPOCERATACEAE Hyatt 1883

First, Carb Tourn: *Aipoceras* Hyatt 1884; Tourn, Belgium (De Koninck 1880); Tourn, Ireland (Foord 1900); Chouteau Lst, Kinderhookian, Missouri and New York (Miller and Furnish 1938); and *Aipoceras*?, Rockford Lst, Kinderhookian, N. Indiana (Gutschick & Treckman 1957). Also *Asymptoceras* Ryckholt 1852; Tourn, Ireland (Foord 1900).

Last, Perm Leonard: *Scyphoceras dionysi*, *S. ellipticum*, and *S. angulatum* Ruzhentsev and Shimansky 1954, Artinskian, South Urals; *Dentoceras latum* Ruzhentsev and Shimansky 1954, Artinskian, South Urals; *Mariceras ferum* Ruzhentsev and Shimansky 1954, Artinskian, South Urals; and *Mariceras* sp., Leonard, Arizonia (see Furnish & Glenister *in* Treatise pt K); *Solenochilus kempae* Miller and Youngquist 1949, lower portion of Lueders Fm, Texas and *Solenochilus* sp., Artinskian, Urals. Other species of *Solenochilus* are present at uncertain Perm horizons in Texas and Kansas. Ruzhentsev & Shimansky 1954, Miller & Youngquist 1949).

Chao (1954) records *Solenochilus*? *auriculus* sp. nov. from the higher part of the Yangsinian of Tanchiashan, Hunan, China. This is said to be probably equivalent to the Maokou Lst (Perm Guad), S.W. China. The siphuncle of this species is not known and the assignment to the genus is tentative. If confirmed this would constitute a record later than those given above.

Comment: Origin probably from Rutoceratidae of the Tainocerataceae according to Kummel (*in* Treatise pt K). Shimansky (1957a) implies the same, though the arrangement of his classification is different. The smallest superfamily of the Nautilida, the Aipocerataceae are rare and poorly known. Kummel (*in* Treatise pt K) gives 3 families and 9 genera only.

Superfamily CLYDONAUTILACEAE Hyatt in Zittel 1900

First, Dev Frasn or Carb Viséan?: *Potoceras dubium* Hyatt 1894. Hyatt suggested the type specimen to be Dev and Schuchert considered an attached brachiopod to be closely comparable with a species from the Iberger Kalk, Dev Frasn, Germany. This type and only specimen was illustrated for the first time and redescribed by Kummel (1963). He submitted the brachiopod to G. A. Cooper who "could not make a positive identification but thought that some Mississippian forms from U.S.A. are more similar to it than any Dev forms. He also adds that the lithology is suggestive of the Viséan". Kummel (*in* Treatise pt K) notes that the specimen is thought probably to have come from the Iberger Kalk or possibly from the Viséan of Belgium. If a Viséan assignment is correct it becomes difficult or impossible to relate the age of *Potoceras* to Viséan, "Lower Carboniferous", or "Mississippian" records of *Liroceras* Teichert 1940, *Bistrialites* Turner 1954, *Peripetoceras* Hyatt 1894 and *Ephippioceras* Hyatt 1884.

Last, Trias Nor: Clydonautilidae: *Clydonautilus* Mojsisovics 1882, *Callaionautilus* Kieslinger 1924, *Cosmonautilus* Hyatt and Smith 1905, *Proclydonautilus* Mojsisovics 1902, and *Styrionautilus* Mojsisovics 1902. Liroceratidae: *Indonautilus* Mojsisovics 1902, *Paranautilus* Mojsisovics 1902, and *Sibyllonautilus* Diener 1915. Gonionautilidae: *Gonionautilus* Mojsisovics 1902. Nor records particularly from Alps, Himalayas, and Timor. Also West N. America. (Kummel 1953a). Relative levels of extinction within Nor unknown (Kummel 1953b).

Comment: Origin unknown (Kummel in Treatise pt K), or possibly from Rutoceratidae of the Tainocerataceae (Shimansky 1957a and see Treatise pt K, fig. 281, p. K 387). Kummel (*in* Treatise) gives 5 families and 21 genera.

Superfamily NAUTILACEAE de Blainville 1825

First, Trias Carn: *Cenoceras trechmanni* Kummel 1953, Carn bed c, Otamita Stream, Hokonui Hills, New Zealand (Kummel 1953b and *in* Treatise pt K).

Extant: five species of *Nautilus* restricted to S.W. Pacific (Stenzel *in* Treatise pt K).

Comment: Origin from Syringonautilidae of the Trigonocerataceae. Near extinction of nautiloids at close of Trias. No Rhaet records. From single surviving genus *Cenoceras* came new radiation in Jur. Early Jur fauna is homogeneous and of nearly world wide distribution. Subsequent diversification in later Jur, Cret, and early Tert with decline in mid-Tert (Kummel 1953b and *in* Treatise pt K). Kummel (*in* Treatise) gives 6 families and 29 genera.

Chapter 14: Mollusca: Cephalopoda (Nautiloidea)

Order VOLBORTHELLIDA Kobayashi 1937

First, Camb L. Camb: *Volborthella* Schmidt 1888, L. Camb, U.S.S.R., Norway, Sweden, Poland, Canada, and Australia; *Salterella* Billings 1861, L. Camb, N. America, Greenland, Scotland, and Asia (Prantl 1948, Teichert *in* Treatise pt K).

Last, Camb M. Camb: *Volborthella* Schmidt 1888, M. Camb, Bohemia (Paradoxides Shs, Skryje), and Poland; *Vologdinella* Balashov 1962, M. Camb, Chinghiz, Kazakhstan, U.S.S.R. (Prantl 1948, Balashov *in* Ruzhentsev 1962, Teichert *in* Treatise pt K).

Comments: See Introduction p. 431.

REFERENCES

ASTROVA, G. G. & ZHURAVLEVA, F. A. 1959. [Discovery of bryozoans and nautiloids in the Ordovician and Silurian of Podoly.] *Paleont. Zh.* 1959, **4,** 154–6.

BALASHOV, Z. G. 1959. [Some new nautiloid species of the Ordovician, Silurian, and Devonian of the S.S.S.R.] *Materialui k "Osnovam Paleontologhii"*, 3, 37–46.

—— 1960. [New Ordovician nautiloids of the S.S.S.R.] *Ministerstva Geol. and Okhrany Nedr S.S.S.R., Novye Vidy Drevnikh Rasteniy i Bespozvonochnyk S.S.S.R.*, 2, 123–36.

BARRANDE, J. 1865–77. *Système silurien du centre de la Bohême*, 2. Prague.

BLAKE, J. F. 1882. *A monograph of British fossil Cephalopoda Pt. 1, Introduction and Silurian species.* London.

BÜLOW, E. v. 1915. Orthoceren und belemnitiden der Trias von Timor. *Paläontologie von Timor*, Lief. 4, Abh. 7, 1–72. Stuttgart.

CHAO, K. K. 1954. Permian cephalopods from Tanchiashan, Hunan. *Acta palaeont. sin.*, **2,** 1–58.

CHLUPÁČ, I. 1955. Stratigraphical study of the oldest Devonian beds of the Barrandian. *Sborn. ústřed. Úst. geol.*, **21,** 91–134.

COOPER, G. A. et al. 1942. Correlation of the Devonian sedimentary formations of North America. *Bull geol. Soc. Am.*, **53,** 1729–94.

DIENER, C. 1919. Nachträge sur Kenntnis der Nautiloideenfauna der Hallstätter Kalke. *Denkschr. Akad. Wiss. Wien*, **96,** 751–78.

DONOVAN, D. T. 1964. Cephalopod phylogeny and classification. *Biol. Rev.*, **39,** 259–87.

FLOWER, R. H. 1941. Development of the Mixochoanites. *J. Paleont.*, **15,** 523–48.

—— 1943. Studies of Palaeozoic nautiloids. I. Tissue remnants in the phragmocone of *Rayonnoceras. Bull. Am. paleont.*, **28,** (109), 1–13.

—— 1945. Classification of Devonian nautiloids. *Am. Midl. Nat.*, **33,** 675–724.

—— 1952a. New Ordovician cephalopods from Eastern North America. *J. Paleont.*, **26,** 24–59.

—— 1952b. The ontogeny of *Centroceras*, with remarks on the phylogeny of the Centroceratidae. *J. Paleont.*, **26,** 519–28.

—— 1954. Cambrian cephalopods. *Bull. New Mex. St. Bur. Mines*, **40,** 1–51.

—— 1955a. Status of Endoceroid classification. *J. Paleont.*, **29,** 329–71.

—— 1955b. Saltations in nautiloid coiling. *Evolution, Lancaster, Pa.*, **9,** 244–60.

—— 1957. Studies of the Actinoceratida. *Mem. Inst. Min. Technol. New Mex.*, **2,** 1–100.

—— 1958. Some Chazyan and Mohawkian Endoceratida. *J. Paleont.*, **32,** 433–58.

—— 1961. Major divisions of the Cephalopoda. *J. Paleont.*, **35,** 569–74.

—— 1962a. The pharagmocone of *Ecdyceras. Mem. Inst. Min. Technol. New Mex.*, **9,** 1–29.

—— 1962b. Part 1, Revision of *Buttsoceras;* Part 2, Notes on the Michelinoceratida. *Mem. Inst. Min. Technol. New Mex.*, **10,** 1–58.

—— 1963. New Ordovician Ascoceratida. *J. Paleont.*, **37,** 69–85.

—— 1964a. The nautiloid order Ellesmeroceratida (Cephalopoda). *Mem. Inst. Min. Technol. New Mex.*, **12,** 1–234.

—— 1964b. Nautiloid shell morphology. *Mem. Inst. Min. Technol. New Mex.*, **13,** 1–79.

—— & GORDON, M. 1959. More Mississippian belemnites. *J. Paleont.*, **33,** 809–42.

—— & KUMMEL, B. 1950. A classification of the Nautiloidea. *J. Paleont.*, **24,** 604–616.

—— & TEICHERT, C. 1957. The cephalopod order Discosorida. *Paleont. Contrib. Univ. Kans.*, **6,** 1–144.

FOERSTE, A. F. 1925a. Cephalopoda of Lake Timiskaming area and certain related species. *Mem. geol. Surv. Can.*, **145**, 64–93.

—— 1925b. Cephalopods from Nesnayemi and Sulmeneva Fjords in Novaya Zemlya. *Rep scient. Results Norw. Exped Nova Zemlya*, **31**, 1–38.

—— 1926. Actinosiphonate, trochoceroid, and other cephalopods. *J. scient. Labs Denison Univ.*, **21**, 285–384.

—— & TEICHERT, C. 1930. The actinoceroids of East-Central North America. *J. scient. Labs Denison Univ.*, **25**, 201–96.

FOORD, A. H. 1897–1903. Monograph of the Carboniferous Caphalopoda of Ireland. *Palaeontogr. Soc. [Monogr.]*, 1–234.

GORDON, M. 1964a. Carboniferous cephalopods of Arkansas. *Prof. Pap. U.S. geol. Surv.*, **460**, 1–322.

—— 1964b. California Carboniferous cephalopods. *Prof. Pap. U.S. geol. Surv.*, **483A**, 1–25.

GUTSCHICK, R. C. & TRECKMAN, J. F. 1957. Lower Mississippian cephalopods from the Rockford Limestone of Northern Indiana. *J. Paleont.*, **31**, 1148–53.

HEDE, J. E. 1921. Gottlands Silurstratigrafi. *Sver. geol. Unders.* Ser. C, **305**.

—— 1960. The Silurian of Gotland. Guide to Excursion C.17. *21st Inst. geol. Congr.*

HOLLAND, C. H. 1965. The Siluro-Devonian boundary. *Geol. Mag.*, **102**, 213–21.

HOUSE, M. R. 1962. Observations on the ammonoid succession of the North American Devonian. *J. Paleont.*, **36**, 247–84.

—— 1965. A study in the Tornoceratidae: the succession of *Tornoceras* and related genera in the North American Devonian. *Phil. Trans. R. Soc.* **250B**, 79–130.

HYATT, A. 1883–4. Genera of fossil cephalopods. *Proc. Boston Soc. nat. Hist.*, **22**, 253–338.

—— 1894. Phylogeny of an acquired characteristic. *Proc. Am. phil. Soc.*, **32**, 349–647.

KIESLINGER, A. 1924. Die nautiloideen der mittleren und oberen Trias von Timor. *Jaarb. Ned.-Oost-Indië*, **51** (1922), 53–124, *nachtrag* 127–45.

KOBAYASHI, T. 1935. On the phylogeny of the primitive nautiloids, with descriptions of *Plectronoceras liaotungensis*, new species and *Iddingsia* (?) *shantungensis*, new species. *Jap. J. Geol. Georg.*, **12**, 17–26.

KONINCK, L. G. de,. 1880. Faune Calcaire Carbonifère de la Belgique, Part II. *Annls Mus. r. Hist. nat. Belg.*, (Palaeont), **5**, 1–133.

KUMMEL, B. 1953a. American Triassic coiled nautiloids. *Spec. Pap. geol. Soc. Am.*, 250, 1–104.

—— 1953b. The ancestry of the family Nautilidae. *Breviora*, **21**, 1–7.

—— 1963. Miscellaneous nautilid type species of Alpheus Hyatt. *Bull. Mus. comp. Zool. Harv.*, **128**, 325–68.

LAI, CHAI-GEEN. 1965. Ordovician and Silurian Cephalopods from Hanzhung and Ningkiang fo Shensi. *Acta palaeont. sin.*, **13**, 308–342.

LINDSTRÖM, G. 1890. The Ascoceratidae and the Lituitidae of the Upper Silurian Formation of Gotland. *K. svenska Vetensk-Akad. Handl.*, **23**, 1–54.

MARTINSSON, A. 1964. Palaeocope ostracodes from the Well Leba 1 in Pomerania. *Geol. Fören. Stockh. Förh.*, **86**, 125–61.

MELVILLE, R. V. 1959. Proposed use of the Plenary Powers to suppress the generic names *Orthoceros* Brünnich, 1771, and *Orthocera* Modeer, 1789 so as to stabilise the generic name *Orthoceras* Bruguière, 1789 (Class Cephalopoda, Order Nautiloidea). *Bull. zool. Nom.*, **17**, 9–24.

MILLER, A. K. 1932. The Mixochanitic Cephalopods. *Stud. nat. Hist. Iowa Univ.*, **14** (4), 1–67.

——, DOWNS, H. R. & YOUNGQUIST, W. 1949. Some Mississippian cephalopods from Central and Western United States. *J. Paleont.*, **23**, 600–12.

——, DUNBAR, C. O. & CONDRA, G. E. 1933. The nautiloid cephalopods of the Pennsylvanian System in the Mid-Continent region. *Neb. Geol. Surv. (Bull.)*, **9**, 1–240.

—— & FURNISH, W. M. 1938. Lower Mississippian nautiloid cephalopods of Missouri. *Univ. Mo. Stud.*, **13**, 140–78.

—— & YOUNGQUIST, W. 1949. American Permian nautiloids. *Mem. geol. Soc. Am.*, **41**, 1–218.

Chapter 14: Mollusca: Cephalopoda (Nautiloidea)

MOJSISOVICS, E. von 1882. Die cephalopoden der Mediterranen Triasprovinz. *Abh. geol. Reich-sanst., Wien,* **10,** 1–322.

—— 1899. Upper Triassic cephalopoda faunae Himálaya. *Mem. geol. Surv. India, Palaeont. indica,* ser. 15, **3,** pt 1, 1–157.

NAKAZAWA, K. 1959. Two cephalopod species from the Norian Nariwa Group in Okayama Prefecture, West Japan. *Jap. J. Geol. Georg.,* **30,** 127–33.

PRANTL, F. 1948. On the occurrence of the genus *Volborthella* Schmidt in Bohemia (Nautiloidea). *Sb. nár. Mus. Praze,* (Ser. B), **4,** 1–13.

RUEDEMANN, R. 1906. Cephalopods of the Beekmantown and Chazy Formations of the Champlain Basin. *Bull. N.Y. St. Mus.,* **90,** 393–611.

RUZHENTSEV, V. E. (Editor). 1962. *Osnovy paleontologii, Mollyuski: Golovonogie,* 1. Akademii Nauk SSSR, Moscow.

—— & SHIMANSKY, V. N. 1954. [Lower Permian coiled and curved nautiloids of the Southern Urals.] *Trudy paleont. Inst.,* **50,** 1–152

SCHINDEWOLF, O. H. 1942. Evolution im Lichte der Paläontologie. *Jena. Z. Med. Naturw.,* **75,** 324–54.

SHIMANSKY, V. N. 1957a. [Systematics and phylogeny of the order Nautilida.] *Byull. mosk. Obschch. Ispỹt. Prir. (Otdel Geol.),* **32,** 105–20.

—— 1957b. [Oncoceratida from the Carboniferous.] *Dokl. Akad. nauk SSSR,* **112,** 532–32.

—— 1961a. [*Argocheilus* Shimansky, nom. nov.] *Paleont. Zh.,* **2,** 128.

—— 1961b. [On the evolution of the Actinoceratoidea of the Carboniferous.] *Paleont. Zh.,* **3,** 33–40.

STUMBUR, Kh. A. 1962. [Distribution of the nautiloids in the Ordovician of Estonia (with a description of some new genera).] *Geoloogia.-Inst. Uurim.,* **10,** 131–48.

TREATISE K. 1964. TEICHERT, C. *et al.* Cephalopoda-General features, Endoceratoidea, Actinoceratoidea, Nautiloidea, Bactritoidea, *in* MOORE, R. C. (Editor) *Treatise on Invertebrate Paleontology,* Part K. University of Kansas Press.

TROEDSSON, G. T. 1926. On the Middle and Upper Ordovician faunas of Northern Greenland, 1. Cephalopods. *Meddr Grønland.,* **71,** 1–157.

TURNER, J. S. 1951. On the Carboniferous nautiloids: *Orthocera gigantea* J. Sowerby and allied forms. *Trans. R. Soc. Edinb.,* **62,** 169–90.

ULRICH, E. O., FOERSTE, A. F., MILLER, A. K. & UNKLESBAY, A. G. 1944. Ozarkian and Canadian cephalopods Part III. Longicones and summary. *Spec. Pap. geol. Soc. Am.,* **58,** 1–226.

UNKLESBAY, A. G. & YOUNG, R. S. 1956. Early Ordovician nautiloids from Virginia. *J. Paleont.,* **30,** 481–91.

WILSON, A. E. 1961. Cephalopoda of the Ottawa formation of the Ottawa-St. Lawrence Lowland. *Bull. geol. Surv. Can.,* **67,** 1–106.

[Professor] C. H. Holland, PH.D. F.G.S.
Department of Geology, Trinity College, Dublin 2, Ireland.

CHAPTER 15

Mollusca: Cephalopoda (Ammonoidea)

Contributors: D. T. DONOVAN, F. HODSON, M. K. HOWARTH,
M. R. HOUSE, E. T. TOZER & C. W. WRIGHT

Introduction. The Bactritina are included here for convenience. Otherwise the classification follows that of the Treatise L rather closely except for the Anarcestina where Erben's (1964, 1965) arrangement of superfamilies is adopted. Elsewhere differences are noted in the text except for the Ceratitina where Tozer gives author reference in parentheses for families which have subsequently been revised. Although it has been disputed in the past, and even recently (Donovan 1964), the balance of recent evidence, especially that of Erben (1964, 1965), favours an origin of the early coiled ammonoids from the straight bactritids probably in the Siegen.

Stratigraphical references follow the standard adopted for the volume. Tozer, however, prefers to use a stage nomenclature in which Griesbachian + Dienerian = Induan, and Smithian + Spathian = Olenek (Tozer 1956b). For the Dev zonal references follow House (1962, p. 249), other systems follow standard practice, and references are given for differences.

Suborder BACTRITINA Shimanskiy 1951

Family BACTRITIDAE Hyatt 1884

First, Ord Arenig: *Eobactrites sandbergeri* (Barrande), Upper D beds, Sárka, Czechoslovakia (Schindewolf 1933, p. 69, 70), U. Didymograptus Sh. Norway (Sweet 1958).

Last, Perm: *Bactrites* spp., U. Perm, Urals, Sicily, etc. (see Shimanskiy *in* Orlov 1962).

Comment: Although Flower (1964 p. 107), who interprets the genus widely, doubts whether *Eobactrites* is a bactritid, Erben (*in* Treatise K495) considers that the discovery of recent Sil bactritids makes it more probable that they do belong to the group.

Family PARABACTRITIDAE Shimanskiy 1951

First, Carb Viséan: *Parabactrites* (?) *pygmaeum* (de Koninck) Belgium. This form may not belong here in which case the group is found only in L. Perm.

Last, Perm ? Leon: *Akastioceras, Microbactrites,* southern Urals (Shimanskiy 1954, Shimanskiy *in* Orlov 1962).

Suborder ANARCESTINA Miller and Furnish 1954

Superfamily MIMOSPHINCTACEAE Erben 1964

First, Dev Sieg: *Anetoceras* (*Erbenoceras*) spp., Hunsrückschiefer, U. Sieg, Germany (Erben 1964).

Last, Dev Eifel: *Convoluticeras discordans* Erben, Daleje Sh, (L. Eifel Czechoslovakia).

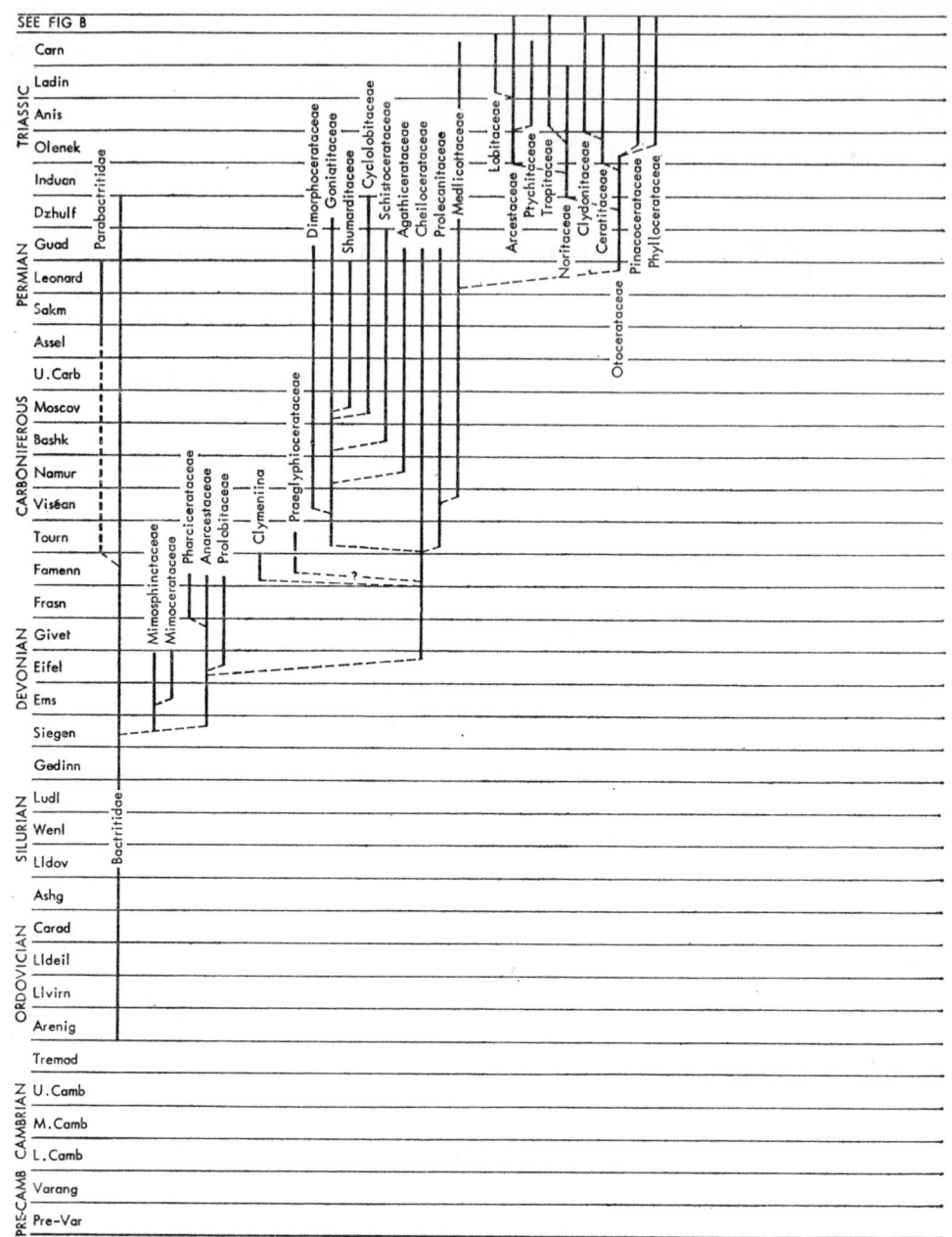

TAXA   AMMONOIDEA

CONTRIBUTORS   D. T. Donovan, F. Hodson, M. K. Howarth, M. R. House, E. T. Tozer

FIG. 15.1 A

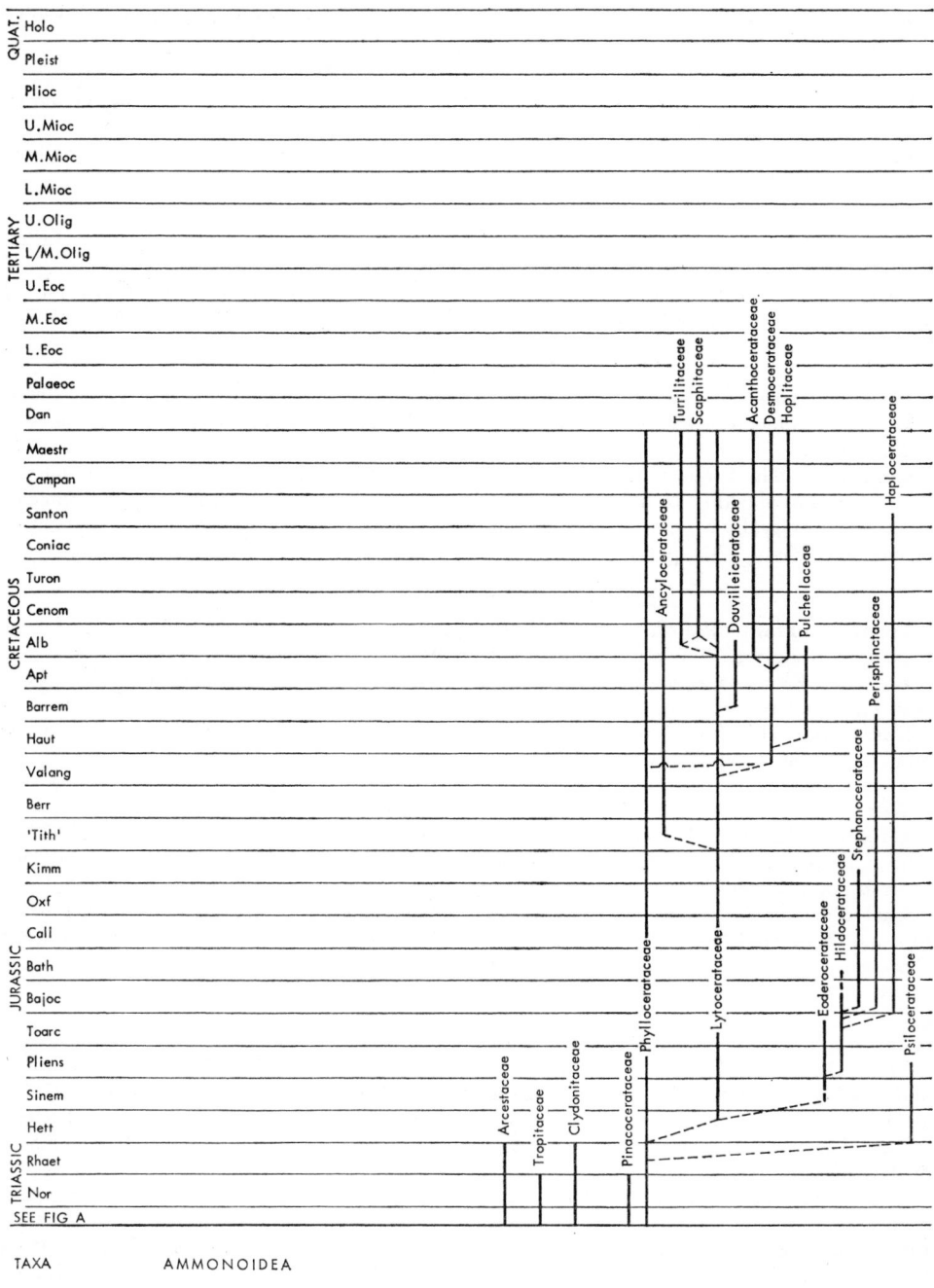

TAXA   AMMONOIDEA

CONTRIBUTORS   D. T. Donovan, M. K. Howarth, E. T. Tozer, C. W. Wright

FIG. 15.1 B

Talenticeras from Victoria, Australia may be Eifel as may *Teicherticeras* spp. from the same locality (Erben 1965).

Superfamily MIMOCERATACEAE Steinmann 1890

First, Dev Ems: *Gyroceratites* spp., U. Ems, Rheinisches Schiefergebirge, Germany (Walliser 1962, Erben 1964 p. 153).

Last, Dev Eifel: *Gyroceratites gracilis* and *G.* spp., Wissenbacherschiefer, Germany (Walliser 1962, Erben 1964).

Superfamily ANARCESTACEAE Steinmann 1890

First, Dev Siegen: *Mimagoniatites* spp., U. Siegen, Germany and Czechoslovakia (Erben 1964, p. 202).

Last, Dev Famenn: *Werneroceras* sp. nov, L. Famenn, Germany (Schindewolf 1937a, pl. 19, fig. 8). This is probably not a *Werneroceras*, but *Archoceras* is common in the late Frasn.

Superfamily PROLOBITACEAE Wedekind 1913

First, Dev Eifel: *Sobolewia globularis* Petter, Jugleri Z., Saura Valley, N. Africa (Petter 1959).

Last, Dev Famenn: *Cycloclymenia planorbiformis* (Münster), Speciosa Z., Germany (Schindewolf 1923, p. 416).

Comment: This group possibly includes two quite separate stocks. No members are known from the Frasn, and this stratigraphical gap separates the *Sobolewia* group from a later Famenn group which typically have more complex sutures, apart from *Raymondiceras* which is thought to belong here (House 1962, p. 262).

Superfamily PHARCICERATACEAE Hyatt 1900

First, Dev Frasn: *Pharciceras* spp. and other genera, Lunulicosta Z., Best documented from Germany (Wedekind 1917) and N. Africa (Petter 1959).

Last, Dev Famenn: *Manticoceras superstes* (Wedekind) and *M. nehdense* Lange from the Curvispina Z., Germany (Schindewolf 1923, Lange 1929, p. 33).

Comment: This short-lived group showed remarkably widespread distribution and is known on all continents except for S. America.

Suborder CLYMENIINA Hyatt 1884

First, Dev Famenn: *Platyclymenia sandbergeri* Wedekind, *Rectoclymenia steinmanni* Wedekind and others, Delphinus Z., Germany (Schindewolf 1923, Wedekind 1908). *Acanthoclymenia* Dev Frasn is not a clymenid.

Last, Dev Famenn: eight genera in Famenn, Sphaeroides Z., Germany (Schindewolf 1937b), England (Selwood 1960) and elsewhere. Records from the "L. Carb." refer to Dev Etrouengt specimens.

Suborder GONIATITINA Hyatt 1884

Superfamily CHEILOCERATACEAE Frech 1897

First, Dev Eifel: *Parodiceras discoideum* (Hall) Jugleri Z., Saura Valley, N. Africa (Petter 1949) and possibly Germany. This species occurs about the Eifel/Giv boundary in N.Y. State (House 1965). Considered to be derived from the Anarcestaceae (*op. cit.*).   [M.R.H.]

Last, Perm Guad: probably *Imitoceras pygmaeum* (Gemmellaro 1887), Sosio Beds (L. Guad), Sicily, Italy.

Comment: Carb and Perm representatives constitute family Imitoceratidae Ruzhentsev 1950, comprising genera *Imitoceras* Schindewolf 1923, *Gattendorfia* Schindewolf 1920, *Kazhakstania* Librovitch 1940 and possibly *Huanites* Chao 1940, which has serrated lobes and *Irinoceras* Ruzhentsev 1947, with trifid ventral lobe; Last might be primitive Pronoritid.   [F.H.]

Superfamily PRAEGLYPHIOCERATACEAE Ruzhenstev 1957

First, Dev Famenn: *Praeglyphioceras pseudosphaericum* (Frech 1902), Platyclymenia Z., Enkeberg, Germany.   [M.R.H.]

Last, Carb Tourn: *Karagandoceras galeatum* Librovitch 1940, Gattendorfia Z., N. Kazakhstan, U.S.S.R.

Superfamily GONIATITACEAE de Haan 1825

First, Carb Tourn: probably *Muensteroceras oweni* (Hall) 1860 and *"Goniatites" allei* Winchell 1862, Marshall Fm, Michigan, U.S.A., associated with Gattendorfia Z. fauna. *"G." allei* has been assigned to the genus *Beyrichoceras* but is probably a primitive girtyoceratid.

Last, Perm Dzhulf: possibly *Pseudogastrioceras abichianum* (Muller 1897), U. Perm, Armenia, U.S.S.R.

Comment: Superfamily is here interpreted as including *Pericyclaceae* Ruzhentsev 1960 *ex* Hyatt 1900, and restricted to forms with 8 entire lobes in septal suture with ventral lobe divided by median saddle. Includes family Pericyclidae Hyatt 1900, Muensteroceratidae Librovitch 1957, Nomismoceratidae Librovitch 1957, Goniatitidae de Haan 1825, Girtyoceratidae Moore 1946, Homoceratidae Spath 1934, Reticuloceratidae Librovitch 1957, Gastrioceratidae Hyatt 1884, (Neoicoceratidae Hyatt 1900), Pseudoparalegoceratidae Librovitch 1957 and Paragastrioceratidae Ruzhentsev 1951.

Superfamily SCHISTOCERATACEAE (*ex* Schisticeratidae Schmidt 1929)

First, Carb Bashk: *Paralegoceras iowense* (Meek & Worthen 1860) and *P. texanum* (Shumard), Atokan Stage (U. Bashk), Oklahoma, U.S.A.

Last, Perm Guad: *Adrianites dunbari* Miller & Furnish 1940, Capitanian (U. Guad), U.S.A. It does not seem possible to separate the adrianitids from the schistoceratids at superfamily level. Exclusive of adrianitids, the latest schistoceratid appears to be *Metalegoceras evolutum* (Haniel 1915), Bitauni Beds, Upper Artinskian, Timor.

Comment: Derived from Goniatitaceae *via Paralegoceras* Hyatt 1884, and comprising Goniatitids with at least 10 entire lobes in septal suture, includes Adrianitaceae Schindewolf 1931.

Constituent families: Schistoceratidae Schmidt 1929, Metalegoceratidae Plummer & Scott 1937, Welleritidae Plummer & Scott 1937, Adrianitidae Schindewolf 1931, Dunbaritidae Miller & Furnish 1957, Hoffmannidae Spath 1934, Clinolobidae Miller & Furnish 1957. The last four families comprise the Adrianitaceae (*auctt.*) ranging from *Dunbarites rectilaterale* Miller 1930, Prouddenites Z., Missourian, U.S.A. to *Adrianites dunbari* Miller & Furnish 1940.

Superfamily AGATHICERATACEAE Arthaber 1911

First, Carb Namur: *Proshumardites karpinskyi* Rauser-Tschernoussova 1928, Eumorphoceras Z.

Last, Perm Guad: Various species of *Agathiceras* from Sosie Beds, Sicily, Italy; Basleo Beds, Timor, and Word Fm (Texan), U.S.A., all L. Guad.

Comment: Derived from Goniatitaceae from *Mesoglyphioceras granosus* (Portlock) stock of U. Viséan *via Dombarites tectus* Librovtich 1957, L. Namur, to *Proshumardites*, L. Namur. Characteristic sutural complication by lateral lobe becoming trifid and developing three independent lobes giving suture line with 12 undivided lobes.

Constituent family: Agathiceratidae Arthaber 1911.

Superfamily DIMORPHOCERATACEAE Hyatt 1884

First, Carb Viséan: *Paradimorphoceras brancoi* (Holzapfel 1889), Pericyclus Z. (IIy), L. Viséan, Germany.

Last, Perm Guad: *Epithalassoceras ruzhencevi* Miller & Furnish 1940, Word Fm (L. Guad), U.S.A.

Comment: Involute shells with narrow, acute or keeled venters derived from Goniatitaceae with 8 lobes in septal suture. Lobes usually divided by adventitious saddles which encroach up flanks to form digitate saddles. Anthracoceratids with adventitious saddles or with delayed appearance of same arise by neotony from dimorphoceratids.

Constituent families: Dimorphoceratidae Hyatt 1884, Anthracoceratidae Plummer & Scott 1937, Berkhoceratidae Librovitch 1957 and Thalassoceratidae Hyatt 1884.

Superfamily SHUMARDITACEAE Plummer and Scott 1937

First, Carb Moscov: *Aktubites trifidus* Ruzhentsev 1955, Moscovian, U.S.S.R.

Last, Perm Leonard: *Perinites hilli* (Smith 1903), Artinskian, U.S.A.

Constituent families: Shumarditidae Plummer & Scott 1937 and Perrinitidae Miller & Furnish 1940.

Superfamily CYCLOLOBITACEAE Zittel 1895

First, Carb Moscov: *Peritrochia* sp., Wellerites Z. (Moscov), Des Moines, U.S.A.

Last, Perm Dzhulf: Possibly *Cyclolobus* (*Krafftoceras*) *krafti* Diener 1903, Himalayas.

Constituent families: Marathonitidae Ruzhentsev 1938, Popanoceratidae Hyatt 1900, Cyclolobidae Zittel 1895.

Superfamily PROLECANITACEAE Hyatt 1884

First, Carb Tourn: *Prolecanites lyoni* (Meek & Worthen 1860), Gattendorfia Z. (L. Tourn), Europe, U.S.S.R., U.S.A. and Australia.

Last, Perm Guad: possibly *Daraelites meeki* Gemmellaro 1887, Sosio Beds, Sicily, Italy.

Comment: Multilobed with lobes undivided, later members have finely denticulated lateral lobe.

Constituent families: Prolecanitidae Hyatt 1884 and Daraelitidae Tchernow 1907.

Superfamily MEDLICOTTACEAE Karpinsky 1889

First, Carb Viséan: *Pronorites cyclolobus* (Phillips 1836) and *Tridentites tridens* (Schmidt 1925), both U. Viséan.

Last, Trias Carn: *Sageceras*. [F.H]

Suborder CERATITINA Hyatt 1884

Superfamily OTOCERATACEAE Hyatt 1900

First, Perm Leonard: *Paraceltites elegans* Girty 1908, Bone Spring Fm, Artinskian, Texas, U.S.A. (Miller & Furnish 1940). [F.H. & E.T.T.]

Last, Trias Olenek: members of the Family Dieneroceratidae Kummel 1952, Smithian (Kummel & Steele 1962). [E.T.T.]

Comment: Derived from Meddicottids. Root stock of Mesozoic Ammonoids. [F.H.]

Constituent families: Xenodiscidae Frech 1902, Perm Leonard-Dzhulf; Araxoceratidae Ruzhencev 1959, Perm Dzhulf; Anderssonoceratidae Ruzhencev 1959, Perm Dzhulf?; Otoceratidae (Ruzhencev 1959), Trias Induan (Griesbachian); Ophiceratidae Arthaber 1911, Trias Induan (Griesbachian-Dienerian); Dieneroceratidae Kummel 1952, Trias Olenek (Smithian). [F.H. & E.T.T.]

Superfamily NORITACEAE Karpinsky 1889

First, Trias Induan: *Proptychites scheibler* Diener, Griesbachian.

Last, Trias Ladin: *Norites subcarinatus* Hauer (Diener 1915).

Constituent families (and subfamilies): Gyronitidae Waagen 1895, Trias Induan (Dienerian); Flemingitidae Hyatt 1900, Trias Induan (Dienerian)-Olenek (Smithian); Xenoceltitidae Spath 1930, Trias Olenek (Smithian-Spathian); Paranoritidae Spath 1930, Trias Induan (Dienerian)-Olenek (Smithian); Proptychitidae Waagen 1895, Trias Induan (Griesbachian)-Olenek (Spathian) (Proptychitinae, Griesbachian-Spathian; Owenitinae, Smithian); Paranannitidae Spath 1930, Trias Olenek (Smithian-Spathian) (Paranannitinae, Smithian-Spathian; Columbitinae, Spathian); Ussuriidae Spath 1930, Trias Olenek (Smithian); Hedenstroemiidae Waagen 1895, Trias Induan (Dienerian)-Anis (Hedentroemiinae, Dienerian-Spathian; Lanceolitinae, Smithian; Aspenitinae, Smithian-Spathian; Beneckeiinae, Olenek

450

Chapter 15: Mollusca: Cephalopoda (Ammonoidea)

(Spathian)-Anis; Kashmiritidae Spath 1930, Trias Olenek (Smithian); Meekoceratidae Waagen 1895, Trias Olenek (Meekoceratinae, Smithian; Arctoceratinae, Smithian-Spathian); Dagnoceratidae (Kiparisova 1961), Trias Olenek (Spathian)-Anis; Noritidae Karpinsky 1889, Trias Olenek (Spathian)-Ladian; Prionitidae (Tozer 1961), Trias Olenek (Smithian); Sibiritidae Tozer 1961, Trias Olenek (Spathian)-Anis.

Superfamily CERATITACEAE Mojsisovics 1879

First, Trias Olenek: members of the Families Stephanitidae Mojsisovics 1879 Smithian (Spath 1934).

Last, Trias Carn: *Perrinoceras novaditus* Johnston, L. Carn (Johnston 1941) and members of Family Carnitidae Arthaber 1911 (Diener 1915).

Constituent families: Stephanitidae Mojsisovics 1879, Trias Olenek (Smithian); Tirolitidae Mojsisovics 1882, Trias Olenek (Smithian?-Spathian); Dinaritidae (Tozer 1965a), Trias Olenek (Spathian); Hellenitidae Kummel 1952, Trias Olenek (Spathian); Acrochordiceratidae Arthaber 1911, Trias Anis; Beyrichitidae Spath 1934, Trias Olenek (Spathian)-Ladin; Ceratitidae Mojsisovics 1879, Trias Anis-Ladin; Danubitidae Spath 1951, Trias Anis; Balatonitidae Spath 1951, Trias Anis; Hungaritidae Waagen 1895, Trias Olenek (Spathian)-L. Carn; Carnitidae Arthaber 1911, Trias Carn; Proteusitidae Spath 1951, Trias Anis; Aplococeratidae Spath 1951, Trias Anis-Ladin.

Superfamily CLYDONITACEAE Mojsisovics 1879

First, Trias Anis: *Nevadites hyatti* (Smith) (Silberling 1962).

Last, Trias Rhaet: *Choristoceras marshi* Hauer, etc. (Diener 1915).

Constituent families: Trachyceratidae Silberling 1956, Trias Anis-M. Nor; Clydonitidae Mojsisovics 1879, Trias L. Carn-U. Nor; Clionitidae Arabu 1932, Trias L. Carn-U. Nor; Arpaditidae Hyatt 1900, Trias Ladin-U. Nor; Heraclitidae Diener 1920, Trias Nor; Lecanitidae Hyatt 1900, Trias Ladin-L. Carn; Cyrtopleuritidae Diener 1925, Trias L. Carn-M. Nor; Tibetitidae Hyatt 1900, Trias Ladin-Nor; Buchitidae Hyatt 1900, Trias L. Carn-U. Nor; Thisbitidae Spath 1951, Trias L. Carn-M. Nor; Noridiscitidae Spath 1951, Trias Nor; Distichitidae Diener 1920, Trias L.-M. Nor; Choristoceratidae Hyatt 1900, Trias L. Carn-Rhaet; Cochloceratidae Hyatt 1900, Trias Nor.

Superfamily TROPITACEAE Mojsisovics 1875

First, Trias Anis: *Tropigymnites planorbis* (Hauer) (Diener 1915).

Last, Trias Nor: members of the Families Tropiceltitidae, Celtitidae, Metasibiritidae, Haloritidae (Diener 1915) and Didymitidae (Diener 1915, Kutassy 1932).

Constituent families (and subfamilies): Tropitidae Silberling 1959, Trias L. Carn-L. Nor; Tropiceltitidae Spath 1951, Trias L. Carn-Nor; Celtitidae Mojsisovics 1893, Trias Anis-U. Nor; Metasibitidae Spath 1951, Trias Nor; Haloritidae Mojsisovics 1893, Trias Ladin-U. Nor (Haloritinae ↔ Carn-U. Nor; Sagenitinae —, Ladin-U. Nor; Episculinitinae —, Carn-U. Nor); Didymitidae Haug 1894, Trias Nor.

Superfamily LOBITACEAE Mojsisovics

First, Trias Ladin; *Lobites bouei* Mojsisovics (Diener 1915).

Last, Trias Carn: *Coroceras sandbergeri* Mojsisovics, etc., Trias Carn (Diener 1915).

Superfamily ARCESTACEAE Mojsisovics 1875

First, Trias Olenek: *Procarnites kokeni* Arthaber, etc., Spathian (Spath 1934).

Last, Trais Rhaet: *Arcestes rhaeticus* Clark and *Cladiscites* sp. (Diener 1915).

Constituent families: Arcestidae Mojsisovics 1875, Trias Anis-Rhaet; Johannitidae Mojsisovics 1882, Trias Anis-L. Carn; Sphingitidae Arthaber 1911, Trias L. Carn-Nor; Cladiscitidae Zittel 1884, Trias Anis-Rhaet; Megaphyllitidae (Popov 1962), Trias Olenek (Spathian)-Rhaet; Nathorstitidae Spath 1951, Trias Ladin.

451

Superfamily PTYCHITACEAE Mojsisovics 1882

First, Trias Anis: *Ismidites marmarensis* (Arthaber) (Diener 1915) and *Isculites hauerinus* (Stoliczka) (Spath 1951).

Last, Trias Carn: *Hyattites praefloridus* (Mojsisovics) and *Nannites spurius* Münster, both L. Carn (Diener 1915).

Constituent families: Ptychitidae Mojsisovics 1882, Trias Anis-L. Carn; Isculitidae Spath 1951, Trias Anis-Ladin; Nannitidae Diener 1897, Trias Ladin-L. Carn.

Superfamily PINACOCERATACEAE Mojsisovics 1879

First, Trias Olenek; *Eogymnites arthaberi* (Diener), Spathian (Diener 1915).

Last, Trias Nor: *Pinacoceras metternichi* (Hauer), etc, U. Nor (Diener 1915).

Constituent families: Pinacoceratidae Mojsisovics 1879, Trias Anis-U. Nor; Gymnititdae Waagen 1895, Trias Olenek (Spathian)-L. Carn. [E.T.T.]

Suborder PHYLLOCERATINA Arkell 1950

Superfamily PHYLLOCERATACEAE Zittel 1884

First, Trias Olenek: *Leiophyllites* Diener, "Columbitan" (i.e. U. Olenek), Kwangsi prov., China (Chao 1959); *Eophyllites* Spath, U.Olenek, Albania and Greece (Spath 1934, p. 293); *Palaeophyllites* Welter, U.Olenek, Timor (Spath 1934, p. 296). [D.T.D. & M.K.H.]

Last, Cret Maestr: *Neophylloceras hetonaiense* Matsumoto, *Phyllopachyceras* sp. ind., U. Maestr, Marca Sh member of Moreno Fm, Panoche Hills, San Joaquin Valley, California (Matsumoto 1960, p. 44).

Constituent families: As in Treatise L.

Comment: The superfamily arose from *Dieneroceras* of the Otocerataceae in the Olenek (Kummel 1952). It persisted relatively unchanged to the top of the Cret, being the only superfamily to cross the Trias-Jur boundary, and then gave rise (largely via the Lytocerataceae) to all Jur and Cret ammonites. [M.K.H.]

Suborder LYTOCERATINA Hyatt 1889

Superfamily LYTOCERATACEAE Neumayr 1876

First, Jur Hett: *Pleuroacanthites* Canavari, Calliphyllum Z., Austria (Lange 1952, pp. 60–61). [D.T.D.]

Last, Cret Maestr: *Tetragonites (Saghalinites)* (?) sp., U. Maestr, Moreno Fm, California (Matsumoto 1960, p. 59); *Gaudryceras* Grossouvre, *Pseudophyllites* Kossmat, *Tetragonites* Kossmat, *Vertebrites* Marshall and *Zelandites* Marshall are all recorded from L. Maestr, Europe, Asia, Africa, Australasia. [M.K.H. & C.W.W.]

Constituent families: As in Treatise L.

Comment: Superfamily derived from Ussuritidae or Discophyllitidae of the Phyllocerataceae at top of Trias, after which the main stream remained relatively unchanged to the top of the Cret, but offshoots gave rise to most of the remaining Jur and Cret superfamilies.

Superfamily ANCYLOCERATACEAE Meek 1876

First, Jur 'Tith': *Protancyloceras* spp., M. Tith, Rogoznik Beds, near Neumarkt, southern Poland (Zittel 1870); bed i, Jebel Gara, Kurdistan (Spath 1950), and Viñales Lst, Cuba (Imlay 1942). Above records are all known to be M. Tith. Genus also occurs in Tith at less accurately known horizons in southern France, Tunisia, Crimea, Mexico and Peru.

Last, Cret Alb: *Ptychoceras closteroide* Etheridge, U.Alb., Point Charles Beds, Darwin Fm, Point Charles, Northern Territory, Australia (Whitehouse 1928); *P.* cf. *glaber* (Whiteaves), U. Alb, Mont Raynaud, Madagascar (Collignon 1932); *Ptychoceras forbesianum* Stoliczka, *P. glaber* (Whiteaves), U.Alb, L.Utatur Group, Madras, India (Kossmat 1895, p. 150); *P. glaber* (Whiteaves), U.Alb, Cumshewa Inlet, Queen Charlotte Islands, British Columbia, Canada (Whiteaves 1884, p. 213).

Chapter 15: Mollusca: Cephalopoda (Ammonoidea)

Constituent families: Protancyloceratidae Breistroffer 1947, Tith-Valang; Bochianitidae Spath 1922, "Tith"-L.Apt; Ptychoceratidae Meek 1876, Haut-U.Alb; Crioceratitidae Wright 1952, Haut-U. Apt; Hemihoplitidae Spath 1924, Haut-Barrem; Heteroceratidae Hyatt 1900, Barrem-Apt; Pedioceratidae Hyatt 1900, Haut-L.Apt; Ancyloceratidae Meek 1876, Barrem-Apt.

Comment: Origin unknown, but has been suggested as from late Jur Protetragonitidae.
[M.K.H.]

Superfamily TURRILITACEAE Meek 1876

First, Cret Alb: *Hamites pseudattenuatus* Casey, L. Alb, Mammillatum Zone, Kitchini Sz., Old Coprolite workings, West Dereham, Norfolk, England (Casey 1961, p. 96).

Last, Cret Maestr: *Baculites* sp. ind., U. Maestr, Casimirovensis Z., Poland (Jeletsky 1951, p. 76); *Baculites* sp. ind., *Didymoceras sandersorum* (Stephenson), U. Maestr, Kemp Clay, Texas (Stephenson 1941, pp. 407, 416); *Baculites rex* Anderson, U. Maestr, Marca Sh member, Moreno Fm, Panoche Hills, San Joaquin Valley, California (Matsumoto 1960, p. 44).

Constituent families: As Treatise L, but excluding Ptychoceratidae Meek, 1876 (incl. in Ancyloceratceae).

Comment: Origin of superfamily in Lytoceratidae possible but yet to be proved.

Superfamily SCAPHITACEAE Meek 1876

First, Cret Alb: *Eoscaphites circularis* (J. de Sowerby), *E. subcircularis* (Spath), U. Alb, Inflatum Z., Varicosum Sz., bed X, Folkestone, Kent., and many other localities in southern England and France (Wiedmann 1965, p. 404). *Zuluscaphites* van Hoepen, M. Alb, is probably not a scaphitid.

Last, Cret Maestr: *Hoploscaphites constrictus* (J. Sowerby), U. Maestr, U. Casimirovensis Z., Denmark and Poland (Jeletzky 1951, pp. 71, 76); *Discoscaphites* spp., U. Maestr, Fox Hills Sst, S. Dakota (Cobban & Reeside, 1952, p. 1021), Kemp Clay, Texas (Stephenson 1941, p. 428).

Constituent families: Scaphitidae Meek 1876, U.Alb-Maast; Labeceratidae Spath 1925, M.Alb-U.Alb.

Comment: Origin of superfamily was probably in the Lytocerataceae (Treatise L), but Wiedmann (1965) claims that the origin is in *Hamites* of the Turrilitaceae. [M.K.H. & C.W.W.]

Suborder AMMONITINA Hyatt 1889

The classification adopted is basically that of the Treatise L, but the superfamilies arising in the L. Cret, i.e. the Desmocerataceae, Douvilleicerataceae, Pulchelliaceae, Hoplitaceae and Acanthocerataceae are modified according to the views put forward by Casey (1960–1965). The superfamily Spirocerataceae of the *Treatise* is included in the Perisphinctaceae as a family. [M.K.H.]

Superfamily PSILOCERATACEAE Hyatt 1867

First, Jur Hett: *Neophyllites* cf. *imitans* Lange, Planorbis Z., Antecedens Sz., N.W. Germany (Hoffmann 1962, p. 165); *Psiloceras planorbis* (J. de C. Sowerby), Planorbis Z., Planorbis Sz., S. Wales (Trueman 1920, p. 100) and elsewhere. Correlation of Antecedens Sz. of N.W. Germany with Planorbis Sz of Britain is unknown.

Last, Jur Pliens: *Radstockiceras* Buckman, Jamesoni Z., not earlier than Polymorphus Sz., England (Tutcher & Trueman 1925, p. 601). [D.T.D.]

Constituent families: as in Treatise L.

Comment: superfamily derived from Ussuritidae of the Phylloceratoceae at Rhaet/Hett boundary.

Superfamily EODEROCERATACEAE Spath 1929

First, [Jur Sinem; *Microderoceras birchi* (J. Sowerby), L. Sinem, Semicostatum Z, Scipionianum Sz., division V at Endingen, Württemberg, Germany (Wallisser 1956). Both specific determination and horizon need confirmation before this can be accepted as the earliest representative]. Jur Sinem: *Microderoceras birchi* (J. Sowerby), L. Sinem, Turneri Z., Birchi Subz., bed 74g, Black Ven, Charmouth, Dorset, England (Lang 1923). This genus appears at this or perhaps slightly earlier horizon at other localities in Britain, France and Germany. There is an unconfirmed record of a fragment said to have come from bed 52, west of Lyme Regis, Dorset, England.

Last, Jur Toarc: *Catacoeloceras confectum* Buckman and *C. dumortieri* (Maubeuge), Variabilis Z., L. Cotswolds Sands, Gloucestershire, England (Buckman 1889), and *Collina mucronata* (d'Orbigny) and *Catacoeloceras crassum* (Young & Bird) (incl. *C. raquineanum* (d'Orbigny)), Swabia (Krumbeck 1944) and Aveyron (Monestier, 1922). [*Sphaerocoeloceras brocchiiforme* Jaworski said to be from the topmost Toarc (Levesquei Z.), Argentina, and accepted as the last genus of Dactylioceratidae in the Treatise (L 254), is probably a L. Liassic Eoderoceratidae. Its associated *"Dumortieria" pusilla* Jaworski, by which it was dated as Toarc, is a L. Liassic *Arnioceras* (Jaworski 1926b).]

Constituent families: As Treatise L.

Comment: Origin of superfamily uncertain, but probably from some Lytocerataceae family such as Ectocentritidae. An independent origin in the Lytocerataceae has often been postulated for the family Dactylioceratidae (Spath 1936, Arkell 1949), but derivation of *Prodactylioceras* from some Eoderocerataceae genus like *Coeloderoceras* in the Ibex Z., seems to be more likely.

Superfamily HILDOCERATACEAE Hyatt 1867

First, Jur Pliens: *Protogrammoceras mellahense* Dubar, L. Pliens, Ibex Z., bed 3m below *Tropidoceras stahli* bed, south of Mellaha, south-east of Gourrama, High Atlas, and north of Jebel Izouggart, west of Ziz, Morocco (Dubar 1961). Other records of *Protogrammoceras* and *Fuciniceras* from Ibex Z. of High Atlas (Dubar 1961); Gemmellaro's (1884, p. 200, pl. 5, figs. 17, 18) Ibex Z. *Harpoceras* from Galati, Sicily, Italy, is doubtful. Davoei Z. species occur in same region (Dubar 1961, Du Dresnay 1963).

Last, Jur Bath: *Vastites vastus* Arkell, L. Bath, Zigzag Z., Brambleditch Quarry, Doulting, Somerset, England (Arkell 1951). Jur U. Bajoc: *Diplesioceras diplesium* Buckman, Garantiana Z., Vetney Cross, Bridport, Dorset, England (Buckman 1920). Both above genera based on single specimens that are only doubtfully referred to the superfamily, though it is difficult to place them elsewhere. Last undoubted representatives are Sonninidae genera *Dorsetensia* (abundant, wide distribution), *Bajocia* (Normandy, France) and *Poecilomorphus* (Europe, Africa), all from Humphriesianum Z., M. Bajoc.

Constituent families: As Treatise L.

Comment: *Protogrammoceras* and *Fuciniceras* derived from Eoderocerataceae genus *Tropidoceras* in Ibex Z., L. Pleins, in central Mediterranean—north Africa region.

Superfamily STEPHANOCERATACEAE Neumayr 1875

First, Jur Bajoc: *Docidoceras* Buckman and *Trilobiticeras* Buckman, M. Bajoc, Sowerbyi Z., Discites Sz., Fossil Bed, Bradford Abbas, Sherborne, Dorset, England (Buckman 1893, Arkell 1952).

Last, Jur Kimm: *Amoeboceras anglicum* (Salfeld) and *A. krausei* (Salfeld), L. Kimm, Pseudomutabilis Z., Ringstead Bay and Black Head, Osmington, Dorset, England (Arkell 1947, pl. 4). *Hoplocardioceras decipiens* Spath, ?Pseudomutabilis Z., oil shs at top of *Amoebites* Shs, Milne Land, Greenland (Spath 1935).

Constituent families: As in Treatise L.

Comment: *Docidoceras* probably derived from Hildocerataceae genus *Erycites* in the L. Bajoc.

Superfamily PERISPHINCTACEAE Steinmann 1890

First, Jur Bajoc: *Parabigotites crassicostatus* Imlay, M. Bajoc, Sauzei Z., Kialagvik Fm, Alaska Peninsula, Fitz Creek Siltst, north side of Cook Inlet, and Tuxedni Fm, Talkeetna Mts, Alaska (Imlay 1964); *Leptosphinctes jaworskii* Westermann, Sauzei Z., Cerro Tricolor, Mendoza, Argentina (Jaworski 1926a, p. 416, pl. 13, fig. 8; Westermann 1956, p. 268). Earliest European representatives of superfamily are all from U. Bajoc, Subfurcatum Z.

Last, Cret Haut: *Craspedodiscus discofalcatus* (Lahusen) and spp., *Simbirskites decheni* (Roemer) and spp., L. U. Haut, Decheni Z., Ulyanovsk (formerly Simbirsk), Russia (Luppov & Drushchitz

Chapter 15: Mollusca: Cephalopoda (Ammonoidea)

1958, pl. 42), Russian platform (Gerasimov 1962, p. 102), Crimea (Drushchitz & Kudryavtseva 1960); *Hertleinites aguila* Imlay, U. Haut?, Aguila Z., Ono Fm, California (Imlay 1960, Casey 1964b, p. 322) *Craspedodiscus* spp., Tealby Limestone, N. Lincs, and base of B beds, Speeton, Yorks (Spath 1924, pp. 78, 79).

Constituent families: As in Treatise L, plus Spiroceratidae Hyatt, 1900, U. Bajoc-U. Oxf (Donovan & Hölder 1958).

Comment: Derivation of whole superfamily either from a M. Bajoc genus of Stephanoceratidae or from *Erycites* (Hammatoceratidae) has been postulated.

Superfamily HAPLOCERATACEAE Zittel 1884

First, Jur Bajoc: *Praestrigites praenuntius* Buckman, L. or M. Bajoc, Concavum Z. or Sowerbyi Z., Discites Sz., Ironshot Bed, Horn Park Quarry, Beaminster, Dorset, England (Buckman 1910, p. 77; 1924, pl. 466).

Last, Cret Santon: *Binneyites rugosus* Cobban, Clioscaphites vermiformis Z., L. Santon, nodules in Marias River Sh, 234–252 ft below top of Kelvin Member, east bank of Marias River, 11 miles S.W. of Shelby, Toole county, Montana, U.S.A. (Cobban 1961).

Constituent families: As Treatise L, plus Binneyitidae Reeside 1927, M.Alb (*Falciferella* Casy)—L.Santon.

Comment: *Strigoceras, Lissoceras* and *Bradfordia* all appear simultaneously in the Sowerbyi Z., M. Bajoc. *Praestrigites* is said to appear in the zone below at the top of the L. Bajoc and is probably the earliest representative. Derivation of superfamily not clear, but possibly from a Hammatoceratidae genus such as *Eudmetoceras* Buckman, 1920. Inclusion of family Binneyitidae is due to the discovery of transitionary specimens from the Aconeceratinae (Casey 1961, p. 118; Wright 1963, p. 602). Successive derivation of members of the superfamily from Phylloceratae has been suggested, but is not supported by direct evidence and seems less likely than evolution of the superfamily as a continuous stream. [M.K.H.]

Superfamily DESMOCERATACEAE Zittel, 1895

First, Cret Valang: *Eodesmoceras celestini* (Pictet & Campiche), U. Valang, Sainte-Croix, Switzerland; *E. haughtoni* Spath, U. Valang, Uitenhage, South Africa (Spath 1930, p. 141).

Last, Cret Maestr: *Pachydiscus egertoni* (Forbes), U. Maestr, lower Casimirovensis Z., Crimea (Jeletzky 1951, p. 76); *Pachydiscus* cf. *colligatus* (Binkhorst), U. Maestr, *Sphenodiscus pleurisepta* Zone, Coahuila, Mexico (Böse & Cavins 1927, pp. 186, 306).

Constituent families: As in Treatise L.

Comment: Origin of superfamily uncertain and could be polyphyletic (see Casey 1961, p. 140). [M.K.H. & C.W.W.]

Superfamily PULCHELLIACEAE Hyatt 1903

First, Cret Haut: *Psilotissotia* cf. *favrei* (Ooster), U. Haut, Sayni Z., bed 3, Craus, Ardèche, France (Sayn & Roman 1905, p. 634), and Combovin and Crest, Drôme, France (Sayn 1903, p. 142).

Last, Cret Alb: *Trochleiceras balearense* Fallot & Termier, L. Alb, Mammillatum Z., Komihevitra, Madagascar (Collignon 1950, p. 48—"*Magneticeras*"). The same species has also been recorded by Solignac (1927, p. 145) from beds in the Bau Arada region of Tunisia that contain *Douvilleiceras mammillatum* amongst other ammonites, and from the basal Alb, Sierra Mediana, Alicante, Spain (Wiedmann 1962, p. 323).

Constituent families: Pulchelliidae Hyatt 1903, U.Haut—U.Apt; Trochleiceratidae Breistroffer 1952, L.Alb.

Comment: Origin of superfamily uncertain, but may be from *Barremites* of the Desmocerataceae.

Superfamily ACANTHOCERATACEAE Hyatt 1900

First, Cret Alb: *Proleymeriella anterior* (Brinkmann), L. Alb, Tardefurcata Z., Schrammeni Sz., canal excavation at Schwicheldt, near Peine, 30 km east of Hannover, Germany (Brinkmann 1937).

Last, Cret Maestr: *Sphenodiscus* spp., Sphenodiscus Z. (but not Casimirovensis Z. at top of Maestr), Europe (Jeletzky 1951, pp. 18, 74), Tinton Formation, New Jersey (Reeside 1962, p. 136), Kemp Clay, Texas (Stephenson 1941, p. 434), *Sphenodiscus pleurisepta* Z., north Mexico (Böse & Cavins 1927), Fox Hills Sst, S. Dakota (Cobban & Reeside 1952). Other species known from M. East, India, Africa, Madagascar and South America but position within Maestr not known.

Constituent families: As in Treatise L, but excluding Binneyitidae Reeside 1927 (see Haplocerataceae), and including Leymeriellidae Breistroffer 1951, L. Alb—M. Alb, and Forbesiceratidae Wright 1952, U. Alb—Cenom (Casey 1957).

Comment: *Proleymeriella* and hence the whole superfamily has been shown to have evolved from the Desmocerataceae genus *Callizoniceras* (Brinkmann 1937, Casey 1957).

Superfamily HOPLITACEAE Douvillé 1890

First, Cret Alb: *Farnhamia* spp. and *Anadesmoceras* sp., L. Alb, Tardefurcata Z., Farnhamensis Sz., Farnham, Surrey, England (Casey, 1965, p. 463).

Last, Cret Maestr: *Hoplitoplacenticeras lafresnayanum* (d'Orbigny), L. Maestr, Neubergicus Z., Calcaire à *Baculites*, Fresville, Manche, France (Grossouvre 1894, p. 121). Authenticity of the above record based on a single specimen has never been questioned, but all other dateable records of *Hoplitoplacenticeras* are from the Vari Z., U. Campan, of Europe, Africa, North and South America.

Constituent families: Hoplitidae Douvillé, 1890, L. Alb—Cenom; Schloenbachiidae Parona & Bonarelli 1897, U. Alb—Turon; Placenticeratidae Hyatt 1900, U. Alb—Maestr; Engonoceratidae Hyatt 1900, L. Alb—L. Turon.

Comment: Both *Farnhamia* and *Anadesmoceras* were probably derived from *Uhligella* of the Desmocerataceae.

Superfamily DOUVILLEICERATACEAE Parona & Bonarelli 1897

First, Cret Barrem: *Paraspiticeras* Kilian, U. Barrem, S. E. France and Wernsdorfer Beds, Austria.

Last, Cret Alb: *Douvilleiceras clementinum* (d'Orbigny), Lower Gault, M. Alb, Dentatus Z., Benettianus Sz., Aube, Paris basin, France (Casey 1962, p. 263). *Astiericeras astierianum* (d'Orbigny), lower M. Alb, Escragnolles, France, is regarded as a descendant of *Douvilleiceras* and therefore the last of the superfamily by Wright (1957 Treatise L) and Wiedmann (1965), but is regarded as member of the Scaphitaceae by Casey (1961, p. 175).

Constituent families: Douvilleiceratidae Parona & Bonarelli 1897, U. Barrem-basal M. Alb.; Deshayesitidae Stoyanow 1949, L. Apt—U. Apt.; Parahoplitidae Spath 1922, U. Apt—L. Alb. (Casey 1961, p. 173).

Comment: The superfamily is said to have had two independent origins. Douvilleiceratidae probably arose from a member of the Lytoceratidae in the Barrem. The Deshayesitidae probably arose at the base of the Apt from *Callizoniceras* of the Desmoceratidae. The family Parahoplitidae is an offshoot of one of the other two families (Casey 1961, p. 174). [M.K.H.]

REFERENCES

ARKELL, W. J. 1947. The geology of the country around Weymouth, Swanage, Corfe and Lulworth. *Mem. geol. Surv. U.K.*, 386 pp., 19 pls.

—— 1949. Jurassic ammonites in 1949. *Sci. Prog. Lond.*, **37**, 401–17.

—— 1951. A monograph of English Bathonian ammonites. Part 1, 1–46, pls 1–4. *Palaeontogr. Soc.* [*Monogr.*].

—— 1952. A monograph of English Bathonian ammonites. Part 3, 73–102, pls 9–12. *Palaeontogr. Soc.* [*Monogr.*].

BÖSE, E. & CAVINS, O. A. 1927. The Cretaceous and Tertiary of southern Texas and northern Mexico. *Bull. Univ. Tex. Bur. econ. Geol. Technol.*, **2748**, 1–357, pls 1–19.

Chapter 15: Mollusca: Cephalopoda (Ammonoidea)

BRINKMANN, R. 1937. Biostratigraphie des Leymeriellenstammes nebst Bemerkungen zur Paläogeographie des nordwestdeutschen Alb. *Mitt. Geol. St Inst. Hamb.*, **16,** 1–18.

BUCKMAN, S. S. 1889. On the Cotteswold, Midford and Yeovil Sands, and the division between the Lias and the Oolite. *Q. Jl. geol. Soc. Lond.*, **45,** 440–73.

—— 1893. The Bajocian of the Sherborne district; its relation to subjacent and superjacent strata. *Q. Jl geol. Soc. Lond.*, **49,** 479–522.

—— 1910. Certain Jurassic (Lias-Oolite) strata of south Dorset; and their correlation. *Q. Jl geol. Soc. Lond.*, 66, 52–89.

—— 1920. *Type Ammonites*, volume 3, part 23, pls 168–180. London.

—— 1924. *Type Ammonites*, volume 5, part 44, pls 458–476. London.

CASEY, R. 1957. The Cretaceous ammonite genus *Leymeriella*, with a systematic account of its British occurrences. *Palaeontology*, **1,** 28–59, pls 7–10.

—— 1960–1965. A monograph of the Ammonoidea of the Lower Greensand, 6 parts, 546 pp., 90 pls. *Palaeontogr. Soc. [Monogr.]*.

—— 1964b. The Cretaceous Period. *Q. Jl geol. Soc. Lond.*, **120S,** 193–202.

CHAO, K. 1959. Lower Triassic ammonoids from western Kwangsi, China. *Palaeont. Sin.*, (B), 355 pp., 45 pls.

COBBAN, W. A. 1961. The ammonite family Binneyitidae in the western interior of the United States. *J. Paleont.*, **35,** 737–758, pls 87–89.

—— & REESIDE, J. B., Jr. 1952. Correlation of the Cretaceous formations of the western interior of the United States. *Bull. geol. Soc. Am.*, **63,** 1011–1044.

COLLIGNON, M. 1932. Les ammonites pyriteuses de l'Albien supériour du Mont Raynaud à Madagascar. *Annls géol. Madagascar*, **2,** 1–36, pls 1–4.

—— 1950. Recherches sur les faunes albiennes de Madagascar. III, —L'Albien de Komihevitra. *Annls. géol. Madagascar*, **17,** 19–54, pls 3–9.

DIENER, C. 1915. Cephalopoda Triadica *in Fossilium Catalogus (Animalia)*, **8.**

DONOVAN, D. T. 1964. Cephalopod phylogeny and classification. *Biol. Rev.*, **39,** 259–87.

—— & HÖLDER, H. 1958. On the existence of heteromorph ammonoids in the Lias. *Neues Jb. Geol. Paläont., Mh.*, **1958,** 217–220.

DRUSHCHITZ, V. V. & KUDRYAVTSEVA, M. P. 1960. [*Atlas of Lower Cretaceous faunas in the northern Caucasus and the Crimea*]. 701 pp., 150 pls. Moscow (Russian).

DUBAR, G. 1961. Les Hildoceratidae du Domérien des Pyrénées et l'apparition de cette famille au Pleinsbachien inférieur en Afrique du nord. *Annls Servs inf. géol. Mém. Bur. Rech. géol. geophys. min*, **1961** (4), 245–57.

DU DRESNAY, R. 1963. Quelques ammonites de la partie inférieure du Pliensbachien (Carixien et Domerian pro parte) du jbel Bou-Rharraf (Haut Atlas oriental). *Notes Mem. Serv. Mines Carte géol. Maroc*, **23,** 141–164.

ERBEN, H. K. 1964. Die evolution der ältesten Ammonoidea, Leif. 1. *Neues Jb. Geol. Paläont., Abh.*, **120,** 107–212.

—— 1965. Die evolution der ältesten Ammonoidea, Leif, 2. *Neues Jb. Geol. Paläont., Abh.*, **122,** 275–312.

FLOWER, R. H. 1964. The nautiloid order Ellesmeroceratida (Cephalopoda). *Mem. Inst. Min. Technol. New Mex.*, **12,** 1–234.

FRECH, F. 1902. Über devonische Ammoneen. *Beitr. Paläont. Geol. Ost.-Ung.*, **14,** 27–112.

GEMMELLARO, G. G. 1884. Sui fossili degli strati a *Terebratula aspasia* della contrada Rocche Rosse presso Galati (Provincia di Messina). *Giorn. Sci. nat. econ. Palermo*, **16,** 167–218, pls 1–7.

—— 1887. La fauna dei calcari con Fusulina della valle del Fiume Sosio (nella provincia di Palermo). *Giorn. Sci. nat. econ. Palermo*, **19,** 1–160, pls 1–10.

GERASIMOV, P. A., MIGACHEVA, E. E., NAIDIN, D. P. & STEPLIN, B. P. 1962. [*Regional Geology of the U.S.S.R. 5. Jurassic and Cretaceous deposits of the Russian Platform*], 196 pp.. Moscow (Russian).

GROUSSOUVRE, A. de 1894. Recherches sur la Craie supérieure. Part 2, Paléontologie, les ammonites de la Craie supérieur. *Mém. Serv. Carte géol. dét. Fr.*, 264 pp., 39 pls.

Hoffmann, K. 1962. Lias und Dogger im Untergrund der Niederrheinischen Bucht. *Fortschr. Geol. Rheinld. Westf.* **6**, 105–184.

House, M. R. 1962. Observations on the ammonoid succession of the North American Devonian. *J. Paleont.*, **36**, 247–284.

—— 1965. A study in the Tornoceratidae. *Phil. Trans. R. Soc.* (B), **250**, 79–130.

Imlay, R. W. 1942. Late Jurassic fossils from Cuba and their economic significance. *Bull. Soc. geol. Am.* **53**, 1417–1478, pls 1–12.

—— 1960. Ammonites of early Cretaceous age (Valanginian and Hauterivian) from the Pacific Coast States. *Prof. Pap. U.S. geol. Surv.*, **334-F**, 163–228, pls 24–43.

—— 1964. Middle Bajocian ammonites from the Cork Inlet region, Alaska. *Prof. Pap. U.S. geol. Surv.*, **418-B**, 60 pp., 29 pls.

Jaworski, E. 1926a. Beiträge zur Paläontologie und Stratigraphie des Lias, Doggers, Tithons und der Unterkreide in den Kordilleren im Süden der Provinz Mendoza (Argentinien). Teil 1. Lias und Dogger. *Geol. Rdsch.*, **17A**, 373–427, pls 11–13.

—— 1926b. La fauna del Lias y Dogger de la cordillera Argentina en la parte meridional de la provincia de Mendoza. *Actas Acad. nac. Cienc. Cordoba*, **9**, 135–318, pls 1–4.

Jeletzky, J. A. 1951. Die Stratigraphie und Belemnitenfauna des Obercampan und Maastricht Westfalens, Nordwestdeutschland und Dänemarks sowie einige allgemeine Gliederungs—Probleme der jüngeren borealen Oberkreide Eurasiens. *Beih. geol. Jb.*, **1**, 142, 7 pls.

Johnston, F. N. 1941. Trias at New Pass Nevada (New Lower Karnic Ammonoids). *J. Paleont*, **15**, 447–491.

Kiparisova, L. D. 1961. [Palaeontological Fundamentals for the Stratigraphy of Triassic Deposits of the Primor'ye Region, Part I, Cephalopod Mollusca.] *Trudÿ vses. nauchno-issled. geol. Inst.* new series, **48** (Russian).

Kossmat, F. 1895. Untersuchungen über die Süddindische Kreideformation. *Beitr. Paläont. Geol. Öst.-Ung.*, **9**, 97–203, pls 15–25.

Krumbeck, L. 1944. Zur Stratigraphie und Faunenkunde des Lias Zeta in Nordbayern. Teil 2. *Z. dt. geol. Ges.*, **96**, 1–71.

Kummel, B. 1952. A classification of the Triassic ammonoids. *J. Paleont.*, **26**, 847–853.

—— & Steele, G. 1962. Ammonites from the *Meekoceras graciltatus* zone at Crittenden Spring, Elko County, Nevada. *J. Palaeont.*, **36**, 638–703.

Kutassy, A. 1932. Cephalopoda Triadica (II) *in Fossilium Catalogus* (*Animalia*), **56**.

Lang, W. D. 1923. Shales-with-"Beef", a sequence in the Lower Lias of the Dorset Coast. *Q. Jl. geol. Soc. Lond.*, **79**, 47–66.

Lange, W. 1929. Zur kenntnis des Oberdevons am Enkeberg und bei Balve (Sauerland). *Abh. preuss. geol. Landesanst.* (N.F.), **119**, 1–132.

—— 1952. Der Untere Lias am Fonsjoch (östliches Karwendelgebirge) und seine Ammonitenfauna. *Palaeontographica* **102A**, 49–162.

Librovitch, L. S. 1940. [Carboniferous Ammonoids of North Kazakhstan *in Paleontology of U.S.S.R.*, Vol. IV, Part 9. Fasc. 1]. Academii Nauk SSSR (Russian).

Luppov, N. P. & Drushchitz, V. V. 1958. *in* Orlov, Yu. A. (Editor). *Osnovy Paleontologii.* [*Mollusca-Cephalopoda II, Ammonoidea, Dibranchiata.*] Moscow (Russian).

Matsumoto, T. 1960. Upper Cretaceous ammonites of California. Part 3. *Mem. Fac. Sci. Kyushu Univ.* (D), Special vol. **2**, 1–204, pls 1–2.

Miller, A. K. & Furnish, W. M. 1940. Permian Ammonoids of the Guadalupe Mountain Region and Adjacent areas. *Spec. Pap. geol. Soc. Am.*, **26**, 242 pp., 44 pls.

Monestier, J. 1922. Sur la stratigraphie paléontologique du Toarcien inférieur et du Toarcien moyen dans la région SE de l'Aveyron. *Bull. Soc. géol. Fr.* (4), **21**, 322–344.

Orlov, Y. A. (Editor) 1962. *Osnovy Paleontologii., Mollyuski: Golovonogie*, 1. Akademii Nauk SSSR, Moscow.

Petter, G. 1959. Goniatites Dévoniennes du Sahara. *Mém. Carte géol. Algér. Paléont.* **2**, 1–313.

Popov, Y. N. 1962. [New species of Ammonoids from the Olenek Stage of the upper Yana River and the Lena-Olenek interfluve.] *Trudÿ nauchno-issled. Geol. Inst. Arkt.*, **127** 176–189 (Russian).

Chapter 15: Mollusca: Cephalopoda (Ammonoidea)

REESIDE, J. B. 1962. Cretaceous ammonites of New Jersey. *In* H. G. Richards *et al*, 1962, The Cretaceous fossils of New Jersey, part 2. *Bull. geol. Surv. Jers.*, **61** (2), 113–137, pls 68–75.

RUZHENCEV, V. E. 1959. [Classification of the superfamily *Otocerataceae*.] *Paleont. Zh.*, 1959, no. 2, 56–67 (Russian).

SAYN, G. 1903. *in* Proceedings of meeting of 16th March, 1903. *Bull. Soc. géol. Fr.* (4), **3**, 142–143.

—— & ROMAN, F. 1905. L'Hauterivien et le Barrémien de la rive droite du Rhône et du Bas—Languedoc. *Bull. Soc. géol. Fr.* (4), **4**, 605–640.

SCHINDEWOLF, O. H. 1923. Beiträge zur kenntnis des Paläozoicums in Oberfranken, Osthüringen und dem Sächsischen Vogtlande (1). *Neues Jb. Miner. geol. Paläont.*, **49**, 250–357, 393–509.

—— 1933. Vergleichende Morphologie und Phylogenie der Anfangskammern tetrabranchiater Cephalopoden. *Abh. Preuss. geol. Landesanst.* (N.F.), **148**, 1–115.

—— 1937a. Zwei neue bemerkenswerte Goniatiten Gattungen des rhenischen Oberdevons. *Jb. preuss. geol. Landesanst., Berg Akad.*, **58**, 242–256.

—— 1937b. Zur Stratigraphie und Paläontologie der Wocklumer Schichten (Oberdevon). *Abh. preuss. geol. Landesanst.* (N.F.), **178**, 1–132.

SELWOOD, E. B. 1960. The ammonoid and trilobite faunas of the Upper Devonian and Lowest Carboniferous rocks of the Launceston area of Cornwall. *Palaeontology*, **3**, 153–185.

SHIMANSKIY, V. N. 1954. Pryamye nautiloidei i bactritoidei sakmarskogo i artinskogo yarusov yuzhnogo Urala. *Trudȳ paleont. Inst.* **44**, 1–156.

SILBERLING, N. J. 1959. Pre-Tertiary Stratigraphy and Upper Triassic Paleontology of the Union District, Shoshone Mountains, Nevada. *Prof. Pap. U.S. Geol. Surv.*, **322.**

—— 1962. Stratigraphic Distribution of Middle Triassic Ammonites at Fossil Hill, Humboldt Range, Nevada. *J. Paleont.*, **36,** 153–160.

SMITH, J. P. 1903. The Carboniferous ammonoids of America. *Monogr. U.S. geol. Surv.*, **42,** 1–211, pls 1–29.

SOLIGNAC, M. 1927. Étude géologique de la Tunisie septentrionale. *Carte Geol. Tunisie*, 756 pp.

SPATH, L. F. 1924. On the ammonites of the Speeton Clay and the subdivisions of the Neocomian. *Geol. Mag.*, **61,** 73–89.

—— 1930. On the Cephalopoda of the Uitenhage Beds. *Ann. S. Afr. Mus.*, **28,** 131–158, pls 13–15.

—— 1934. *Catalogue of the fossil cephalopoda in the British Museum (Natural History). Part IV. The Ammonoidea of the Trias (I).* 521 pp., 18 pls. London, British Museum (Natural History).

—— 1935. The upper Jurassic invertebrate faunas of Cape Leslie, Milne Land. 1, Oxfordian and Lower Kimmeridgian. *Meddr. Grønland*, **99** (2), 82 pp., 15 pls.

—— 1936. The ammonites of the Green Ammonite Beds of Dorset. *Q. Jl geol. Soc. Lond.* **92,** 438–55, pl. 38.

—— 1950. A new Tithonian ammonoid fauna from Kurdistan, northern Iraq. *Bull. Brit. Mus. nat. Hist. Geol.*, **1,** 93–146, pls 6–10.

—— 1951. *Catalogue of the fossil cephalopoda in the British Museum (Natural History). Part V. The Ammonoidea of the Trias (II).* London, British Museum (Natural History).

STEPHENSON, L. W. 1941. The larger invertebrate fossils of the Navarro Group of Texas. *Bull. Univ. Tex. Bur. econ. Geol. Technol.*, **4101,** 641 pp., 95 pls.

SWEET, W. H. 1958. The Middle Ordovician of the Oslo region, Norway, 10. Nautiloid cephalopods. *Norsk geol. Tidsskr.*, **38,** 1–178.

TOZER, E. T. 1961. Triassic Stratigraphy and Faunas, Queen Elizabeth Islands, Arctic Archipelago. *Mem. geol. Surv. Brch Can.*, **316.**

—— 1965a. Latest Lower Triassic Ammonoids from Ellesmere Island and Northeastern British Columbia. *Bull. Geol. Surv. Can.*, **123.**

—— 1965b. Lower Triassic Stages and Ammonoid Zones of Arctic Canada. *Geol. Surv. Pap. Can.*, **65-12.**

TREATISE, K. 1964. Mollusca 3: Nautiloidea *in* Moore, R. C. (Editor) *Treatise on Invertebrate Paleontology*, Part K. University of Kansas Press.

TREATISE, L. 1957. ARKELL, W. J., *et al.* Mollusca 4: Ammonoidea *in* MOORE, R. C. (Editor) *Treatise on Invertebrate Paleontology*, Part L. University of Kansas Press.

TRUEMAN, A. E. 1920. The Liassic rocks of the Cardiff district. *Proc. Geol. Ass. Lond.* **31,** 93–107.

TUTCHER, J. W. & TRUEMAN, A. E. 1925. The Liassic rocks of the Radstock district (Somerset). *Quart. J. Geol. Soc. Lond.* **81,** 595–666.

WALLISER, O. H. 1956. Chronologie des Lias α zwischen Fildern und Klattgau (Arieten-schichten, Sudwestdeutschland). *Neues Jb. Geol. Paläont., Abh.,* **103,** 181–222, pls 10, 11.

—— 1962. Die Arten der Gattung *Gyroceratites* H. v. Meyer 1831 (Ammonoidea, Unter-bis Mitteldevon). *Neues Jb. Geol. Paläont., Mh.* for 1962, 565–576.

WEDEKIND, R. 1908. Die Cephalopodenfauna des höheren Oberdevon am Enkeberge. *Neues Jb. Miner. Geol. Paläont.,* 26, 565–634.

—— 1917. Die Genera der Palaeoammonoidea (Goniatiten). *Palaeontographica,* **62,** 85–184.

WESTERMANN, G. 1956. Phylogenie des Stephanocerataceae und Perisphinctaceae des Dogger. *Neues Jb. Geol. Paläont., Abh.,* **103,** 233–279.

WHITEAVES, J. F. 1884. On the fossils of the coal bearing deposits of the Queen Charlotte Islands collected by Mr. G. M. Dawson in 1878. *Geol. Surv. Can.,* Mesozoic Fossils **1,** 3, 191–262, pls 22–33.

WHITEHOUSE, F. W. 1928. The correlation of the marine Cretaceous deposits of Australia. *Rep. Australas. Ass. Advmt Sci.,* **18,** 275–280.

WIEDMANN, J. 1962. Habitus, Skulptur und Sutur bei Kreide-Ammonoideen. *Neues Jb. Geol. Paläont., Abh.,* **114,** 317–332, pl. 18.

—— 1965. Origin, limits and systematic position of *Scaphites. Palaeontology,* **8,** 397–453, pls 53–60.

WRIGHT, C. W. 1963. Cretaceous ammonites from Bathurst Island, northern Australia. *Palaeontology,* **6,** 597–614, pls 81–87.

ZITTEL, K. A. 1870. Fauna der ältern Cephalopodenführenden Tithonbildungen. *Palaeontographica,* Suppl. **1,** 1–192, pls 1–5.

[Professor] D. T. DONOVAN, D.SC. PH.D. F.L.S. F.G.S.
Department of Geology, University College, Gower Street, London W C 1.

[Professor] F. HODSON, PH.D. F.G.S.
Department of Geology, The University, Southampton.

M. K. HOWARTH, B.SC. PH.D. F.G.S.
Department of Palaeontology, British Museum (Natural History), Cromwell Road, London S W 7.

[Professor] M. R. HOUSE M.A. PH.D. F.G.S.
Department of Geology, The University, Kingston upon Hull, Yorkshire.

E. T. TOZER, M.A. PH.D. F.R.C.S. F.G.S.
Geological Survey of Canada, Department of Energy, Mines & Resources, Ottawa, Canada.

C. W. WRIGHT, M.A. F.G.S.
37 Phillimore Gardens, London W 8.

CHAPTER 16

Mollusca: Cephalopoda (Coleoidea)

Contributors: D. T. DONOVAN & J. M. HANCOCK

Order BELEMNOIDEA Steinmann 1907

There is disagreement at the present time on the classification of the earliest Belemnoidea, and their relation to the Bactritoidea from which they are probably derived (see Flower and Gordon 1959, Shimansky 1960, Erben 1964, Jeletzky 1965). There is no doubt that there are belemnoids at least as early as the Namurian, but the variety of this fauna suggests that they had developed before this (Upper Devonian?). Their similarity to the Parabactritidae of Shimansky is such that Flower and Gordon thought that the Parabactritidae might be belemnoids, but Shimansky and Erben are convincing in making a distinction, although Erben suggests that the Belemnoidea s.s. are derived from the Parabactritidae. A fragment, which may be a belemnoid, from the Devonian (Eifel?) of Couvain, Belgium, is figured by Koninck (1843).

The classification used here is conservative. For Jeletzky the only pre-Jurassic belemnoid is *Eobelemnites* Flower (Namurian), and the forms here considered under the subfamily Aulacoceratinae are assigned to a separate order—the Aulacocerida. For Erben some of the Aulacoceratinae are Belemnoidea s.s. (e.g. *Mojsisovicsteuthis convergens* (v. Hauer) from the Karnian), and some are a separate order the Protobelemnoidea which Erben believes are derived from the Bactritidae, not the Parabactritidae.

There is disagreement on what is the last belemnoid. There are genera which are intermediate between belemnoids and sepiids. I have placed *Bayanoteuthis* (Eocene), which probably had a rostrum of calcite, in the Belemnoidea. But *Styracoteuthis* (Eocene) whose rostrum has lost all the details of its internal structure through recrystallisation, was probably of aragonite (like *Vasseuria*, see Curry 1955), and is here considered to be a sepiid.

Family BELEMNITIDAE d'Orbigny 1845

Subfamily AULACOCERATINAE Bernard 1895 emend

First, Carb Namur: *Paleoconus bakeri* Flower and Gordon, *Hematites barbarae* Flower and Gordon, *H. burbankensis* Flower and Gordon, *Bactritimimus ulrichi* Flower and Gordon, *B. girtyi* Flower and Gordon, L. Eumorphoceras Z. (E[1]), Arkansas, U.S.A., Fayetteville Shale; Utah, U.S.A., Chainman Shale (Flower and Gordon 1959). *Eobelemnites caneyense* Flower from the Caney Shale in Oklahoma is not accurately dated but is about the same age.

Last, Jur Toarc: *Ausseites* spp., Alps, Appenines, Corsica, Spain, Peru.

Comment: This subfamily probably embraces two distinct groups: see remarks on the order as a whole.

The Fossil Record, pp. 461–467. Geological Society of London, 1967. Printed in Northern Ireland.

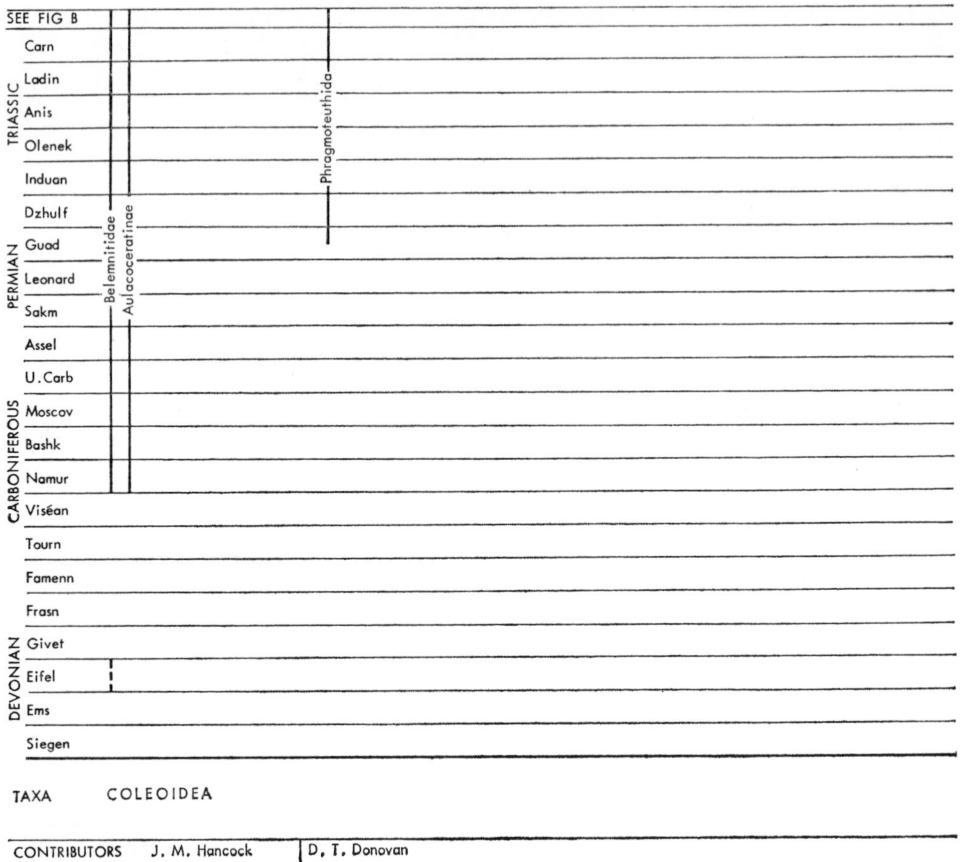

SEE FIG B					
TRIASSIC Carn					
Ladin		Phragmoteuthida			
Anis					
Olenek					
Induan					
PERMIAN Dzhulf	Belemnitidae	Aulacoceratinae			
Guad					
Leonard					
Sakm					
Assel					
CARBONIFEROUS U.Carb					
Moscov					
Bashk					
Namur					
Viséan					
Tourn					
DEVONIAN Famenn					
Frasn					
Givet					
Eifel					
Ems					
Siegen					

TAXA   COLEOIDEA

CONTRIBUTORS   J. M. Hancock | D. T. Donovan

FIG. 16.1 A

Subfamily PASSALOTEUTHINAE Naef 1922

First, Jur L.Sinem: *Nannobelus acutus* (Miller), Bucklandi Z., west Europe (Werner 1912).

Last, Jur U.Bajoc: *Megateuthis gigantea* auct., west Europe.

Comment: I am uncertain if *Coeloteuthis* Lissajous 1906 should be placed in a separate sub-family—the Coeloteuthinae Naef 1922; in any case the horizons of this rare genus are poorly recorded, but it is probably U.Sinem to L.Pliens.

Subfamily HASTATINAE Stolley 1919

First, Jur L.Pliens: *Hastites* spp., west Europe. There is uncertainty about which species appears first and when. In Dorset, England, *H. fustiformis* Lang and *H. spadix-ari* (M. Simpson) appear in the Ibex Z. (valdani Subz.) (Lang 1928). In the Schwabian Jura, according to Schwegler (1962, 148-54), *H. charmouthensis* (Mayer) is earlier than the true *H. clavatus* (Schlotheim), but both appear in the lower part of Lias *Gamma* (= L.Pliens) but the zone is not given. There are old records (e.g. Phillips 1866) of *Belemnites clavatus* from the U. Sinem (Raricostatum Z.).

Last, Cret L.Cenom: (i) *Neohibolites minimus* var. *ultimus* (d'Orbigny), Mantelli Z., S.E. England, Glauconitic Marl and Lower Chalk; Russian platform, Exogyra conica Z., (Naidin 1964); Madagascar, Martimpreyi Z (Collignon 1959). Some records of *Belemnites ultimus* from the Cenomanian actually refer to *Actinocamax primus* Arkhangelsky (e.g. Hume 1897). *Neohibolites stilus* (Blandford), Cenom, Madagascar.

462

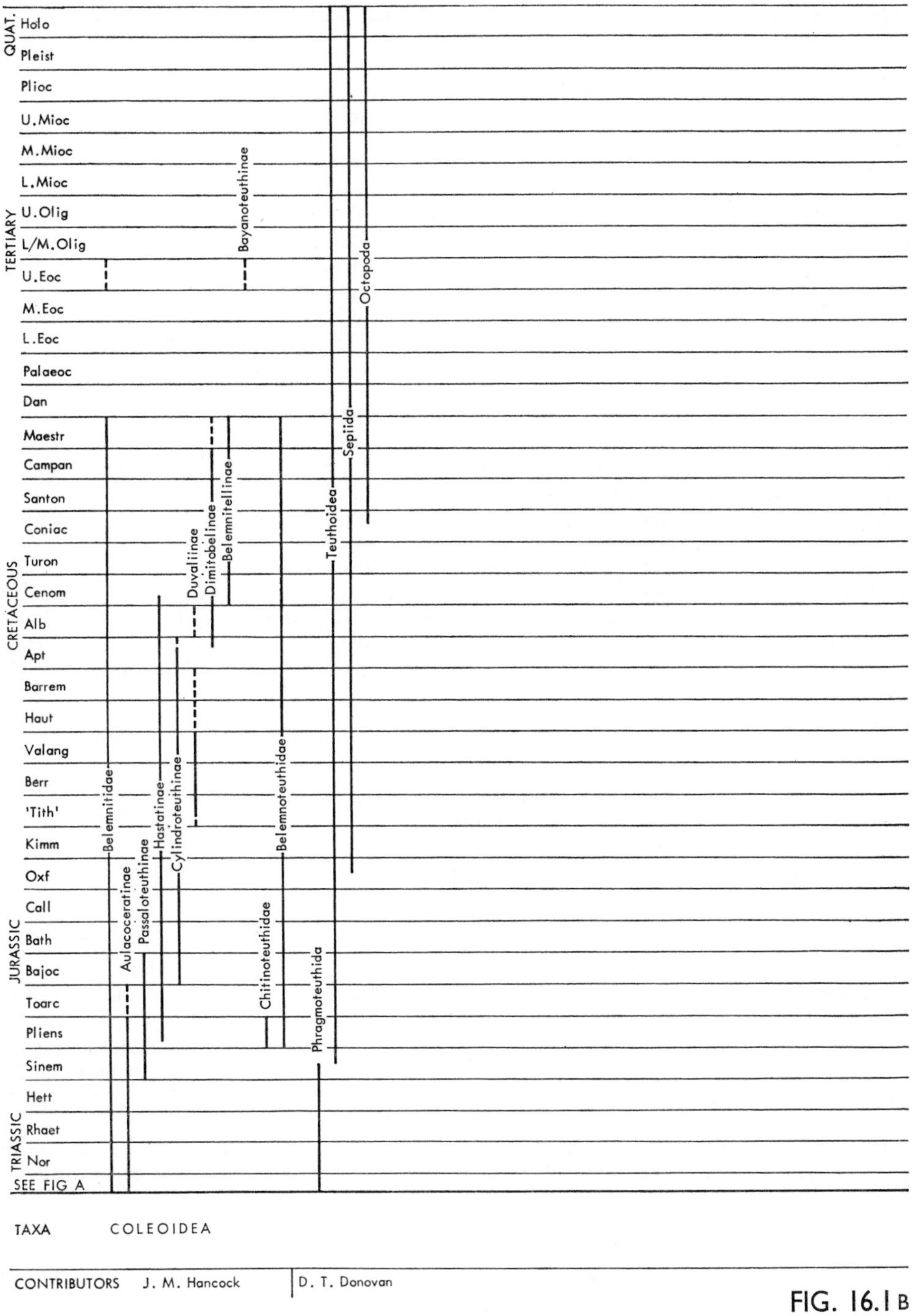
QUAT.
Holo
Pleist
Plioc
U.Mioc
M.Mioc
L.Mioc
TERTIARY
U.Olig
L/M.Olig
U.Eoc
M.Eoc
L.Eoc
Palaeoc
Dan
Maestr
Campan
Santon
Coniac
CRETACEOUS
Turon
Cenom
Alb
Apt
Barrem
Haut
Valang
Berr
'Tith'
Kimm
Oxf
Call
JURASSIC
Bath
Bajoc
Toarc
Pliens
Sinem
Hett
TRIASSIC
Rhaet
Nor
SEE FIG A
Bayanoteuthinae
Octopoda
Sepida
Teuthoidea
Belemnitellinae
Dimitobelinae
Duvaliinae
Belemnoteuthidae
Belemnitidae
Cylindroteuthinae
Hastatinae
Passaloteuthinae
Aulacoceratinae
Chitinoteuthidae
Phragmoteuthida
TAXA COLEOIDEA
CONTRIBUTORS J. M. Hancock | D. T. Donovan

FIG. 16.1 B

(ii) *Parahibolites tourtiae* Weignera, Mantelli Z., Russian platform, Exogyra conica Z. (Naidin 1964); Poland; Germany.

Subfamily CYLINDROTEUTHINAE Stolley 1919 emend Naef 1922

First, Jur Bajoc: *Cylindroteuthis blainvilli* (Voltz), *C. alpina* (Ooster), *C. (Holcobelus) munieri* (Deslongchamps), relative ages of these species unknown, W. Europe.

Last, Cret Apt: *Oxyteuthis depressus* Stolley, probably L.Apt, Fissicostatus Z. (Bodei Subz.), but exact horizon in Sutterby Marl, Lincolnshire, England, not recorded; the base of this fm contains ammonites of horizons through nearly whole of L.Apt and the main mass of the Marl is U.Apt (Nutfieldensis Z.). *Oxyteuthis gracilis* Frebold, U. Apt, Koldeway Island, northern East Greenland; *Belemnites jarneri* and *B. borealis* Frebold from the same locality are probably also *Oxyteuthis* (Frebold 1935).

Comment: The Cylindroteuthinae are probably an offshoot of the Passaloteuthinae; the age of the first Cylindroteuthid depends on where the dividing line is placed. Naef (1922) suggests that *Belemnites trabeculus* Lissajous (U.Pliens) may be an intermediate.

Subfamily DUVALIINAE Pavlow 1913

First, Jur "Tith": *Conobelus conophorus* (Oppel), *Duvalia tithonica* Oppel, Transitorius Z., Czechoslovakia, Stramberg Beds; also known from France, Spain, Sicily and Crimea. Stevens (1963) says *Duvalia* appears in Europe in the early "Tith".

Last, Cret Alb?: *Duvalia effrenata* Rothpletz, Vilser Alps, Austria, Gaultmergel (Rothpletz 1886). *Duvalia inaequilateralis* v.Eichwald, Chasik Island, Alaska, Gault (Eichwald 1871).

Comment: Schwegler (1949, 306) suggests that there is a small group of forerunners of this subfamily ("Produvalia") as early as L.Malm. (?Oxf). It is generally considered that pre-Tith belemnites with lateral grooves which have been referred to Duvaliinae (e.g. Lissajous, 1925, 30) are members of the Hastatinae, e.g. *Belemnopsis* and *Dicoelites*. Similarly *"Pseudobelus" stoliczkai* Spengler and *"P". blandfordi* Spengler, from the U.Alb L. Utatur Group, S. India (Spengler 1910) are *Parahibolites*. The Albian records of *Duvalia* above, are of doubtful date, and it may well be that the subfamily is entirely pre-Apt.

Subfamily DIMITOBELINAE Whitehouse 1924

First, Cret L.Apt?: *Peratobelus australis* (Phillips), Queensland, Blythesdale Group.

Last, Cret Maestr: *Dimitobelus hectori* Stevens, Amuri Bluff, New Zealand, 4-6 ft. below Teredo Limestone, Haumurian stage (Stevens 1965).

Comment: Limited geographically to south India, New Guinea, Australia and New Zealand.

Subfamily BELEMNITELLINAE Pavlow 1913

First, Cret L.Cenom: *Actinocamax (Praeactinocamax) primus* Arkhangelsky, Mantelli Z., Russian platform (Naidin 1964); Glauconite Sands, Co. Antrim, Ireland (Hancock 1961).

Last, Cret U.Maestr: *Fusiteuthis polonica* Kongiel, Casimirovensis Z., middle Vistula valley, central Poland, horizon z (Kongiel 1962).

Belemnella casimirovensis (Skolozdrówna) and about three other allied species, Casimirovensis Z., Russian platform, Crimea and north Caucasus (Gerasimov *et al.* 1962), central Poland (Kongiel 1962), Denmark (Birkelund 1957), Maastricht Tuff, the Netherlands (Limburg) and Belgium (Schmid 1959).

Comment: *"Belemnites" upwarensis* Keeping from the Aptian is not considered to belong to this subfamily. Apart from one record from northern South America, limited geographically to the northern part of the northern hemisphere.

Subfamily BAYANOTEUTHINAE Naef 1922 emend.

First and **Last,** Tert U.Eoc: *Bayanoteuthis rugifer* (Schloenbach), Bremier, France, Sables de Beauchamp; also Bavaria and Italy.

Comment: The other members of the Neobelemnitidae Pavlow are here considered part of the Sepiida.

Chapter 16: Mollusca: Cephalopoda (Coleoidea)

Family CHITINOTEUTHIDAE Müller-Stoll 1936

First, Jur L.Pliens: *Chitinoteuthis* sp.indet., Kirchheim, Schwabian Jura, Lias (Gamma). Roger (1952, 708) records the family in the Lower Lias of south France.

Last, Jur U.Pliens: *Chitinoteuthis decidua* Müller-Stoll, *C. crassicristata* Müller-Stoll, Schwabian Jura, Lower Depressus Beds (Müller-Stoll 1936).

Family BELEMNOTEUTHIDAE Zittel 1885

First, Jur L.Pliens: *Xiphoteuthis elongata* de la Beche, Jamesoni Z. (s.l.), Lyme Regis, England.

Last, Cret "Maestr": *Greenlandibelus rosenkrantzi* (Birkelund), Agatdalen valley (Angmartussut), Nugssuaq, West Greenland (Birkelund 1956).

Comment: *Permoteuthis* Rosenkrantz 1946 from the Permian of east Greenland, is here considered a member of the Phragmoteuthida, but this family is still used to accommodate a rather wide variety of forms. [J.M.H.]

Order OCTOPODA Leach 1817

First, Cret Coniac: *Palaeoctopus newboldi* (H. Woodward), Fish Beds of Sahel-Alma, Lebanon (Roger 1944). **Extant.**

Comment: According to Jeletzky (1965) *Palaeoctopus* is probably a "specialized representative of Cirromorphina". The only other fossil octopods are argonauts which are known from the Miocene onwards.

Order SEPIIDA Leach 1817

First, Jur U.Oxf: *Voltzia* [? = *Trachyteuthis*] *palmeri* Schevill, Jagua Fm, Cuba (Schevill 1950). **Extant.**

Comment: Jeletzky (1965) regards Jurassic records of sepiids as doubtful. In his view the earliest undoubted sepiid is *Belemnosella* Naef 1922 first known from Palaeoc.

Order TEUTHOIDEA Naef 1916

First, Jur Sinem: *Loligosepia bucklandi* (Voltz) Turneri Z., Dorset, England (Buckland 1837 pl.28, figs. 6, 7, pl. 29, figs. 1–3, pl. 30). **Extant.**

Comment: Relationship of *Loligosepia* to living Vampyromorpha is an open question. The above record assumes that one follows Jeletzky (1965) who includes the vampyromorphs as a suborder of Teuthoidea. The horizon of the examples figured by Buckland is recorded as Lias. A comparable specimen in B.M.(N.H.) (C4639) is dated as Turneri Zone by ammonites in the matrix.

Order PHRAGMOTEUTHIDA Jeletzky 1964

First, U.Perm: *Permoteuthis groenlandica* Rosenkrantz, Clavering Island, East Greenland (Rosenkrantz 1946).

Last, L.Jur: England (unpublished; information from L. Bairstow). [D.T.D.]

REFERENCES

BIRKELUND, T. 1956. Upper Cretaceous Belemnites from West Greenland. *Meddr Grønland*, **137,** no. 9.

—— 1957. Upper Cretaceous Belemnites from Denmark. *K. danske Vidensk. Selsk. Skr. (biol.),* **9,** no. I.

BUCKLAND, W. 1837. *Geology and mineralogy considered with reference to Natural Theology.* 2nd Ed. London: Wm. Pickering; 2 vols.

COLLIGNON, M. 1959. Corrélations sommaires entre les dépôts du Crétacé supérieur de Madagascar et ceux de l'Europe Occidentale, ... *C.r. Congr. Socs. sav. Paris Sect. Sci., Colloque sur le Crétacé Supérieur Français, Dijon* 1959, 41–52.

CURRY, D. 1955. The Occurrence of the Dibranchiate Cephalopods *Vasseuria* and *Belosepiella* in the English Eocene, with Notes on their Structure. *Proc. malacol. Soc. Lond.,* **31,** 3–22.

EICHWALD, E. von 1871. *Geognostisch-paläontologische Bemerkungen über die Halbinsel Mangischlak und die Aleutischen Inseln.* pp. 88–200, St Petersburg.

ERBEN, H. K. 1964. Bactritoidea. *in* MOORE, R. C. (Editor) *Treatise on Invertebrate Paleontology,* Part K. 491–505. University of Kansas Press.

FLOWER, R. H. & GORDON, M., Jr. 1959. More Mississippian Belemnites. *J. Paleont.,* **33,** 809–42, pl. 112–116.

FREBOLD, H. 1935. Marines Aptien von der Koldewey Insel (Nördliches Ostgrönland). *Meddr. Grønland,* **95,** no. 4.

GERASIMOV, P. A., MEEGACHEVA, E. E., NAIDIN, D. P. & STERLIN, B. P. 1962. [Jurassic and Cretaceous Sediments of the Russian Platform]. *Och. Geol. SSSR,* **5** (Russian).

HANCOCK, J. M. 1961. The Cretaceous System in Northern Ireland. *Q. J. geol. Soc. Lond.,* **117,** 11–36.

HUME, W. F. 1897. The Cretaceous strata of County Antrim. *Q. J. geol. Soc. Lond.,* **53,** 540–606.

JELETZKY, J. A. 1965 Taxonomy and Phylogeny of Fossil Coleoidea (=Dibranchiata). *Geol. Surv. Pap. Can.,* **65-2.**

KONGIEL, R. 1962. On belemnites from Maestrichtian, Campanian and Santonian sediments in the Middle Vistula valley (Central Poland). *Pr. Muz. Ziemi,* **5,** 3–148, pl. 1–21.

KONINCK, L. de 1843. Notice sur un coquille fossile des terrains anciens de Belgique. *Bull. Acad. r. Belg. Cl. Sci.,* **10,** 207–8, 1 plate.

LANG, W. D. 1928. The Belemnite Marls of Charmouth, a Series in the Lias of the Dorset Coast. *Q. J. geol. Soc. Lond.,* **84,** 179–257, pl. 13–18.

LISSAJOUS, M. 1925. Répertoire alphabétique des Bélemnites jurassiques précédé d'un essai de classification. *Trav. Lab. Géol. Univ. Lyon,* **8.**

MÜLLER-STOLL, H. 1936. Beitrage zur Anatomie der Belemnoidea. *Nova Acta Leop.* (new series), **4,** 159–226, pl. 56–69.

NAEF, A. 1922. *Die Fossilen Tintenfische.* Jena.

NAIDIN, D. P. 1964. [*Upper Cretaceous Belemnites of the Russian Platform and adjoining regions*]. Moscow University (Russian).

PHILLIPS, J. 1866. A monograph of British Belemnitidae: Jurassic; part 2. *Palaeontgr. Soc.* [*Monogr.*]

ROGER, J. 1944. Phylogénie des céphalopodes octopodes: *Palaeoctopus newboldi* (Sowerby 1846) Woodward. *Bull. Soc. géol. Fr.* (5), **14,** 83–98.

—— 1952. Sous-classe des Dibranchiata *in* Piveteau, J. *Traité de Paléontologie,* **2,** 689–755.

ROSENKRANTZ, A. 1946. Krogbarnende Cephalopoder fra Østgrønlands Perm. *Meddr. Dansk geol. Foren.,* **11,** 160–161.

ROTHPLETZ, A. 1886. Geologisch-paläontologische Monographie der Vilser Alpen, etc. *Palaeontographica,* **33,** 1-180, pl. 1–17.

SCHEVILL, W. E. 1950. An Upper Jurassic sepioid from Cuba. *J. Paleont.* **24,** 99-101.

SCHMID, F. 1959. Biostratigraphie du Campanien-Maastrichtien du N E de la Belgique sur la base des Bélemnites. *Annls, Soc. géol. Belg.,* **82,** B235–56.

SCHWEGLER, E. 1949. Vorläufige Mitteilung über Grundsätze und Ergebnisse einer Revision der Belemnitenfauna des Schwäbischen Jura. *Neues Jb. Miner. Geol. Paläont. Mh.* for 1949, 294–306.

—— 1962. Revision der Belemnitenfauna des Schwäbischen Jura. *Palaeontographica,* **120,** 121–64.

SHIMANSKY, V. N. 1960. New Mississippian Belemnites (review of Flower and Gordon 1959 in Russian). *Paleont. Zh.,* **2,** 158–62.

SPENGLER, E. 1910. Die Nautiliden und Belemniten des Trichinopoly distrikts. *Beitr. Paläont. Geol. Öst.-Ung.,* **23,** 125–57, pl. 11–14.

STEVENS, G. R. 1963. Faunal Realms in Jurassic and Cretaceous Belemnites. *Geol. Mag.,* **100,** 481–97.

—— 1965. The Jurassic and Cretaceous Belemnites of New Zealand and a Review of the Jurassic and Cretaceous Belemnites of the Indo-Pacific Region. *Palaeont. Bull., Wellington,* **36.**

Chapter 16: Mollusca: Cephalopoda (Coleoidea)

WERNER, E. 1912. Über die Belemniten des schwäbischen Lias und die mitihnen verwandten Formen des Braunen Jura (Acoeli). *Palaeontographica*, **59,** 103–46, pl. 10–13.

WHITEHOUSE, F. W. 1924. Dimitobelidae—A New Family of Cretaceous Belemnites. *Geol. Mag.*, **61,** 410–6.

[Professor] D. T. Donovan, D.SC. PH.D. F.L.S. F.G.S.
Department of Geology, University College, Gower Street, London W C 1.

J. M. Hancock, M.A. PH.D. F.G.S.
Department of Geology, King's College, Strand, London W C 2.

CHAPTER 17

Mollusca: Scaphopoda and Bivalvia

Contributor: N. J. MORRIS

The Bivalvia are classified following Newell (1965) with minor modifications evident in the text. Much of the ground work of this chapter was carried out by the late Dr. L. R. Cox, o.b.e. f.r.s., to whom the author is greatly indebted, and I would like to thank Mr. R. J. Cleevely of the British Museum (Natural History) for much help rendered.

The Bivalvia and Scaphopoda show a number of characters suggesting affinities with the Monoplacophora. They are bilaterally symmetrical molluscs. A number of early Bivalvia have muscle scars directly comparable with the living monoplacophoran *Neopilina*. Among Ordovician forms a number of Nuculoida (Barrande 1881, pls. 271–278), the early lucinoid *Babinka* (McAlester 1965) and *"Sanguinolites" pellicoi* de Verneuil (family uncertain) (Born 1918, pl. 24, Fig. 3b) have 6 to 8 pairs of pedal retractor muscles. *Babinka* has a series of small muscles comparable with the ctenidial muscles of the Monoplacophora (McAlester 1965, p. 235).

The eight pairs of pedal muscles that may be primitive and evidence for the ancestral metamerism of the Mollusca are greatly reduced in numbers in the vast majority of Bivalvia.

The Scaphopoda retain the head and radula found in the Amphineura, the Gasteropoda, some Cephalopoda and the Monoplacophora. Their deposit feeding habit is comparable to that of *Nuculana*. Mantle fusion along their ventral margin during development (Yonge 1957) suggests an affinity with primitive Bivalvia.

The Bivalvia may have separated as a distinct group of Mollusca by lateral compression as an adaption to burrowing or ploughing through a soft substrate, i.e. originally infaunal. Primitive forms including the Ribeiroida attain this having a simple folded shell with a gape along the anterior, ventral and posterior margins; but more advanced groups develop an elastic ligament dorsally joining two calcified shells.

Alternative modes of life, usually epifaunal, include byssal fixation clearly present in *Byssonychia*, (Ambonychiidae) first appearing in the mid-Ordovician but may also have occurred in the L. Ordovician Ribeirioid *Euchasma*. Cementation held to be a development of byssal attachment (Yonge 1962) is first recognised in the Permian *Pseudomonotis* (Pterioida) and also occurring in the oysters, the Plicatuliadae, *Placunopsis*, the pectinid *Hinnites*, the Spondylidae, the rudists (Hippuritoida) and the Chamacea. A swimming habit occurs in some Pectinidae and Limidae and is also reported in the Posidoniidae (Jefferies & Minton 1965).

Bivalve planktonic larval stages (Ockleman 1965) have been recognised as far back as the Llandeillo (Ord.) (personal observation). Adaptions to burrowing include the juxtaposition and fusion of various mantle layers (Yonge 1957); posterior dorsal fusion of all three layers may be recognised in the Poromyoida throughout their history by posterior extension of their shell and ligament. Fusion of the two inner layers to form siphons recognised by the possession of a pallial

---

The Fossil Record, pp. 469–477. Geological Society of London, 1967. Printed in Northern Ireland.

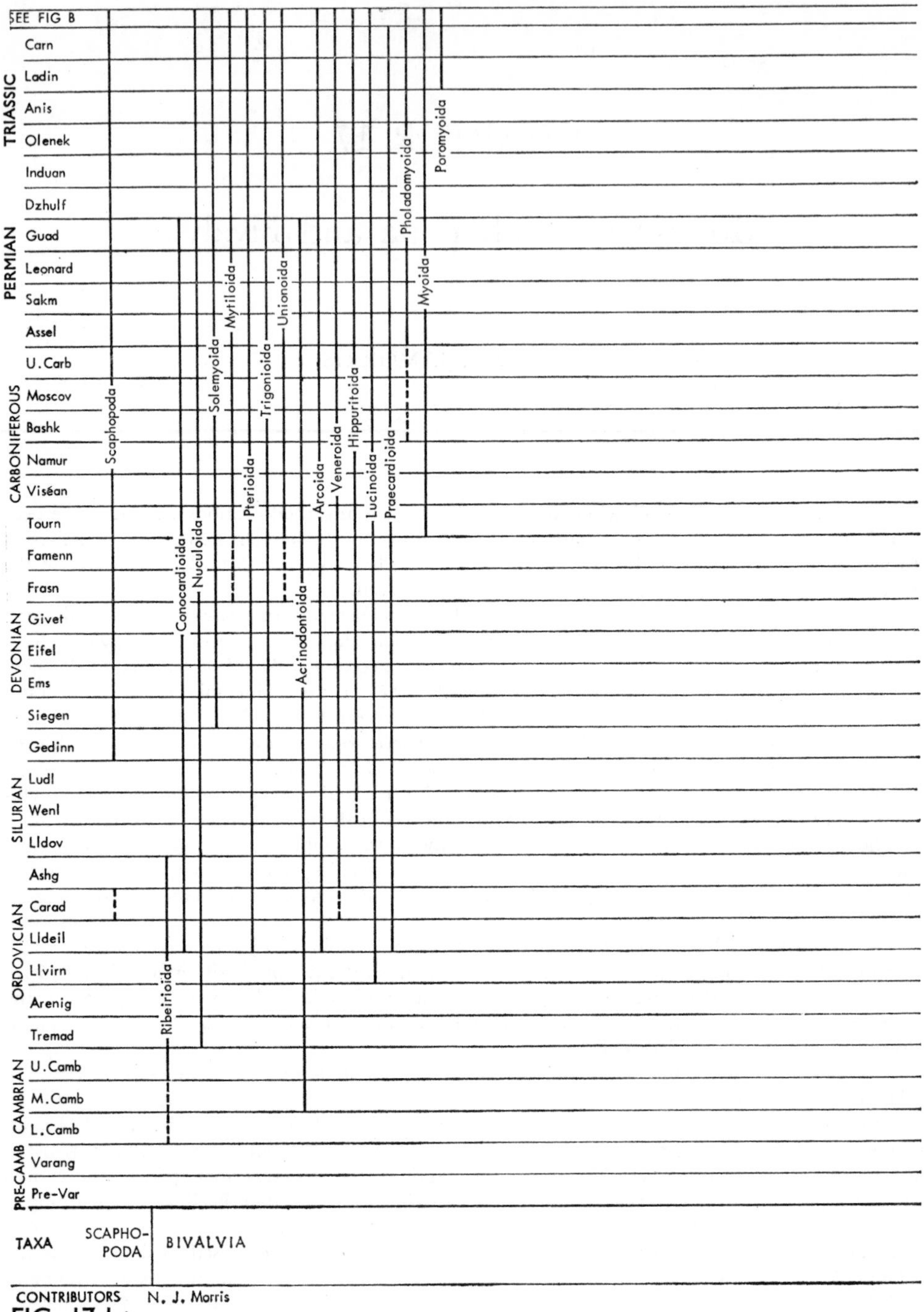
SEE FIG B
Carn
Ladin
Anis
Olenek
Induan
Dzhulf
Guad
Leonard
Sakm
Assel
U.Carb
Moscov
Bashk
Namur
Viséan
Tourn
Famenn
Frasn
Givet
Eifel
Ems
Siegen
Gedinn
Ludl
Wenl
Lldov
Ashg
Carad
Lldeil
Llvirn
Arenig
Tremad
U.Camb
M.Camb
L.Camb
Varang
Pre-Var
TRIASSIC
PERMIAN
CARBONIFEROUS
DEVONIAN
SILURIAN
ORDOVICIAN
CAMBRIAN
PRE-CAMB
Scaphopoda
Conocardioida
Nuculoida
Solemyoida
Mytiloida
Pterioida
Trigonioida
Unionoida
Actinodontoida
Arcoida
Veneroida
Hippuritoida
Lucinoida
Praecardioida
Pholadomyoida
Myoida
Poromyoida
Ribeirioida
TAXA
SCAPHO-PODA
BIVALVIA
CONTRIBUTORS
N. J. Morris

FIG. 17.1 A

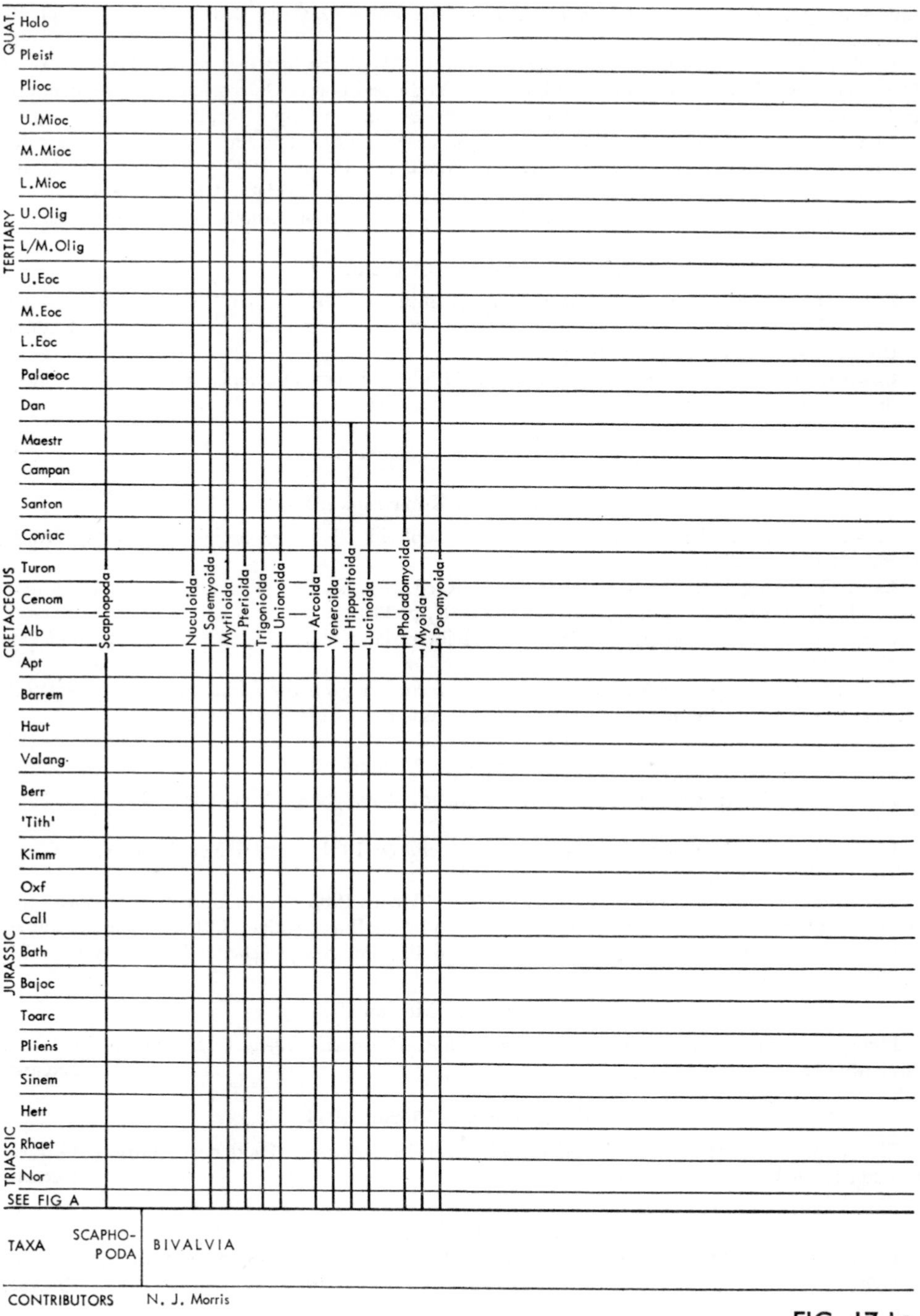
QUAT.
Holo
Pleist
Plioc
U.Mioc
M.Mioc
L.Mioc
U.Olig
L/M.Olig
U.Eoc
M.Eoc
L.Eoc
Palaeoc
Dan
Maestr
Campan
Santon
Coniac
Turon
Cenom
Alb
Apt
Barrem
Haut
Valang.
Berr
'Tith'
Kimm
Oxf
Call
Bath
Bajoc
Toarc
Pliens
Sinem
Hett
Rhaet
Nor
TERTIARY
CRETACEOUS
JURASSIC
TRIASSIC
SEE FIG A
Scaphopoda
Nuculoida
Solemyoida
Mytiloida
Pterioida
Trigonioida
Unionoida
Arcoida
Veneroida
Hippuritoida
Lucinoida
Pholadomyoida
Myoida
Poromyoida
TAXA
SCAPHO-
PODA
BIVALVIA
CONTRIBUTORS
N. J. Morris

FIG. 17.1 B

sinus is first recorded in *Allorisma monensis*, Lower Carboniferous, Great Britain (Hind 1900, pl. 48, Figs. 13, 14).

Rock-boring Bivalvia *Lithophaga carbonarius* (Hind) (Mytilidae) are first recorded in the Lower Carboniferous (Hind 1896, p. 80) and both these and coral borers Gastrochaenidae are common in Jurassic rocks. Wood borers (Pholadidae) first occur in the Upper Jurassic.

The majority of Bivalvia are filter feeders (Jørgensen 1966). The few exceptions include the Poromyoida (Yonge 1928), carnivorous; the Nuculoida (Yonge 1939), deposit feeders; the Leptonacea (Lucinoida), commensal (Boss 1965); and the Tridacnidae (Yonge 1936) and the cardiid *Corculum* (Kawaguti 1950) which have symbiotic zooxanthellae in their mantles.

Class SCAPHOPODA Bronn 1862

First, Dev Siegin/Ems: *Prodentalium martini* (Whitfield) 1882, Upper Helderberg Limestone, Dublin, Ohio, U.S.A.. **Extant.**

Constituent taxa: as in *Treatise* pt. I.

Comment: *Dentalium acus* Eichwald, Ord. U.S.S.R. is not sufficiently known to be placed with certainty in the Scaphopoda.

Class BIVALVIA Linnaeus

Order RIBEIRIOIDA Kobayashi 1954

First, L.–M. Camb: *Heraultia varensalensis* Cobbold 1935, "Georgian", Hérault, France (Cobbold 1935, p. 38).

Last, Ord Ashg: *Pinnocaris curvata* Cowper Reed, Starfish Bed, Drummuck Gp, Ardmillan Ser., Thraive Glen, Scotland. (Cowper-Reed 1907, p. 110).

Constituent taxa: Eopteriidae Miller 1889, Ribeiriidae Kobayashi 1933, and Technophoridae Miller 1889.

Comment: Many species of *Technophorus* are recorded from the Cinncinnati Fm. of Eastern N. America and are therefore approximately the same age as *Pinnocaris* above.

Order CONOCARDIOIDA Neumayr 1881

First, Ord Lldeil: *Conocardium beecheri* Raymond. Chazy Fm, New York (Raymond 1916, p. 337).

Last, Perm Guad: *Conocardium tschernischewi* Licharev 1931, Vaga River Area, N. U.S.S.R. (Newell 1940, p. 286).

Comment: *Conocardium superstes* & *C.* sp. indet. Healy 1908 Rhaet, Burma, are poorly preserved, but more likely to belong to the Poromyacea or the Burmesiidae. Other species attributed to *Conocardium* occurring in the Trias are assigned to different groups (Diener & Kutassy 1923–31, p. 442).

Order NUCULOIDA Morton 1963

First, Ord Tremad: *Ctenodonta famatinensis* and *Palaeoneilo iruyensis* Harrington 1938. N. Argentina (Harrington 1938, p. 131–3). **Extant.**

Order SOLEMYOIDA Morton 1963

First, Dev Siegen: *Dystactella telliniformis* Hall 1833, Upper Helderberg Group, Ontario Canada (Hall 1885, p. 513). **Extant.**

Order MYTILOIDA Férrusac 1822

First, U. Dev: *Mytilops praecedens* (Hall 1884), Chemung Group, New York (Hall 1884, p. 267). **Extant.**

Constituent taxa: (Newell 1965) Mytilacae and Pinnacae.

Comment: The Mytilacae closely resemble the Modiomorphidae (? = Modiolopsidae) (Actinodontoida) and may have evolved directly from them. "Mytiloid shells" Tremad G.B.

(Jones & Woodward 1893) are superimposed shells of *Lingulella* sp. *Atrina costata* (Phillips) 1836 L. Carb. Visean is one of the earliest Pinnacae (Hind 1901, p. 1).

Order PTERIOIDA Newell 1965

First, Ord Lldeil: *Clionychia mytiloides* Hall, *C. marginalis* & *Ambonychia curvata* Raymond 1905, Chazy Fm, N. York (Bassler 1915). **Extant.**

Comment: Some Ambonychiidae, which have reduced the anterior part of their shell, possess a prominent byssal gape without developing the elongated straight hinge of the more typical pterioids. They appear to be a separate offshot from the cyrtodonts or closely related actinodonts.

A number of Caradocian forms attributed to *Pterinea* or *Leptodesma* are thin-shelled with a straight hinge posterior to the umbones but no sign of attenuation of the hinge. These may belong to the "Modiolopsidae" (? = Modiomorphidae). They include "*Modiolopsis*" *orbicularis* (J. de C. Sowerby), *Leptodesma ardmillanensis* Hind and *Pterinea parva* Parks 1928.

The first record of a true Pterioid seems to be *Leptodesma* cf. *transversa* Hind, Carad, Cyclocrinus Beds, Norway (Soot-Ryen 1960, p. 107). *Pterinea crassa* Thoral 1935, L. Arenig, Montagne Noire, France may belong to the ribeirioid genus *Eopteria* Billings but does not appear to belong to the Pterioida.

The pectinoids are believed to have developed from the Silurian *Rhombopteria* (Newell 1938). Oysters first appear in the Triassic, e.g. *Lopha cristadiformis* (Schlotheim) (Seilacher 1954).

Order TRIGONIOIDA Dall 1889

First, Dev Gedinn: *Schizodus tumidus* Hall 1885, Upper Helderberg Fm, New York (Hall 1885). **Extant.**

Constituent Taxon: Trigoniacea as understood by Newell 1965 (p. 18) but excluding the Lyrodesmatidae here included in the Actinodontoida and the Trigonioididae here included in the Unionida.

Comment: *Praemyophoria? antiqua* Khalfin 1958, L. Carad., Anderkanskii Stage, Kazakstan, is not sufficiently well-known to be attributed to this group.

Order UNIONOIDA Stoliczka 1871

First, Dev Frasn–Famenn: *Archanodon jukesi* (Baily), Kiltorcan Beds, Kilkenny, Eire (Newton 1899). **Extant.**

Comment: Possibly derived from the Modiomorphidae.

Order ACTINODONTOIDA Douvillé 1912

First, Camb M. Camb: *Lammellodonta simplex* Vogel, Munero Beds, Zaragoza province, Spain. (Vogel 1962).

Last, Perm Guad: *Taimyria taimyrensis* Lutkevich, Taimyr Peninsula, arctic Siberia, U.S.S.R., (Orlov 1960).

Constituent Texa: Modiomorphidae Miller 1877, L. Ord-Perm; Cycloconchidae Ulrich 1893, Ord; Lamellodontidae Vogel 1962, M. Camb; Carydiidae Haffer 1959, Dev; and Lyrodesmatidae Ulrich 1894, L. Ord-U. Sil.

Comment: *Modiolopsis sanbernardica* & *Cosmogoniophorina tenuicostata* Harrington 1938 from the L. Ord, Trem of N. Argentina (Modiomorphidae) are the first of the genera of the more familiar Families Modiomorphidae, Cyclochonchidae and Caridiidae which Newell has grouped (Newell 1965, p. 18) as this order which are ancestral to many of the modern forms.

The Modiomorphidae apparently gave rise directly to the *Mytiloida*. The Cycloconchidae apparently gave rise to the Arcoida and Pterioida via the Cyrtodontidae. The Carydiidae are related to or gave rise to some of the heterodonts, while the Cycloconchidae may have given rise to the Veneroida including the Carditidae via *Ortonella*, and possibly the Trigonioida via the Lyrodesmatidae.

"*Modiolopsis*" *bocagei* Delgado 1904 from the L. Camb of Portugal may be a Conchostracan (Teixeira 1952, p. 169).

The Fossil Record, Part II

Order ARCOIDA Stoliczka 1871

First, Ord Lldeil: *Cyrtodonta* spp. Chazy Fm, E. N. America, *C. canadensis & breviuscula* Billings, *C. scala & solitaria* Raymond (Bassler 1915). **Extant.**

Comment: *Parallelodon antiquus*, *Cyrtodonta lata* Barrois & *C. obtusa* McCoy from the Arenig-Llanvirn, Grès Armoricain, France might belong to this group, but are not well enough illustrated to be certain. *Glyptarca primaeva*, *Palaearca oboloidea & P. hopkinsoni* Hicks 1873, from Arenig Beds of St. Davids, Wales are unrecognisable, as are *Parallelodon* spp. Termier (1950, p. 88), U. Llvirn, Morocco.

The connection between the Cyrtodontidae and the Arcacea is not firmly established.

Order VENEROIDA Adams & Adams 1858

First, Ord Carad-Ashg: *Ortonella hainesi* (Miller) 1874. Cinncinnati Fm, E. N. America (Ulrich 1893, p. 669). **Extant.**

Comment: *Cypricardinia lineata* Hind 1910 Carad, Girvan, Scotland, appears not to belong here.

Heterodonts of the Triassic including *Pachycardia* and *Heminajas*, probably related to early Carditidae may have given rise to the Crassatellidae, Arcticacae, Corbiculacae, and Veneracae through such Jurassic forms as *Pseudotrapezium* and *Pronoella* (Casey 1952, p. 121–176).

The Astartidae have been separate from the Carditidae since the Permian and possibly as far back as the Devonian.

The Cardiniidae may have arisen from the Triassic *Trigonodus* which is also probably related to the Carditidae.

The Chamacae may have arisen from byssally attached Carditidae during the Cretaceous.

The Myoconchidae and possibly *Hippopodium* are derived from the Permophoridae which may also be related to the Carditidae.

A number of groups at present included in this order are of uncertain ancestry; the Tellinacae, which apparently gave rise to the Solenacae (Davies 1935, p. 145) and possibly also the Mactracae; the Cardiacae and related Tridacnacae; and the Glossacae. Each has a history back into the Jurassic or late Triassic but their relationship to earlier forms remains obscure. This is also the case of the Tertiary and Recent fresh water mussels Dreisseniacae.

Order HIPPURITOIDA Newell 1965

First, Sil ?Wenl: *Megalomoidea canadensis* (Hall) 1852. Coral Lmst., above Clinton Gp., Niagara Series, N. America.

Last, Cret U. Maestr: *Hippurites castroi* (Vidal) 1874, *Agria moroi* (Vidal) 1878, *Praeradiolites boucheroni* (Bayle) 1878 & *P. leymeriei* (Bayle) 1881, Lychnus Marls, Catalonia, Spain. (See Toucas 1909, p. 124, tabl. 4).

Comment: *Ischyrodonta* Ulrich, U. Ord (Cyrtodontidae), may be an ancestor.

Order LUCINOIDA Dall 1889

First, Ord Llvirn: *Babinka prima* Barrande 1881, Šárka Beds, Bohemian Basin (McAlester 1965). **Extant.**

Constituent Taxa: Lucinacea, Leptonacea and Cyamacea including all the families listed by Newell (1965, p. 19).

Order PRAECARDIOIDA Newell 1965

First, Ord Lldeil: *Psiloconcha senecta* (Sardeson) 1896, St. Peters Sandstone, Minn. U.S.A. (Bassler 1915, p. 1057).

Last, Trias Carn: *?Cardiomorpha cassiana* (Bittner) 1895, St. Cassian Beds, Tyrol, N. Italy. In my opinion the Praecardioda have independently given rise to various families of the Myoida and Pholadomyoida. The author can see very little difference between the genus *Cardiomorpha* common in the Carboniferous and the Ceratomyidae. However, pending further investigation, they are retained in the Pholadomyoida. *Cardiomorpha cassiana* may belong to either taxon.

Chapter 17: Mollusca: Scaphopoda and Bivalvia

Cardiomorpha nuggetensis Trechmann, Carn, New Zealand is wrongly placed. *Sanguinolites pellicoi* de Verneuil & Barrande, and *S. guirandi* Thoral both L. Ord Europe, do not belong to this group.

Order PHOLADOMYOIDA Newell 1965

First, U. Carb: *Praeundulomya insolitus* (Thomas 1928), from Peru is the earliest species attributed to the Pholadomyoida which appear to be directly descended from the Praecardioida.

Extant.

Order MYOIDA Stoliczka 1870

Whereas this group is held to be distinct from the Praecardioida and Pholadomyoida by many molluscan workers, in the opinion of the writer they appear to have been derived from the Praecardioida, probably the Edmondiidae. The earliest form found with a *Corbula*-like hinge structure is *Scaldia fragilis* de Koninck, Tournaisian, Belgium.

The Myacae may have developed from late Jurassic Pholadomyoida although their shell structure and porcelaneous nature have led a number of workers to suggest an affinity with the Veneroida.

Order POROMYOIDA Pelseneer 1906

First, Trias Ladin: *Cuspidaria triassica* (Stoppani), Southern Alps (Bittner 1895, p. 9) (Diener & Kutassy 1923–31, p. 244).

Extant.

Comment: The hinges of the several species of Triassic *Cuspidaria* (Bittner 1895, pl. 1) are unknown as is the case of the Mesozoic genus *Cercomya* Agassiz 1843 generally referred to the Lanternulidae. Similarities between the rounded anterior and elongate posterior rostrum of some species of *Cercomya* on the one hand and *Cuspidaria* on the other lead to some doubt of the authenticity of Mesozoic species of *Cuspidaria* until their hinges have been investigated. The general shape of these Mesozoic forms is nevertheless strongly reminiscent of recent Cuspidariidae.

REFERENCES

BAILY, W. H. 1861. Explanations to sheets 147 and 157 of the maps of the Geological Survey of Ireland.

BARRANDE, J. 1881. *Systeme silurien du centre de la Bohême*, Vol. 6, *Classe des Mollusques, Ordre Acéphalés*. Prague & Paris (in 4 vols).

BARROIS, C. 1891. Mémoire sur la faune du Grés armoricain, *Annls Soc. géol. N.*, **19**, 134–237.

BASSLER, R. S. 1915. Bibliographic index of American Ordovician & Silurian fossils, *Bull. U.S. natn. Mus.*, **92**, 1–1521 (2 vols.).

BILLINGS, E. 1861–65. *Palaeozoic fossils*. Geological Survey of Canada, Montreal.

BITTNER, A. 1895. Lamellibranchiaten der Alpinen Trias. 1 Theil: Revision der Lamellibranchiaten von Sct. Cassian. *Abh. geol. Bundesanst, Wien*, **18**, 1.

BORN, A. 1918. Die *Calymene tristani* = Stufe (mittleres Untersilur) bei Almaden, ihre Fauna, Gliederung und Verbreitung *Abh. Senckenb. naturforsch. Ges.*, **36**, 309–358.

Boss, K. J. 1965. Symbiotic Erycinacean bivalves, *Malacologia*, **3**, 183–195.

CASEY, R. 1952. Some genera and sub-genera, mainly new of Mesozoic heterodont lamellibranchs. *Proc. malac. Soc., Lond.*, **29**, 121–176.

COBBOLD, E. S. 1921. The Cambrian horizons of Comley (Shropshire) and their Brachiopoda, Pteropoda, Gasteropoda, etc. *Quart. Jl. geol. Soc. Lond.*, **76**, 325–386.

—— 1935. Lower Cambrian faunas from Hérault, France. *Ann. Mag. nat. Hist.*, 10th Ser., **16**, 25–48.

DAVIES, A. M. 1935. *The composition of Tertiary faunas. Tertiary faunas—1: Mollusca*. Murby, London.

DIENER, C. & KUTASSY, A. 1923/31. *Fossilium Catalogus—1: Animalia*, Pars 19 & 51, Lamellibranchiata triadica. Junk, Berlin.

EICHWALD, C. E. von. 1855–60. *Lethaea Rossica, ou Paléontologie de la Russie*, Vol. 1—*L'ancienne période* (2 vols. & atlas). Stuttgart.

HALL, J. 1852. *Natural history of New York—VI. Palaeontology* Vol. ii: Organic remains of the lower middle division of the New York system. New York.

—— 1884. *Natural history of New York—VI. Palaeontology* Vol. v: *Lamellibranchiata—1.* Monomyaria of the Upper Helderberg, Hamilton and Chemung Groups. New York.

—— 1885. *Natural history of New York—VI. Palaeontology* Vol. v: *Lamellibranchiata—2.* Containing descriptions and figures of the Dimyaria of the Upper Helderberg, Hamilton, and Chemung groups. New York.

HARRINGTON, H. J. 1938. Sobre las faunas del Ordoviciano inferior del Norte Argentino. *Revta Mus. La Plata* (N.S.), **1** Secc. Paleont., 109–289.

HICKS, H. 1873. On the Tremadoc rocks in the neighbourhood of St. David's, South Wales, and their fossil contents. *Quart. Jl geol. Soc. Lond.,* **29,** 39–52.

HIND, W. 1896–1905. A Monograph of the British Carboniferous lamellibranchs (2 vols.), *Palaeontogr. Soc.* [*Monogr.*].

—— 1910. The lamellibranchs of the Silurian rocks of Girvan. *Trans. R. Soc. Edinb.,* **47,** 479–548.

JEFFERIES, R. P. S. & MINTON, P. 1965. The mode of life of two Jurassic species of 'Posidonia' (Bivalvia). *Palaeontology,* **8,** 156–185.

JONES, T. R. & WOODWARD, H. 1893. On some Palaeozoic *Phyllopodous* and other fossils. *Geol. Mag.,* **40,** 198–203.

JØRGENSON, C. B. 1966. *Biology of suspension feeding.* Pergamon Press, Oxford.

KAWAGUTI, S. 1950. Observations on the heart shell *Corculum cardissa* (L.) and its associated zooxanthellae. *Pacif. Sci.,* **4,** 43–49.

KHALFIN, L. L. 1958. Lamellibranch molluscs from the Ordovician of Chu-Iliyskiye Gor. *Trudȳ geol. Inst. Leningr.,* **9,** 139–196 (in Russian).

KOBAYASHI, T. 1954. Fossil Estherians and allied fossils. *J. Fac. Sci. Tokyo Univ.,* II, **9,** 1–192 (see postscript p. 183).

KONINCK, L. de. 1841. *Description des animaux fossiles qui se trouvent dans le terrain carbonifere de Belgique.* Liége.

KUHN, O. 1932. *Fossilium Catalogus—1: Animalia, Pars 54 Rudistae.* Junk, Berlin.

LUTKEVICH, E. M. 1951. Stratigrafiya verbhnepermskikh otlozhenii Kamskogo Priuralya. *Trudȳ vses. neft. nausch.-issled. geol-razv. Inst.,* **39,** 1951: 124, illust.

LUDBROOK, N. H. 1960. Scaphoda. In *Treatise on invertebrate paleontology,* Part I: *Mollusca 1.* Lawrence, pp. 37–41.

McALESTER, A. L. 1965. Systematics, affinities, and life habits of *Babinka,* a transitional Ordovician lucinoid bivalve. *Palaeontology,* **8,** 231–246.

MOORE, R. C. (Ed.) 1960. *Treatise on Invertebrate Paleontology,* Part I: *Mollusca 1.* Lawrence.

MURCHISON, R. E. 1854. *Siluria.* London.

NEWELL, N. D. 1938. Late Paleozoic pelecypods: Pectinacea. *Bull. geol. Surv. Kansas,* **10,** 1–23.

—— 1965. Classification of the Bivalvia. *Amer. Mus. Novit.,* No. 2206, 1–25.

NEWELL, N. D. *et al.* 1940. Invertebrate fauna of the late Permian Whitehorse sandstone. *Bull. Geol. Soc. Am.,* **51,** 261–336.

NEWTON, R. B. 1899. On *Archanodon jukesi* (Forbes MS) Baily sp., from the Old Red Sandstone of Monmouthshire. *Geol. Mag.,* **46,** 245–251.

OCKELMANN, K. W. 1965. Developmental types in marine bivalves and their distribution along the Atlantic coast of Europe. *Proc. 1st Europ. Malac. Congr.,* pp. 25–35.

ORLOV, Y. A. (Editor). 1960. *Osnovui Paleontologii—3, Mollusca* (in Russian).

PARKS, W. A. 1928. Faunas and stratigraphy of the Ordovician Black Shales and related rocks in Southern Ontario. *Trans. R. Soc. Can.,* IV, **22,** 39–92.

RAYMOND, P. E. 1905. The fauna of the Chazy Limestone. *Am. J. Sci.,* **20,** 353–382.

—— 1916. The pelecypoda of the Chazy Formation. *Ann. Carneg. Mus.,* **10,** 325–343.

REED, F. R. C. 1907. Sedgwick Museum notes Crustacea, etc., from Girvan. *Geol. Mag.,* **54,** 108–115.

SARDESON, F. W. 1896. The Saint Peter Sandstone. *Bull. Minn. Acad. nat. Sci.,* **4,** 64–88.

SEILACHER, A. 1954. Ökologie der triassischen muschel *Lima lineata* (Schloth.) und ihrer Epöken. *Neues Jb. Geol. Paläont. Mh.*, **4**, 163–183.

SOOT-RYEN, H. & T. 1960. The Middle Ordovician of the Oslo region, Norway, ii Pelecypoda. *Norsk. geol. Tidsskr.*, **40**, 81–122.

TEIXEIRA, C. 1952. La faune cambriense de Vila Boim au Portugal. *Bolm. Soc. geol. Port.*, **10**, 169–188.

TERMIER, G. & H. 1950. Paléontologie Marocaine 11. Invertébres de l'Ere Primaire. 3—Mollusques. *Notes Mém. Serv. Mines Carte géol. Maroc*, **78**, 246.

THOMAS, H. D. 1928. An upper Carboniferous fauna from the Amotape Mountains, Northwestern Peru. *Geol. Mag.*, **65**, 215–234.

THORAL, M. 1955. *Contribution à l'étude paléontologique de l'Ordovicien inférieur de la Montagne Noire et revision sommaire de la faune cambrienne de la Montagne Noire.* Montpelier.

TOUCAS, A. 1907–1909. Études sur la classification et l'evolution des Radiolitides. *Mém. Soc. géol. Fr. Paléont.*, No. 36.

ULRICH, E. O. 1893. New and little known Lamellibranchiata from the Lower Silurian rocks of Ohio and adjacent states. *Rep. Invest. Div. geol. Surv. Ohio*, **7**, 627–693.

VOGEL, K. 1962. Muscheln mit Schosszähnen aus dem spanischen Kambrium und ihre Bedeutung für die Evolution der Lamellibranchiaten. *Abh. dt. Akad. Wiss. Berl.* Math.-Naturn. Kl., **1962**, 197–244.

WHITFIELD, R. P. 1893. Contributions to the palaeontology of Ohio. *Rep. Invest. Div. geol. Surv. Ohio*, **7**, 407.

YONGE, C. M. 1928. Structure and function of the organs of feeding and digestion in the septibranchs, *Cuspidaria* and *Poromya*. *Phil. Trans. R. Soc.* (B) **216**, 221–263.

—— 1936. Mode of life, feeding, digestion and symbiosis with zooanthellae in the Tridacnidae. *Scient. Rep. Gt. Barrier Reef Exped.*, **1**, 283–321.

—— 1939. The protobranchiate mollusca; a fundamental interpretation of their structure and evolution. *Phil. Trans. R. Soc.*, B, **230**, 79–147.

—— 1957. Mantle fusion in the Lamellibranchia. *Pubbl. Staz. zool. Napoli*, **29**, 151–171.

—— 1962. On the primitive significance of the byssus in the Bivalvia and its effects in evolution. *J. mar. biol. Ass. U.K.*, **42**, 113–125.

N. J. Morris, B.A. F.G.S.
Department of Palaeontology, British Museum (Natural History), Cromwell Road, London SW 7.

CHAPTER 18

Arthropoda: Protarthropoda and Trilobitomorpha

Contributors: J. W. COWIE, W. T. DEAN, R. GOLDRING,
W. D. I. ROLFE, A. W. A. RUSHTON, J. T. TEMPLE
& R. P. TRIPP.

Supersubphylum PROTARTHROPODA Lankester 1904

Subphylum ONYCHOPHORA Grube 1853

Order PROTONYCHOPHORA Hutchinson 1930

First and **Last,** M.Camb: *Aysheaia pedunculata* Walcott, Bathyuriscus-Elrathina Z., Burgess Shale, British Columbia. *Xenusion* Pompeckj, ?Pre-Camb-Camb (Pleist drift), Germany, may be Onychophora but age unknown (Treatise O and W, Glaessner 1962).
Comment: Ancestor of Euonychophora Hutchinson, Quat Holo.

Supersubphylum EUARTHROPODA Lankester 1904

Subphylum TRILOBITOMORPHA Størmer 1944

Class TRILOBITOIDEA Størmer *in* Moore 1959

Subclass MARRELLOMORPHA Beurlen 1934

First and **Last,** M.Camb: *Marrella splendens* Walcott, Bathyuriscus-Elrathina Z., British Columbia (Treatise O; Simonetta 1962, ref. *in* Whittington & Rolfe 1963, p. 19). *Mimetaster* Gürich, Dev Siegen, has been regarded as a later marrellomorph (Dechaseaux *in* Piveteau 1953), but may be a crustacean metanauplius (Treatise R). *Pygaspis* Beurlen 1934, Perm Assel, is not Marrellomorpha but Crustacea Pygocephalomorpha (Brooks 1962).

Subclass MEROSTOMOIDEA Størmer 1944

First, L.Camb: *Sidneyia*? [*Amiella*] *prisca* (Mansuy *in* Deprat & Mansuy) 1912, Palaeolenus Z., Indochina (Simonetta 1964). *S.groenlandica* Cleaves, Pre-Camb Varang, is inorganic (Rolfe 1963). The L. Camb taxa erected by Vologdin (1965) are based on pseudofossils, probably rolled-up mud flakes.
Last, M.Camb: *Sidneyia, Leanchoilia, Naraoia* Walcott and ?*Emeraldoides* Simonetta, Bathyuriscus-Elrathina Z., British Columbia (Treatise O). Other genera reassigned to Chelicerata Aglaspida (Simonetta 1964); *Synaustrus* Riek, Trias Olenek, is not Merostomoidea but Crustacea Euthycarcinoidea.

The Fossil Record, pp. 479–497. Geological Society of London, 1967. Printed in Northern Ireland.

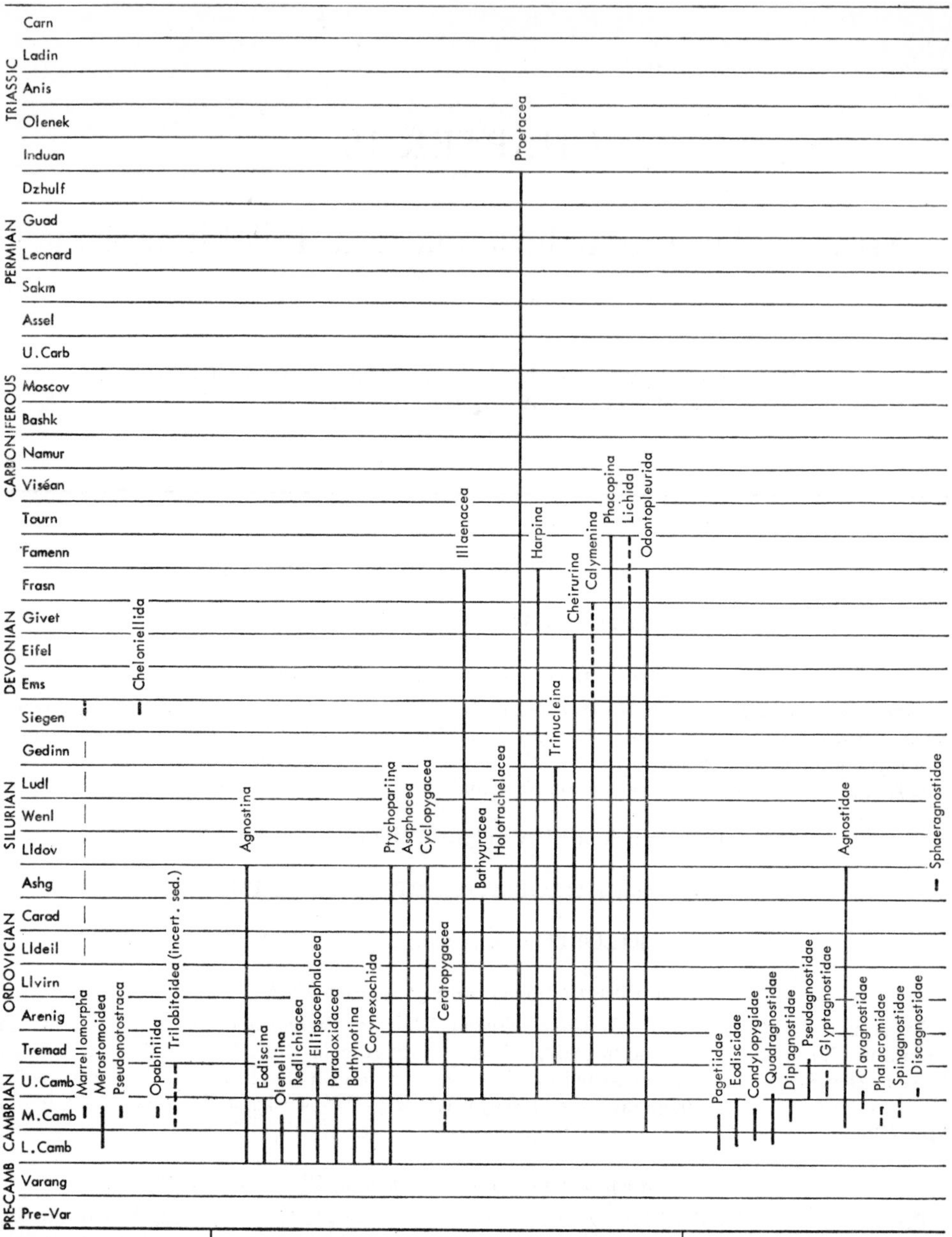

FIG. 18.1 A

Chapter 18: *Arthropoda: Protarthropoda and Trilobitomorpha*

Subclass PSEUDONOTOSTRACA Raymond 1935

First and **Last,** M.Camb: *Burgessia* and *Waptia* Walcott, Bathyuriscus-Elrathina Z., British Columbia (Treatise O).

Subclass uncertain

Order CHELONIELLIDA Broili 1933

First and **Last,** Dev Siegen: *Cheloniellon calmani* Broili, Hunsrückschiefer, Germany (Treatise O).

Order OPABINIIDA Størmer 1944

First and **Last,** M. Camb: *Opabinia regalis* Walcott, Bathyuriscus-Elrathina Z., British Columbia (Treatise O).

TRILOBITOIDEA incertae sedis

First and **Last,** M.Camb: *Yohoia, Helmetia, Mollisonia* Walcott, *Houghtonites* Raymond 1931, Bathyuriscus-Elrathina Z., British Columbia. *Tontoia* Walcott, ?Albertella Z., Arizona, is a doubtful, earlier record; *Yohoia*?, U.Camb, Siberia, may be a later record (Novozhilov *in* Orlov 1960, p. 195). [W.D.I.R.]

Class TRILOBITA Walch 1771

Introduction: The classification of Treatise O has been adopted as a framework because of its general availability to readers, but it should be emphasised that there is at present no generally acceptable major classificatory scheme for the trilobites. Where individual families are considered by contributors to be defined and interpreted in current usage with sufficient objectivity and agreement, they are used as the basis for detailed documentation; where these criteria are not met, documentation is at a level appropriate to the present state of knowledge. [J.T.T.]

Order AGNOSTIDA Kobayashi 1935

Suborder AGNOSTINA Salter 1864

Classification of Agnostina: from Öpik 1961 and 1963; genera *incertae familiae* omitted.

Family CONDYLOPYGIDAE Raymond 1913

First, L.Camb: *Condylopyge* sp. nov. (Rushton MS), U. Prot. Z., England; *Mallagnostus* Howell is no agnostid (Rasetti *in* Rushton MS).
Last, M.Camb: *Pleuroctenium bifurcatum* (Illing), U. P. davidis Z. (= Pt. punct. Z.), N. Atlantic Province (Hutchinson 1962).

Family QUADRAGNOSTIDAE Howell 1935
(=PERONOPSIDAE Westergård)

First, L.Camb: *Eoagnostus roddyi* Resser & Howell, U. Olenellus Z., Pennsylvania (Resser & Howell 1938).
Last, U.Camb: *Hypagnostus* sp. (undescribed), G. stolidotus Z. (? = Crep. Z.), Queensland (Öpik 1961 p. 58).

Family DIPLAGNOSTIDAE Whitehouse 1936

First, M.Camb: *Diplagnostus* sp. (undescribed), U. Pt. gibb. Z., Queensland. (Öpik 1961).
Last, M.Camb: *Oidalagnostus trispinifer* Westergård, U. L. laev. Z., N. Atlantic Province (Westergård 1946, Hutchinson 1962).

Family PSEUDAGNOSTIDAE Whitehouse 1936

First, U.Camb: species of *Pseudagnostus* (undescribed), O'Hara Sh., (= Ced. Z.), Queensland (Öpik 1956, p. 22).

TABLE: Suggested correlation of North American and European Cambrian trilobite zones, based on publications by Henningsmoen, Lochman, Lochman & Wilson, Öpik, Palmer, Rasetti, Robison, and Westergård, and incorporating unpublished studies by J. W. Cowie and A. W. A. Rushton. Throughout the Cambrian correlation between the two provinces is still only provisional, but the vertical dividing line is thickened at horizons where the evidence for the suggested correlation is considered stronger than elsewhere. The European Middle Cambrian zones are grouped into stages as follows: A, P. oelandicus; B, P. paradoxissimus; C, P. forchhammeri.

[J. W. C., A.W.A.R., J.T.T.]

	NORTH AMERICAN ZONES	EUROPEAN ZONES	
UPPER	Saukia	6	Acerocare
	Ptychaspis-Prosaukia	5	Peltura
	Conaspis	4	Leptoplastus
		3	Parabolina
	Elvinia		
	Dunderbergia		
	Prehousia	2	Olenus
	Dicanthopyge		
	Aphelaspis		
	Crepicephalus	1	A. pisiformis
	Cedaria		
MIDDLE	Bolaspidella	C	L. laevigata J. brachymetopa G. nathorsti
		B	Pt. punctuosus H. parvifrons Pt. atavus
	Bath.-Elrath.		Pt. gibbus
	Glossopleura		
	Albertella	A	P. pinus
	Plag.-Pol.		P. insularis
LOWER	U. Olenellus		Protolenus
	L. Olenellus		Callavia-Holmia

Last, Ord Tremad: *Machairagnostus tmetus* Harrington & Leanza, L.Tremad., *Parabolina argentina* Z., Argentine (Harrington & Leanza 1957).

Family GLYPTAGNOSTIDAE Whitehouse 1936

First, U.Camb: *Glyptagnostus stolidotus* Öpik, base of Crep. Z., Queensland, Alabama, Nevada (Palmer 1962).
Last, U.Camb: *Agnostotes inconstans* Öpik, *Irvingella tropica* Z. (= Elv. Z.), Queensland (Öpik 1963a). *Lotagnostus,* possibly this family, occurs later.

Family AGNOSTIDAE M'Coy 1849

First, M.Camb: *Ptychagnostus praecurrens* (Westergård), P. pinus Z., Sweden (Westergård 1946).
Last, Ord Ashg: *Trinodus tardus* (Barrande), U.Ashg, Dalmanitina Beds, Poland (Kielan 1960).
Comment: includes Ptychagnostinae Kobayashi, Agnostinae M'Coy, Micragnostinae Howell, Geragnostinae Howell, Trinodidae Howell (Öpik 1961).

Family CLAVAGNOSTIDAE Howell 1937

First, M.Camb: *Clavagnostus repandus* (Westergård), J. brach. Z., Sweden (Westergård 1946).
Last, U.Camb: *Aspidagnostus rugosus* Palmer, basal Aphel. Z., Nevada (Palmer 1962).

Family PHALACROMIDAE Hawle & Corda 1847

First and **Last,** M.Camb: *Phalacroma bibullatum* (Barrande), ? Pt. atav. Z. or H. parv. Z., Europe (Illing 1916).
Comment: genus *Phalacroma* only (Öpik 1961).

Family SPINAGNOSTIDAE Howell 1935

First and **Last,** M.Camb: *Spinagnostus franklinensis* Howell, C. vermontensis Z. (= P. forchhammeri Stage), Vermont (Howell 1937).
Comment: genus *Spinagnostus* only (Öpik 1961).

Family DISCAGNOSTIDAE Opik 1963

First and **Last,** U.Camb: *Discagnostus spectator* Öpik, *Glyptagnostus stolidotus* Z., Queensland (Öpik 1963a).

Family SPHAERAGNOSTIDAE Kobayashi 1939

First and **Last,** Ord Ashg: Species of *Sphaeragnostus,* e.g. *S. gaspensis europeensis,* M. Ashg, *Staurocephalus clavifrons* Z., N. Atlantic Province, (Kielan 1960).

Suborder EODISCINA Kobayashi 1939

Classification of Eodiscina: as in Treatise O.

Family PAGETIIDAE Kobayashi 1935

First, L.Camb: *Hebediscus attleborensis* (Shaler & Foerste), Call.-Holm. Z., N. Atlantic Province (Cobbold 1921, Hutchinson 1962); or *H. marocana* Hupé, L.Timhgitian, Morocco (Hupé 1960).
Last, M.Camb: *Pagetia* cf. *bootes* Walcott, Bath.-Elrath. Z., British Columbia (Rasetti 1951).

Family EODISCIDAE Raymond 1913

First, L.Camb: *Serrodiscus bellimarginatus* (Shaler & Foerste), Call.-Holm. Z., N. Atlantic Province (Cobbold 1921, Hutchinson 1962); or *S. speciosus* and *Calodiscus* spp., U. Olenellus Z., New York State (Lochman 1956).
Last, M.Camb: *Eodiscus armatus* Hutchinson (blind form), P. forchhammeri Stage, S.E. Newfoundland (Hutchinson 1962); *Opsidiscus bilobatus* (Westergård) (oculate form), L. laev. Z., Sweden (Westergård 1946). [A.W.A.R.]

The Fossil Record, Part II

Order REDLICHIIDA Richter 1933

Suborder OLENELLINA Resser 1938

Family OLENELLIDAE Vogdes 1893

First, L. Camb: *Fallotaspis tazemmourtensis* Hupé, Z. I, Morocco and L. Olenellus Z., Campito Sst, California (Hupé 1953, tabs. 2 and 3; Hupé & Nelson 1964, pp. 621–623).
Last, L./M. Camb: *Olenellus* and other genera, U. Olenellus Z. and Prot. Z., e.g. St. Piran Sst, Canada (Rasetti 1951, pp. 53–55, 81–87) and lower M. Camb, Morocco (Hupé 1960, p. 81).

Family DAGUINASPIDIDAE Hupé 1953

First, L. Camb: *Daguinaspis*, L. Olenellus Z., Campito Sst, California (Hupé & Nelson 1964, pp. 621–623).
Last, L. Camb: *Daguinaspis ambroggii* Hupé & Abadie, *D. (D.) latifrons* Hupé, Z. III, Morocco (Hupé 1953, tabs 2 & 3).

Suborder REDLICHIINA Harrington 1959

Superfamily REDLICHIACEA Poulsen 1927

Family REDLICHIIDAE Poulsen 1927

First, L. Camb: *Pararedlichia pulchella*, *P. rochi*, *P. subtransversa* Hupé, Z. I, Morocco (Hupé 1953, tabs. 2 and 3).
Last, M. Camb: *Redlichia idonea* Whitehouse and *R. chinensis* Walcott, P. ins. Z., Thorntonia and Beetle Creek fms, Queensland, Australia (Öpik 1956, p. 17).

Family NEOREDLICHIIDAE Hupé 1953

First and **Last,** L. Camb: Morocco, Spain, U.S.S.R., Korea.

Family SAUKIANDIDAE Hupé 1953

First and **Last,** L. Camb: Morocco, Spain.

Family GIGANTOPYGIDAE Hupé 1953

First and **Last,** L. Camb: Morocco, Spain.

Family DESPUJOLSIIDAE Harrington 1959

First and **Last,** L. Camb: Morocco. (Treatise O).

Family YINITIDAE Hupé 1953

First and **Last,** M. Camb: Korea, China.

Family ABADIELLIDAE Hupé 1953

First, L. Camb: *Abadiella bourgini*, *A. meteora* Hupé, Z. III, Morocco (Hupé 1953, tabs. 2 and 3).
Last, M. Camb: *Redlichina*, Siberia, U.S.S.R.

Family DOLEROLENIDAE Kobayashi 1951

First and **Last,** L. Camb: Prot. Z., Spain.

Superfamily ELLIPSOCEPHALACEA Matthew 1887

Family ELLIPSOCEPHALIDAE Matthew 1887

First, L. Camb: *Ellipsocephalus*, Europe, Morocco, Canada, Australia.
Last, M./U. Camb: ?*Manchurocephalus*, L. laev. Z./A. pis. Z., Manchuria (Treatise O).

484

Chapter 18: *Arthropoda: Protarthropoda and Trilobitomorpha*

Family PROTOLENIDAE Richter & Richter 1948

First, L. Camb: Europe, Morocco, Asia, Canada (Treatise O).
Last, M. Camb: *Protolenus, Kingaspis, Strenuella,* Poland (Orlowski 1964, p. 42).

Family YUNNANOCEPHALIDAE Hupé 1953

First and **Last,** L. Camb: China.

Superfamily PARADOXIDACEA Hawle & Corda 1847

Family PARADOXIDIDAE Hawle & Corda 1847

First, L. Camb: *Metadoxides richterorum* Sdzuy, Prot. Z., Bunte Sandsteine und Schiefer, Cantabrian Mts (León and Asturias), Spain. (Lotze 1958, p. 737).
Last, M. Camb: *Paradoxides forchhammeri* Angelin, ? L. laev. Z., Scandinavia (Westergård 1953, p. 36); *Centropleura phoenix* Öpik (if referable to fam.), Proampyx agra Z. (= L. laev. Z.), Queensland (Öpik 1961, p. 34).

Family HICKSIIDAE Hupé 1953

First and **Last,** L. Camb: Portugal, Spain.

Suborder BATHYNOTINA Lochman-Balk 1959

Family BATHYNOTIDAE Hupé 1953

First and **Last,** L./M. Camb: Arctic Asia & Eastern N. America.

Order CORYNEXOCHIDA Kobayashi 1935

Family DORYPYGIDAE Kobayashi 1935

First, L. Camb: *Kootenia,* U. Olenellus Z., Americas, Greenland, Eurasia, Australia.
Last, U. Camb: *Holteria* and *Olenoides,* Americas, Asia, Australia.

Family OGYGOPSIDAE Rasetti 1951

First, L. Camb: *Ogygopsis batis* (Walcott), U. Olenellus Z., Nevada (Palmer 1964, pp. 6–7).
Last, M. Camb: *Ogygopsis,* N. America.

Family ORYCTOCEPHALIDAE Beecher 1897

First, L. Camb: *Lancastria roddyi* (Walcott) and *Goldfieldia pacifica* Palmer, U. Olenellus Z., N. America (Palmer 1964, pp. 7–8).
Last, M. Camb: *Oryctocare geikei* Walcott, Bol. Z., N. America (Resser 1939, p. 14).

Family DOLICHOMETOPIDAE Walcott 1916

First and **Last,** L./U. Camb (Treatise O).

Family CORYNEXOCHIDAE Angelin 1854

First and **Last,** M. Camb (Treatise O).

Family ZACANTHOIDIDAE Swinnerton 1915

First, L. Camb: *Prozacanthoides* and *Zacanthopsis,* U. Olenellus Z., N. America.
Last, M. Camb: *Zacanthoides,* Bol. Z., Americas (Treatise O).

Family DINESIDAE Lermontova 1940

First and **Last,** L./M. Camb (Treatise O). [J.W.C.]

Order PTYCHOPARIIDA Swinnerton 1915

Suborder PTYCHOPARIINA Richter 1933

Classification: Within Ptychopariina classification is very provisional and subjective and there is little agreement among authors on either definition or content of family-group and superfamily-group taxa. Detailed listing of first and last specific occurrences would, except in the few cases treated separately below, give spurious exactitude to a very confused situation, and is not attempted. In the following alphabetical list the ranges of the families are based, unless stated otherwise, on the family limits as interpreted in Treatise O.

Constituent families: Agraulidae Raymond, L.-U. Camb; Alokistocaridae Resser, Camb U. Olenellus Z.-Dund. Z.; Andrarinidae Raymond, M. Camb-U. Camb Parab. Z.; Anomocaridae Poulsen, M.-U. Camb; Asaphiscidae Raymond, M.-U. Camb; Avoninidae Lochman, M.-U. Camb; Bolaspididae Howell, M. Camb; Burlingiidae Walcott (see below); Catillicephalidae Raymond, U. Camb; Cheilocephalidae Shaw (*sensu* Palmer 1965), U. Camb Aphel. Z.-Elv. Z.; Conocoryphidae Angelin, L. Camb-Ord Tremad; Cooslellidae Palmer, U. Camb Ced. Z. & Crep. Z.; Crepicephalidae Kobayashi, Camb ?Plag.-Pol. Z-Crep. Z.; Damesellidae Kobayashi, M.-U. Camb; Diceratocephalidae Lu, U. Camb; Dikelocephalidae Miller, U. Camb Ptych.-Pros. Z. & Sauk. Z.; Dokimocephalidae Kobayashi, U. Camb Dund. Z.-Ptych.-Pros. Z.; Elviniidae Kobayashi, U. Camb; Emmrichellidae Kobayashi, M. Camb-L. Ord; Eurekiidae Hupé, U. Camb Ptych.-Pros. Z. & Sauk. Z.; Glaphuridae Hupé (see below); Housiidae Hupé, U. Camb Dican. Z.-Elv. Z.; Hungaiidae Raymond, U. Camb; Hypermecaspididae Harrington & Leanza, L.-M. Ord; Idahoiidae Lochman, U. Camb Elv. Z.-Sauk. Z.; Illaenuridae Vogdes, U. Camb Ptych.-Pros. Z. & Sauk. Z.; Kaolishaniidae Kobayashi, U. Camb; Kingstoniidae Kobayashi, M. Camb Bol. Z.-U. Camb; Komaspididae Kobayashi (see below); Leiostegiidae Bradley, M. Camb-L. Ord; Liostracinidae Raymond, ?M.Camb-U.Camb ?Ptych.-Pros. Z.; Loganellidae Rasetti, U. Camb; Lonchocephalidae Hupé, M. Camb Bol. Z.-U. Camb; Marjumiidae Kobayashi, M. Camb-Ord Tremad; Menomoniidae Walcott, M. Camb Bol. Z.-U. Camb ?Elv. Z. (Palmer 1965); Nepeidae Whitehouse (*sensu* Öpik 1963b), M. Camb-early U. Camb; Norwoodiidae Walcott, U. Camb-L. Ord; Olenidae Burmeister (see below); Pagodiidae Kobayashi, M. Camb-L. Ord; Papyriaspididae Whitehouse, M.-U. Camb; Parabolinoididae Lochman, U. Camb Con. Z. & Ptych.-Pros. Z.; Pterocephaliidae Kobayashi, U. Camb Aphel. Z.-Elv.Z.; Ptychaspididae Raymond, U. Camb (Con. Z.-Sauk. Z. in U.S.A.); Ptychopariidae Matthew, L. Camb-L. Ord; Raymondinidae Clark, U. Camb; Remopleurididae Hawle & Corda, U. Camb-Ord Ashg; Saukiidae Ulrich & Resser, U. Camb (Ptych.-Pros. Z.-Sauk. Z. in U.S.A., early U. Camb in SW China); Shirakiellidae Hupé, U. Camb; Shumardiidae Lake (see below); Solenopleuridae Angelin, M. Camb-L. Ord; Telephinidae Marek (see below); Tricrepicephalidae Palmer, U. Camb Ced. Z. & Crep. Z.

Family BURLINGIIDAE Walcott 1908

First, M. Camb: *Burlingia laevis* Westergård, P. pin. Z., Sweden (Westergård 1936, p. 32).
Last, U. Camb: *Schmalenseeia amphionura* Moberg, A. pis. Z., Sweden (Westergård 1947, p. 22); *S. spinulosa* Lazarenko, ? zone, U.S.S.R. *Fissocephalus* Lermontova is excluded from family.

Family GLAPHURIDAE Hupé 1953

First, Ord Tremad: *Glaphurus alimbeticus* Balashova, U.S.S.R. (Balashova 1961, p. 137).
Last, Ord Carad, ?Ashg: several spp. of *Glaphurus* & *Glaphurina* (attrib. to fam. doubtful), U.S.A. & U.S.S.R. (Ulrich 1930b; Chugaeva 1958); also undescribed forms, Ashg, Ireland (Dean M.S.).

Family KOMASPIDIDAE Kobayashi 1935

First, M. or U. Camb: *Komaspis typa* & *K. convexus* Kobayashi, Olenoides Z., S. Korea (Kobayashi 1935, p. 141; Öpik 1963a, p. 95). *Terechtaspis* Repina, L. Camb, is excluded from family.
Last, Ord ?Arenig: spp. of *Carolinites*, Eire & W. U.S.A. (Stubblefield 1950, p. 345; Hintze 1953, p. 21); also undescribed forms, Ashg, Ireland (Dean M.S.).

Chapter 18: Arthropoda: Protarthropoda and Trilobitomorpha

Family OLENIDAE Burmeister 1843

First, U. Camb: *Olenus alpha* Henningsmoen, A. pis. Z., Norway (Henningsmoen 1957, p. 100).
Last, Ord Carad: *Triarthrus linnarssoni* Thorslund, Sweden (Thorslund 1940, p. 128); *T. eatoni* (Hall), New York (Whittington 1957, p. 941).

Family SHUMARDIIDAE Lake 1907

First, U. Camb: spp. of *Shumardia* & *Eoshumardia*, E. Asia (Kobayashi 1935, p. 211).
Last, Ord Ashg: *Shumardia polonica* Kielan, Poland (Kielan 1960, p. 159).

Family TELEPHINIDAE Marek 1952

First, Ord Llvirn: *Telephina sulcata* Nikolaisen, $3c\gamma$–$4a\alpha_1$ transition, Norway (Nikolaisen 1963, p. 353).
Last, Ord Ashg: *Telephina* various spp., Europe (Ulrich 1930b).   [J.T.T.]

Suborder ASAPHINA Salter 1864

Superfamily ASAPHACEA Burmeister 1843

Family ASAPHIDAE Burmeister 1843

First, U.Camb: *Charchaqia norini* Troedsson (1937, p. 46), China; *Promegalaspides kinnekullensis* Westergård (1939, p. 4), Sweden; *Yuepingia niobiformis* Lu (1956, p. 371), SW China.
Last, Ord Ashg: *Ectenaspis beckeri* (Slocum), N. America (Raymond 1920, p. 292).

Family TAIHUNGSHANIIDAE Sun 1931

First, Ord Tremad: *Asaphellina* spp., *Taihungshania* spp., SW France, N. America (Ross 1951, p. 109; Thoral 1935, p. 218).
Last, Ord Llvirn: *Omeipsis huangi* (Sun), China (Kobayashi 1951, p. 16).

Family TSINANIIDAE Kobayashi 1933

First and **Last,** U.Camb: China. Includes *Dictyites dictys* (Walcott) and *Tsinania* spp. (Kobayashi 1933, p. 134).

Family NILEIDAE Angelin 1854

First, Ord Tremad: includes *Borthaspis innotata* (Salter), Wales; *Nileus limbatus* Brögger, Sweden; *Symphysurus* spp., Scandinavia, SW France. (Lake 1942, p. 311; Stubblefield 1951, p. 440; Tjernvik 1956, p. 208).
Last, Ord Carad: *Barrandia cordai* (M'Coy), *B. radians* (M'Coy), England, Wales (Whittard 1961, p. 222).

Family DIKELOKEPHALINIDAE Kobayashi 1936

First, Ord Tremad: *Birmanites birmanicus* (Reed 1915, p. 30), Burma; *Leimitzia bavarica* (Barrande), Germany (Sdzuy 1955, p. 37); *Asaphopsoides villebruni* (Bergeron), SW France (Thoral 1935, p. 287).
Last, Ord Llvirn: *Hungioides bohemicus* (Perner), Czechoslovakia (Prantl & Přibyl 1948, p. 14).

Superfamily CYCLOPYGACEA Raymond 1925

Family CYCLOPYGIDAE Raymond 1925

First, Ord Tremad: *Cyclopyge genatenta* Stubblefield & Bulman (1927, p. 138), England.
Last, Ord Ashg: several genera in Europe, including *Cyclopyge*, *Ellipsotaphrus*, *Microparia* s.s., *M.* (*Degamella*), *Psilacella* and *Symphysops* (Marek 1961; Whittard 1952).

Superfamily CERATOPYGACEA Linnarsson 1869

Family CERATOPYGIDAE Linnarsson 1869

First, M. Camb: *Proceratopyge* spp. (Westergård 1948, p. 5), Sweden. According to Kobayashi (1935, p. 273) *Kogenium* is of M. Camb age in eastern Asia, but Öpik (1963a, p. 98) suggests U. Camb age.

Last, Ord Tremad: several genera including *Ceratopyge* and *Hysterolenus* Scandinavia, *Onychopyge* and *Pseudohysterolenus*, Argentina (Harrington & Leanza 1957, pp. 187, 191; Moberg & Segerberg 1906, p. 84; Regnéll & Hede 1960, p. 15; Størmer 1940, p. 140).

Suborder ILLAENINA Jaanusson 1959

Superfamily ILLAENACEA Hawle and Corda 1847

Family STYGINIDAE Vogdes 1890

First, Ord Arenig: *Raymondaspis limbata* (Angelin), Scandinavia (Skjeseth 1955, p. 21; Whittington 1950, p. 549).

Last, Ord Ashg: *Stygina latifrons* (Portlock), Britain, Scandinavia (Harper 1948, p. 50; Skjeseth 1955, p. 13; Whittington 1950, p. 547).

Family THYSANOPELTIDAE Hawle and Corda 1847

First, Ord Carad: *Eobronteus benoratus* Sinclair (1949, p. 45), Quebec, Canada.

Last, Dev Frasn: *Scutellum, Scabriscutellum*, Germany, Czechoslovakia (R. & E. Richter 1926, p. 242; Šnajdr 1960, p. 48).

Family ILLAENIDAE Hawle and Corda 1847

First, Ord Arenig: *Dysplanus, Illaenus* and *Platillaenus* spp., Scandinavia (Jaanusson 1957).
Last, Sil Ludl: *Bumastus hornyi* Šnajdr (1957, p. 115), Czechoslovakia.

Superfamily BATHYURACEA Walcott 1886

Family BATHYURIDAE Walcott 1886

First, Ord Tremad: *Agerina praematura* Tjernvik (1956, p. 200), Sweden.
Last, Ord Carad: *Bathyurus, Raymondites*, eastern N. America (Whittington 1953).

Family LECANOPYGIDAE Lochman 1953

First, U.Camb: *Lecanopyge, Platydiamesus, Rasettia* and *Resseraspis*, especially in eastern N. America (Lochman 1953, p. 889).
Last, Ord Arenig: *Strigigenalis* spp., North America (Whittington 1953, p. 671).

Superfamily HOLOTRACHELACEA Warburg 1925

Family Holotrachelidae Warburg 1925

First and **Last,** Ord Ashg: *Holotrachelus*, the only known genus, is widely distributed in Britain, Scandinavia, eastern N. America and Russia (Cooper 1930, p. 374; Warburg 1925, p. 147; Weber 1948, p. 46).   [W.T.D.]

Superfamily PROETACEA Salter 1864

Family PROETIDAE Salter 1864

First, Ord: numerous poorly documented records to proetids in M. and U. Ord. Also *Paryfenus* Hadding, low M.Ord Sweden.

Last, Perm Leonard?: *Neoproetus, Permoproetus* Sicily, Crimea, Timor? (Ruggieri 1959, Toumansky 1935).

Last, with anteriorly tapering to inversely pyriform glabella *Weania librovitchi* (Weber), Carb Viséan, ?Namur, Urals (Campbell & Engel 1963); eight taxa to U. Viséan (Osmólska 1962, Erben 1961). (Subfamilies as in Treatise O.)

Family PHILLIPSIIDAE Oehlert 1886

Family not homogeneous (Hessler 1963, 1965)

First, Dev Famenn: *Perliproetus catharinae* Maksimova, Prolobites Z., Urals (Maksimova 1955) if included in family. *Moschoglossis, Piltonia,* Wocklumeria Z., England, Belgium, U.S.S.R. (Kirghiz), (Goldring 1958), *Pudoproetus* Wocklumeria Z., Urals, U.S.S.R. Louisiana Lst, U.S.A. (Hessler op. cit.). *Breviphillipsia, Elliptophillipsia, Griffithidella, Thigriffides, Phillipsia, Cummingella* make appearance Gattendorfia Z. and Chouteau Lst. *Palaeophillipsia,* Sugiyama (Japan) from L. Carb, not Famenn (Endo & Matsumoto 1962).

Last, Perm Guad/Dzhulf: trilobite records from the Permian are not well dated. It is certain that *Ditomopyge* continues into the upper Guad or Dzhulf in the Salt Range (Pakistan) (Grant 1966) and possibly as high elsewhere in Asia.

Families OTARIONIDAE Richter & Richter 1926
& AULACOPLEURIDAE Angelin 1854

First, Ord Arenig: *Otarion insolitum* (Dean 1966, p. 337), S. W. France.

Last, Dev Famenn: *Otarion stigmatophthalmus* Richter, Cheiloceras Z., Germany (Richter & Richter 1926). *Coignouina acanthina* (Coignou) Namur, England (Reed 1943) regarded as brachymetopid, but other species included in genus belong to Otarionidae. Hessler (1965) records *Otarion* sp. in L. Carb, Chouteau Lst, U.S.A.

Family BRACHYMETOPIDAE Prantl & Přibyl 1950

First, Dev Gedinn: *Cordania cyclurus, C. macrobius, C. falcata,* Helderberg, N. America (Quebec, Maine, New York, Tennessee, Okla.) (Whittington 1960).

Last, Perm Dzhulf: *Cheiropyge chitichun* Diener (1897, 1903), Himalayas, (*Panarchaegonus* Öpik, Ord-Sil, assigned to Proetidae.) [R.G.]

Family PHILLIPSINELLIDAE Whittington 1950

First and **Last,** Ord Carad-Ashg: *Phillipsinella parabola* (Barrande 1852), Králův Dvůr Sh (Ashg), Bohemia; widespread in Ashg, earlier (Carad) in Norway (Størmer 1953).

Family CELMIDAE Jaanusson 1956

First and **Last,** Ord ? Llvirn: *Celmus granulatus* Angelin, ? Expansus Lst, Östergötland, Sweden; ? 2 other spp. (Jaanusson 1956).

Family PLETHOPELTIDAE Raymond 1925

Referred genera range from U. Camb Ced. Z., western U.S.A., to L. Ord, U.S.A. & U.S.S.R. (Lochman-Balk & Wilson 1958, Maksimova 1962).

Family DIMEROPYGIDAE Hupé 1953

First, Ord ?Arenig: 2 spp. of *Dimeropygiella,* Pogonip Group, W. U.S.A. (Hintze 1953).

Last, Ord Ashg: *Toernquistia nicholsoni* (Reed), Keisley Lst, N. England (Whittington 1950). [J.T.T.]

Suborder HARPINA Whittington 1959

Family HARPIDAE Hawle and Corda 1847

First, Ord Tremad: *Australoharpes depressus* Harrington & Leanza (1957, p. 195), Argentina.

Last, Dev Frasn: *Harpes neogracilis* R. & E. Richter (1926, p. 112), Europe.

Family HARPIDIDAE Whittington 1950

First, U.Camb: *Fissocephalus* spp., Lermontova (1951, p. 16), Russia; *Loganopeltoides* spp., N. America (Rasetti 1945, p. 46).

Last, Ord Arenig: *Loganopeltis depressa* Rasetti (1943, p. 103), N. America.

Family ENTOMASPIDIDAE Ulrich in Bridge 1930

First, U.Camb: *Entomaspis radiatus* Ulrich (1930a, p. 213), N. America.

Last, Ord Tremad: *Hypothetica rawi* Ross (1951, p. 113), N. America.

Suborder TRINUCLEINA Swinnerton 1915

Family TRINUCLEIDAE Hawle and Corda 1947

First, Ord Arenig: *Myttonia confusa* Whittard (1955, p. 29), Shelve Inlier, Welsh Borderland; *Hanchungolithus primitivus* (Born), SW France (Dean, 1966, p. 281). Both species in D. extensus Z.

Last, Ord Ashg: mostly *Tretaspis* spp., widespread in Europe and eastern N. America but especially so in Scandinavia, where last is *T. latilimba broeggeri* Størmer (1945, p. 403). Also *Cryptolithus* in Scotland and Ireland (Lamont 1935, p. 317; Reed 1935, p. 1; Fearnsides *et al.* 1907, p. 121; Harper 1948, p. 50).

Family OROMETOPIDAE Hupé 1955

First and Last, Ord Tremad to Arenig: Widespread in Europe and S. America. *Orometopus* only known genus; all species of Tremad or Arenig age. (Harrington & Leanza 1957, p. 197; Stubblefield & Bulman 1927, p. 133; Tjernvik 1957, p. 269).

Family DIONIDIDAE Gürich 1908

First, Ord Llvirn: *Dionide turnbulli* Whittington & *D. jubata* Raymond, England & Wales (Whittard 1958, p. 95); *Dionidella incisa* Prantl & Přibyl (1948, p. 3) & *Trinucleoides reussi* (Barrande), Czechoslovakia (Whittington 1940, p. 255).

Last, Ord Ashg: *Dionide* spp., Czechoslovakia and Poland (Kielan 1960, p. 161).

Family RAPHIOPHORIDAE Angelin 1854

First, Ord Arenig: *Ampyx* spp. widespread in Anglo-Welsh area, SW France and Scandinavia, *Lonchodomas* recorded in Sweden. (Thoral 1935, p. 305; Tjernvik 1957, p. 270; Whittard 1955, p. 15).

Last, Sil Ludl: *Raphiophorus parvulus* Forbes (*in* Phillips & Salter 1848, p. 350), Shropshire, England.

Family ENDYMIONIIDAE Raymond 1920

First, Ord Llvirn: *Endymionia* spp., eastern N. America (Whittington 1965, p. 324).

Last, Ord Carad: *Salteria* spp., Scotland and eastern N. America (B.N. Cooper 1953, p. 13; Reed 1903, p. 43).

Family ALSATASPIDIDAE Turner 1940

First, Ord Arenig: *Falanaspis aliena* Tjernvik (1957, p. 272), Sweden.

Last, Ord Llvirn: *Seleneceme* spp., Britain, N. America (Whittard 1960, p. 118).

Family HAPALOPLEURIDAE Harrington and Leanza 1957

First, Ord Tremad: *Hapalopleura* spp., *Rhadinopleura eurycephala* Harrington & Leanza (1957, p. 205), S. America; *Clavatellus* spp. Poletaeva (1955, p. 172), Russia.

Last, Ord Arenig: *Araiopleura reticulata* Harrington & Leanza (1957, p. 209), S. America.

Family ITYOPHORIDAE Warburg 1925

First, Ord Carad: *Frognaspis stoermeri* Nikolaisen, Norway.

Last, Ord Ashg: *Ityophorus undulatus* Warburg, Sweden.

Chapter 18: *Arthropoda: Protarthropoda and Trilobitomorpha*

Order PHACOPIDA Salter 1864

Suborder CHEIRURINA Harrington and Leanza 1957

Family CHEIRURIDAE Salter 1864

First, U. Camb: *Eocheirurus* spp., Russia (Rozova 1960, p. 16).
Last, Dev Eifel: *Crotalocephalus sternbergi* (Boeck), Czechoslovakia (Prantl 1946, p. 11).

Family PLIOMERIDAE Raymond 1913

First, Ord Tremad: *Parapilekia bohemica* (Růžička), Czechoslovakia. Other genera include *Anacheirurus*, Wales, and *Protopliomerops*, N. & S. America, Asia (Havlíček *et al.* 1958, p. 28; Ross 1951, p. 131; Harrington & Leanza 1957, p. 217).
Last, Ord Ashg: *Placoparia (Hawleia) prantli* Kielan (1960, p. 125), Poland.

Family ENCRINURIDAE Angelin 1854

First, Ord Arenig: *Cybele bellatula* (Dalman), Scandinavia (Størmer 1940, p. 140).
Last, Sil Ludl: *Encrinurus stubblefieldi* Tripp (1962, p. 471), England; *Encrinurus transiens* (Barrande), *Cromus beaumonti* (Barrande), Czechoslovakia, N. America (Horný 1962, p. 904; Churkin & Langenheim 1960, p. 268).

Suborder CALYMENINA Swinnerton 1915

Family CALYMENIDAE Burmeister 1843

First, Ord Tremad: *Pharostomina oepiki* Sdzuy (1955, p. 31), Germany; *P. trapezoidalis* (Harrington), Argentina (Harrington & Leanza 1957, pp. 223, 276).
Last, Dev ?Ems: *Calymene interjecta* Barrande, Czechoslovakia.

Family HOMALONOTIDAE E. J. Chapman 1890

First, Ord Trem: *Bavarilla hofensis* (Barrande), Germany (Sdzuy 1955, p.35).
Last, Dev ?Givet: *Dipleura dekayi* Green, N. & S. America (Kozłowski 1923, p.20).

Suborder PHACOPINA Struve 1959

Family PHACOPIDAE Hawle and Corda 1947

First, Ord Ashg: *Phacops primaevus* Clarke, eastern N. America (G. A. Cooper 1930, p. 385).
Last, Dev Famenn: *Cryphops*, *Dianops*, *Phacops* spp. incl. *P. accipitrinus* (Phillips), Europe (Goldring 1955, pp. 30, 46; R. & E. Richter 1926, p. 242; 1951, p. 221).

Family DALMANITIDAE Vogdes 1890

First, Ord Arenig: *Ormathops borni*, SW France (Dean 1966, p. 292).
Last, Dev Frasn: *Asteropyge* spp., Europe (R. & E. Richter 1926, p. 243).

Family CALMONIIDAE Delo 1935

First, Sil Wenl: *Acaste downingiae* (Murchison), England (R. & E. Richter 1954, p. 16).
Last, Dev (M.): *Cryphaeoides rostratus* (Kozłowski) & *Schistostylus brevicaudatus* (Kozłowski), Sicasica Fm, Bolivia (Delo 1935, pp. 410, 416).

Family PTERYGOMETOPIDAE Reed 1905

First, Ord Arenig: *Pterygometopus sclerops* (Dalman), Scandinavia (Whittington 1950, p. 538).
Last, Ord Ashg: several genera widely distributed in Europe, Russia and eastern N. America. Include *Achatella*, *Calliops*, *Calyptaulax*, *Chasmops* and *Liocnemis* (Delo 1940; Kielan 1960).

Family MONORAKIDAE Kramarenko 1952

First, Ord Carad: *Isalaux canonensis* Frederickson & Pollak (1952, p. 643), N. America, *I.* spp., Russia (Maksimova 1962, p. 101).

Last, Ord Ashg: *Elasmaspis, Evenkaspis, Ceratevenkaspis, Monorakos* and *Parevenkaspis*, Russia (Kramarenko 1952; 1956). [W.T.D.]

Order LICHIDA Moore 1959

Family LICHIDAE Hawle and Corda 1847

First, Ord Tremad: *Lichas klouceki* Růžička 1926, Bohemia.

Last, Dev(U.): *Craspedarges wilcanniae* Gürich 1901, U. Dev, Australia.

Comment: Ancestral taxon uncertain. Greatest abundance in M. Ord; bizarre spinose genera in Dev. Some individuals extremely large–70 cm in length. Wide distribution.

Family LICHAKEPHALIDAE Tripp 1957

First and **Last,** Ord Tremad: *Lichakephalus erbeni* Sdzuy 1955, Germany. [R.P.T.]

Order ODONTOPLEURIDA Whittington 1959

Family ODONTOPLEURIDAE Burmeister 1843

First, Ord Arenig: *Selenopeltis binodosus*, SW France (Dean 1966, p. 334).

Last, Dev Frasn: *Radiaspis radiata* (Goldfuss), Germany (R. & E. Richter 1926, pp. 109, 242).

Family EOACIDASPIDIDAE Poletaeva 1957

First, M. Camb: *Acidaspides lermontovae* Chernysheva (1953, p. 81), Russia.

Last, U. Camb: *Belovia calva* (Chernysheva), *Eoacidaspis salairica* Poletaeva (1957, p. 162), Russia. [W.T.D.]

REFERENCES

BALASHOVA, E. A. 1961. [Some Tremadoc trilobites of the Atkyubinsk district.] *Trudỹ geol. Inst., Leningr.*, **18**, 102–145, 4pls. (Russian).

BARRANDE, J. 1852. *Système silurien du Centre de la Bohême* Vol. I, Trilobites. Prague & Paris.

BROOKS, H. K. 1962. The Paleozoic Eumalacostraca of North America. *Bull. Am. Paleont.*, **44,** 163–338.

CAMPBELL, K. S. W. & ENGEL, B. A. 1963. The faunas of the Tournaisian Tulcumba Sandstone and its members in the Werrie and Belvue synclines, New South Wales. *J. geol. Soc. Aust.,* **10**, 55–122, 9 pls.

CHANG, W. T. 1949. Ordovician trilobites from Kaiping Basin, Hopei. *Bull. geol. Soc. China,* **29,** 111–125, 2 pls.

CHERNYSHEVA, N. E. 1953. [*Middle Cambrian Trilobites of Eastern Siberia, Part* 1.] 1–116, pls. 1–8. (Russian).

CHUGAEVA, M. N. 1958. [Trilobites of the Ordovician of the Chu-Ili mountains.] *Trudỹ geol. Inst., Leningr.*, **9**, 5–138, 11 pls. (Russian).

CHURKIN, M. & LANGENHEIM, R. L. 1960. Silurian strata of the Klamath Mountains, California. *Am. J. Sci.,* **258**, 258–273, 4 figs.

COBBOLD, E. S. 1921. The Cambrian Horizons of Comley (Shropshire) and their Brachiopoda, Pteropoda, Gasteropoda, etc. *Q. Jl Geol. Soc. Lond.*, **76**, 325–386, pl. 21–24.

COOPER, B. N. 1953. Trilobites from the Lower Champlainian Formations of the Appalachian Valley. *Mem. geol. Soc. Am.,* **55**, 1–69, 19 pls.

COOPER, G. A. 1930. New species from the Upper Ordovician of Percé. *Am. J. Sci.,* **20,** 365–392, pls. 4, 5.

DEAN, W. T. 1966. The Lower Ordovician stratigraphy and Trilobites of the Landeyran Valley and the neighbouring part of the Montagne Noire, south-western France. *Bull. Br. Mus. (Nat. Hist.) Geol.*, **12**, 245–353, pls. 1–21.

DELO, D. M. 1935. A revision of the phacopid trilobites. *J. Paleont.*, **9**, 402–420, 45 figs.

—— 1940. Phacopid trilobites of North America. *Spec. Pap. geol. Soc. Am.*, **29**, 135 pp., 13 pls.

DIENER, C. 1897. The Permocarboniferous fauna of Chitichun. *Mem. geol. Surv. India Palaeont. Indica* (15), **1**, (1), 1–105, 13 pl.

—— 1903. Permian fossils of the central Himalayas. *Mem. geol. Surv. India Palaeont. Indica* (15), **1**, (5), 1–204, 10 pl.

ENDO, R. & MATSUMOTO, E., 1962. Permo-Carboniferous trilobites from Japan. *Sci. Rep. Saitama Univ.* (B), **4**, 149–172, 3 pl.

ERBEN, H. K. 1961. Blinding and Extinction of certain Proetidae (Tril.). *J. paleont. Soc. India*, **3**, 82–104.

FEARNSIDES, W. G., ELLES, G. L. & SMITH, B. 1907. The Lower Palaeozoic rocks of Pomeroy. *Proc. R. Ir. Acad.*, **26**, 97–128.

FREDERICKSON, E. A. & POLLACK, J. M. 1952. Two trilobite genera from the Harding Formation (Ordovician) of Colorado. *J. Paleont.*, **26**, 641–644, 6 figs.

GOLDRING, R. 1955. The Upper Devonian and Lower Carboniferous trilobites of the Pilton Beds in N. Devon. *Senckenberg. Leth.*, **36**, 27–48, 2 pls.

—— 1958. Lower Tournaisian Trilobites in the Carboniferous Limestone Facies of the southwest province of Great Britain and of Belgium. *Palaeontology*, **1**, 231–244, pl. 43.

GLAESSNER, M. F. 1962. Pre-Cambrian Fossils. *Biol. Rev.*, **37**, 467–494.

GRANT, R. E. 1966. Late Permian trilobites from the Salt Range, West Pakistan. *Palaeontology*, **9**, 64–73, pl. 13.

GÜRICH, G. 1901. Ueber eine neue Lichas-Art aus dem Devon von Neu-Süd-Wales, und über die Gattung Lichas überhaupt. *Neues Jb. Miner. Geol. Palaont. BeilBd.*, **14**, 519–39, pl. 18, figs. 1–8, pl. 20.

HARPER, J. C. 1948. The Ordovician and Silurian rocks of Ireland. *Proc. Lpool geol. Soc.*, **20**, 48–67.

HARRINGTON & LEANZA, A. F. 1957. Ordovician trilobites of Argentina. *Univ. Kansas, Dept. Geol. Spec. Pub.*, **1**, 276 pp., 140 figs.

HAVLÍČEK, V., HORNÝ, R., CHLUPÁČ, I. & ŠNAJDR, M. 1958. *Führer zu den Geologischen Exkursionen in das Barrandium.* Sbírka geol. prův., No. 1, 1–171.

HENNINGSMOEN, G. 1957. The trilobite family Olenidae, with description of Norwegian material and remarks on the Olenid and Tremadocian Series. *Skr. norske Vidensk Akad.* I Mat.–Nat. Kl., **1957**, 1–303, 31 pls.

HESSLER, R. R. 1963. Lower Mississippian trilobites of the family Proetidae in the United States, part I. *J. Paleont.*, **37**, 543–563, pl. 59–62.

—— 1965. Lower Mississippian trilobites of the family Proetidae in the United States, part II. *J. Paleont.*, **39**, 248–264, pl. 37–40.

HINTZE, L. F. 1953. Lower Ordovician trilobites from western Utah and eastern Nevada. *Bull. Utah geol. miner. Surv.*, **48**, i–vi, 1–249, 28 pls.

HORNÝ, R. J. 1962. Das mittelböhmische Silur. *Geologie*, **8**, 873–916, 26 figs.

HOWELL, B. F. 1937. Cambrian *Centropleura vermontensis* fauna of northwestern Vermont. *Bull. geol. Soc. Am.*, **48**, 1147–1210, pl. 1–6.

HUPÉ, P. 1953. Contribution à l'étude du Cambrien inférieur et du Précambrien III de l'Anti-Atlas Marocain. *Notes Mém. Serv. Mines Carte géol. Maroc*, **103**, tabs. 2 and 3.

—— 1960. Sur le Cambrien inférieur du Maroc. *21st Int. Geol. Congr.*, Sec. 8, 75–85.

—— & NELSON, C. A. 1964. Sur l'existence de *Fallotaspis* et *Daguinaspis*, trilobites marocains dans le Cambrien inférieur de California et ses conséquences. *C.r. hebd. Séanc. Acad. Sci., Paris*, **258**, 621–3.

HUTCHINSON, R. D. 1962. Cambrian Stratigraphy and Trilobite Faunas of Southeastern Newfoundland. *Bull. geol. Surv. Canada*, **88**, 1–156, pl. 1–25.

ILLING, V. C. 1916. The Paradoxidian Fauna of Part of the Stockingford Shales. *Q. Jl geol. Soc. Lond.*, **71**, 386–448, pl. 28–38.

JAANUSSON, V. 1956. On the trilobite genus *Celmus* Angelin, 1854. *Bull. geol. Instn Univ. Upsala*, **36**, 35–49, pl.

—— 1957. Unterordovizische Illaeniden aus Skandinavien. *Bull. geol. Instn Univ. Upsala*, **37**, 79–165, 10 pls.

KIELAN, Z. 1960. Upper Ordovician trilobites from Poland and some related forms from Bohemia and Scandinavia. *Palaeont. pol.*, **11**, 1–198, pl. 1–36.

KOBAYASHI, T. 1933. Upper Cambrian of the Wuhutsui Basin, Liaotung, with special reference to the limit of the Chaumitian (or Upper Cambrian) of Eastern Asia, and its subdivision. *Jap. J. Geol. Geog.*, **11**, 55–155, pls. 9–15.

—— 1935. The Cambro-Ordovician formations and faunas of South Chosen. Palaeontology., Pt. III. Cambrian faunas of South Chosen with a special study on the Cambrian trilobite genera and families. *J. Fac. Sci. Tokyo Univ.*, **4**, 49–344, pls. 1–24.

—— 1951. On the Ordovician trilobites in central China. *J. Fac. Sci. Tokyo Univ.*, **8**, 1–87, pls. 1–5.

KOZŁOWSKI, R. 1923. Faune dévonienne de Bolivie. *Annls Paléont.*, **12**, 1–112, 10 pls.

KRAMARENKO, N. N. 1952. Novye trilobity iz Silura Bassejna reki Podkamennaja Tunguska. *Dokl. Akad. nauk SSSR*, **86**, 401–404, 9 figs.

—— 1956. [New representatives of the Ordovician trilobite genus *Monorakos* Schmidt of the Siberian Platform.] *Materials for the Principles of Palaeontology* No. 1, *Trudy paleont. Inst.*, 49–55, pl. 1. (Russian).

LAKE, P. 1942. A monograph of the British Cambrian trilobites. Pt. 13. *Palaeontogr. Soc. [Monogr.]*, 307–332, pls. 44–46.

LAMONT, A. 1935. The Drummuck Group, Girvan; a stratigraphical revision, with descriptions of new fossils from the lower part of the Group. *Trans. geol. Soc. Glasgow*, **19**, 288–332, pls. 7–9.

LERMONTOVA, E. V. 1951. [Upper Cambrian trilobites and brachiopods of Boshche-Kul (Northeast Kazakhstan).] *Trudy vses. nauchnoissled. geol. Inst.*, 1–49, 6 pls. (Russian).

LOCHMAN, C. 1953. Analysis and discussion of nine Cambrian trilobite families. *J. Paleont.*, **27**, 889–896.

—— 1956. Stratigraphy, paleontology and paleogeography of the *Elliptocephala asaphoides* strata in Cambridge and Hoosick quadrangles, New York. *Bull. geol. Soc. Am.*, **67**, 1331–1396, pl. 1–10.

LOCHMAN-BALK, C. & WILSON, J. L. 1958. Cambrian biostratigraphy in North America. *J. Paleont.*, **32**, 312–350.

LOTZE, F. 1958. Zur stratigraphie des spanischen Kambriums. *Geologie*, **7** (3–6), 727–750, table.

LU, Y-H. 1956. An Upper Cambrian trilobite faunule from eastern Kueichou. *Acta palaeont. sin.*, **4**, 365–372, pl. 1.

—— 1957. Trilobita. In *Index fossils of China*, Invertebrata, Pt. 3, 249–294, pls. 137–155.

MAKSIMOVA, Z. A. 1955. [Trilobites of the Middle and Upper Devonian of the Urals and northern Mugodzhar]. *Trudy vses. nauchnoissled geol. Inst.*, **3**, 1–263, 18 pl. (Russian).

—— 1962. [Trilobites of the Ordovician and Silurian of the Siberian platform]. *Trudy vses. nauchnoissled. geol. Inst.*, **76**, 1–215, 18 pls. (Russian).

MÄNNIL, R. 1962. [A faunistic characterisation of the Porkuni Stage]. *Geoloogia-Inst. Uurim.*, **10**, 115–127.

MAREK, L. 1961. The trilobite family Cyclopygidae Raymond in the Ordovician of Bohemia. *Rozpr. ústřed. Úst. geol.*, **28**, 1–84, 6 pls.

MOBERG, J. C. & SEGERBERG, C. O. 1906. Bidrag till Kännedomen om Ceratopygeregionen. *Acta Univ. lund.* (2nd Series), **2**, 1–113, 7 pls.

NIKOLAISEN, F. 1963. The Middle Ordovician of the Oslo region, Norway. 14. The trilobite family Telephinidae. *Norsk geol. Tidsskr.*, **43**, 345–399, 4 pls.

ÖPIK, A. A. 1956. Cambrian geology of Queensland, *In* El sistema cambrico, su paleogeografia y el problema de su base; part 2, 1–24. *20th Int. Geol. Congr., Mexico.*

—— 1961. The geology and palaeontology of the headwaters of the Burke River, Queensland. *Bull. Bur. Miner. Resour. Geol. Geophys. Aust.*, **53**, 1–249, pl. 1–24.

—— 1963a. Early Upper Cambrian Fossils from Queensland, *Bull. Bur. Miner. Resour. Geol. Geophys. Aust.*, **64**, 1–133, pl. 1–9.

—— 1963b. *Nepea* and the Nepeids (Trilobites, Middle Cambrian, Australia). *J. geol. Soc. Aust.*, **10**, 339–341, figs 1, 2.

ORLOV, YU. A. (Editor) 1960. *Osnovy paleontologii, Chlenistonogiye, trilobito-obraznyye i rakoobraznyye.* Moscow.

ORLOWSKI, S. 1964. Middle Cambrian and its fauna in the eastern part of the Holy Cross Mts. *Studia geol. polon.* **16**, 1–94, pls. 1–15.

OSMÓLSKA, H. 1962. Famennian and Lower Carboniferous Cyrtosymbolinae (Trilobita) from the Holy Cross Mountains, Poland. *Acta palaeont. pol.*, **7**, 52–222, 17 pl.

PALMER, A. R. 1962. *Glyptagnostus* and associated trilobites in the United States. *Prof. Pap. U.S. geol. Surv.*, **374-F**, 1–49, pl. 1–6.

—— 1964. An unusual Lower Cambrian trilobite fauna from Nevada. *Prof. Pap. U.S. geol. Surv.*, **483-F**, 1–14, pls 1–3.

—— 1965. Trilobites of the Late Cambrian Pterocephaliid Biomere in the Great Basin, United States. *Prof. Pap. U.S. geol. Surv.*, **493**, 1–105, 20 pls.

PHILLIPS, J. & SALTER, J. W. 1848. Palaeontological Appendix to Professor John Phillips' Memoir on the Malvern Hills, compared with the Palaeozoic districts of Abberley, etc. *Mem. geol. Surv. U.K.*, **2** (1), 331–386, pls. 4–30.

PIVETEAU, J. (Editor) 1953. *Traité de Paléontologie*, **3**. Paris.

POLETAEVA, O. K. 1957. [Cambrian representatives of Odontopleuroidea Prantl and Přibyl emend. Hupé 1955]. *Ezheg. vses. paleont. Obsthch*, **16**, 162–5, 3 figs. (Russian).

PRANTL, F. 1946. Some abnormalities in *Crotalocephalus* Salter (Trilobitae). *Bull. int. Acad. tchéque Sci.*, **48**, 1–16, 2 pls.

—— & PŘIBYL, A. 1948. Some new or imperfectly known Ordovician trilobites from Bohemia. *Bull. int. Acad. tchéque Sci.*, **49**, 1–23, pls. 1–3.

RASETTI, F. 1943. New Lower Ordovician trilobites from Lévis, Quebec. *J. Paleont.*, **17**, 101–104, pl. 19.

—— 1945. Evolution of the facial suture of the trilobites *Loganopeltoides* and *Loganopeltis*. *Am. J. Sci.*, **243**, 44–50, 1 pl.

—— 1951. Middle Cambrian Stratigraphy and faunas of the Canadian Rocky Mountains. *Smithson. misc. Collns*, **116**, no. 5, 1–277, pl. 1–34.

RAYMOND, P. E. 1920. Some new Ordovician trilobites. *Bull. Mus. comp. Zool. Harv.*, **54**, 273–296.

REED, F. R. C. 1903. The Lower Palaeozoic trilobites of the Girvan District, I. *Palaeontogr. Soc.* [*Monogr.*], 1–48, pls. 1–6.

—— 1915. Supplementary Memoir on new Ordovician and Silurian fossils from the Northern Shan States. *Mem. geol. Surv. India Palaeont. Indica*, N.S., **6** (1).

—— 1935. The Lower Palaeozoic trilobites of Girvan. Supplement No. 3. *Palaeontogr. Soc.* [*Monogr.*], 1–64, pls. 1–4.

—— 1943. The genera of British Carboniferous trilobites. *Ann. Mag. nat. Hist.*, (11), **10**, 54–65.

REGNÉLL, G. 1960. The Lower Palaeozoic of Scania. *In* Regnéll, G. and Hede, J. E., Guide to Excursions Nos. A22 and C17. *21st Int. geol. Congr.*

RESSER, C. E. 1939. The Spence Shale and its fauna. *Smithson. misc. Collns*, **97**, No. 12, 1–29.

RESSER, C. E. & HOWELL, B. F. 1938. Lower Cambrian *Olenellus* Zone of the Appalachians. *Bull. geol. Soc. Am.*, **49**, 195–248, pls 1–13.

RICHTER, R. & E. 1926. Die Trilobiten des Oberdevons, Beiträge zur Kenntnis devonischer Trilobiten, 4. *Abh. preuss. geol. Landesanst.*, **99**, 1–314, 12 pls.

—— 1951. Der Beginn des Karbons im Wechsel der Trilobiten. *Senckenberg. Leth.* **32**, 219–266, pls. 1–5.

—— 1954. Die Trilobiten des Ebbe-Sattels und zu vergleichende Arten (Ordovizium, Gotlandium/Devon). *Abh. senckenb. naturforsch. Ges.*, **488**, 1–76, pls. 1–12.

ROBISON, R. A. 1964. Middle-Upper Cambrian Boundary in North America. *Bull. geol. Soc. Am.*, **75**, 987–993, figs. 1, 2.

ROLFE, W. D. I. 1963. Catalogue of type specimens in the invertebrate paleontological collections of the Museum of Comparative Zoology, Arthropoda. *Bull. Mus. comp. Zool. Harv.*, **129**, 369–398.

ROSS, R. J. 1951. Stratigraphy of the Garden City Formation in northeastern Utah, and its trilobite faunas. *Bull. Peabody Mus. nat. Hist.*, **6**, 1–161, pls. 1–36.

Rozova, A. V. 1960. [Upper Cambrian trilobites of Salair (Tolstochikhinsky suite).] *Trudý Inst. geol. geofiz. Akad. nauk SSSR (Sib. otdel.)*, **5**, 1–116, pls. 1–8. (Russian).

Ruggieri, G. 1959. Una nuova trilobite del Permiano del Sosio (Sicilia). *Memorie Inst. geol. miner. Univer. Padova*, **21**, 3–10, 1 pl.

Růžička, R. 1926. Fauna vrstev Eulomových Rudniho ložiska u Holoubkova (v Ouzkém). (Faune des couches à Euloma du gisement ferrugineux près de Holoubkov (à Ouzky).) *Rospr. čsl. Akad. Věd*, **35**, no. 39, 1–26, pl. 1–3.

Sdzuy, K. 1955. Die Fauna der Leimitz-Schiefer (Tremadoc). *Abh. senckenb. naturforsch. Ges.*, **492**, 1–74, pl. 1–8.

Simonetta, A. M. 1964. Osservazione sugli artropodi non trilobiti della 'Burgess Shale' (Cambriano medio). *Monitore zool. ital.*, **72**, 215–231.

Sinclair, G. W. 1949. The Ordovician trilobite *Eobronteus*. *J. Paleont.*, **23**, 45–56, pls. 12–14.

Skjeseth, S. 1955. The Middle Ordovician of the Oslo region, Norway. 5. The trilobite family Styginidae. *Norsk. geol. Tidsskr.*, **35**, 9–28, pls. 1–5.

Šnajdr, M. 1957. Klasifikace čeledě Illaenidae (Hawle & Corda) v českém starším paleozoiku. *Sb. ústřed Úst. geol.*, [*Pal.*] **23**, 125–284, pls. 1–12.

—— 1960. Studie o čeledi Scutelluidae (Trilobitae). *Rozpr. ústřed. Úst. geol.*, **26**, 1–263, pls. 1–36.

Størmer, L. 1940. Early descriptions of Norwegian trilobites. The type specimens of C. Boeck, M. Sars and M. Esmark. *Norsk geol. Tidsskr.*, **20**, 113–151, pls. 1–3.

—— 1945. Remarks on the *Tretaspis* (*Trinucleus*) Shales of Hadeland. *Norsk. geol. Tidsskr.*, **25**, 379–426, pls. 1–4.

—— 1953. The Middle Ordovician of the Oslo region, Norway. 1. Introduction to stratigraphy. *Norsk geol. Tidsskr.*, **31**, 37–141, 6 pls.

Stubblefield, C. J. 1950. A new Komaspid Genus of wide distribution in early Ordovician times. *Ann. Mag. nat. Hist.* (12), **3**, 341–352, pl. 2.

—— 1951. Further renaming of the Tremadoc trilobite genus *Psilocephalus* Salter. *Geol. Mag.*, **88**, 440.

—— & Bulman, O. M. B. 1927. The Shineton Shales of the Wrekin District. *Q. Jl geol. Soc. Lond.*, **83**, 99–146, pls. 3–5.

Thoral, M. 1935. *Contribution à l'étude paléontologique de l'Ordovicien inférieur de la Montagne Noire et révision sommaire de la faune cambrienne de la Montagne Noire.* Univ. Paris, Thèse, Faculté des Sci., 1–363, pls. 1–35.

Thorslund, P. 1940. On the Chasmops Series of Jemtland and Södermanland (Tvären). *Sver. geol. Unders. Afh.* (C), **436**, 1–191, 15 pls.

Tjernvik, T. E. 1956. On the early Ordovician of Sweden. *Bull. Geol. Instn Univ. Upsala*, **36**, 107–284, pls. 1–11.

Toumansky, O. G. 1935. *The Permo-Carboniferous trilobites of the Crimea*, 1–56, 12 pl. Glavnoe Geologo-Hydro-Geodezicheskoe Upravlenie, Moscow and Leningrad.

Treatise O. 1959. Moore, R. C. (Editor). *Treatise on Invertebrate Paleontology, Part O:* Harrington, H. J. *et al.*, Arthropoda 1. University of Kansas Press.

Treatise W. 1962. Moore, R. C. (Editor) *Treatise on Invertebrate Paleontology, Part W:* Hass, W. H. *et al.* Miscellanea. University of Kansas Press.

Tripp, R. P. 1962. The Silurian trilobite *Encrinurus punctatus* (Wahlenberg) and allied species. *Palaeontology*, **5**, 460–477, pls. 65–68.

Troedsson, G. T. 1937. On the Cambro-Ordovician faunas of Western Ouruq tagh, eastern T'ien-shan. *Palaeont. sin.* new series B, **2**, 1–74, pls. 1–10.

Ulrich, E. O. 1930a. *In* Bridge, J. Geology of the Eminence and Cardareva Quadrangles. *Missouri Bur. Geol. Mines*, **24**, 212–222, pls 19–21.

—— 1930b. Ordovician trilobites of the family Telephidae and concerned stratigraphic correlations. *Proc. U.S. natn Mus.*, **76**, (21), 1–88, 8 pls.

Vologdin, A. G. 1965. Otkrytiye ostatkov ogromnykh pantsirnykh zhivotnykh v Karagasskoy svite Vostochnogo Sayana. *Dokl. Akad. Nauk SSSR*, **161** (6), 1426–1429.

Warburg, E. 1925. The trilobites of the Leptaena Limestone in Dalarne. *Bull. Geol. Instn Univ. Upsala*, **17**, 1–450, pls. 1–11.

WEBER, V. N. 1948. [Trilobites of the Silurian rocks, no. 1, Lower Silurian trilobites.] *Monografii Paleont. SSSR*, **69**, 1–113, pls. 1–11. (Russian).

WESTERGÅRD, A. H. 1936. *Paradoxides oelandicus* Beds of Öland, with the account of a diamond boring through the Cambrian at Mossberga. *Sver. geol. Unders. Afh.* (C), **394**, 1–66, pls 1–12.

—— 1939. Swedish Cambrian Asaphidae. *Sver. geol. Unders. Afh.* (C), **421**, 1–16, pls. 1–3.

—— 1946. Agnostidea of the Middle Cambrian of Sweden. *Sver. geol. Unders. Afh.* (C), **447**, 1–140, pl. 1–16.

—— 1947. Supplementary notes on the Upper Cambrian trilobites of Sweden. *Sver. geol. Unders. Afh.* (C), **489**, 1–34, pls 1–3.

—— 1948. Non-agnostidean trilobites of the Middle Cambrian of Sweden, I. *Sver. geol. Unders. Afh.* (C), **498**, 1–32, pls. 1–4.

—— 1953. Non-agnostidean trilobites of the Middle Cambrian of Sweden, III. *Sver. geol. Unders. Afh.* (C), **526**, 1–58, pls. 1–8.

WHITTARD, W. F. 1952. Cyclopygid trilobites from Girvan and a note on *Bohemilla*. *Bull. Br. Mus. (Nat. Hist.), Geol.*, **1**, 305–324, pls. 32, 33.

—— 1955. The Ordovician trilobites of the Shelve Inlier, West Shropshire, 1. *Palaeontogr. Soc.* [*Monogr.*], 1–40, pls. 1–4.

—— 1958. The Ordovician trilobites of the Shelve Inlier, West Shropshire, 3. *Palaeontogr. Soc.* [*Monogr.*], 71–116, pls. 10–15.

—— 1960. The Ordovician trilobites of the Shelve Inlier, West Shropshire, 4. *Palaeontogr. Soc.* [*Monogr.*], 117–162, pls. 16–21.

—— 1961. The Ordovician trilobites of the Shelve Inlier, West Shropshire, 5. *Palaeontogr. Soc.* [*Monogr.*], 163–196, pls. 22–25.

WHITTINGTON, H. B. 1950. Sixteen Ordovician genotype trilobites. *J. Paleont.*, **24**, 531–565, pls. 68–75.

—— 1953. North American Bathyuridae and Leiostegiidae (Trilobita). *J. Paleont.*, **27**, 647–678, pls. 65–69.

—— 1957. Ontogeny of *Elliptocephala, Paradoxides, Sao, Blainia*, and *Triarthrus* (Trilobita). *J. Paleont.*, **31**, 934–946, 2 pls.

—— 1959. Silicified Middle Ordovician Trilobites: Remopleurididae, Trinucleidae, Raphiophoridae, Endymioniidae. *Bull. Mus. comp. Zool. Harv.*, **121**, 371–497, 36 pl.

—— 1960. *Cordania* and other trilobites from the Lower and Middle Devonian. *J. Paleont.*, **34**, 405–420, pl. 51–54.

—— 1965. Trilobites of the Ordovician Table Head Formation, Western Newfoundland. *Bull. Mus. comp. Zool. Harv.*, **132** (4), 275–442, pls. 1–68.

—— & ROLFE, W. D. I. (Editors), 1963. *Phylogeny and evolution of Crustacea.* Spec. Publ. Mus. comp. Zool. Harv., 192 pp.

J. W. COWIE, PH.D. F.G.S.
Department of Geology, The University, Queen's Buildings, Bristol 8.

W. T. DEAN, PH.D. F.G.S.
Department of Palaeontology, British Museum (Natural History), Cromwell Road, London s w 7.

R. GOLDRING, PH.D. F.G.S.
Department of Geology, The University, Reading, Berkshire.

W. D. I. ROLFE, PH.D. F.G.S.
Hunterian Museum, The University, Glasgow w 2, Scotland.

A. W. A. RUSHTON, PH.D.
Geological Survey and Museum, Institute of Geological Sciences, Exhibition Road, London s w 7.

J. T. TEMPLE, M.A. PH.D. F.G.S.
Department of Geology, Birkbeck College, Malet Street, London w c 1.

R. P. TRIPP,
High Wood, Botsom Lane, West Kingsdown, Sevenoaks, Kent.

CHAPTER 19

Arthropoda: Chelicerata, Pycnogonida, Palaeoisopus, Myriapoda and Insecta

Contributors: R. A. CROWSON, W. D. I. ROLFE, J. SMART,
C. D. WATERSTON, E. C. WILLEY & R. J. WOOTTON

Subphylum CHELICERATA Heymons 1901

Class MEROSTOMATA Dana 1852

Subclass XIPHOSURA Latreille 1802

The classification of Novozhilov (*in* Rohdendorf 1962b) is used here without prejudice.

Order AGLASPIDA Walcott 1911

First, Camb L.Camb: *Paleomerus hamiltoni* Størmer, Kinnekulle, Sweden (Størmer 1955). The first form assigned to the order without doubt is *Beckwithia typa* Resser M.Camb: Marjum Fm, Weeks Canyon, Utah (Raasch 1939).

Last, Ord Carad: *Neostrabops martini* Caster and Macke, Maysville Fm, Ohio (Caster and Macke 1952).

Order CHASMATASPIDIDA Caster and Brooks 1956

First and **Last,** Ord Llvirn?: monotypic order known from *Chasmataspis laurencii* Caster and Brooks, sediments in the Chazyan hiatus of Canada, Tennessee, U.S.A. (Caster and Brooks 1956).

Order SYNZIPHOSURA Packard 1886

First, Sil Wenl: *Neolimulus falcatus* Woodward and *Cyamocephalus loganensis* Currie, Logan Water, Lanarkshire, Scotland (Woodward 1868, Currie 1927).

Last, Dev Siegen: *Weinbergina opitzi* Richter and Richter, Hunsrückschiefer, Rheinland, Germany (Richter and Richter 1929).

Order LIMULINA Richter and Richter 1929

First, Dev Gedinn: *Kiaeria limuloides* Størmer, Downtonian, Ringerike, Norway (Størmer 1934). **Extant.**

Comment: Represented by extant species belonging to the genera *Limulus, Tachypleus* and *Carcinoscorpius*.

Order EURYPTERIDA Burmeister 1843

The classification of Caster and Kjellesvig-Waering (1964) is used here without prejudice.

The Fossil Record, pp. 499–534. Geological Society of London, 1967. Printed in Northern Ireland.

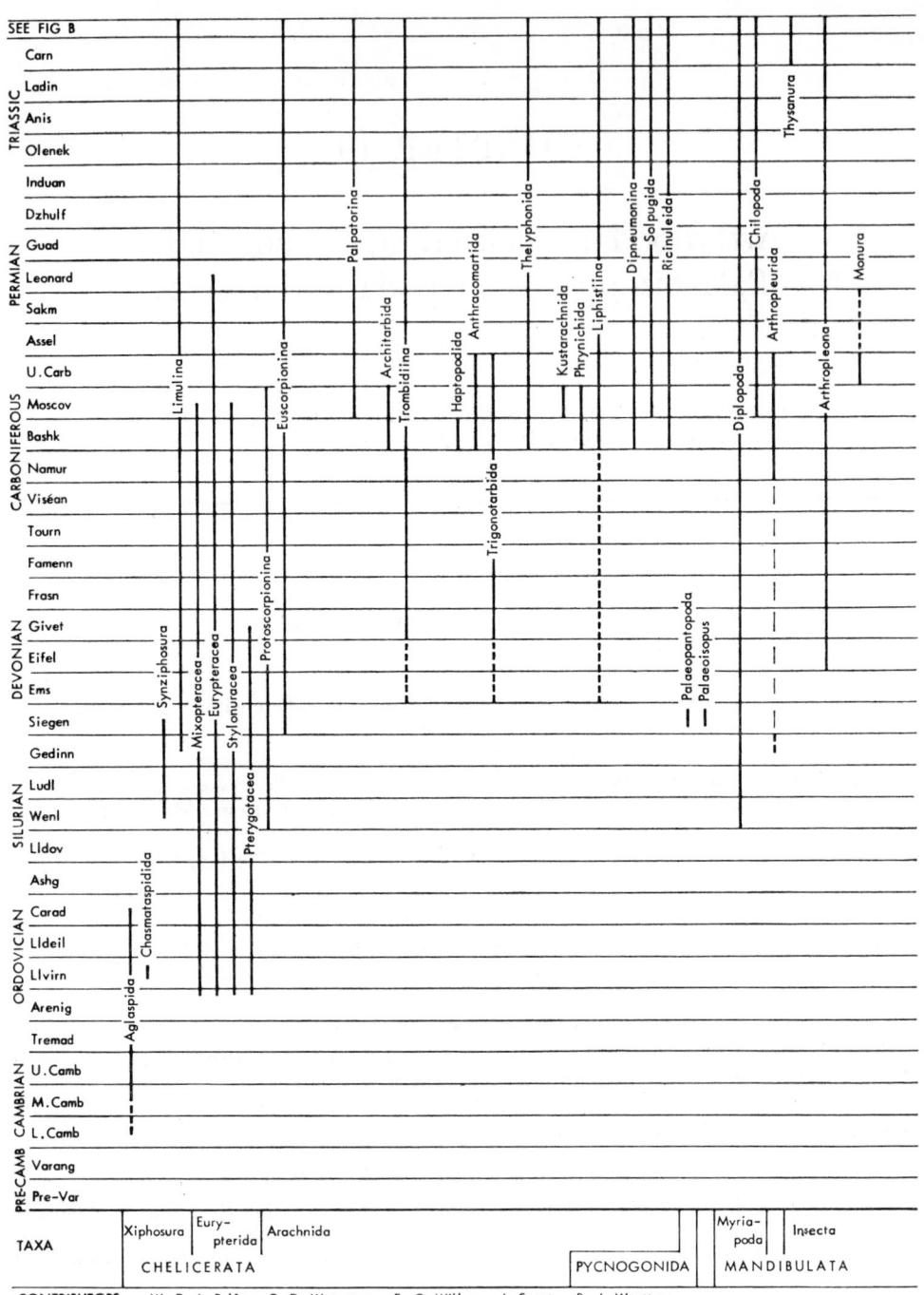

FIG. 19.1 A

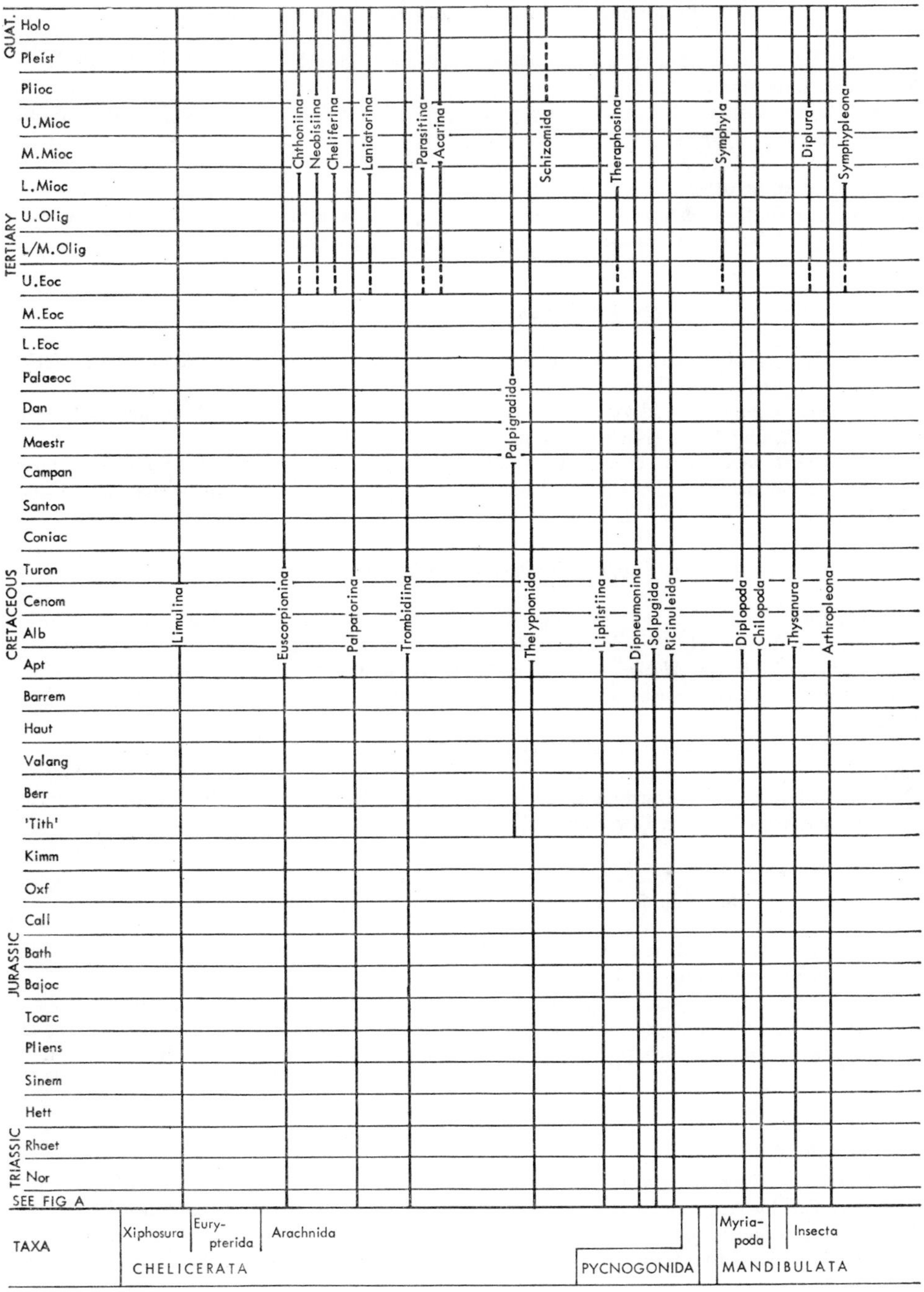
QUAT.
Holo
Pleist
TERTIARY
Plioc
U.Mioc
M.Mioc
L.Mioc
U.Olig
L/M.Olig
U.Eoc
M.Eoc
L.Eoc
Palaeoc
Dan
CRETACEOUS
Maestr
Campan
Santon
Coniac
Turon
Cenom
Alb
Apt
Barrem
Haut
Valang
Berr
'Tith'
JURASSIC
Kimm
Oxf
Call
Bath
Bajoc
Toarc
Pliens
Sinem
Hett
TRIASSIC
Rhaet
Nor
SEE FIG A
Limulina
Euscorpionina
Chthoniina
Neobisiina
Cheliferina
Palpatorina
Laniatorina
Trombidiina
Parasitina
Acarina
Palpigradida
Thelyphonida
Schizomida
Liphistiina
Theraphosina
Dipneumonina
Solpugida
Ricinuleida
Symphyla
Diplopoda
Chilopoda
Thysanura
Diplura
Arthropleona
Symphypleona
TAXA
Xiphosura
Eury-pterida
Arachnida
CHELICERATA
PYCNOGONIDA
Myria-poda
Insecta
MANDIBULATA

CONTRIBUTORS W. D. Rolfe, C. D. Waterston, E. C. Willey, J. Smart, R. J. Wootton

FIG. 19.1 B

The Fossil Record, Part II

Superfamily MIXOPTERACEA Caster and Kjellesvig-Waering 1955

First, Ord Arenig–Llvirn: *Eocarcinosoma ruedemanni* (Flower), Deepkill Fm, Rensselair Co., New York State (Flower 1945).

Last, Carb Moscov: *Mycterops ordinatus* Cope, Allegheny Fm, Beaver Co., Pennsylvania and *Mycterops mathieui* (Pruvost), Westphalian, Belgium (Kjellesvig-Waering 1959); also fragments of the same genus from Mazon Creek, Illinois (Kjellesvig-Waering 1963).

Constituent families: Megalograptidae Caster and Kjellesvig-Waering, Ord Carad-Ashg; Mixopteridae Caster and Kjellesvig-Waering, Sil Wenl-Dev Gedinn; Carcinosomatidae Størmer, Ord Arenig–Llvirn-Dev Gedinn; Mycteropidae Cope, Carb Moscov.

Superfamily EURYPTERACEA Burmeister 1843

First, Ord Arenig–Llvirn: *Waeringopterus? priscus* (Ruedemann) Deepkill Fm, Mt. Merino, Hudson, New York State (Leutze 1961).

Last, Perm Leonard: *Adelophthalmus sellardsi* (Dunbar) Wellington Fm, Dickinson Co., Kansas and Red Rock, Oklahoma (Kjellesvig-Waering 1948).

Constituent families: Hughmilleriidae Kjellesvig-Waering, Ord Carad-Perm Leonard; Slimoniidae Novozhilov, Ord Arenig–Llvirn-U. Carb; Eurypteridae Burmeister, Ord Carad-Dev Siegen.

Superfamily STYLONURACEA Diener 1924

First, Ord Arenig–Llvirn: *Dolichopterus antiquus* Ruedemann, Deepkill Fm, Mt. Merino, Hudson, New York State (Ruedemann 1942).

Last, Carb Moscov: *Mazonipterus cyclophthalmus* Kjellesvig-Waering, Carbondale Fm, Mazon Creek, Illinois and *Hibbertopterus? potens* (Hall) Allegheny Fm, Pennsylvania (Kjellesvig-Waering 1963).

Constituent families: Dolichopteridae Kjellesvig-Waering and Størmer, Ord Arenig–Llvirn-Dev Siegen; Stylonuridae Diener, Ord Carad-Carb Moscov; Rhenopteridae Størmer, Dev Siegen-Givet; Woodwardopteridae Kjellesvig-Waering, L. Dev-Carb Viséan; Hibbertopteridae Kjellesvig-Waering, Dev Famenn?-Perm.

Superfamily PTERYGOTACEA Clarke and Ruedemann 1912

First, Ord Arenig–Llvirn: *Pterygotus (Pterygotus?) deepkillensis* Ruedemann, Deepkill Fm, Deepkill, New York State (Ruedemann 1934).

Last, Dev (M.): *Pterygotus (Pterygotus) bolivianus* Kjellesvig-Waering, Metacryphaeus caffer Z., Sicasica Series, Bolivia (Kjellesvig-Waering 1964); also *Pterygotus (Pterygotus) dicki* Peach, Dev Givet, Thurso Flagstone Group, M. Old Red Sandstone, Caithness, Scotland (Peach 1883).

[C.D.W.]

Class ARACHNIDA Lamarck 1801

Introduction. The classification used is that of Petrunkevitch (Treatise P), which differs slightly from that used by Waterlot (*in* Piveteau 1953), Millot (*in* Grassé 1949) and Dubinin (*in* Rohdendorf 1962b), although the last groups the eurypterids and the scorpions together. According to Wills (1959, 1960) and Kjellesvig-Waering (1966) the classification of the scorpions requires revision.

Many fossil arachnids come from certain horizons in the Carboniferous coal measures of Europe and North America. The amber of localities such as the Baltic coast and Chiapas, Mexico, has produced many excellently preserved specimens. Exceptional conditions, as occurred during the formation of the Rhynie Chert of Aberdeenshire and the onyx marble of Arizona, have also resulted in particularly well preserved fossil material. "The fossil record of Arachnida is therefore very incomplete" (Petrunkevitch *in* Treatise P).

Subclass LATIGASTRA Petrunkevitch 1949

Order SCORPIONIDA Latreille 1817

Suborder PROTOSCORPIONINA Petrunkevitch 1949

First, Sil Wenl: *Dolichophonus loudonensis* (Laurie), U.Sil, Pentland Hills, Scotland (Laurie 1899).

Last, Carb Moscov: *Mazonia woodiana* Meek and Worthen, Francis Creek shales and lst, Mazon Creek, Illinois (Meek and Worthen 1868, Petrunkevitch 1949).

Comments: *Mazonia woodiana* as well as *Gigantoscorpius willsi* Störmer, Carb Tourn-Viséan, Calciferous Sandstone Series, near Langholm, Scotland, which has affinities with *M. woodiana* (see Störmer 1963), may not belong to this suborder (see introduction, and Kjellesvig-Waering 1966); but since the Wenl-L.Dev scorpions are closely related (Kjellesvig-Waering 1966) possible **Last,** Dev Ems: gen. et sp. indet. (Störmer 1960), Nellenköpchen Gruppe, Alken a.d. Mosel, Germany, which is considered to have affinities with *Proscorpius* (Kjellesvig-Waering 1966).

Suborder EUSCORPIONINA Petrunkevitch 1949

First, Dev Siegen: *Palaeoscorpius devonicus* Lehmann, Hunsrückschiefer, Germany (Lehmann 1944). **Extant.**

Comment: *P. devonicus* is known from a unique specimen (Petrunkevitch 1953).

Order PSEUDOSCORPIONIDA Latreille 1817

Suborder CHTHONIINA Beier 1932

First, Tert U. Eoc–L/M. Olig): *Chthonius* and *Heterolophus*, Baltic amber (Treatise P). **Extant.**

Suborder NEOBISIINA Beier 1932

First, Tert U. Eoc–L/M. Olig: *Neobisium, Garypinus, Geogarypus* and *Pseudogarypus*, Baltic amber (Treatise P). **Extant.**

Suborder CHELIFERINA Hagen 1878

First, Tert U. Eoc–L/M. Olig: Six genera belonging to three families, Baltic amber (Treatise P). **Extant.**

Order PHALANGIDA Perty 1833

Suborder PALPITORINA Thorell 1876

First, Carb Moscov: *Nemastomoides longipes* (Petrunkevitch) and *N. depressus* (Petrunkevitch), Francis Creek shales and lst, Mazon Creek, Illinois (Petrunkevitch 1913, 1953), each known from one specimen. **Extant.**

Suborder LANIATORINA Thorell 1876

First, Tert U. Eoc–L/M. Olig: *Gonyleptes*, Baltic amber (Treatise P). **Extant.**

Suborder CYPHOPHTHALMINA Simon 1879

No fossil record.

Order ARCHITARBIDA Petrunkevitch 1949

(no suborders erected)

First, Carb Bashk: *Goniotarbus tuberculatus* (Pocock), *G. angulatus* (Pocock), *Mesotarbus intermedius* Petrunkevitch, *M. hindi* (Pocock), *M. angustus* (Pocock) and *Leptotarbus torpedo* (Pocock) all from Similis-pulchra Z., Coseley, near Dudley, England (Petrunkevitch 1953).

Last, Carb Moscov: *Orthotarbus nyranensis* Petrunkevitch, Coal Measures (Westphalian D), Nýřany, Czechoslovakia (Petrunkevitch 1953). *Geratarbus bohemicus* Petrunkevitch may also come from this horizon in the coal measures of Nýřany.

Comment: No stratigraphical details are available for *Phalangiotarbus subovalis* (Woodward), Carb Bashk–Moscov, Coal Measures of Burnley, England, and *Ophiliotarbus kliveri* Waterlot, Carb, Westphalian, Sarre, Germany.

Order ACARIDA Nizsch 1818

Suborder NOTOSTIGMATINA With 1903

No fossil record.

Suborder HOLOTHYRINA Reuter 1909

No fossil record.

Suborder TETRAPODILINA Bremi 1872

No fossil record.

Suborder TROMBIDIINA Dugès 1839

First, Dev Ems–Givet: *Protacarus crani* Hirst, Rhynie Chert Bed, M. Old Red Sandstone, Aberdeenshire, Scotland (Hirst 1923). **Extant.**

Suborder PARASITINA Reuter 1909

First, Tert U. Eoc–L/M. Olig: *Seius*, Baltic amber (Treatise P). **Extant.**

Suborder ACARINA Leach 1815

First, Tert U. Eoc–L/M. Olig: 19 families represented by 44 genera, Baltic amber (Treatise P)
Extant.

Subclass STETHOSTOMATA Petrunkevitch 1949

Order HAPTOPODIDA Pocock 1911

(no suborders erected)

First, Carb Bashk: *Pleisiosiro madeleyi* Pocock, Communis Z., Sparth Bottoms, Rochdale, Lancashire, England. The only specimen known from this locality has been erroneously labelled *Architarbus rotundatus* Scudder (Petrunkevitch 1953).

Last, Carb Bashk: *Pleisiosiro madeleyi* Pocock, Similis-pulchra Z., Coseley, near Dudley, England (Petrunkevitch 1953).

Comment: This is a monospecific order. Nine specimens of this species are known; details of eight of these have been considered above. No details have been found in the literature for the ninth specimen.

Order ANTHRACOMARTIDA Karsch 1882

(no suborders erected)

First, Carb Bashk: *Cleptomartus denuiti* (Pruvost), Assise de Charleroi (Westphalian A), Morlanwelz, Hainaut, Belgium (Pruvost 1930).

Last, Carb U.Carb: *Pleomartus palatinus* (Ammon), Stephanian, Brücken, Pfalz, Germany (Petrunkevitch 1953).

Comment: Stratigraphical details for *Anthracomartus voelkelianus* Krasch and *A. granulatus* Frič both of Carb, Silesia are not available.

Chapter 19: Arthropoda: Chelicerata, Pycnogonida, Palaeoisopus, Myriapoda, Insecta

Subclass SOLUTA Petrunkevitch 1949

Order TRIGONOTARBIDA Petrunkevitch 1949

(no suborders erected)

First, Dev Ems–Givet: *Palaeocharinoides hornei* Hirst, *Palaeocharinus scourfieldi* Hirst, *P. rhyniensis* Hirst, *P. calmani* Hirst, *P. kidstoni* Hirst and twelve other unnamed species assigned to the genus *Palaeocharinus*, Rhynie Chert Bed, M. Old Red Sandstone, Aberdeenshire, Scotland (Hirst 1923).

Last, Carb U.Carb: *Trigonomartus arnoldi* Petrunkevitch, middle Stephanian, Decazeville, southern France (Petrunkevitch 1955).

Comment: No stratigraphical details are available for *Vratislava silesica* (Romer), Carb, Coal Measures, near Klodzko (Glaz), Poland.

Subclass CAULOGASTRA Pocock 1893

Superorder LATISTERNA Petrunkevitch 1949

Order PALPIGRADIDA Thorell 1888

(no suborders erected)

First, Jur 'Tith': *Sternarthron zitteli* Haase, Lithographischenschiefer, Solenhofen, Germany (Haase 1890). **Extant.**

Superorder CAMAROSTOMATA Petrunkevitch 1949

Order THELYPHONIDA Latreille 1804

(no suborders erected)

First, Carb Bashk: *Prothelyphonus britannicus* (Pocock), Similis-pulchra Z., Coseley, near Dudley, England (Petrunkevitch 1953). **Extant.**

Order SCHIZOMIDA Petrunkevitch 1945

(no suborders erected)

First, Tert ?Plioc: *Calcitro fischeri* Petrunkevitch, *Onychothelyphonus bonneri* Pierce and *Calcoscizomus latisternum* Pierce, onyx marble, Bonner, Arizona (Petrunkevitch 1945, Pierce 1950, 1951). **Extant.**

Order KUSTARACHNIDA Petrunkevitch 1913

(no suborders erected)

First and **Last,** Carb Moscov: *Kustarachne tenuipes* Scudder, *K. conica* Petrunkevitch and *K. extincta* (Melander), Francis Creek shales and lst, Mazon Creek, Illinois (Petrunkevitch 1949, 1953).

Comment: These three species have been described from unique specimens, but no details of their stratigraphical position in the Mazon Creek section are available.

Superorder LABELLATA Petrunkevitch 1949

Order PHRYNICHIDA Petrunkevitch 1945

(no suborders erected)

First, Carb Bashk: *Graeophonus carbonarius* Scudder, Joggins Mines, Nova Scotia, Canada (Petrunkevitch 1949), *G. anglicus* Pocock, Similis-pulchra Z., Coseley, near Dudley, England (Petrunkevitch 1953) and *G. anglicus* (= *Protophrynus carbonarius* Pruvost 1930 (Petrunkevitch 1953)), Assise de Charleroi (Westphalian B), Belgium (Pruvost 1930).

Last, Carb Moscov: *Graeophonus carbonarius* Scudder, *Thelyphrynus elongatus* Petrunkevitch and

505

Protophrynus carbonarius Petrunkevitch, Francis Creek shales and lst, Mazon Creek, Illinois (Petrunkevitch 1949) and *Graeophonus anglicus* Pocock, England (Petrunkevitch 1953).

Order ARANEIDA Clerck 1757

Suborder LIPHISTINA Pocock 1892

First, possibly Dev Ems–Givet: *Palaeocteniza crassipes* Hirst, Rhynie Chert Bed, M. Old Red Sandstone, Aberdeenshire, Scotland (Hirst 1923). If this species does not belong to this suborder, then **First,** Carb Bashk: *Eocteniza silvicola* Pocock and *Protocteniza britannica* Petrunkevitch, Similis-pulchra Z., Coseley, near Dudley, England (Petrunkevitch 1953). **Extant.**

Comment: No stratigraphical details are available for *Protolycosa anthracophila* Romer, Carb, Upper Silesia, Poland.

Suborder THERAPHOSINA Sundervall 1830

First, Tert U. Eoc–L/M. Olig: *Clostes*, Baltic amber and possibly *Eopluridina*, Tert Olig, Colorado (Treatise P). **Extant.**

Comment: *Eoatypus woodwardii* McCook 1888 is wrongly described as being Tert Eoc, Garnet Bay, Isle of Wight, England (McCook 1888). It is in fact from the Bembridge Limestone (Olig) of Gurnard Bay, Isle of Wight. McCook had doubts about its systematic position.

Suborder HYPOCHILINA Petrunkevitch 1933

No fossil record.

Suborder DIPNEUMONINA Latreille 1817

First, Carb Bashk: *Archaeometa nephilina* Pocock and *Arachnometa tuberculata* Petrunkevitch, Similis-pulchra Z., Coseley, near Dudley, England (Petrunkevitch 1953). **Extant.**

Comment: No stratigraphical details are available for *Dinopilio parvus* Petrunkevitch, Coal Measures from tip at Chislet Colliery, Kent, England.

Suborder APNEUMONINA Dahl 1913

No fossil record.

Superorder ROSTRATA Petrunkevitch 1949

Order SOLPUGIDA Leach 1815
(no suborders erected)

First, Carb Moscov: *Protosolpuga carbonaria* Petrunkevitch, Francis Creek shales and limestones, Mazon Creek, Illinois (Petrunkevitch 1949). **Extant.**

Superorder PODOGONA Cook 1899

Order RICINULEIDA Thorell 1892
(no suborders erected)

First, Carb Bashk: *Curculiodes granulatus* Petrunkevitch, Lenisulcata Z., Coal Measures, Shipley pit, Bradford, England (Petrunkevitch 1949). **Extant.** [E.C.W.]

Subphylum PYCNOGONIDA Latreille 1810

The classification of J. W. Hedgpeth (*in* Treatise P) is used here.

Order PANTOPODA Gerstaecker 1863

Extant: represented by the families Nymphonidae Wilson 1878; Pallenidae Wilson 1878; Colossendeidae Hoek 1881; Ammotheidae Dohrn 1881; Tanystylidae Shimkevich 1913; Phoxichilidiidae Sars 1891; Endeidae Norman 1908; Pycnogonidae Wilson 1878.

Chapter 19: Arthropoda: Chelicerata, Pycnogonida, Palaeoisopus, Myriapoda, Insecta

Order PALAEOPANTOPODA Broili 1930

First and **Last** Dev Siegen: monotypic order known from *Palaeopantopus maucheri* Broili, Hunsrückschiefer, Germany. (Broili 1929). [C.D.W.]

ARTHROPODA: Incertae sedis

Genus PALAEOISOPUS Broili 1928

First and **Last,** Dev Siegen: *Palaeoisopus problematicus* Broili, Hunsrückshiefer, Germany (Broili 1928).

Subphylum MANDIBULATA

Class CRUSTACEA

(see Chapter 20)

Class MYRIAPODA Leach 1814

Introduction. The classification of Laurentiaux (*in* Piveteau 1953) and Sharov (*in* Rohdendorf 1962b) has been adopted. In general, the remarks on the fossil record of the Arachnida (see page 502) also apply to this class.

Subclass SYMPHYLA Ryder 1880

First, Tert U. Eoc–L/M. Olig: *Scoloprendrella* sp., Baltic amber (Bachofen von Echt 1942). **Extant.**

Subclass PAUROPODA Lubbock 1866

No fossil record.
Comment: Small myriapods (1–1·5 mm). Their absence from Tert amber could be considered significant.

Subclass DIPLOPODA Blainville-Gervais 1844

First, Sil Wenl: *Archidesmus loganensis* Peach, Logan Water, Lesmahagow, Scotland (Peach 1898). **Extant.**
Comment: *Archidesmus macnicoli* Peach and four species of *Kampecaris*, all from Dev L. Old Red Sandstone from various localities in Great Britain, and some Carb species (see Peach 1882, 1898, Brade-Birks 1923, Clarke 1952) and *Archidesmus loganensis* are problematic diplopods, and have not been assigned to any order.
Constituent orders: (after Sharov 1962b) Pseudophognatha Latzel 1884, L.Olig-Holo; Palaeocoxopleura Verhoeff 1928, Carb-Perm; Eurysterna Verhoeff 1926, Carb-Trias; Palaeomorpha Verhoeff 1928, Carb; Armadillomorpha Verhoeff 1887 (= Oniscomorpha Pocock 1887), Cret-Holo; Nematophora Verhoeff 1913, L.Olig-Holo; Polydesmoidae Pocock 1887, L.Olig-Holo; Juliformia Saussure & Humbert 1872, L.Olig-Holo; Colobognatha Brandt 1834, L.Olig-Holo.

Subclass CHILOPODA Leach 1814

First, Carb Moscov: *Latzelia primordialis* Scudder, *Eileticus anthracinus* Scudder, *E. aequalis* Scudder, *Palenarthus impressus* Scudder, *Ilyodes divisa* Scudder and *I. elongata* Scudder, Francis Creek shales and limestones, Mazon Creek, Illinois (Scudder 1890). **Extant.**
Comment: *Eileticus* may be a crustacean (Pruvost 1919). [E.C.W.]

Subclass ARTHROPLEURIDA Waterlot 1934

Probably Myriapoda, although critical data lacking (Rolfe & Ingham 1967, Treatise R).
First, Carb Namur: *Arthropleura* aff. *mailleuxi* Pruvost, Ostrauer Schichtengruppe, Czechoslovakia (Přibyl 1960). *Bundenbachiellus* Broili, Dev Siegen, and *Camptophyllia* Gill, Carb Bashk, may also be Arthropleurida (Treatise R).

507

Last, U.Carb: *Arthropleura fayoli* Boule 1893 and *A.*sp.Remy & Remy 1959, Stephanian C, France and Germany (Van Straelen 1931; Guthörl 1936; Waterlot *in* Piveteau 1953).

[W.D.I.R.]

Class INSECTA

The classification adopted is based on that of Imms (1957); deviations are inevitable because that classification does not cover the fossil orders.

The earliest fossil insect is believed to be an Apterygote of the Order Collembola. Until quite recently it was believed that the earliest certainly winged insects were members of the Orders Palaeodicytoptera, Dictyoptera and Paraplecoptera found in the Upper Carboniferous. Rohdendorf (1961a) has, however, recently reported on an enigmatic Devonian fossil for the reception of which he has erected the Order Archeoptera, which appears to be a winged insect (see p. 515). Most fossil insects consist of wings and in many cases these are fragmentary; the morphology of the insect wing has recently been reviewed in some detail by Seguy (1959).

Smart (1963) has briefly reviewed the phylogeny of both extant and fossil orders of Insects and the field of palaeoentomology has been reviewed by Martynova (1961).

The classification of the fossil orders is discussed at some length by Laurentiaux (*in* Piveteau 1953), and Carpenter (*in* Treatise R) is anticipated with much interest. Other works dealing with Insects that the palaeoentomologist may need to consult are Carpenter (1954b *in* Brues, Melander & Carpenter), Grassé (1949, 1951b), Rohdendorf (1962b) and Rohdendorf, Bekker-Migdisova, Martynova & Sharov (1961).

Subclass I APTERYGOTA

First, Dev Eifel: See Order Collembola below. References: Dennis (1949b) and Imms (1957).

Order THYSANURA Latreille 1796 (= THYSANURA ECTOTROPHI auctt.)

First, Trias ?Carn: *Triassomachilis uralensis* Sharov 1948, Nakyz, Bashkir A.S.S.R., U.S.S.R.
Extant.

Order DIPLURA Börner 1904 (= THYSANURA ENTOTROPHI auctt.)

First, Tert U. Eoc–L/M Olig: *Campodea darwini* Silvestri 1912, Baltic Amber.   **Extant.**

Order PROTURA Silvestri 1907.

No fossil record.   **Extant.**

Order COLLEMBOLA Lubbock 1862

First, Dev Eifel; see Suborder Arthropleona below.   **Extant.**

Suborder ARTHROPLEONA Börner 1901

First, Dev Eifel: *Rhyniella praecursor* Hirst and Maulik 1926, Rhynie, Aberdeen, Scotland.
Extant.

Suborder SYMPHYPLEONA Börner 1901

First, Tert U. Eoc–L/M. Olig: *Sminthurus succineus* Stach 1922 and eleven other species (Handschin 1926), Baltic Amber.   **Extant.**

Order MONURA Sharov 1951

First, Carb U. Carb: *Dasyleptus lucasi* Brongniart 1885, Commentry, France.
Last, Perm (Lower; Kuznetsk series, correlation uncertain): *Dasyleptus brongniarti* Sharov 1957, Kuznetsk Basin, Kemerov District, U.S.S.R.
Reference: Martynova (1962)

Subclass II PTERYGOTA

The classification adopted in Imms (1957) is followed here with the fossil orders inserted. This classification is based on the condition of the wing pads in the pre-imaginal instars and the presence or absence of a pupal stage in the life-history. Neither of these criteria are satisfactory for dealing with fossil insects which can only be placed in such a classification by making use of other characteristics and making presumptions in respect of the development of the wings and the life-history.

An alternative classification, originally developed by Martynov (1925a *et seq.*), based on the structure of the wings themselves and on their mode of articulation is available. This classification has much merit for the palaeoentomologist since many "fossil insects" consist only of wings! The groupings of orders in this classification are indicated in the text below. It is used by Jeannel (1949) where he discusses the classification and phylogeny of the orders of Insects including those known only as fossils.

Division I EXOPTERYGOTA (= HEMIMETABOLA)

(a) Palaeopteran Orders (= PALAEOPTERA, PALAEOPTERYGOTA, *auctt.*)

First, Carb Bashk: see Orders Odonata, Archodonata, Palaeodictyoptera and Protodonata below.

Of the seven orders in this group five are extinct and two are extant.

Order EPHEMEROPTERA Imms 1934 (= EPHEMERIDA Leach 1817)

First, Carb U. Carb: see Suborder Protephemeroptera below.   **Extant.**

Suborder PROTEPHEMEROPTERA Handlisch 1906

First and **Last,** Carb U. Carb: *Triplosoba pulchella* Brongniart 1893, Commentry, France.

Suborder PLECTOPTERA Packard 1886 (emend. Tillyard 1932)

First, Perm Leonard: *Protereisma permianum* Sellards 1907, Elmo, Kansas, U.S.A.   **Extant.**
References: Carpenter (1963a), Rohdendorf (1962a) and Tshernova (1965).

Order ODONATA Fabricius 1792

First, Carb Bashk: see Suborder Eomeganisoptera below.   **Extant.**
Comment: On analysis most authors, dealing with the overall systematics of this order, recognize the same segregates within which they place the various genera, families, etc., but they differ in the taxonomic status given to them. Below no particular author is followed; the three suborders of extant Odonata of Imms (1957) are listed with four further suborders which accommodate fossil forms. References: Fraser (1957) and Rohdendorf (1962a).

Suborder EOMEGANISOPTERA Rohdendorf 1962

First and **Last,** Carb Bashk: *Erasipteron larischi* Pruvost 1934. According to Kukalova (1964a) the fossil came from "the top mudstone of the coal seam 31 (D) in the mine President Gottwald (formerly Frantisek) at Horni Sucha, Upper Silesian Coal Basin, Czechoslovakia. According to K. Patteisky (1928) and S. Dybova (1959) the seam was deposited in Namurian C".
Comment: Kukalova (1964a) has re-examined and reported on the unique holotype of *Erasipteron larischi.*

Suborder ARCHIZYGOPTERA Handlirsch 1906

First, Trias (M. or U; correlation uncertain): *Triassagrion australiense* Tillyard, 1922, Ipswich, Queensland, Australia.
Last, Jur Oxf–Call: *Protomyrmeleon handlirschi* Martynov 1927, Karatau, Kazakhstan, U.S.S.R.

Suborder PROTANISOPTERA Carpenter 1931

First, Perm Leonard: *Ditaxineura anomalostigma* Tillyard 1925, Elmo, Kansas, U.S.A. and one other species from Kansas, one from Tshekarda and two from Kuznetsk Basin, Kemerov District, U.S.S.R.
Last, Perm Dzhulf: *Polytaxineura stanleyi* Tillyard 1935, Belmont, N.S.W., Australia.

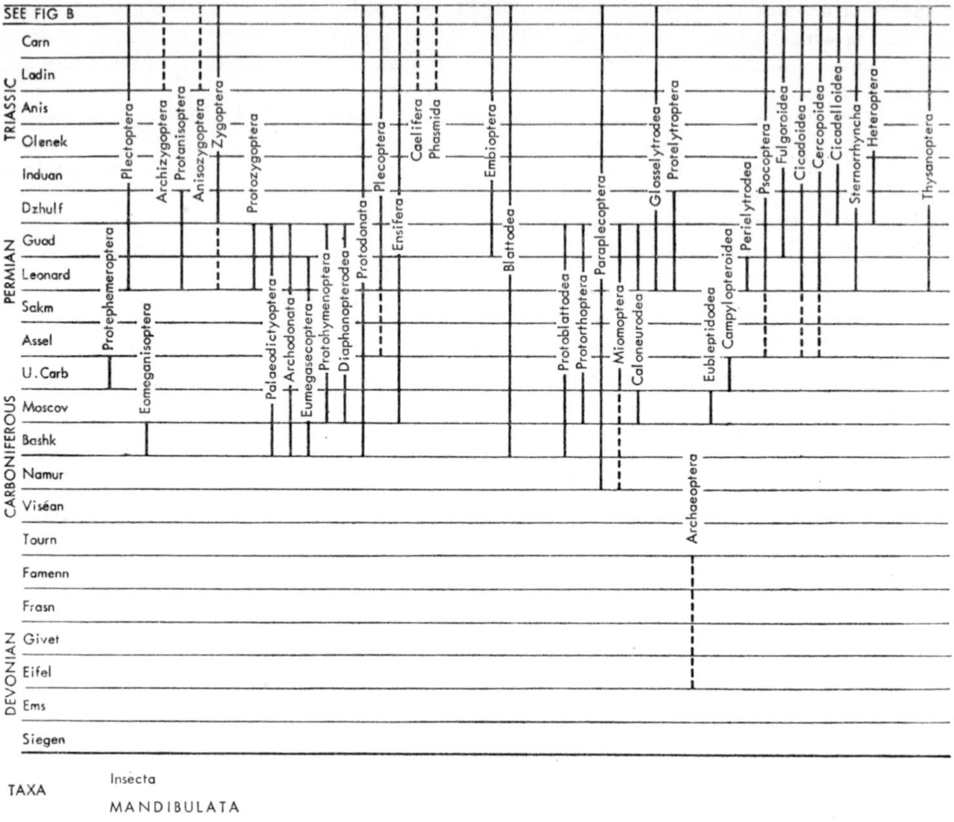

FIG. 19.2A

CONTRIBUTORS   J. Smart,   R. J. Wootton

Suborder ANISOZYGOPTERA Handlirsch 1906

First, Trias (Middle or Upper; correlation uncertain): *Mesophlebia antinodalis* Tillyard 1916 and *Triassophlebia stigmatica* Tillyard 1922, Ipswich, Queensland, Australia.   **Extant.**

Suborder ZYGOPTERA Selys 1840

First, Perm (Upper; correlation uncertain): *Permagrion falklandicum* Tillyard 1928, Bodie Creek Head, Falkland Islands.   **Extant.**

Suborder ANISOPTERA Selys 1840

First, Jur Torac: *Liassogomphus propinquus* (Bode 1905), U. Lias, Hatdorf bei Fallersleben, Brunswick, Germany.   **Extant.**

Suborder PROTOZYGOPTERA Tillyard 1925

First, Perm Leonard: *Kennedya mirabilis* Tillyard 1925, Elmo, Kansas, U.S.A. and five other species from Kansas and one from Nizhnee Moshevo, Perm District, U.S.S.R.

Last, Perm Guad: *Sushkinia parvula* Martynov 1930, Tikhie Gory, U.S.S.R. and four other species from the same place and Iva Gora, Archangelsk District, U.S.S.R.

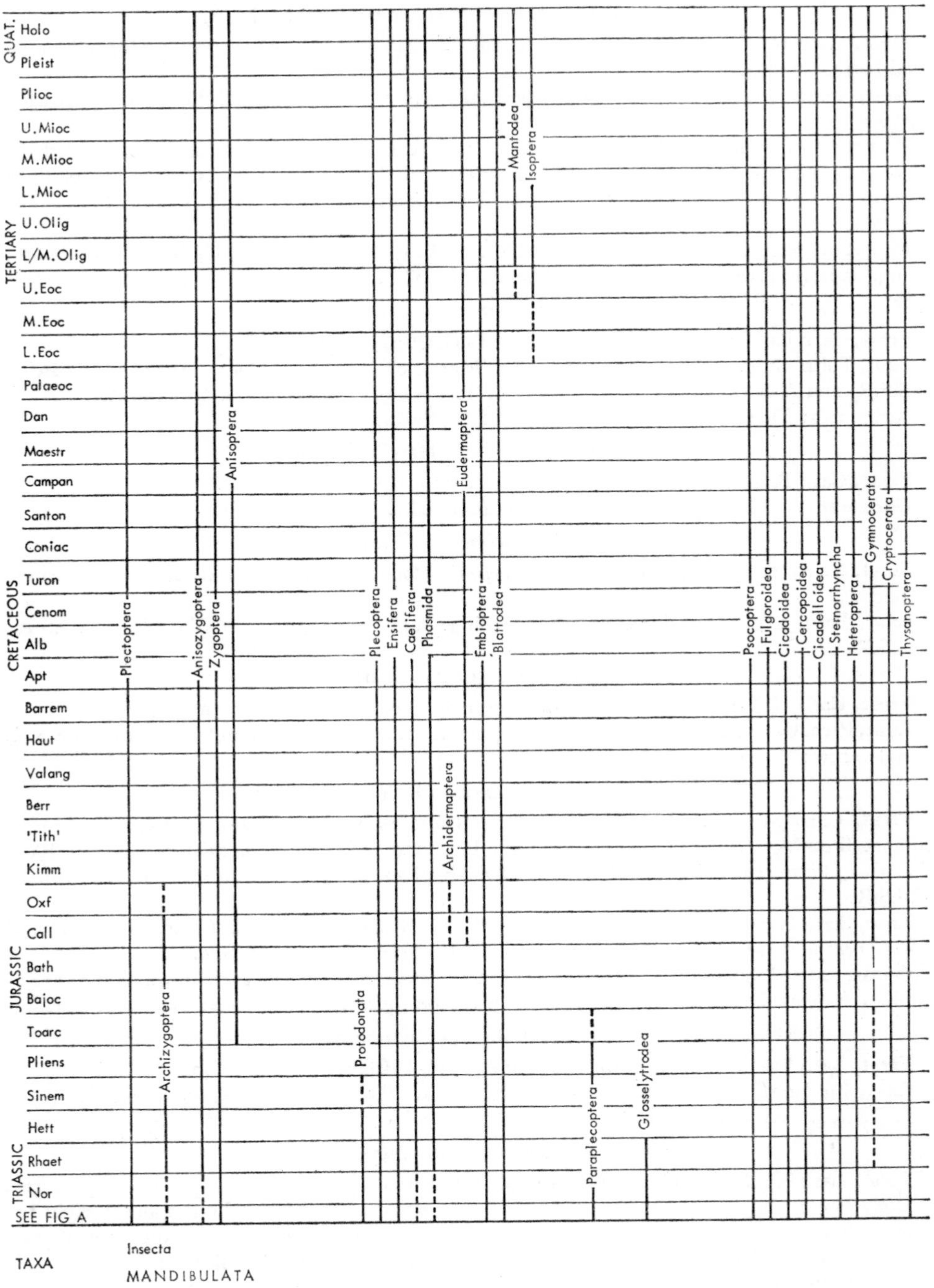

FIG. 19.2B

511

Order PALAEODICTYOPTERA Goldenberg 1854

First, Carb Bashk: *Severinopsis vetusta* Kukalova 1958 and two other species, Upper Silesian Coal Basin, Czechoslovakia.

Last, Perm Guad: *Eohymen maculipennis* Martynov 1937, Kargala, Orenburgh District, U.S.S.R.

Comments: Following Carpenter (1954b) and Kukalova (1963b) we have not divided the order into suborders. Other authorities have divided the group up and raised some of these divisions to ordinal status (See, for instance, Laurentiaux (*in* Piveteau 1953) and Rohdendorf (1962a)).

Important papers dealing with this Order are: Carpenter (1954b, 1965) Kukalova (1963b), Laurentiaux (*in* Piveteau 1953) and Rohdendorf (1962a).

Order ARCHODONATA Martynov 1932

First, Carb Bashk: *Rectineura lineata* Bolton 1934, Sturry, Kent, England.

Last, Perm Guad: *Permothemis libelluloides* (Martynov 1932), Iva-Gora, Archangelsk district, U.S.S.R. and *Ideliella decora* G. Zalesskii 1937, Tikhie Gory, Tatar A.S.S.R., U.S.S.R.

References: Demoulin (1954) and Rohdendorf (1962a).

Order MEGASECOPTERA Handlirsch 1906

First, Carb Bashk: see Suborder Eumegasecoptera below.

Comment: Rohdendorf's (1962a) classification is followed.

Suborder EUMEGASECOPTERA Carpenter 1947

First, Carb Bashk: *Brodioptera cumberlandensis* Copeland 1957, Plarrsboro, Nova Scotia, Canada.

Last, Perm Leonard: *Vorkutia tshernovi* Rohdendorf 1947, Vorkuta Basin, Komi A.S.S.R., U.S.S.R.

Suborder PROTOHYMENOPTERA Carpenter, 1947

First, Carb U. Carb: *Aspidothorax triangularis* Brongniart 1894, Commentry, France.

Last, Perm Guad: *Ivahymen constrictus* Martynov 1931, Iva-Gora, Archangelsk district, U.S.S.R.

References: Carpenter (1947, 1951).

Order DIAPHANOPTERODEA Rohdendorf 1962

First, Carb Moscov: *Prochoroptera calopteryx* Handlirsch 1911, Mazon Creek, near Morris, Illinois. Possibly *Tchirkovaea guttata* Zalesskii 1932 and *Philiasptilon masculosum* Zalesskii 1932 L.Carb-L. Perm (correlation uncertain), L. Balakhonka ser., Kuznetsk Basin, Kemerov District, U.S.S.R.

Last, Perm Guad: *Kuloja expansa* Martynov 1928, *Parakuloja paurovenosa* (Martynov 1931) and *Eukuloja cubitalis* (Martynov 1931), Iva-Gora, Archangelsk district, U.S.S.R.

Comment: Rohdendorf (1962a) has suggested a series of three suborders to which the various families recognised by himself and other authors can be allocated. Reference: Carpenter (1963b).

Order PROTODONATA Brongniart 1893 (= MEGANISOPTERA Martynov 1932)

First, Carb Bashk: *Typus durhami* Carpenter 1960, Durham, Georgia, U.S.A.

Last, Jur Hett/Sinem: *Liadotypus relictus* Martynov 1937, Shurab, Kirgisia, U.S.S.R.

Reference: Carpenter (1960).

(b) Polyneopteran or Orthopteroid Orders

First, Carb Namur: See Order Paraplecoptera, below at p. 514. **Extant.**

Comment: Of the fifteen orders in this group seven are extinct; the remaining eight are extant. There are some comments on the phylogenetic relationships of the orders in Zeuner (1939). Some authors would place the Order Zoraptera (see p. 516) here rather than with the paraneopteran Orders (see p. 516). See also comments on Protoblattodea below at p. 514.

Order PLECOPTERA Burmeister 1839

First, Perm Leonard: *Uralonympha varica* Zalesskii 1939, and *Perlopsis filicornis* Martynov 1940, Tshekarda, Perm District, U.S.S.R. (both nymphs); and *Palaeoperla exacta* Sharov 1961, Perm

Order MIOMOPTERA Martynov 1927

First, Carb U. Carb: *Archimioptera carbonaria* Guthörl 1939, Saarland, Germany; or Carb Namur: *Metropator pusillus* Handlirsch 1906, Altamont, Pennsylvania.

Last, Perm Guad: *Palaeomantis schmidti* Handlirsch 1904, Tikhie Gory, Tatar A.S.S.R., four spp. from Iva Gora, Archangelsk District; and one from Ilyinski Ser (correlation uncertain), Kuznetsk Basin, Kemerov District, Siberia.

Comment: The genera comprised in this order were distributed by Carpenter (1954b) amongst Protorthoptera, Protoperlaria and Psocoptera but the order has been maintained by Martynova (1962) and Kukalova (1963a). Carpenter (1965) has placed *Metropator* (Carb Namur) in Miomoptera (see p. 518).

Order CALONEURODEA Martynov 1938

First, Carb Moscov: *Euthyneura lecomtei* Pruvost 1919 and *Emphyloptera lecrivaini* Pruvost 1919, Lens, Pas-de-Calais, France.

Last, Perm Guad: *Euthygramma parallellum* (Martynov 1928), Iva-Gora and Sheimo-Gora, Archangelsk District, U.S.S.R. and three other species from the same localities and from Tikhie Gory, Tatar A.S.S.R., U.S.S.R.

References: Carpenter (1943a, 1961), Laurentiaux (*in* Piveteau 1953), Martynov (1938b) and Martynova (1962).

Order GLOSSELYTRODEA Martynov 1938

First, Perm Leonard: *Permoberotha villosa* Tillyard 1932 and several other species, Elmo, Kansas.

Last, Trias Rhaet: *Mesojurina sogjutensis* Martynov 1943, Issyk-Kul, Kirgisia, U.S.S.R.

References: Martynov (1938a) and Martynova (1952, 1962).

Order PROTELYTROPTERA Tillyard 1931

First, Perm Leonard: *Protelytron permianium* Tillyard 1931 and 13 other spp. from Elmo, Kansas, U.S.A.; 8 spp. from Obora, Moravia, Czechoslovakia; and 1 from Tshekarda, Perm District, U.S.S.R.

Last, Perm Dzhulf: *Protocoleus mitchelli* Tillyard 1934, Belmont, New South Wales, Australia.

Comment: We follow Carpenter and Kukalova (1964) and place *Protocoleus* here; we do not recognise the Order Protocoleoptera Tillyard 1934, erected for the reception of this genus. Reference: Kukalova (1964c).

Orders Incertae Sedis

Placed here are four orders erected by various authors about which we feel that too little is known to allow of their placement in a formal classification. All are Palaeozoic. We regard the Orders Protocoleoptera Tillyard 1924 and Paracoleoptera Laurentiaux 1953 as being merged in Protelytroptera and Coleoptera respectively (see above and 525).

Order ARCHAEOPTERA Rohendorf 1961

First and **Last,** Dev (Upper): *Eopterum devonicum* Rohdendorf 1961, Upper Devonian, Komi A.S.S.R., U.S.S.R.

Comment: The fossil is a little enigmatic and it is difficult fully to elucidate its nature. It is to be hoped that more specimens can be obtained because the occurrence of a winged insect in the Devonian is a matter of major significance when considering the phylogeny of the class. It is figured in Rohdendorf (1961a, 1962b).

Order EUBLEPTIDODEA Laurentiaux 1953

First and **Last,** Carb Moscov: *Eubleptus danielsi* Handlirsch 1906, Mazon Creek, nr. Morris, Illinois, U.S.A.

Comment: Carpenter (1965) assigns *Eubleptus* to the Order Palaeodictyoptera (see page 512).

Suborder CAMPYLOPTEROIDEA Carpenter 1943

First and **Last,** Carb U.Carb: *Campyloptera eatoni* Brongniart 1894, Commentry, France.

Comment: The monotypic family Campylopteridae and the Suborder Campylopteroidea (Order Megasecoptera) were "tentatively" erected by Carpenter (1943b) who said that a "distinct order will probably be needed eventually" for the species. However, he omitted the family from his (1954) key to the families of Megasecoptera. Laurentiaux (*in* Piveteau 1953) recognised the suborder.

Order PERIELYTRODEA Zalessky 1948

First and **Last,** Perm Leonard: *Perielyton mirabile* Zalessky 1948, Tshekarda, Perm District, U.S.S.R.

Reference: Sharov (1962b).

(c) Paraneopteran or Hemipteroid Orders

First, Perm Leonard: see Order Hemiptera, Suborder Homoptera below at p. 516.

The six orders grouped here are rather loosely associated. Some authors would place the Zoraptera with the Polyneopteran or Orthopteroid orders (See p. 512). The six orders are all extant.

Order ZORAPTERA Silvestri 1913

No fossil record. **Extant.**

Comment: Small insects with a body length of about 3 mm. and a wing-span of 7 mm. which eluded the neoentomologist until 1913! Reference: Dennis (1949a).

Order PSOCOPTERA Shipley 1904

First, Perm Leonard: *Dichentomum tinctum* Tillyard 1926, Elmo, Kansas, U.S.A., and several other spp. from Kansas and Perm District, U.S.S.R., also three spp. from Kuznetsk Basin, Kemerov District, U.S.S.R. (L. Perm; correlation uncertain). **Extant.**

References: Bekker-Migdisova & Vishnyakova (1962) and Carpenter (1932, 1933).

Order SIPHUNCULATA Latreille 1825 (= ANOPLURA Leach 1815)

No fossil record. **Extant.**

Comment: The sucking lice, usually associated with mammals.

Order MALLOPHAGA Nitzsch 1918

No fossil record. **Extant.**

Comment: The Chewing or Bird Lice which are not, however, exclusively associated with birds. [J.S. & R.J.W.]

Order HEMIPTERA Linnaeus 1758

First, Perm Leonard: see Suborder Homoptera below. **Extant.**

Comment: The two Suborders, Homoptera and Heteroptera, are often given separate ordinal status. References: Bekker-Migdisova (1962) and Evans (1956).

Suborder HOMOPTERA Leach 1815

First, Perm Leonard: *Archescytina permiana* Tillyard 1926, Elmo, Kansas, U.S.A., and many other Archescytinidae from Elmo, and from Tshekarda, Perm District, and Kuznetsk Basin, Kemerov District, (Kuznetsk Series, correlation uncertain), U.S.S.R., and *Tshekardaella tshekardensis* Bekker-Migdisova 1960, Tshekarda, Perm District, U.S.S.R. **Extant.**

Comment: *Protoprosbole straeleni* Laurentiaux 1952, Carb Namur, Monceau-Fontaine, Belgium; *Blattoprosbole tomiensis* Bekker-Migdisova 1958, and *Archeglyphis crassinervis* Martynov

1935, M. Carb, L. Balakhonka Series (correlation uncertain), Kuznetsk Basin, Kemerov District, U.S.S.R., and *Dictyocicada antiqua* Brongniart 1885, U. Carb, Commentry, France, have all been claimed to be Homoptera. The position of each is uncertain; *B. tomiensis* and *A. crassinervis* are the most probable Homoptera.

References: Bekker-Migdisova (1960a,b, 1961) and Evans (1963).

Series COLEORRHYNCHA Myers & China 1929

No fossil record. **Extant.**

Comment: Members of the Family Actinoscytinidae (U. Perm-U. Jur) have been claimed to be Coleorrhyncha (Bekker-Migdisova, 1958), as have the Mesozoic Ipsviciidae (China, 1962). Both suggestions are probably wrong. China's proposal to include the only known coleorrhynchous family, the Peloridiidae, in the Auchenorrhyncha is not here followed.

Series AUCHENORRHYNCHA Dumeril 1806

First, Perm (Lower: Kuznetsk Series, correlation uncertain): see Superfamilies Cicadoidea and Cercopoidea below. **Extant.**

Comment: Evans (1964) has discussed the diversity and possible origins of this group.

Superfamily CICADOIDEA

First, Perm (Lower; Kuznetsk Series, correlation uncertain): *Evanscicada speciosa* (Bekker-Migdisova, 1961) and several other species, Kuznetsk Basin, Kemerov District, U.S.S.R. **Extant.**

Comment: *Archeglyphis crassinervis* Martynov 1930, U. Carb, L. Balakhonka Series, Kuznetsk Basin, Kemerov District, U.S.S.R., has been claimed to belong to a cicadoid family (Martynov 1930, Bekker-Migdisova 1961). It is, however, poorly preserved and is here regarded as *incertae sedis*.

Superfamily FULGOROIDEA

First, Perm Guad; *Scytophara extensa* Martynov 1937, and *Scytocixius mendax* Martynov 1937, Kargala, Orenburg District, U.S.S.R. **Extant.**

Comment: *Neuropibrocha* and *Kaltanopibrocha* Bekker-Migdisova 1961 (L. Perm; Kuznetsk Series correlation uncertain), Kuznetsk Basin, Kemerov District, U.S.S.R., are here regarded as *incertae. sedis*.

Superfamily CERCOPOIDEA

First, Perm (Lower; Kuznetsk Series correlation uncertain): *Scytinoptera picturata* Bekker-Migdisova 1961 and 5 other spp. Kuznetsk Basin, Kemerov District, U.S.S.R. **Extant.**

Comment: *Scytinoptera* and related genera, previously thought cicadelloid, probably cercopoid (Evans 1964).

Superfamily CICADELLOIDEA

First, Perm Dzhulf: *Homaloscytina plana* Tillyard 1926, Belmont, N.S.W., Australia. **Extant.**

Comment: Permian supposed cicadelloids have usually been placed in the Scytinopteridae (e.g. Evans 1956, Bekker-Migdisova 1962). *Scytinoptera*, though, is probably cercopoid (Evans 1964), and definite Permian cicadelloids are hard to determine.

Series STERNORRHYNCHA Amyot and Serville 1843

First, Perm Leonard: *Tshekardaella tshekardensis* Bekker-Migdisova 1948, Tshekarda, Perm District, U.S.S.R. **Extant.**

Comment: Series usually divided into 4 superfamilies; but assignment of fossils too controversial to be worthwhile here. Archescytinidae, many spp. Leonard-Dzhulf, may be sternorrhynchous (Martynov 1933, Bekker-Migdisova 1960b, etc.) but thought auchenorrhynchous by Evans (1956, etc.)

Suborder HETEROPTERA Latreille 1810

First, Perm Dzhulf: *Actinoscytina belmontensis* Tillyard 1926, and *Paraknightia magnifica* Evans 1943, Belmont, N.S.W., Australia. **Extant.**

Comments: Most fossil Heteroptera have been insufficiently described and need re-examination. Many described fossils cannot, therefore, safely be assigned to either of the two series into which the suborder is divided. The two species cited above are both Heteroptera but otherwise *incerae sedis*.

Series GYMNOCERATA Fieber 1851

First, Jur Call–Oxf: *Lygaenocoris prynadai* Popov 1961, and three other spp., Karatau, Kazakhstan, U.S.S.R. **Extant.**

Comment: *Darniopsis tragopea* Bekker-Migdisova 1958, and three spp. of *Ceresopsis* Bekker-Migdisova 1958, Trias Rhaet, Issyk-Kul, Kirgisia, U.S.S.R., and many species from the Lias, Mecklenburg and Lower Saxony, Germany (Handlirsch 1906, 1938; Bode 1953) may well be earlier records. The family Dunstaniidae Tillyard 1916 (L.-U. Trias) are Homoptera.

Series CRYPTOCERATA Fieber 1851

First, Jur Pliens: *Shurabella lepyroniopsis* Bekker-Migdisova 1949, locality II, nr. Shurab, Tadzhikistan, U.S.S.R. **Extant.**

Comment: *Triassocoris myersi* Tillyard 1922 may belong here (Southwood & Leston 1959, Bekker-Migdisova 1962). [R.J.W.]

Order THYSANOPTERA Haliday 1836

First, Perm Leonard: *Permothrips longipennis* Martynov 1935, Tshekarda, Perm District, U.S.S.R. **Extant.**

Reference: Martynova (1962).

Division II ENDOPTERYGOTA (= HOLOMETABOLA)

(d) Oligoneopteran Orders

First, Carb U. Carb: see Order Neuroptera, Superfamily Raphidioidea below at p. 519.

Comments: Mecoptera, with Lepidoptera, Trichoptera, Diptera and Siphonaptera are frequently designated the "Panorpoid Complex". *Metropator pusillus* Handlirsch 1906 from the Upper Carboniferous of North America, "Near Altamont Colliery, Pennsylvania, Nordamerika. Lower-Pottsville, Lower Lykens Group. Unteres Obercarbon" in U.S. National Museum (Handlirsch 1906: 112–113) has been considered by some authors to be a member of the Order Mecoptera and, therefore, by inference, an endopterygote insect with a holometabolous life-history. If this assignment be correct then *Metropator* and not *Fatjanoptera* may be the earliest endopterygote Insect. The assignment to Mecoptera on the basis of the features of the fossil (an incomplete wing) can be questioned and, of course, nothing is known of its life-history. Carpenter (1965) has, in fact, placed *Metropator* in the polyneopteran exopterygote Order Miomoptera! (see also under Eumecoptera on p. 522)

All orders of the Endopterygota are extant.

Order NEUROPTERA Linnaeus 1758.

First, Carb. U. Carb: See Suborder Megaloptera, Superfamily Raphidioidea, below at p. 519.

Comments: The Neuroptera along with the Mecoptera are orders of considerable interest not only as insects but in respect of their zoo-geography and palaeontological record. Authors are by no means in agreement on the classification of the Neuroptera. We propose to follow Imms (1957), mainly as a matter of convenience, (1) in the initial division of the order in to two sub-orders, and (2) in the classification of the Suborder Megaloptera. However, we propose to follow Berland & Grassé (1951) in recognising five rather than four superfamilies of the Suborder Planipennia.

Authors also differ in the status to be accorded to the various taxonomic segregates even when agreeing on their delimitation. *Permoberotha* Tillyard 1932 and *Permoberothella* Riek 1953 have both been removed from Neuroptera and placed in Glosselytrodea by Martynova (1961).

We outline below the classification adopted and append a few notes indicating how it compares with other classifications.

Order NEUROPTERA

Suborder Megaloptera with Superfamilies Sialoidea and Raphidioidea.

Suborder Planipennia with Superfamilies Ithonoidea, Coniopterygoidea, Osmyloidea, Hemerobioidea and Myrmeleontoidea.

Notes.

1. Berland & Grassé (1951) and Martynova (1962) designate the superfamilies Sialoidea and Raphidioidea as Orders Megaloptera and Raphidioptera. They also treat the Suborder Planipennia as an order. They accord subordinal rank to the taxonomic segregates of Planipennia here designated superfamilies.

2. Martynova (1962) places the families comprised in Ithonoidea and Osmyloidea in a segregate designated the Suborder Polystoechotidea.

3. Imms (1957) has the families here comprised in Osmyloidea within the Superfamily Hemerobioidea.

4. Handlirsch (1925) and Tillyard (1926) are two other important authors on the Neuroptera.

Suborder MEGALOPTERA Latreille 1802

First, Carb U. Carb/Perm; See Superfamily Raphidioidea below.   **Extant.**

Superfamily SIALOIDEA.

First, Perm (Lower; Kuznetsk series, correlation uncertain): *Permosialis sibirica* Martynova 1961, with *P. asiatica* Martynova 1961 and *P. matutina* Martynova 1961, Kuznetsk Basin, Kemerov District, U.S.S.R.   **Extant.**

Comment: The larva of a sialid, *Mormolucoidea articulatus* Hitchcock 1858 has been described from the Trias of Turner's Falls, Massachusetts, U.S.A.

Constituent families: Corydalidae and Sialidae.

Superfamily RAPHIDIOIDEA

First, Carb U. Carb or Perm (Lower; Burgukli Series, correlation uncertain see comment below): *Fatjanoptera mnemonica* Martynova 1961, Tunguska Basin, Krasnoyarsk region, U.S.S.R.   **Extant.**

Comment: Martynova (1961) gives the age of the L. Burgukli Series as Carb. N.Shvedov, *Lexique Stratigraphique International* II, U.S.S.R., part I pp. 259–260 considers it L. Perm, with a flora comparable with that of Leon beds in the Pechora river basin, Komi A.S.S.R., U.S.S.R.

Suborder PLANIPENNIA Heymons 1915

First, Perm (Lower): see Superafmily Ithonoidea below.   **Extant.**

Superfamily CONIOPTERYGOIDEA Enderlein 1905

First, Tert U. Eoc–L/M. Olig: *Coniopteryx timidus* (Hagen 1854), Baltic Amber.   **Extant.**
Constituent family: Coniopterygidae Burmeister 1839.

Superfamily ITHONOIDEA

First, Perm (Lower; Kuznetsk Series, correlation uncertain): *Permithonopsis kaltanensis* Martynova 1961 (with *P. perantiqua* Martynova 1961 and *P. sharovi* Martynova 1961), Kuznetsk Basin, Kemerov District, U.S.S.R.   **Extant.**

Comment: The discontinuity of the distribution of the extant genera is remarkable: *Ithone* and *Heterithone*—Australia; *Oliarce*—California; *Rapisma*—Himalayas.

Constituent families: Ithonidae Tillyard 1919 and Permithonidae Tillyard 1922 (= Permegalomidae Martynova 1952 and Permopsychopsidae Riek 1953).

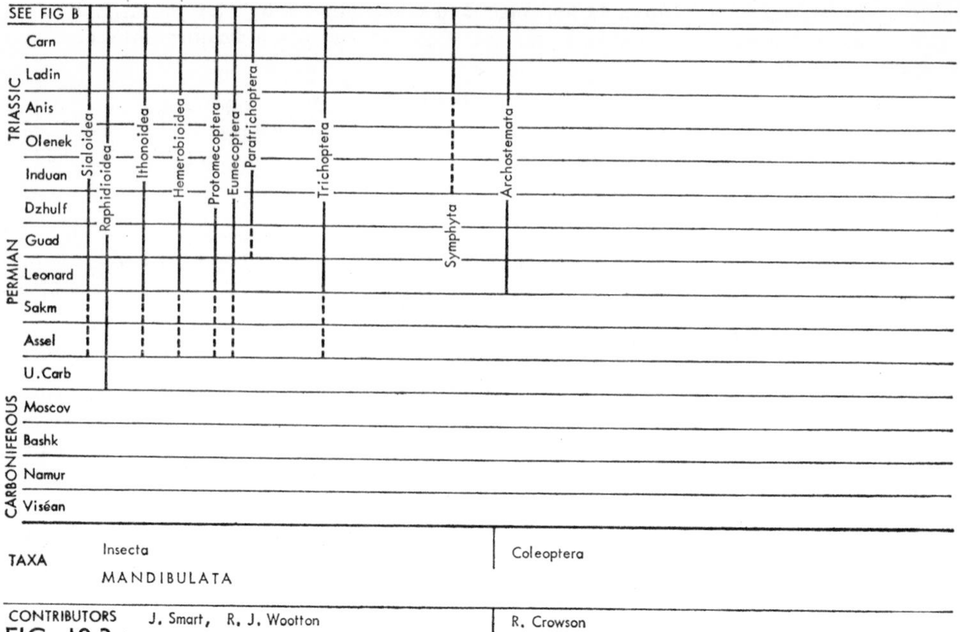
SEE FIG B
TRIASSIC
Carn
Ladin
Anis
Olenek
Induan
PERMIAN
Dzhulf
Guad
Leonard
Sakm
Assel
U.Carb
CARBONIFEROUS
Moscov
Bashk
Namur
Viséan
Sialoidea
Raphidioidea
Ithonoidea
Hemerobioidea
Protomecoptera
Eumecoptera
Paratrichoptera
Trichoptera
Symphyta
Archostemata
TAXA
Insecta
MANDIBULATA
Coleoptera
CONTRIBUTORS
J. Smart, R. J. Wootton
R. Crowson

FIG. 19.3 A

Superfamily OSMYLOIDEA Brauer 1868

First, Trias Rhaet: *Petrushevskia borisi* Martynova 1958, Issyk-Kul, Kirgisia, U.S.S.R. **Extant.**

Constituent families: Osmylidae Brauer 1868, Osmylitidae Martynova 1949, Mesopolystoechotidae Martynova 1949, Dilaridae Handlirsch 1906, Berothidae Handlirsch 1908, Sisyridae Handlirsch 1906, Mantispidae Westwood 1840, and Polystoechotidae Handlirsch 1906.

Superfamily HEMEROBIOIDEA Westwood 1840

First, Perm (Lower; Kuznetsk Series, correlation uncertain) *Palaemerobius latibasis* Martynova 1961, Kuznetsk Basin, Kemerov District, U.S.S.R. **Extant.**

Constituent families: Psychopsidae Handlirsch 1908, Chrysopidae Hagen 1866, Hemerobiidae Westwood 1840, Kalligrammatidae Handlirsch 1906, Brongniartiellidae Martynova 1949, Palaemerobiidae Martynov 1928, Sialidopseidae Zalessky 1926 (= Permosisyridae Martynov 1933), Mesochrysopidae Handlirsch 1908, Sympherobiidae Brues & Melander 1932, Apochrysidae Brues & Melander 1910.

Superfamily MYRMELEONTOIDEA Burmeister 1829

First, Trias Rhaet: *Sogjuta speciosa* Martynova 1958, Issyk-Kul, Kirgisia, U.S.S.R. **Extant.**

Constituent families: Myrmeleontidae Burmeister 1829 (= Myrmeleonidae *auctt.*), Nymphidae Brauer 1868, Nemopteridae Hagen 1861, Ascalaphidae Schneider 1845, Solenoptilidae Handlirsch 1906, Nymphitidae Handlirsch 1906, Stilbopterygidae Tillyard 1926 and Myoidactylidae Handlirsch 1925.

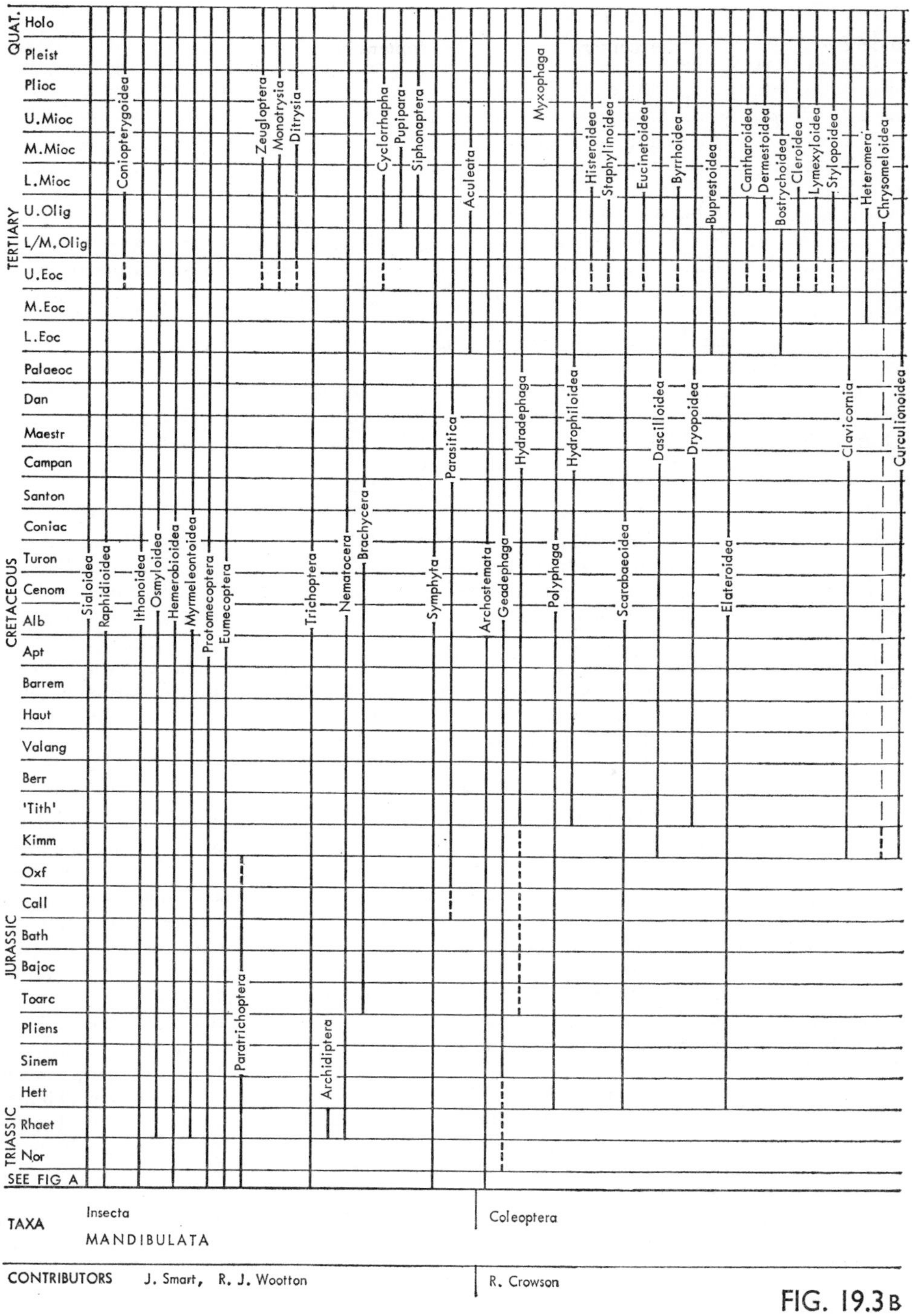
QUAT.
Holo
Pleist
TERTIARY
Plioc
U.Mioc
M.Mioc
L.Mioc
U.Olig
L/M.Olig
U.Eoc
M.Eoc
L.Eoc
Palaeoc
Dan
CRETACEOUS
Maestr
Campan
Santon
Coniac
Turon
Cenom
Alb
Apt
Barrem
Haut
Valang
Berr
'Tith'
Kimm
JURASSIC
Oxf
Call
Bath
Bajoc
Toarc
Pliens
Sinem
Hett
TRIASSIC
Rhaet
Nor
SEE FIG A
Coniopterygoidea
Zeugloptera
Monotrysia
Ditrysia
Cyclorrhapha
Pupipara
Siphonaptera
Aculeata
Myxophaga
Histeroidea
Staphylinoidea
Eucinetoidea
Byrrhoidea
Buprestoidea
Cantharoidea
Dermestoidea
Bostrychoidea
Cleroidea
Lymexyloidea
Stylopoidea
Heteromera
Chrysomeloidea
Hydradephaga
Hydrophiloidea
Dascilloidea
Dryopoidea
Clavicornia
Curculionoidea
Parasitica
Brachycera
Sialoidea
Raphidioidea
Ithonoidea
Osmyloidea
Hemerobioidea
Myrmeleontoidea
Protomecoptera
Eumecoptera
Trichoptera
Nematocera
Symphyta
Archostemata
Geadephaga
Polyphaga
Scarabaeoidea
Elateroidea
Paratrichoptera
Archidiptera
TAXA
Insecta
MANDIBULATA
Coleoptera
CONTRIBUTORS
J. Smart, R. J. Wootton
R. Crowson

FIG. 19.3B

The Fossil Record, Part II

Order MECOPTERA Packard 1886

First, Perm Leonard: see under suborders Protomecoptera and Eumecoptera below. **Extant.**

Comments: In the arrangement which follows, where we recognise four sub-orders, Proto-mecoptera, Eumecoptera, Paratrichoptera, and Neomecoptera, we have relied much on Marty-nova (1962) and on the important survey of the group by Grassé (1951a) in which he took cog-nisance of both extant and fossil forms. We include the suborder Protodiptera Tillyard 1937 in Paratrichoptera, following Martynova (1962). Suborder Paramecoptera Tillyard 1919, known only from two incomplete wings cannot be safely assigned to any of the suborders.

The taxonomy of the order has been complicated by the enigmatic nature of many of the fossils—some merely fragments of wings—assigned, probably quite correctly, to it. This has resulted in the erection of a great many families for their reception and the authorities are not in agreement as to which might be synonyms of which (See further in notes under Suborder Eumecoptera).

Some authors treat the order simply as comprising a series of families and make no attempt to group them in any way.

The literature on the Mecoptera is extensive, some of the more important references, relating especially to phylogeny, are: Carpenter (1930, 1954a, 1965), Crampton (1930), Hinton (1958), Grassé (1951a), Imms (1944), Martynova (1948, 1959, 1962) and Riek (1953).

Suborder PROTOMECOPTERA Tillyard 1917

First, Perm Leonard: *Platychorista venosa* Tillyard 1926, Elmo Kansas, U.S.A., *Marimerobius splendens* Zalesskii 1946, Tshekarda, Perm District, U.S.S.R., and many spp. from Perm (Lower; Kuznetsk Series., correlation uncertain), Kuznetsk Basin, Kemerov District, U.S.S.R. **Extant.**

Comment: Represented at the present time by the rare species: *Merope tuber* Newman 1838, Eastern U.S.A. *Austromerope poulteni* Killington 1933, Australia; and *Notiothauma reedi* McLachlan 1877, Chile.

Constituent families: Protomeropidae Tillyard 1926 (=Platychoristidae Carpenter 1930), Archipanorpidae Tillyard 1917, Kaltanidae Martynova 1958, Tomiochoristidae Martynova 1958, Permomeropidae Reik 1953 and the two families Meropidae Handlirsch 1906 and Notiothaum-idae Esben-Petersen 1921 to which the extant species are assigned.

Suborder EUMECOPTERA Tillyard 1917

First, Perm Leonard: *Permopanorpa formosa* Tillyard 1926, Elmo, Kansas, U.S.A. and many other spp. from Elmo, Kansas; and from the Urals, and the Kuznetsk Basin (Kuznetsk Series), U.S.S.R. **Extant.**

Comment: *Metropator pusillus* Handlirsch 1906, Carb Namur, Pennsylvania, was placed in Mecoptera by Tillyard (1926). This assignment was questioned by Carpenter (1930) but was accepted by Martynova (1962) who placed it in Order Eumecoptera. Crampton (1930) assigned *Metropator* to the Order Protorthoptera. Carpenter (1965) has now assigned *Metropator* to the Order Miomoptera. (See also p. 518). We consider it here as *incert. sed.*

Constituent families: Agetopanorpidae Carpenter 1930[+0], Anormochoristidae Tillyard 1926, Belmontiidae Tillyard 1919[0] Cladochoristidae Reik 1953[+], Idelopanorpidae Zalessky 1929[0], Lithopanorpidae Carpenter 1930[+], Mesochoristidae Tillyard 1926[0], (= Eosetidae Tindale 1944), Mesopanorpidae Tillyard 1918[+0], Metropatridae Handlirsch 1906, Neorthophlebiidae Handlirsch 1920[+], Orthophlebiidae Handlirsch 1906, Parachoristidae Tillyard 1926[+], Permo-centropidae Martynov 1933, Permochoristidae Tillyard 1918[+], Permopanorpidae Tillyard 1926[+], Petromantidae Handlirsch 1904[+], Protochoristidae Tillyard 1926[+], Protopanorpidae Handlirsch 1937, Stereochoristidae Tillyard 1919[+], Tychtopsychidae Martynova 1958 and Xenochoristidae Riek 1953[+], the extant families: Bittacidae Enderlein 1910 (= Bittacusidae

---

[0] ⋯ These families are comprised in the family Permochoristidae Tillyard by Martynova (1962); she assigns Cladochoristidae to Order Trichoptera.

[+] ⋯ These families are comprised in the family Orthophlebiidae Handlirsch by Carpenter (1954b).

522

Handlirsch, 1906), Choristidae Tillyard 1919, Nannochoristidae Tillyard 1917 and Panorpidae Stephens 1835.

Suborder PARATRICHOPTERA Tillyard 1919

First, Perm (Upper; Ilyinsk Series, correlation uncertain); *Permotipula borealis* Martynova 1961, Kuznetsk Basin, Kemerov District, U.S.S.R. or Perm Dzhulf: *Permotipula patricia* Tillyard 1929, *Robinjohnia tillyardi* Martynova 1948, *Permotanyderus ableptus* Riek 1953 and *Choristotanyderus nanus* Riek 1953, Belmont and Warner's Bay, N.S.W., Australia.

Last, Jur Call–Oxf: *Pseudopolycentropus latipennis* Martynov 1927, Karatau, Kazakhstan, U.S.S.R.

Comments: Constitution and validity of suborder queried by Riek (1956), but accepted by Martynova (1959, 1961, 1963).

Widely believed that the Order Diptera must have arisen from Paratrichoptera but see Imms (1944) on comparison of Diptera with *Nannochorista*, etc., Suborder Eumecoptera.

Constituent families: Permotipulidae Tillyard 1937 (= Robinjohniidae Martynova 1948), Pseudopolycentropididae Handlirsch 1921 (= "Pseudocentropidae Handlirsch 1921" of Laurentiaux 1953), Pseudodipteridae Martynova 1961, Choristopsychidae Martynov 1937, Mesopsychidae Tillyard 1917, Liassophilidae Tillyard 1933, Triassopsychidae Tillyard 1919, Permotanyderidae Riek 1953 and Dobbertiniidae Handlirsch 1921.

Suborder NEOMECOPTERA Crampton 1930

No fossil record. The suborder comprises but one species *Boreus hymenalis* Latreille 1816, an obscure, apterous insect of holarctic distribution. Hinton (1958) would remove the Neomecoptera from the Mecoptera and set them apart with full ordinal status. **Extant.**

Order LEPIDOPTERA Linnaeus 1758

First, Tert U. Eoc–L/M. Olig: many spp. from Baltic amber. **Extant.**

Comments: It is now generally accepted that the families Palaeontinidae Handlirsch 1906 and Dunstaniidae Tillyard 1916 are Homoptera and not Lepidoptera.

Eoses triassica Tindale 1944 was thought to be a Lepidopteran and was treated as representing a Suborder Eoneura Tindale 1944 by Laurentiaux (*in* Piveteau 1953) but Riek (1955) presents convincing evidence that the species is a synomym of *Mesochorista proavita* Tillyard 1916 (Family Mesochoristidae, Suborder Eumecoptera; see p. 522).

The classification below is that of Imms (1957). Other references: Kuznetsov (1941), Laurentiaux (1953), Rebel (1936) and Riek (1955).

Suborder ZEUGLOPTERA Chapman 1916

First, Tert U. Eoc–L/M. Olig: *Micropteryx proavitalla* Rebel 1936, Baltic Amber. **Extant.**

Suborder MONOTRYSIA Borner 1938

First, Tert U. Eoc–L/M. Olig: *Electrocrania immensipalpia* Kuznetsov 1941 and many others from Baltic Amber. **Extant.**

Suborder DITRYSIA Borner 1938

First, Tert U. Eoc–L/M. Olig: *Palaeoscardiites mordvilkoi* Kuznetsov 1941 and many others from Baltic Amber. **Extant.**

Order TRICHOPTERA Kirby 1913

First, Perm (Lower; Kuznetsk Series, correlation uncertain): *Microptysma sibiricum* Martynova 1958, Kuznetsk Basin, Kemerov District, U.S.S.R. **Extant.**
Reference: Martynova (1962). [J.S. & R.J.W.]

Order DIPTERA Linnaeus 1758

First, Trias Rhaet: see Suborders Archidiptera, and Nematocera. **Extant.**

Comments: Laurentiaux (*in* Pivetean 1953) says "Le Trias inférieur de l'est de la France, dont la faune reste inédite, a livré les plus anciennes traces de diptères, associées précurseurs encore comtemporains, paratrichoptères (Pseudodiptera) et aux permochoristides. Cette découverte ramène a l'ordre du jour, le problème du berceau géographique".

We follow the classification of Imms (1957) with the addition of a suborder set up by Rohdendorf for the accommodation of certain fossils described by him.

Rohdendorf in a series of papers (see refs. below) has elaborated a very interesting phylogenetic classification of Diptera (adopted in Rohdendorf 1962a): unfortunately this classification has not yet received the critical attention of English-language writers.

The Permian fossil, *Permotipula patricia* Tillyard 1929, is now regarded as definitely not in any way belonging to the Diptera but is assigned to the Suborder Paratrichoptera.

References: Imms (1944, 1957), and Rohdendorf (1946, 1951, 1959, 1961b, 1964).

Suborder ARCHIDIPTERA Rohdendorf 1961

First and **Last,** Trias Rhaet: Several species described by Rohdendorf (1962a), including: *Dictyodiptera multinervis, Paradictyodiptera triachalis, Dipterodictya tipuloidea, Hyperoplyneura phryganeoidea, Dyspolyneura longipennis* and *Diplopolyneura mirabilis*, Issyk-kul, Kirgisia, U.S.S.R.

Suborder NEMATOCERA Latreille 1825

First, Trias Rhaet: Many species described by Rohdendorf (1962a), including: *Eopolyneura tenuinervis, Pareopolyneura costalis, Musidoromima crassinervis, Tipulodictya minima, Architipula radiata, Architendipes tshernovskiji, Rhaetomyiacosta, Rhaetofungivora reticulate, Palaeoplecia rhaetica, Phragmiligoneura incerta, Oligophryne fungivoroides* and *Protorhyphus turanicus*, Issyk-Kul, Kirgisia, U.S.S.R. **Extant.**

Suborder BRACHYCERA Macquart 1834

First, Jur Torac: *Protobrachyceron liasinum* Handlirsch 1938, Upper Lias, Dobbertin, Mecklenberg, Germany. **Extant.**

Suborder CYCLORRHAPHA

First, Tert U. Eoc–L/M. Olig: many species referrable to extant genera in Baltic Amber.
Extant.

Suborder PUPIPARA

First, Tert U. Olig: *Ornithoponus rottensis* Statz 1940, Graugruner Schiefer, Rott, Germany.
Extant.

Order SIPHONAPTERA Latreille 1825 (= APHANIPTERA Kirby 1826)

First, Tert U. Eoc–L/M. Olig: *Palaeopsylla klebsiana* Dampf 1910, Baltic Amber. **Extant.**
Comment: Holland (1964) has reviewed the scant knowledge of fossil fleas. [J.S.]

Order HYMENOPTERA Linnaeus 1758

First, Trias (Lower; Madigen Series, correlation uncertain): see under Suborder Symphyta below. **Extant.**
Comment: Reviews of our information about fossil Hymenoptera will be found in Laurentiaux (*in* Piveteau 1953) and Martynova (1962).

Suborder SYMPHYTA Gerstaecker 1867

First, Trias (Lower; Madigen Series, correlation uncertain). *Triassoxyela foveolata* Rasnitzyn 1964 and nine other species, Madigen, Kirgisia, U.S.S.R. **Extant.**
Constituent superfamilies: Xyeloidea Benson 1951, L. Trias (correlation uncertain) see *Triassoxyela* above; Megalodontoidea Ross 1937, Jur Call–Oxf; Siricoidea Ross 1937, Jur Call–Oxf; Orussoidea Bischoff 1926; Cephoidea Ross 1937, Tert L/M Olig. All extant.
References: Rasnitzyn (1963, 1964).

Suborder APOCRITA Gerstaecker 1867

First, Jur Call–Oxf: see under Section Parasitica below. **Extant.**
Comment: For convenience we here employ the traditional but obsolete division of the suborder into Parasitica and Aculeata.

Section PARASITICA Kirby 1837

First, Jur Call–Oxf: *Mesaulacinus oviformis* Martynov 1925 and *Mesohelorus muchini* Martynov 1925, Karatau, Kazakhstan, U.S.S.R. **Extant.**
Constituent superfamilies: Cynipoidea Ashmead, Cret (correlation uncertain): Ichneumonoidea Konow, Jur Call–Oxf, (See *Mesaulacinus* above): Chalcidoidea Ashmead, Cret (correlation uncertain): Serphoidea Kieffer, Jur Call–Oxf, (see *Mesohelorus* above); Bethyloidea Handlirsch, Tert L/M Olig. All Extant.

Section ACULEATA Latreille 1807

First, Tert L. Eoc: *Eoponera berryi* Carpenter 1930, Wilcox, Tennessee. **Extant.**
Comment: The aculeates probably underwent their principal radiation in the Cretaceous, but no certain fossils of this age are known. *Cretavus sibiricus* Sharov 1957, Cret Coniac–Santon–Campan, Kas river, Krasnoyarsk Region, U.S.S.R., has been claimed to be aculeate, but is here regarded as *incert. sed.*
Constituent superfamilies: Scolioidea Ashmead, Tert L/M Olig; Formicoidea Ashmead, Tert L. Eoc (see *Eoponera* above); Pompiloidea Berland, Tert L/M Olig; Vespoidea Ashmead, Tert L/M Olig; Sphecoidea Ashmead, Tert L/M Olig; Apoidea Ashmead, Tert L/M Olig. All Extant. [J.S. & R.J.W.]

Order COLEOPTERA Linnaeus 1758

First, Perm Leonard: *Tshekardocoleus magnus* Rohd. & *T. minor* Ponomarenko, Kungursk series, Urals, Russia (Rohdendorf & Ponomarenko 1962). **Extant.**
Comment: Fossils of this order usually readily recognisable and common from Upper Permian onwards.

Suborder ARCHOSTEMATA Kolbe 1911

First: As for Coleoptera. 2 extant families, Cupedidae & Micromalthidae. **Extant.**
Comment: The Lower Permian fossils all more or less aberrant in elytral structure. All Permian specimens in which ventral structures are seen agree in this with family Cupedidae, though some have elytra unlike extant Cupedidae and resembling various Polyphaga.

Suborder ADEPHAGA Clairville 1806

Section GEADEPHAGA

First, Jur ?Sinem: *Notokistus brodiei* Handlirsch (1908) (?Carabidae), Lower Lias, Gloucestershire, England. **Extant.**
Comment: Ponomarenko informs me (*in litt.*) that he has seen fossils apparently intermediate between Cupedidae and Geadephaga from Triassic deposits in Russia.

Section HYDRADEPHAGA

First, Jur ?Toarc: *Angaragabus jurassicus* Ponomarenko (1963) (?Noteridae; *Liadytes avus* Ponom. from same deposits may be adult of same species), Angara River, Siberia, USSR. **Extant.**
Comment: Large Dytiscid-like forms occur in Solnhofen Lithographic Stone, 'Tith' (Handlirsch 1908); *Coptoclava longipoda* Ping (Ponomarenko 1961) from Lower Cretaceous of China apparently the larva of an Amphizoid-like form.

Suborder MYXOPHAGA Crowson 1955

No fossil record.
Comment: Existing species very small, probably overlooked as fossils.

Suborder POLYPHAGA Emery 1886

First, Jur Hett: *Aphodiites protogaea* Heer (1865), Lower Lias, Schambelen, Aargau, Switzerland. **Extant.**
Comment: Suborder reliably separable from Archostemata and Myxophaga only by lack of noto-pleural suture in prothorax, a character rarely visible in fossils.

Superfamily HYDROPHILOIDEA (PALPICORNIA auctt.)

First, Jur 'Tith': *Pseudohydrophilus avitus* Heyden (?Hydrophilidae), Lithographic stone, Solnhofen, Germany (Handlirsch 1908). **Extant.**
Comment: Most distinctive feature of the superfamily is in antennae, very rarely visible in fossils.

Superfamily HISTEROIDEA Crowson 1955

First, Tert U. Eoc–L/M. Olig: several spp., Baltic Amber, Kaliningrad region, U.S.S.R. (Klebs 1910). **Extant.**
Comment: The group should be recognisable in fossils from truncate elytra and general form.

Superfamily STAPHYLINOIDEA Ganglbauer 1895

First, Tert U. Eoc–L/M. Olig: several spp. and several families, Baltic Amber, Kaliningrad region, U.S.S.R. (Klebs 1910). **Extant.**
Comment: Family Staphylinidae readily recognisable in fossils, but other families not so.

Superfamily SCARABAEOIDEA (LAMELLICORNIA auctt.)

First, as for Polyphaga (*q.v.*). **Extant.**
Comment: Probably the first Polyphagan group to develop a distinctive facies, recognisable in fossils.

Superfamily EUCINETOIDEA Crowson 1960

First, Tert U. Eoc–L/M. Olig: *Brachelodes motschulskyi* and other spp., (Helodidae), Baltic Amber, Kaliningrad region, U.S.S.R. (Yablokoff-Khnzorian 1961). **Extant.**
Comment: Klebs (1910) also lists spp. of Clambidae from Baltic Amber. *Praemordella martynovi* Scegoleva-Barovskaya (U.Jur, Kara-Tau, U.S.S.R; see Rohdendorf & Ponomarenko 1962), attributed to Mordellidae, might well be a Eucinetid.

Superfamily DASCILLOIDEA Boving & Craighead 1931

First, Jur Kimm: *Mesodascilla jacobsoni* Martynov (see Rohdendorf & Ponomarenko 1962) (Dascillidae), Kara-Tau, U.S.S.R. **Extant.**

Superfamily BYRRHOIDEA Boving & Craighead 1931

First, Tert U. Eoc–L/M. Olig: several spp. (Byrrhidae), Baltic Amber, Kaliningrad region, U.S.S.R. (Klebs 1910). **Extant.**
Comment: Fossils will be difficult to distinguish from Chelonariidae, Limnichidae, Nosodendridae, etc..

Superfamily DRYOPOIDEA Boving & Craighead 1931

First, Jur 'Tith': *Parasilphites angusticollis* Oppenheimer probably family Dryopidae, Lithographic stone, Solnhofen, Germany (Handlirsch 1908). **Extant.**
Comment: *Tersus crassicornis* Martynov (Jur Kimm: Kara-Tau, U.S.S.R.; Rohdendorf & Ponomarenko 1962), described as Elateridae, could as well belong in this superfamily.

Superfamily BUPRESTOIDEA Crowson 1955

First, L. Eoc: *Chlorodema primordialis* (Pongracz), family Buprestidae, Brown Coal, Geiseltal, Germany (Haupt 1950). **Extant.**

Comment: Many Mesozoic fossils attributed to Buprestidae, but unreliably in absence of ventral structures.

Superfamily ELATEROIDEA Leng 1920

First, Jur Hett: *Megacentrus tristis* Heer (1865) (?Elateridae), Lower Lias, Schambelen, Switzerland. **Extant.**

Comment: *Tersus crassicornis* Martynov may belong here or in Dryopoidea (*q.v.*).

Superfamily CANTHAROIDEA Reitter 1906

First, Tert U. Eoc–L/M. Olig: several families and many spp., Baltic Amber, Kaliningrad region, U.S.S.R. (Klebs 1910). **Extant.**

Comment; In fossils, probably liable to confusion with Cleroidea, Lymexyloidea, Heteromera and perhaps some Dascilloidea or Staphylinoidea.

Superfamily DERMESTOIDEA Crowson 1955

First, Tert U. Eoc–L/M. Olig: several spp, of Dermestidae, Baltic Amber, Kaliningrad region, U.S.S.R. (Klebs 1910). **Extant.**

Comment: The group will not be readily recognisable in Mesozoic fossils.

Superfamily BOSTRYCHOIDEA Kolbe 1908

First, L. Eoc: *Venablesia colluvium* Britton (1960) (Anobiidae), London Clay, Bognor, England. **Extant.**

Comment: The special form of the prothorax should aid the recognition of this group among older fossils, though this is approached in Curculionoidea–Scolytidae.

Superfamily CLEROIDEA Böving & Craighead 1931

First, Tert U. Eoc–L/M. Olig: *Prospinoza baltica* Crowson (1964) (Cleridae). Klebs (1910) lists several spp. each of families Trogossitidae, Cleridae, Melyridae; Baltic Amber, Kaliningrad region, U.S.S.R. **Extant.**

Comment: Group not likely to be readily recognized in Mesozoic fossils.

Superfamily LYMEXYLOIDEA Böving & Craighead 1931

First, Tert U. Eoc–L/M. Olig: 3 genera of Lymexylidae, Baltic Amber, Kaliningrad region, U.S.S.R. (Klebs 1910). **Extant.**

Superfamily STYLOPOIDEA (STREPSIPTERA auctt.).

First, Tert U. Eoc–L/M. Olig: *Mengea tertiaria* Menge, Baltic Amber, Kaliningrad region, U.S.S.R. (Ulrich 1943). **Extant.**

Comment: *Mengea* notably more primitive than extant Stylopoids, suggests that ancestry of the group not much older than Tertiary.

Superfamily CUCUJOIDEA Böving & Craighead 1931

Section CLAVICORNIA

First, Jur Kimm: *Nitidulina eclavata* Martynov, Kara-Tau, U.S.S.R. (Rohdendorf & Ponomarenko 1962). **Extant.**

Comment: *Parandrexis* Martynov, from the same locality, probably belongs in Clavicornia rather than Cerambycidae.

The Fossil Record, Part II

Section HETEROMERA

First, Tert M. Eoc: *Eodromus agilis* (Meunier) (Tenebrionidae), Brown Coal, Geiseltal, Germany (Haupt 1950). **Extant.**

Comment: Mesozoic fossils attr. to Heteromera all doubtful, e.g. the Jurassic (Kara-Tau) spp. *Necromera baeckmanni* (see Chrysomeloidea) and *Praemordella martynovi* Sceg.-Bar. (see Eucinetoidea).

Superfamily CHRYSOMELOIDEA (PHYTOPHAGA auctt.)

First, Tert M. Eoc: *Eosagra subparallela* Haupt (1950), Brown coal, Geiseltal, Germany. (Chrysomelidae). **Extant.**

Comment: *Necromera baeckmanni* Martynov (Jur Kimm, Kara-Tau, U.S.S.R.) seems to me likely to be an ancestral Cerambycid type rather than a Heteromeran.

Superfamily CURCULIONOIDEA (RHYNCHOPHORA auctt.)

First, Jur Kimm: *Archaeorrhynchus tenuicornis* Martynov (?Nemonychidae), Kara-Tau, U.S.S.R. (Rohdendorf & Ponomarenko 1962). **Extant.**

Comment: Group readily recognisable by rostrate head. [R.A.C.]

Order STREPSIPTERA Kirby 1913

Imms (1957) gives this group full ordinal status. This procedure is questioned by many authors who regard the insects comprised in the order as constituting a Superfamily, Stylopoidea, of the Order Coleoptera. It is so treated on page 527. [J.S. & R.J.W.]

REFERENCES

BACHOFEN VON ECHT, A. F. 1942. Über die Myriapoden des Bernstein. *Palaeobiologica*, **7**, 394–403.

BEKKER-MIGDISOVA, E. E. 1958. [New Homopterous insects, Part 1]. *Mater. Osnov. paleont.* **2**, 57–67 (Russian).

—— 1960a. [Palaeozoic Homoptera of the U.S.S.R. and the question of the phylogeny of the Order]. *Paleont Zh.*, **3**, 28–42 (Russian).

—— 1960b. [New Permian Homoptera of the European part of the U.S.S.R.]. *Trudy paleont. Inst.*, **76**, 1–112 (Russian).

—— 1961. Homoptera, *in* ROHDENDORF, BEKKER-MIGDISOVA, MARTYNOVA & SHAROV 1961. (*q.v.*).

—— 1962. Various groups, *in* ROHDENDORF, B. B. (Editor) 1962b. (*q.v.*).

—— & VISHNYAKOVA, V. N. 1962. Psocoptera, *in* ROHDENDORF, B. B. (Editor) 1962b. (*q.v.*).

BERLAND, L. & GRASSÉ, P.-P. 1951. Super-Ordre des Néuroptéroïdes, *in* GRASSÉ, P.-P. (Editor) 1951, (*q.v*).

BODE, A. 1953. Die Insektenfauna des Ostniedersächsischen Oberen Lias. *Palaeontographica.*, **103A**, 1–375.

BRADE-BIRKS, G. 1923. Notes on Myriapoda XXVIII. *Kampecaris tuberculata* nov. sp. from the Old Red Sandstone of Ayrshire. *Proc. R. phys. Soc. Edinb.*, **20**, 277–280.

BRITTON, E. B. 1960. Beetles from the London Clay at Bognor Regis, Sussex. *Bull. Br. Mus. nat. Hist., Geol.*, **4**, 29–50.

BROILI, F. 1928. Crustaceenfunde aus dem rheinischen Unterdevon, I. Über extremitätenresten. *Sber. bayer. Akad. Wiss. (Math.-Natuh. Abt.)*, 1928, 197–201.

—— 1929. Beobachtungen an neuen Arthropodenfunden aus den Hunsrückschiefern; ein Pantopode aus dem rheinischen Unterdevon; *Sber. bayer. Akad. Wiss. (Math.-Naturh. Abt.)*, 1929, 272–280, pl. 5.

CARPENTER, F. M. 1930. The Lower Permian insects of Kansas. Part I. *Bull. Mus. comp. Zool. Harv.*, **70**, 69–101.

—— 1932. The Lower Permian insects of Kansas, Part 5. *Am. J. Sci.*, **24**, 1–22.

—— 1933. The Lower Permian insects of Kansas. Part 6 *Proc. Am. Acad. Arts. Sci.*, **68**, 411–503 pl. 1.

—— 1936. The Lower Permian insects of Kansas. Part 7. *Proc. Am. Acad. Arts. Sci.*, **70**, 103–146.

—— 1943a. The Lower Permian insects of Kansas, Part 9. *Proc. Am. Acad. Arts. Sci.*, **75**, 55–84.

—— 1943b. Studies on Carboniferous Insects from Commentry; Part I. Introduction and Families Protagriidae, Meganeuridae and Campylopteridae. *Bull. geol. Soc. Am.*, **54**, 527–554.

—— 1947. Lower Permian insects from Oklahoma, Part 1. *Proc. Am. Acad. Arts. Sci.*, **76**, 25–54.

—— 1950. The Lower Permian insects of Kansas. Part 10. *Proc. Am. Acad. Arts. Sci.*, **78**, 185–210.

—— 1951. Studies on Carboniferous insects from Commentry, France: Part II. The Megasecoptera. *J. Paleont.*, **25**, 336–355.

—— 1954a. The Baltic Amber Mecoptera. *Psyche, Camb.*, **61**, 31–40.

—— 1954b. *In* BRUES, C. T., MELANDER, A. L. and CARPENTER, F. M. Classification of Insects. *Bull. Mus. comp. Zool. Harv.*, **108**, 777–827.

—— 1960. Studies on North American Carboniferous Insects. 1. The Protodonata. *Psyche, Camb.*, **67**, 98–110.

—— 1961. Studies on Carboniferous Insects of Commentry, France; Part III. The Caloneurodea. *Psyche, Camb.*, **68**, 145–153.

—— 1963a. Studies on Carboniferous insects from Commentry, France: Part IV. The Genus *Triplosoba*. *Psyche, Camb.*, **70**, 120–128.

—— 1963b. Studies on Carboniferous Insects of Commentry, France: Part V. The genus *Diaphanoptera* and the order Diaphanopterodea. *Psyche, Camb.*, **70**, 240–256.

—— 1965. Studies on North American Carboniferous insects. 4. The genera *Metropator*, *Eubleptus*, *Hapaloptera* and *Hadentomum*. *Psyche, Camb.*, **72**, 175–190.

—— & KUKALOVA, J. 1964. The structure of the Protelytroptera, with description of a new genus from Permian strata of Moravia. *Psyche, Camb.*, **71**, 193–197.

CASTER, K. E. & BROOKS, H. K. 1956. New Fossils from the Canadian-Chazyan (Ordovician) Hiatus in Tennessee. *Bull. Am. Paleont.*, **36**, 157–99, pls. 12–23.

—— & KJELLESVIG-WAERING, E. N. 1964. Upper Ordovician Eurypterids of Ohio. *Palaeontogr. am.*, **4**, no. 32, 301–54, pls. 43–53.

—— & MACKE, W. B. 1952. An aglaspid Merostome from the Upper Ordovician of Ohio. *J. Paleont.*, **26**, 753–7, pl. 109, fig. 1.

CHINA, W. E. 1962. South American Peloridiidae (Hemiptera-Homoptera: Coleorrhyncha). *Trans. R. ent. Soc., Lond.*, **114**, 131–161.

CLARKE, B. B. 1952. The geology of Dinmore Hill, Herefordshire, with a description of a new Myriapod from the Dittonian rocks there. *Trans. Woolhope nat. Fld Club*, **33**, 222–236.

CRAMPTON, G. C. 1930. The wings of the remarkable archaic Mecopteron *Notiothauma reedi* McLachlan, with remarks on their Protoblattoid affinities. *Psyche, Camb.*, **38**, 1–21.

CROWSON, R. A. 1955. *The Natural Classification of the Families of Coleoptera*, 187 pp. London, Lloyd.

—— 1960. The Phylogeny of Coleoptera. *A. Rev. Ent.*, **5**, 111–134.

—— 1964. A Review of the Classification of Cleroidea. *Trans. R. ent. Soc. Lond.*, **116**, 275–327.

CURRIE, L. D. 1927. On Cyamocephalus, a new Synxiphosuran from the Upper Silurian of Lesmahago, Lanarkshire. *Geol. Mag.*, **64**, 153–7, text fig.

DEMOULIN, G. 1954. Quelques remarques sur les Archodonates. *Bull. Annls. Soc. ent. Belg.*, **90**, 327–337.

DENNIS, R. 1949a. Ordre des Zoraptères, *in* GRASSÉ, P.-P. (Editor), 1949. (*q.v.*).

—— 1949b. Sous-Classe des Aptérygotes, *in* GRASSÉ, P.-P., (Editor), 1949. (*q.v.*).

EVANS, J. W. 1956. Palaeozoic and Mesozoic Hemiptera (Insecta). *Aust. J. Zool.*, **4**, 165–258.

—— 1963. The Phylogeny of the Homoptera. *A. Rev. Ent.*, **8**, 77–94.

—— 1964. The periods of origin and diversification of the Superfamilies of the Homoptera-Auchenorhyncha (Insecta) as determined by a study of the wings of Palaeozoic and Mesozoic fossils. *Proc. Linn. Soc. Lond.*, **175**, 171–181.

FLOWER, R. H. 1945. A new Deepkill Eurypterid; *Am. Midl. Nat.*, **34,** 717–9, fig.

FRASER, F. C. 1957. *A reclassification of the Order Odonata, Handbook No. 12,* 133 pp.. Royal Zoological Soc. N.S.W. (A revised edition of Tillyard & Fraser, (1938–1940). (*q.v.*)).

GRASSÉ, P.-P. (Editor). 1949. *Traité de Zoologie,* **9,** 1117 pp. (Insectes: Paléontologie, Géonémie, Aptérygotes, Ephéméroptères, Odonatoptères, Blattoptéroïdes, Orthoptéroïdes, Dermaptéroïdes, Coléoptères). Masson, Paris.

—— 1951a. Ordre des Mécoptères, *in* GRASSE, P.-P. (Editor). 1951b (*q.v.*).

—— (Editor). 1951b. Traité de Zoologie, **10** (2 fascicules), 1948 pp. (Insectes Supérieurs et Hémiptéroïdes). Masson, Paris.

GUTHÖRL, P. 1936. *Arthropleura,* der Riesengliederfüssler des Oberkarbons und seine Verbreitung in dem europäischen Steinkohlenbecken. *Glückauf,* **72,** 965–975.

HAASE, E. 1890. Beiträge zur Kenntnis der fossilien Arachniden. *Z. dt. geol. Ges.,* **42,** 629–657.

HANDLIRSCH, A. 1906–1908. *Die fossilen Insekten und die Phylogenie der Rezenten Formen.* Engelmann, Leipzig.

—— 1925. Uberordnung: Neuropteroidea Handl. oder Plannipennia (Banks) (Netzflugler). *in* SCHRODER, C. *Handbuch der Entomologie,* **3,** 825–840.

—— 1938. Neue Untersuchungen über die fossilen Insekten mit Ergänzungen und Nächtragen sowie Ausblicken auf phylogenetische, palaeogeographische und allgemein biologische Probleme, Teil II. *Annln naturh. Mus. Wien.,* **49,** 1–240.

HANDSCHIN, E. 1926. Revision der Collembollen des baltischen Bernsteins. *Ent. Mitt.,* **15,** 161–185, 211–223, 330–342.

HAUPT, H. 1950. Die Käfer aus der Eozänen Braunkohle Geiseltales. *Geologica Berl.,* no. 6, vii + 168 pp.

HEER, O. 1865. *Urwelt der Schweiz.* Zürich.

HINTON, H. E. 1958. The phylogeny of the Panorpoid Orders. *A. Rev. Ent.,* **3,** 181–206.

HIRST, S. 1923. On some arachnid remains from the Old Red Sandstone (Rhynie Chert Bed, Aberdeenshire). *Ann. Mag. nat. Hist.* (9), **12,** 455–474.

HOLLAND, G. P. 1964. Evolution, Classification and Host Relationships of Siphonaptera. *A. Rev. Ent.* **9,** 123–146.

ILLIES, J. 1965. Phylogeny and zoogeography of the Plecoptera. *A. Rev. Ent.,* **10,** 117–140.

IMMS, A. D. 1944. On the constitution of the maxillae and labium in Mecoptera and Diptera. *Q. Jl microsc. Sci.,* **85,** 73–96.

—— 1957. *A General Textbook of Entomology,* (RICHARDS, O. W., and DAVIES, R. G. Editors), 886 pp., Methuen, London.

JEANNEL, R. 1949. Classification et Phylogénie des Insectes, *in* GRASSÉ, P.-P. (Editor) 1949 (*q.v.*).

KJELLESVIG-WAERING, E. N. 1948. The Mazon Creek Eurypterid; A Revision of the Genus Lepidoderma. *Ill. St. Mus., Sci. Pap.,* 2 no. 4, 46 pp, 1 text fig, 8 pls.

—— 1959. A taxonomic Review of some late Palaeozoic Eurypterida. *J. Paleont.,* **33,** 251–6, pl. 38.

—— 1963. Pennsylvanian Invertebrates of the Mazon Creek Area. Illinois: Eurypterida. *Fieldiana: Geol.,* 12, no. 6, 85–106.

—— 1964. A Synopsis of the Family Pterygotidae Clarke and Ruedemann, 1912 (Eurypterida) *J. Paleont.,* **38,** 331–61, pls. 53–6.

—— 1966. Silurian scorpions from New York. *J. Paleont.,* **40,** 359–375.

KLEBS, R. 1910. Uber Bernsteineinschlusse in allgemeinen und die Coleopteren meiner Bernsteinsammlung. *Schr. phys.-ökon. Ges. Königsb.,* **51,** 217–242.

KUKALOVA, J. 1959. On the Family Blattinopsidae Bolton, 1925. (Insecta, Protorthoptera). *Rozpr. čsl. Akad. Věd,* Rada M.P.V., **69,** 1–30, pl. 1–2.

—— 1963a. Permian insects of Moravia. 1. Miomoptera. *Sb. geol. Věd* series P, **1,** 7–52, pls. 1–16.

—— 1963b. To the taxonomy of Palaeodictyoptera (Insecta). *Vest. ústřed Úst. geol.,* **38,** 197–200.

—— 1964a. To the Morphology of the oldest known dragon fly *Erasipteron larischi* Pruvost, 1933. *Vest. ústřed Úst. geol.,* **39,** 463–464, 1 plate.

—— 1964b. Permian insects of Moravia, Part 2. *Sb. geol. Věd* series P, **3**, 39–118, 24 plates.

—— 1964c. Permian Protelytroptera, Coleoptera and Protorthoptera (Insecta) of Moravia. *Sb. geol Věd* series P, **6**, 61–98, 8 plates.

KUZNETZOV, N. Y. 1941. [*A revision of the Amber Lepidoptera*], 136 pp. Academii Nauk SSSR, Moscow and Leningrad (Russian with English summary).

LAURIE, M. 1899. On a Silurian scorpion and some additional eurypterid remains from the Pentland Hills. *Trans. R. Soc. Edinb.*, **39**, 575–590.

LEHMANN, W. M. 1944. *Paleoscorpius devonicus* n.g., n.sp., ein Skorpion aus dem rheinischen Unterdevon. *Neues Jb. Miner. Geol. Paläont., Mh.*, 1944, 177–185.

LEUTZE, W. P. 1961. Arthropods from the Syracuse Formation, Silurian of New York. *J. Paleont.*, **35**, 49–64, pls. 15–16.

McCOOK, H. C. 1888. A new fossil spider, *Eoatypus woodwardii*. *Proc. Acad. nat. Sci. Philad.*, 1888, 200–202.

MARTYNOV, A. V. 1925a. Über zwei Grundtypen der Flügel bei den Insekten und ihre Evolution. *Z. Morph. Ökol. Tiere*, **4**, 465–501.

—— 1925b. [To the knowledge of fossil insects from Jurassic beds in Turkestan, Part 2]. *Izd. Akad. nauk. SSSR*, **19**, 569–598 (Russian).

—— 1928. A new fossil form of Phasmatodea from Galkino (Turkestan) and on Mesozoic Phasmids in general. *Ann. Mag. nat. Hist.* (10), **1**, 319–328.

—— 1930. [Palaeozoic Insects from the Kuznetz Basin]. *Izv. glav. geol.-razved. Uprav.*, **49** (10), 73–100 (Russian).

—— 1933. [On the Permian family Archescytinidae (Homoptera) and its relationship]. *Izv. Akad. nauk SSSR*, for 1933, 833–894. (Russian).

—— 1937. [Wings of termites and phylogeny of Isoptera and of allied groups of Insects] *in N. V. Nassonov Commerative volume*, 93–150. Inst. Evol. Morph., Akademii Nauk SSSR, Moscow and Leningrad (Russian with English summary).

—— 1938a. [On a new Permian order of orthopterous insects, Glosselytrodea]. *Izv. Akad. nauk SSSR Ser. Biol.*, for 1938, 187–206 (Russian).

—— 1938b. [Permian fossil insects from the Archangelsk District. Part V]. *Trudy Paleont. Inst.*, **7**(3), 69–80 (Russian).

MARTYNOVA, O. M. 1948. [Material on the evolution of the Mecoptera]. *Trudy Paleont. Inst.*, **14**, 1–77 (Russian).

—— 1952. [The Order Glosselytrodea in Permian deposits of the Kemerov District]. *Trudy Paleont. Inst.*, **40**, 187–196 (Russian).

—— 1959. [Phylogenetic inter-relationships of insects of the mecopteroid complex]. *Trudy Inst. Morf. Zhivot.*, **27**, 221–229 (Russian).

—— 1961. Palaeoentomology. *Ann. Rev. Ent.*, **6**, 285–293.

—— 1962. Various groups *in* ROHDENDORF, B. B. (Editor). 1962. (*q.v.*).

MEEK, F. B. & WORTHEN, A. H. 1868. Arachnida, pp. 560–563 *in Geological Survey of Illinois*, Volume 3, Springfield, Illinois.

PEACH, B. N. 1882. On some fossil myriapods from the Old Red Sandstone of Forfarshire. *Proc. R. phys. Soc. Edinb.*, **7**, 177–188.

—— 1883. On the occurrence of Pterygotus and a limuloid in the Caithness Flagstones and on the nature and mode of formation of "Adam's Plates". *Proc. R. phys. Soc. Edinb.*, **7**, 343–50, pl. 7.

—— 1898. On some new myriapods from the Palaeozoic rocks of Scotland. *Proc. R. phys. Soc. Edinb.*, **14**, 113–126.

PETRUNKEVITCH, A. 1913. A monograph of the terrestrial Paleozoic arachnids of North America. *Trans. Conn. Acad. Arts. Sci.*, **18**, 1–137.

—— 1949. A study of Paleozoic Arachnida. *Trans. Conn. Acad. Arts Sci.*, **37**, 60–315.

—— 1953. Paleozoic and Mesozoic Arachnida of Europe. *Mem. geol. Soc. Am.*, **53**, 128 pp., 58 plates.

—— 1955. *Trigonotarbus arnoldi*, a new species of fossil arachnid from southern France. *J. Paleont.*, **29**, 475–477.

531

PIERCE, W. D. 1950–1951. Fossil arthropods from the onyx marble. *Bull. Sth. Calif. Acad. Sci.*, **49,** 101–104 and **50,** 34–49.

PIVETEAU, J. (Editor) 1953. *Traité de Paléontologie*, Volume 3. Paris, Masson.

PONOMARENKO, A. G. 1961. [On the systematic position of *Coptoclava* Ping]. *Paleont. Zh.*, **3,** 67–72 (Russian).

—— 1963. [Early Jurassic Water-beetles from Angara]. *Paleont. Zh.*, **4,** 128–131 (Russian).

PŘIBYL, A., 1960. Nove poznatky o Svrchnokarbonske sladkovodni a kontinentalni faune z Ostravskokarvinske oblasti. *Rozpr. čsl. Akad. Věd.*, **70,** 1–71.

PRUVOST, P. 1919. La faune du terrain Houiller du Nord de la France. *Mem. Serr. carte géol. det. Fr.*

—— 1930. La faune continentale du terrain houiller de la Belgique. *Mém. Mus. r. Hist. nat. Belg.*, **44,** 206–217.

RAASCH, G. O. 1939. Cambrian Merostomata. *Spec. Pap. geol. Soc. Am.*, **19,** 146 pp, pl. 1–21, fig. 1–14.

RAGGE, D. R. 1955. *The wing-venation of the Orthoptera Saltatoria, with notes on dictyopteran wing-venation.* British Museum (Natural History), London.

RASNITZYN, A. P. 1963. [Late Jurassic Hymenoptera of Karatau]. *Paleont. Zh.*, 1963, (1), 86–99 (Russian).

—— 1964. [New Triassic Hymenoptera of Central Asia]. *Paleont. Zh.*, 1964, (1), 88–96 (Russian).

REBEL, H. 1936. Mikrolepidopteren aus dem baltischen Bernstein. *Naturwissenschaften*, **24** (33), 519–520.

RICHTER, R. & RICHTER, E. 1929. Weinbergina opitzi, n.g., n.sp., ein Schwertträger (Merost., Xiphos.) aus dem Devon (Rheinland). *Senckenbergiana*, **11,** 193–209, figs. 1–4.

RIEK, E. F. 1953. Fossil Mecopteroid insects from the Upper Permian of New South Wales. *Rec. Aust. Mus.*, **23,** 55–87.

—— 1955. Fossil Insects from the Triassic beds at Mt. Crosby, Queensland. *Aust. Jl Zool.*, **3**(4): 654–691.

—— 1956. A re-examination of the Mecopteroid and Orthopteroid fossils (Insecta) from the Triassic beds of Denmark Hill, Queensland, with descriptions of further specimens. *Aust. J. Zool.*, **4,** 98–110.

ROHDENDORF, B. B. 1946. [The evolution of the wing and the Phylogeny of Oligoneura (Diptera, Nematocera)]. *Trudy paleont. Inst.*, **13** (2), 1–108, 16 pls. (Russian with an English summary).

—— 1951. [Organs of locomotion of two-winged insects and their origin]. *Trudy paleont. Inst.*, **35,** 1–179 (Russian).

—— 1959. Die Bewegungsorgane der Zweiflugerinsekten und ihre Entwichlung, parts I-III. *Wiss. Z. Humbolt-Univ. Berl.*, **8,** 73–119, 269–308 and 435–454 (ROHDENDORF 1951 translated into German).

—— 1961a. [The description of the first winged insect from the Devonian Beds of the Timan (Insecta, Pterygota)]. *Ent. Obozr.*, **40,** 485–489, 2 figs. (Russian with English summary).

—— 1961b. Neue Angaben uber das System der Dipteren. *Proc. 11th Int. Congr. Ent., Wien,* 1960, **I,** 153–158.

—— 1962a. Various groups *in* ROHDENDORF, B. B. (Editor) 1962b (*q.v.*).

—— (Editor). 1962b. *Osnovy Paleontologii: Chlenistonogie Trakheinye i Khelitserovye.* Akademii Nauk SSSR, Moscow.

—— 1964. [Historical development of two-winged insects]. *Trudy paleont. Inst.*, **100,** 1–311. (Russian).

——, BEKKER-MIGDISOVA, E. E., MARTYNOVA, O. M. & SHAROV, A. G. 1961. [Palaeozoic insects of the Kuznetsk Basin]. *Trudy paleont. Inst.*, **85,** 1–705 (Russian).

—— & PONOMARENKO, A. G. 1962. *In* ROHDENDORF, B. B. (Editor) 1962b (*q.v.*).

ROLFE, W. D. I. & INGHAM, J. K. 1967. Limb structure, affinity and diet of the Carboniferous "centipede" *Arthropleura*. Scott. *J. Geol.*, **3** (1): in press.

RUEDEMANN, R. 1934. Eurypterids in Graptolite Shales. *Am. J. Sci.*, **157,** 374–85.

—— 1942. Some new Eurypterids from New York, in Paleontology and Geology, Cambrian and Ordovician Fossils, pt. 2. *Bull. N.Y. St. Mus.*, **327**, 24–9.

SCUDDER, S. H. 1890. New Carboniferous myriapoda from Illinois. *Mem. Boston. Soc. nat. Hist.*, **4**, 417–442.

—— 1893. Tertiary Rynchophorous Coleoptera. *Monographs U.S. geol. Surv.*, **21**.

SEGUY, E. 1959. Introduction a l'etude morphologique de l'aile des Insectes. *Mem. Mus. natn. Hist. nat., Paris*, Ser. A, **21**, 1–238.

SMART, J. 1953. On the wing-venation of *Physemacris variolosa* (Linn.) (Insecta; Pneumoridae). *Proc. zool. Soc. Lond.*, **123**, 199–202.

—— 1956. On the wing-venation of Chaetessa and other Mantids (Insecta; Mantodea). *Proc. zool. Soc. Lond.*, **127**, 545–553.

—— 1963. Explosive Evolution and the Phylogeny of Insects. *Proc. Linn. Soc., Lond.*, **172**, 125–126.

SHAROV, A. G. 1961a. On the system of the orthopterous insects. *Proc. 11th. Int. Congr. Ent., Wien*, **1**, 295–296.

—— 1961b. The origin of the Order Plecoptera. *Proc. 11th. Int. Congr. Ent., Wien*, **1**, 296–298.

—— 1962a. Redescription of *Lithophotona floccosa* Cock. (Manteodea) with some notes of the manteod wing venation. *Psyche, Camb.*, **69**, 102–106.

—— 1962b. Various groups *in* ROHDENDORF, B. B. (Editor) 1962b (*q.v.*).

SOUTHWOOD, T. R. E. & LESTON, D. 1959. *Land and water bugs of the British Isles.* Warne, London and New York.

STØRMER, L. 1934. Merostomata from the Downtonian Sandstone of Ringerike, Norway. *Skr. norske Vidensk-Akad.* 1933, no. 10, 1–125, pl. 1–12, figs. 1–39.

—— 1955. A new Merostome from the Lower Cambrian of Kinnekulle, Sweden. *Ark. Zool.* (2) 9, nr 25, 507–19.

—— 1960. A scorpion-like eurypterid from the Lower Devonian of Germany. *21st Int. geol. Congr.*, part XXII, 87–91.

—— 1963. *Gigantoscorpius willsi*, a new scorpion from the Lower Carboniferous of Scotland and its associated preying organisms. *Skr. norske Vidensk-Akad.*, new series, No. 8, 171 pp., 22 plates.

TILLYARD, R. J. 1926. Order Neuroptera, *in The insects of Australia and New Zealand*, chap. 23, pp. 308–325. Angus & Robertson, Sydney.

—— & FRASER, F. C. 1938–1940. A reclassification of the Order Odonata. Based on some new interpretations of the venation of the Dragonfly Wings. *Aust. Zool.*, **9**, 125–169, 195–221, 349–396 (see FRASER 1957).

TREATISE, P. 1955. MOORE, R. C. (Editor). *Treatise on Invertebrate Paleontology, Part P:* STØRMER, L., PETRUNKEVITCH, A. AND HEDGPETH, J. W., Chelicerata with sections on Pycnogonida and Palaeoisopus. University of Kansas Press.

TREATISE, R. (in press). MOORE, R. C. (Editor). *Treatise on Invertebrate Paleontology, Part R:* Arthropoda 4, University of Kansas Press.

TREATISE, W. 1962 MOORE, R. C. (Editor). *Treatise on Invertebrate Paleontology, Part W:* HAAS, W. H. *et al.* Miscellanea. University of Kansas Press.

TSHERNOVA, O. A. 1965. [Some Fossil Mayflies (Ephemeroptera, Mesthodidae) from Permian-beds of the Ural]. *Ent. Obozr.*, **44**, 353–361 (Russian).

ULRICH, W. 1943. Die Mengeiden und die Phylogenie der Strepsipteren. *Z. Parasit Kde*, **13**, 62–101.

VAN STRAELEN, V., 1931. *Crustacea Eumalacostrac (Crustaceis decapodis exclusis).* Foss. Cat. 1, pars 48, 98 pp.

WILLS, L. J. 1959–1960. The external anatomy of some Carboniferous "Scorpions". *Palaeontology*, **1**, 261–282 and **3**, 276–332.

WOODWARD, H. 1868. On a new limuloid crustacean (*Neolimulus falcatus*) from the Upper Silurian of Lesmahagow, Lanarkshire. *Geol. Mag.*, **5**, 1–5.

YABLOKOFF-KHNZORIAN, S. M. 1961. [Representatives of the family Helodidae (Coleoptera) from the Baltic Amber]. *Paleont. Zh.*, **1**, 108–116 (Russian).

Zeuner, F. E. 1939. *Fossil Orthoptera Ensifera*. British Museum (Natural History), London.

—— 1960. A Triassic insect fauna from the Molteno beds of S. Africa. *Proc. 11th. Int. Congr. Ent., Wien*, **1**, 304–306.

R. A. Crowson, PH.D.
Department of Zoology, The University, Glasgow 2, Scotland.
W. D. I. Rolfe, PH.D. F.G.S.
Hunterian Museum. The University, Glasgow 2, Scotland.
J. Smart, PH.D. F.L.S. F.Z.S.
Department of Zoology, Downing Street, Cambridge.
C. D. Waterston, PH.D. F.R.S.E. F.M.A.
Royal Scottish Museum, Edinburgh 1, Scotland.
E. C. Willey, PH.D. F.G.S.
Geology Department, University of New England, Armidale, New South Wales, Australia.
R. J. Wootton, PH.D.
Department of Zoology, The University, Exeter, Devon.

CHAPTER 20

Arthropoda: Crustacea

Contributors: R. H. BATE, J. S. H. COLLINS, J. E. ROBINSON
& W. D. I. ROLFE

Class CRUSTACEA Pennant 1777

Subclass BRANCHIOPODA Latreille 1817

Series ANOSTRACA Sars 1846

Order EUANOSTRACA Preuss 1951

First, Dev Siegen: *Gilsonicaris rhenana* Van Straelen 1943, Hunsrückschiefer, Germany (Tasch *in* Whittington & Rolfe 1963). *Opabinia* Walcott, M.Camb, may be Anostraca; *Rochdalia* Woodward, Carb Bashk, is an insect nymph and not anostracan (Rolfe 1967). **Extant.**

Order LIPOSTRACA Scourfield 1926

First and **Last,** Dev Siegen–Eifel: *Lepidocaris rhyniensis* Scourfield, Rhynie Chert, Scotland (Tasch *in* Whittington & Rolfe 1963).

Order? ENANTIOPODA Birshteyn *in* Orlov 1960

First and **Last,** Carb Namur: *Tesnusocaris goldlichi* Brooks 1955, Tesnus Fm, Texas (Birshteyn *in* Orlov 1960). Although thought by Brooks and Birshteyn to be the first representative of the present Subclass Cephalocarida Sanders 1955, Hessler (Treatise R ms.) denies this, and the genus has been compared with Anostraca (Tiegs & Manton 1958).

Series PHYLLOPODA Latreille 1802

Order NOTOSTRACA Sars 1867

First, Carb Namur: *Lynceites cansoensis* Copeland 1957, Canso Group, Nova Scotia (Copeland 1957). *Protocaris* Walcott, L.-M.Camb, (Størmer 1944, ref. *in* Treatise 0) and *Douglasocaris* Caster & Brooks 1956, Ord Arenig?, may be ancestral but inadequately known (Brooks *in* Whittington & Rolfe 1963). Order? Ribeirida Kobayashi 1954, U.Camb-Ord, are not Notostraca but Mollusca Bivalvia (see page 472). *Parvancorina* Glaessner 1958, Pre-Camb Varang, has been compared with Notostraca (Glaessner 1962) but data inadequate. **Extant.**

Order KAZACHARTHRA Novozhilov 1957

First and **Last,** Jur Hett–Toarc: *Iliella, Ketmenia* Chernyshev 1940, *Almatium, Kungeja, Kysyltamia, Panacanthocaris* Novozhilov 1957, *Jeanrogerium* Novozhilov 1960, Lias, Kazakhstan S.S.R. (Novozhilov *in* Orlov 1960; Novozhilov 1960).

The Fossil Record, pp. 535–563. Geological Society of London, 1967. Printed in Northern Ireland.

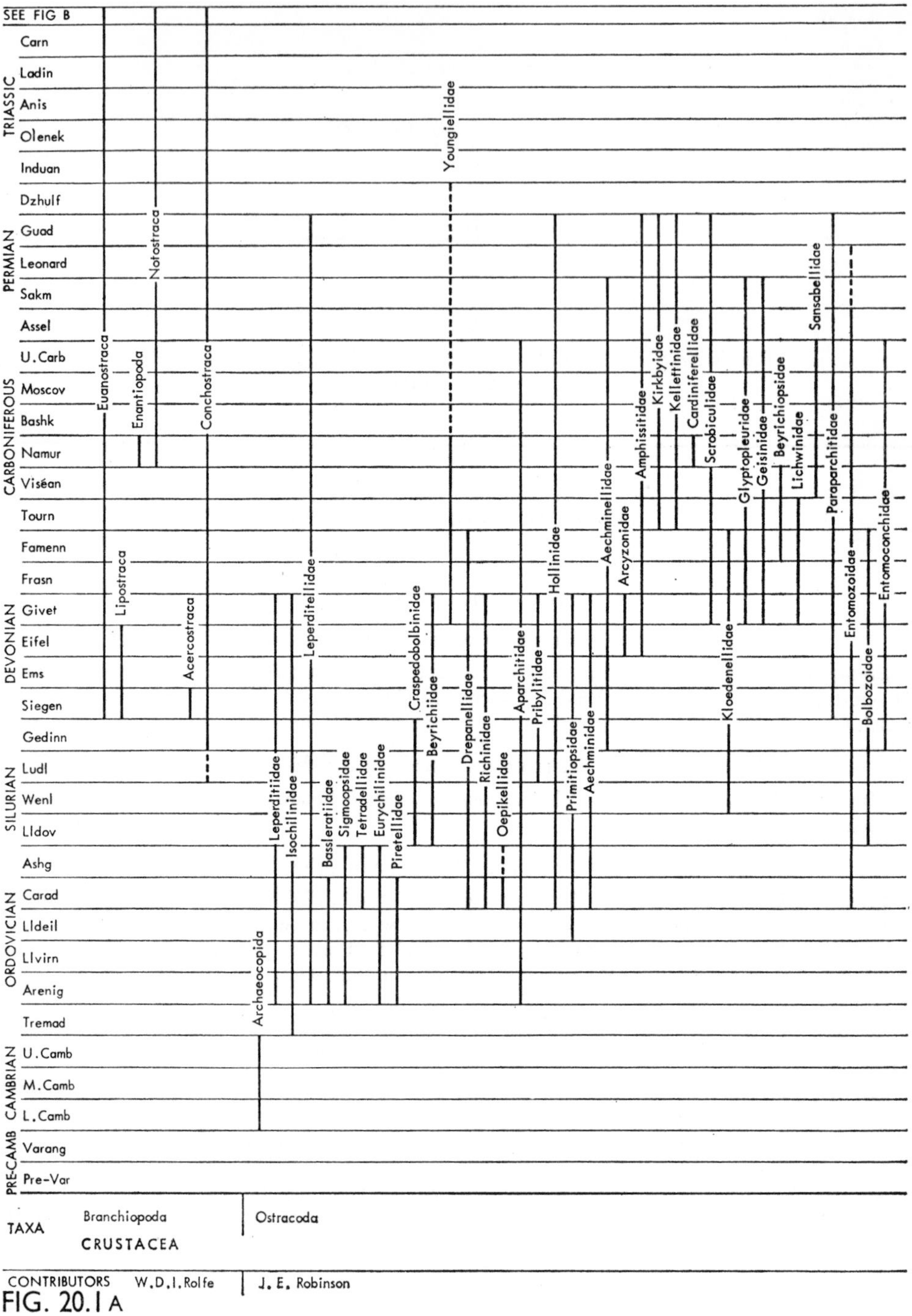
SEE FIG B
TRIASSIC
Carn
Ladin
Anis
Olenek
Induan
PERMIAN
Dzhulf
Guad
Leonard
Sakm
Assel
CARBONIFEROUS
U.Carb
Moscov
Bashk
Namur
Viséan
Tourn
DEVONIAN
Famenn
Frasn
Givet
Eifel
Ems
Siegen
Gedinn
SILURIAN
Ludl
Wenl
Lldov
ORDOVICIAN
Ashg
Carad
Lldeil
Llvirn
Arenig
Tremad
CAMBRIAN
U.Camb
M.Camb
L.Camb
PRE-CAMB
Varang
Pre-Var
Euanostraca
Lipostraca
Enantiopoda
Notostraca
Acercostraca
Conchostraca
Archaeocopida
Leperditiidae
Isochilinidae
Leperditellidae
Bassleratiidae
Sigmoopsidae
Tetradellidae
Eurychilinidae
Piretellidae
Craspedobolbinidae
Beyrichiidae
Youngiellidae
Drepanellidae
Richinidae
Oepikellidae
Aparchitidae
Pribylitidae
Hollinidae
Primitiopsidae
Aechminidae
Aechminellidae
Arcyzonidae
Amphissitidae
Kirkbyidae
Kellettinidae
Cardiniferellidae
Scrobiculidae
Kloedenellidae
Glyptopleuridae
Geisinidae
Beyrichiopsidae
Lichwinidae
Sansabellidae
Paraparchitidae
Entomozoidae
Bolbozoidae
Entomoconchidae
TAXA
Branchiopoda
CRUSTACEA
Ostracoda
CONTRIBUTORS
W.D.I. Rolfe
J. E. Robinson

FIG. 20.1 A

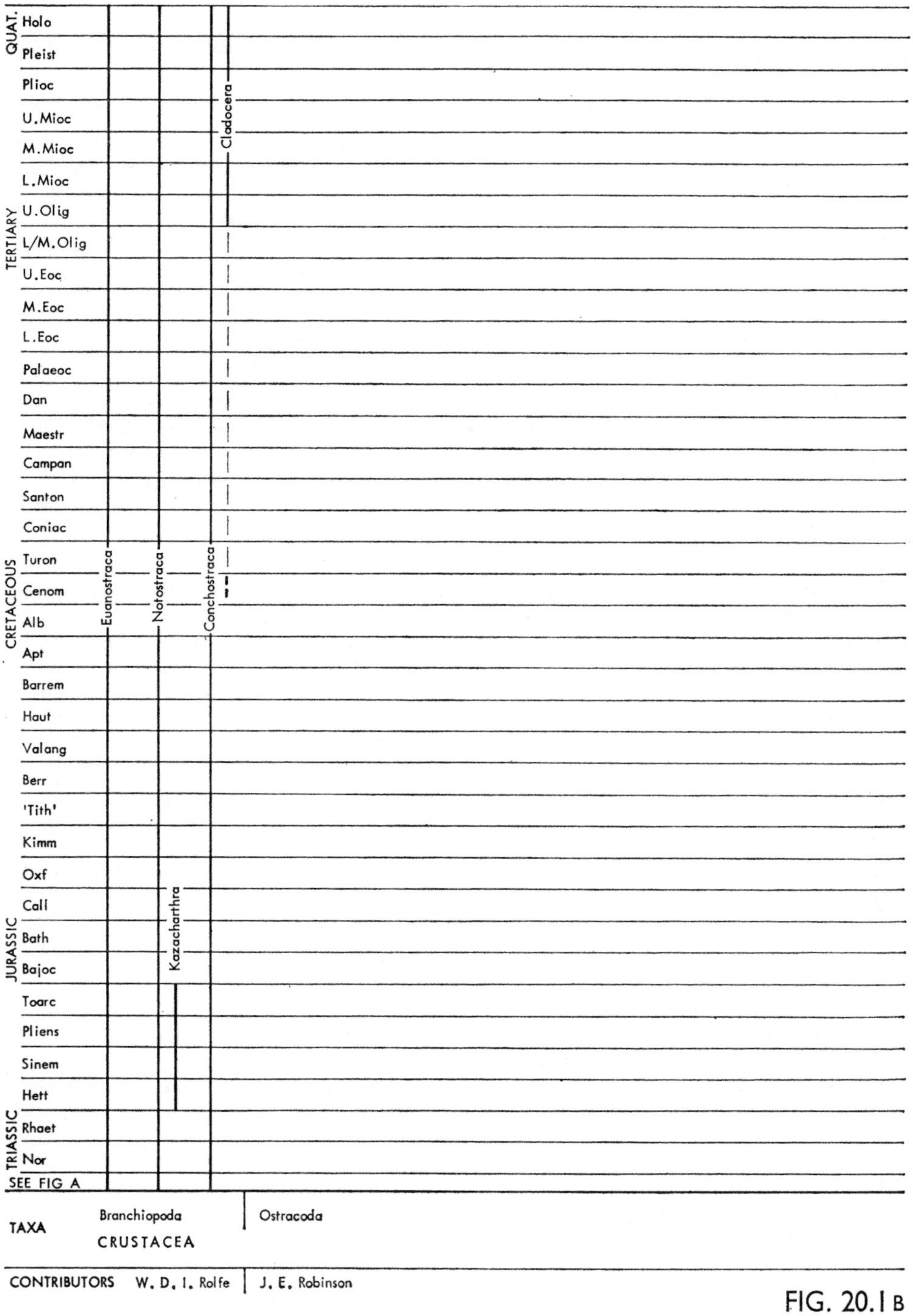

		Euanostraca	Notostraca	Conchostraca	Cladocera	Kazacharthra
QUAT.	Holo					
	Pleist					
TERTIARY	Plioc				Cladocera	
	U.Mioc					
	M.Mioc					
	L.Mioc					
	U.Olig					
	L/M.Olig					
	U.Eoc					
	M.Eoc					
	L.Eoc					
	Palaeoc					
	Dan					
CRETACEOUS	Maestr					
	Campan					
	Santon					
	Coniac					
	Turon					
	Cenom	Euanostraca	Notostraca	Conchostraca		
	Alb					
	Apt					
	Barrem					
	Haut					
	Valang					
	Berr					
JURASSIC	'Tith'					
	Kimm					
	Oxf					
	Call					Kazacharthra
	Bath					
	Bajoc					
	Toarc					
	Pliens					
	Sinem					
	Hett					
TRIASSIC	Rhaet					
	Nor					
	SEE FIG A					

TAXA	Branchiopoda	Ostracoda
	CRUSTACEA	

| CONTRIBUTORS | W. D. I. Rolfe | J. E. Robinson |

FIG. 20.1 B

Order ACERCOSTRACA Lehmann 1955

First and **Last,** Dev Siegen: *Vachonisia rogeri* (Lehmann) 1955, Hunsrückschiefer, Germany (Novozhilov *in* Orlov 1960).

Order CONCHOSTRACA Sars 1846

First, Sil Ludl–Dev Gedinn: *Asmussia? buchoti* (Péneau 1937), Schistes du Moulin de Régereau, France (*cf.* Péneau 1962). *Eoasmussia heintzi* Soot-Ryen, Ord Carad, Peltifer Z., Norway, is an isolated earlier occurrence (Soot-Ryen 1960); four genera in Dev Ems (Novozhilov 1961). Camb "Conchostraca" of Ulrich & Bassler 1931 are Ostracoda (Treatise Q). **Extant.**

Comment: May be derived, together with Ostracoda Archaeocopida, from Camb Lepidittidae Kobayashi 1954, although uncertain whether the latter are Bivalvia Ribeirida, Ostracoda or Conchostraca (Tasch *in* Whittington & Rolfe 1963).

Order CLADOCERA Latreille 1829

First, Tert U. Olig: *Daphnia fossilis* Heyden 1862, Blätterkohlen, Rott, Germany (Rolfe 1963). *Daphnia?* sp., Cret Cenom, Perucer Schichten, Czechoslovakia (Fritsch 1910), is probably an earlier record. Cladoceran ephippia reported from Pre–Camb Varang - L. Camb, Visingsö Fm, Sweden (Ewetz 1933), are known only from thin sections and hence difficult to verify. *Lynceites* Goldenberg 1870, U. Carb is not Cladocera but Notostraca (Guthörl 1934). **Extant.**

(W.D.I.R.)

Subclass OSTRACODA Latreille 1806

Palaeocopida as an order does not embrace all Palaeozoic ostracodes. Valve orientation, muscle scar pattern, and sheer size, separate Leperditicopida Scott 1961, while still other ostracodes merit separation as Archaeocopida Sylvester-Bradley 1961, on grounds of shell composition and fundamental simplicity if not for their Cambrian age. Recently, a further group of Cambrian ostracodes has become known possessing phosphatic shell, regarded as suborder Phosphatocopina Muller 1964, of the Archaeocopida.

Order ARCHAEOCOPIDA Sylvester-Bradley 1961

First, Camb L. Camb: *Bradoria* Matthew 1899, *Beyrichona* Matthew 1886, *Hipponicharion* Matthew 1886, *Indiana* Matthew 1902, and several other genera, mainly N. America–Europe (Sylvester-Bradley *in* Treatise Q).

Last, Camb U. Camb: *Falites angustiduplicata* Müller (1964), Peltura scarabaeoides Z., Sweden.

Order LEPERDITICOPIDA Scott 1961

Family LEPERDITIIDAE Jones 1856

First, Ord (L.): *Heterochilina obliqua* Poulsen (1937), Narwhal Sound Fm, Greenland.

Last, Dev Givet: *Hermannina waldschmiti* (Paeckelmann 1922), U. Stringocephalus Beds. In Treatise Q range of *Leperditia* is extended to U. Dev.

Comment: Main occurrence, Sil cosmopolitan. Much confusion in older literature swells later range of this family and of the type genus. May extend down into U. Camb (see Treatise Q).

Family ISOCHILINIDAE Swartz 1949

First, Ord Tremad: *Isochilina gregaria* (Whitfield), Beekmantown, Vermont.
Last. Dev (M.): *Isochilina scapha* Stewart (1930), Silica Sh, Ohio.

Order PALAEOCOPIDA Henningsmoen 1953

Ostracoda now classified as Palaeocopida figure in some of the earliest attempts to use ostracodes as fossils defining stratigraphical horizons. Later in time, Ulrich and Bassler, working on the Ord and Sil deposits of the Appalachians, formulated a series of ostracode faunal zones for the middle Sil Clinton. In all, nine zones were given the names of nine ostracode species, all members of the Zygobolbinae, a subfamily of the Beyrichiidae, (1923 Maryland Geol Survey, Silurian Volume). Forty years later, Martinsson, working upon the classic Silurian sections of Gotland, not only discovered important facts upon beyrichid morphology and systematics, but was able to outline an impressive stratigraphy based upon these palaeocopes. Zygobolbids are still almost exclusively North America, but European Beyrichiidae are now recorded in Northern Canada, and in the Maritime Provinces. The correlation of horizons in the Welsh Borderland may be in prospect.

Since the publication of the 'Bibliographic Index of Paleozoic Ostracoda' by Bassler and Kellett (1934), many hundred new species, genera, and families have been published, and the beginnings of what is virtually a new approach to taxonomy have developed. The appreciation of growth stages, sex dimorphism, and attention to structures previously regarded as simply ornamentational, has led to changes in classification, often at family level. Such changes and reallocations were afoot when Treatise Q was in preparation in 1960. Understandably its final form of 1961 appears today in need of revision, its thirty nine families in need of closer scrutiny and perhaps some fusion.

From quite another standpoint, reviewing the palaeocope record, it becomes evident that there are still unfortunate time gaps which have not yet been studied adequately, or may not yet have been available for study. For example, the U. Ord-L. Sil, the L. Dev, U. Dev benthonic fauna, and Perm marine fauna. Furthermore, it still has not been possible to integrate fully the Russian record into the overall picture, which might overcome some of these deficiencies. Above all, however, attention is focussed upon the Permo-Trias hiatus, which in Ostracodes involves the change from fauna dominated by Palaeocopida, to fauna dominated by Podocopida. In recent years, Trias faunas described from Austria by Kollmann, and from Thuringia by Beutler and Gründel, have shown some degree of intermingling of the two faunas, while increasingly, podocope features are recognised in late Palaeozoic kloedenellids for example.

Family LEPERDITELLIDAE Ulrich and Bassler 1906

First, Ord Arenig: *Conchoprimitia gammae* Öpik (1937), L. Arenig (B II), Estonia.
Last, Perm Guad: *Coryellina indicata* Sohn (1954), L. Guad, Texas.
Comment: Main occurrence, Ord-Sil N.W. Europe and U.S.A. Heterogeneous group, imperfectly classified at present. Jurassic *Cryptophyllus* (Treatise Q) needs verification.

Family BASSLERATIIDAE Schmidt 1941

Considered in sense of Jaanusson (1957), and including Quadrijugatoridae Kesling and Hussey 1953, of Treatise Q.
First, Ord Arenig: *Steusslofia polynodulifera* Hessland (1949), L. Arenig, Sweden; *Tallinellina* sp., M. estonica Z., Ringsaker, Norway (Jaanusson 1957, p. 355).
Last, Ord Carad: *Tallinella? hloubertensis*, U. Carad (dε_2), Bohdalec Fm, Czechoslovakia. Jaanusson (1957, p. 343)
Comment: Main occurrence M. Ord. U.S.A. and Baltic-W. Europe. Origins difficult to assess being close to beginning of palaeocope record. May give rise to piretellids, tetradellids, and sigmoopsids.

Family SIGMOOPSIDAE Henningsmoen 1953

First, Ord Arenig: *Glossomorphites* n. sp., L. Arenig, Sweden (Tjernvik 1956, p. 163).
Last, Ord Ashg: *Oecematobolbina* sp., D. complanatus Z., Sweden (Jaanusson 1957, p. 403).
Comment: Main occurrence L.-M. Ord, Baltic-W. Europe.

Family TETRADELLIDAE Swartz 1936

First, Ord Carad: *Tetradella quadrilirata* (Hall and Whitfield 1875), Black River, U.S.A.
Last, Ord Ashg: *Tetradella carinata* Keenan (1951), Maquoketa Fm, U.S.A.
Comment: Main occurrence M. Ord, N. America. Name *Tetradella* widely and indiscriminately used in the literature, but adherence to genotype characters after Kesling and Hussey (1953)

can restrict time range to Ord. Origins possibly in sigmoopsids (Jaanusson 1957, Henningsmoen 1965), from which separation may be artificial (Henningsmoen 1965, p. 386; Pokorny 1965, p. 139).

Family EURYCHILINIDAE Ulrich and Bassler 1923

Considered in sense of Henningsmoen (1953) and Jaanusson (1957), not Treatise Q.
First, Ord Arenig: *Chilobolbina lativelata* Jaanusson (1957), (BIIβ), Estonia.
Last, Ord Ashg: *Laccochilina tarda* Henningsmoen (1954), (5b), Dalmanitina Beds, Norway.
Comment: Main occurrence Ord, N. America and Europe; later records need verification. Range extension in Treatise Q to U. Dev based on *Bicornellina* Zaspelova 1952, but upon illustrations alone this may have kirkbyid or drepanellid affinity rather than eurychilinid.

Family PIRETELLIDAE Öpik 1937

First, Ord Arenig: *Euprimites reticulogranulatus* Hessland (1949), Red Orthoceras Lst, Sweden and (BIIIγ), Estonia.
Last, Ord Carad: *Piretella acmaea* Öpik (1937), U. Carad, (FIc), Estonia.
Comment: Main occurrence M. Ord, Baltic. Origins considered eurychilinid (Kesling 1957), or bassleratid (Jaanusson 1957, p. 275).

Family CRASPEDOBOLBINIDAE Martinsson 1962

First, Sil Lldov: *Craspedobolbina unculifera* Martinsson (1962), U. Lldov, Sweden.
Last, Dev Gedinn: *Hemsiella* cf. *maccoyiana* (Jones 1855), Baltic Beyrichienkalk (Martinsson 1964).
Comment: Main occurrence Sil cosmopolitan. Origins still sought in early Sil, possibly Siberia (Martinsson 1962, p. 360). *Cr. dietrichi* Kummerow 1924, Baltic Drift, no longer considered to be from U. Ord.

Family BEYRICHIIDAE Matthew 1886

First, Sil Lldov: *Beyrichia (B) halliana* Martinsson (1962), U. Lldov, Sweden.
Last, Dev Givet: *Kozlowskiella kozlowskii* Příbyl (1953), Poland.
Comment: Main occurrence Sil cosmopolitan. Origins held include eurychilinid via piretellids (Kesling 1957, p. 71), or eurychilinid (Jaanusson 1957). Additional families may be required for late Sil and Dev beyrichiids. Absolute upper limit may reach Carb Viséan.

Family YOUNGIELLIDAE Kellet 1933

First, Dev Givet: *Youngiella givetiana* Rozhdestvenskaya (1962), Bashkiria, U.S.S.R.
Last, Perm (U.): *Moorea facilis* Schneider (1958), Kazan Region, U.S.S.R.
Comment: Main occurrence Tourn-Namur, Europe; U. Miss.-Perm, N. America. Orlov (1960) extends range back to Ord, broken in Sil, resuming in Dev to continue to Perm.

Family DREPANELLIDAE Ulrich and Bassler 1923

First, Ord Carad: *Drepanella crassinoda* (Ulrich), Kentucky.
Last, Dev Famenn: *Neodrepanella* Zaspelova 1952, U.S.S.R. (Scott & Hessland *in* Treatise Q).

Family RICHINIDAE Scott 1961

First, Ord Carad: *Pseudulrichia bivertex* (Ulrich 1879), Trenton, Kentucky.
Last, Dev Givet: *Richina selenicristata* Stover (1956), uppermost Hamilton, Moscow Fm, New York.
Comment: Heterogeneous assemblage, poorly classified at present.

Family OEPIKELLIDAE Jaanusson 1957

First, Ord Carad: *Oepikella tvaerensis* Thorslund (1940), Sweden.
Last, Ord (U.): ? *Oepikella* (Hessland *in* Treatise Q).

Comment: Jaanusson (1957) erected the monotypic subfamily Oepikellinae within the Eurychilinidae Ulrich and Bassler. Hessland (*in* Treatise Q, p. 169) elevated this to family status.

Family APARCHITIDAE Jones 1901

First, Ord Arenig: *Aparchites reticuliferus* Hessland (1949), Sweden.
Last, Carb U. Carb: *Cyathus kellumi* Bradfield (1935), Virgil Stage, Oklahoma.
Comment: Main occurrence Ord. Family ill-defined, and absolute range difficult to assess from literature.

Family PRIBYLITIDAE Pokorny 1958

First, Sil Ludl: ? *Microchilina jarovensis* Bouček (1936), Přídolí Stage, middle (eβ), Czechoslovakia.
Last, Dev Givet: *Pribylites moravicus* Pokorny (1950). Red Coral Lst, Celechovic, Czechoslovakia.

Family HOLLINIDAE Swartz 1936

First, Ord Carad: *Grammolomatella* sp., Carad (4b), Norway (Jaanusson 1957).
Last, Perm Guad: *Hollinella occidentalis* (Girty 1910), Texas.
Comment: Origin possibly in sigmoopsids (Jaanusson 1957), or tetradellids (Henningsmoen 1965).

Family PRIMITIOPSIDAE Swartz 1936

First, Ord Lldeil: *Anisocyamus elegans* (Harris 1957), Tulip Creek, Oklahoma.
Last, Dev Givet: *Polenovula crassa* (Polenova 1955), S.W. Urals. Martinsson (1960) erects subfamily Polenovulinae for this species of Polenova, and records further M. Dev primitiopsids from Poland.
Comment: Main occurrence Sil Wenl-Ludl, Baltic-W. Europe.

Family AECHMINIDAE Bouček 1936

First, Ord Carad: *Aechmina ?bispinata* Kraft (1962), Edinburg Lst, U.S.A.
Last, Dev (M.): *Aechmina choanobasota* Kesling (1952), Traverse Group, U.S.A.
Comment: Main occurrence Sil, Europe.

Family AECHMINELLIDAE Sohn 1961

First, Dev Gedinn: *Bicornella tricornis* Coryell and Cuskley (1934), Haragan Sh, Oklahoma.
Last, Perm Sakm: *Cornigella binoda* Kellett (1933), Oklahoma.
Comment: Range extended to M. Perm in Treatise (Q 125) but record not traced.

Family ARCYZONIDAE Kesling 1961

First, Dev Eifel: *Arcyzona subquadrata* (Ulrich 1891), Onondaga Lst, U.S.A. (Kesling 1961).
Last, Dev Givet: *Amphizona asceta* Kesling and Copeland (1954), Windom Sh, U.S.A.

Family AMPHISSITIDAE Girty 1910

First, Dev Eifel: *Amphissites tener omphalotus* Becker (1964), Germany.
Last, Perm Guad: *Amphissites knighti* Sohn (1954), L. Word Fm, Texas.
Comment: Main occurrence Carb Europe-N. America. Early occurrence of these ornamented kirkbyacea (Amphissitidae and Arcyzonidae) encourages idea of possible beyrichid (strepulid) ancestry.

Family KIRKBYIDAE Ulrich and Bassler 1906

First, Carb Tourn: *Kirkbya* sp, Lower Limestone Sh., K Z., Forest of Dean, England (personal observation).
Last, Perm Guad: *Kirkbya permiana* Jones 1859, Magnesian Lst, Durham, England.
Comment: Forms studied by Kollmann from Austrian U. Trias have kirkbyid affinity (Kollmann 1963, p. 17, p. 63).

Family KELLETTINIDAE Sohn 1954

First, Carb Tourn: *Kellettina* sp, Lower Limestone Sh., K Z., Forest of Dean, England (personal observation).
Last, Perm Guad: *Kellettina vidriensis* (Hamilton 1942), L. Word, Texas.
Comment: Main occurrence Carb, Europe–N. America.

Family CARDINIFERELLIDAE Sohn 1953

First and **Last,** Carb Namur: *Cardiniferella bowsheri* Sohn (1953), Chester (Helms Fm), U.S.A.
Comment: May represent a merodont subfamily of Kirkbyiidae (Gründel 1965).

Family SCROBICULIDAE Posner 1951

First, Dev Givet: *Bideirella reticulata* Stover (1956), U. Hamilton, New York.
Last, Perm Guad: *Roundyella dorsopapillosa* Sohn (1954), Leonard, Texas.
Comment: Main occurrence Viséan–Namur, Europe–U.S.S.R. May represent a family within Kirkbyacea (Gründel 1965).

Family KLOEDENELLIDAE Ulrich and Bassler 1908

First, Sil Wenl: *Kloedenella cornuta* Ulrich and Bassler var *praenuntia* Swartz (1933), U. Rochester, Pennyslvania.
Last, Dev Famenn: *Dizygopleura clara* Polenova (1952), U.S.S.R.
Comment: Main occurrence M. Sil–M. Dev. Orgins obscure, possibly beyrichid (e.g. Henningsmoen 1953). *Eokloedenella* Kraft 1962 could be leperditellid. Definitive judgement on family awaited in publication by Guber and Jaanusson (Bull. geol. Insts Univ. Upsala). The writer is in agreement with views of Pokorny (1965, pp. 203–6), seeing present families Glyptopleuridae, Beyrichiopsidae, and Geisinidae as integral parts of Kloedenellidae to large extent. Present consideration of range restricted to those Devonian forms relateable to sense of Ulrich and Bassler (1923).

Family GLYPTOPLEURIDAE Girty 1910

First, Dev Givet: *Marginia sculpta* var *multicostata* Polenova (1952), U. Givet, Samara Bend, U.S.S.R.
Last, Perm Sakm: *Glyptopleura triserta* Harris and Lalicker (1932), Texas.
Comment: Main occurrence Tourn-Viséan, Europe; Namur–Moscov, U.S.A. Origins in kloedenellid stock. Neither *Svantonites* Pokorny 1950, nor *Glyptopleura cracens* Kesling and Kilgore 1952, possible first records, appears to be glyptopleurid from illustrations. On the other hand, *Marginia sculpta multicostata* does.

Family GEISINIDAE Sohn 1961

First, Dev Givet: *Knoxiella accepta* Polenova (1952) (regarded synonym *Hypotetragona* Morey 1935, Treatise Q), U. Givet, Samara Bend, U.S.S.R.
Last, Perm Sakm: *Geisina upsoni* Kellett (1933), U. Wolfcamp, Texas.
Comment: Main occurrence U. Dev–Carb Viséan, Europe; Penn, U.S.A.

Family BEYRICHIOPSIDAE Henningsmoen 1953

First, Dev Famenn: *Tambovia prima* Samoilova (1951), U.S.S.R.
Last, Carb Viséan: *Beyrichiopsis cornuta* Jones and Kirkby 1886, U. Viséan, Northumberland and Scotland, Britain.
Comment: Main occurrence Tourn Europe, Canada. Strong affinity with Glyptopleuridae; both perhaps at most subfamilies of Kloedenellidae.

Family LICHWINIDAE Posner 1950

First, Dev Givet: *Evlanella germanica* Becker (1964), Germany.
Last, Carb Tourn: *Lichwinia lichwinensis* Posner 1950, *Kalugia ivanovi* Posner (1950); U.S.S.R.

Comment: Main occurrence U. Dev U.S.S.R. Possible kloedenellid ancestry, in turn suggestive of Mesozoic cytherelloids.

Family SANSABELLIDAE Sohn 1961

First, Carb Viséan: *Sansabella inflata* Geis (1932), Salem Lst, Miss, U.S.A.
Last, Carb, U. Carb: *Sansabella brevis* Cooper (1946), L. Virgil, Illinois.
Comment: Main occurrence U. Miss, Chester, U.S.A. In most characters akin to contemporary kloedenellids.

Family PARAPARCHITIDAE Scott 1959

First, Dev Siegen: *Paraparchites mesleri* Bassler (1941), Camden Fm, Missouri.
Last, Perm Guad: *Paraparchites marathonensis* Hamilton (1942), L. Guad, Texas.
Comment: Main occurrence Tourn–Viséan, Europe; Miss–Penn, U.S.A.

Order MYODOCOPIDA Sars 1866

Suborder MYODOCOPINA Sars 1866

Family ENTOMOZOIDAE Přibyl 1951

First, Ord ?Carad: *Rhomboentomozoe pygmaea* (Ruedemann 1901).
Last, Perm: *Richteria* or *Entomozoe* (Sylvester–Bradley *in* Treatise Q).
Comment: Main occurrence, greatest diversity and number of recognized species U. Dev Europe. Family has spindle-pattern in time range, being most diversified in late Devonian Kulm facies, attenuated before and after. From German literature, could be considered pre-eminent as stratigraphically significant ostracodes. Subspecies employed to this end. (Gründel 1962, Rabien 1954, Sylvester–Bradley *in* Treatise Q).

For remaining families of the Myodocopina, as listed below, ranges only are given as by Sylvester–Bradley (*in* Treatise Q).

BOLBOZOIDAE Bouček 1936 Sil-Dev
ENTOMOCONCHIDAE Brady 1868 Dev-Carb
CYPROSINIDAE Whidborne 1890 (monotypic) Dev
THAUMATOCYPRIDIDAE Müller 1906 (monotypic) Jur (M.)—extant
CYPRIDINIDAE Baird 1850 ?Carb—extant
CYLINDROLEBERIDIDAE Müller 1906 extant
CYPRELLIDAE Sylvester–Bradley 1961 (monotypic) Carb
RHOMBINIDAE Sylvester–Bradley 1951 Carb
SARSIELLIDAE Brady and Norman 1896 ?Dev—extant
HALOCYPRIDIDAE Dana 1852 extant.   [J.E.R.]

Suborder CLADOCOPINA Sars 1866

Family POLYCOPIDAE Sars 1866

First, Carb Viséan: *Discoidella ampla* Cooper (1941), *D. pendens and D. simplex* Croneis & Gale 1939; L. Chesterian, Illinois, U.S.A. *Discoidella* cf. *convexa* Croneis & Borger 1941, Derbyshire, England, (Robinson 1959). Robinson (unpublished MS.) has also found *Discoidella* sp. from the Lower Viséan, Northumberland, England.   **Extant.**
Comment: Represented at the present time by *Polycope* Sars 1966. Marine.

Order PODOCOPIDA Müller 1894

Suborder PLATYCOPINA Sars 1866

Family CAVELLINIDAE Egorov 1950

First, Sil Ludl (L): *Gotlandella martinssoni* Adamczak (1966); Mulde beds, Gotland, Sweden.
Last, Perm Guad: *Cavellina ellipticalis* Hamilton 1942. Word Fm, Texas, U.S.A.

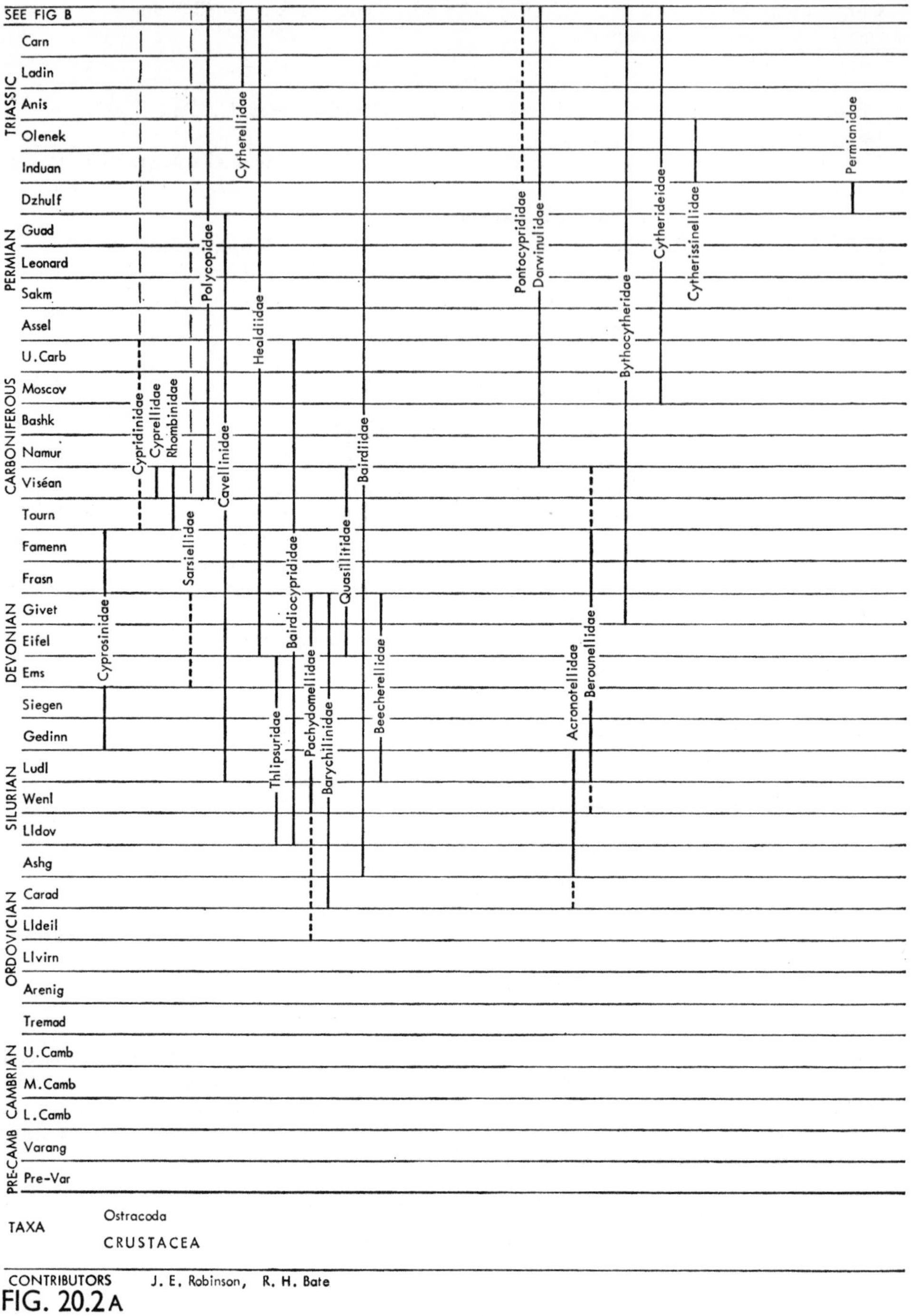
SEE FIG B
TRIASSIC
Carn
Ladin
Anis
Olenek
Induan
PERMIAN
Dzhulf
Guad
Leonard
Sakm
Assel
CARBONIFEROUS
U.Carb
Moscov
Bashk
Namur
Viséan
Tourn
DEVONIAN
Famenn
Frasn
Givet
Eifel
Ems
Siegen
Gedinn
SILURIAN
Ludl
Wenl
Lldov
ORDOVICIAN
Ashg
Carad
Lldeil
Llvirn
Arenig
Tremad
CAMBRIAN
U.Camb
M.Camb
L.Camb
PRE-CAMB
Varang
Pre-Var
Cypridinidae
Cyprellidae
Rhombinidae
Polycopidae
Cytherellidae
Cavellinidae
Sarsiellidae
Cyprosinidae
Healdiidae
Bairdiocyprididae
Thlipsuridae
Pachydomellidae
Barychilinidae
Quasillitidae
Bairdiidae
Beecherellidae
Pontocyprididae
Darwinulidae
Acronotellidae
Berounellidae
Bythocytheridae
Cytherideidae
Cytherissinellidae
Permianidae
TAXA
Ostracoda
CRUSTACEA
CONTRIBUTORS
J. E. Robinson, R. H. Bate

FIG. 20.2A

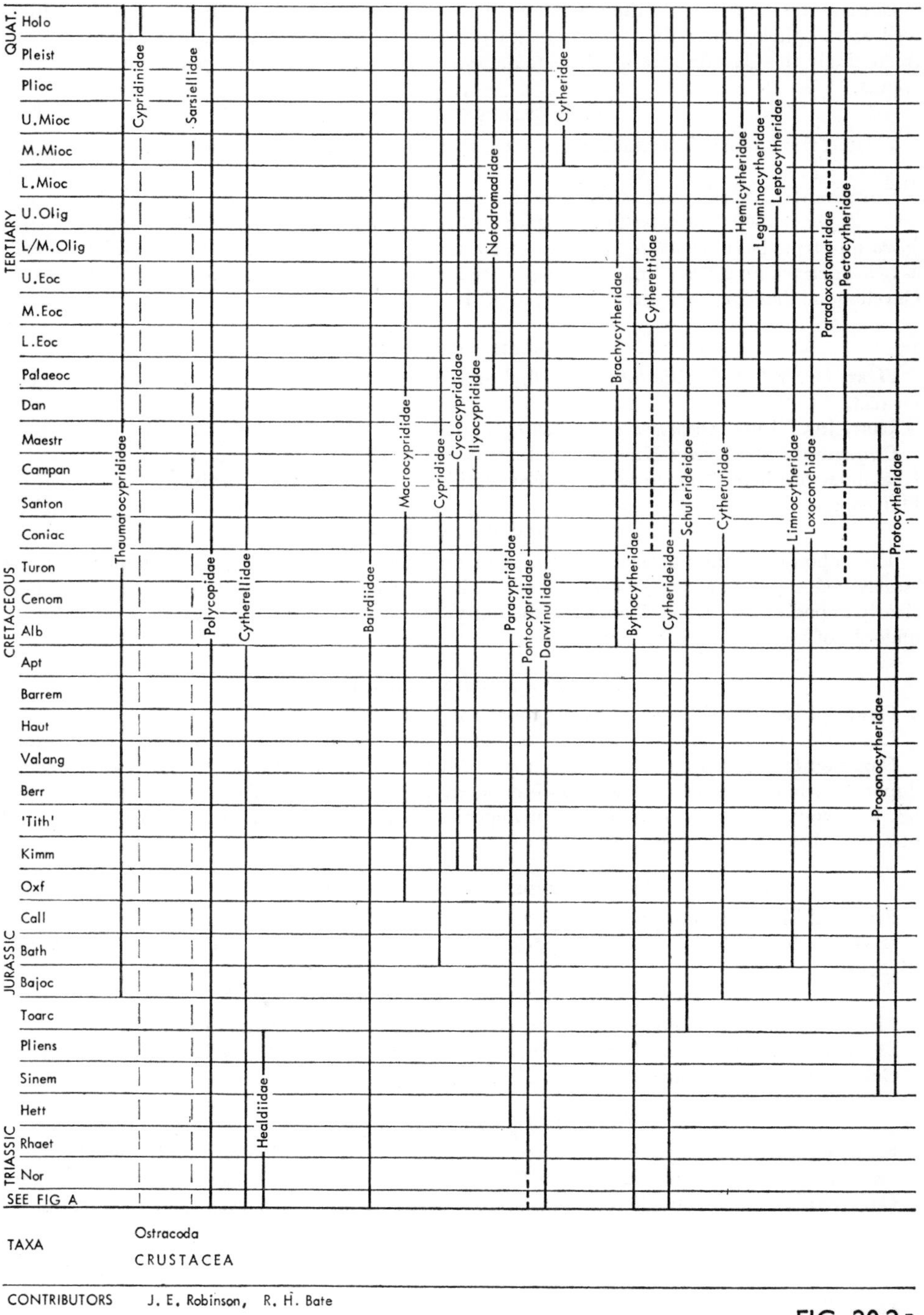
QUAT.
Holo
Pleist
Plioc
U.Mioc
M.Mioc
L.Mioc
TERTIARY
U.Olig
L/M.Olig
U.Eoc
M.Eoc
L.Eoc
Palaeoc
Dan
Maestr
Campan
Santon
Coniac
CRETACEOUS
Turon
Cenom
Alb
Apt
Barrem
Haut
Valang
Berr
'Tith'
Kimm
Oxf
Call
JURASSIC
Bath
Bajoc
Toarc
Pliens
Sinem
Hett
TRIASSIC
Rhaet
Nor
SEE FIG A
Cypridinidae
Sarsiellidae
Thaumatocyprididae
Polycopidae
Cytherellidae
Healdiidae
Bairdiidae
Macrocyprididae
Cyprididae
Cyclocyprididae
Ilyocyprididae
Notodromadidae
Paracyprididae
Pontocyprididae
Darwinulidae
Cytheridae
Brachycytheridae
Bythocytheridae
Cytherettidae
Cytherideidae
Schulerideidae
Cytheruridae
Hemicytheridae
Leguminocytheridae
Leptocytheridae
Limnocytheridae
Loxoconchidae
Paradoxostomatidae
Pectocytheridae
Progonocytheridae
Protocytheridae
TAXA
Ostracoda
CRUSTACEA
CONTRIBUTORS
J. E. Robinson, R. H. Bate

FIG. 20.2B

Comment: Significantly the Cavellinidae are pre-Triassic, thus fulfilling stratigraphically as well as morphologically the characteristics expected in forms ancestral to the Cytherellidae. Accordingly the Cavellinidae are here taken out of the Metacopina and placed into the Platycopina.

Family CYTHERELLIDAE Sars 1866

First, Trias Ladin: *Cytherelloidea* n.sp.1 & n.sp.2, Sohn 1964, Grantsville Fm, Nevada, U.S.A.
Extant.

Comment: Represented at present time by species of *Cytherelloidea* Alexander 1929 and *Cytherella* Jones 1849, the latter first appearing in L. Jur. All members of family marine. *Cytherelloidea* appears to be restricted to much warmer waters than *Cytherella* (Sohn 1962). Family regarded as being derived from Cavellinidae through a reduction in the number of muscle scars. It is to the Cavellinidae that the Palaeozoic "cytherellas" belong.

Family HEALDIIDAE Harlton 1933

First, Dev Eifel: *Healdia bohemica* Příbyl and Šnajdr 1950, Choteč Fm, nr. Prague, Czechoslovakia.
Last, Jur Pliens: *Ogmoconcha amalthei*(Quenstedt 1858), *O. contractula* Triebel 1941, Europe.
Comment: *Robsoniella* Kuznetsova 1956 is not considered to belong to this family. The Healdiidae are here grouped with the Cavellinidae (from which they probably evolved) in the Platycopina. [R.H.B.]

Suborder METACOPINA Sylvester-Bradley 1961

This suborder of the PODOCOPIDA represents an attempt in 1961 to group together what are largely podocopan ancestral stocks, and which in due course it may be possible to relate more clearly to podocopan descendants upon the basis of their shell structures. The time range for the majority of Metacopina is late Palaeozoic.

Family THLIPSURIDAE Ulrich 1894

First, Sil Lldov: *Thlipsura corpulenta* Jones and Holl 1869, England.
Last, Dev (M.): *Thlipsura thyridioides* Swartz and Swain 1941, Onondaga, W. Virginia.
Comment: Main occurrence Sil, Europe; M. Dev, U.S.A. Often regarded as root stock of duplicature-bearing ostracodes with differentiated hinge structures, such structural patterns may not be wholly reliable in establishing phylogenies (Pokorny 1965, p. 88). "New genus Thilpsuracea?" has recently been recorded from late M. Trias of Nevada (Sohn 1964, p. 40).

Family BAIRDIOCYPRIDIDAE Shaver 1961

First, Sil Lldov: *Cytherellina siliqua* Jones 1855, Shropshire, England.
Last, Carb U. Carb: *Pseudobythocypris kellettae* Cordell (1952), U. Pennsylvanian, Virgil, Missouri.

Family PACHYDOMELLIDAE Berdan and Sohn 1961

First, ? Ord: *Tubulibairdia* sp., U.S.A. (Berdan and Sohn *in* Treatise Q p. 373).
Last, Dev Givet: *Tubulibairdia windomensis* Swartz and Oriel (1948), Windom Sh, New York.
Comment: Main occurrence L.-M. Dev.

Family BARYCHILINIDAE Ulrich 1894

First, Ord Carad: *Barychilina ordoviciana* Teichert (1937), Washington Land, Greenland.
Last, Dev Givet: *Barychilina tryphera* Kesling and Kilgore (1952), Genshaw Fm, Michigan.
Comment: The Carboniferous *Venula*, considered as possible barychilinid in Treatise Q, seems out of place in the family.

Family QUASILLITIDAE Coryell and Malkin 1936

First, Dev (M.): *Jenningsina catenulata* (Van Pelt 1933), Bell Sh, Michigan.
Last, Carb Viséan: *Graphiadactyllis arkansana* (Girty 1910), *G.* n. sp., U. Viséan, Yorkshire, England (personal observation).

Comment: Main occurrence M. Dev; N. America, North Africa, Europe. Family may encompass the two families Bufinidae Sohn and Stover 1961, and Ropolonellidae Coryell and Malkin 1936; these have shorter range (Dev) and differentiating characters not easy to appreciate. Quassilitacea were originally considered Podocopina by Sylvester–Bradley and assigned relationship to the later Cytheracea, which is still possible but not yet clarified by intermediate links (Sylvester–Bradley 1956, p. 11). [J.E.R.]

Suborder PODOCOPINA Sars 1866

Family BAIRDIIDAE Sars 1888

First, Ord Ashg: *Bairdia griffithiana, B.murchisoniana* and *B.salteriana* Jones & Holl (1868), Bala Series, Ireland. **Extant.**

Comment: Represented at present time by species of *Bairdia* McCoy 1844, *Bythocypris* Brady 1880 and *Triebelina* Bold 1946. Marine. Hessland (1949) records several species of *Bythocypris* from the L. Ord. of Sweden. This is, in fact, a present-day genus and its presence in the Palaeozoic must be regarded as extremely doubtful.

Family BEECHERELLIDAE Ulrich 1894

First, Sil Ludl: *Acanthoscapha decurtata* (Bouček 1936), Pristiograptus ultimus Z., Kolednik, Czechoslovakia.

Last, Dev Givet: *Acanthoscapha devonica* (Kesling & Sohn 1958) New York.

Comment: *Beecherella trapezoides* Gibson 1955 U. Dev, is almost certainly not a member of this genus or family.

Family MACROCYPRIDIDAE Müller 1912

First, Jur Oxf: *Macrocypris* sp. 51 Oertli 1959, Seewen, Switzerland. **Extant.**

Comment: The above species is possibly first appearance of the genus. All Palaeozoic species and most Mesozoic species referred to *Macrocypris* do not belong here. By L. Cret. the genus is represented by a number of valid species. Represented at the present time by *Macrocypris* Brady 1867 and *Macrocypria* Sars 1923. Marine.

Family CYPRIDIDAE Baird 1845

First, Jur Bath: *Protoargilloecia impurata* Ljubimova (1955), Volga-Ural region, U.S.S.R. **Extant.**

Comment: Family includes all the present day freshwater cyprids. Some living genera are: *Cypris* Müller 1776, *Cypridopsis* Brady, 1867, *Heterocypris* Claus 1893, *Disopontocypris* Mandelstam 1956, and *Candona* Baird 1845. The freshwater Carb-Perm genus *Carbonita* Strand 1928 is probably ancestral to some of the Mesozoic cyprids but has not yet been assigned to any particular family. The Cyprididae are almost certainly polyphyletic.

Family CYCLOCYPRIDIDAE Kaufmann 1900

First, Jur Kimm: *Cetacella inermis* Martin (1958), Thören, Germany. **Extant.**

Comment: All members of this family are freshwater in habit and most abundant at the present day.

Family EUCANDONIDAE Swain 1961

Comment: Not a valid family, various genera placed therein in Treatise Q have been put here into the Cyprididae for the time being.

Family ILYOCYPRIDIDAE Kaufmann 1900

First, Jur Kimm: *Rhinocypris jurassica* (Martin 1940), N.W.Germany. **Extant.**

Comment: This family is represented at the present time by *Ilyocypris* Brady & Norman 1889 and more importantly in the Mesozoic by the genus *Cypridea* Bosquet 1852 which has a world-wide distribution in fresh-brackish water sediments. *Cultella* Ljubimova 1959, from the Trias, U.S.S.R. is not considered to belong here.

Family NOTODROMADIDAE Kaufmann 1900

Comment: Palaeoc—Extant. Freshwater family.

Family PARACYPRIDIDAE Sars 1923

First, Jur Hett: *Paracypris* sp., Chitry-les-Mines, France (Oertli 1963). **Extant.**
Comment: The above is taken as the first definite record of this family. Sohn (1964) records *Paracypris?* sp. from U. Trias of Alaska whilst Styk (1962) records this genus from the Mushelkalk of Poland. Ostracodes having a *Paracypris*-type outline are recorded from the Silurian onwards but are regarded as extremely doubtful. The Triassic records listed above are not illustrated and are not included as definite at this stage. Represented at the present time by *Paracypris* Sars 1866, *Aglaiella* Daday 1910 [etc.].

Family PONTOCYPRIDIDAE Müller 1894

Comment: ?Dev—Trias—Extant. Appearance in Dev extremely doubtful.

Family DARWINULIDAE Brady & Norman 1889

First, Carb Namur: *Darwinula berniciana* (Jones 1884), Yoredale Series, Northumberland, England. **Extant.**
Comment: *Darwinula* Brady & Robertson 1885 is a long ranging genus occurring at the present time. Useful as an ecological indicator of freshwater sediments, though may occur in slightly brackish water conditions. A number of L. Carb ostracodes currently placed in the genus *Carbonita* Strand 1928 may more correctly belong to *Darwinula*.

Family CYTHERIDAE Baird 1850

First, Tert M. Mioc: *Cnestocythere lamellicosta* Triebel (1950), Tortonian, Austria. **Extant.**
Comment: Family mainly represented by living species, e.g. *Cythere lutea* Brady & Norman 1889. *Camptocythere* Triebel 1950 does not belong here (Bate 1963). Marine.

Family ACRONOTELLIDAE Swartz 1936

Comment: U. Ord—U. Sil.

Family BEROUNELLIDAE Sohn & Berdan 1960

Comment: Sil—Dev—?L. Carb.

Family BRACHYCYTHERIDAE Puri 1954

First, Cret Alb: *Alatacythere robusta* (Jones & Hinde 1890) Gault, Folkestone, England.
Extant.
Comment: *Brachycythere tumidosa* Swartz & Swain 1946 described from U. Jur of U.S.A. is not a *Brachycythere*. *Amphicythere* Triebel 1954, *Apatocythere* Triebel 1940, *Dordoniella* Apostolescu 1955, and *Macrodentina* (including *Dictyocythere* and *Polydentina*) Martin 1940 are here removed from the family—*Amphicythere*, *Apatocythere*, and *Dordoniella* to the Schulerideidae and *Macrodentina* to the Progonocytheridae. Represented at the present time by species of *Brachycythere* Alexander 1933, *Bosquetina* Keij 1957, and *Pterygocythereis* Blake 1933. Marine.

Family BYTHOCYTHERIDAE Sars 1926

First, Dev Givet: *Monoceratina casei* Warthin (1934), Norway Point Fm, Michigan, U.S.A.
Extant.
Comment: *Monceratina cooperi* Swain 1953 recorded from L. Dev Tennessee, is not considered here to belong to that genus. Represented in present-day seas by *Bythoceratina* Hornibrook 1952, *Bythocythere* Sars 1866, *Monoceratina* Roth 1928 [etc].

Family CYTHERETTIDAE Triebel 1952

First, Cret: *Paracytheretta* spp. Several undescribed species recorded from Senonian of Europe by Van Morkhoven (1963, p. 236). Previous first appearance of genus: *Paracytheretta reticosa* Triebel (1941), Tert Palaeoc, Denmark. **Extant.**

Comment: Marine. Genera living today include *Cytheretta* Müller 1894 and *Loculicytheretta* Ruggieri 1954.

Family CYTHERIDEIDAE Sars 1925

First, Carb Moscov: *Basslerella acuminata* Cooper (1946), McLeansboro Group, Illinois. **Extant.**

Comment: *Basslerella* Kellett 1935 is considered to be a direct ancestor of *Cytheridea* Bosquet 1852 (Kellett 1935). Represented at present time by *Cyprideis* Jones 1857 and *Cytheridea* [etc.]

Family SCHULERIDEIDAE Mandelstam 1959

First, Jur Toarc: *Praeschuleridea ventriosa* (Plumhoff 1963) Germany. Genus common L.Bajoc of Germany, Switzerland and England. **Extant.**

Comment: Represented at the present time by at least one species: *Cuneocythere semipunctata* (Brady 1867) which occurs in North European seas (Van Morkhoven 1963). All representatives of this family are marine. Evolutionary series *Praeschuleridea-Schuleridea (Schuleridea)-Schuleridea (Aequacytheridea)* stratigraphically important.

Family CYTHERISSINELLIDAE Kashevarova 1958

Comment: L.Trias, U.S.S.R. only.

Family CYTHERURIDAE Müller 1894

First, Jur Bajoc: *Cytheropterina comica* Bate (1963) and *C. gravis* Bate (1963). Yorkshire, England. **Extant.**

Comment: A species of *Cytheropteron*-type has been observed in the Toarc England by R.A. Field. This as yet unpublished record will further extend the range of this family. Represented at the present time by the marine ostracodes *Cytherura* Sars 1866 and *Cytheropteron* Sars 1866 [etc.]

Family ENTOCYTHERIDAE Hoff 1942

Comment: Commensal or subterranean in habit. No known fossil record.

Family HEMICYTHERIDAE Puri 1953

First, Tert L.Eoc: *Urocythere(Pokornyella)ventricosa* (Bosquet 1852), U.Ypresian, Belgium. **Extant.**

Comment: Represented at the present time by *Caudites* Coryell & Fields 1937, *Hemicythere* Sars 1925, *Aurila* Pokorny 1955 [etc.]. Marine.

Family KLIELLIDAE Schäfer 1945

Comment: No known fossil record, present day forms only.

Family LEGUMINOCYTHERIDAE Howe 1961

First, Tert Palaeoc: *Leguminocythereis parallelokladia* Munsey (1953), Midway Group, Alabama. This species may eventually be found not to be congeneric with *Leguminocythereis* Howe 1936. Specifically, however, it still retains its position as being the first appearance of the family. Family important in Eoc and Olig, U.S.A. and Europe. **Extant.**

Comment: Only *Basslerites* Howe 1937 represents this family at the present day. Marine.

Family LEPTOCYTHERIDAE Hanai 1957

First, Tert U.Eoc: *Callistocythere kaiata* Hornibrook (1952), Kaiatan and Runangan Stages(= Bartonian), Jackson's Paddock, New Zealand. **Extant.**

Comment: Represented at the present time by *Leptocythere* Sars 1925, *Callistocythere* Ruggieri 1953 [etc.]. Species of *Leptocythere* favour colder waters, often brackish, while those of *Callistocythere* are more common in warmer marine waters (Van Morkhoven 1963).

Family LIMNOCYTHERIDAE Klie 1938

First, Jur Bath: *Timiriasevia mackerrowi* Bate, *Theriosynoecum kirtlingtonense* Bate, *Timiriasevia* sp. and *Bisulcocypris* sp.*A* & sp.*B*. Bate (1965) Oxfordshire, England. **Extant.**

Comment: Mandelstam (1947) first described *Timiriasevia* (*T. epidermiformis*) from Jur of Asia. The precise age of the sediments concerned is not known. *Limnocythere* Brady 1868, *Gomphocythere* Sars 1924 and *Metacypris* Brady & Robertson 1870 are present-day members of this essentially freshwater to brackishwater family.

Family LOXOCONCHIDAE Sars 1925

First, Jur Bajoc: *Cytheromorpha? greetwellensis* Bate (1963), Lincoln, England. **Extant.**

Comment: This family is essentially Tertiary to present day in range. The presence of a species externally resembling *Cytheromorpha* within M. Jur suggests that an extension of the range of this family is possible. Both *Cytheromorpha* Hirschmann 1909 and *Loxoconcha* Sars 1866 are mesohaline to littoral in habit.

Family PARADOXOSTOMATIDAE Brady & Norman 1889

Comment: Mioc—Extant. Largely composed of present-day genera.

Family PECTOCYTHERIDAE Hanai 1957

First, Cret Turon–Maestr: *Arcacythere chapmani* Hornibrook (1952), Piripauan (Senonian), New Zealand. **Extant.**

Comment: *Dolocythere* Mertens 1956 has been removed from this family and placed into the Cytherideidae (Bate 1963). Represented in present-day seas by *Munseyella* Bold 1957.

Family PERMIANIDAE Schneider 1947

Comment: U. Perm, U.S.S.R. only.

Family PROGONOCYTHERIDAE Sylvester-Bradley 1948

First, Jur Sinem: *Micropneumatocythere reticulata* (Klingler & Neuweiler 1959), Germany.

Last, Cret Maestr: *Neocythere roemeriana* (Bosquet 1847), Sichen and St. Pietersberg, nr. Maastricht, Netherlands.

Comment: An important family in Bajoc and Bath. Has tended to become something of a "sack" family into which an assortment of unrelated genera has been placed. Attempts are being made to clarify the position of this family (see Bate 1963). Separation of the *Lophocythere*-*Pleurocythere*-types from the *Progonocythere*-types might soon become necessary.

Family PROTOCYTHERIDAE Ljubimova 1955

First, Jur Sinem: *Ektyphocythere betzi* (Klingler & Neuweiler 1949), Germany; *Ektyphocythere luxuriosa* (Apostolescu 1959), France. **Extant.**

Comment: Family raised from level of subfamily (Bate 1963) to include *Ektyphocythere* Bate 1963 *Kirtonella* Bate 1963 and *Systenocythere* Bate 1963. Other genera included are *Protocythere* Triebel 1938, *Veenia* Butler & Jones 1957, *Buntonia* Howe 1935 and *Quasibuntonia* Ruggieri 1958. The last two genera represent this family at the present time. Marine.

Family PSAMMOCYTHERIDAE Klie 1938

Comment: Represented by the present-day genus *Psammocythere* Klie 1936. No known fossil record.

Chapter 20: Arthropoda: Crustacea

Family SCHIZOCYTHERIDAE Howe 1961

First, Cret Cenom: *Amphicytherura* sp. Van Morkhoven (1963) gives no further details than this but explains that he has observed a number of as yet undescribed species from Cret and L. Palaeoc of Europe, North Africa, and the Middle East. **Extant.**

Comment: Almost certainly a polyphyletic family based upon the possession of a schizodont hinge. Present day genera include *Paijenborchella* Kingma 1948 and *Neomonoceratina* Kingma 1948. Marine.

Family SINUSUELLIDAE Kashevarova 1958

Comment: U. Perm, U.S.S.R. only.

Family TOMIELLIDAE Mandelstam 1956

Comment: Perm of U.S.S.R. only.

Family TRACHYLEBERIDIDAE Sylvester-Bradley 1948

First, Jur Bajoc: *Oligocythereis fullonica* (Jones & Sherborn 1888), Oolith de Royaumeix, Dieulouard, France (Oertli 1963). **Extant.**

Comment: *Oligocythereis* Sylvester-Bradley 1948 may be regarded as being the ancestral genus of this family. Some present-day genera are *Trachyleberis* Brady 1898, *Bradleya* Hornibrook 1952, *Echinocythereis* Puri 1954 [etc.]. Marine. The L. -M. Jur genus *Trachycythere* Triebel & Klingler 1959 has been removed from this family and placed into the Progonocytheridae. Similarly *Veenia* Butler & Jones 1957 and *Buntonia* Howe 1935 have been removed to the Protocytheridae.

Family XESTOLEBERIDIDAE Sars 1928

First, Cret Santon: *Xestoleberis* sp., Bouches-du-Rhône, France, (Oertli 1963). **Extant.**

Comment: The first described species of *Xestoleberis* would appear to be *X. opina* Schmidt 1948 which occurs in Cret Campan, U.S.A. Family represented at the present time by *Xestoleberis* Sars 1866, *Uroleberis* Triebel 1958 [etc.]. Marine. [R.H.B.]

Subclass EUTHYCARCINOIDEA Gall & Grauvogel 1964

First and **Last,** Trias Olenek: *Euthycarcinus kessleri* Handlirsch, and *E.* [*Synaustrus*] *brookvalensis* (Riek 1964), Grès à Voltzia, France and Beacon Hill Shales, Hawkesbury Sandstone, Australia (Gall & Grauvogel 1964; Riek 1964).

Subclass MAXILLOPODA Dahl 1956

Series COPEPODA H. Milne-Edwards 1830

First, Tert M./U.Mioc: *Cletocamptus* sp. and Cyclopoida gen. et sp. indet., Barstow Fm, California (Palmer 1960). *Castexia douvillei* Mercier 1937 (= *Canceripustula nocens* Solov'yev 1961), Jur Call, is known only as cysts on the echinoid *Collyrites*, possibly formed by a parasitic copepod (Mercier 1937; Solov'yev 1961). *Euthycarcinus* and Cyclina have been regarded as Copepoda but are here treated separately. **Extant.**

[W.D.I.R.]

Series CIRRIPEDIA Burmeister 1834

Order THORACICA Darwin 1851

Suborder LEPADOMORPHA Pilsbry 1916

First, Carb Moscov: *Praelepas jaworskii* Tschernischew 1930, Donez and Kusnetzk Basins, Russia. Sil, *Cyprilepas holmi* Wills (1963), Oesel, Estonia, is referred to this order, but insufficient evidence makes taxonomic position uncertain. **Extant.**

Constituent families: Praelepadidae Withers 1953, Carb, Russia. Scalpellidae Pilsbry 1916, Trias Rhaet, Westbury Beds, England; present distribution, all oceans (Withers 1928).

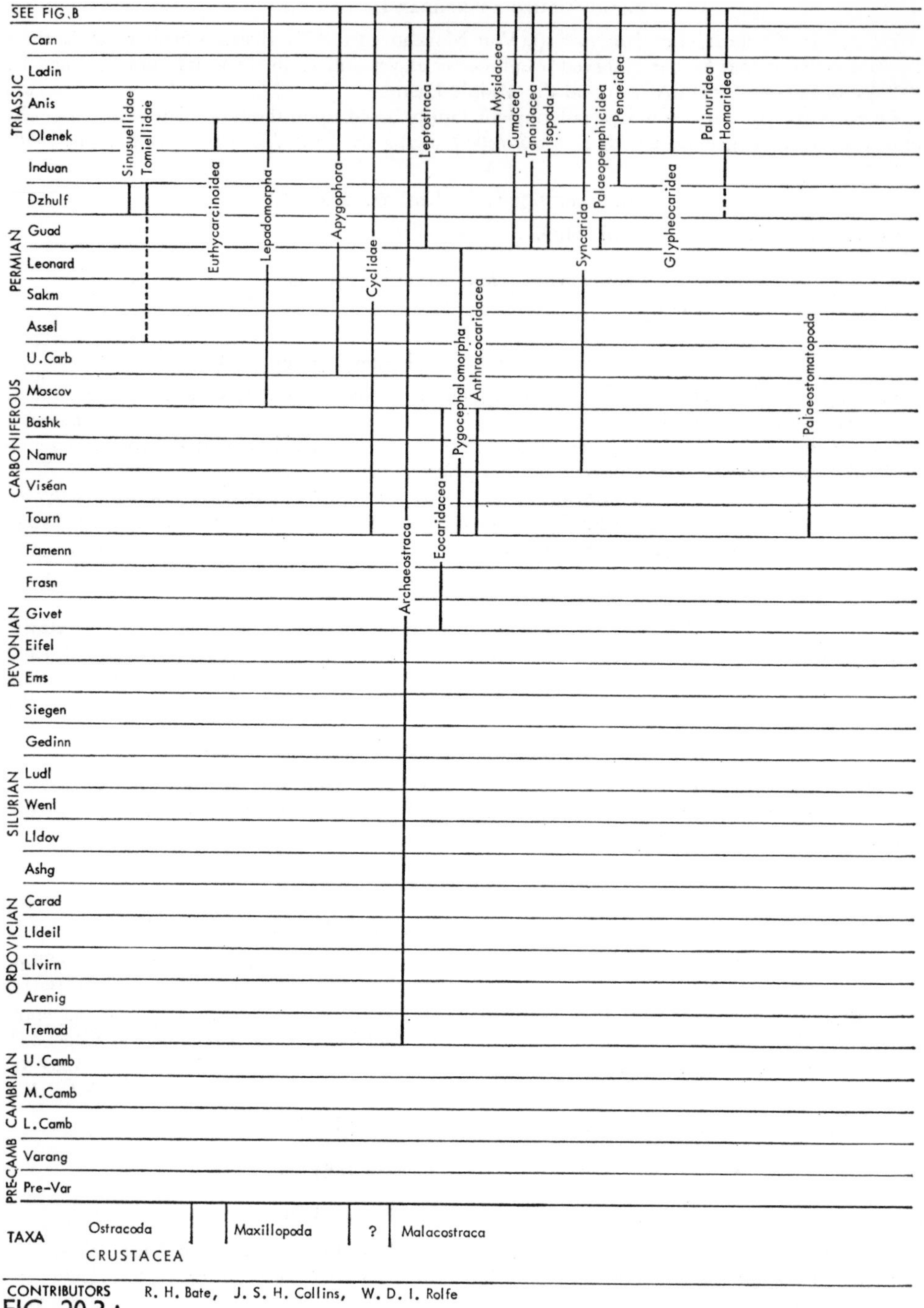
SEE FIG.B
TRIASSIC
Carn
Ladin
Anis
Olenek
Induan
PERMIAN
Dzhulf
Guad
Leonard
Sakm
Assel
CARBONIFEROUS
U.Carb
Moscov
Bashk
Namur
Viséan
Tourn
DEVONIAN
Famenn
Frasn
Givet
Eifel
Ems
Siegen
Gedinn
SILURIAN
Ludl
Wenl
Lldov
ORDOVICIAN
Ashg
Carad
Lldeil
Llvirn
Arenig
Tremad
CAMBRIAN
U.Camb
M.Camb
L.Camb
PRE-CAMB
Varang
Pre-Var
Sinusuellidae
Tomiellidae
Euthycarcinoidea
Lepadomorpha
Apygophora
Cyclidae
Archaeostraca
Leptostraca
Eocaridacea
Pygocephalomorpha
Anthracocaridacea
Mysidacea
Cumacea
Tanaidacea
Isopoda
Syncarida
Palaeopemphicidea
Penaeidea
Glypheocaridea
Palinuridea
Homaridea
Palaeostomatopoda
TAXA
Ostracoda
Maxillopoda
?
Malacostraca
CRUSTACEA
CONTRIBUTORS R. H. Bate, J. S. H. Collins, W. D. I. Rolfe

FIG. 20.3 A

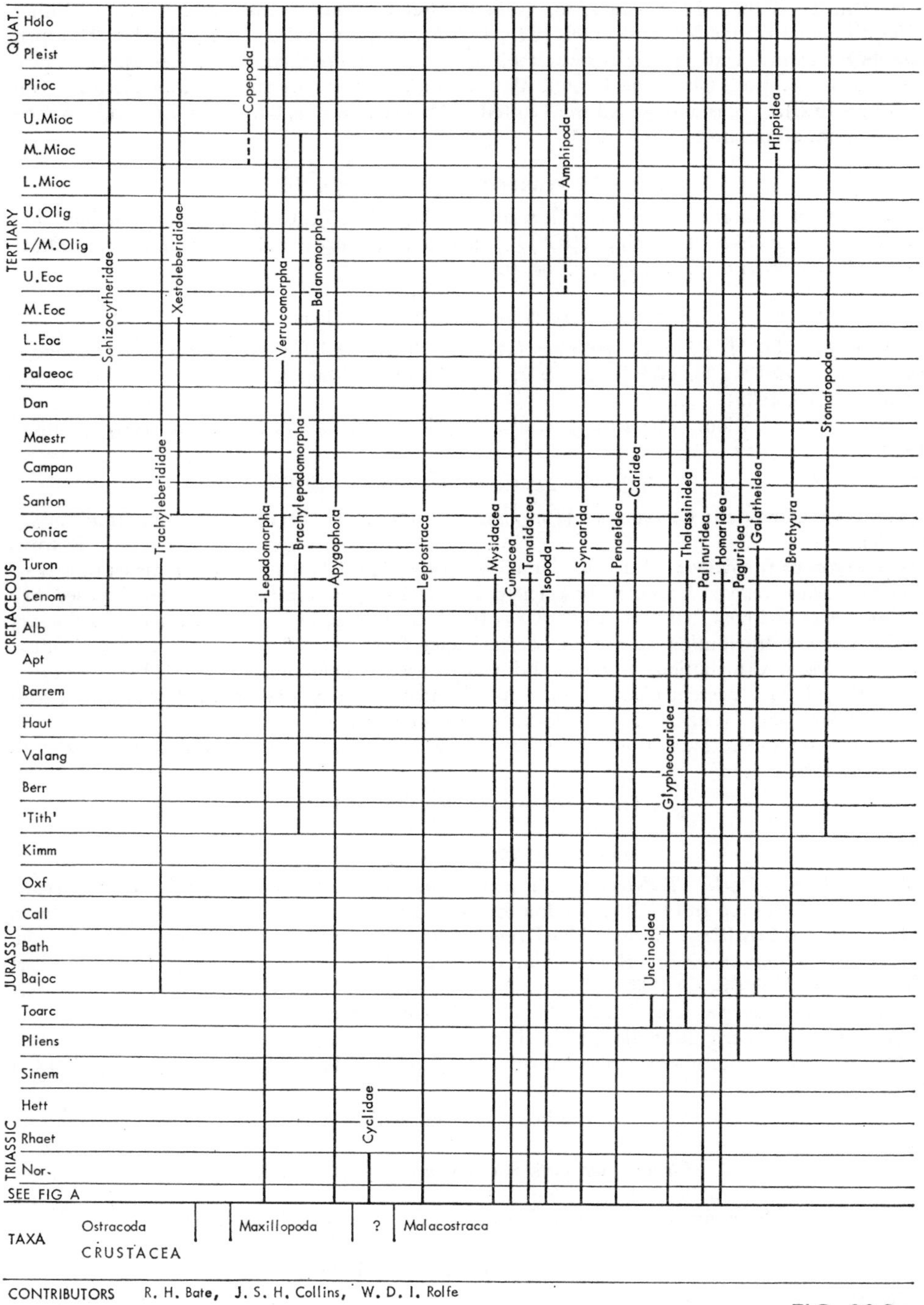
QUAT.
Holo
Pleist
Plioc
U.Mioc
M.Mioc
L.Mioc
TERTIARY
U.Olig
L/M.Olig
U.Eoc
M.Eoc
L.Eoc
Palaeoc
Dan
Maestr
Campan
Santon
Coniac
Turon
Cenom
CRETACEOUS
Alb
Apt
Barrem
Haut
Valang
Berr
'Tith'
Kimm
Oxf
Call
JURASSIC
Bath
Bajoc
Toarc
Pliens
Sinem
Hett
TRIASSIC
Rhaet
Nor.
SEE FIG A
Schizocytheridae
Trachyleberididae
Xestoleberididae
Copepoda
Lepadomorpha
Verrucomorpha
Brachylepadomorpha
Balanomorpha
Apygophora
Cyclidae
Leptostraca
Mysidacea
Cumacea
Tanaidacea
Isopoda
Amphipoda
Syncarida
Penaeidea
Caridea
Uncinoidea
Glypheocaridea
Thalassinidea
Palinuridea
Homaridea
Paguridea
Galatheidea
Hippidea
Brachyura
Stomatopoda
TAXA
Ostracoda
Maxillopoda
?
Malacostraca
CRUSTACEA
CONTRIBUTORS R. H. Bate, J. S. H. Collins, W. D. I. Rolfe

FIG. 20.3 B

Stramentidae Withers 1920, Cret?Alb, Syria to Cret Campan, Europe and U.S.A. (Withers 1935). Oxynaspididae Nilsson-Cantell 1921, Tert M. Eoc, Auversian, U. Bracklesham; present distribution, world wide, generally between Lats. 40° N & S (Withers 1953). Lepadidae Darwin 1851, Tert M. Eoc, Claiborne Group, Weches Fm, Texas; present distribution, all oceans (Withers 1953). Trilasmatidae Nilsson-Cantell 1924, Tert. U. Eoc, Bartonian, England; present distribution, all oceans.

Suborder VERRUCOMORPHA Pilsbry 1916

First, Cret Cenom: *Proverruca* (?) *nodosa* Withers (1935), Chalk detritus, England and *Schreteriella cenomanica* Kolosváry (1958), "Sandstone", Bozovics Südsiebenburger. **Extant.** Present distribution of *Verruca* spp., all oceans.

Suborder BRACHYLEPADOMORPHA Withers 1924

First, Jur 'Tith': *Pycnolepas fimbriata* (Withers 1912), Red Lst, Nesseldorf and Stramberg, Moravia. *Brachylepas* H. Woodward 1901, Cret Turon to Maestr, England and N.W. Europe (Withers 1928, 1935).
Last, Tert M.Mioc: *Pycnolepas paronai* (De Alessandri 1895), Helvetian, Italy (Withers 1953).

Suborder BALANOMORPHA Pilsbry 1916

First, Cret Campan: *Catophragmus* (*Pachydiadema*) *cretaceum* Withers (1935), A. mammillatus Z., Sweden. **Extant.**
Constituent families: Chthamalidae Pilsbry 1916, Cret Campan Sweden; present distribution, all oceans. *Chthamalus darwini* Bosquet 1857, Cret Campan, Limbourg, Holland is based on a recent species (Withers 1935). Balanidae Gray 1925: Balaninae, Tert M.Eoc, Hungary (Kolosváry 1947); present distribution, all oceans. Tetraclitinae, Tert L/M.Olig, Lattorfian, Italy (Withers 1953); present distribution, tropical and warm seas. Chelonibiinae, Tert U.Olig, France (Kolosváry 1955); present distribution, tropical and warm temperate seas. Coronulinae, Tert Plioc, Astian, Italy (Withers 1953); present distribution, all oceans.
Comment: Ord, *Eobalanus* and Dev *Protobalanus* Ruedemann 1924, U.S.A., are not balanids (Davadie 1963).

Order ACROTHORACICA Gruvel 1905

Suborder APYGOPHORA Berndt 1907

First, Carb U.Carb: *Trypetesa caveata* Tomlinson 1963, U.S.A.. Dev, unidentified burrows recorded from Europe and U.S.A. (Rodda & Fisher 1962). **Extant.**
Constituent families: Trypetesidae Kruger 1940, Carb U.Carb, U.S.A.; present distribution, all oceans (Tomlinson 1963). Rogerellidae Codez and Saint-Seine 1957, Jur, England to Tert Plioc, France (Saint-Seine 1955). Zapfellidae Codez and S.-Seine 1957, Trias, Europe to Tert Plioc, Italy and Algeria (Codez and S.-Seine 1957, Saint-Seine 1954).
Comment: Generic distinctions of fossil spp are based primarily on shape and size of burrow in host and presence or absence of peduncular pit (Rodda & Fisher 1962). [J.S.H.C.]

Subclass incertae sedis

Order? CYCLINA Richter *in* Dittler *et al.* 1933

Superfamily CYCLOIDEA Glaessner 1928 (*non* Whitehouse 1941)

Family CYCLIDAE Packard 1885

First, Carb Tourn: Seven species of *Cyclus* de Koninck 1841 (*non* Anton 1837), Carboniferous Limestone, England, Ireland and ?U.S.S.R., and Glencartholm Volcanic Group, Upper Caninia Z., (C_2S_1), Scotland (Hopwood 1925; Chernyshev 1933).

Chapter 20: Arthropoda: Crustacea

Last, Trias Nor: *Cyclocarcinus serratus, Mesoprosopon triasinum* Stolley 1914, *Carcinaspis pustulosa* Schafhäutl 1863, and *?Halicyne elongata* Reuss 1867, Pedata and Hallstätter Kalk, Austria, Germany (Glaessner 1928). *?Gen. et sp. nov.* Stoppani 1865, p. 36, pl. 1 fig. 6, Trias Rhaet may be a later cycloid (*fide* Glaessner). *Mesoprosopon?* Lörenthey & Beurlen 1929, Trias Rhaet, is not Cyclina.

Comment: Variously regarded as Copepoda (Glaessner *in* Trümpy 1957, Kramarenko 1961), Branchiura (Hopwood 1925) and Phyllocarida (Glaessner 1928).

Subclass MALACOSTRACA Latreille 1802

Series PHYLLOCARIDA Packard 1879

Order ARCHAEOSTRACA Claus 1888

First, Ord Tremad: *Caryocaris mcoyi* (Etheridge 1892), *C.? scanica* (Moberg & Segerberg 1906), and *C.*spp., Bryograptus-Clonograptus Z., New Zealand, New York, Sweden, Nevada, Yukon. *Canadaspis* Novozhilov *in* Orlov 1960, M.Camb, and other Camb genera are not known to be Malacostraca (Rolfe *in* Whittington & Rolfe, 1963). Bradorina Raymond 1935, L.Camb-Ord Tremad, are not Archaeostraca (Treatise Q).

Last, Trias Carn: *Austriocaris carinata* and *A. striata* Glaessner 1931, Reingrabner Schiefer, Austria (Roger *in* Piveteau 1953).

Order LEPTOSTRACA Claus 1880

First, Perm Guad: *Nebalia? bentzi* Malzahn 1958, Zechsteinmergel CaI, Germany (Rolfe *in* Whittington & Rolfe 1963). **Extant.**

Series EUMALACOSTRACA Grobben 1892

The classification of the Eumalacostraca which follows is after Brooks (1962) with modification following Burkenroad (1963) and Fryer (1965). This is a horizontal classification and inevitably tends to obscure the relationships of annectant forms.

Superorder EOCARIDA Brooks 1962 *emend.* Burkenroad 1963, Fryer 1965

Order EOCARIDACEA Brooks 1962

First, Dev Givet: *Devonocaris cuylerensis* (Wells 1957), Terebratum Z., New York.
Last, Carb Bashk: *Palaemysis dunlopi* Peach 1908, Modiolaris Z., Airdrie Blackband Ironstone, Scotland (Brooks 1962).

Order PYGOCEPHALOMORPHA Beurlen 1930

First, Carb Tourn: *Tealliocaris* Peach 1908 and *Pseudogalathea* Peach 1883, Zaphrentis Z. (Z_2)-Upper Caninia Z. (C_2S_1), Scotland, England, France (Van Straelen 1931). 'Dev' records of *Amphipeltis* Salter 1863 refer to *Pygocephalus* Huxley 1857, Carb Bashk (Brooks 1962, p. 257).
Last, Perm Leonard: *Mamayocaris jepseni* Brooks 1962, Opeche Fm, South Dakota.

Superorder PERACARIDA Calman 1904

Order ANTHRACOCARIDACEA Brooks 1962

First, Carb Tourn: *Acadiocaris novascotica* (Copeland 1957), upper Horton Group, Nova Scotia. May be ancestral Tanaidacea or related to Spelaeogriphacea Gordon or Thermosbaenacea Monod (Brooks 1962), but ordinal status uncertain (Fryer 1965).
Last, Carb Bashk: *Acadiocaris? landsboroughi* (Peach 1908), Communis–Lower Similis-Pulchra Z., Scotland (Brooks 1962).

Order MYSIDACEA Boas 1883

First, Trias Olenek: *Schimperella beneckei* and *S.kessleri* Bill 1914, Grès à Voltzia, France. *Anthracomysis* Van Straelen 1922, Carb Namur, may be an earlier record but data inadequate (Brooks 1962). Earlier records refer to Eocaridacea. **Extant.**

Order CUMACEA Kröyer 1846

First, Perm Guad: *cf. Nannastacus* sp. Malzahn *in* Glaessner & Malzahn 1962 p. 254, Zechsteinmergel CaI, Germany. **Extant.**

Order TANAIDACEA Hansen 1895

First, Perm Guad: *Ophthalmapseudes rhenanus* (Malzahn) 1957, Zechsteinmergel CaI, Germany (Glaessner & Malzahn 1962). *Oxyuropoda* Carpenter and Swain 1908, Dev Famenn, may be an earlier record, but critical features lacking and might also be Isopoda or Anthracocaridacea. **Extant.**

Order ISOPODA Latreille 1817

First, Perm Guad: *Palaeophreatoicus sojanensis* Birshteyn 1962 and *Protamphisopus reichelti* Malzahn *in* Glaessner & Malzahn 1962, Spiriferovyi Horizont, Arkhangel'sk, U.S.S.R. and Zechsteinmergel CaI, Germany (Birshteyn 1962; Glaessner & Malzahn 1962). *Houghtonites* Raymond 1931, M.Camb, probably not Isopoda but Trilobitoidea (Rolfe 1963). **Extant.**

Order AMPHIPODA Latreille 1816

First, Tert U.Eoc–L/M.Olig: *Palaeogammarus sambiensis* Zaddach 1864 and *P. balticus* Lucks 1928, Bernstein Fm, Kaliningrad, U.S.S.R. (Baltic amber) (Birshteyn *in* Orlov 1960). *Corophioides* Smith, Camb-Cret, trace fossil, may indicate presence of older Amphipoda (Treatise W). *Necrogammarus* Woodward 1871, Sil Ludl, is not Amphipoda but Myriapoda? (Peach 1899 see Piveteau 1953, p. 396); *Amphipeltis* and *Diplostylus* Salter 1863, Carb Bashk, are not Amphipoda but Pygocephalomorpha (Brooks 1962). **Extant.**

Superorder SYNCARIDA Packard 1885

First, Carb Namur: *Palaeosyncaris dakotensis* Brooks 1962 and *Squillites spinosus* Scott 1938, Heath Shale, N. Dakota and Montana. Dev records refer to Eocaridacea; *Acadiocaris* [*Palaeocaris*] *novascotica* (Copeland) and *Anthracocaris scotica* (Peach), Carb Tourn, are not Syncarida (Brooks 1962). **Extant.**

Superorder EUCARIDA Calman 1904

Order DECAPODA Latreille 1802

Classification after Balss 1957, Burkenroad 1963 and Glaessner 1960.

Suborder incertae sedis

Section PALAEOPEMPHICIDEA *nov.*

First and **Last,** Perm Guad: *Palaeopemphix* Gemmellaro 1890, Sosio beds, Sicily (Burkenroad 1963).

Suborder DENDROBRANCHIATA Bate 1888

Section PENAEIDEA de Haan 1849

First, Trias Induan: *Antrimpos madagascariensis* Van Straelen 1933, Schistes à Claraia, Madagascar (Van Straelen 1933, ref. *in* Balss & Grüner 1961). *Waptia* Walcott, M. Camb, has been compared with a penaeid protozoea, but data inadequate (Whittington & Rolfe 1963). **Extant.**

Suborder PLEOCYEMATA Burkenroad 1963

Supersection NATANTIA Boas 1880

Section CARIDEA Dana 1852 [EUCYPHIDEA Ortmann 1890]

First, Jur Call: *Udora gevreyi, U.minuta* Van Straelen 1923, Macrocephalus-Calloviense Z., France (Glaessner 1929). *Praeatya* Woodward 1868, Jur Hett-Pliens, is probably Glypheocaridea

(Beurlen & Glaessner 1930, ref. *in* Balss & Grüner 1961). *Oplophorus?* sp. Remy 1954, Lualaba Series, Congo, is not Trias but Jur Kimm. **Extant.**

Section? UNCINOIDEA Beurlen 1930

First and **Last,** Jur Toarc: *Uncina posidoniae* Quenstedt, Falciferum-Bifrons Z., Germany (Beurlen 1930, ref. *in* Balss & Grüner 1961).

Supersection REPTANTIA Boas 1880

Section MACRURA Latreille 1806

Subsection GLYPHEOCARIDEA Beurlen & Glaessner 1930 *emend.* Glaessner 1960
First, Trias Olenek: *Litogaster? luxoviensis* Etallon, Grès bigarré, France.
Last, Tert L.Eoc: *Trachysoma scabrum* Bell, London Clay, England and Kanev beds, Ukraine S.S.R. (Glaessner 1929).

Subsection THALASSINIDEA Dana 1852
First, Jur Toarc: *Magila? bonjouri* (Etallon), Upper Lias, France (Glaessner 1929).
Extant.

Subsection PALINURIDEA Borradaile 1907
First, Trias Carn: *Tetrachela raiblana* (Bronn) and *Platypleon nevadensis* Van Straelen 1936, Raibler Schichten and Reingrabner Schiefer, Austria, and Luning Fm, Nevada (Glaessner 1931; Van Straelen 1936; refs *in* Balss & Grüner, 1961). **Extant.**

Subsection HOMARIDEA Boas 1880 [NEPHROPSIDEA Ortmann 1896; ASTACIDEA Dana 1852]
First, Perm-Trias Dzhulf-Induan: *Protoclytiopsis antiqua* Birshteyn, borehole, West Siberia (Birshteyn 1958). **Extant.**

Section ANOMALA de Haan 1850 *emend.* Boas 1880

Subsection PAGURIDEA Henderson 1888
First, Jur Pliens: *Palaeopagurus* aff. *deslongchampsi* Van Straelen 1925, Jamesoni Z., France (Glaessner 1929). **Extant.**

Subsection GALATHEIDEA Henderson 1888
First, Jur Bajoc: *Olinaecaris carinatus* Van Straelen 1925, Murchisonae Z., France (Glaessner 1929). **Extant.**

Subsection HIPPIDEA de Haan 1849
First, Tert L/M.Olig: *Blepharipoda brucei* Rathbun, Lincoln Fm, Washington State (Glaessner 1929). **Extant.**

Section BRACHYURA Latreille 1802
First, Jur Pliens: *Eocarcinus praecursor* Withers, and *Goniodromites? liasicus* Beurlen, Davouei Z., England, and Jamesoni-Davouei Z., Bornholm, Denmark (Withers 1932; Beurlen 1932; refs *in* Balss & Grüner 1961). Perm-Trias records refer to Cyclina. **Extant.**

Superorder HOPLOCARIDA Calman 1904

Order PALAEOSTOMATOPODA Brooks 1962 *emend.* Burkenroad 1963, Fryer 1965
First, Carb Tourn: *Archaeocaris vermiformis* Meek, New Providence Fm, Kentucky.
Last, Carb Namur: *Archaeocaris fraiponti* (Van Straelen), Assise de Chokier, Belgium (Brooks 1962).

Order STOMATOPODA Latreille 1817
First, Jur 'Tith': *Clausia lithographica* Oppenheim, *Sculda pennata* Münster, *S.pusilla*, *S.spinosa* Kunth, Lithographicum Z., Germany (Van Straelen 1931). *cf. Sculda* Kuhn 1952, Jur Toarc, Tenuicostatum Z., Germany, may be an earlier record (Kuhn 1952). *Necroscilla* Woodward 1879, Carb Bashk-Moscov, is not Stomatopoda but Pygocephalomorpha (Brooks 1962). **Extant.**

REFERENCES

ADAMCZAK, F. 1966. On Kloedenellids and Cytherellids (Ostracoda Platycopa) from the Silurian of Gotland. *Acta Universitatis Stockholmiensis cont. geol.* **15,** 7–21.

APOSTOLESCU, V. 1959. Ostracodes du Lias du Bassin de Paris. *Revue Inst. fr. Pétrole,* **14,** 795–826, 4 pls.

BALSS, H. 1957. Decapoda, *in* Bronns H. G. *Klassen und Ordnungen des Tierreichs,* **5,** Abt. 1, Buch 7, Lief. 12, 1505–1672; Leipzig.

—— & GRÜNER, H.-E. 1961. Decapoda, *in* Bronns, H. G. *Klassen und Ordnungen des Tierreichs,* **5,** Abt. 1, Buch 7, Lief. 15, 1979–2169; Leipzig.

BASSLER, R. S. 1941. Ostracoda from the Devonian (Onondaga) Chert of West Tennessee. *J. Wash. Acad. Sci.,* **31,** 21–27.

BATE, R. H. 1963. Middle Jurassic Ostracoda from North Lincolnshire. *Bull. Br. Mus. nat. Hist., Geol.,* **9,** 19–46, 13 pls.

—— 1965. Freshwater ostracods from the Bathonian of Oxfordshire. *Palaeontology,* **8,** 749–759, pls. 109–11.

BECKER, G. 1964. Palaeocopida (Ostracoda) aus dem Mitteldevon der Sötenicher Mulde. *Senckenberg. leth.,* **45,** 45–113, pls. 6–15.

BEUTLER, G. & GRÜNDEL, J. 1963. Die ostracoden der Unteren Keupers im bereich des Thuringer Beckens. *Freiberger Forsch.* **164,** 35–71.

BIRSHTEYN, YA. A. 1958. Drevneyshiy predstavitel' otryada desyatinogikh rakoobraznykh *Protoclytiopsis antiqua* gen. nov. sp. nov. iz Permskikh otlozheniy zapadnoy Sibiri. *Dokl. Akad. nauk SSSR,* **122**(3), 477–480. [Transl.2007, B.R.G.M., Paris.]

—— 1962. *Palaeophreatoicus sojanensis* gen. et sp.nov. i nekotoryye voprosy filogenii i zoogeografii rabnonogikh rakoobraznykh (Isopoda). *Paleont. Zh.,* **1962**(3), 65–80. [Transl. PZ62-3-8, A.G.I., Washington D.C.]

BOSQUET, J. 1847. Description des Entomostracés fossiles de la Craie de Maestricht. *Mem. Soc. r. Sci. Liége,* **4,** 353–378, 4 pls.

—— 1852. Description des Entomostraces fossiles des terrains Tertiaires de la France et de la Belgique. *Mém. cour. Mém. Sav. étr. Acad. r. Sci. Belg.,* **24,** 142pp.

BOUČEK, B. 1936. Die Ostracoden des böhmischen Ludlows (Stufe eℬ). *Neues Jb. Geol. Paläont. Abh.,* **76,** 31–98.

BRADFIELD, H. H. 1935. Pennsylvanian ostracodes of the Ardmore Basin, Oklahoma. *Bull. Am. Paleont.,* **22,** 1–172.

BROOKS, H. K. 1962. The Paleozoic Eumalacostraca of North America. *Bull. Am. Paleont.,* **44**(202), 163–338.

BURKENROAD. M. D. 1963. The evolution of the Eucarida (Crustacea, Eumalacostraca), in relation to the fossil record. *Tulane Stud. Geol.,* **2**(1), 2–17.

CHERNYSHEV, B. I. 1933. Arthropoda s Urala i drugikh mest SSSR. *Mater. tsentr. nauchno-issled. geol.-razved. Inst.,* sb. 1, paleont. i strat. 15–24.

CODEZ, J. & SAINT-SEINE, R. DE. 1957 Révision des Cirripèdes Acrothoraciques Fossiles. *Bull. Soc. géol. Fr.* (6), **7,** 699–719.

COOPER, C. L. 1946. Pennsylvanian Ostracodes of Illinois. *Bull. Ill. St. geol. Surv.,* **70,** 177 pp., 21 pls.

COPELAND, M. J. 1957. The arthropod fauna of the Upper Carboniferous rocks of the Maritime Provinces. *Mem. geol. Surv. Brch Can.,* **286,** 5 + 110 pp.

CORDELL, R. J. 1952. Ostracodes from the Upper Pennsylvanian of Missouri. *J. Paleont,* **26,** 74–112.

CORYELL, H. N. & CUSKLEY, V. A. 1934. Some new ostracodes from the White Mound Section of the Haragan shale, Murray County, Oklahoma. *Amer. Mus. Novi.,* **748,** 1–12.

DAVADIE, C. 1963 *Étude des balanes d'Europe et d'Afrique.* 146 pp., pl. 1–55; Centre Nationale de Recherche Scientifique, Paris.

EWETZ, C. E. 1933. Einige neue Fossilfunde in der Visingsöformation. *Geol. För. Stockh. Förh.,* **55**(3), 506–518.

FRITSCH, A. 1910. *Miscellanea palaeontologica, II Mesozoica.* Prague.

FRYER, G. 1965. Studies on the functional morphology and feeding mechanism of *Monodella argentarii* Stella (Crustacea: Thermosbaenacea). *Trans. R. Soc. Edinb.*, **66**(4), 49–90.

GALL, J.-C. & GRAUVOGEL, L. 1964. Un arthropode peu connu, le genre *Euthycarcinus* Handlirsch. *Annls Paléont.*, **50**(1), 18 pp.

GEIS, H. L. 1932. Some Ostracodes from the Salem Limestone, Mississippian, of Indiana. *J. Paleont.*, **6,** 149–188.

GIRTY, G. H. 1910. New genera and species of Carboniferous fossils from the Fayetteville shale of Arkansas. *Ann. N.Y. Acad. Sci.*, **20,** 189–238.

GLAESSNER, M. F. 1928. Zur Frage der ältesten fossilen Krabben. *Zentbl. Miner. Geol. Paläont.*, for 1928, Abt. B, 388–398.

—— 1929. *Crustacea Decapoda.* Foss. Cat. 1, Pars **41,** 464 pp.

—— 1960. The fossil decapod Crustacea of New Zealand and the evolution of the Order Decapoda. *Palaeont. Bull., Wellington*, **31,** 79 pp.

—— 1962. Pre-Cambrian fossils. *Biol. Rev.*, **37,** 467–494.

—— & MALZAHN, E. 1962. Neue Crustaceen aus dem niederrheinischen Zechstein. *Forstchr. geol. Rheinld Westf.*, **6,** 245–264.

GRÜNDEL, J. 1962. "Zur phylogenetik und Taxionomie der *Entomozoidae* (Ostracoda) unter-Ausschluss der Bouciinae." *Geologie*, **10,** 1184–1203.

—— 1962. Zur Taxionomie der Ostracoden der *Gattendorfia-Stufe* Thuringiens. *Freiberger Forsch-Hft* series C, **151,** 51–105.

—— 1965. Zur Kenntnis der Kirkbyacea (Ostracoda). *Freiberger Forschhft* series C, **182,** 49–61.

GUTHÖRL, P. 1934. Die Arthropoden aus dem Carbon und Perm des Saar-Nahe-Pfalz-Gebietes. *Abh. Preuss. geol. Landesanst.*, **164,** 219 pp.

HALL, J. & WHITFIELD, R. P. 1875. Description of invertebrate fossils, mainly from the Silurian System. *Rep. geol. Surv. Ohio*, **2**(2), 101–105, pl. 4.

HAMILTON, I. B. 1942. Ostracodes from the Upper Permian of Texas. *J. Paleont.*, **16,** 712–718, pl. 110.

HARRIS, R. W. 1957. Ostracoda of the Simpson Group. *Bull. Okla. Geol. Surv.*, **75.**

—— & LALICKER, C. G. 1932. New Upper Carboniferous ostracoda from Oklahoma and Kansas. *Am. Midland Nat.*, **13,** 396–409.

HENNINGSMOEN, G. 1953. Classification of Paleozoic straight-hinged ostracods. *Norsk geol. Tidsskr.*, **31,** pp 185–288, pl. 1–2.

—— 1954. Silurian Ostracods from Oslo Region, 1. Beyrichiacea. With a revision of the Beyrichiidae. *Norsk geol. Tidsskr.*, **34,** pp 15–71, pl 1–8.

—— 1965. On certain features of Palaeocope Ostracodes. *Geol. För. Stockh. Förh.*, **86,** pp 329–334.

HESSLAND, I. 1949. Investigations of the Lower Ordovician of the Siljan District, Sweden. *Bull. geol. Instn Univ. Upsala*, **33,** pp. 99–408, pl 1–26.

HOPWOOD, A. T. 1925. On the family Cyclidae Packard. *Geol. Mag.*, **62,** 289–309.

HORNIBROOK, N. DE B. 1952. Tertiary and Recent marine Ostracoda of New Zealand. Their origin, affinities and distribution. *Bull. N.Z. geol. Surv.*, **18,** 1–82.

JAANUSSON, V. 1957. Middle Ordovician Ostracodes of Central and Southern Sweden. *Bull. geol. Instn Univ. Upsala*, **37,** pp. 173–422, pls I–XV.

JONES, T. R. 1884. Notes on the late Mr. George Tate's specimens of Lower Carboniferous Entomostraca from Berwickshire and Northumberland. *Proc. Berwick Nat. Club.*, **10,** 312–326, pl. 2.

—— & HINDE, G. J. 1890. A supplementary monograph of the Cretaceous Entomostraca of England and Ireland. *Palaeontogr. Soc. [Monogr.]*.

—— & HOLL, H. B. 1868. Notes on Palaeozoic Entomostraca, No. 8. Some Lower Silurian Species from the Chair of Kildare, Ireland. *Ann. Mag. nat. Hist.* (4) **2,** 54–62, pl. 7.

—— & KIRKBY, J. W. 1886. Notes on the Palaeozoic bivalved Entomostraca No. 22. On some undescribed species of the British Carboniferous Ostracoda. *Ann. Mag. nat. Hist.* (5)., **18,** 249–264, pls. 6–9.

—— & Kirkby, J. W. 1886. On some fringed and other ostracoda from the Carboniferous series. *Geol. Mag.*, **23**, 433–439, pls. 11–12.

—— & Sherborn, C. D. 1888. On some Ostracoda from the Fullers-earth Oolite and Bradford Clay. *Proc. Bath nat. Hist. Fld Club*, **6**, 249–278, 5 pls.

Keenan, J. E. 1951. Ostracodes from the Maquoketa Shale of Missouri. *J. Paleont.*, **25**, 561–574.

Kellett, B. 1933. Ostracodes of the Upper Pennsylvanian and the Lower Permian strata of Kansas, I. *J. Paleont.*, **7**, 59–108, pls. 13–16.

—— 1935. Ostracodes of the Upper Pennsylvanian and the Lower Permian strata of Kansas. *J. Paleont.*, **9**, 132–166, pls. 16–18.

Kesling, R. V. 1952. Ostracodes of the Families Leperditellidae, Primitiidae, Drepanellidae, Aechminidae and Kirkbyidae from the Middle Devonian Bell Shale Michigan. *Contrib. Mus. Paleont. Univ. Mich.* **10**, 21–44, pls. 1–5.

—— 1957. Origin of Beyrichid Ostracods. *Contrib. Mus. Paleont. Univ. Mich.*, pp 57–80, pls 1–7.

—— & Copeland M. J. 1954. A new kirkbyid ostracod from the Wanakah member of the Middle Devonian Ludlowville formation in western New York. *Contr. Mus. Paleont. Univ. Mich.*, **11,** 153–166.

—— & Hussey, R. C. 1953. A new family and genus of ostracod from Ordovician Bill's Creek shale of Michigan. *Contr. Mus. Paleont. Univ. Mich.* pp 77–95.

—— & Kilgore, J. E. 1952. Ostracods of the families Leperditellidae, Drepanellidae, Glyptopleuridae, Kloedenellidae Bairdiidae, Barychylinidae and Thlipsuridae from the Genshaw Formation of Michigan. *Contr. Mus. Paleont. Univ. Mich.*, **10**, 1–19, pls. 1–4.

—— & Sohn, I. G. 1958. The Palaeozoic Ostracode genus *Alanella* Bouček 1936. *J. Paleont.*, **32,** 517–524, pl. 78.

Klingler, W. & Neuweiler, F. 1959. Leitende Ostracoden aus dem deutschen Lias ℬ. *Geol. Jber.* **76,** 373–410, 6 pls.

Kollmann, K. 1963. *in* Excursion guides of 8th European Micropaleontological Colloquium, Austria. pp. 14–19, pp, 61–65.

Koslováry, G. 1947. Eine neue Balanidae aus dem ungarischen Eözan. *Ann. Hist-Nat Mus. Nat. Hungarica*, **40,** 305–307.

—— 1955. Über stratigraphische Rolle der fossilen Balaniden. *Acta Biol., Szeged*, **5,** 183–189, fig. 1–6.

—— 1958. Ein neuer operculator Cirripedier aus der Kreide. *Paläont. Z.*, **32,** 1/2, 38–39.

Kraft, J. C. 1962. Morphologic and systematic relationships of some Middle Ordovician ostracodes. *Mem. geol. Soc. Am.*, **86.**

Kramarenko, N. N. 1961. Predstavitel' Cyclidae (Crustacea) iz Nizhnepermskikh otlozhenii Priural'ya. *Paleont. Zh.*, for 1961 no. 2, 84–89.

Kuhn, O. 1952. Neue Crustacea Decapoda und Insecta aus dem Untersten Lias von Nordfranken. *Palaeontographica*, **101A,** 153–166.

Ljubimova, P. S. 1955. [Ostracods of Cretaceous formations of the eastern area of the Mongolian National Republic and their importance to stratigraphy]. *Trudÿ vses. neft. nauchnoissled. geol.-razv. Inst.* new series, **93,** 1–174 (Russian).

Mandelstam, M. I. 1947. [Ostracods of the Middle Jurassic Deposits of the Mangislaka Peninsula] *in* [Microfauna, Petroleum occurrence, Caucasus Emba and Central Asia], 239–262, 2 pls. VNIGRI. (Russian).

Martin, G. P. R. 1940. Ostracoden des norddeutschen Purbeck and Wealden. *Senckenberg. leth.*, **22,** 275–361.

—— 1958. *Cetacella*, eine neue Ostracoden-gattung aus dem Kimmeridge Nord-wesdeutschland. *Palaont. z.* **32,** 190–196.

Martinsson, A. 1960. Primitiopsid Ostracodes from the Ordovician of Oklahoma and the Systematics of the Family Primitiopsidae. *Bull. geol. Instn Univ. Upsala*, **38,** pp 139–154, pl I–III.

—— 1962. Ostracodes of the family Beyrichiidae from the Silurian of Gotland. *Bull. geol. Instn Univ. Upsala*, **41,** 1–369.

—— 1964. Palaeocope Ostracodes from the Well Leba I in Pomerania. *Geol. För. Stockh. Förh.,* **86,** 125–161.

MERCIER, J. 1937. Zoothylacies d'échinide fossile provoquées par un crustacé: *Castexia douvillei* nov. gen., nov.sp. *Bull. Soc. géol. Fr.* (5), **6,** 149–154.

MÜLLER, K. J. 1964. Ostracoda (Bradorina) mit phosphatischen Gehäusen aud dem Ober-kambrium von Schweden. *Neues Jb. Geol. Paläont., Abh.,* **121,** 1–46.

MUNSEY, G. C. 1953. A Paleocene Ostracoda fauna from the Coal Bluff marl member of the Naheola Formation of Alabama. *J. Paleont.,* **27,** 1–20.

NOVOZHILOV, N. I. 1960. Position systématique des Kazacharthra (arthropodes) d'après de nouveaux matériaux des monts Ketmen et Sajkan (Kazakhstan SE et NE). *Bull. Soc. géol. Fr.* (7), **1,** 265–269.

—— 1961. Dvustvorchatye listonogie Devona. *Trudȳ paleont. Inst.,* **81,** 132 pp.

OERTLI, H. J. 1959. Malm ostrakoden aud dem schweizerischen Juragebirge. *Denkschr. schweiz. naturf. Ges.,* **83,** 1–44, pls. 1–7.

—— 1963. *Mesozoic Ostracod Faunas of France.* 57 pp., 90 pls. Leiden.

ÖPIK, A. 1937. *Ostracoda from the Ordovician Uhaku and Kukruse Formations of Estonia.* Geol. Inst. Univ. Tartu, **50,** 1–74, pls. 1–15.

ORLOV, YU. A. (Editor) 1960. *Osnovy paleontologii, Chlenistonogiye, trilobitoobraznyye i rakoobraznyye.* Akademii Nauk SSSR, Moscow.

PAECKELMANN, W. 1922. Der Mittel devonische Massenkalk der Bergischen Landes. *Abh. preuss. geol. landesanst.,* **91,** 1–112.

PALMER, A. R. 1960. Miocene copepods from the Mojave Desert, California. *J. Paleont.,* **34,** 447–452.

PÉNEAU, J. 1962. pp. 191–201 in Erben, H. K. (*ed.*), *Symposiums Band, 2 Internationale Arbeitstagung über die Silur/Devon-Grenze und die Stratigraphie von Silur und Devon, Bonn-Bruxelles* 1960. Stuttgart.

PIVETEAU, J. (Editor) 1953. *Traité de paléontologie,* **3,** Masson, Paris.

PLUMHOFF, F. 1963. Die Ostracoden des Oberaalenium und tiefen Unterbajocium (Jura) des Gifhomer Trogcs. N.W. Deutschland. *Abh. senckenb. naturforsch Ges.,* **503,** 1–100, pls. 1–12.

POKORNY, V. 1950. The ostracods of the Middle Devonian Red Coral limestone of Celechovic. *Sb. ústřed. Úst. geol.,* **17,** 513–632, pls. 1–5.

—— 1965. *Principles of Zoological Micropalaeontology,* Vol. 2 (English Translation), Pergamon, Oxford.

POLENOVA, E. N. 1952. Ostrakody verkhnei chasti zhivetskogo yarusa russkoi platformy Mikro-fauna SSSR V. *Trudȳ vses. neft. nauchno-issled. geol.-razv. Inst.,* **60,** 65–156, pls. 1–15.

—— 1955. Ostrakody devona Valga-Uralskoi oblasti. *Trudȳ vses. neft. nauchno-issled. geol.-razv. Inst.,* **87,** 191–287, pls. 1–15.

POSNER V. M. 1950. *Lichwininae in* EGOROV, V. G. 1950. *Ostrakody franskogo yarusa russkoi plat-formy,* 141 pp. VNIGRI, Moscow.

POULSEN, C. 1937. On the Lower Ordovician faunas of east Greenland. *Meddr Grøl.,* **119,** (3), 72 pp., 8 pls.

PŘÍBYL, A. 1953. The ostracodes of the Middle Devonian (Givetian) of Poland in the profile Grzegarzewick in the Gory Swietokrzyskie *Sb. ústřed Úst. geol.,* **20,** 233–344.

—— & SNAJDR, M. 1950. [On new Ostracoda from the Choteč Limestones (Middle Devonian) of Holyne near Prague]. *Sb. st. geol. Úst. čsl. Repub.* **17,** 101–179, 5 pls (Czech).

QUENSTEDT, F. A. 1856–58. *Der Jura,* 823 pp, 100 pls. Tübingen.

RABIEN, A. 1954. Zur Taxonomie und Chronologie der oberdevonischen Ostracoden. *Abh. hess. Landesamt. Bodenforsch.,* **9,** 1–286.

RIEK, E. F. 1964. Merostomoidea (Arthropoda, Trilobitomorpha) from the Australian Middle Triassic. *Rec. Aust. Mus.,* **26**(13), 327–332.

ROBINSON, J. E. 1959. The Ostracod Fauna of the Shale Facies of the Cawdor Limestones, North End of Cawdor Quarry, Derbyshire. *Q. Jl geol. Soc. Lond.,* **114,** 435–448, 3 figs.

RODDA, P. U. & FISCHER, W. L. 1962. Upper Paleozoic Acrothoracic Barnacles from Texas. *Tex. J. Sci.,* **14,** 460–479.

ROLFE, W. D. I. 1963. Catalogue of type specimens in the invertebrate paleontological collections of the Museum of Comparative Zoology, Arthropoda. *Bull. Mus. comp. Zool. Harv.*, **129**, 369–398.

—— 1967. *Rochdalia*, a Carboniferous insect nymph. *Palaeontology*, **10**, 307–313.

ROSS, A. 1965. A new cirripede from the Eocene of Georgia. *Q. J. Fla Acad. Sci.*, **28**, 59–67, fig. 1–2.

ROZHDESTVENSKAYA, A. A. 1962. *in Brachiopods, ostracods, spores of Middle and Upper Devonian of Bashkiria, U.S.S.R.* Akad Nauk S.S.R. Moscow.

RUEDEMANN, R. 1901. Trenton conglomerate of Rysedorph Hill, Rensselaer County, New York, and its fauna. *Bull. N.Y. State Mus.*, **49**, 71–94, pls. 5–7.

SAINT-SEINE, R. DE 1954. Existance de Cirripèdes acrothoraciques des le Lias. *Zapfella pattei* nov. gen. nov. sp. *Bull. Soc. géol. Fr.* (6), **4**, 447–451, pl. 18–20.

—— 1955. Les Cirripèdes Acrothoraciques Echinicoles. *Bull. Soc. géol. Fr.* (6), **5**, 299–303, pl. 16–17.

SAMOILOVA, R. B. 1951. Materiali k izugeniyu mikrofauni Devona top Moskovnogo Basseina.

SCHNEIDER, G. 1958. *in Mikrofauna SSR*, **9**, p 257., VNIGRI.

SOHN, I. G. 1953. *Cardiniferella* n gen. the type of a new family of Carboniferous Ostracoda. *J. Wash. Acad. Sci.*, **43**, 166–68.

—— 1954. Ostracoda from the Permian of the Glass Mountains, Texas. *Prof. Pap. U.S. geol. Surv.*, **264-A**, 1–23, pls. 1–5.

—— 1964. Significance of Triassic Ostracodes from Alaska and Nevada. *Prof. Pap U.S. geol. Surv.* **501-D**, 40–42.

SOLOV'YEV, A. N. 1961. Parazit *Canceripustula nocens* u pozdneyurskogo morskogo ezha. *Paleont. Zh.*, for **1961**, no. 4, 115–119.

SOOT-RYEN, H. 1960. The Middle Ordovician of the Oslo region, Norway. 12, Notostraca and Conchostraca. *Norsk geol. Tidsskr.*, **40**, 123–132.

STEWART, G. A. 1930. Additional species from the Silica shale of Lucas County, Ohio. *Ohio. J. Sci.*, **30**, 52–58, 1 pl.

STOPPANI, A. 1865. Géologie et paléontologie des Couches à *Avicula contorta* en Lombardie. *Paléont. Lombarde* Séries 3.

STOVER, L. E. 1956. Ostracoda from the Windom Shale (Hamilton) of Western New York. *J. Paleont.*, **30**, 1092–1142.

STYK, O. 1962. [Triassic microfauna in borings of Sulechow and Ksiaz]. (Abstr.). *Kwart. geol.*, **6**, 732–733 (Polish).

SWARTZ, F. M. 1933. Dimorphism and orientation in ostracodes of the family Kloedenellidae from the Silurian of Pennsylvania. *J. Paleont.*, **7**, 231–260.

—— 1936. Revision of the Primitiidae and Beyrichiidae, with new Ostracoda from the Lower Devonian of Pennyslvania. *J. Paleont.*, **10**, 541–586, pls. 78–89.

—— & ORIEL, S. S. 1948. Ostracoda from Middle Devonian Windom Beds in Western New York. *J. Paleont.*, **22**, 541–565.

—— & SWAIN, F. M. 1941. Ostracodes of the Middle Devonian Onondaga beds of central Pennsylvania. *Bull. geol. Soc. Am.*, **52**, 381–458.

SYLVESTER-BRADLEY, P. C. 1956. The structure, evolution and nomenclature of the Ostracod hinge. *Bull. Br. Mus. nat. Hist., Geol.*, **3**, 1–21.

TEICHERT, C. 1937. A new Ordovician fauna from Washington Land North Greenland. *Meddr Grønl.*, **119**, no. 1. 65 pp., 7 pls.

THORSLUND, P. 1940. On the Chasmops Series of Jamtland and Sodermanland (Tvären) *Sver. geol. Unders. Afh.* series C., **436**, 191 pp., 15 pls.

TIEGS, O. W. & MANTON, S. M. 1958. The evolution of the Arthropoda. *Biol. Rev.*, **33**, 255–337.

TJERNVIK, T. 1956. On the early Ordovician of Sweden. Stratigraphy and fauna. *Bull. geol. Instn Univ. Upsala*, **36**, 107–284.

TOMLINSON, J. T. 1963. Acrothoracican Barnacles in Paleozoic Myalinids. *J. Paleont.*, **37**, 164–166, pl. 23.

TREATISE O 1959. HARRINGTON, H. J., *et al.* Arthopoda 1: General Features, Protarthropoda,

Chapter 20: Arthropoda: Crustacea

Euarthropoda-General Features, Trilobitomorpha *in* MOORE, R. C. (Editor) *Treatise on Invertebrate Paleontology*, part O. University of Kansas Press.

TREATISE Q 1961. BENSON, R. H. *et al.* Arthropoda 3. Crustacea: Ostracoda *in* MOORE, R. C. (Editor) *Treatise on Invertebrate Paleontology*, Part Q. University of Kansas Press.

TREATISE R (in press). Arthropoda 4. Branchiopoda, Cirripeda, Malacostraca, Myriapoda, Insecta *in* MOORE, R. C. (Editor) *Treatise on Invertebrate Paleontology*, part R.

TREATISE W 1962. HASS, W. H. *et al.* Miscellanea *in* MOORE, R. C. (Editor) *Treatise on Invertebrate Paleontology*, part W. University of Kansas Press.

TRIEBEL, E. 1941. Zur morphologie und Oekologie des fossilen Ostracoden. *Senckenberg. leth.*, **23**, 294–400.

―― 1950. Homöomorphe Ostracoden-Gattungen. *Senckenberg. leth.*, **31**, 313–330.

TRÜMPY, R. 1957. Ein Fund von *Halicyne* (Crustacea incertae sedis) im mittleren Muschelkalk des Wutachtales. *Eclog. geol. Helv.*, **50**, 544–553.

TSCHERNISCHEW, B. I. 1930. Cirripedien aus dem Bassin des Donez und von Kusnetzk, *Zool. Anz.*, **92**, 26–27, 7 figs.

ULRICH, E. O. 1879. Descriptions of new genera and species of fossils from the Lower Silurian about Cincinnati. *J. Cincinnati Soc. Nat. Hist.*, **2**.

―― 1891. New and little known American Paleozoic Ostracoda. *J. Cincinnati Soc. Nat. Hist.*, **13**, 173–211.

―― & BASSLER, R. S. 1906. New American Paleozoic Ostracoda. Notes and descriptions of Upper Carboniferous genera and species. *Proc. U.S. Nat. Mus.*, **30**, 149–164.

―― & ―― 1923. Paleozoic Ostracoda pp 271–391 & Ostracoda pp 500–704, pl 36–65 in *Silurian*, Maryland Geological Survey, Baltimore.

VAN MORKHOVEN, F.P.C.M. 1963. *Post-Palaeozoic Ostracoda.* **2**, 478 pp. Amsterdam.

VAN PELT 1933. Some ostracodes from the Bell Shale, Middle Devonian of Michigan. *J. Paleont.*, **7**, 326–342, pl. 39.

VAN STRAELEN, V. 1931. *Crustacea Eumalacostraca (Crustaceis decapodis exclusis).* Foss. Cat. 1, Pars **48**, 98 pp.

WARTHIN, A. S. 1934. Common Ostracoda of the Traverse Group. *Contrib. Mus. Paleont. Mich. Univ.*, **4**, 205–206.

WHITTINGTON, H. B. & ROLFE, W. D. I. (*ed.*) 1963. *Phylogeny and evolution of Crustacea.* Special publication of the Museum of Comparative Zoology, Harvard University. 192 pp.

WILLS, L. J. 1963. *Cyprilepas holmi* Wills 1962, a pedunculate cirripede from the Upper Silurian of Oesel, Estonia. *Palaeontology*, **6**, 161–165, pl. 22.

WITHERS, T. H. 1928–1953. *Catalogue of Fossil Cirripedia in the Department of Geology, British Museum (Natural History)*: 1928 *Triassic and Jurassic*. xii + 154, 12 pls; 1935 *Cretaceous*. xvi + 434, 50 pls; 1953 *Tertiary*. xv + 396, 64 pls. London, British Museum (Natural History).

R. H. BATE, PH.D. F.G.S.
Department of Palaeontology, British Museum (Natural History) Cromwell Road, London
S W 7.

J. S. H. COLLINS, A.I.A.T. F.G.S.
63 Oakhurst Grove, East Dulwich, London S E 22.

J. E. ROBINSON, PH.D. F.G.S.
Department of Geology, University College, Gower Street, London W C 1.

W. D. I. ROLFE, PH.D. F.G.S.
Hunterian Museum, The University, Glasgow W 2.

CHAPTER 21

Echinodermata: Pelmatozoa

Contributors: R. P. S. JEFFERIES, K. A. JOYSEY,
C. R. C. PAUL & W. H. C. RAMSBOTTOM

Class CARPOIDEA

Introduction: The Carpoidea are an unnatural group. Mitrata and Cornuta are more closely related to each other than to the other carpoids, and the Digitata are probably best placed in the Eocrinoidea.

Order SOLUTA

First, Ord ?Tremad: Undetermined Dendrocystitid, probably L. Tremad (Ubaghs 1963b).

Last, Dev Gedinn-Siegen: *Rutroclypeus junori* Withers, *R. victoriae* Gill and Caster, *R. withersi* Gill and Caster, Victoria, Australia; *or "Rutroclypeus" globulus* (Dehm) Dev Siegen, Germany (Dehm 1934, Gill & Caster 1960).

Order CINCTA

First and **last,** Camb M. Camb: *Trochocystites bohemicus* Barrande (Barrande 1887; Jaekel 1900, 1918; Bather 1913), *Trochocystoides parvus* Jaekel (1918), both Bohemia; *Gyrocystis platessa* Jaekel (1918), S. France; *Decacystis hispanicus* Gislén (1927), Spain.

Order CORNUTA

First, Camb M. Camb: *Ceratocystis perneri* Jaekel, Bohemia (Jaekel 1900, Bather 1913).

Last, Ord Ashg: *Cothurnocystis elizae* Bather, *C. curvata* Bather, Scotland (Bather 1913).

Order MITRATA

First, Ord Tremad-Arenig: *Peltocystis cornuta* Thoral and *Chinianocarpos thorali* Ubaghs, U. Tremad or L. Arenig, S. France (Thoral 1935, Ubaghs 1961).

Last, Dev Eifel-Givet: *Dalejocystis casteri* Prokop, Bohemia (Prokop 1963).

Order DIGITATA

First, Ord Arenig: *Rhipidocystis baltica* Jaekel, U. Arenig, Leningrad region, U.S.S.R.

Last, Ord Carad: *R. robusta* Hecker, M. Carad, Leningrad region, U.S.S.R. and Estonia (Hecker 1940).

Class CYCLOIDEA

First and and **Last,** Camb M. Camb: *Cymbionites craticula* Whitehouse (1941), Queensland, Australia. It is probably an Eocrinoid.

The Fossil Record, pp. 565–581. Geological Society of London, 1967. Printed in Northern Ireland.

Class CYAMOIDEA

First and **Last,** Camb M. Camb: *Peridionites navicula* Whitehouse (1941), Queensland, Australia.

Comment: Probably an Eocrinoid or digitate "carpoid" related to *Rhipidocystis*.

Class HELICOPLACOIDEA

First and **Last,** Camb L. Camb: *Helicoplacus curtisi, H. gilberti* Durham and Caster, California, Nevada (U.S.A.), Alberta (Canada). (Durham & Caster 1963, Durham 1964).   [R.P.S.J.]

Class CYCLOCYSTOIDEA Miller & Gurley 1895

First, Ord Carad: *Cyclocystoides billingsi* Wilson 1946, Hull or Rockland beds, Ottawa River, Ontario, Canada.

Last, Dev Ems: *Cyclocystoides* sp., Cultrijugatus Z., Oberkoblenz Schichten, Lissingen, Gerolstein, Eifel, Germany (Sieverts-Doreck 1951).

Introduction to 'Cystoids' and allied groups. 'Cystoidea', Eocrinoidea and Paracrinoidea have frequently been regarded as belonging to one class. 'Cystoidea' themselves are here regarded as an artificial group, and are divided into Classes Rhombifera and Diploporita; families are as in Kesling 1963 except that *Trematocystis* (? = *Holocystites*) is removed from Aristocystitidae to form Trematocystidae nov. All references for documentation will be found listed in Bassler & Moodey (1943) unless otherwise mentioned.

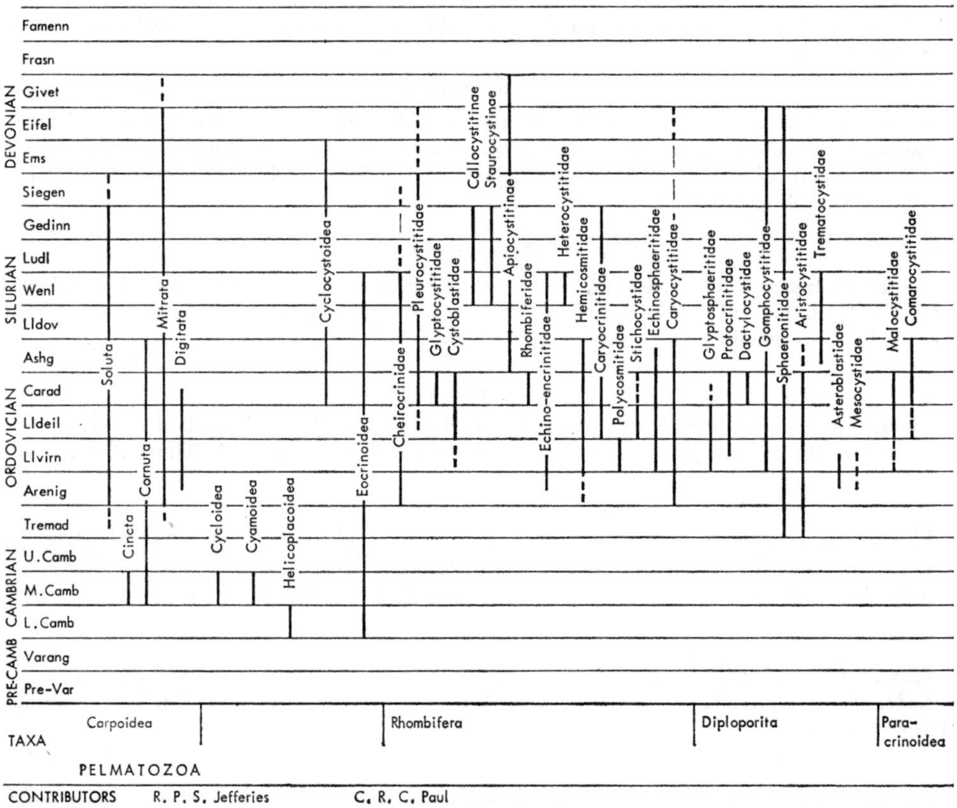

FIG. 21.1 A

Chapter 21: Echinodermata: Pelmatozoa

Chapter 21: *Echinodermata: Pelmatozoa*

Class EOCRINOIDEA Jaekel 1918

First, Camb L. Camb: *Lepidocystis wanneri* Foerste, Kinzers Fm, York, Penna., U.S.A..

Last, Sil Wenl: *Lysocystites* (2 spp.) Niagaran Lst, Racine, Wisconsin, and St. Paul, Ind., U.S.A..

Comment: A heterogeneous collection of primitive pelmatozoa (see Ubaghs 1963a, p. 25.) for which no satisfactory classification exists. There are less than 20 established genera of which about half are monotypic. The group includes several evolutionary lines, of which one leads to the Rhombifera (Cystoidea). The Eocrinoid *Macrocystella* (Ord Tremad-Lldeil) is on morphological grounds directly ancestral to Rhombiferan *Cheirocrinus* (Ord Arenig-Sil Wenl). This line may continue much further back and include *Protocystites meneviensis* Hicks 1872, M. Camb, and 'Cystoid plates' Cobbold 1931, L. Camb. Probably also ancestral to the Crinoidea, Diploporita (Cystoidea) and Paracrinoidea, but no suitable morphological ancestors known.

Class RHOMBIFERA Zittel 1879

Superfamily GLYPTOCYSTITIDA Bather 1899

Family CHEIROCRINIDAE Jaekel 1899

First, Ord Arenig: *Cheirocrinus lanquedocianus* Thoral, Miquelina miqueli Beds (basal Arenig), Montaigne Noire, France.

Last, Sil Wenl-Ludl: *Cheirocrinus tertius* (Barrande), E2 (U. Wenl-L. Ludl), Lodenitz and Sedlitz, Bohemia (Bassler & Moodey 1943, sub *Leptocystis*). Cf. *Cheirocrinus giganteus* (Leuchtenberg), Dev Siegen (L.), Bassin de Chateaulin, France (Pruvost & le Maitre 1943) is doubtful.

Comment: The earliest Rhombiferan family. Very widespread; N. America, Europe, Asia and Australia.

Family PLEUROCYSTITIDAE Neumayr 1889

First, Ord Lldeil-Carad: *Pleurocystites watkinsi* Strimple, Bromide Fm (U. Lldeil-L. Carad), S.W. of Ardmore, Okla., U.S.A. (Strimple 1948).

Last, Dev ?Eifel: *Regulaecystis* sp. nov., Shales, Triangle Point, Torquay, Devon, England (Paul 1967). Scrutton (1966) considers these shales to be L. Givet.

Comment: This family is unknown from Sil rocks.

Family GLYPTOCYSTITIDAE Bather 1899

First, Ord Carad: *Glyptocystites grandis* Sinclair, Kirkfield Fm., Kirkfield, Ontario, Canada (Sinclair 1945).

Last, Ord Carad: *Glyptocystites* (4 spp.), M. Trenton Lst, Quebec, Canada (Sinclair 1948) and Mich., U.S.A. (Kesling 1961).

Family CYSTOBLASTIDAE Jaekel 1899

First, Ord Llvirn-Lldeil: *Cystoblastus leuchtenbergi* Volborth, Echinosphaerites Lst, C1 (U. Llvirn-Lldeil), Pavlovsk, U.S.S.R..

Last, Ord Carad: *Cystoblastus kokeni* Jaekel, Kuckers Sh, C2, Kuckers, Estonia.

Family CALLOCYSTITIDAE Bernard 1895

Subfamily CALLOCYSTITINAE Bernard 1895

First, Sil Wenl: *Callocystites* (2 spp.), Rochester Sh, Grimsby, Ontario, Canada and Lockport, N.Y., U.S.A..

Last, Dev Gedinn: *Sphaerocystites* (4 spp.), Keyser Fm, Maryland, W. Va., and Penna., U.S.A..

Subfamily STAUROCYSTINAE Jaekel 1899

First, Sil Wenl: *Staurocystis quadrifasciatus* (Pearce) and *Pseudocrinites bifasciatus* Pearce, Wenlock Lst, Walsall and Dudley, England (Paul 1966b).

Last, Dev Gedinn: *Pseudocrinites* (7 spp.), Keyser Fm., Penna, W. Va., and Maryland, U.S.A..

The Fossil Record, Part II

Subfamily APIOCYSTITINAE Jaekel 1899

First, Ord Ashg: *Lepadocystis moorei* (Meek), Elkhorn Fm., Indiana & Ohio, U.S.A..

Last, Dev Frasn: *Strobilocystites schucherti* Thomas, Shell Rock Fm., Nora Springs, Iowa, U.S.A. (Thomas 1924).

Family RHOMBIFERIDAE Kesling 1962

First and **Last,** Ord Carad: *Rhombifera bohemica* Barrande, D4, Wraz, Bohemia (Bassler & Moodey 1943, sub Tiaracrinidae, Crinoidea).

Family ECHINOENCRINITIDAE Bather 1899

First, Ord Arenig (U.): *Echinoencrinites* (2 spp.) and *Eutretocystis* (2 spp.), Walchow Fm., B2, Iswas & Leningrad, U.S.S.R..

Last, Sil Wenl: *Glansicystis baccata* (Forbes), Wenlock Lst, Walsall, Dudley, England (Paul 1966b).

Superfamily HEMICOSMITIDA Jaekel 1918

Family HETEROCYSTITIDAE Jaekel 1918

First and **Last,** Sil Wenl: *Heterocystites armatus* Hall, Shelby Dolomite, Lockport, N.Y., U.S.A..

Family HEMICOSMITIDAE Jaekel 1918

First, Ord Arenig-Llvirn: *Hemicosmites elongatus* Pander, Walchow or Kunda Fms., B2 or B3 (U. Arenig-L. Llvirn), Pulkowa & Popofka, U.S.S.R..

Last, Ord Ashg: *Hemicosmites grandis* Jaekel and *Tricosmites tricornis* (Jaekel) Borkholm Lst (U. Ashg), Hasbal & Nömmsküll, Estonia.

Family CARYOCRINITIDAE Bernard 1895

First, Ord Lldeil: *Caryocrinites* (3 spp.), Naungkangyi Beds, Sedaw, Burma.

Last, Dev Gedinn: *Strybalocystites elongatus* Rowley, Bailey Lst, Perry Co., Mo., U.S.A..

Superfamily POLYCOSMITIDA Jaekel 1918

Family POLYCOSMITIDAE Jaekel 1918

First and **Last,** Ord Llvirn: *Polycosmites bohemicus* Jaekel, D1, Vosek, Bohemia.

Family STICHOCYSTIDAE Jaekel 1918

First, Ord Lldeil: *Stichocystis* sp., Shihtzepu Shale, Kweichou, China (Sun 1936).

Last, Ord Lldeil-Carad: *Stichocystis geometrica* (Ang.), Kullsberg Lst (U. Lldeil-M. Carad), Dalarna, Sweden (Bassler & Moodey 1943; Regnéll 1945). *Stichocystis alutacea* (Ang.), Ord Ashg, is not a *Stichocystis*.

Superfamily CARYOCYSTITIDA Jaekel 1918

Family ECHINOSPHAERITIDAE Neumayr 1889

First, Ord Llvirn: *Echinosphaerites ellipticus* Eichwald, Kunda Fm, B3, (L. Llvirn), Reval, Estonia.

Last, Ord Ashg: *Echinosphaerites* sp., Swindale Lst (M. Ashg), Knock, Westmoreland, England(Paul 1967).

Family CARYOCYSTITIDAE Jaekel 1918

First, Ord Arenig: *Heliocrinites echinoides* Leuchtenberg, Walchow Fm., B2 (U. Arenig), Pulkowa and Zarskoje Selo, U.S.S.R.; exact age uncertain. First record of certain age is *Heliocrinites* (2 spp.), Ord L. Llvirn: Kunda Fm., B3, Reval, Estonia.

Chapter 21: Echinodermata: Pelmatozoa

Last, Ord Ashg: *Heliocrinites* (2 spp.), Cystoid Lst (U. Ashg), Cautley, Yorks., England (Paul 1967). *?Heliocrinites* sp., Dev Eifel, Sud Oranais, Algeria (le Maitre 1958a), is doubtful.

Class DIPLOPORITA Muller 1854

Superfamily GLYPTOSPHAERITIDA Bernard 1895

Family GLYPTOSPHAERITIDAE Bernard 1895

First, Ord Llvirn: *Glyptosphaerites leuchtenbergi* (Volborth), Kunda Fm, B3 (L. Llvirn), Pulkowa, U.S.S.R..

Last, Ord Lldeil-Carad: *Glyptosphaerites suecicus* (Ang.), L. Chasmops Lst (U. Lldeil-L. Carad), Dalarna, Sweden (Regnéll 1945).

Family PROTOCRINITIDAE Bather 1899

First, Ord Llvirn: *Protocrinites fragum* (Eichwald), Duboviki Fm., C1 (U. Llvirn), Pulkowa and Zarskoje Selo, U.S.S.R..

Last, Ord Carad: *Protocrinites* (2 spp.), Wasselem Beds, D3 (U. Carad), Spitham and Jewe, Estonia.

Family DACTYLOCYSTIDAE Jaekel 1899

First, Ord Carad: *Dactylocystis schmidti* Jaekel & *Estonocystis antropoffi* Jaekel, Hemicosmites Beds, D1 (M. Carad), Reval, Estonia (Bassler & Moodey 1943, *D. schmidti* sub *Proteroblastus*).

Last, Ord Carad: *Revalocystis mickwitzi* (Jaekel), Wesenberg Fm, E (U. Carad), Reval, Estonia.

Family GOMPHOCYSTITIDAE Miller 1889

First, Ord Llvirn: *Pyrocystites* (3 spp.), D1, Wosek, Bohemia.

Last, Dev Eifel: *?Gomphocystites californicus* Stauffer, Kennet Fm., Kearsage, Calif., U.S.A.

Superfamily SPHAERONITIDA Neumayr 1889

Family SPHAERONITIDAE Neumayr 1889

First, Ord Tremad: *Palaeosphaeronites crateriformis* (Růžička), Trenice Beds, Holoubkov, Czechoslovakia (Prokop 1964).

Last, Dev Eifel: *Eucystis* (at least 4 spp.), Sud Oranais, Algeria; Chalonnes, France; Azzel Mathi, Central Sahara (le Maitre 1958b), Morocco (Termier & Termier 1950), Konèprusy and near Prague, Czechoslovakia (Prokop 1964).

Comment: Very common in Ord and Dev, but so far unknown in Sil.

Family ARISTOCYSTITIDAE Neumayr 1889

First, Ord Tremad: *Calix dorecki* Sdzuy, Leimitz-Schiefern, Frankenwald, Germany (Sdzuy 1955).

Last, Ord Carad: *Amphoracystis, Hippocystis* & *Aristocystites*, Lodenitz, Zahorzan etc., Bohemia (Bassler & Moodey 1943). '*Holocystites*' *gyrinus* Miller and 5 other spp. from Racine Dolomite (Sil Wenl) of Illinois, U.S.A., may belong to this family as restricted here.

Family HOLOCYSTITIDAE Miller 1889

First, Ord Ashg: *Trematocystis* sp. nov., Swindale Lst (M. Ashg), Knock, Westmorland, England (Paul 1967).

Last, Sil Wenl: '*Holocystites*' (60 'spp.'), Racine Dolomite, and Osgood Shs, U.S.A.

Superfamily ASTEROBLASTIDA Bather 1900

Comment: All members of the Superfamily Asteroblastida are placed in the Blastoidea by Bassler & Moodey (1943).

Family ASTEROBLASTIDAE Bather 1900

First, Ord Arenig: *Asteroblastus* (2 spp.), Walchow Fm, B2 (U. Arenig), Pulkowa, U.S.S.R.
Last, Ord Llvirn: *Asteroblastus, Asterocystis* and *Metasterocystis*, Kunda Fm, B3 (L. Llvirn), Estonia and U.S.S.R.

Family MESOCYSTIDAE Bather 1899

First and **Last,** Ord Arenig-Llvirn: *Mesocystis pusirefskii* (Hoffman), Walchow or Kunda Fms., B2 or B3 (U. Arenig-L. Llvirn), Leningrad, U.S.S.R.

Class PARACRINOIDEA Regnéll 1945

Comment: Families as in Bassler & Moodey (1943) who regarded them as rhombiferan cystoids.

Family MALOCYSTITIDAE Bather 1899

First, Ord Llvirn-Lldeil: *Canadocystis, Malocystites, Platycystites*, Chazyan Lst (U. Llvirn-Lldeil), N.E. U.S.A. and Canada.
Last, Ord Carad: *Amygdalocystites* (5 spp.), Hull Lst and Kirkfield Fm, Kentucky, U.S.A.; Quebec and Ontario, Canada.

Family COMAROCYSTITIDAE Bather 1899

First, Ord Lldeil-Carad: *Sinclairocystis* (3 spp.), Bromide Fm (U. Lldeil-L. Carad), Sulphur, Okla., U.S.A. (Strimple 1952).
Last, Ord Ashg: *Comarocystites* or *Sinclairocystis* sp., Starfish Bed (U. Ashg), Threave Glen, Girvan, Scotland (Paul 1966a). [C.R.C.P.]

Class CRINOIDEA

Introduction. The classification used follows that of Ubaghs and Sieverts-Doreck (*in* Piveteau 1953) except that the inclusion of the Order Coronata among the Crinoidea follows from the demonstration by Fay (1961b) of the presence of branching arms in the order.

Order CORONATA Jaekel 1918

First, Ord Lldeil: *Mespilocystites bohemicus* Barrande 1887, band d2 of Barrande, Bohemia (Regnéll 1948b, p. 39).
Last, Sil Ludl: *Stephanoblastus mirus* (Barrande); band E2 of Barrande, Bohemia (Regnéll 1945, p. 193).

Subclass INADUNATA Wachsmuth and Springer 1885

Order HYBOCRINIDA Jaekel 1918

First, Ord Llvirn: *Baerocrinus parvus* Jaekel, Kunda Fm, near Leningrad, Russia (Regnéll 1948b).
Last, Sil Lldov: *Cornucrinus longicornis* Regnéll, Dalarna, Sweden (Regnéll 1948a).

Order DISPARIDA Moore and Laudon 1943

First, Ord Arenig: *Iocrinus? cambriensis* (Hicks), Ramsey Island, Wales (Ramsbottom 1961).
Last, Perm Guad: *Neocatillocrinus incissus* Wanner, *Paracatillocrinus granulatus* Wanner, *P. spinosus* Wanner and *Xenocatillocrinus wrighti* Wanner, all from Basleo, Timor (horizon *fide* Glenister and Furnish 1961, p. 680).

Order CLADIDA Moore and Laudon 1943

Suborder DENDROCRININA Bather 1899

First, Ord Lldeil: *Merocrinus salopiae* Bather and *Pandoracrinus mincopensis* Ramsbottom, Meadowtown Beds, Shropshire, England.
Last, Carb Viséan: *Goniocrinus incipiens* (Hall), U. Burlington Lst, Iowa, U.S.A.

Chapter 21: Echinodermata: Pelmatozoa

Suborder POTERIOCRINITINA Jaekel 1918

First, Dev Siegen: *Propoteriocrinus scopae* Schmidt and *Rhenocrinus ramossissmus* Schmidt, Hunsrück Beds, Germany.

Last, Trias Rhaet: *Encrinus cassianus* Laube, Salzkammergut, Austria, and *E. granulosus* Münster, Bavarian Alps, Germany (Biese 1934).

Suborder CYATHOCRINITINA Bather 1899

First, Ord Lldeil: *Carabocrinus geometricus* Hudson, Valcour Lst, Lake Champlain, New York, U.S.A.; *Palaeocrinus chapmani* (Billings). "Chazy Limestone", Canada. *Tetractocrinus compactus* Jaekel, Walchow or Kunda Fm, Leningrad, Russia may be earlier but is an abnormal form.

Last, Perm Guad: *Ceratocrinus* [Cyathocrinitidae] and numerous genera of Hypocrinidae from Basleo, Timor (horizon *fide* Glenister & Furnish 1961, p. 380).

Subclass FLEXIBILIA Zittel 1879

Order TAXOCRINIDA Springer 1913

First, Ord Carad: *Protaxocrinus elegans* (Billings) and *P. laevis* Billings, Trenton, Lst, Ottawa, Canada.

Last, Carb Namur: *Taxocrinus whitfieldi* (Hall), Chester Glen Dean Lst, Illinois, U.S.A. Also *Onychocrinus parvus* Miller and Gurley, probably from Glen Dean Lst, Indiana, U.S.A., but insufficiently known.

Order SAGENOCRINITIDA Springer 1913

First, Sil Lldov: *Clidochirus americanus* Springer and *C. ulrichi* Foerste, Brassfield Lst, Dayton, Ohio, U.S.A.

Last, Perm Guad: Numerous genera of Homalocrinidae and Lecanocrinidae from Basleo, Timor (Bassler & Moody 1943). Horizon *fide* Glenister & Furnish (1961, p. 680).

Subclass CAMERATA Wachsmuth and Springer 1885

Order DIPLOBATHRIDA Moore and Laudon 1943

Suborder ZYGODIPLOBATHRINA Ubaghs 1953

First, Ord Lldeil: *Cleiocrinus perforatus* (Hudson), Valcour Lst, Lake Champlain, New York, U.S.A.

Last, Dev Gedinn-Siegen: *Spyridiocrinus cheuxi* (Oehlert), L. Dev, near Angers, France.

Suborder EUDIPLOBATHRINA Ubaghs 1953

First, Ord Lldeil: *Hercocrinus beacheri* Hudson, *H. elegans* Hudson, *H. ornatus* Hudson, *Rhaphanocrinus gemmeus* Hudson, Valcour Lst, Lake Champlain, New York, U.S.A. Also *Deocrinus asperatus* Billings, Aylmer Fm, Montreal, Canada.

Last, Carb Viséan: *Rhodocrinites baccatus* (Wright), L. Lst Group, P_2 Z., east and west Scotland.

Order MONOBATHRIDA Moore and Laudon 1943

Suborder TANAOCRININA Moore 1952

First, Ord Ashg: *Tanaocrinus typus* Wachsmuth and Springer, *Compsocrinus harrisi* (S. A. Miller), *C. miamiensis* (S. A. Miller) and *Canistrocrinus richardsoni* (Wetherby), all from Waynesville Lst, Ohio, U.S.A. Also *Xenocrinus multiramus* Ramsbottom and *X.* sp. (Ramsbottom 1961), Starfish Bed, Girvan, Scotland.

Last, Perm Guad: *Wannerocrinus glans* Marez Oyens, *Neodichocrinus nanus* Wanner, and *Stomiocrinus* spp., all from Basleo, Timor (horizon *fide* Glenister & Furnish 1961, p. 680). Also *Paragaricocrinus mediterraneous* Yakovlev, Sicily, Italy.

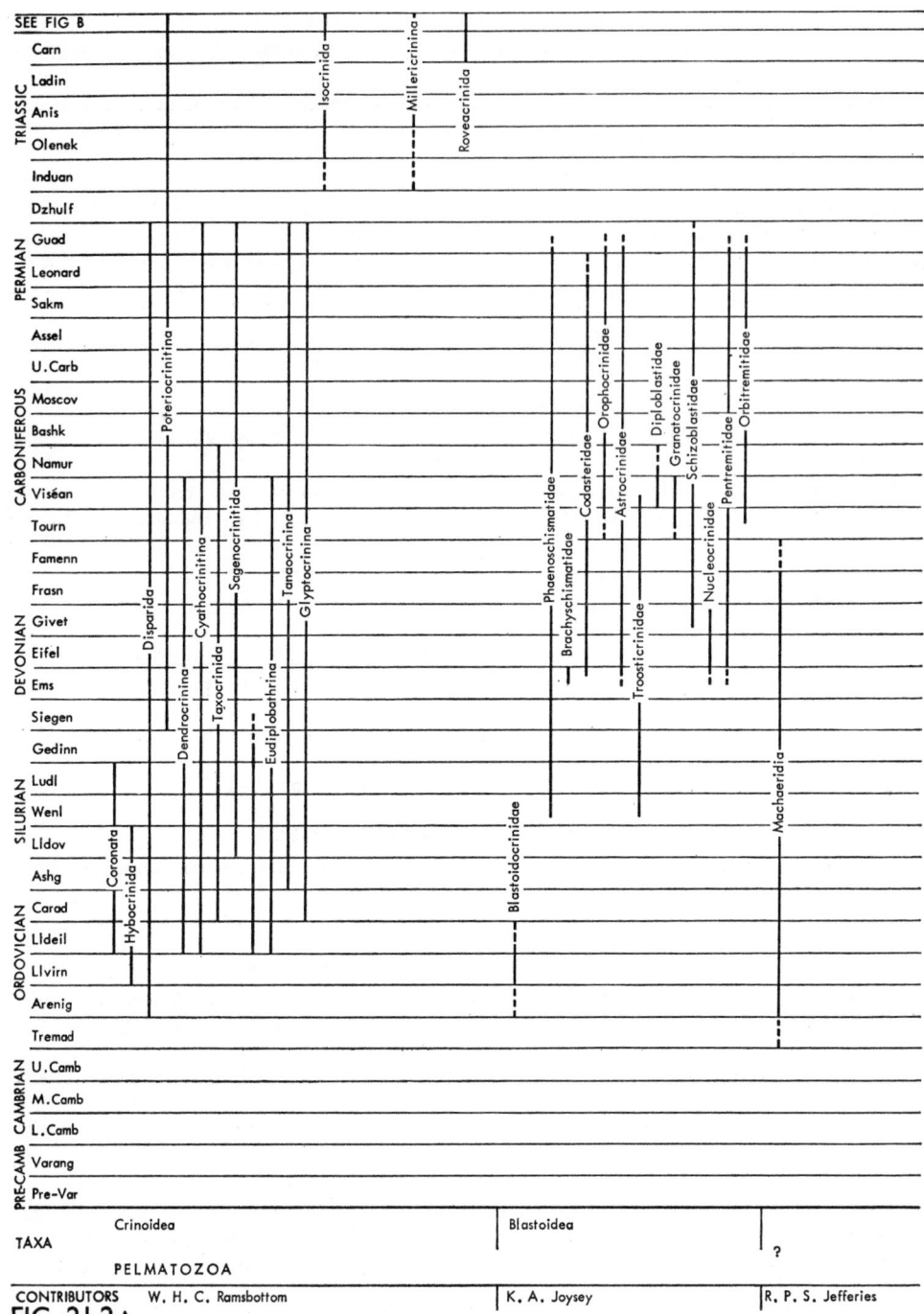

FIG. 21.2A

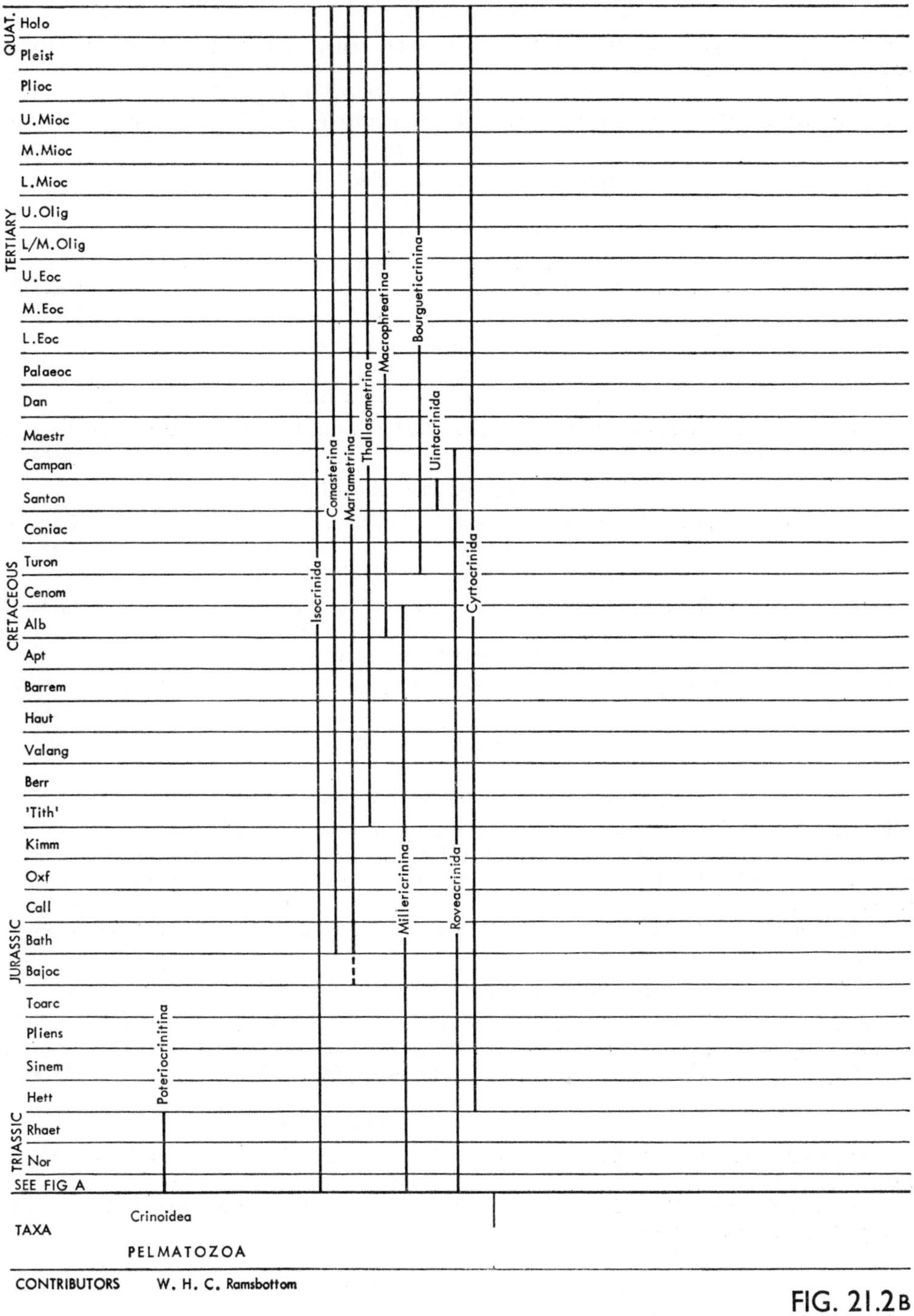
QUAT.
Holo
Pleist
Plioc
U.Mioc
M.Mioc
L.Mioc
TERTIARY
U.Olig
L/M.Olig
U.Eoc
M.Eoc
L.Eoc
Palaeoc
Dan
Maestr
Campan
Santon
Coniac
CRETACEOUS
Turon
Cenom
Alb
Apt
Barrem
Haut
Valang
Berr
'Tith'
Kimm
Oxf
Call
JURASSIC
Bath
Bajoc
Toarc
Pliens
Sinem
Hett
TRIASSIC
Rhaet
Nor
SEE FIG A
Isocrinida
Comasterina
Mariametrina
Thallasometrina
Macrophreatina
Bourgueticrinina
Uintacrinida
Cyrtocrinida
Millericrinina
Roveacrinida
Poteriocrinitina
TAXA
Crinoidea
PELMATOZOA
CONTRIBUTORS
W. H. C. Ramsbottom

FIG. 21.2B

Suborder GLYPTOCRININA Moore 1952

First, Ord Carad: *Schizocrinus nodosus* Hall, stems only, Platterville Lst (Black River), Wisconsin, U.S.A. (Ockerman 1926).

Last, Perm Guad: *Eutelecrinus poculiformis* Wanner, *Plesiocrinus pyriformis* Wanner, and species of *Platycrinites* and *Pleurocrinus*, all from Basleo, Timor (horizon *fide* Glenister & Furnish 1961, p. 680).

Subclass ARTICULATA Miller 1821

Order ISOCRINIDA Sieverts-Doreck 1953

First, Trias Induan-Olenek: *Isocrinus dubius* Goldfuss and *Pentacrinus* sp. [both stem fragments], Werfener Schichten, Bavarian Alps, Germany (Beise 1934). **Extant.**

Order COMATULIDA Clark 1908

Suborder COMASTERINA Gislén 1924

First, Jur Bath: *Palaeocomaster stellatus* Gislén, Bath, England, and *P. schlumbergeri* (Loriol), Calvados, France. **Extant.**

Suborder MARIAMETRINA Gislén 1924

First, Jur Bajoc-Bath: *Solanocrinus coliticus* Gislén, England. **Extant.**

Suborder THALLASOMETRINA Gislén 1924

First, Jur 'Tith': *Pterocoma formosa* (Walther), Solenhofen, Germany. **Extant.**

Suborder MACROPHREATINA Clark 1909

First, Cret Alb: *Roimetra columbiana* Clark, M. Villeta Fm, Naranjille, Colombia (Clark 1944). **Extant.**

Order MILLERICRINIDA Sieverts-Doreck 1953

Suborder MILLERICRININA Sieverts-Doreck 1953

First, Trias: *Dadocrinus gracilis* (von Buch), *D. grundeyi* Jaekel and *D. kinischi* Wachsmuth and Springer, Unterer Wellenkalk (Lower Muschelkalk), Germany. The first of these also occurs in correlatives in the Alpine Trias, and isolated columnals referred to *Dadocrinus*? occur in the Bunter (Biese 1934).

Last, Cret Alb: *Cyclocrinus variolarius* (Seeley), Red Chalk, Hunstanton, England (Rasmussen 1961).

Suborder BOURGUETICRININA Sieverts-Doreck 1953

First, Cret Turon: *Bourgueticrinus fischeri* (Geinitz), Kent, Yorkshire, Isle of Wight, all in England, and Saxony, Germany. Also *B. ellipticus* (Miller), H. planus Z, England. There is a doubtful Jur form known only from columnals (Rasmussen 1961, p. 168). **Extant.**

Order UINTACRINIDA Zittel-Broili 1924

First, Cret Santon: *Uintacrinus socialis* Grinnel, lower part of Marsupites testudinarius Z, England, also Germany, France, Italy, Australia and N. America.

Last, Cret Santon: *Marsupites testudinarius* (Schlotheim) and *Uintacrinus anglicus* Rasmussen, top of *M. testudinarius* Z, Sussex, England.

Order ROVEACRINIDA Sieverts-Doreck 1953

First, Trias Carn: *Somphocrinus mexicanus* Peck, Mexico (Peck 1948).
Last, Cret Campan: *Saccocoma cretacea* Bather, England (Rasmussen 1961).

Chapter 21: Echinodermata: Pelmatozoa

Order CYRTOCRINIDA Sieverts-Doreck 1953

First, Jur Hett: *Cotyloderma oppeli* Terquem, Lorraine, and *Cyclocrinus hausmanni* (Roemer), Thuringia, Germany. Also *Cotyloderma* sp., Dijon, France. **Extant.**

[W.H.C.R.]

Class BLASTOIDEA Say 1825

Introduction

During recent years blastoid classification has been in a state of rapid change, largely owing to the activities of Fay, in preparation for the relevant volume of the 'Treatise', which has not yet been published. Whereas Bassler and Moodey (1943) recognized 42 genera of Eublastoidea grouped into 13 families, Fay (1964) recognized 75 genera (including 22 new genera described by Fay in the period 1960–63), grouped into 12 families. Only 6 family names are common to the two classifications, and only 2 of these include substantially the same group of genera (Troosticrinidae and Pentremitidae). Fay's 1964 classification is used in the present work, without commitment, solely because it is the only classification which includes Fay's new genera. Nearly all the forms at one time included in the Order Protoblastoidea Bather have been transferred to other classes, but for the present, the Order Parablastoidea Hudson has been retained in the Class Blastoidea, although it is not so included by Fay (1961a).

Fay's classification into families is based largely on the nature of the hydrospires and the hydrospire openings. These are important characters and some of the resultant families are probably natural groups, but in other cases, mechanical pigeon-holing based on too few characters has brought together several diverse groups of genera which appear to have little else in common (e.g. Astrocrinidae).

The characters of many blastoids are not yet known in sufficient detail to allow their final placing in Fay's scheme of classification. There is little doubt that many genera will be moved from one family to another during the next few years, as old material is redescribed. For example, in the period between his provisional classification of 1961 and his revised classification of 1964, Fay himself changed the family assignment of 10 genera. Subsequently, other workers have rejected 1 of Fay's genera, and have transferred 2 genera to different families (Breimer & Macurda 1965).

Some of these changes will inevitably affect the range charts. When Breimer and Macurda (1965) redescribed the badly weathered holotype (and only known specimen) of the type-species of *Calycoblastus* they returned this genus to the Pentremitidae from the Granatocrinidae. This did not alter the range of the Pentremitidae, but it changed the last known member of the Granatocrinidae from Perm Leonard to Carb Viséan. The magnitude of this change also gives emphasis to the uneven stratigraphical distribution of blastoid genera, which according to Fay's data is as follows: Silurian 3; Devonian 15; Mississippian 36; Pennsylvanian 3; Permian 19. Apart from the extreme rarity of Pennsylvanian material, it is significant that 74 of the genera are confined to a single geological system, and only *Pentremites* itself (Miss.-Penn.) crosses a system boundary. This suggests that in blastoid systematics the concept of a genus has often been influenced by stratigraphical criteria.

Subsequently to Fay's 1964 classification 4 new genera have been described, but two of these (*Pyramiblastus* Macurda and *Malchiblastus* McKellar) could not be assigned to a family with any confidence, which suggests that the definition of some family boundaries may already require revision in the light of new observations (Macurda 1964b, McKellar 1966).

In several of his publications Fay has suggested possible phylogenetic links between genera, but it is considered premature to include these on the chart, partly because several links would run backwards in time, and partly because several of Fay's 1961 within-family links have become cross-family links in his 1964 classification. The resultant polyphyletic origin of some families may well be correct, but these particular links clearly need to be reconsidered.

During the current period of activity in blastoid studies many species are being transferred from one genus to another, and so in the present work special attention has been given to type-species, because they have greater significance in fixing the stratigraphical occurrence of a genus.

Fay (1961a) provided an excellent bibliography of blastoid literature, and a few subsequent publications are included in Fay (1964). Hence, the present list of references only includes publications which are not listed in either Fay (1961a) or Fay (1964), both of which are key references for the present work.

Order PARABLASTOIDEA Hudson 1907

Family BLASTOIDOCRINIDAE Bather 1899

First, Ord Arenig-Llvirn: *Blastocystis rossica* Jaekel 1918 (= *Blastoidocrinus carchariadens* Schmidt 1874 (*non* Billings)). Orthoceras Lst, Kunda Fm (B₃), Pulkova, Leningrad region (Schmidt 1874).

Last, Ord Lldeil: *Blastoidocrinus carchariadens* Billings 1859, Valcou rLst. U. Chazyan Stage, Lake Champlain, N.Y. State, and Aylmer Fm, uppermost Chazyan Stage, Montreal, Quebec, Canada (Bassler & Moodey 1943).

Order FISSICULATA Jaekel 1918

Family PHAENOSCHISMATIDAE Etheridge & Carpenter 1886

First, Sil Wenl: *Decaschisma pentalobus* (Hall) [type-species], and *Decaschisma pulchellum* (Miller & Dyer), Waldron Sh, Indiana, U.S.A. (Fay 1961).

Last, Perm Guad: *Dipteroblastus permicus* Wanner [type-species], *Thaumatoblastus longiramus* Wanner [type-species], *T. longispinus* Wanner, and *Neoschisma timorense* Wanner, Basleo Beds, Timor (Wanner 1940). Also *Notoblastus brevispinus* Brown [type-species], Branxton Subgroup, Maitland (Upper Marine) Group, New South Wales, Australia (Brown 1941), but this Australian record may be Perm Leonard (Glenister & Furnish 1961).

Family BRACHYSCHISMATIDAE Fay 1961

First and **Last,** Dev Ems: *Brachyschisma corrugatum* (Reimann) [type-species], and two other spp. of this genus, Onondaga Lst, Williamsville, New York, U.S.A. (Fay 1961, 1962).

Family CODASTERIDAE Etheridge & Carpenter 1886

First, Dev Ems: *Heteroschisma pyramidatus* (Shumard), Columbus Lst, Ohio, and Jeffersonville Lst, Kentucky, U.S.A. (Fay 1961, Cline & Heuer 1950), this assuming that all species which Fay (1961) included in *Trionoblastus* Fay should be transferred to *Heteroschisma* Wachsmuth. The type-species *Heteroschisma gracile* Wachsmuth, Thunder Bay Lst, Michigan, U.S.A., is Dev Givet (Bassler & Moodey 1943).

Last, Perm Leonard: *Paracodaster miloradovitchi* Yakovlev [type-species], Artinskian of Petchora Basin, Urals, U.S.S.R. (Yakovlev 1940).

Family OROPHOCRINIDAE Jaekel 1918

First, Carb Tourn: *Orophocrinus stelliformis* (Owen & Shumard) [type-species], Burlington Lst, Iowa (Fay 1961), and several other spp. of this genus from Tourn of N America and Europe (Joysey & Breimer 1963, Macurda 1965).

Last, Perm Guad: *Anthoblastus stelliformis* Wanner [type-species], *Microblastus pocilloformis* Eykeren [type-species], and *Timoroblastus coronatus* Wanner [type-species], Basleo Beds, Timor (Wanner 1940, Van Eykeren 1942). *Indoblastus granulatus* Wanner [type-species], also from Basleo Beds, has been transferred to Astrocrinidae (Breimer and Macurda 1965).

Family ASTROCRINIDAE Austin & Austin 1843

First, Dev Ems: *Cryptoschisma schultzii* (d'Archiac & Verneuil) and *Pentremitidea pailletti* (Verneuil), Caliza de Ferroñes and Caliza de Arnao, Asturias and León. Spain (Fay 1961).

Last, Perm Guad: *Angioblastus variabilis* Wanner [type-species] *Angioblastus depressus* Wanner, *Ceratoblastus nanus* Wanner, [type-species], *Nannoblastus pyramidatus* Wanner [type-species], *Pterotoblastus gracilis* Wanner [type-species] and four other spp. of this genus, Basleo Beds, Timor

(Wanner 1940). Also *Indoblastus granulatus* Wanner [type-species], Basleo Beds, Timor (Wanner 1940), recently transferred from Orophocrinidae (Breimer & Macurda 1965). *Sagittoblastus* Yakovlev, type-species *S. wanneri* Yakovlev, Mount Divia Series, Krasnooufimsk, Urals, U.S.S.R. (Perm Leonard), is now regarded as a synonym of *Angioblastus* Wanner (Yakovlev 1926, Yakovlev & Ivanov 1956, Hecker 1964).

Order SPIRACULATA Jaekel 1918

Family TROOSTICRINIDAE Bather 1899

First, Sil Wenl: *Troosticrinus reinwardti* (Troost) [type-species], Louisville Lst, Kentucky and Tennessee, U.S.A. (Bassler & Moodey 1943).

Last, Carb Viséan: *Metablastus varsouviensis* (Worthen), *Metablastus wortheni* (Hall), Warsaw Lst, Illinois and Missouri, U.S.A. *Metablastus nitidulus* (Miller & Gurley) and *Metablastus wachsmuthi* (Gurley), Salem Lst, Indiana, U.S.A., are all Viséan, but *Metablastus lineatus* (Schumard) [type-species], Burlington Limestone, Illinois, U.S.A. is Tourn. Also *Tricoelocrinus woodmani* (Meek & Worthen) [type-species], ranges Keokuk Lst? to Warsaw Lst, Indiana, U.S.A., so crossing Tourn-Viséan boundary (Fay 1961). *Tricoelocrinus* (?) *belfordi* Crockford & Brown, from Perm of Australia was subsequently reassigned as *Rhopaloblastus* (?) *belfordi* (Crockford & Brown) (Brown 1941).

Family DIPLOBLASTIDAE Fay 1964

First, Carb Viséan: *Diploblastus glaber* (Meek & Worthen) [type-species], St. Louis Lst, Illinois; St. Genevieve Lst, Kentucky; Gasper and Warsaw Lst, Alabama, U.S.A. (Fay 1961).

Last, Carb Namur: *Nodoblastus librovitchi* (Yakovlev) [type-species], Daibar Mt, Aktyubinsk Prov., Kazakstan, U.S.S.R. (Fay 1963).

Family GRANATOCRINIDAE Fay 1961

First, Carb Tourn: *Tanaoblastus roemeri* (Schumard) [type-species], several other spp. of *Tanaoblastus* and *Poroblastus chouteauensis* (Peck), Chouteau Lst, Missouri, U.S.A. (Kinderhookian). *Granatocrinus* Hall, *Carpenteroblastus* Rowley, *Monadoblastus* Fay, *Poroblastus* Fay, *Cryptoblastus* Etheridge & Carpenter, *Dentiblastus* Macurda all have type-species in Osagean of North America (Fay 1961, Macurda 1964). Also *Mesoblastus crenulatus* (Roemer) [type-species], Tournai, Belgium (Fay 1961).

Last, Carb Viséan: *Heteroblastus cumberlandi* Etheridge & Carpenter [type-species], Yoredael Series (D_2 subzone), Northumberland, England (Etheridge & Carpenter 1886), and *Monoschizoblastus rofei* (Etheridge & Carpenter) [type-species], Carboniferous Lst, Fermanagh and Leitrim (D_1 subzone), Ireland (Etheridge & Carpenter 1886, Oswald 1955). Also *Cribroblastus* Hambach and *Ptychoblastus* Fay both have type-species in Meramic of North America (Fay 1961). *Calycoblastus tricavatus* Wanner, Bitauni Beds, Timor (Perm Leonard) has been transferred back to the Pentremitidae (Breimer & Macurda 1965). A new genus, *Malchiblastus* McKellar, type-species *Mesoblastus* ? *australis* Etheridge, Neerkol Fm, Stanwell, Queensland, Australia (Carb Moscov) has been tentatively regarded as ? Granatocrinidae (McKellar 1966), but as this assignment was based partly on similarity in shape to *Calycoblastus*, it is at present regarded as being too uncertain to be included on the chart.

Family SCHIZOBLASTIDAE Fay 1961

First, Dev Givet: *Strongyloblastus petalus* Fay [type-species], Tichenor Lst, New York, U.S.A. (Fay 1962).

Last, Perm Guad: *Deltoblastus elongatus* (Wanner) [type-species] according to Fay, Amarissi Beds, Timor (Wanner 1940, Fay 1961), and according to Fay's interpretation 14 other spp. of this genus from Basleo Beds and Amarissi Beds, Timor. (Fay 1961 states: "In each case where Wanner recognised a variety I have raised it to the rank of species.")

The Fossil Record, Part II

Family NUCLEOCRINIDAE Bather 1899

First, Dev Ems: *Elaeacrinus verneuili* Roemer [type-species], Onondaga Lst, Indiana, U.S.A., and *Elaeacrinus venustus* (Miller & Gurley), Columbus Lst, Ohio, U.S.A. (Fay 1961).

Last, Dev Givet: *Placoblastus obovatus* (Barris) [type-species], and *Placoblastus ehlersi* Fay & Reimann, Thunder Bay Lst, Michigan, U.S.A., and *Nucleocrinus elegans* Conrad [type-species], Moscow Fm, New York, U.S.A., and several other spp. of these two genera at slightly lower horizons within Givet, N. America (Fay 1961, Fay & Reimann 1962).

Family PENTREMITIDAE d'Orbigny 1851

First, Dev Ems: *Cordyloblastus wachsmuthi* (Etheridge & Carpenter), *Cordyloblastus malladai* (Etheridge & Carpenter) and *Cordyloblastus gilbertsoni* (Etheridge & Capenter), base of Santa Lucia Lst, Colle, León, Spain, and *Cordyloblastus clavatus* (Schultze), top of Santa Lucia Lst, Colle, León, Spain (Breimer 1962 and pers. comm. 1966). *C. clavatus* also occurs in Eifel of Kergavan, Finistère, France (Philippot & Morzadec 1965) and Nollenbach, Eifel, Germany (Etheridge & Carpenter 1886). The designated type-species is *Cordyloblastus acutangulus* (Schultze), Pelm, Eifel, Germany (Fay 1961).

Last, Perm Guad: *Rhopaloblastus timoricus* Wanner [type-species], Basleo Beds, Timor (Wanner 1940). *Calycoblastus tricavatus* Wanner [type-species], Bitauni Beds, Timor (Perm Leonard), has been returned to this family from the Granatocrinidae (Breimer & Macurda 1965).

Family ORBITREMITIDAE Bather 1899

First, Carb Tourn: *Globoblastus norwoodi* (Owen & Schumard), type-species, Burlington Lst, Iowa, Illinois and Missouri, U.S.A. (Beaver 1961, Fay 1961). Also *Doryblastus melonianus* (Schmidt), Tournaisian Lst, (correlated with C_1 subzone of Avonian), Velbert, Germany (Fay 1961).

Last, Perm Guad: *Orbitremites malaianus* Wanner, Basleo Beds, Timor (Wanner 1940). Fay (1964) listed *Orbitremites* as confined to Mississippian, apparently not accepting that *O. malaianus* belongs to this genus. If this were so, then the last *Orbitremites* would be Carb Viséan: *Orbitremites derbiensis* (Sowerby) [type-species], Middle Lst (D_2 subzone), Yorkshire and Derbyshire, England (Joysey 1959), and *Orbitremites derbiensis musatovi* Arendt, Steshevo horizon (C_1^2 st), near Mitino on River Oka, U.S.S.R. (Arendt 1960). *O. malaianus* is here accepted as belonging to *Orbitremites;* for the purposes of the range chart, even if the genus were to be split, this species would still be the last known member of the Orbitremitidae.

[K.A.J.]

Class MACHAERIDIA

First, Ord Trem Arenig: *Plumulites bohemicus* Barrande, Bohemia (Barrande 1872).

Last, Dev?Frasn-Famenn: *Turrilepas newberryi* (Whitfield) (Hall & Clarke 1888).

Comment: The Machaeridia are more likely to be molluscs than echinoderms (Wolberg 1938).

[R.P.S.J.]

REFERENCES

ARENDT, J. A. 1960. Novyi podvid blastoidei ig Podmoskovnogo baseina. *Byull. mosk. Obshch. Ispÿt. Prir. geol.* Section, **35,** 149–150.

BARRANDE, J. 1852–1911. *Système silurien du centre de la Bohême.* Paris.

BASSLER R. S. & MOODEY, M. W. 1943. Bibliographic and faunal index of Paleozoic Pelmatozoan echinoderms. *Spec. Pap. geol. Soc. Am.* **45.**

BATHER, F. A. 1913. Caradocian Cystidea from Girvan. *Trans. R. Soc. Edinb.* **49,** 359–529, pl. 1–6.

BEAVER, H. H. 1961. Morphology of the blastoid *Globoblastus norwoodi. J. Paleont.,* **35,** 1103–1112, pl. 129–130.

BIESE, W. 1934. Crinoidea triadica. *Fossilium catalogus*, 1, Animalia, pars 66.

BREIMER, A. 1962. A monograph on Spanish Palaeozoic Crinoidea. *Leidse Geol. Meded.*, **27**, 1–189, 16 pls.

—— & Macurda, D. B. 1965. On the systematic position of some blastoid genera from the Permian of Timor. *Kon. Ned. Akad. Wet., Amsterdam Proc.* Series B., **68**, 209–217.

CLARK, A. H. 1944. A new fossil Comutulid from the Cretaceous of Cundinamarca, Colombia. *J. Wash. Acad. Sci.*, **34**, 303–8.

COBBOLD, E. S. 1931. Additional fossils from the Cambrian rocks of Comley, Shropshire. *Q. J. geol. Soc. Lond.*, **87**, 459–511, pls. 38–41.

DEHM, R. 1934. Untersuchungen an Cystoideen des Rheinischen Unterdevons. *Sber. bayer. Akad. Wiss.* for 1934, pls. 2.

DURHAM, J. W. 1964. The Helicoplacoidea and some possible implications. *Yale Scient. Mag.*, 39 (2), 24–8.

—— & Caster, K. E. 1963. Helicoplacoidea: a new class of echinoderms. *Science, N.Y.*, **140** 820–2.

FAY, R. O. 1961a. Blastoid Studies. *Paleont. Contr. Univ. Kansas*, (No. 27). Echinodermata, art. 3, 1–147, pl. 1–54.

—— 1961b. The type species of *Stephanocrinus* Conrad. *Okla. Geol. Notes*, **21**, 236–8.

—— 1962. *Brachyschisma*, a Middle Devonian blastoid from New York. *Okla. Geol. Notes*, **22**, 103–108.

—— 1964. An outline classification of the Blastoidea. *Okla. Geol. Notes*, **24**, 81–90.

—— & Reimann, I. G. 1962. Some brachiolar and ambulacral structures of blastoids. *Okla. Geol. Notes*, **22**, 30–49.

GILL, E. D. & CASTER, K. E. 1960. Carpoid echinoderms from the Silurian and Devonian of Australia. *Bull. Am. Paleont.*, **41**, 5–71, pl. 1–10.

GISLÉN, T. 1924. Echinoderm studies. *Zool. Bidr. Upps.*, **9**, 1–316.

—— 1927. A new Spanish carpoid. *Ark. Zool.*, **19**, (2) 1–3.

GLENISTER, B. F. & FURNISH, W. M. 1961. The Permian ammonoids of Australia. *J. Paleont.*, **35**, 673–736.

HALL, J. & CLARK, J. M. 1888. Trilobites and other Crustacea of the Oriskany, Upper Heldesberg, Hamilton, Portage Chemung and Catskill Groups. in *Geol. Surv. New York. vol.* 7, *Paleontology*, xiv + 236 pp, 36 pls.

HECKER, R. F. 1940. Carpoidea, Eocrinoidea und Ophiocistia des Ordoviziums des Leningrader Gebietes und Estlands. *Trudÿ Inst. paleont.*, **9**, 1–81, pl. 1–10.

—— 1964. *Osnovy Paleontologii*, **10**, 1–381, 10 pl. Akademii Nauk SSSR, Moscow.

HICKS, H. 1872. On some undescribed fossils from the Menevian Group of Wales. *Q. J. geol. Soc. Lond.*, **28**, 173–183, p. 5–7.

JAEKEL, O. 1899. *Stammesgeschichte der Pelmatozoen 1, Thecoidea und Cystoidea.* Berlin.

—— 1900. *Über Carpoideen, eine neue Klasse von Pelmatozoen. Z. dt. geol. Ges.*, **52**, 661–77.

—— 1918. Phylogenie und System der Pelmatozoen. *Paläont. Z.*, **3**, 1–128.

JOYSEY, K. A. & BREIMER, A. 1963. The anatomical structure and systematic position of *Pentablastus* (Blastoidea) from the Carboniferous of Spain. *Palaeontology*, **6**, 471–490, pl. 66–69.

KESLING, R. V. 1961. A new *Glyptocystites* from the Middle Ordovician strata of Michigan. *Contr. Mus. Paleont. Univ. Mich.*, **17**, 59–76, pl. 1–3.

—— 1963. Key for the classification of cystoids. *Contr. Mus. Paleont. Univ. Mich.*, **18**, 101–116.

MACURDA, D. B. 1964a. *Dentiblastus*, a new blastoid genus from the Burlington Limestone (Mississippian). *J. Paleont.*, **38**, 367–372, pl. 58.

—— 1964b. A new spiraculate blastoid *Pyramiblastus*, from the Mississippian Hampton Formation of Iowa. *Contr. Mus. Paleont. Univ. Mich.*, **19**, 105–114, pl. 1.

—— 1965. The functional morphology and stratigraphic distribution of the Mississippian blastoid genus *Orophocrinus. J. Paleont.*, **39**, 1045–1096, pl. 121–126.

McKELLAR, R. G. 1966. A revision of the blastoids "*Mesoblastus* ? *australis*," "*Granatocrinus* ? *wachsmuthii*" and "*Tricoelocrinus* ? *carpenteri*", described by Etheridge (1892) from the Carboniferous of Queensland. *Mem. Qd Mus.*, **14**, 191–198, pl. 24.

MAITRE, D. LE. 1958a. Contribution a l'étude des faunes Dévoniennes d'Afrique de Nord. l. Échinodermes. *Bull. Serv. Carte géol. Algér. Trav. réc.* N.S., **20**, 115–152, pl. 1–3.

—— 1958b. Le genre *Eucystis* Angelin dans le Dévonien. Présence de *Eucystis flavus* (Barrande) dans le Dévonien Moyen du Sahara Central. *C.r. somm. Séanc. Soc. géol. Fr*, **13**, 304–307.

MILLER, S. A. 1889. *North American Geology and Paleontology.* 664 pp. Cinncinnati, Ohio.

OCKERMAN, G. 1926. Fauna of the Galena Limestone near Appleton. *Trans. Wisconsin Acad. Sci.*, **22**, 99–142.

PAUL, C. R. C. 1966a. On the occurrence of *Comarocystites* or *Sinclairocystis* (Paracrinoidea: Comarocystitidae) in the Starfish Bed, Threave Glen, Girvan. *Geol. Mag.*, **102**, 474–477, pl. 20.

—— 1966b. A monograph of British Silurian cystoids. *Bull. Brit. Mus. nat. Hist.*, **13**, 297–356, 10 pls.

—— 1967. New records of Cystoids from Britain. *Proc. Geol. Soc. Lond.* (in press).

PECK, R. E. 1948. A Triassic crinoid from Mexico. *J. Paleont.*, **22**, 81–4

PIVETEAU, J. (Editor) 1953. *Traité de Paléontologie*, **3**. Masson, Paris.

PHILIPPOT, A. & MORZADEC, P. 1965. Deux Blastoïdes nouveaux du Devonien du Massif armoricain. *C.r. Somm. Séanc. Soc. géol. Fr.*, **8**, 258.

PROKOP, R. J. 1963. *Dalejocystis*, n. gen., the first representative of the Carpoidea in the Devonian of Bohemia. *J. Paleont.*, **37**, 648–50, pl. 83–4.

—— 1964. Sphaeronitoidea Neumayr of the Lower Palaeozoic of Bohemia. (Cystoidea, Diploporita). *Sb. geol. Pal.*, **15**, 7–38, pl. 1–8.

PRUVOST, P. & MAITRE, D. LE. 1943. Observations sur le bord orientale du Bassin de Chateaulin. *Bull. Serv. Carte géol. Fr.*, **93, 213**, 81–94.

RAMSBOTTOM, W. H. C. 1961. A monograph on British Ordovician Crinoidea. *Palaeontogr. Soc.* [*Monogr.*].

RASMUSSEN, H. W. 1961. A monograph on the Cretaceous Crinoidea. *Biol. Skr.* **12**(1) 1–428.

REGNÉLL, G. 1945. Non-crinoid Pelmatozoa from the Paleozoic of Sweden. *Meddn Lunds. geol. miner. Instn*, **108**, 1–255.

—— 1948a. Swedish Hybocrinida (Crinoidea Inadunata Disparata: Ordovician—Lower Silurian) *Ark. Zool.*, **40**, A, 9.

—— 1948b. An outline of the succession and migration of non-crinoid Pelmatozoan faunas in the Lower Paleozoic of Scandinavia. *Ark. f. Kem, Miner. Geol.*, **26**A, 1–55.

SCHMIDT, T. 1874. Uber einige neue und wenig bekannte baltisch-silurische Petrefacten. *Zap. imp. Akad. Nauk* (7), **21**, no. 11, 48 pp., 4 pls.

SCRUTTON, C. T. 1966. The ages of some coral faunas in the Torquay area. *Proc. Ussher Soc.*, **1**, 186–188.

SDZUY, K. 1955. Cystoideen aus dem Leimitz-Schiefern (Tremadoc). *Senckenberg. leth.*, **35**, 269–276, pl. 1.

SIEVERTS-DORECK, H. 1951. Über *Cyclocystoides* Salter & Billings und eine neue Art aus dem belgischen und rheinischen Devon. *Senckenbergiana*, **32**, 9–30.

SINCLAIR, G. W. 1945. An Ordovician faunule from Quebec. *Can. Fld Nat.*, **59**, 71–74, pl. 2.

—— 1948. Three notes on Ordovician cystoids. *J. Paleont.*, **22**, 301–314, pl. 42–44.

STRIMPLE, H. L. 1948. *Pleurocystites watkinsi* n. sp. from the Bromide Formation of Oklahoma. *Am. J. Sci.*, **246**, 761–764, pl. 1.

—— 1952. Two new species of *Sinclairocystis*. *J. Wash. Acad. Sci.*, **42**, 158–160, figs. 1–9.

SUN, Y. C. 1936. On the occurrence of *Aristocystis* faunas in China. *Bull. geol. Soc. China*, **15**, 477–488, pl. 1–2.

TERMIER, H. & TERMIER, G. 1950. *Paléontologie Marocaine, vol. 2.* Paris.

THOMAS, A. O. 1924. Echinoderms from the Iowa Devonian. *Rep. Iowa geol. Surv.* **29**, 387–505, pl. 35–56.

THORAL, M. 1935. *Contribution a l'étude paléontologique de l'Ordovicien inférieur de la Montagne Noire et révision sommaire de la faune cambrienne de la Montagne Noire*, 362 pp., 35 pls. Montpellier.

UBAGHS, G. 1961. Un échinoderme nouveau de la classe des Carpoïdes dans l'Ordovicien inférieur du département de l'Hérault (France). *C.r. hebd. Séanc. Acad. Sci., Paris*, **253**, 2738–40.

—— 1963a. *Rhopalocystis destombesi* n. g., n. sp. Éocrinoide de l'Ordovicien Inférieur (Tréma-docien Supérieur) du Sud Marocain. *Notes Mém. Serv. Mines Carte géol. Maroc.*, **23**, 25–40, pl. 1–3.

—— 1963b. *Cothurnocystis* Bather, *Phyllocystis* Thoral and an undetermined member of the order Soluta (Echinodermata, Carpoidea) in the uppermost Cambrian of Nevada. *J. Paleont.*, **37**, 1133–42, pl. 151–2.

WHITEHOUSE, F. W. 1961. The Cambrian faunas of North-Eastern Australia Pt. 4. Early Cambrian echinoderms similar to the larval stages of recent forms. *Mem. Qd. Mus.*, **12**, 1–28, pl. 1–4.

WILSON, A. E. 1946. Echinodermata of the Ottawa formation of the Ottawa-St. Lawrence Lowland. *Bull. geol. Surv. Can.*, **4**, v + 61 pp., 6 pls.

WOLBURG, J. 1938. Beitrag zum Problem der Machaeridia. *Paläont. Z.*, **20**, 289–98.

R. P. S. Jefferies, B.A. PH.D. F.G.S.
Department of Palaeontology. British Museum (Natural History), Cromwell Road, London s w 7.

K. A. Joysey, M.A. PH.D. F.G.S.
University Museum of Zoology, Downing Street, Cambridge.

C. R. C. Paul,
Museum of Palaeontology, University of Michigan, Ann Arbor, Michigan, U.S.A.

W. H. C. Ramsbottom M.A. PH.D. F.G.S.
Institute of Geological Sciences, Ring Road, Halton, Leeds 15, Yorkshire.

CHAPTER 22

Echinodermata: Eleutherozoa

Contributors: B. N. FLETCHER, G. M. PHILIP & C. W. WRIGHT

Subphylum ECHINOZOA Haeckel in Zittel 1895

[Classes Helicoplacoidea Durham & Caster 1963 and Cyclocystoidea Miller & Gorley 1895, placed in Echinozoa in Treatise U, are documented in Chapter 21 of this volume—Ed.]

Class EDRIOASTEROIDEA Billings 1858

First, Camb M.Camb: *Stromatocystites walcotti* Schuchert, Olenellus Beds, East Arm, Boone Bay, Newfoundland (Schuchert 1919).

Last, Carb Namur: *Hemicystites ? carbonarius* Bassler, Bluefield Group, Adds Valley, Western Virginia, U.S.A. (Bassler 1936).

Constituent families: Agelocrinitidae Jaekel, M.Camb-Carb Namur; Edrioasteridae Bather, Ord Carad; Cyathocystidae Bather, Ord Llvirn-Ashg; ? Steganoblastidae Bather, Ord Carad.

Comment: The Steganoblastidae (based on *Astrocystites* Whiteaves) can only be referred questionably to this class.

Class OPHIOCISTIOIDEA Sollas 1899

First, Ord Arenig: *Volchovia mobilis* Gekker, Magalaspis lst (B$_{II}$), Volkhov, Leningrad district, U.S.S.R. (Gekker 1940).

Last, Dev Eifel: *Rhenosquama westfalica* Richter, Selscheider beds, Ebbelinghausen, Westphalia, Germany (Richter 1930).

Constituent families: Eucladidae Gregory, Sil Ludl; Rhenosquamidae Richter, Dev Eifel; Sollasinidae Fedotov, Sil Wenl-Ludl; Volchoviidae Gekker, Ord Arenig.

Comment: Ophiocistioids are known only from Europe and U.S.S.R.

Class INCERTAE SEDIS

Order MEGALAPODA MacBride & Spencer 1938

First and **Last,** Ord Ashg: *Eothuria beggi* MacBride & Spencer, Drummock Group, Girvan, Ayrshire, Scotland (MacBride & Spencer 1938).

Constituent family: Eothuriidae MacBride & Spencer.

Comment: The genus *Eothuria*, originally described as a plated holothurian, is probably best considered as an early aberrant echinoid related to the Lepidocentroida.

The Fossil Record, pp. 583–599. Geological Society of London, 1967. Printed in Northern Ireland.

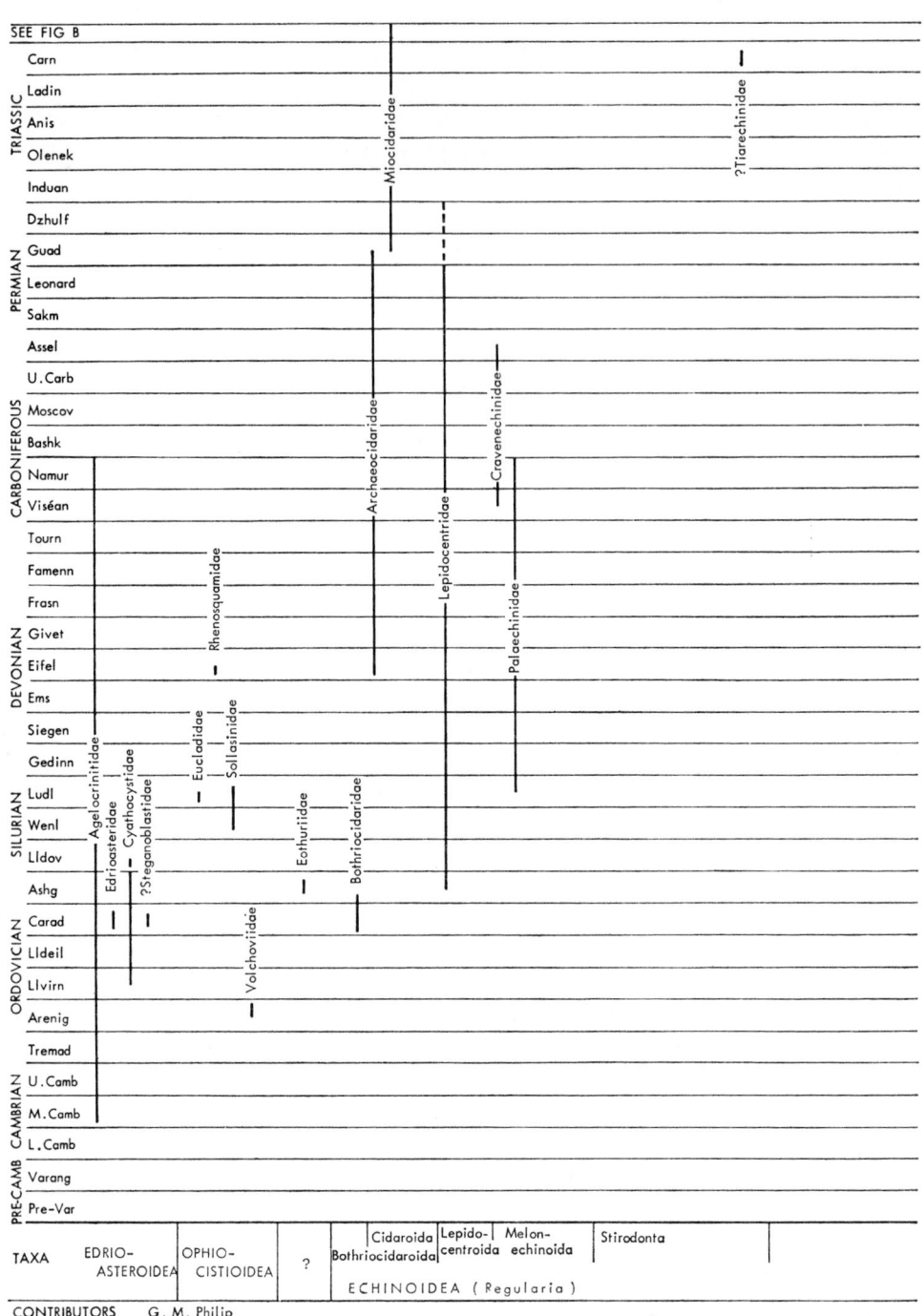

FIG. 22.1 A

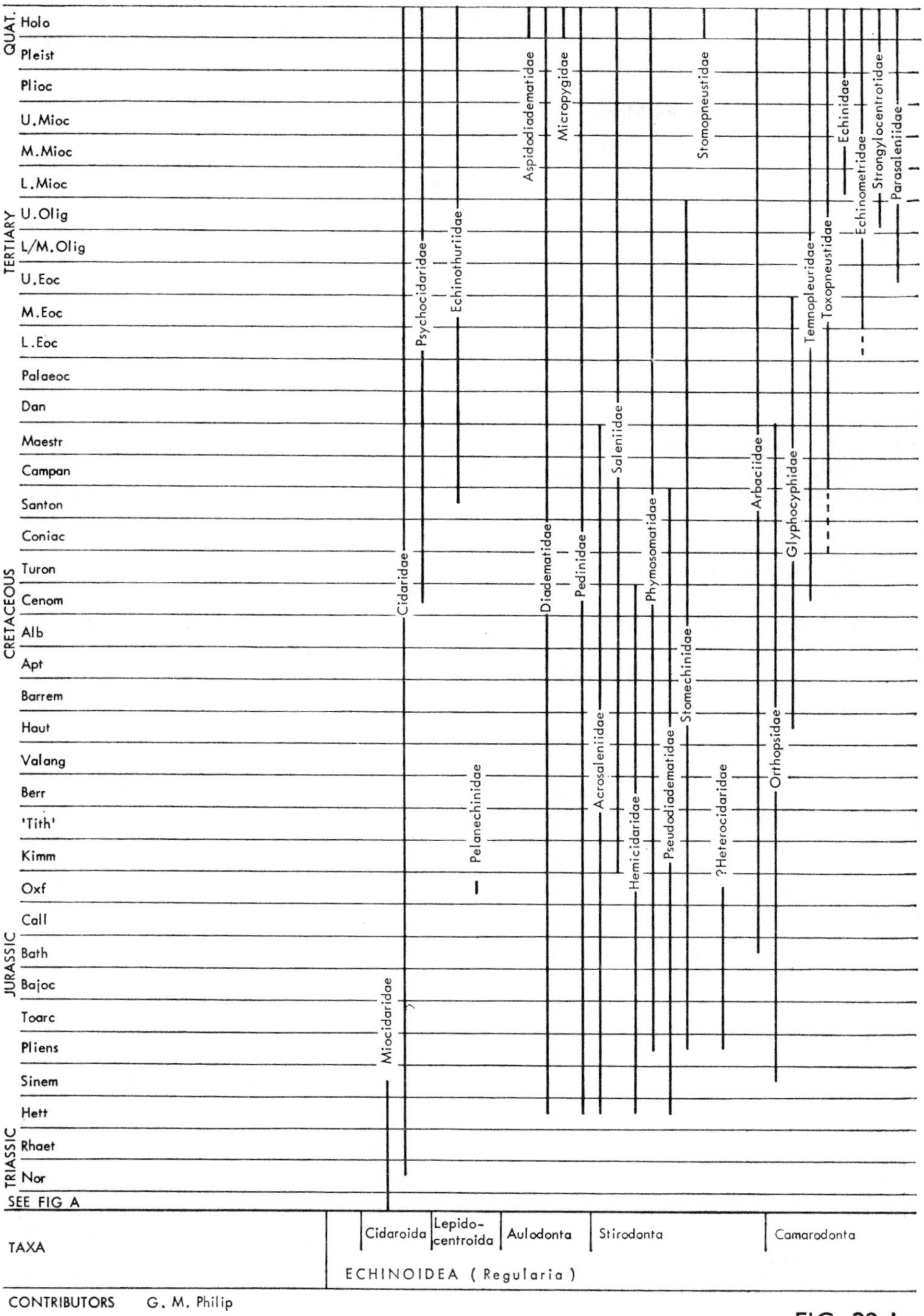

QUAT.
Holo
Pleist
TERTIARY
Plioc
U.Mioc
M.Mioc
L.Mioc
U.Olig
L/M.Olig
U.Eoc
M.Eoc
L.Eoc
Palaeoc
Dan
CRETACEOUS
Maestr
Campan
Santon
Coniac
Turon
Cenom
Alb
Apt
Barrem
Haut
Valang
Berr
'Tith'
Kimm
JURASSIC
Oxf
Call
Bath
Bajoc
Toarc
Pliens
Sinem
Hett
TRIASSIC
Rhaet
Nor
SEE FIG A
Miocidaridae
Cidaridae
Psychocidaridae
Echinothuriidae
Pelanechinidae
Aspidodiadematidae
Diadematidae
Micropygidae
Pedinidae
Acrosaleniidae
Saleniidae
Hemicidaridae
Phymosomatidae
Pseudodiadematidae
Stomechinidae
Stomopneustidae
?Heterocidaridae
Arbaciidae
Orthopsidae
Glyphocyphidae
Temnopleuridae
Toxopneustidae
Echinidae
Echinometridae
Strongylocentrotidae
Parasaleniidae
TAXA
Cidaroida
Lepido-centroida
Aulodonta
Stirodonta
Camarodonta
ECHINOIDEA (Regularia)
CONTRIBUTORS G. M. Philip

FIG. 22.1 B

Class ECHINOIDEA

Subclass REGULARIA Latreille 1825

Superorder PSEUDOECHINACEA Mortensen 1935

Order BOTHRIOCIDAROIDA Zittel 1879

First, Ord Carad: *Bothriocidaris pahleni* Schmidt, Johvi stage (D_I), Estonia (Jackson 1912; Männil 1962).

Last, Ord Ashg: *Bothriocidaris eichwaldi* Männil, Vormsi stage (F_{IC}), Estonia (Männil 1962).

Constituent family: Bothriocidaridae Klem.

Superorder PERISCHOECHINACEA McCoy 1849

Order CIDAROIDA Claus 1880

First, Dev Eifel: *Xenocidaris clavigera* Schultze, Gerolstein, Eifel, Germany (Schultze 1866). *Siluricidaris* Regnéll (1956), based on radioles from the Ludlovian of Gotland, is not certainly a cidaroid. Austin (1848 p. 293) recorded what is apparently an archeocidaroid from the Wenl Lst, Gliddon Hill, Shropshire, England, but the specimen has not been described, and has apparently been lost (Jackson 1912 p. 236). **Extant.**

Constituent families: Archaeocidaridae McCoy, Dev Eifel-Perm Guad; Cidaridae Gray, Trias Nor-extant; Miocidaridae Durham & Melville, Perm Guad-Jur Sinem; Psychocidaridae Ikeda, Cret Cenom-extant.

Comment: The Cretaceous genus *Tylocidaris* is referred to the Psychocidaridae (Philip 1963a). Present distribution, all oceans, particularly the Indo-Pacific region.

Order LEPIDOCENTROIDA Mortensen 1934

(= ECHINOCYSTITOIDA Jackson 1912)

Suborder LEPIDOCENTRINA Mortensen 1934

First, Ord Ashg: *Aulechinus grayae* Bather & Spencer and *Ectinechinus lamonti* MacBride & Spencer, Drummock Group, Girvan, Ayrshire, Scotland (MacBride & Spencer 1938). *Myriastiches gigas* Sollas was thought to be Ord Lldeil (MacBride & Spencer 1938), but the Sil age originally given by Sollas is apparently correct (Durham & Melville 1957).

Last, Perm ?Dzhulf: *Proechinus anatoliensis* Kier, Gomaniibrik Fm, Diyarbakir Province, Turkey (Kier 1965).

Constituent family: For present purposes only one family, Lepidocentridae Lovén, is recognized in this sub-order.

Suborder ECHINOTHURIINA Claus 1880

First, Jur Oxf: *Pelanechinus corallinus* (Wright), Coralline Oolite, Malton, Yorkshire, England, and elsewhere (Groom 1887). **Extant.**

Constituent families: Echinothuriidae Thomson, Cret Santon-extant; Pelanechinidae Groom, Jur Oxf.

Order MELONECHINOIDA Mortensen 1934

First, Sil Ludl: *Gotlandechinus balticus* Regnéll, Klinteberget, Klinteberg Group, Gotland (Regnéll 1956). *Palaechinus* sp. of Mitchell (1897) Sil Ludl, Yass, N.S.W., is probably a cystoid; *"Wrightella" phillipsia* (Forbes 1848) Sil Lldov, Malvern Hills, Welsh Borderland, may be a melonechinoid but is imperfectly known.

Last, Perm Assel: *Xenechinus parvus* Kier, Niel Ranch Fm, Texas (Kier 1958; Ross 1963 p. 25).

Constituent families: Cravenechinidae Hawkins, Carb Viséan-Perm Assel; Palaechinidae McCoy, Sil Ludl-Carb Namur.

Chapter 22: Echinodermata: Eleutherozoa

Superorder DIADEMATACEA Duncan 1889

Order AULODONTA Jackson 1912

Suborder ASPIDODIADEMINA Mortensen 1939

Extant.

Constituent family: Aspidodiadematidae Duncan.
Comment: No fossil representatives of this suborder are known for certain, although Mortensen (1940, p. 21) has suggested that Cret *Tiaridia batnensis* (Cotteau) and Jur *Eosalenia miranda* Lambert may be aspidodiadematids.

Suborder DIADEMINA Duncan 1889

First, Jur Hett: *Eodiadema parvulum* (Tornquist), Angulata Z, Naihingen, Württemberg, Germany (Tornquist 1908). **Extant.**
Constituent families: Diadematidae Gray, Jur Hett-extant; Micropygidae Mortensen, extant.

Suborder PEDININA Mortensen 1939

First, Jur Hett: *Diademopsis heeri* Merian, Schambelen, Asrgau, Switzerland, and other Hett spp., France (Lambert & Thiéry 1910 p. 198). The Carn species referred by Bather (1909) and Lambert & Thiéry (1910 p. 195) to *Mesodiadema*, as presently known, cannot be accepted as diadematacoid echinoids. **Extant.**
Constituent family: Pedinidae Duncan.

Order STIRODONTA Jackson 1912

Suborder CALYCINA Gregory 1900

First, Jur Hett: *Acrosalenia chartroni* Lambert, Revrac, Vendée, France (Lambert 1904).
Extant.
Constituent families: Acrosaleniidae Gregory, Jur Hett-Cret Maestr; Saleniidae L. Agassiz, Jur Kimm-extant.

Suborder PHYMOSOMINA Mortensen 1904

First, Jur Hett: *Plesiocidaris florida* (Merian), Gürbefall, Bernese Alps, Switzerland (Desor & de Loriel 1869 p. 93); *Hessotiara minor* Lambert and *Pseudodiadema primaevum* Lambert, Revrac, Vendée, France (Lambert 1904). *Diplopodia veronensis* (Böhm 1884 p. 761) is listed by Lambert & Thiéry (1910 p. 186) as a Trias Rhaet species, but is apparently younger. **Extant.**
Constituent families: Hemicidaridae Wright, Jur Hett-Cret Cenom; Phymosomatidae Pomel, Jur Pliesn-extant; Pseudodiadematidae Pomel, Jur Hett-Cret Santon; Stomechinidae Pomel, Jur Pliesn-Tert U.Olig; Stomopneustidae Meissner, extant; ? Heterocidaridae Mortensen, Jur Pliesn-Jur Oxf; ? Tiarechinidae Gregory, Trias Carn.

Suborder ARBACIINA Gregory

First, Jur Bath: *Atopechinus cellensis* Thiéry, Celles, Ardèche; also *Acroaster michaleti* Lambert, France (Colligon & Lambert 1928). **Extant.**
Constituent family: Arbaciidae Gray.

Order CAMARODONTA Jackson 1912

Suborder ORTHOPSINA Mortensen 1942

First, Jur Sinem: *Orthopsis parvituberculata* (Boehm), Verona, Italy (Boehm 1884).
Last, Cret Maestr: *Orthopsis perlata* Noetling, Dés Valley, Mari Hills, Baluchistan, Pakistan (Noetling 1897), and other species.
Constituent family: Orthopsidae Duncan.

Suborder TEMNOPLEURINA Mortensen 1942

First, Cret Haut: *Hemidiadema neocomiensis* (Cotteau), Auxerre (Yonne), France (Cotteau 1858–1880 p.184). **Extant.**

Constituent families: Glyphocyphidae Duncan, Cret Haut-Tert M.Eoc; Temnopleuridae Agassiz, Cret Cenom-extant; Toxopneustidae? Cret Santon-extant.

Suborder ECHININA Claus 1876

First, Tert ?M.Eoc: *Echinometra thomsoni* Haime, Baluchistan, Pakistan, (d'Archiac & Haime 1853). **Extant.**

Constituent families: Echinidae Gray, Tert L.Mioc-extant; Echinometridae Gray, Tert M.Eoc-extant; Strongylocentrotidae Gregory, Tert U.Olig-extant; Parasaleniidae Mortensen, Tert U.Eoc-extant.

Comment: The oldest polyporous echininids are discussed elsewhere (Philip 1965b).

Subclass IRREGULARIA Latreille 1825

Superorder GNATHOSTOMATA Zittel 1879

Order HOLECTYPOIDA Duncan 1889

Suborder HOLECTYPINA Duncan 1889

First, Jur Pliens: *Plesiechinus reynesi* Desor, Margaritatus Z., Cabanous (Aveyron), France, Cotteau (1867–1874 p.455).

Last, Cret Maestr: *Galerites sulcatoradiatus* Goldfuss, Fox-les-Caves, Belgium (Smiser 1935) and other Maestrichtian species in Europe and Pakistan (Noetling 1898).

Constituent families: Conulidae Lambert, Cret Haut-Maestr; Discoidiidae Lambert, Cret Apt-Maestr; Galeritidae Gray, Cret Santon-Maestr; Holectypidae Lambert, Jur Pliens-Cret Maestr; Pygasteridae, Jur Pliens-Cret Cenom.

Suborder ECHINONEINA H. L. Clark 1925

First, Jur Call: *Pygopyrina icaunensis* (Cotteau), Yonne, and elsewhere, France and Switzerland (Cotteau 1867–1874 p.396). **Extant.**

Constituent family: Echinoneidae L. Agassiz & Desor.

Comment: It is possible that *Pygopyrina* and other Jur genera placed by Mortensen (1948) in this family may be better referred to the Conulidae.

Order CLYPEASTEROIDA A. Agassiz 1873

Suborder CLYPEASTERINA A. Agassiz 1873

First, Tert U.Eoc: *Clypeaster biarritzensis* Cotteau, Lou Cout près Biarritz, France, and other species (Cotteau 1889–1894 p.228). **Extant.**

Constituent families: Arachnoididae Duncan, Tert U.Olig-extant; Clypeasteridae L. Agassiz, Tert U.Eoc-extant.

Suborder SCUTELLINA Haeckel 1896

First, Cret Maestr: *Echinocyamus placenta* (Goldfuss) and *Fibularia subglobosus* (Goldfuss), St Pieters, Maastricht, Holland (Goldfuss 1826 p.135). **Extant.**

Constituent families: Astriclypeidae Stefanini, Tert L/M.Olig-extant; Fibulariidae Gray, Cret Maestr-extant; Laganidae Desor, Tert U.Eoc-extant; Neolaganidae Durham, Tert U.Eoc-Tert U.Olig; Rotulidae, Tert L.Mioc-extant; Scutellidae Gray, Tert M.Eoc-extant.

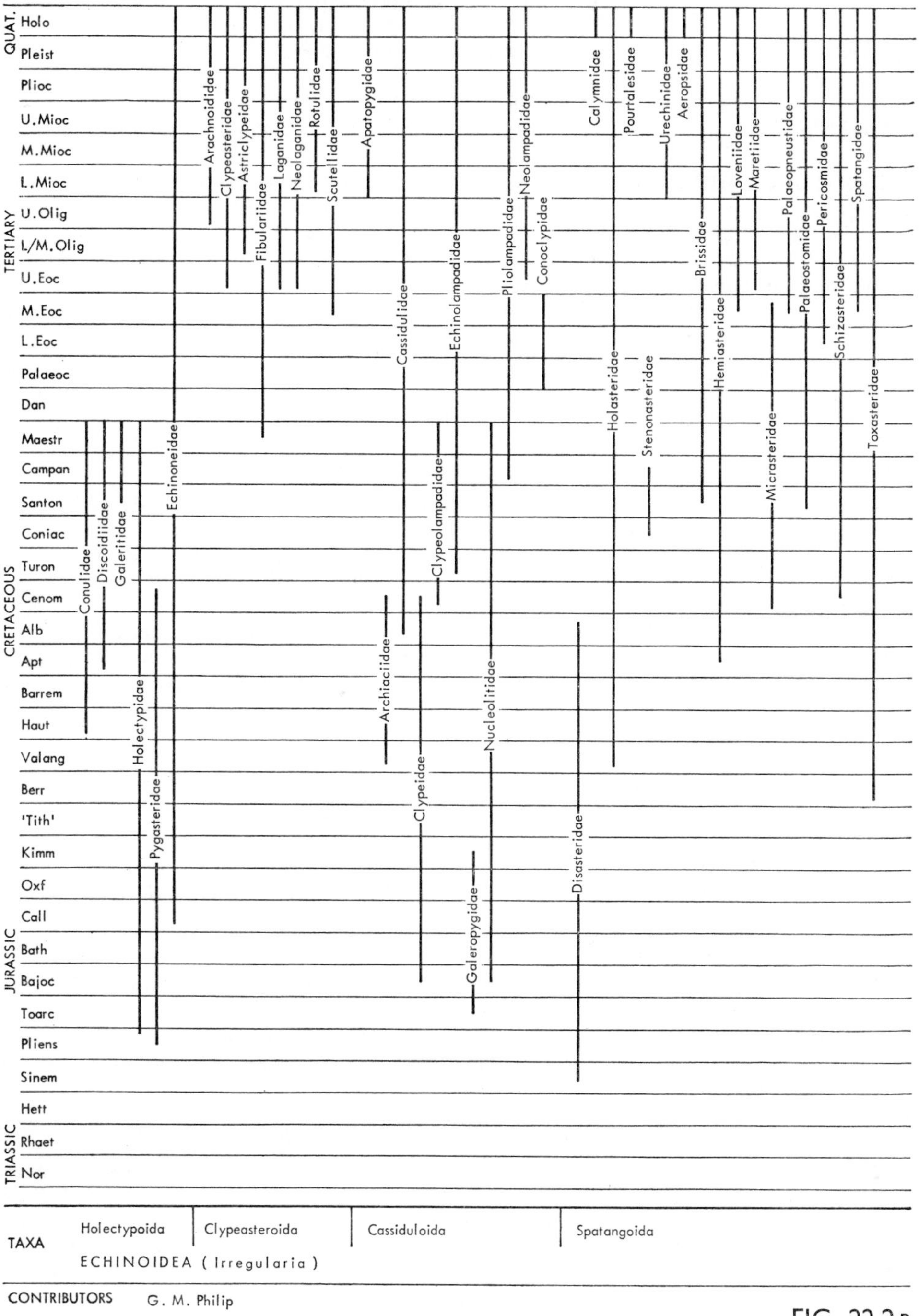
QUAT.
Holo
Pleist
TERTIARY
Plioc
U.Mioc
M.Mioc
L.Mioc
U.Olig
L/M.Olig
U.Eoc
M.Eoc
L.Eoc
Palaeoc
Dan
CRETACEOUS
Maestr
Campan
Santon
Coniac
Turon
Cenom
Alb
Apt
Barrem
Haut
Valang
Berr
'Tith'
Kimm
Oxf
Call
JURASSIC
Bath
Bajoc
Toarc
Pliens
Sinem
Hett
TRIASSIC
Rhaet
Nor
Arachnoididae
Clypeasteridae
Astriclypeidae
Fibulariidae
Laganidae
Neolaganidae
Rotulidae
Scutellidae
Apatopygidae
Cassidulidae
Echinolampadidae
Pliolampadidae
Neolampadidae
Conoclypidae
Calymnidae
Pourtalesidae
Urechinidae
Aeropsidae
Brissidae
Hemiasteridae
Loveniidae
Maretiidae
Palaeopneustidae
Palaeostomidae
Pericosmidae
Schizasteridae
Spatangidae
Toxasteridae
Holasteridae
Stenonasteridae
Micrasteridae
Conulidae
Discoidiidae
Galeritidae
Echinoneidae
Holectypidae
Pygasteridae
Clypeolampadidae
Archiaciidae
Clypeidae
Nucleolitidae
Galeropygidae
Disasteridae
TAXA
Holectypoida
Clypeasteroida
Cassiduloida
Spatangoida
ECHINOIDEA (Irregularia)
CONTRIBUTORS
G. M. Philip

FIG. 22.2B

The Fossil Record, Part II

Superorder ATELOSTOMATA Zittel

Order CASSIDULOIDA Claus 1880

Suborder CASSIDULINA Claus 1880

First, Jur Toarc: *Galeropygus priscus* Cotteau, Solliès-Pont (Var), France (Cotteau 1867–1874). **Extant.**

Constituent families: Apatopygidae Tert L.Mioc-extant; Archiaciidae Cotteau & Triger, Cret Valang-Cenom; Cassidulidae L. Agassiz & Desor, Cret Alb-extant; Clypeidae Lambert, Jur Bajoc-Cret Cenom; Clypeolampadidae Kier, Cret Cenom-Maestr; Echinolampidae Gray, Cret Turon-extant; Galeropygidae Lambert, Jur Toarc-Kimm; Nucleolitidae L. Agassiz & Desor, Jur Bajoc-Cret Maestr; Pliolampadidae Kier, Cret Campan-extant.

Suborder NEOLAMPADINA Philip 1963

First, Tert U.Eoc: *Pisolampas concinna* Philip, Tortachilla Lst, Aldinga, South Australia (Philip 1963b). **Extant.**

Constituent family: Neolampadidae Lambert.

Suborder CONOCLYPINA Zittel 1879

First, Tert Palaeoc: *Conoclypus sindensis* (Duncan & Sladen), Ranikot Series, Petiani, W., Pakistan and other species (Duncan & Sladen 1882).

Last, Tert M.Eoc: *Conoclypus rostratus* (Duncan & Sladen), Khirthar Ser, Hills E. of Trak, W. Sind, Pakistan, and other species (Duncan & Sladen 1884).

Constituent family: Conoclypidae Zittel.

Comment: Dr. Porter Kier (*in litt*, May 1965) records a clypeasteroid lantern in the genus *Haimea*. It seems likely, therefore, that the Oligopygidae, elsewhere questionably referred to the Conoclypina (Philip 1965a p. 59), should be transferred to the Clypeasteroida.

Order SPATANGOIDA Claus 1876

Suborder PROTOSTERNINA Mortensen 1907

First, Jur Sinem: *Pygomalus prior* (Desor), Aargau, Switzerland and France (Beurlen 1934).

Last, Cret Alb: *Collyropsis moussoni* (Desor), Swiss Alps (Beurlen 1934).

Constituent family: Disasteridae Gras 1848.

Comment: Only the family Disasteridae is recognized in this suborder (Jesionek-Szymańska 1963).

Suborder MERIDOSTERNINA Mortensen 1907

First, Cret Valang: *Holaster cordatus* Dubois, Fontanil (Isère) and elsewhere, France (d'Orbigny 1854–1860 p. 81). **Extant.**

Constituent families: Calymnidae Mortensen, extant; Holasteridae Picet, Cret Valang-extant, Pourtalesidae A. Agassiz, extant; Stenonasteridae Lambert, Cret Coniac-Cret Campan; Urechinidae Duncan, Tert L.Mioc-extant.

Suborder AMPHISTERNINA Mortensen 1907

First, Cret Berr: *Toxaster laffitei* Devries, Bel Kheir (Aures), Algeria and *T.rochi* Lambert, Morocco (Devries 1960). **Extant.**

Constituent families: Aeropsidae Lambert, extant; Brissidae Gray, Cret Santon-extant; Hemiasteridae H. L. Clark, Cret Apt-extant; Loveniidae Lambert, Tert M.Eoc-extant; Maretiidae Lambert, Tert U.Eoc-extant; Micrasteridae Lambert, Cret Cenom-Tert M.Eoc; Palaeopneustidae A. Agassiz, Tert M.Eoc-extant; Palaeostomidae Lovén, Cret Santon-extant; Pericosmidae Lambert, L.Eoc-extant; Schizasteridae Lambert, Cret Cenom-extant; Spatangidae Gray, Tert M.Eoc-extant; Toxasteridae Lambert, Cret Berr-extant. [G.M.P.]

Class HOLOTHUROIDEA

General Comment. Apart from a few exceptional occurrences (e.g. in the Jur Kimm, Solenhofen Lst), the fossil record of the holothurians consist of dissociated sclerites. All the families documented below, except the first two, are founded on distinctive types of sclerites.

Family HOLOTHURIIDAE Ludwig 1889

First, Jur Kimm: *Protholothuria armata* Giebel, Gravesiana Z., Solenhofen Lst, Germany (Clark 1912, Frizzell & Exline 1955). **Extant.**

Family SYNAPTIDAE Oestergren 1898

First, Jur Kimm: *Pseudocaudina brachyura* Broili, Gravesiana Z., Solenhofen Lst, Germany (Frizzell & Exline 1955). **Extant.**

Family CALCLAMNIDAE Frizzell & Exline 1955

First, Dev Givet: *Eocaudina septaforaminalis* Martin, Cedar Valley Fm, Iowa (Martin 1952). **Extant.**

Family THEELIIDAE Frizzell & Exline 1955

First, Dev Givet: *Protocaudina hexagonaria* Martin, Cedar Valley Fm, Iowa (Martin 1952). **Extant.**

Family ACHISTRIDAE Frizzell & Exline 1955

First, Carb Viséan: *Achistrum nicholsoni* Etheridge, D2 Z., Hurlet Lst, Fordel, Scotland (Frizzell & Exline 1955).
Last, Cret Barrem: *Achistrum monochordata* Hodson, Harris & Lawson. Speeton, England (Fletcher 1965).

Family STICHOPITIDAE Frizzell & Exline 1955

First, Carb Viséan: *Tetravirga etheridgei* Frizzell & Exline and *Tetravirga fordelensis* Frizzell & Exline, D2 Z., Hurlet Lst, Fordel, Scotland (Frizzell & Exline 1955). **Extant.**

Family ETHERIDGELLIDAE Frizzell & Exline 1955

First, Carb U. Carb: *Etheridgella porosa* Croneis, Wayland sh Fm, Eastland, Texas (Frizzell & Exline 1955).
Last, Jur Oxf: *Frizzellus irregularis* Hampton, Cordatum Z., Dorset (Hampton 1958).

Family CALCLYRIDAE Frizzell & Exline 1955

First and **Last,** Perm Guad: *Calclyra eiseliana* Spandel, Zechstein, Thüringen, Germany (Spandel 1898, Frizzell & Exline 1955).

Family KALIOBULLITIDAE Kristan-Tollmann 1963

First and **Last,** Trias Rhaet: *Kaliobullites umbo* Kristan-Tollmann, Korallenbach, Aussee, Austria (Kristan-Tollmann 1963).

Family PRISCOPEDATIDAE Frizzell & Exline 1955

First, Jur Sinem: *Staurocumites* cf. *bartensteini* Deflandre-Rigaud, Bucklandi Z., d'Osmanville, France (Rioult 1961). **Extant.**

Family CALCANCORIDAE Frizzell & Exline 1955

First, Jur Oxf: *Calcancora sieboldii* (Münster), Streitberg, Germany (Frizzell & Exline 1955). **Extant.**

Family SYNAPTITIDAE Frizzell & Exline 1955

First, Jur Oxf: *Synaptites irregularis* Deflandre-Rigaud, Villers-sur-Mer, France (Deflandre-Rigaud 1949). **Extant.**

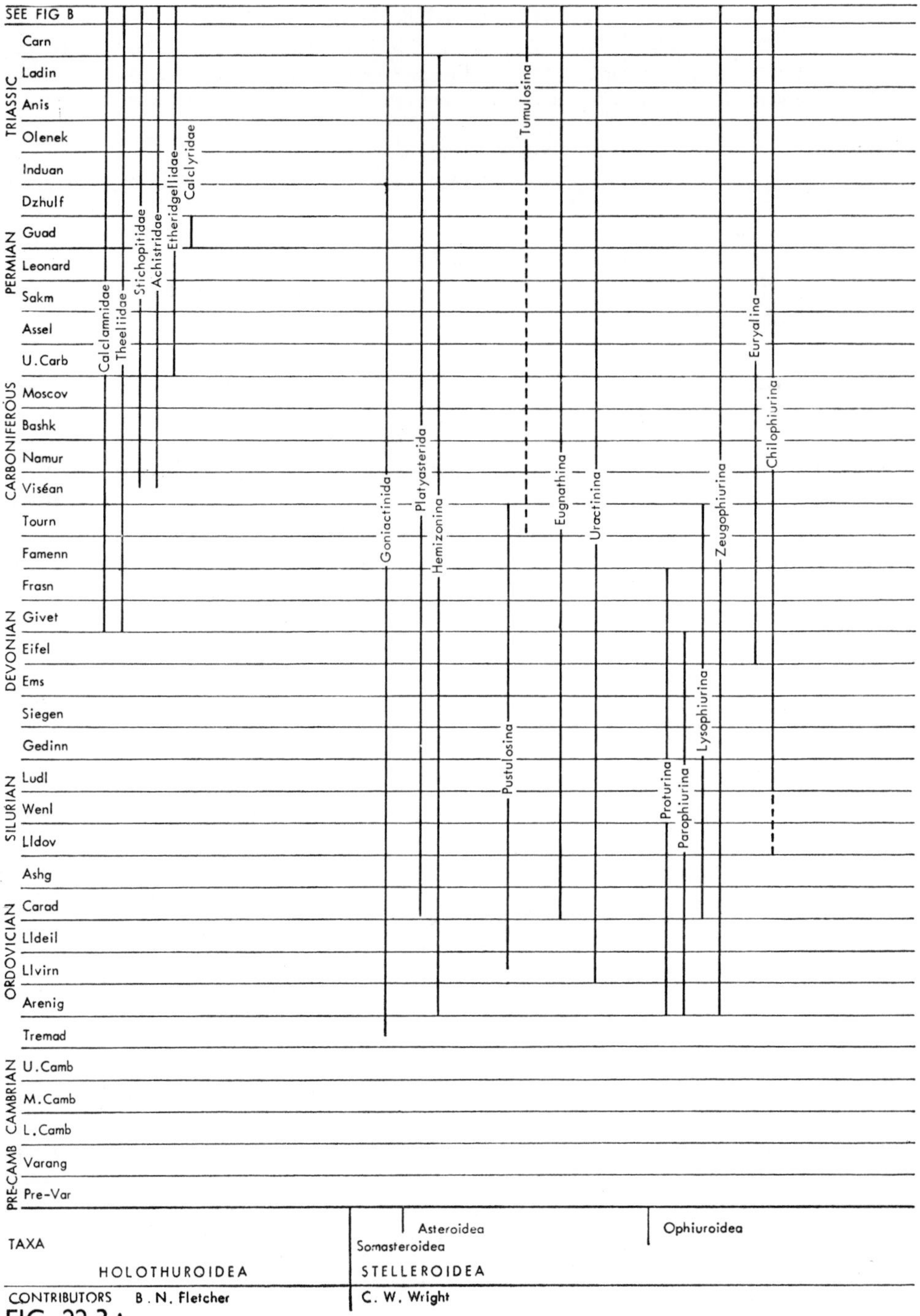

SEE FIG B

TRIASSIC
Carn
Ladin
Anis
Olenek
Induan

PERMIAN
Dzhulf
Guad
Leonard
Sakm
Assel
U.Carb

CARBONIFEROUS
Moscov
Bashk
Namur
Viséan
Tourn
Famenn
Frasn

DEVONIAN
Givet
Eifel
Ems
Siegen
Gedinn

SILURIAN
Ludl
Wenl
Lldov

ORDOVICIAN
Ashg
Carad
Lldeil
Llvirn
Arenig
Tremad

CAMBRIAN
U.Camb
M.Camb
L.Camb

PRE-CAMB
Varang
Pre-Var

Calclamnidae
Theeliidae
Stichopitidae
Achistridae
Etheridgellidae
Calclyridae

Goniactinida
Platyasterida
Hemizonina
Pustulosina
Tumulosina
Euagnathina
Uractinina
Zeugophiurina
Chilophiurina
Euryalina
Lysophiurina
Proturina
Parophiurina

TAXA

HOLOTHUROIDEA

Asteroidea
Somasteroidea

Ophiuroidea

STELLEROIDEA

CONTRIBUTORS   B . N . Fletcher

C. W. Wright

FIG. 22.3 A

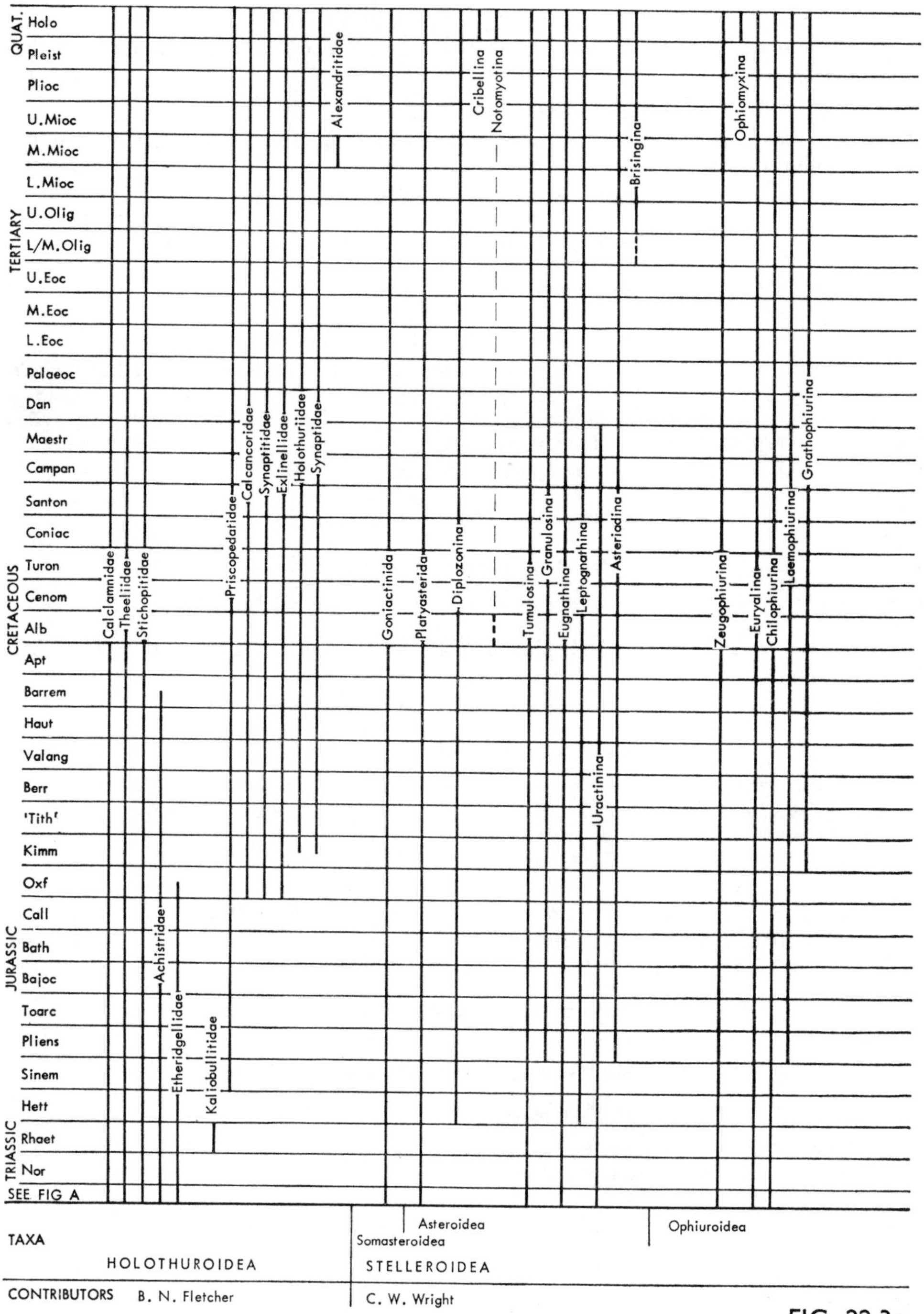

QUAT.
Holo
Pleist
Plioc
U.Mioc
M.Mioc
L.Mioc
TERTIARY
U.Olig
L/M.Olig
U.Eoc
M.Eoc
L.Eoc
Palaeoc
Dan
Maestr
Campan
Santon
Coniac
CRETACEOUS
Turon
Cenom
Alb
Apt
Barrem
Haut
Valang
Berr
'Tith'
Kimm
Oxf
JURASSIC
Call
Bath
Bajoc
Toarc
Pliens
Sinem
Hett
TRIASSIC
Rhaet
Nor
SEE FIG A
Calclamnidae
Theeliidae
Stichopitidae
Achistridae
Etheridgellidae
Kaliobullitidae
Priscopedatidae
Calcancoridae
Synaptitidae
Exlinellidae
Holothuriidae
Synaptidae
Alexandritidae
Goniactinida
Platyasterida
Diplozonina
Cribellina
Notomyotina
Tumulosina
Granulosina
Eugnathina
Leptognathina
Uractinina
Asteriadina
Brisingina
Zeugophiurina
Ophiomyxina
Euryalina
Chilophiurina
Laemophiurina
Gnathophiurina
TAXA
Asteroidea
Somasteroidea
Ophiuroidea
HOLOTHUROIDEA
STELLEROIDEA
CONTRIBUTORS
B. N. Fletcher
C. W. Wright

FIG. 22.3B

Family EXLINELLIDAE Deflandre-Rigaud 1961

First, Jur Oxf: *Exlinella frizzelli* Deflandre-Rigaud, Villers-sur-Mer, France (Deflandre-Rigaud 1962). **Extant.**

Family ALEXANDRITIDAE Kristan-Tollmann 1964

First and **Last,** Tert M. Mioc: *Alexandrites alexandri* Kristan-Tollmann, Burgenland, Austria (Kristan-Tollmann 1964). (B.N.F.)

Subphylum ASTEROZOA Zittel, 1895

Class STELLEROIDEA Lamarck, 1801

Subclass SOMASTEROIDEA Spencer, 1951

Order GONIACTINIDA Spencer, 1951

First, Ord Tremad: *Chinianaster levyi* Thoral, *Villebrunaster thorali* Spencer and *Ampullaster ubaghsi* Fell, U.Tremad, Herault, France (Spencer, 1951). **Extant.**
Constituent families: Chinianasteridae Spencer, Ord Tremad (U.)-Arenig (L.); Villebrunasteridae Fell, Ord Tremad (U.); Platasteriidae Caso, extant; Archegonasteridae Spencer, Ord Arenig (U.); Archophiactinidae Spencer, Ord Ashg-Dev (U.).

Subclass ASTEROIDEA Lamarck, 1816

Order PLATYASTERIDA Spencer, 1951

First, Ord Carad: *Platanaster ordovicus* Spencer, Shropshire, England (Spencer, 1919). **Extant.**
Constituent families: Palasteriscidae Gregory, Ord Carad-Dev Eifel; Luidiidae Verrill, Tert Mioc-extant.

Order PAXILLOSIDA Perrier, 1884

Suborder HEMIZONINA Spencer, 1951

First, Ord Arenig; *Petraster ramseyensis* Hicks, L.Arenig, S.Wales (Spencer, 1918).
Last, Trias Ladin: *Trichasteropsis weissmanni* (Münster), Muschelkalk, Germany.
Constituent families: Petrasteridae Spencer, Ord Arenig-Sil; Lepidasteridae Gregory, Sil Wenl-Dev. (U.); Palasterinidae Gregory, L.Sil-Trias Ladin.

Suborder DIPLOZONINA Spencer & Wright, 1966

First, Jur Hett: *Plesiastropecten hallovensis* Peyer, Switzerland (Hess, 1955). **Extant.**
Constituent family: Astropectinidae Gray.

Suborder CRIBELLINA Fisher, 1911

Extant.
Constituent families: Gonipectinidae Verrill; Porcellanasteridae Sladen.

Suborder NOTOMYOTINA Ludwig, 1910

First, Cret ?Alb: *Benthopecten?* sp., U.Alb, Yorkshire, England (Treatise U). **Extant.**
Constituent family: Benthopectinidae Verrill.

Order VALVATIDA Perrier, 1884

Suborder PUSTULOSINA Spencer, 1951

First, Ord Llanv: *Protopalaeaster* sp., Czechoslovakia (Spencer 1950).
Last, Carb Tourn: *Neopalaeaster crawfordsvillensis* (Miller), Keokuk group, Indiana (Schuchert, 1915).

Constituent families: Palaeasteridae Miller, Sil Wenl-? Carb Perm; Hudsonasteridae Schuchert, Ord Arenig (U.)-U.Sil; Neopalaeasteridae Schuchert, Carb Tourn; Mesopalaeasteridae Schuchert, Ord Ashg-Dev Frasn; Xenasteridae Gregory, Eifel; Promopalaeasteridae Schuchert, Ord Carad-Sil; Eoactinidae Spencer, Sil.

Suborder TUMULOSINA Spencer & Wright, 1966

First, Carb Perm: *Monaster clarkei* (de Koninck), New South Wales (Etheridge, 1892).
Extant.
Constituent families: Monasteridae Schuchert, Carb Perm; Stauranderasteridae Spencer, Jur Bath-Tert Dan; Sphaerasteridae Schöndorf, Jur Oxf-extant.

Suborder GRANULOSINA Perrier, 1894

First, Jur Pliens: *Pycinaster mortenseni* Mercier, Calvados, France (Mercier, 1935). **Extant.**
Constituent families: Odontasteridae Verrill, Jur ?Bajoc-extant; Chaetasteridae Sladen, extant; Archasteridae Viguier, Tert ? Mioc-extant; Goniasteridae Forbes, Jur Pliens-extant; Oreasteridae Fisher, extant; Ophidiasteridae Verrill, Cret Cenom-extant; Radiasteridae Fisher, extant.

Order SPINULOSIDA Perrier, 1884

Suborder EUGNATHINA Spencer & Wright, 1966

First, Ord Carad: *Schuchertia stellata* (Billings), Trenton Fm, Canada. **Extant.**
Constituent families: Taeniactinidae Spencer, Ord Carad-Carb Tourn; Lepyriactinidae Spencer & Wright, Sil Wenl; Schuchertiidae Schuchert, Ord Carad-Sil Wenl; Helianthasteridae Gregory, Dev Eifel; Solasteridae Perrier, Jur Pliens-extant; Tropidasteridae Wright, Jur Pliensb; Korethrasteridae Danielsson & Koren, extant; Pythonasteridae Sladen, extant; Pterasteridae Perrier, extant.

Suborder LEPTOGNATHINA Spencer & Wright 1965

First, Jur Hett: *Diclidaster gevreyi* de Loriol, Ardêche, France (Loriol, 1897). **Extant.**
Constituent families: Asterinidae Gray, Jur Bajoc-extant; Ganeriidae Sladen, extant; Poraniidae Perrier, extant; Echinasteridae Verrill, ? U.Cret-extant; Valvasteridae Viguier, Hett-extant; Acanthasteridae Sladen, extant; Mithrodiidae Viguier, extant; Metrodiridae Sladen, extant.

Order FORCIPULATIDA Perrier, 1884

Suborder URACTININA Spencer & Wright, 1966

First, Ord Llvirn: *Bohemaster primula* Jaekel and undescribed member of Cnemidactinidae, Czechoslovakia (Spencer, 1950).
Last, Cret Maestr: *Arthraster cristatus* Spencer, England (Spencer, 1913).
Constituent families: Cnemidactinidae Spencer, Ord Llvirn-Ashg; Urasterellidae Schuchert, Ord Llvirn-Carb Perm; Calliasterellidae Schöndorf, Carb Tourn-Cret Maestr.

Suborder ASTERIADINA Fisher, 1928

First, Jur Pliens: *Asterias* (sensu lato) *gaveyi* Forbes, England (Wright, 1863-1880).
Extant.
Constituent families: Heliasteridae Viguier, extant; Zoroasteridae Sladen, extant; Asteriidae Gray, Jur Pliens-extant.

Suborder BRISINGINA Fisher, 1928

First, Tert Olig: undescribed member of Brisingidae, California (Durham, 1964). **Extant.**
Constituent family: Brisingidae Sars, Tert Olig-extant.

The Fossil Record, Part II

Subclass OPHIUROIDEA Gray, 1840

Order STENURIDA Spencer, 1951

Suborder PROTURINA Spencer & Wright, 1966

First, Ord Arenig: *Pradesura jacobi* (Thoral), L.Arenig, Herault, France (Spencer, 1951).
Last, Dev Frasn: *Ptilonaster princeps* Hall, New York (Schuchert, 1915).
Constituent families: Pradesuridae Spencer, Ord Arenig-Dev Eifel; Phragmactinidae Spencer, Ord Ashg; Rhopalocomidae Spencer & Wright, Sil Ludl-Carb Frasn; Bdellacomidae Spencer & Wright, Sil Ludl-Dev Eifel.

Suborder PAROPHIURINA Jaekel, 1923

First, Ord Arenig: *Eophiura bohemica* Schuchert, *Palaeura neglecta* Schuchert, U.Arenig, Czechoslovakia (Spencer, 1951).
Last, Dev Eifel: *Medusaster rhenanus* Stürtz, Germany (Lehmann, 1957).
Constituent families: Eophiuridae Schöndorf, Ord Arenig; Palaeuridae Spencer, Ord Arenig-Dev Eifel; Stenasteridae Schuchert, Ord Carad-Ashg.

Order OEGOPHIURIDA Matsumoto, 1915

Suborder LYSOPHIURINA Gregory, 1896

First, Ord Carad: *Protaster salteri* (Salter), L.Carad, Wales (Spencer, 1934).
Last, Carb Tourn: *Euzonosoma montanum* (Raymond), Madison fm, Montana (Spencer 1934, p. 418).
Constituent families: Encrinasteridae Schuchert, Ord Ashg-Carb Tourn; Protasteridae Miller, Ord Carad-Carb Tourn.

Suborder ZEUGOPHIURINA Matsumoto, 1929

First, Ord Arenig: *Hallaster* sp., U. Arenig, Czechoslovakia (Spencer, 1951).   **Extant.**
Constituent families: Lapworthuridae Gregory, L.Ord-L.Dev; Furcasteridae Stürtz, U.Ord-Carb Tourn; Klasmuridae Spencer, U.Dev; Ophiocanopidae Mortensen, extant.

Order PHRYNOPHIURIDA Matsumoto, 1915

Suborder OPHIOMYXINA Fell, 1962

Extant.
Constituent family: Ophiomyxidae Ljungman.

Suborder EURYALINA Lamacck, 1816

First, Dev Eifel: *Eospondylus primigenius* (Stürtz), *Kentrospondylus decadactylus* Lehmann, Germany (Lehmann, 1957).   **Extant.**
Constituent families: Eospondylidae Spencer & Wright, Dev Eifel; Onychasteridae Miller, L.Carb; Asteronychidae Muller & Troschel, Cret ? Santon-extant; Asteroschematidae Verrill, extant; Gorgonocephalidae Ljungman, Tert Olig-extant; Euryalidae Gray, extant.

Order OPHIURIDA Lamarck, 1816

Suborder CHILOPHIURINA Matsumoto, 1915

First, Sil: *Argentinaster bodenbenderi* Ruedemann, Argentina (Ruedemann, 1916).   **Extant.**
Constituent families: Ophiurinidae Gregory, Sil-Carb Tourn; Ophiuridae Lyman, Carb Tourn-extant; Ophioleucidae Matsumoto, Jur ? Pliens-extant; Ophiocomidae Ljungman, Jur ? Oxf-extant; Ophionereididae Ljungman, extant; Ophiodermatidae Ljungman, Jur Pliens-extant.

Chapter 22: Echinodermata: Eleutherozoa

Suborder LAEMOPHIURINA Matsumoto, 1917

First, Jur Pliens: *Ophiacantha ? dorecki* Hess, Switzerland (Hess, 1962). **Extant.**
Constituent families: Ophiacanthidae Perrier, Jur ? Pliens-extant; Hemieuryalidae
Verrill, Jur ? Pliens-extant.

Suborder GNATHOPHIURINA Matsumoto, 1915

First, Jur Kimm: *Ophiothrix ? royeri* (de Loriol), Switzerland (Hess, 1960). **Extant.**
Constituent families: Amphilepididae Matsumoto, extant; Ophiactidae Matsumoto,
extant; Amphiuridae Ljungman, Cret Cenom-extant; Ophiothricidae Ljungman, Jur Kimm-
extant. [C.W.W.]

REFERENCES

D'ARCHIAC, A. & HAIME, J. 1853. *Description des animaux fossiles du Groupe Nummulitique de l'Inde.*
1–373, pl. 1–36. Paris.
AUSTIN, T. 1848. Observations on the Cystidae of M. von Buch, and the Crinoidea generally.
Q. Jl geol. Soc. Lond. **4,** 291–294.
BASSLER, R. S. 1936. New species of American Edrioasteroidea. *Smithson. Misc. Collns,* **95**(6),
1–33.
BATHER, F. A. 1909. Triassic Echinoderms of Bakony. *Resultate wiss. Erforschung Balatonsees,*
Paläont. **1**(6).
BEURLEN, K. 1934. Monographie der Echinoiden-Familie Collyritidae d'Orb. *Palaeontographica,*
80A, 41–144.
BOEHM, G. 1884. Beitrag zur kenntniss der grauen Kalke in Venetien. *Z. dt. geol. Ges.,* **36,**
737–782, pl. 15–26.
CLARKE, H. L. 1912. Fossil Holothurians. *Science, N.Y.,* **35,** 274–278.
COLLIGON, M. & LAMBERT, J. 1928. Espèces nouvelles d'Échinides fossiles établies par Paul
Thiéry. *Bull. géol. Soc. Fr.* (4), **28,** 261–271, pl. 20–21.
COTTEAU, G. 1858–1880. *Échinides nouveaux ou peu connus.* 1re Série. (extracted from *Rev. Mag.*
Zool.)
—— 1867–1874. *Paléontologie Française. Tome IX. Terrain jurassique. Échinides irréguliers.* Paris.
—— 1889–1894. *Paléontologie Française. Terrain tertiaire. Échinides éocènes. Tome II.* Paris.
DEFLANDRE-RIGAUD, M. 1949. Revision du Manipule Synaptites, sclérites de Holothurides
fossiles. *Bull. Inst. océanogr. Monaco,* no. 946, 1–11.
—— 1962. Contribution à la connaissance des sclérites d'Holothurides Fossiles. *Mém. Mus.*
natn Hist. nat., Paris series C, **11** (1), 1–123.
DESOR, E. & DE LORIOL, P. 1868–1872. *Échinologie Helvétique. Échinides de la Periode Jurassique.*
Wiesbaden & Paris.
DEVRIES, A. 1960. Contribution a l'étude de quelques groupes d'Echinides fossiles d'Algérie.
Publs Serv. Carte géol. Algér., Mem. Paléont., **3.**
D'ORBIGNY, A. 1854–1860. *Paléontologie Française. Terrain crétacé. Échinoides irréguliers,* VI, Paris.
DUNCAN, P. M. & SLADEN, W. P. 1882–1886. Fossil Echinoidea of Western Sind and the Coast
of Biluchistan and of the Persian Gulf, from the Tertiary formations. *Mem. géol. Surv. India*
Palaeont. indica (14), **1**(3), 1–382, pl. 1–58.
DURHAM, J. W. 1964. *In* ZULLO, V. A. *et al.* The echinoid genus *Salenia* in the Eastern Pacific.
Palaeontology, **7,** 331–349.
—— & MELVILLE, R. V. 1957. A classification of echinoids. *J. Paleont.,* **31,** 242–272.
ETHERIDGE, R. 1892. A monograph of the Carboniferous and Permo-Carboniferous Invertebrata
of New South Wales. Part II. Echinodermata, Annelida, and Crustacea. *Mem. geol. Surv.*
N.S.W. (Palaeontology), **5,** 67–131, pl. 12–22.
FLETCHER, B. N. 1965. Holothurian sclerites from the Speeton clay. *Nature, Lond.,* **208,** 281.
FORBES, D. 1848. *In* PHILLIPS, J. & SALTER, W. J. Palaeontological Appendix to Professor John
Phillips Memoir on the Malvern Hills. *Mem. geol. Surv. U.K.,* **2**(1), 384–385, pl. 29.

Frizzell, D. L. & Exline, H. 1955. Monograph of Fossil Holothurian Sclerites. *Tech. Bull. Sch. Mines Metall Univ. Mo.*, **89**, 1–204, pl. 1–11.

Gekker, R. F. 1940. Carpoidea, Eocrinoidea i Ophiocistia nizhnego silura Leningradskoy oblasti i Estonii. *Trudy paleont. Inst.*, **9**(4), 5–82.

Goldfuss, A. 1826. *Petrefacta Germaniae* I, 1–252. Dusseldorf.

Groom, T. T. 1887. On some new features in *Pelanechinus corallinus*. *Q. Jl geol. Soc. Lond.*, **43**, 703–714.

Hampton, J. S. 1958. *Frizzellus irregularis*, a new holothurian sclerite from the Upper Bathonian of the Dorset coast, England. *Micropaleontology*, **4**, 309–316.

Hess, H. 1955. Die fossilen Astropectiniden (Asteroidea). *Schweiz. paläont. Abh.*, **71**, 1–113, pl. 1–4, text fig. 1–62.

—— 1960. Ophiurenreste aus dem Malm des Schweitezr Juras und des Departments Haut-Rhin. *Eclog. geol. Helv.*, **53**, 385–421, text fig. 1–50.

—— 1962. Mikropaläontologische Untersuchungen an Ophiuren. *ibid.*, **55**, 595–656, text fig. 1–142.

Jackson, R. T. 1912. Phylogeny of the Echini, with a revision of Paleozoic species. *Mem. Boston Soc. nat. Hist.*, **7**, 1–433, pl. 1–76.

Jesionek-Szymańska, W. 1963. Échinides irréguliers du Dogger de Pologne. *Acta palaeont. pol.*, **8**, 293–414.

Kier, P. M. 1958. Permian echinoids from West Texas. *J. Paleont.*, **32**, 889–892, pl. 114.

—— 1965. Evolutionary trends in Paleozoic echinoids. *J. Paleont.*, **39**, 436–465.

Kristan-Tollmann, E. 1963. Holothurien-Sklerite aus der Trias der Ostalpen. *Sber. öst. Akad. Wiss.*, **172**, 351–380, pl. 1–10.

—— 1964. Holothurien-Sklerite aus dem Torton des Burgenlandes, Österreich. *Sber. öst. Akad. Wiss.*, **173**, 75–100, pl. 1–9.

Lambert, J. 1904. Note sur L'infralias de la Vendée et des Deuxsevres (Suite). IV—Echinides. *Bull. geol. Soc. Fr.* (4), **3**, 538–544, pl. 18 (partim).

—— & Thièry, P. 1909–1925. *Essai de nomenclature raisonnée des échinides*, 1–607. Chaumont.

Lehmann, W. M. 1957. Die Asterozoen in den Dachschiefern des rheinischen Unterdevons. *Abh. hess. Landesamt. Bodenforsch.*, **21**, 160 p., 55 pl., 31 text-figs.

Loriol, M. P. de 1897. Notes pour servir à l'etude des Échinodermes [VI]. *Revue suisse Zool.*, **5**.

Macbride, W. & Spencer, W. K. 1938. Two new Echinoidea, *Aulechinus* and *Ectinechinus*, and an adult plated holothurian, *Eothuria*, from the Upper Ordovician of Girvan, Scotland. *Phil. Trans. R. Soc.*, **229B**, 91–136, pl. 10–17.

Männil, R. 1962. The taxonomy and morphology of Bothriocidaris (Echinoidea). *Geoloogia-Inst. Uurimi*, **9**, 143–190, 5 pl. (Russian).

Martin, W. R. 1952. Holothuroidea from the Iowa Devonian. *J. Paleont.*, **26**, 728–729.

Mercier, J. 1935. Les Stellérides mésozoiques du Bassin de Paris (bordure occidentale). *Mém. Soc. linn. Normandie* (n.s. geol.), **1**, 1–66, pl. 1–3.

Mitchell, J. 1897. On the occurrence of the genus *Palaechinus* in the Upper Silurian rocks of New South Wales. *Proc. Linn. Soc. N.S.W.*, **22**, 258–259.

Mortensen, T. 1940. *A monograph of the Echinoidea*, III(1); C. A. Reitzel, Copenhagen, 1–370.

—— 1948. Idem, IV(1). 1–363.

Noetling, F. 1897. Fauna of Baluchistan and N. W. Frontier of India. Part 3. Fauna of the Upper Cretaceous (Mäestrichtien) Beds of the Mari Hills. *Mem. geol. Surv. India Palaeont. indica* (16), **1**, 1–79, pl. 1–21.

Philip, G. M. 1963a. The Tertiary echinoids of south-eastern Australia. I. Introduction and Cidaridae (1). *Proc. R. Soc. Vict.*, **76**, 181–226, pl. 21–26.

—— 1963b. Two Australian Tertiary neolampadids and the classification of cassiduloid echinoids. *Palaeontology*, **6**, 718–726, pl. 106–107.

—— 1965a. Classification of echinoids. *J. Paleont.*, **39**, 45–62.

—— 1965b. The Tertiary echinoids of south-eastern Australia. III. Stirodonta, Aulodonta, and Camarodonta (1). *Proc. R. Soc. Vict.*, **78**, 181–196, pl. 26–29.

Regnéll, G. 1956. Silurian echinoids from Gotland. *Ark. Miner., Geol.* **2**, 155–178, pl. 1–4.

RICHTER, R. 1930. Schuppenrohren als Anzeiger von zwei im deutschen Devon neuen Echinodermen-Gruppen (Edrioasteroidea Billings und Ophiocistia Sollas?). *Senckenberg. Leth.*, **12,** 279–304.

RIOULT, M. 1961. Les sclerites d'Holothuries du Lias, *in* Colloque sur les Lias français. *Mém. Bur. Rech. géol. min.*, **4,** 121–153.

ROSS, C. A. 1963. Standard Wolfcamp series (Permian), Glass Mountains, Texas. *Mem. geol. Soc. Am.*, **88,** 1–205, pl. 1–29.

RUEDEMANN, R. 1916. Paleontologic Contributions from the New York State Museum.

SCHUCHERT, C. 1915. Revision of Paleozoic Stelleroidea with special reference to North American Asteroidea. *Bull. U.S. natn. Mus.*, **88,** 311 pp.

—— 1919. A Lower Cambrian edrioasterid, *Stromatocystites walcotti*. *Smithson. Misc. Collns.*, **70**(1), 1–8.

SCHULTZE, L. 1866. Monographie der Echinodermen des Eifler Kalkes. *Denksch. Akad. Wiss. Wien*, **26,** 1–118.

SMISER, J. S. 1935. A monograph of the Belgian Cretaceous echinoids. *Mém. Mus. r. Hist. nat. Belg.*, **68,** 1–98, pl. 1–9.

SPANDEL, E. 1898. Die Echinodermen aus deutschen Zechsteins. *Abh. naturhist. Ges., Nürnberg*, **11,** 17–45.

SPENCER, W. K. 1913. The evolution of the Cretaceous Asteroidea. *Phil. Trans. R. Soc.*, **202B,** 99–177, pl. 9–10.

—— 1914–1940. British Palaeozoic Asterozoa. Parts 1–10. *Palaeontogr. Soc.* [*Monogr.*], 540 p., 37 pl., 348 text fig.

—— 1950. Asterozoa and the study of Palaeozoic faunas. *Geol. Mag.*, **87,** 393–408.

—— 1951. Early Palaeozoic Starfish. *Phil. Trans. R. Soc.* **235B,** 87–129, pl. 2–8, text fig. 1–24.

TORNQUIST, A. 1908. Die Diatematoiden des württembergischen Lias. *Z. dt. geol. Ges.*, **60,** 378–430, pl. 15–19.

TREATISE U. 1966. Echinodermata 3: Asterozoa, Echinozoa, etc. *In* MOORE, R. C. (Editor) *Treatise on Invertebrate Paleontology.* University of Kansas Press.

WRIGHT, T. 1863–1880. British Fossil Echinodermata of the Oolitic formations: vol. 2, Asteroidea and Ophiuroidea. Parts 1–3. *Palaeontogr. Soc.* [*Monogr.*], 203 pp., 21 pl.

B. N. Fletcher, PH.D. F.G.S.
    Plot 13, Linkdale Estate, Maldon Road, Gt. Boddow, Essex.
G. M. Philip, M.SC. PH.D. F.G.S.
    Geology Department, University of New England, Armidale, New South Wales, Australia.
C. W. Wright, M.A. F.G.S.
    37 Phillimore Gardens, Kensington, London W 8.

CHAPTER 23

Chordata: Hemichordata (including Graptolithina), Pogonophora, Urochordata and Cephalochordata

Contributors: C. H. HOLLAND, R. B. RICKARDS, D. SKEVINGTON,
I. STRACHAN & L. B. H. TARLO

Introduction. The classification of the Chordata is that employed by Tarlo (1960). The reasons for including the Hemichordata and Pogonophora within the Chordata, rather than giving them the rank of independent phyla as in the Zoological Record, are discussed in detail in a more recent account (Tarlo 1967). [L.B.H.T.]

Phylum CHORDATA

Subphylum HEMICHORDATA

Class PTEROBRANCHIA Lankester 1878

Order RHABDOPLEURIDA Fowler 1892

First, Ord Llvirn: *Rhabdopleuroides expectatus* Kozłowski, Vaginoceras Lst, Poznan, Poland (Kozłowski 1961). **Extant.**

Order CEPHALODISCIDA Fowler 1892

First, Ord Tremad: *Eocephalodiscus polonicus* Kozłowski, Glauconitic Sst, Wysoczki, S. Poland (Kozłowski 1949). **Extant.** [L.B.H.T.]

Class GRAPTOLITHINA Bronn 1846

Order DENDROIDEA Nicholson 1872

Family DENDROGRAPTIDAE Roemer in Frech 1897

First, Camb U. Camb: *Callograptus antiquus* Ruedemann, *Dendrograptus edwardsi major* Ruedemann, and *D. hallianus moneymakeri* Ruedemann, Nolichucky Sh, Tennessee (Ruedemann 1947); other approximately coeval species of *Dictyonema, Callograptus, Dendrograptus* and *Aspidograptus* from: U. Wilberns Fm, Texas (Decker 1945); Deadwood Fm, S. Dakota; Trempeleau Fm, Gaspé (Eau Claire) Quebec (Ruedemann 1933, 1947); and Potsdam Fm, New York (Hall 1865). A dendroid graptolite, undescribed, but possibly *Dendrograptus*, has been obtained from the M.Camb, P. davidis Z, Comley, England.

Last, Carb Namur *Dictyonema* sp. (undescribed, mentioned Bulman 1955 *in* Treatise V p. 18) Eumorphoceras Z (E_1) Yorkshire, England.

Constituent genera: As in Treatise V but excluding *Reticulograptus* Wiman which is a tuboid.

Family ANISOGRAPTIDAE Bulman 1950

First, Ord Tremad; undescribed forms referable to *Bryograptus* mentioned Tjernvik (1958), D. flabelliforme desmograptoides Z., Flagabro, Scania.

Last, Ord Lldeil-Carad (L): *Calyxdendrum graptoloides* Kozłowski, Poznan and Warsaw, Poland (Kozłowski 1960).

Constituent genera: *Anisograptus* Ruedemann, *Adelograptus* Bulman, *Bryograptus* Lapworth, *Clonograptus* Hall and Nicholson, *Radiograptus* Bulman, *Staurograptus* Emmons, *Triograptus* Monsen, *Kiaerograptus* Spjeldnaes 1963, *Calyxdendrum* Kozłowski 1960.

Family ACANTHOGRAPTIDAE Bulman 1938

First, Camb U. Camb: *Acanthograptus priscus* Ruedemann, Trempealeauan Stage, Jordan Sst Afton, Minnesota and Arbuckle Lst, Oklahoma (Ruedemann 1947).

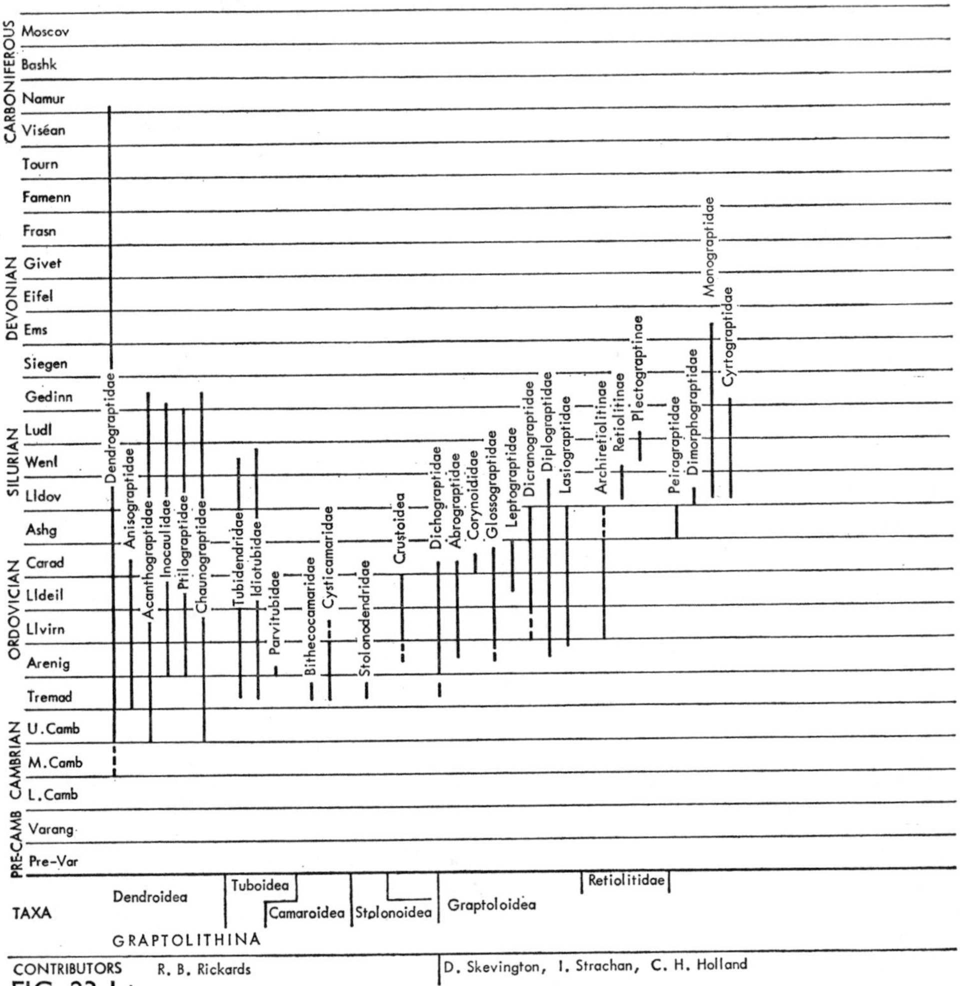

FIG. 23.1·A

CONTRIBUTORS   R. B. Rickards   D. Skevington, I. Strachan, C. H. Holland

Chapter 23: Chordata: Hemichordata, Pogonophora, Urochordata and Cephalochordata

Last, Dev Gedinn: *Palaeodictyota rotundatum* Bouček, *P. textorium* (Počta) and *P. undulatum* (Počta), hercynicus Z, Lochkov Lst, Kasor, Czechoslovakia (Bouček 1957).

Constituent genera: *Acanthograptus* Spencer, *Coremagraptus* Bulman, *Palaeodictyota* Whitfield. *Dyadograptus* Obut is not recognized here.

Family INOCAULIDAE Reudemann 1947

First, Ord Arenig: *Thallograptus diffluens* Ruedemann, and *T. gracilis* Ruedemann, St. Paul's Group, Newfoundland (Ruedemann 1947).

Last, Dev Gedinn: *Inocaulis multiramous* Ruedemann, Manlius Lst, Cayugan Series, Syracuse, N. America (Ruedemann 1947).

Constituent genera: *Inocaulis* Hall, *Thallograptus* Ruedemann, *Estoniocaulis* Obut, *Crinocaulis* Obut, *Boucekocaulis* Obut. The ranges of genera placed doubtfully in this family (*Diplospirograptus* Ruedemann, *Medusaegraptus* Ruedemann, *Palmatophycus* Bouček) are not considered in the above section. The contributor does not agree with the erection of a separate order (Bouček 1957) to accommodate the inocaulids.

Family PTILOGRAPTIDAE Hopkinson 1875

First, Ord Arenig: Several species of *Ptilograptus* from Deepkill Sh and equivalents, N. America (Ruedemann 1947), from San Remo, Australia (Thomas 1960) and from St. David's, Pembrokeshire, Wales (Hopkinson 1873).

Last, Sil Ludl: *Ptilograptus pribyli* Bouček, Pridoli Beds, Velka Chuchle, Czechoslovakia (Bouček 1957).

Family CHAUNOGRAPTIDAE Bulman 1955

First, Camb U. Camb: *Mastigograptus macrotheca* Ruedemann, Lyell Fm, Alberta, Canada (Ruedemann 1947).

Last, Dev Gedinn: *Chaunograptus gracilis* Clarke, Grande Grève Lst, Quebec, Canada and *C. gonothecatus* Decker, Haragan Fm, Oklahoma (Ruedemann 1947).

Constituent genera: *Chaunograptus* Hall and *Mastigograptus* Ruedemann; *Ascograptus* Ruedeman and *Haplograptus* Ruedemann are only doubtfully placed in this family. There seems to be a case for placing the chaunograptids in a separate order but this should be deferred until their morphology is known in more detail. The order Dithecoidea Obut is based upon forms even less well known structurally than *Chaunograptus* itself, and the erection of the order is here considered premature.

Order TUBOIDEA Kozłowski 1938

Family TUBIDENDRIDAE Kozłowski 1949

(= MULTITUBIDAE Skevington 1963)

First, Ord Tremad: *Tubidendrum bulmani* Kozłowski, Poland (Kozłowski 1949).

Last, Sil Wenl: *Reticulograptus thorsteinssoni* Bulman and Rickards (in press), Cornwallis Island, Canadian Arctic.

Constituent genera: *Tubidendrum* Kozłowski and *Reticulograptus* Wiman (= *Multitubus* Skevington). Several Sil Ludl species placed in *Reticulograptus* (see Bouček 1957) must now be referred to this genus with reserve, and are not included above.

Family IDIOTUBIDAE Kozłowski 1949

First, Ord Tremad: *Idiotubus typicalis* Kozłowski and several other *Idiotubus* species, *Calycotubus infundibulatus* Kozłowski, *Conitubus siculoides* Kozłowski, *Dendrotubus wimani* Kozłowski, Poland (Kozłowski 1949).

Last, Sil Wenl: *Cyclograptus rotandentatus* Spencer, Niagara Fm, Ontario (Ruedemann 1947), and *C. multithecatus* Bouček, Cyrtograptus radians Z., Lodenice, Czechoslovakia (Bouček 1957).

Constituent genera: *Idiotubus* Kozłowski, *Calycotubus* Kozłowski, *Conitubus* Kozłowski, *Cyclograptus* Spencer, *Dendrotubus* Kozłowski, *Discograptus* Wiman, *Galeograptus* Wiman. The genera *Calyptograptus* Spencer, *Epigraptus* Eisenack, and *Rhodonograptus* Počta are only doubtfully placed in this family.

Family PARVITUBIDAE Skevington 1963

First and **Last,** Ord Arenig: *Parvitubus oelandicus* (Bulman), Öland, Sweden (Skevington 1963, Bulman 1936).
Constituent genus: *Parvitubus* Skevington.

Order CAMAROIDEA Kozłowski 1938

Family BITHECOCAMARIDAE Bulman 1955

First and **Last,** Ord Tremad: *Bithecocamara gladiator* Kozłowski, Poland (Kozłowski 1949).
Constituent genus: *Bithecocamara* Kozłowski.

Family CYSTICAMARIDAE Bulman 1955

First, Ord Tremad: *Cysticamara accollis* Kozłowski, *Flexicollicamara bryozoaeformis* Kozłowski, *Graptocamara hyperlinguata* Kozłowski, *Tubicamara coriacea* Kozłowski, Poland (Kozłowski 1949) and *Syringotaenia bystrowi* Obut, U.S.S.R. (Obut 1963).
Last, Ord Arenig-Llvirn: *Graptocamara hyperlinguata* Kozłowski, Hagudden, Öland, Sweden (Skevington 1963).
Constituent genera, *Cysticamara* Kozłowski, *Flexicollicamara* Kozłowski, *Graptocamara* Kozłowski, *Tubicamara* Kozłowski, *Syringotaenia* Obut.

Order STOLONOIDEA Kozłowski 1938

Family STOLONODENDRIDAE Bulman 1955

First and **Last,** Ord Tremad: *Stolonodendrum uniramosum* Kozłowski, and *S. parasiticum* Kozłowski, Poland (Kozłowski 1949).
Constituent genus, *Stolonodendrum* Kozłowski.

Order CRUSTOIDEA Kozłowski 1962

(no families erected)

First, Ord Arenig–Llvirn: *Lapworthicrusta aenigmatica* Kozłowski, Sarbia, Poland (Kozłowski 1962).
Last, Ord (M.): *Bulmanicrusta modesta* Kozłowski, *Wimanicrusta urbaneki* Kozłowski, and *W. cristaelingulata* Kozłowski, Zakroczym, Poland (Kozłowski 1962).
Comment: All the known crustoids have been obtained from erratic boulders, not all of which have been dated with certainty. [R.B.R.]

Order GRAPTOLOIDEA Lapworth 1875

Suborder DIDYMOGRAPTINA Lapworth 1875

Family DICHOGRAPTIDAE Lapworth 1873

First, Ord ?Tremad; *Didymograptus novus* Berry 1960, *D. primigenius* Bulman 1950a, ?*D.* sp.Bulman 1954, *D.? stoermeri* Erdtmann 1965, *D.pritchardi* Hall 1899, *D.taylori* Hall 1899, *D.norvegicus* Monsen 1925, *D.klotschichini* Obut 1961. With the recognition of bithecae on *D.kiaeri* Monsen(Spjeldnaes 1963), further doubt has been cast on the true graptoloid nature of the Tremadocian "didymograptids". In the lowest beds of the Arenig, however, there are several species of *Tetragraptus* and *Didymograptus* (Monsen 1937, Berry 1960, Thomas 1960) and it is probable that true graptoloids do occur in the Tremadocian.
Last, Ord Carad: *Didymograptus superstes* Lapw. and *D.serratulus* Hall, gracilis Z., Glenkiln Sh, Scotland (Elles and Wood, 1901–18)

Chapter 23: Chordata: Hemichordata, Pogonophora, Urochordata and Cephalochordata

Family ABROGRAPTIDAE Mu 1958

First, Ord Arenig: *Dinemagraptus warkae* Kozłowski, ?hirundo Z., erratic block of Baltic limestone (Kozłowski 1951).

Last, Ord Carad: *Abrograptus formosus* Mu and other genera and species, gracilis Z., Hulo Sh., China (Mu 1962)

Family CORYNOIDIDAE Hopkinson and Lapworth 1875

First, Ord Carad: *Corynoides calicularis* Nicholson, gracilis Z., cosmop. (Strachan 1949).

Last, Ord Carad: *Corynoides curtus* Lapw., clingani Z., cosmop. (Strachan 1949).

Comment: *Corynites* Kozłowski 1956, the other genus in the family, is known only from erratic boulders but is probably also Carad.

Family LEPTOGRAPTIDAE Lapworth 1880

First, Ord Lldeil: *Nemagraptus explanatus*(Lapw.) and *N. pertenuis*(Lapw.), teretiusculus Z., Wales (Elles 1940).

Last, Ord Carad: *Leptograptus flaccidus*(Hall) and vars., linearis Z., cosmop.(Elles and Wood 1901–18, Ross and Berry 1963, Thomas 1960).

Family DICRANOGRAPTIDAE Lapworth 1873

First, Ord Llvirn: *Dicellograptus moffatensis* Carruthers, bifidus Z., Wales (Hopkinson and Lapworth 1875).

Last, Ord Ashg: *Dicellograptus anceps* Nicholson, anceps Z., Hartfell Sh, Scotland (Elles and Wood 1901–18). [I.S.]

Suborder GLOSSOGRAPTINA Jaanusson 1960

Constituent family: Glossograptidae Lapworth 1873 emended (syn. with Cryptograptidae Hadding 1915).

Family GLOSSOGRAPTIDAE Lapworth 1873 emended

First, Ord Arenig: *Glossograptus acanthus* Elles & Wood, *Glossograptus* sp (p). indet., *Cryptograptus antennarius* (Hall) and *Cryptograptus hopkinsoni* (Nicholson); hirundo Z., cosmop. (Jackson 1962; Mu & Lee 1958; Spjeldnaes 1953; etc.). *Glossograptus?* sp. Monsen, P. densus (3b γ) and P. angustifolius elongatus (3b δ) Z., (? = nitidus + gibberulus Z.), Lower Didymograptus Shale, Scandinavia (Monsen 1937; Hede 1951), probably belongs in *Phyllograptus* (Bulman 1950b). Presence of *C. hopkinsoni* in gibberulus Z., Skiddaw Slates, England, doubtful (Jackson 1962).

Last, Ord Carad: *Cryptograptus tricornis* (Carruthers), clingani Z., Scotland (Elles & Wood 1908), Australia (Thomas & Keble 1933) and elsewhere.

Comment: Origin cryptogenetic (Bulman 1963a); from *Isograptus* (Thomas 1960). Extinction relatively sudden; no known descendants.

Suborder DIPLOGRAPTINA Lapworth 1880 emended

Constituent families: As in Bulman 1963a p. 417.

Family DIPLOGRAPTIDAE Lapworth 1873

First, Ord Arenig: *Glyptograptus shelvensis* Bulman and *Glyptograptus austrodentatus anglicus* Bulman, gibberulus Z., Shelve Church Beds, Shropshire, England (Bulman 1963b). Presence of *Diplograptus* sp(p). indet. in Ca2-Ca3 Z. (= gibberulus Z.), Castlemaine Series, Victoria, Australia, is doubtful (Harris 1935 p. 320). [D.S.]

Last, Sil Lldov: *Petalograptus tenuis*(Barrande) and *P. altissimus* Elles and Wood, griestonensis Z., Czechoslovakia (Bouček and Přibyl 1941)

Climacograptus ultimus Ruedemann 1925 from the Bertie Waterlime (Ludlovian) of New York is probably a poorly preserved specimen of *Gothograptus nassa*(Holm) (personal examination). [I.S.]

Comment: Origin cryptogenetic. Family probably monophyletic, but rapidly undergoing primary division into two groups (*dentatus* and *austrodentatus*) based on mode of proximal end development. Considerable thecal cladogenesis gives a wide variety of descendants in hirundo-bifidus Z. (Bulman 1963b).

Family LASIOGRAPTIDAE Lapworth 1879

First, Ord Arenig: *Hallograptus inutilis* (Hall), hirundo (3bε) Z., Lower Didymograptus Shale, Norway (Spjeldnaes 1953).

Last, Ord Ashg: *Nymphograptus velatus* Elles & Wood, anceps Z., Upper Hartfell Shales, Scotland (Elles & Wood 1908).

Comment: Family probably derived by excessive thecal differentiation from early Diplograptidae of *austrodentatus* group (Bulman 1963b).

Family RETIOLITIDAE Lapworth 1873

Subfamily ARCHIRETIOLITINAE Bulman 1955

First, Ord Llvirn: *Retiograptus tentaculatus* Hall, dentatus Z., Point Levis, Quebec (Raymond 1914); dentatus Z., Deep Kill, New York (Ruedemann 1902); and elsewhere in North America.

Last, Ord Carad-Ashg: *Archiretiolites regimontanus* Eisenack, linearis-anceps Z., Harju Series, East Baltic, NW Europe (Eisenack, 1935).

Comment: Subfamily possibly derived by excessive thecal differentiation from early Diplograptidae along several lines of descent; relationship to Silurian Retiolitinae and Plectograptinae uncertain (Bulman *in* Treatise V; 1963a). [D.S.]

Subfamily RETIOLITINAE Lapworth 1873

First, Sil Lldov: *Retiolites perlatus* Nicholson, gregarius Z., Birkhill Sh and Stockdale Sh, British Isles (Elles and Wood 1901–18).

Last, Sil Wenl: *Retiolites geinitzianus* Barrande, murchisoni Z., Europe (Elles and Wood 1901–18, Bouček and Münch 1944).

Subfamily PLECTOGRAPTINAE Bouček and Münch 1952

First, Sil Wenl: *Plectograptus*(?) *textor* Bouček and Münch, rigidus Z., Motol Beds, Bohemia (Bouček and Münch 1952).

Last, Sil Ludl: *Plectograptus macilentus* Törnquist and *Spinograptus spinosus*(Wood), nilssoni Z., Europe (Bouček and Münch 1952, Wood 1900). [I.S.]

Family PEIRAGRAPTIDAE Jaanusson 1960

First and **Last,** Ord Ashg: *Peiragraptus fallax* Strachan, Vaureal Fm, Anticosti Id., Canada (Strachan 1954). Family monotypic; probably derived from Diplograptidae by modification of mode of development. Restricted to Canada. [D.S.]

Family DIMORPHOGRAPTIDAE Elles and Wood 1908

First, Sil Lldov: *Akidograptus acuminatus*(Nicholson) and *A.ascensus* Davies, acuminatus Z., Birkhill Sh, Scotland (Davies 1929).

Last, Sil Lldov: *Rhaphidograptus toernquisti*(Elles and Wood), convolutus Z., Birkhill Sh., Scotland (Bulman 1960, p.67).

Suborder MONOGRAPTINA Lapworth 1880

Family MONOGRAPTIDAE Lapworth 1873

First, Sil Lldov: *Monograptus atavus* Jones, vesiculosus Z., Europe (Elles 1925, Stein 1965). Other slender monograptids with simple thecae also occur in this zone. [I.S.]

Last, Dev Ems: *Monograptus* spp., Dvorce-Prokop Lst, top Pragian Stage directly below boundary with Zlíchovian Stage, uppermost L. Ems, Central Bohemia, Czechoslovakia (Bouček, personal communication; also Jaeger, personal communication).

The fauna is said to include *Monograptus* cf. *yukonensis* Jackson and Lenz, and probably two other species. It is shortly to be described by Professor Bouček (now see Bouček 1966).

Traditionally the graptoloidea have been regarded as extending only to the top of the Sil; indeed the continued presence of monograptids, particularly in Central and Eastern Europe, has been regarded as diagnostic of a Sil age. Changing views of correlation about the Sil-Dev boundary have only recently allowed the equation of the supposedly youngest monograptid bearing strata (up to M. hercynicus Z.) with the Dev Gedinn and Siegen (for summary see Holland 1965).

M. hercynicus Perner (widespread in Europe, N. Africa, and Asia) and the associated *M. kayseri* Perner have been described by Jaeger (1959). *M. belketaiefensis* Planchon (1964) and *M. anngueurensis* Legrand (1965), both from the Sahara, N. Africa, are recorded above *M. hercynicus* and their associated faunas are said to indicate a basal Pragian (probably uppermost Siegen) age.

M. yukonensis, Road River Fm, Yukon, N. America (Jackson and Lenz 1963) is said, on brachiopod evidence, to be early Gedinnian in age. Graptolite evidence has been taken to imply the lower part of M. hercynicus Z. or earlier. Professor Bouček (personal communication) suggests that his new fauna from Bohemia may have implications in dating the Yukon species.

[C.H.H.]

Family CYRTOGRAPTIDAE Bouček 1933

First, Sil Lldov: *Diversograptus attenuatus* Hopkinson, cyphus Z., Thuringia (Manck 1923, Münch 1952)

Last, Dev Gedinn: *Linograptus posthumus* Richter, hercynicus Z., Central Europe (Jaeger 1959). [I.S.]

Class ENTEROPNEUSTA Gegenbaur 1870

No certain fossil record, but could be represented by trace fossils of U-shaped burrows.

Extant.

Subphylum POGONOPHORA Johannson 1937

First, L. Camb: *Hyolithellus micans* (Billings); L. Camb, E. Greenland; M. Camb Clay, Bornholm, Denmark (Poulsen 1963). **Extant.**

Subphylum UROCHORDATA

Class ASCIDIACEA Blainville 1824

First, Perm Guad: *Permosoma tunicatum* Jaekel, L. Zechstein, Sosio-kalk, Palazzo Adriano, Sosio, Sicily (Jaekel 1918). **Extant.**

Class THALIACEA van der Hoeven 1850

No known fossil record. Problematica, Olig, Engi-Matt, Switzerland, claimed by Peyer (1957) to represent salps, shown by Dzulynski and Slaczka (1959, 1960) and Pavoni (1959) to be skip marks or roll-markings of fish vertebrae. **Extant.**

Class APPENDICULARIA Lahille 1890

No known fossil record. *Oesia disjuncta*, M. Camb, Burgess Shale, British Columbia, Canada, claimed by Lohmann (1922) to represent an appendicularian, shown by Tarlo (1960) to be an annelid. **Extant.**

UROCHORDATA INCERTAE SEDIS

Ainiktozoon loganense, Sil, Wenl, Lanarkshire, Scotland, claimed by Scourfield (1937) to represent new group of urochordate, shown by Tarlo (1960) to possess compound eye and thus more probably to be an arthropod.

607

The Fossil Record, Part II

Subphylum CEPHALOCHORDATA Owen 1846

No known fossil record. *Scaumenella mesacanthi*, Dev Frasn, Scaumenac Bay, Quebec, Canada, described by Graham-Smith (1935) as a new form of chordate close to cephalochordates, subsequently interpreted by Tarlo (1960) as ammocoete larva. *Jamoytius kerwoodi*, Sil Wenl, Lanarkshire, Scotland, claimed by White (1946, 1958) to belong to group representing possible ancestor of cephalochordates, subsequently interpreted by Stensiö (1958) as an anaspid. This latter was confirmed by Tarlo (1960) and later by Ritchie (1960).   **Extant.** [L.B.H.T.]

REFERENCES

BERRY, W. B. N. 1960. Graptolite Faunas of the Marathon Region, West Texas. *Univ. Tex. Publs*, **6005**.

BOUČEK, B. 1957. The dendroid graptolites of the Silurian of Bohemia. *Rozpr. ústřed. Úst. geol.*, **23**, 1–294.

—— 1966. Eine neue und bisherjungste Graptolithen—Fauna aus dem böhmischen Devon. *N. Jb. Geol. Paläont. Mh.*, 1966, 3, 161–8.

—— & MÜNCH, A. 1944. Die Retioliten des mitteleuropäischen Llandovery und unteren Wenlock. *Rozpr. čsl. Akad. Věd Uměni*, **53**, no. 41.

—— & —— 1952. Central European Retiolites of the Upper Wenlock and Ludlow. *Sb. ústřed. Úst. geol.*, **19**, 104–51.

—— & PŘIBYL, A. 1941. O rodu *Petalolithus* Suess z ceskeho siluru. *Rozpr. čsl. Akad. Věd. Uměni*, **51**, no. 11.

BULMAN, O. M. B. 1936. On the graptolites prepared by Holm. 7. The graptolite fauna of the Lower *Orthoceras* Limestone of Hälludden, Öland and its bearing on the evolution of the Lower Ordovician graptolites. *Ark. Zool.*, **26A**, 1–52.

—— 1950a. Graptolites from the Dictyonema Shales of Quebec. *Q. Jl geol. Soc. Lond.*, **106**, 63–99.

—— 1950b. On some Ordovician graptolite assemblages of Belgium. *Bull. Mus. r. Hist. nat. Belg.*, **26**, 1–8.

—— 1954. The graptolite fauna of the Dictyonema Shales of the Oslo Region. *Norsk. geol. Tidsskr.*, **33**, 1–40.

—— 1960. Some morphologically intermediate genera in graptolite phylogeny. *21st Int. geol. Cong.*, pt. 22, 65–70.

—— 1963a. The evolution and classification of the Graptoloidea. *Q. Jl geol. Soc. Lond.*, **119**, 401–18.

—— 1963b. On *Glyptograptus dentatus* (Brongniart) and some allied species. *Palaeontology*, **6**, 665–89.

DAVIES, K. A. 1929. Notes on the Graptolite Faunas of the Upper Ordovician and Lower Silurian. *Geol. Mag.*, **66**, 1–27.

DECKER, C. 1945. The Wilburns Upper Cambrian graptolites from Mason, Texas. *Univ. Tex. Publs*, **4401**, 13–61.

DZULYNSKI, S. & SLĄCZKA, A. 1959. Directional structures and sedimentation of the Krosno Beds (Carpathian flysch.). *Roczn. pol. Tow. geol.*, **28**(3), 205–260.

—— 1960. Sole markings produced by fish bones acting as tools. *Roczn. pol. Tow. geol.*, **30**, (2), 249–255.

EISENACK, A. 1935. Neue Graptolithen aus Geschieben baltischen Silurs. *Paläont. Z.*, **17**, 73–90.

ELLES, G. L. 1925. The Characteristic Assemblages of the Graptolite Zones of the British Isles. *Geol. Mag.*, **62**, 337–47.

—— 1940. The stratigraphy and faunal succession in the Ordovician rocks of the Builth-Llandrindod Inlier, Radnorshire. *Q. Jl geol. Soc. Lond.*, **95**, 383–445.

—— & WOOD, E. M. R. 1901–18. A monograph of British graptolites. *Palaeontogr. Soc.* [*Monogr.*]

ERDTMANN, B.-D. 1965. Eine spät-tremadocische graptolithenfauna von Töyen in Oslo. *Norsk geol. Tidsskr.*, **45**, 97–112.

GRAHAM-SMITH, W. 1935. *Scaumenella mesacanthi* gen. et sp. n., a peculiar organism from the Upper Devonian of Scaumenac Bay, P.Q., Canada. *Ann. Mag. nat. Hist.* (10), **16**, 473–476.

HALL, J. 1865. Graptolites of the Quebec group. Figures and descriptions of Canadian organic remains. *Canada geol. Surv.*, decade 2, 151 pp.

HALL, T. S. 1899. Victorian graptolites: Part II. The graptolites of the Lancefield Beds. *Proc. R. Soc. Vict.* (new series), **77**, 164–78.

HARRIS, W. J. 1935. The graptolite succession of Bendigo East with suggested zoning. *Proc. R. Soc. Vict.*, **47**, 314–37.

HEDE, J. E. 1951. Boring through Middle Ordovician—Upper Cambrian in the Fågelsång district, Scania (Sweden). *Acta Univ. lund.*, **76**, 1–84.

HOLLAND, C. H. 1965. The Siluro-Devonian boundary. *Geol. Mag.*, **101**, 213–221.

HOPKINSON, J. 1873. On some graptolites from Upper Arenig Rocks of Ramsay Island, St David's. *Geol. Mag.*, **10**, 518–519.

—— & LAPWORTH, C. 1875. Descriptions of the Graptolites of the Arenig and Llandeilo Rocks of St. David's. *Q. Jl geol. Soc. Lond.*, **31**, 631–72.

JACKSON, D. E. 1962. Graptolite zones in the Skiddaw Group in Cumberland, England. *J. Paleont.*, **36**, 300–13.

—— & LENZ, A. C. 1963. A new species of *Monograptus* from the Road River Formation, Yukon. *Palaeontology*, **6**, 751–753.

JAEGER, H. 1959. Graptolithen und Stratigraphie des jungsten Thüringer Silurs. *Abh. dt. Akad. Wiss. Berl.*, 1959, no. 2, 1–197.

JAEKEL, O. 1918. Über fragliche Tunicaten aus dem Perm Siciliens. *Paläont. Z.*, **2**, 66–74.

KOZŁOWSKI, R. 1949. Les Graptolithes et quelques nouveaux groupes d'animaux du Trémadoc de la Pologne. *Palaeont. pol.*, **3**, 1–235.

—— 1951. Sur un remarquable Graptolithe ordovicien. *Acta geol. pol.*, **2**, 86–93.

—— 1956. Nouvelles observations sur les Corynoididae. *Acta palaeont. pol.*, **1**, 259–69.

—— 1960. *Calyxdendrum graptoloides* n.gen., n.sp.. A graptolite intermediate between the Dendroidea and the Graptoloidea. *Acta palaeont. pol.*, **5**, 107–125.

—— 1961. Découverte d'un Rhabdopleuride (Pterobranchia) Ordovicien. *Acta palaeont. pol.*, **6**, 3–16.

—— 1962. Crustoidea—nouveau groupe de graptolites. *Acta palaeont. pol.*, **7**, 3–52.

LEGRAND, P. 1965. Quelques nouveaux graptolites à la limite des systèmes Silurien et Dévonien au Sahara Algérien. (Résumé). *In* Colloque sur le Dévonien inférieur et ses limites, Rennes 1964. *Mem. Bur. Rech. Geol. Min.*, **33**, 53–56. (a longer version was circulated as a duplicated preprint in 1964).

LOHMANN, N. H. 1922. *Oesia disjuncta* Walcott, eine Appendiculaire aus dem Kambrium. *Mitt. zool. St. Inst. Hamb.*, **38**, 69–75.

MANCK, E. 1923. Untersilurische Graptolithenarten der Zone 10 des Obersilurs, ferner *Diversograptus* gen. nov. sowie einige neue Arten anderer Gattungen. *Natur, Lpz.*, **14**, 282–9.

MONSEN, A. 1925. Über eine neue ordovicische Graptolithenfauna. *Norsk. geol. Tidsskr.*, **8**, 147–88.

—— 1937. Die Graptolithen fauna im unteren Didymograptus-schieffer (Phyllograptusschieffer) Norwegens. *Norsk. geol. Tidsskr.*, **16**, 57–267.

MU, A. T. 1958. *Abrograptus*, a new graptolite genus from the Hulo Shale (Middle Ordovician) of Kiangshan, Western Chekiang. *Acta palaeont. sin.*, **6**, 259–66.

—— 1962. New materials of Abrograptidae. *Acta palaeont. sin.*, **10**, 1–8.

—— & LEE, C. K. 1958. Scandent graptolites from the Ningkuo Shale of the Kiangshan-Changshan area, western Chekiang. *Acta palaeont. sin.*, **6**, 391–427.

MÜNCH, A. 1952. Die Graptolithen aus dem anstehenden Gotlandium Deutschlands und der Tschechslowakei. *Geologica, Berl.*, **7**.

OBUT, A. M. 1961. [Graptolites in the Tremadocian and adjacent deposits of the Aktyubinskoi and Orenburgskoi Regions]. *Trudy geol. Inst., Leningr.*, **18**, 146–150 (Russian).

—— 1963. Dendroids from the N.W. Russian Platform. *Trudy vses. neft. nauchno-issled. geol.-razv. Inst.*, **78**, 26–57, 12 plates.

PAVONI, N. 1959. Rollmarken von Fischwirbeln aus den oligozänen Fischschiefern von Engi-Matt (Kt. Glarus). *Eclog. geol. Helv.*, **52**(2), 941–949.

PEYER, B. 1957. Über bisher als Fahrten gedentete problematische Bildungen aus den oligozänen Fischschiefern des Sernftales. *Schweiz. paläont. Abh.*, **73**, 4–34.

PLANCHON, J. P. 1964. A propos de la survivance des graptolites dans le Dévonien: découverte d'une nouvelle espèce (*Monograptus belketaiefensis*) dans le Dévonien inférieur du Sahara septentrional. *C. r. hebd. Séanc. Acad. Sci., Paris*, **258**, 4813–4815.

POULSEN, V. 1963. Notes on *Hyolithellus* Billings, 1871, class *Pogonophora* Johannson, 1937. *Biol. Medd. Dan. Vid. Selsk.*, **23**, (12), 1–15.

PŘIBYL, A. 1948. Bibliographic index of Bohemian Silurian graptolites. *Knih. st. geol. Úst. čsl. Repub.*, **22**.

RAYMOND, P. E. 1914. The succession of faunas at Levis, Quebec. *Am. J. Sci.*, **38**, 523–30.

RITCHIE, A. 1960. A new interpretation of *Jamoytius kerwoodi* White. *Nature, Lond.*, **188**, 647–649.

ROSS, R. J. & BERRY, W. B. N. 1963. Ordovician Graptolites of the Basin Ranges in California, Nevada, Utah, and Idaho. *Bull. U.S. geol. Surv.*, **1134**.

RUEDEMANN, R. 1902. Graptolite facies of the Beekmantown formation in Rennselaer County, New York. *Bull. N. Y. St. Mus.*, **52**, 546–75.

—— 1925. Some Silurian (Ontarian) faunas of New York. *Bull. N. Y. St., Mus.*, **265**.

—— 1933. Cambrian graptolite faunas of North America. *Bull. publ. Mus., Milwaukee*, **13**, no. 3, 307–348.

—— 1947. Graptolites of North America. *Mem. geol. Soc. Am.*, **19**, 1–652.

SCOURFIELD, D. J. 1937. An anomalous fossil organism, possibly a new type of Chordate, from the Upper Silurian of Lesmahagow, Lanarkshire. *Ainiktozoon loganense*, gen. et sp. nov. *Proc. R. Soc.*, **121B**, 533–547.

SKEVINGTON, D. 1963. Graptolites from the Ontikan Limestones (Ordovician) of Öland, Sweden. I: *Dendroidea, Tuboidea, Camaroidea* and *Stolonidea*. *Bull. geol. Instn Univ. Upsala.*, **42**, no. 6, 1–62.

SPJELDNAES, N. 1953. The Middle Ordovician of the Oslo Region, Norway. 3. Graptolites dating the beds below the Middle Ordovician. *Norsk. geol. Tidsskr.*, **31**, 171–84.

—— 1963. Some Upper Tremadocian graptolites from Norway. *Palaeontology*, **6**, 121–31.

STEIN, V. 1965. Stratigraphische und paläontologische Untersuchungen im Silur des Frankenwaldes. *Neues Jb. Geol. Paläont. Abh.*, **121**, 111–200.

STENSIÖ, E. A. 1958. Les Cyclostomes Fossiles. *In:* Grassé, P. *Traité de Zoologie*, **13**, (1), 173–425.

STRACHAN, I. 1949. On the genus *Corynoides* Nicholson. *Geol. Mag.*, **86**, 153–60.

—— 1954. The structure and development of *Peiragraptus fallax* gen. et sp. nov. A new graptolite from the Ordovician of Canada. *Geol. Mag.*, **91**, 509–13.

TARLO, L. B. H. 1960. The invertebrate origins of the vertebrates. 21st *Int. geol. Congr.*, **22**, 113–123.

—— 1967. *The Pattern of Vertebrate Evolution.* Edinburgh.

THOMAS, D. E. 1960. The zonal distribution of Australian graptolites. *J. Proc. R. Soc. N.S.W.*, **94**, 1–58.

—— & KEBLE, R. A. 1933. The Ordovician and Silurian rocks of the Bulla-Sunbury area, and a discussion of the sequence of the Melbourne area. *Proc. R. Soc. Vict.*, **45**, 33–84.

TJERNVIK, T. E. 1958. The Tremadocian Beds at Flagabro in South-Eastern Scania (Sweden). *Geol. För. Stockh. Förh.*, **80**, 260–276.

TREATISE V. 1955. MOORE, R. C. (Editor). *Treatise on Invertebrate Paleontology, Part V:* BULMAN, O. M. B. Graptolithina with section on Enteropneusta and Pterobranchiata, University of Kansas Press.

WHITE, E. I. 1946. *Jamoytius kerwoodi*, a new chordate from the Silurian of Lanarkshire. *Geol. Mag.*, **88**, 89–97.

—— 1958. Original environment of the Craniates. *In: Studies on Fossil Vertebrates*, 212–234.

WOOD, E. M. R. 1900. The Lower Ludlow Formation and its Graptolite-Fauna. *Q. Jl geol. Soc. Lond.*, **56**, 415–90.

[Professor] C. H. Holland, PH.D. F.G.S.
Department of Geology, Trinity College, Dublin 2, Ireland.
R. B. Rickards, PH.D. F.G.S.
Department of Geology, Trinity College, Dublin 2, Ireland.
D. Skevington, PH.D.
Department of Geology, University College, Gower Street, London W 1.
I. Strachan, PH.D. F.G.S.
Department of Geology, The University, Birmingham 15.
L. B. H. Tarlo, D.SC. PH.D. F.L.S. F.A.Z. F.G.S.
Department of Geology, The University, Reading, Berkshire.

CHAPTER 24

Miscellanea

Contributors: C. DOWNIE, D. W. FISHER, R. GOLDRING & F. H. T. RHODES

Phylum UNCERTAIN

Order CONODONTOPHORIDA Eichenberg 1930

A utilitarian classification is used here, based on Hass (*Treatise*, Part W, 1962) with amendments based on Lindström (1964) and Rhodes & Müller (1966). Some new and a few other genera are here included in Hass' classification for the first time. The use of this classification does not imply that the present author believes that it has any phylogenetic value. It is used here only because it represents the best available taxonomic framework for treating the conodonts in the present volume. Studies of conodont assemblages (e.g. Rhodes 1952 and Walliser 1964) suggest that it has little phylogenetic significance, and the increasing recognition of "natural" conodont taxa will inevitably involve radical taxonomic revision.

Family DISTACODONTIDAE Bassler 1925

First, Camb M. Camb: *Furnishina furnishi* Müller and *Oneotodus tenuis* Müller, Ptychagnostus gibbus Z., Vestergötland, Sweden (Müller 1959; see also Cygan and Koucky 1963). Other Camb distacodids are probably relatively younger than these (Müller 1959, Tab. 3). There is some doubt as to whether such Camb genera as *Westergaardodina* are true conodonts.

Last, Dev Famenn: *Acodina delata* Stauffer, and *A. zionensis* Stauffer, "to II", Morvan, France (Lys, Serre, Mauvier and Grekoff 1961; see also Sannemann 1955; Stauffer 1938, 1940).

Family BELODONTIDAE Huddle 1934

First, Camb M. Camb: *Coelocerodontus? bisulcata* (Müller). Ptychagnostus gibbus Z., Vestergötland, Sweden (Müller 1959). *Hertzina*, the new genus to which Müller referred this species, is here regarded as a junior subjective synonym of *Coelocerodontus*.

Last, Dev Famenn: *Belodella triangularis* (Stauffer) "to IIB", Morvan, France (Lys, Serre, Mauvier and Grekoff 1961).

Family COLEODONTIDAE Branson & Mehl 1944

Subfamily COLEODONTINAE Branson & Mehl 1944

First, Ord ?Lldeil: *Coleodus simplex* Branson and Mehl and *C. pectiniformis* Youngquist and Cullison, Dutchtown Fm, Missouri, U.S.A. (Youngquist and Cullison, 1946).

Last, Carb Viséan: *Bactrognathus communis* Hass and *B. penehamata* Hass, Chappel Lst, Texas, U.S.A. (Hass 1959; see also Collinson, Scott and Rexroad 1962). *Hindeodina* is here regarded as a junior subjective synonym of *Hindeodella*.

The Fossil Record, pp. 613–626. Geological Society of London, 1967. Printed in Northern Ireland.

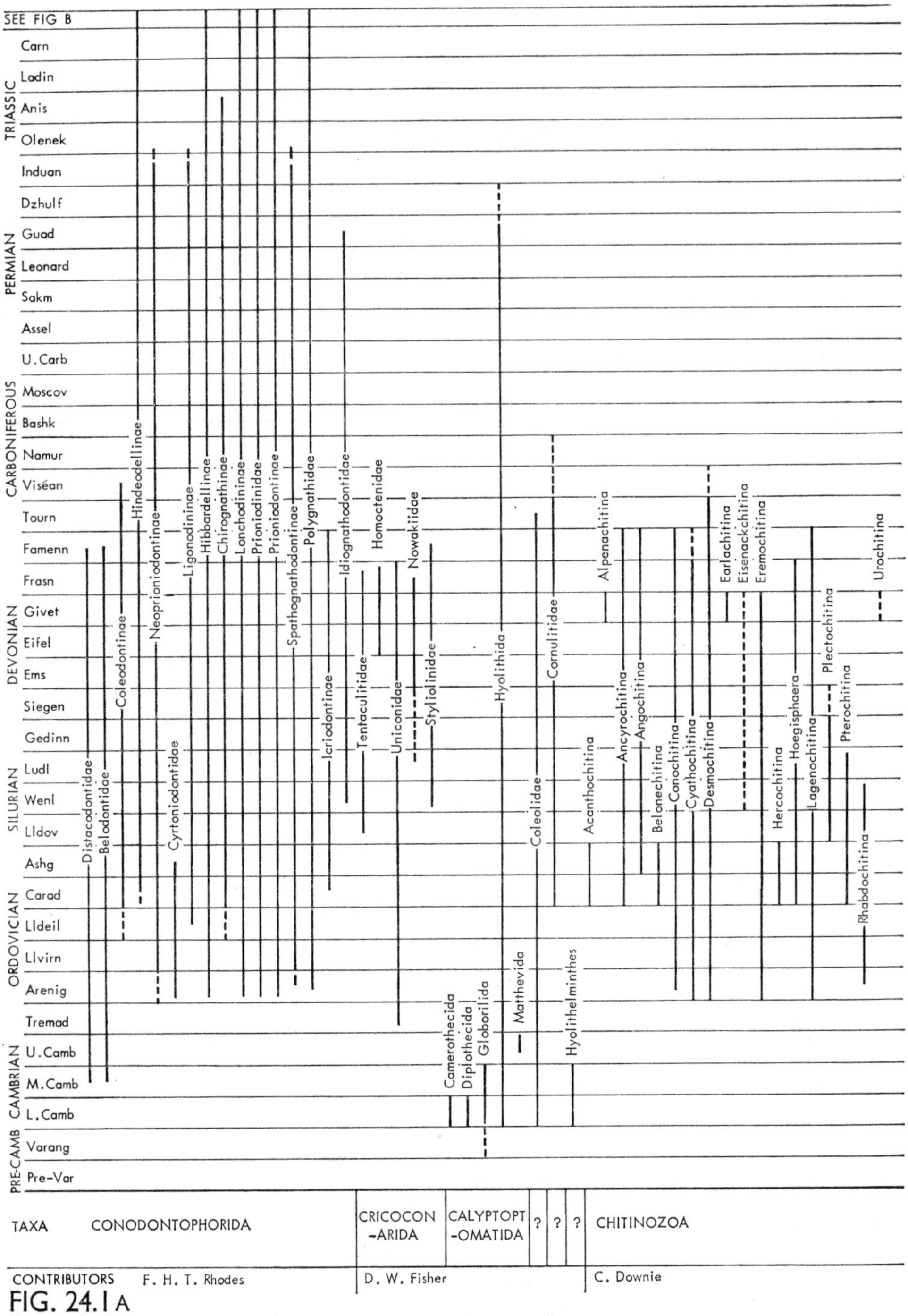

SEE FIG B
Carn
Ladin
Anis
Olenek
Induan
Dzhulf
Guad
Leonard
Sakm
Assel
U.Carb
Moscov
Bashk
Namur
Viséan
Tourn
Famenn
Frasn
Givet
Eifel
Ems
Siegen
Gedinn
Ludl
Wenl
Lldov
Ashg
Carad
Lldeil
Llvirn
Arenig
Tremad
U.Camb
M.Camb
L.Camb
Varang
Pre-Var

TRIASSIC
PERMIAN
CARBONIFEROUS
DEVONIAN
SILURIAN
ORDOVICIAN
CAMBRIAN
PRE-CAMB

Hindeodellinae
Neoprioniodontinae
Coleodontinae
Ligonodininae
Hibbardellinae
Chirognathinae
Lonchodininae
Prioniodinidae
Prioniodontinae
Spathognathodontinae
Polygnathidae
Idiognathodontidae
Homoctenidae
Nowakiidae
Distacodontidae
Belodontidae
Cyrtoniodontidae
Icriodontinae
Tentaculitidae
Uniconidae
Styliolinidae
Hyolithida
Cornulitidae
Coleolidae
Acanthochitina
Ancyrochitina
Angochitina
Belonechitina
Conochitina
Cyathochitina
Desmochitina
Alpenachitina
Hercochitina
Hoegisphaera
Lagenochitina
Plectochitina
Pterochitina
Earlachitina
Eisenackchitina
Eremochitina
Rhabdochitina
Urochitina

Camerothecida
Diplothecida
Globorilida
Matthevida
Hyolithelminthes

TAXA	CONODONTOPHORIDA	CRICOCON-ARIDA	CALYPTOPT-OMATIDA	?	?	?	CHITINOZOA
CONTRIBUTORS	F. H. T. Rhodes	D. W. Fisher					C. Downie

FIG. 24.1 A

Chapter 24: Miscellanea

Subfamily HINDEODELLINAE Hass 1959

First, Ord ?Carad: *Hindeodella serrata* Stauffer, Decorah Sh, Kansas, U.S.A. (Stauffer 1932). Stauffer's only figured specimen is fragmentary and it may be a broken posterior bar of some other genus.

Last, Trias Nor: *Hindeodella triassica* Müller, Hallstätter Kalk, Upper Austria (Huckriede 1958; see also Hirschmann 1959).

Subfamily NEOPRIONIODONTINAE Hass 1959

First, Ord ?Arenig: *Loxodus bransoni* Furnish, Stonehenge Lst, Pennsylvania, U.S.A. (Sando, 1958): Oneota Dolomite, Iowa, Minnesota, U.S.A. (Furnish 1938).

Last, Trias Induan-Olenek: *Neoprioniodus unicornis* Müller and *N. bransoni* Müller, 1300 ft above Meekoceras Z., Nevada, U.S.A. (Clark 1959 p. 307; see also Müller 1956). The Trias specimens referred to this genus differ from older "typical" representatives in having small basal cavities, restricted basal aprons and, in some, though not in the second species, relatively small anterior fangs.

Subfamily CRYTONIODONTINAE Hass 1959

First, Ord Arenig: *Paracordylodus gracilis* Lindström, "Fauna II", Isle of Öland, Sweden (Lindström 1960; see also Lindström 1954).

Last, Ord Ashg (Richmond): *Zygognathus plebia* Branson, Mehl and Branson, *Z. pyramidalis* Branson, Mehl and Branson and *Zygognathus* sp. Branson, Mehl and Branson, Whitewater Fm, Indiana, U.S.A. (Branson, Mehl and Branson 1951).

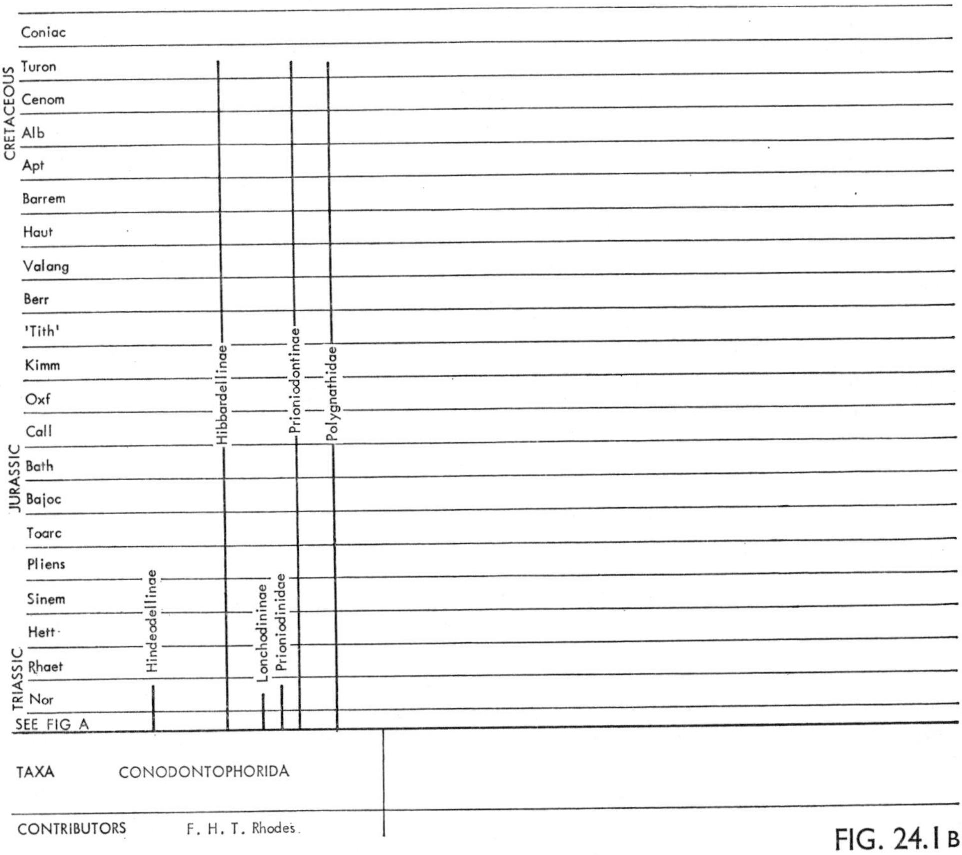

FIG. 24.1 B

The Fossil Record, Part II

Subfamily LIGONODININAE Hass 1959

First, Ord Lldeil: *Ligonodina tortilis* Sweet and Bergström, Pratt Ferry Fm, Alabama, U.S.A. (Sweet and Bergström 1962).

Last, Trias Induan-Olenek: *Ligonodina triassica* Müller, Meekoceras Z., Nevada, U.S.A. (Müller 1956; Clark 1959). The specimens identified as *Ligonodina?* sp. A. and *Ligonodina* sp. B by Tatge (1956) are probably members of the genus *Lonchodina*.

Subfamily HIBBARDELLINAE Müller 1956

First, Ord Arenig: *Oepikodus smithensis* Lindström, "Fauna III", Arenigian Billingen Stage, Isle of Öland, Sweden (Lindström 1960).

Last, Cret Turon: *Roundya* n. sp. A Diebel, Limestone with *Benueites benueensis* Reyment, Mungo River Fm, Cameroons, West Africa (Diebel 1956). There has been some reluctance amongst conodont workers to accept this fauna as indigenous because of the gap between this and the next youngest known faunas of Trias age. This seems to me to be an inadequate reason for rejecting the Cameroon occurrence.

Subfamily CHIROGNATHINAE Branson & Mehl 1944

First, Ord Carad-?Lldeil: *Chirognathus cultidactyla* Sweet, *C. dubia* Branson and Mehl, *C. maniformis* Branson and Mehl, *C. monodactyla* Branson and Mehl, "6.7 feet above base of Harding Sandstone", Colorado, U.S.A. (Sweet 1955. Fifteen other chirognathid species appear above these in the Harding Sst; see also Branson and Mehl 1933 and Stauffer 1935).

Last, Trias Anis: *Parachirognathus? breviramulis* (Tatge), Trochitenkalk, Ceratites Schichten, Thuringen, E. Germany (Hirschmann 1959; see also Tatge 1956).

Subfamily LONCHODININAE Hass 1959

First, Ord Arenig: *Trichonodella alae* Lindström, Limbata Limestone, Isle of Öland, Sweden (Lindström 1960). *Trichonodella? irregularis* Lindström in the same fauna probably represents another genus. *Trichonodella* is here interpreted in the sense defined by Hass (1959, p. W53). See also Lindström, 1964.

Last, Trias Nor: *Lonchodina mülleri* Tatge, "Hallstätter Kalk", Bavaria, Germany, and Styria, Austria: Cyrtopleurites Z., Upper Austria (Huckreide 1958; see also Tatge 1956, Hirschmann 1959 and Müller 1956).

Family PRIONIODINIDAE Bassler 1925

First, Ord Arenig: *Falodus extenuatus* (Lindström), Limbata Lst, Isle of Öland, Sweden (Lindström 1960; see also Lindström 1954).

Last, Trias Nor: *Prioniodina mediocris* (Tatge) "Rosa kalk, um 60m vom Haselgebirge", Upper Austria (Huckreide 1958).

Family PRIONIODONTIDAE Bassler 1925

Subfamily PRIONIODONTINAE Bassler 1925

First, Ord Arenig: *Prioniodus evae* Lindström, Billingen Stage, Isle of Öland, Sweden (Lindström 1960; see also Lindström 1954).

Last, Cret Turon: *Ozarkodina* sp. indet. A Diebel, "Limestone with *Benueites benueensis* Reyment, Mungo River Fm.", Cameroons, W. Africa (Diebel 1956). *Ozarkodina* sp. indet. B Diebel may represent a distinct genus.

Subfamily SPATHOGNATHODONTINAE Hass 1959

First, Ord. Arenig-Llvirn: *Spathognathodus* n. sp. Lindström 1960 (p. 93, Fig. 5.5), Obtusicauda-Gigas Lsts, Isle of Öland, Sweden.

Last, Trias Induan-Olenek: *Spathognathodus conservativa* (Müller) and *S. discreta* (Müller) Meekoceras Z., Nevada, U.S.A. (Müller 1956): *Spathognathodus cristagalli* Huckriede, "Untere Ceratiten schichten", Salt Range, Pakistan (Huckriede 1958).

616

Chapter 24: Miscellanea

The "*Spathognathodus?* sp. ind." illustrated by Diebel from Cret, Cameroons is closer to *Kockelella*, of which it is an approximate homeomorph.

Family POLYGNATHIDAE Bassler 1925

First, Ord Arenig: *Ambalodus* n. sp. 1 Lindström, *A.* n. sp. 2 Lindström, *Amorphognathus* n. sp. 1 Lindström, Expansus Lst, Isle of Öland, Sweden (Lindström 1960).

Last, Cret Turon: *Polygnathus mungoensis* Diebel, "Limestone with *Benueites benueensis* Reyment, Mungo River Fm", Cameroons, W. Africa (Diebel 1956).

Subfamily ICRIODONTINAE Müller & Müller 1957

First, Ord Carad: *Icriodina acuta* (Rhodes), Galena Fm, Iowa, U.S.A. (Ethington 1959).

Last, Dev Famenn: *Icriodus cymbiformis* Branson & Mehl, Montagne Noire, France (Lys & Serre 1957). *Icriodus cornutus* Sannemann, to IIβ, Morvan, France (Lys, Serre, Mauvier & Grekoff 1961). These authors show the species extending up to III (p. 555) and also show *I. nodosus* (Huddle) extending up to toV, but no details are given. (See also Sannemann 1955). Collinson, Scott & Rexroad (1962 Chart 1) show *Icriodus* as being present in the Saverton Fm (to IV–V) but interpret it as probably reworked. They show its last definite occurrence in the Sylamore Fm (to I) of the Mississippi Valley.

Family IDIOGNATHODONTIDAE Harris & Hollingsworth 1933

Subfamily IDIOGNATHODONTINAE Harris & Hollingsworth 1933

First, Sil Wenl: *Kockelella patula* Walliser, patula Z., Carnic Alps, Austria (Walliser 1964).

Last, Perm Guad: *Streptognathodus sulcoplicatus* Youngquist, Hawley and Miller. Phosphoria Fm, Idaho, & San Andés Lst, New Mexico, U.S.A. (Clark & Ethington 1962).

Subfamily BALOGNATHINAE Hass 1959

The status of the only valid genus now included in this family, *Icriodina*, is at present uncertain.

[F.H.T.R.]

REFERENCES

BRANSON, E. B. & MEHL, M. G. 1933. Conodonts from the Harding sandstone of Colorado. *Univ. Mo. Stud.*, **8**, 19–38, 2 pls.

——, MEHL, M. G. & BRANSON, C. C. 1951. Richmond conodonts of Kentucky and Indiana. *J. Paleont.*, **25**, 1–17, pls. 1–4.

CLARK, D. L. 1959. Conodonts from the Triassic of Nevada and Utah. *J. Paleont.*, **33**, 305–312, pls 44–45.

—— & ETHINGTON, R. L. 1962. Survey of Permian conodonts in western North America. *Brigham Young Univ. Stud.*, **9**, 102–114.

COLLINSON, C. W., SCOTT, A. J. & REXROAD, C. B. 1962. Six Charts showing biostratigraphic zones and correlations based on conodonts from the Devonian and Mississippian rocks of the Upper Mississippi Valley. *Circ. Ill. St. geol. Surv.*, **328**, 1–32.

CYGAN, N. E. & KOUCKY, F. L. 1963. *The Cambrian and Ordovician rocks of the east flank of the Big Horn Mountains, Wyoming,* W.G.A.-B.G.S. Guidebook to the North Powder River Basin, pp. 26–37.

DIEBEL, K. 1956. Conodonten in der oberkreide von Kameron. Geologie, **5**, 424–450, pls 1–4.

ETHINGTON, R. L. 1959. Conodonts of the Ordovician Galena formation. *J. Paleont.*, **33**, 257–292, pls 39–41.

FURNISH, W. M. 1938. Conodonts from the Praire du Chien. (Lower Ordovician) beds of the upper Mississippi Valley. *J. Paleont.*, **12**, 318–340, pls 41, 42.

HASS, W. H. 1959. Conodonts from the Chappel limestone of Texas. *Prof. Pap. U.S. geol. Surv.*, **294**, 365–399, pls 46–50.

HIRSCHMANN, C. 1959. Über conodonten aus dem oberen Muschelkalk des Thuringer Beckens. *Freiberger Forschft.* C, **76,** 1–86, pls 1–9.

HUCKRIEDE, R. 1958. Die Conodonten der mediterranean Trias und ihr stratigraphischer Wert. *Paläont. Z.,* **32,** 141–175, pls 10–14.

LINDSTRÖM, M. 1954. Conodonts from the lowermost Ordovician strata of south-central Sweden *Geol. För. Stok. Förh.,* Bd. 76, pp. 517–601, pls 1–7.

——— 1960. A Lower-Middle Ordovician succession of conodont faunas. *21st Int. geol. congr.,* part 7, Ordovician and Silurian stratigraphy and correlations, 88–96.

——— 1964. *Conodonts.* Elsevier Publishing Co., Amsterdam, London, New York.

LYS, M. & SERRE, B. 1957. Etude de conodontes du Devonien et du Carbonifere de la region d'Adrar-Tanezrouft (Sahara). *Inst. Franc. Petrol. Rev.,* **12,** 1035–1066, pls 1–7.

———, SERRE, B., MAUVIER, A. & GREKOFF, N. 1961. Contribution a la connaissance des Micro-faunas du Paleozoique: Etudes Micropaleontologiques (Conodontes, Ostracodes) dans le Devonien superieur du Morvan. *Inst. Franc. Petrol. Rev.,* **16,** no. 5, 538–567, pls 1–5.

MÜLLER, K. J. 1956. Triassic conodonts from Nevada. *J. Paleont.,* **30,** 818–830, pls 95–96.

——— 1959. Kambrische Conodonten. *Z. dt. geol. Ges.,* **111,** 434–465, pls 11–15.

RHODES, F. H. T. 1952. A classification of Pennsylvanian conodont assemblages. *J. Paleont.,* **26,** 886–901, pls 126–129.

——— 1965. Conodont research and taxonomy, 1959–1965. *Paleont. Contr. Univ. Kan.,* in press.

——— & Müller, K. J. 1966. Comments on conodonts. *Paleont. Contr. Univ. Kansas,* Paper 9, 2–5.

SANDO, W. J. 1958. Lower Ordovician section near Chambersburg, Pennsylvania. *Bull. geol. Soc. Am.,* **69,** 837–854.

SANNEMAHN, DIETRICH. 1955. Oberdevonische Conodonten. *Senckenberg. Leth.,* **36,** 123–156.

STAUFFER, C. R. 1932. Decorah shale conodonts from Kansas. *J. Paleont.,* **6,** 257–264, pl. 40.

——— 1935. Conodonts of the Glenwood beds. *Bull. geol. Soc. Am.,* **46,** 125–168, pls 9–12.

——— 1938. Conodonts of the Olentangy shale. *J. Paleont.,* **12,** 411–443, pls 48–53.

——— 1940. Conodonts from the Devonian and associated clays of Minnesota. *J. Paleont.,* **14,** 417–435, pls 58–60.

SWEET, W. C. 1955. Conodonts from the Harding formation (Middle Ordovician) of Colorado. *J. Paleont.,* **29,** 226–262.

——— & BERGSTROM, S. M. 1962. Conodonts from the Pratt Ferry formation (Middle Ordovician) of Alabama. *J. Paleont.,* **36,** 1214–1252.

TATGE, URSULA. 1956. Conodonten aus dem Germanischen Muschelkalk. *Paläont. Z.,* **30,** pp. 108–127, 129–147, pls 5–6.

WALLISER, OTTO H. 1964. Conodonten des Silurs. *Abh. hess. Landes amt. Bodenforsch,* **41,** 1–106, pls 1–32.

YOUNGQUIST, W. L. & CULLISON, J. S. 1946. The conodont fauna of the Ordovician Dutchtown formation of Missouri. *J. Paleont.,* **20,** 579–590, pls 89, 90.   [F.H.T.R.]

Phylum UNCERTAIN

[show greatest affinities to the Mollusca and Annelida]

Class CRICOCONARIDA Fisher 1962

[= Superorder TENTACULITOIDEA of Class CONICONCHIA of Lyashenko (1959) and Class TENTACULITA of Bouček (1964) (partim)]

Order TENTACULITIDA Lyashenko 1955

Poor descriptions and illustrations prohibit placement of *Tentaculites crestensis* Rusconi 1955, *T. empozadensis* Rusconi 1953 and *T. mogotensis* Rusconi 1955 within the Cricoconarida. In fact, their cricoconarid assignment is unproved; they may be cornulitids. All three species are from the L. Ord (stage or series indeterminable) Lasheriana Fm, Empozadense Horizon, Mendoza, Argentina.

Family TENTACULITIDAE Walcott 1886

First, Sil Lldov: *Dicricoconus? minutus* (Hall) 1843, L. Clinton Group (M. Lldov), western N.Y., U.S.A.

Last, Dev Frasn: *Tentaculites donensis* Lyashenko 1959 (nude name, 1955), Semiluk beds (M. Frasn), central Russian Platform, U.S.S.R. *T. semilukianus* Lyashenko 1959 (nude name, 1953), Semiluk beds, central Russian Platform, U.S.S.R. *T. spiculus* Hall 1876, "Chemung" facies (precise position within Frasnian uncertain), south of Ithaca and south of Cortland, N.Y., U.S.A.

Family UNICONIDAE Lyashenko 1955

First, Ord Tremad: *"Tentaculites" lowdoni* Fisher and Young 1955, Chepultepec Lst (L. Canadian) Shenandoah Valley, Virginia, U.S.A.

Last, Dev Frasn: *Uniconus livnensis* Lyashenko 1959, Liven beds (U. Frasn), central Russian Platform, U.S.S.R.

Family HOMOCTENIDAE Lyashenko 1955

[regarded as an Order (Homoctenida) under class Tentaculita by Bouček 1964]

First, Dev Eifel: *Homoctenus(?) hanusi* Bouček 1964, Daleje Sh (L. Eifel), Hlubocepy, Czech.; Thuringia, Germany; Grzegorzorvice, Holy Cross Mts., Poland.

Last, Dev Frasn: *Polycylindrites nalivkini* (Lyashenko) 1954, L. Voronezh beds (U. Frasn), central Russian Platform, U.S.S.R. (Lyashenko 1959).

Comment: Lyashenko (1959) and Bouček (1964) assign *Denticulites* to the Tentaculitidae. As the inner surface is repeated on the exterior, the contributor considers *D.* as an homoctenid. For those who would remove the above two forms from the homoctenids, the following is then the earliest homoctenid: Dev L. Frasn. *Homectenus tikhyi* Lyashenko, Kynov beds, Tatar, A.S.S.R.

Order DACRYOCONARIDA Fisher 1962

Family NOWAKIIDAE Bouček & Prantl 1960

First, Sil Ludl: *Nowakia matlockiensis* (Chapman) 1904 [= *Nowakia acuaria* (Richter) 1854, *fide.* Bouček, 1964], Tanjilian beds (= Jordanian beds of Gill, 1941, U. Leidl), Victoria, Australia. The age of these Australian strata, relative to the European standard, has not yet been determined. Hence first occurrence may be: Dev Gedinn (Z. of *M. hercynicus*): *Paranowakia bohemica* Bouček 1964, lower Lochkov Lst. (Radotin Lst. member), Czechoslovakia.

Last, Dev Frasn: *Crassilina timanica* Lyashenko 1957, Khvorostan beds (Early Frasn), Timan, U.S.S.R. (Lyashenko 1959). *Viriatella spatiosa* Lyashenko 1959, Khvorostan beds, Tatar, A.S.S.R.

Comment: The position of this stratigraphic interval is open to question owing to lack of unanimity on the position of the Sil-Dev boundary in continental Europe.

Family STYLIOLINIDAE Grabau 1912

(*fide.* Lyashenko 1955; unverifiable by me)

First, Sil Wenl: *Styliolina* cf. *laevis* Richter 1854, Z. of *Monograptus riccartonensis*, Zebingyi beds, near Maymyo, Burma (LaTouche 1913). Position within Wenlock uncertain: *"Styliola"* sp., Rochester Fm, Maryland, U.S.A. (Swartz, 1913).

Last, Dev Famenn: *Styliolina* sp., Gowanda Fm (L. Famenn), western N.Y., U.S.A. (Clarke 1904).

The Fossil Record, Part II

Phylum MOLLUSCA

Class CALYPTOPTOMATIDA Fisher 1962

[= superorder HYOLITHOIDEA Syssoiev 1957 (partim)]

Order HYOLITHIDA Matthew 1899

[= class HYOLITHA of Marek 1963 & Marek and Yochelson 1964]

First, Camb L.Camb: Many species of hyolithids occur in Early Cambrian strata on all continents, excluding Antarctica. Which species is oldest is presently indeterminable owing to the lack of precise intercontinental correlation. Among the earliest species are: *Hyolithes corrugatus* Kiaer 1916, Holmia Sh, Tømten, Norway; *H. princeps*, and *H. terranovicus* Walcott, St. Johns Group, Manuels Bay, Newfoundland; *H. strettonensis* Cobbold 1934, Obolella groomi beds, Shropshire, England; *Trapezovitus sinosus* Syssoiev 1958 (Formation not given), Yakutsk, A.S.S.R.; *H. americanus* Billings 1872 and *H. communis* Billings 1872, Cossayuna Group, eastern N.Y., U.S.A.

Last, Perm: Difficulties in exact correlation within the U. Perm prohibit stating which hyolithid was the last. Among these are: *Hyolithes kirkbyi* (as *Theca? kirkbyi* Howse 1857), "Magnesian Limestone Series", Durham, England. Also Perm Upper Guad (*Timorites* Zone): *H. richteri* Geinitz (1861), L. Zechstein, Germany, and Perm Dzhulf: *Macrotheca wynnei* Waagen 1880, U. Productus Lst, Salt Range, India [hyolithid assignment uncertain, probably a gigantic orthothecid hyolithid and, if so, the last of the group].

Constituent Families: (as in *Treatise*, pt. W): Hyolithidae Nicholson 1872, L. Camb-Perm Guad; Ceratothecidae Fisher 1962, Sil Ludl-Dev Gedinn; Orthothecidae Syssoiev 1958, L. Camb-M. Dev, Perm Dzhulf?; Sulcavitidae Syssoiev1 958, L. Camb-Sil Lldov; Pterygothecidae Syssoiev 1958, L. Ord-Dev.

Order GLOBORILIDA Syssoiev 1957

First, Precambrian (late): *Wyattia reedensis* Taylor 1966, Reed Dolostone, White-Inyo mountain area, Inyo County, California.

Last, Camb M. Camb.: *Globorilus globiger* (Saito), 1936, Korea.

Comment: *Wyattia*, assigned questionably to the globorilids by Taylor (1966), occurs in unmetamorphosed strata 900 meters stratigraphically below the earliest olenellids (*Fallotaspis*). If the *Fallotaspis* biozone is to be regarded as the base of the Cambrian system (as it is in the Atlas Mountains of Morocco) then *Wyattia* is a bonafide Precambrian fossil.

The following are monotypic orders of the Class CALYPTOPTOMATIDA.

Order CAMEROTHECIDA Syssoiev 1957

First and Last, Camb L.Camb: *Camerotheca gracilis* Matthew 1885, Canada.

Order DIPLOTHECIDA Syssoiev 1957

First and Last, Camb L.Camb: *Diplotheca acadica* Matthew 1885, Canada.

Order MATTHEVIDA Fisher

[*nom. transl.* Matthevina Fisher 1962]

First and Last, Camb U.Camb: *Matthevia variabilis* Walcott 1885, Hoyt Lst, Saratoga Springs, N.Y., U.S.A.

Comment: Yochelson (1966) has recently proposed that this division be divorced from the Calyptoptomatids and elevated to class rank (Mattheva), under the phylum Mollusca.

Chapter 24: Miscellanea

Phylum MOLLUSCA?

Class UNCERTAIN

Family COLEOLIDAE Fisher 1962

First, Camb L.Camb: *Coleoloides typicalis* Walcott 1889, St. Johns Group, Manuels Bay, Newfoundland. *C. prindlei* Lochman 1956, Cossayuna Group, Washington, Rensselaer, and Columbia Counties, N.Y., U.S.A.

Last, Carb Tourn: *Coleolus missouriensis* Howell 1952, Chouteau Fm (Lower Mississippian = Kinderhookian), Sedalia, Missouri, U.S.A.

Comment: Coleolids were assigned under the Order Hyolithellida by Syssoiev (1957) and as an order (Coleolida) under the Class Tentaculita by Boucek (1964). They are generally agreed to be molluscan but assignment within the Mollusca has varied.

Phylum, Class, Order UNCERTAIN

Family CORNULITIDAE Fisher 1962

[regarded as an Order in the Class Tentaculita by Bouček (1964)]

First, Ord Carad: *Cornulites flexuosus* (Hall) 1847 [as *Tentaculites flexuosa* Hall], Trenton Lst, Trenton Falls, New York, U.S.A.

Last, Carb Tourn-Namur: *Cornulitella carbonaria* (Young), "Carboniferous Limestone Group", Ravenscraig Castle, near Kirkcaldy and Whitehouse, near Linlithgow, England (Etheridge 1880).

Class POGONOPHORA Johannson 1937

(*fide* Poulsen, 1963) [see also p. 621]

Order HYOLITHELMINTHES Fisher 1962

First, Camb L.Camb: *Hyolithellus micans* Billings 1871, Cossayuna Group, New York, U.S.A.; L. Comley Sst, Rushton, Shropshire, England (Cobbold 1934; Lochman, 1956). *H. sinuosus* Cobbold 1921, Obolella groomi beds, Shropshire, England. *H. tortuosus* Cobbold 1934, Acrothele Sh and L. Comley Sst, Rushton, Shropshire, England. *Torellella laevigata* Linarsson var. *Holmi* Kiaer 1916, Holmia Sh, Tømten, Norway (Kiaer 1916).

Last, Camb M.Camb: *Hyolithellus cuyanus* Rusconi 1951 and *H. mendozanus* Rusconi 1951, Isidreana Fm (Villavicense Horiz.), Mendoza, Argentina (Rusconi 1951).

REFERENCES

Bouček, B. 1964. *The Tentaculites of Bohemia*. 215 p, 40 pl., 36 text figs., 6 tables. Prague.

—— & Prantl, F. 1961. Uber einige neue Tentaculiten-Gattungen aus dem bohmische Devon. *Vest. ústred Úst. geol.*, **36**, 385–388, 1 pl.

Clarke, J. M. 1904. Naples fauna in western New York. *N.Y. State Mus. Mem.*, 6, 454 p., (p. 356), 20 pls.

Cobbold, E. S. 1921. The Cambrian horizons of Comley (Shropshire) and their Brachiopoda, Pteropoda, Gasteropoda, etc. *Q. Jl geol. Soc. Lond.*, **76**, 325–386, pl. 21–24.

Etheridge, R., Jr. 1880. A contribution to the study of British Carboniferous tubicolar annelida. *Geol. Mag.*, **7**, 262–264, pl. 7, figs. 37–40.

Fisher, D. W. 1962. Small conoidal shells of uncertain affinities. *In* Moore, R. C. (Editor) *Treatise on Invertebrate Paleontology*, Part W. University of Kansas Press.

Kiaer, J. 1916. The Lower Cambrian Holmia fauna at Tømten in Norway. *K. Norske Nidensk. Skrift.*, 10, 134 p., pl. 1–14.

Lochman, C. 1956. Stratigraphy, paleontology, and paleoecology of the *Elliptocephala asaphoides* strata in Cambridge and Hoosick quadrangles, New York. *Bull. geol. Soc. Am.*, **67**, 1331–1396, pl. 1–10, fig. 1–2.

LYASHENKO, G. P. 1959. [*Devonian Coniconchia in the central district of the Russian Platform.*] V.N.I.G.N.I., p. 1–220, pl. 1–31 (in Russian).

POULSEN, V. 1963. Notes on Hyolithellus Billings, 1871, Class Pogonophora Johannson, 1937. *Biol. Meddr,* **23,** 15 p., 1 fig., 1 tab.

RUSCONI, C. 1951. Más trilobitas cámbricos de San Isidro, Cerro Pelado y Canota. *Revta. Mus. Hist. nat. Mendoza,* **5,** 3–30, 29 figs.

SWARTZ, C. K. 1913. Correlation of Silurian formations in Maryland with those of other areas. *Maryland Geol. Surv.* (Silurian volume), 794 p. (p. 220).

SYSSOIEV, V. A. 1957. On the morphology, systematic position, and systematics of Hyolithoidea. *Dokl. Akad. nauk SSSR,* **116,** 304–307 (in Russian).

—— [in LYASHENKO, G. P. & SYSSOIEV, V. A.]. 1958. Mollusca?; Class Coniconchia *in* ORLOV, Y. A., LUPPOV, N. P. & DRUSCHITS, V. V. (Editors) *Osnovy Paleontologii,* **6,** 179–191, pl. 1–7.

TAYLOR, M. E. 1966. Precambrian mollusc-like fossils from Inyo County, California. *Science,* 153, p. 198–201, 4 text figs.

YOCHELSON, E. L. 1966. Mattheva, a proposed new class of mollusks. *U.S. Geol. Sur. Prof. Paper,* 523-B, 11 p., 1 pl. [D.W.F.]

TRACE-FOSSILS

Invertebrate trace genera are listed alphabetically in Part W of the Treatise and in Häntzschel (1965). Vertebrate trace genera are listed in Kuhn (1963). The five ecological groups proposed by Seilacher (1953) can be recognised from the L. Camb: Pascichnia (grazing trails), Cubichnia (resting trails), Domichia (dwelling burrows), Fodinichnia (feeding burrows), and Repichnia (crawling trails), and the latter three from the upper Pre-Camb. Trace-fossils are a function of animal behaviour, and as Seilacher (op. cit.) has shown, similar traces can be made by different groups of organisms, e.g. bilobitid types. Such types are often long-ranging. Trace genera show stratigraphic change only in so far as the animal group responsible:

1. Made evolutionary changes in the body structures causing the trace, as with appendage changes in vertebrates and arthropods (Seilacher 1960, 1962),

2. Made behavioural changes, as with *Neonereites* (Seilacher 1960),

3. Made environmental changes, as with limulinids and trilobites.

Invertebrate Traces

Many trace genera are known by only a single species and have a very limited geographic and stratigraphic distribution. Such with a wider geographic distribution may be useful index fossils e.g. *Tomaculum problematicum.* Some genera as now defined include synonyms with smaller stratigraphical and geographical range e.g. *Zoophycus* Dev-Tert, includes *Taonurus* Tert, *Spirophyton* Dev-Carb, *Cancellophycus* Jur, etc.

Vertebrate Traces

PISCES

The only definite fish traces known are from the U. Jur Solnhofen Limestone (Abel 1935) and attributed to coelacanth. Only bottom-dwelling fish are likely to leave traces in the sediment and are known to do so in present sediments. The absence of fossil-fish traces may be explained as due, either to the difficulty in recognising and interpreting them, or to the low fossilisation potential of the biofacies concerned. Traces doubtfully attributed to fish include L.Carb crossopterygian traces (Fiege 1951, Kühn 1957). Dipnoan aestivation burrows are known from L.Perm, N. America (Romer & Olson 1954, Vaughn 1964).

AMPHIBIA

No Dev amphibian traces can be substantiated.

First, Carb Viséan: *Hylopus* Dawson Horton Gp, Nova Scotia, Canada (Colbert and Schaeffer 1947). Others possibly in L.Carb, Scotland (Smith 1889) and N. England (Barkas 1873). No amphibian traces known Jur, Cret. Absence due to change in environment.

Chapter 24: Miscellanea

First, Carb U. Carb: *Colletosaurus missouriensis* (Butts) (attributed to *Petrolacosaurus*), Missouri, N. America (Schmidt 1959).

AVES

Bird traces doubtfully present in L.Cret: *Ignotornis* Mehl N. America (Dakota Sst) (Lessertisseur 1955).

MAMMALIA

First, Tert Palaeoc: Alberta (Rutherford & Russel 1928).

WORMS

Many fossil worms are only known from particular or unique deposits. These are listed in the Treatise (W). Trails attributed to worms occur in Precamb strata. *Dickinsonia* Sprigg, *Spriggina floundersi* Glaessner (Australia) are only Precamb body worms. Polychaete scolecodonts are first recorded from Tremad (Whittard 1953). Tubes of sedentarids are known from L. Camb but some recorded may belong to other phyla (Treatise W, p. 164).

REFERENCES

ABEL, O. 1935. *Vorzeitliche Lebensspuren.* Jena.

BARKAS, T. P. 1873. *Illustrated guide to the fish, amphibian, reptillian and supposed mammalian remains of the Northumberland Carboniferous strata.* London.

COLBERT, E. H. & SCHAEFFER, B. 1947. Some Mississippian footprints from Indiana. *Am. J. Sci.,* **245,** 614–623.

FIEGE, K. 1951. Eine Fisch-schwimmspur aus dem Kulm bei Waldeck, usw. *Neues Jb. Geol. Palaont. Mh.,* for 1951, 9–31.

HÄNTZSCHEL, W. 1965. *Vestigia Invertebratorum et Problematica.* Part 108, Fossilium Catalogus, 1, Animalia. Hague.

KÜHN, O. 1957. Eine Fährtenplatte aus dem Unterkarbons. *Paläont Z.,* **31,** 6.

—— 1963. *Ichnia Tetrapodorum.* Part 101, Fossilium Catalogus, 1, Animalia. Hague.

LESSERTISSEUR, J. 1955. Traces Fossiles d'activitié animale et leur significance paléobiologique. *Mém. Soc. géol. Fr.,* **74,** 1–150.

ROMER, A. S. & OLSON, E. C. 1954. Aestivation in a Permian lungfish. *Breviora,* **30,** 1–8.

RUTHERFORD, R. L. & RUSSEL, L. S. 1928. Mammal tracks from the Paskapoo Beds of Alberta. *Am. J. Sci.,* **15,** 262–264.

SCHMIDT, H. 1959. Die Cornberger Fährten im Rahmen der Vierfüssler-Entwicklung. *Abh. hess. Landes-amt Bodenforsch.,* **28,** 1–137.

SEILACHER, A. 1953. Studien zur Palichnologie 1. Über die Methoden der Palichnologie. *Neues Jb. Geol. Paläont. Abh.,* **96,** 421–452.

—— 1960. Lebensspuren als Leitfossilien. *Geol. Rundsch.,* **49,** 41–50.

—— 1962. Form und Function des Trilobiten-Dactylus. *Paläont Z.,* **H. Schmidt-Festband,** 218–227.

SMITH, J. 1889. Note on the occurrence of footprints in the Calciferous Sandstone between West Kilbride and Fairlie. *Trans. geol. Soc. Glasg.,* **9,** 201–203.

TREATISE, W. 1962. Miscellanea *in* MOORE, R. C. (Editor) *Treatise on Invertebrate Paleontology,* Part W. University of Kansas Press.

VAUGHN, P. P. 1964. Evidence of aestivating lungfish from the Sangre de Cristo Formation, Lower Permain of Northern New Mexico. *Contr. Sci.,* **80.**

WHITTARD, W. F. 1953. *Palaeoscolex piscatorum* gen. et sp. nov. a worm from the Tremadocian of Shropshire. *Q. Jl geol. Soc. Lond.,* **109,** 125–136.   [R.G.]

Phylum UNCERTAIN
Order CHITINOZOA Eisenack

Fossils classed in this order are usually individuals isolated from chains or cocoons. Their affinities are in doubt; one likely possibility is that they are egg-cases of an extinct group of annelids.

Their classification, which is presently based largely on gross morphological features and superficial ornament, is sometimes difficult to operate; in particular, the distinction between genera is often blurred. Supra-generic classification is in need of revision in the light of recent discoveries.

Order CHITINOZOA Eisenack

Genus ACANTHOCHITINA Eis.

First, Ord Carad: *A. barbata* Eis., ?Carad, Canada (Jansonius 1964).
Last, Ord Ashg: *A. barbata* Eis., Lyckholm Fm, Estonia (Eisenack 1962).

Genus ALPENACHITINA Dunn & Miller

First and **Last,** Givet: *A. eisenacki* D. & M., Alpena Lst, U.S.A. (Dunn & Miller 1964).

Genus ANCYROCHITINA Eis.

First, Ord Carad: *A. multiradiata* Eis., Jewe Beds, Estonia (Eisenack 1962).
Last, Dev Famenn: *Ancyrochitina* sp. Taug., Algeria (Taugourdeau 1962).

Genus ANGOCHITINA Eis.

First, Ord Ashg: *A. capillata* Eis., Lyckholm Fm, Estonia (Eisenack 1962).
Last, Dev Famenn: *A. dimorpha* Taug. & Jekh., *A. crumena* Taug., Algeria (Taugourdeau and Jekhowsky 1960, Taugourdeau 1962).

Genus BELONECHITINA Jan.

First, Ord Carad: *B. robusta* (Eis.), Laggan Burn Lst, Scotland and Wasalemm's Beds, Estonia (Jansonius 1964, Eisenack 1962).
Last, Ord Ashg: *B. robusta* (Eis.), Lyckholm Fm, Estonia (Eisenack 1962).

Genus CONOCHITINA Eis.

First, Ord Arenig: *C. primitiva* Eis., Glauconite Lst, Estonia (Eisenack 1962).
Last, Dev Famenn: *C. reflexa* Taug. & Jekh., Algeria (Taugourdeau and Jekhowsky 1960).

Genus CYATHOCHITINA Eis.

First, Ord Arenig: *C.* cf. *calix* Eis., Glauconite Sst, Estonia (Eisenack 1958).
Last, Dev Frasn-Famenn: *C. infundibuliformis* Taug. & Jekh., Algeria (Taugourdeau & Jekhowsky 1960).

Genus DESMOCHITINA Eis.

First, Ord Arenig: *D. minor* Eis., Glauconite Sst, Estonia (Eisenack 1962).
Last, Carb Tourn/Viséan: *D.* sp., Goddard Sh, U.S.A. (Wilson & Clarke 1960).

Genus EARLACHITINA Coll. & Scott

First and **Last,** Givet: *E. latipes* Coll. & Scott, Cedar Valley Fm, U.S.A. (Collinson and Scott 1958).

Genus EISENACKCHITINA Jan.

First, Sil ?Wenl: *E. castor* Jan.,? Canada (Jansonius 1964).
Last, Dev Givet: *E. castor* Jan., Home Fm, Canada (Jansonius 1964).

Genus EREMOCHITINA Taug. & Jekh.

First, Ord Arenig: *E. baculata* Taug. & Jekh. and *E. mucronata* Taug. & Jekh., Algeria (Benoit and Taugourdeau 1961).

Last, Dev Givet: *E. cingulata* var *serrata* (Taug. & Jekh.), Algeria (Taugourdeau & Jekhowsky 1960).

Genus HERCOCHITINA Jan.

First and **Last,** Ord Carad/Ashg: *H. crickmayi* Jans., Vaureal Fm, Canada (Jansonius 1964).

Genus HOEGISPHAERA Stapl

First, Ord Carad: *H. utricula*, Taugourdeau, Isotelus gigas Lst, U.S.A. (Taugourdeau 1965).
Last, Dev Frasn: *H. glabra* Stapl., Woodbend Fm, Canada (Staplin 1961).

Genus LAGENOCHITINA Eis.

First, Ord Arenig: *L. esthonica* Eis., Glanconite Sst, Estonia (Eisenack 1962).
Last, Dev Famenn: *L. macrostoma* Taug. & Jekh., and *L. fenestrata* (Taug. & Jekh.) Algeria. (Taugourdeau & Jekhowsky 1960, Taugourdeau 1962).

Genus PLECTOCHITINA Cramer

First, Sil Lldov: *P. longicornis* (Taug. & Jekh.), Algeria (Taugourdeau and Jekhowsky 1961).
Last, Dev Gedinn-Siegen: *P. longicornis* (Taug. & Jekh.). *P. carminae* Cram. and *P. pseudo-agglutinatus* (Taug.), Algeria and San Pedro Fm, Spain (Cramer 1963).

Genus PTEROCHITINA Eis.

First, Ord Carad: *P. retracta* Eis., Reval Fm, Estonia (Eisenack 1962).
Last, Sil Ludl: *P. perivelata* Eis. Beyrichia Lst, Estonia (Eisenack 1955).

Genus RHABDOCHITINA Eis.

First, Ord Arenig: *R. striata* Eis. and *R.* cf. *magna* Eis., Glauconite Lst, Estonia (Eisenack 1962).
Last, Sil Wenl: *R. canna* Defl., Combe d'Ysarne Lst, France (Deflandre 1945). The record of a species in Carb by Taugourdeau 1961 is unsubstantiated.

Genus UROCHITINA Taug. & Jekh.

First and **Last,** Dev ?Givet: *U. globosa* Taug. & Jekh., *U. simplex* Taug. & Jekh. and *U. verrucosa* Taug. & Jekh., Algeria (Taugourdeau & Jekhowsky 1960).

SYNONYMS: AMPULLACHITINA = ANCYROCHITA; CALPICHITINA = HOEGISPHAERA; CLATHRO-CHITINA = ANCYROCHITINA (pars), CYATHOCHITINA (pars); HAPLOCHITINA = LAGENOCHITINA; ILLICHITINA = CYATHOCHITINA; KALOCHITINA = CONOCHITINA; MIRACHITINA and PARACHITINA (not chitinozoa); SPHAEROCHITINA = LAGENOCHITINA; STEPHANOCHITINA = ANGOCHITINA; TANUCHITINA = CYATHOCHITINA.

REFERENCES

BENOIT, A. & TAUGOURDEAU, P. 1961. Sur quelques Chitinozoaires de l'Ordovicien du Sahara. *Revue Inst. fr. Pétrole*, **16,** 1403–21, pl. 1–5.

COLLINSON, C. & SCOTT, A. J. 1958. Chitinozoan faunule of the Devonian Cedar Valley formation. *Circ. Ill. St. geol. Surv.*, **247,** 1–34, pls. 1–3.

CRAMER, F. H. 1963. Microplankton from three Palaeozoic formations in the province of Leon (N.W. Spain). *Leid. geol. Meded.*, **30,** 252–361, pls. 1–24.

DEFLANDRE, G. 1945. Microfossiles des calcaires silurien de la Montagne Noire. *Ann. Paléont*, **31,** 41–75.

DUNN, D. L. & MILLER, T. H. 1964. A disticntive chitinozoa form the Alpena Limestone (Middle Devonian) of Michigan. *J. Paleont.*, **38,** 725–8, pl. 119.

EISENACK, A. 1955. Chitinozoen, Hystrichospharen und andere Mikrofossilien aus dem *Beyrichia*-Kalk. *Senckenbergiana*, **36,** 157–88, pls. 1–5.

—— 1958. Mikrofossilien aus dem Ordovizium des Baltikums. I. Markazitschicht, *Dictyonema*-Schiefer, Glankonitsand, Glaukonitkalk. *Senckenberg. Leth.*, **39,** 389–405, pls. 1–2.

—— 1962. Mikrofossilien aus dem Ordovizium des Baltikums. 2. Vaginatenkalk bis Lykholmer Stufe. *Senckenberg. Leth.*, **43,** 349–66, pl. 44.

JANSONIUS, J. 1964. Morphology and Classification of some chitinozoa. *Bull. Can. Petrol. Geol.*, **12,** 4, 901–18, pls. 1–2.

STAPLIN, F. L. 1961. Reef-controlled distributions of Devonian microplankton in Alberta. *Paleontology*, **4,** 392–424, pls. 48–51.

TAUGOURDEAU, P. 1961. Chitinozoaires du Silurien d'Aquitaine. *Revue Micropaléont.*, **3,** 135–54.

—— 1962. Associations de Chitinozoaires dans quelques sondages de la Region d'Edjele (Sahara). *Revue Micropaléont.*, **4,** 229–36, pl. 1.

—— 1965. Chitinozoaires de l'Ordovicien des U.S.A., Comparison avec les faunes de l'ancien monde. *Revue Inst. fr. Pétrole*, **20,** 463–84, pls. 1–2.

—— & JEKHOWSKY, B. 1960. Répartition et description des Chitinozoaires silure-devoniens de quelques sondages de la C.R.E.P.S., de la C.F.P.A. et de la S.N. Repal au Sahara. *Rev. Inst. fr. Pétrole*, **15,** 119–260, pls. 1–13.

WILSON, L. R. & CLARKE, R. T. 1960. A Mississippian Chitinozoan from Oklahoma. *Okla. Geol. Notes*, **20,** 6, 148–50, pl. 1.   [C.D.]

C. Downie, PH.D. F.G.S.
   Department of Geology, the University, St. George's Square, Sheffield 1.
D. W. Fisher, PH.D.
   Geological Survey, New York State Museum and Science Service, Albany, N.Y., U.S.A.
R. Goldring, PH.D. F.G.S.
   Department of Geology, The University, Reading, Berkshire.
[Professor] F. H. T. Rhodes, D.SC. PH.D. F.G.S.
   Geology Department, University College of Swansea, Singleton Park, Swansea, Wales.

The Fossil Record, Part II

VERTEBRATA

VERTEBRATA

Introduction. The following six chapters document the fossil record of the vertebrates. The chapter headings are the familiar 'classes' of the subphylum Craniata (this term is now generally preferred to Vertebrata, since all vertebrates do not necessarily have vertebrae). However, it will be seen that the Agnatha include two distinct classes, whilst 'Pisces' comprise seven. This should occasion no surprise, since all terrestrial vertebrates are not included in the single class 'Tetrapoda'. In fact in recent years it has become increasingly recognized that the primary aquatic vertebrates represent as varied a group as the terrestrial.

The classifications employed in the chapters themselves frequently vary considerably from those given in current text-books. This is due to the attempt of the contributors to present their data in the framework of as up-to-date a classification as possible. So if parts appear somewhat unfamiliar, readers may rest assured that they will certainly become familiar during the next decade.

Finally, as the different vertebrate classes are frequently grouped into a variety of major divisions, different from those forming the chapter headings, it is hoped that the following table will serve as a useful guide:

AGNATHA	AGNATHANS		
PISCES			ANAMNIOTES
AMPHIBIA			
REPTILIA	GNATHOSTOMES	TETRAPODS	
AVES			AMNIOTES
MAMMALIA			

L. B. H. T.

CHAPTER 25

Agnatha

Contributor: L. B. H. TARLO

Introduction. The Agnatha are frequently divided into two groups—the armoured fossil forms or ostracoderms and the naked living cyclostomes. Stensiö (1927), however, established the close affinity between the lampreys (petromyzonids) and the cephalaspids (Osteostraci) and anaspids, although his thesis that the hagfish (myxinoids) and the pteraspids (Heterostraci) were also similarly related has not met with such ready acceptance. The details of the internal anatomy suggest that the Agnatha belong to two fundamentally distinct classes: the Diplorhina including the Heterostraci and Thelodonti, and the Monorhina which is also divided into two subclasses— the Hyperoartii (Osteostraci, Anaspida and Galeaspida) and Hyperotreti (Myxini). This latter classification is employed here; at the same time the ranks of the taxa documented have been altered to give a standardized format throughout the superclass.

Class DIPLORHINA (PTERASPIDOMORPHI)

Subclass HETEROSTRACI (PTERASPIDES)

Order ASTRASPIDIFORMES Berg 1940

First, Ord Carad: *Astraspis desiderata* Walcott, Harding Sst, Colorado (Ørvig 1958). *Palaeodus* Rohon and *Archodus* Rohon, Ord Arenig, are here accepted as thelodonts (Obruchev 1964).
Last, Ord Ashg: *Pycnaspis splendens* Ørvig, U.Bighorn Fm, Wyoming (Ørvig 1958).

Order ERIPTYCHIIFORMES Tarlo 1962

First, Ord Carad: *Eriptychius americanus* Walcott, Harding Sst, Colorado (Ørvig 1958).
Last, Ord Ashg: "Eriptychiida gen. and sp. indet.", U.Bighorn Fm, Wyoming, (Ørvig 1958). *Tesseraspis* Wills, Dev Gerdinn, assigned by Obruchev (1964) to the eriptychiids is here referred to the psammosteids (Tarlo 1962, 1964).

Order CYATHASPIDIFORMES

Suborder TOLYPELEPIDIDA

First, Sil Wenl: *Tolypelepis* sp., Allen Bay Fm, Cornwallis Island, Canada (Denison 1964).
Last, Dev Gedinn: *Tolypelepis timanica* Obruchev, Eptarmenskaya Series, Timan, Soviet Union (Kossovoi and Obruchev 1962).

The Fossil Record, pp. 629–636. Geological Society of London, 1967. Printed in Northern Ireland.

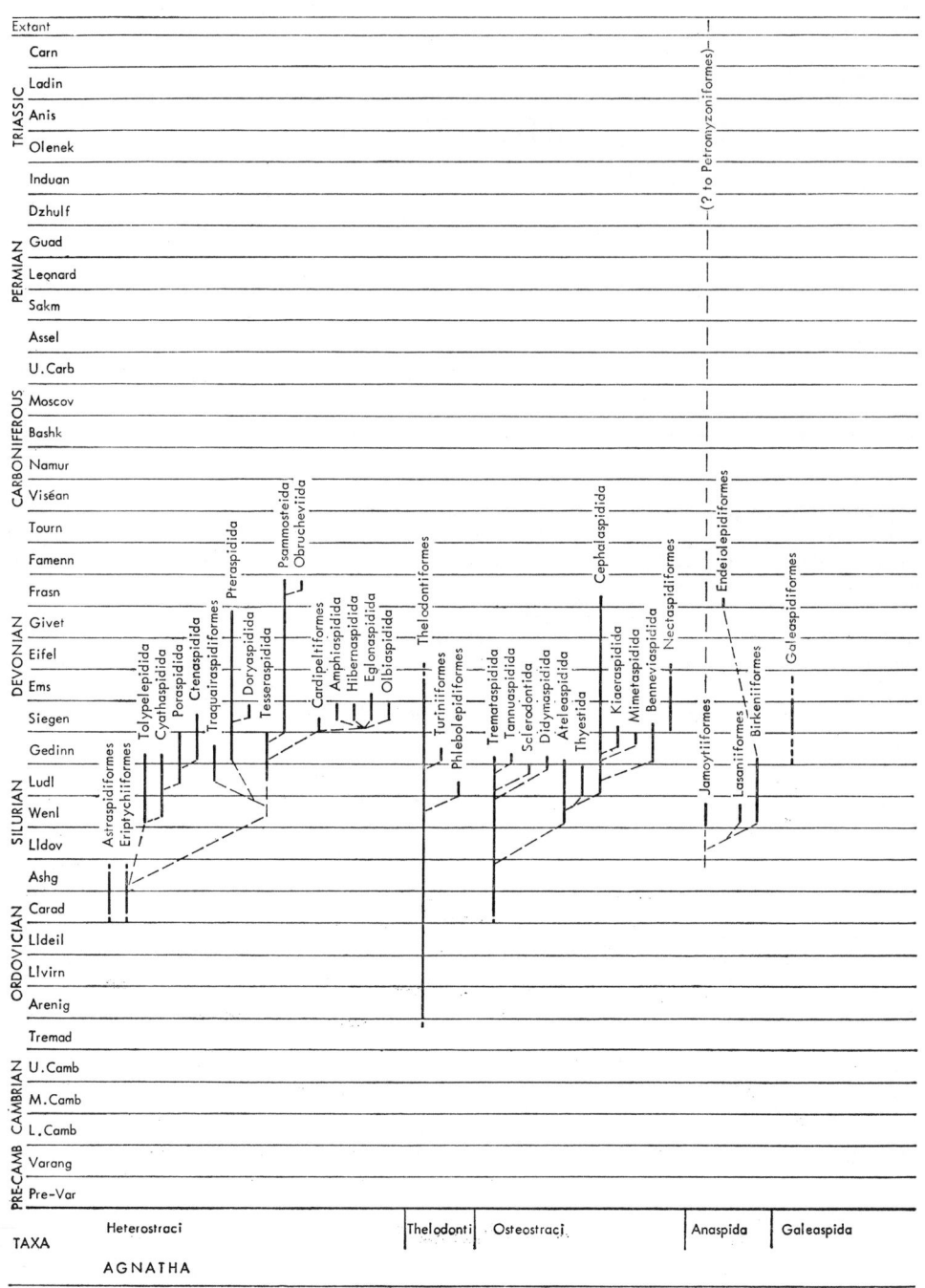

FIG. 25.1 A

Chapter 25: Agnatha

Suborder CYATHASPIDIDA Kiaer 1930

First, Sil Wenl: "Cyathaspid n. gen. A sp. B", Read Bay Fm, Cornwallis Island, Canada (Denison 1964).

Last, Dev Gedinn: *Irregulareaspis stensioi* Zych, U.Chortkov horizon, Podolia, Ukraine, Soviet Union (Obruchev 1964).

Suborder PORASPIDIDA Tarlo 1962

First, Sil Ludl: *Americaspis* sp., Ottisville member, Pennsylvania (Denison 1964).

Last, Dev Gedinn: *Poraspis sericea* (Lankester), Pteraspis crouchi Z., Dittonian, England and *Homalaspidella hitida* (Kiaer), Ben Nevis Div., Red Bay Series, Spitzbergen (Denison 1964). *Allocryptaspis* Denison, Dev Siegen, placed in Poraspidida by Denison (1964) but here assigned to Ctenaspidida (Tarlo 1962, Obruchev 1964). Obruchev (1958) listed possible cyathaspids then believed Eifel, now recognised Ems (1964), Razvedochnin Series, Norilsk, N.W. Siberia, but these remains most probably belong to eglonaspids.

Suborder CTENASPIDIDA Zych 1931

First, Dev Gedinn: cf. *Ctenaspis* sp., Traquairaspis symondsi Z. Dittonian (*sensu* Allen and Tarlo), England and Fraenkelryggen Div., Red Bay Series, Spitzbergen (Denison 1964).

Last, Dev Siegen: *Allocryptaspis elliptica* (Bryant), *A. flabelliformis* (Bryant), *A. laticostata* Denison, and *A. Utahensis* Denison, L. Siegen, Beartooth Butte Fm, Wyoming, Water Canyon Fm, Utah [this genus included in Ctenaspidida by Tarlo (1962) and Obruchev (1964), in Poraspidida by Denison (1964)], and *Putoranaspis prima* Obruchev, and *Aphataspis kiaeri* Obruchev, L. Siegen Kureyka Series, N.W. Siberia, Soviet Union (Obruchev 1964).

Order TRAQUAIRASPIDIFORMES Tarlo 1962

First, Sil Ludl: *Yukonaspis angusta* (Denison), L/M Ludl, Beaver River, Yukon, Canada (Denison 1963, Obruchev 1964). Denison's (1964) revision of the age of this form is not here accepted.

Last, Dev Gedinn: *Traquairaspis symondsi* (Lankester), Pteraspis crouchi Z., Dittonian, England (Ball and Dineley 1961). Obruchev (1964) includes *Weigeltaspis* Dev U.Gedinn in this Order, but this view is not here accepted (Tarlo 1962, 1964). "Indet. heterostracan", Dev Siegen, showing similarities to traquairaspids (Denison 1953) probably an amphiaspid (see Obruchev 1964).

Order PTERASPIDIFORMES

Suborder PTERASPIDIDA Kiaer 1932

First, Dev Gedinn: *Penygaspis* sp., and *Protopteraspis gosseleti* (Leriche), Traquairaspis symondsi Z., Dittonian (*sensu* Allen and Tarlo), England.

Last, Dev Givet: "Pteraspids", Wijde Bay Series, Spitzbergen (Dineley 1955).

Suborder DORYASPIDIDA Heintz *in* Tarlo 1962

First and **Last,** Dev Siegen: *Doryaspis nathorsti* (Lankester), Keltiefjellet (Lykta) Div., Wood Bay Series, Spitzbergen (Friend 1961).

Order PSAMMOSTEIFORMES

Suborder TESSERASPIDIDA Tarlo 1962

First, Sil Ludl: *Tesseraspis denisoni* Tarlo, L/M Ludl, Beaver River, Yukon, Canada (Tarlo 1964). The inclusion of *Tesseraspis* in the Eriptychiiformes by Obruchev (1964) and its exclusion from the Psammosteiformes by Stensiö (1964) are not here accepted.

Last, Dev Gedinn: *Weigeltaspis godmani* Tarlo, Pteraspis crouchi Z., Dittonian, England, *W. alta* Brotzen, *W. brotzeni* Tarlo, Podalaspis lerichei Z., Dittonian, Podolia, Soviet Union, and *W. heintzi* Tarlo, Ben Nevis Div., Red Bay Series, Spitzbergen (Tarlo 1964). Obruchev's (1964) inclusion of *Weigeltaspis* in the Traquairaspidiformes is not here accepted.

631

Suborder PSAMMOSTEIDA Kiaer 1932

First, Dev Siegen: *Drepanaspis carteri* (McCoy), *D. edwardsi* Tarlo, Dartmouth Slates, Cornwall, England (Tarlo 1961, 1964).

Last, Dev Frasn: *Psammosteus grossi* Obruchev, Lovat horizon, Novgorod, Soviet Union. This record placed at base of Famenn by Obruchev (1958) and Tarlo (1964) now accepted as being in Frasn (Karatajute-Talimaa 1964).

Suborder OBRUCHEVIIDA Tarlo 1965

First and **Last,** Dev Frasn: *Obruchevia heckeri* (Obruchev), Nadsnejski horizon, Novgorod, Soviet Union (Tarlo 1964). Stensiö (1964) erroneously included *Cardipeltis*, Dev Siegen, with this group.

Order CARDIPELTIFORMES Tarlo 1962

First and **Last,** Dev Siegen: *Cardipeltis wallacii* Bryant, and *C. sinclairi* Bryant, L. Siegen, Beartooth Butte Fm, Wyoming, Water Canyon Fm, Utah (Denison 1952, 1963).

Order AMPHIASPIDIFORMES

Suborder AMPHIASPIDIDA Obruchev 1938

First and **Last,** Dev Siegen: *Amphiaspis argos* Obruchev, Kureyka Series, N.W. Siberia, Soviet Union (Obruchev 1964).

Suborder HIBERNASPIDIDA Obruchev *in* Tarlo 1962

First and **Last,** Dev Siegen: *Hibernaspis macrolepis* Obruchev, Kureyka Series, N.W. Siberia, Soviet Union (Obruchev 1964).

Suborder EGLONASPIDIDA Tarlo 1962

First, Dev Siegen: *Eglonaspis rostrata* Obruchev, Kureyka Series, N.W. Siberia, Soviet Union (Obruchev 1964).

Last, Dev Ems: *Pelurgaspis macrorhynchis* Obruchev, Razvedochnin Series, N.W. Siberia, Soviet Union (Obruchev 1964). "Eglonaspis ?" from Norilsk, N.W. Siberia listed by Obruchev (1958) as Dev Eifel, now considered Ems.

Suborder OBLIASPIDIDA Obruchev 1964

First and **Last,** Dev Siegen: *Olbiaspis coalescens* Obruchev, *Siberiaspis plana* Obruchev, and *Angaraspis urvantzevi* Obruchev, Kureyka Series, N.W. Siberia, Soviet Union (Obruchev 1964).

Subclass THELODONTI (COELOLEPIDES)

Order THELODONTIFORMES

First, Ord Arenig: *Palaeodus brevis* Rohon, *Archodus elegans* Rohon, Glauconitic Sands, Leningrad, Soviet Union. Identified as tubercles of astraspids by Ørvig (1958), but Obruchev's (1948, 1964) identification as thelodonts here accepted.

Last, Dev Ems or Eifel: "Thelodontida gen. et sp. ident.", Stormbukta, W. Sorkapp Land (= Grey Hoek Series), Spitzbergen (Ørvig 1957a).

Order TURINIIFORMES

First and **Last,** Dev Gedinn: *Turinia pagei* (Powrie), Dittonian (*sensu* Allen and Tarlo), Forfarshire, Scotland.

Order PHLEBOLEPIDIFORMES Berg 1940

First and **Last,** Sil Ludl: *Phlebolepis elegans* Pander, K_1 horizon, L. Ludl, Oesel, Estonia (Obruchev 1964). *Paraplesiobatis heinrichsi* Broili, Dev Siegen or Ems, included by Berg (1955) in Phlebolepidiformes has been shown by Gross (1962) to be a placoderm.

Chapter 25: Agnatha

Class MONORHINA (CEPHALASPIDOMORPHI)

Subclass HYPEROARTII

Superorder OSTEOSTRACI (CEPHALASPIDES)

Order TREMATASPIDIFORMES (OLIGOBRANCHIATA partim)

Suborder TREMATASPIDIDA Heintz 1939

General comments: This suborder is equivalent to Tremataspididae of Obruchev (1964) but with "Didymaspidinae" excluded, and to Group C of suborder Aceraspida of Stensiö (1964), but with "Thyestidae" excluded.

First, Ord Carad: Osteocyte [Tremataspid gen. et sp. indet.], Harding Sst, Colorado (Ørvig 1965).

Last, Dev Gedinn: *Timanaspis kossovoii* Obruchev, Eptarmenskaya Series, Timan, Soviet Union (Kossovoi and Obruchev 1962).

Suborder TANNUASPIDIDA

First and **Last,** Dev Gedinn: *Tannuaspis levenkoi* Obruchev, L. Dev, Tuva, Soviet Union (Obruchev 1956).

Suborder SCLERODONTIDA

First and **Last,** Sil Ludl: *Sclerodus pustuliferus* Agassiz, Ludlow Bone Bed, L. Red Downton Fm, Welsh Borderland, England (Stensiö 1932, Tarlo 1964). This form considered *incertae sedis* by Stensiö (1964).

Suborder DIDYMASPIDIDA

General comments: This suborder equivalent to Group B of Aceraspida of Stensiö (1964).

First, Sil Ludl: *Didymaspis grindrodi* Lankester, L. Red Downton Fm, Welsh Borderland, England (Allen and Tarlo 1963, Tarlo 1964).

Last, Dev Gedinn: *Didymaspis grindrodi* Lankester, Psammosteus Lst Group, Dittonian (*sensu* Allen and Tarlo), Welsh Borderland, England (Allen and Tarlo 1963).

Order CEPHALASPIDIFORMES (OLIGOBRANCHIATA partim)

Suborder ATELEASPIDIDA (ACERASPIDA Stensiö 1958)

General comments: Since they form a clearly defined group, the following are included in this suborder: Stensiö's (1964) Aceraspididae and Hemicyclaspididae of Group A of Aceraspida, and Hirellidae of Orthobranchiata, which are equivalent to Obruchev's (1964) Ateleasididae (= Aceraspididae) of Cephalaspidida and Hemicyclaspididae (incl. Hirellidae) of Kiaeraspidida (= Orthobranchiata).

First, Sil Wenl: *Ateleaspis tesselata* Traquair, "Downtonian", Lesmahagow, Lanarkshire, Scotland (Westoll, 1951).

Last, Dev Gedinn: *Gylenaspis maceacheni* Tarlo and Gurr, Bed 2, L. Dev, Kerrera, Argyllshire, Scotland (Tarlo and Gurr 1966).

Suborder THYESTIDA

General comments: This group classified under Cephalaspidida by Obruchev (1964) and placed in Group C of Aceraspida of Stensiö (1964), i.e. Tremataspidiformes. Here given independent status as major sub-division of Cephalaspidiformes.

First. Sil Ludl: *Thyestes verrucosus* Eichwald, K_1 horizon, L. Ludl. Oesel, Estonia (Obruchev 1964).

Last. Sil Ludl: *Thyestes* sp., U. Red Downton Fm, Downtonian (*sensu* Allen and Tarlo), Welsh Borderland, England (Allen and Tarlo 1963. Tarlo 1964).

The Fossil Record, Part II

Suborder CEPHALASPIDIDA Heintz 1939 (ZENASPIDA Stensiö 1958)

First, Sil Ludl: *Procephalaspis oeselensis* (Robertson), K_1 horizon, L. Ludl, Oesel, Estonia (Obruchev 1964).

Last, Dev Frasn: *Escuminaspis laticeps* (Traquair), and *Alaspis macrotuberculata* Ørvig, Escuminac Beds, Scaumenac Bay, Quebec, Canada (Ørvig 1957b). These two genera provisionally included here by Obruchev (1964) although according to Stensiö (1964) *incertae sedis*.

Order KIAERASPIDIFORMES (ORTHOBRANCHIATA)

Suborder KIAERASPIDIDA Obruchev

First, Dev Gedinn: *Kiaeraspis auchenaspidoides* Stensiö, Ben Nevis Div., Red Bay Series, Spitzbergen (Wängsjö 1952).

Last, Dev Siegen: *Axinaspis whitei* Wängsjö, Kapp Kjeldsen Div., Wood Bay Series, Spitzbergen (Wängsjö 1952).

Suborder MIMETASPIDIDA

First and **Last,** Dev Gedinn: *Mimetaspis exilis* (Wängsjö), and *Mimetaspis hoeli* (Stensiö), Ben Nevis Div., Red Bay Series, Spitzbergen (Wängsjö 1952).

Suborder BENNEVIASPIDIDA

General comments: This suborder consists of Benneviaspididae of Denison (1951) here raised to subordinal rank, and includes Stensiö's (1964) Boreaspididae, Hoelaspididae and Benneviaspididae which he has as independent families of the Order Orthobranchiata (= Kiaeraspidiformes).

First, Dev Gedinn: *Ectinaspis heintzi* Wängsjö, Fraenkelryggen Div., Red Bay Series, Spitzbergen (Wängsjö 1952). According to Steniö (1964) "Osteostraci *incertae sedis*", but probably Benneviaspididae.

Last, Dev Siegen: *Boreaspis costata* Wängsjö, Keltiefjellet Div., Wood Bay Series, Spitzbergen (Friend 1961).

Order NECTASPIDIFORMES Stensiö 1958

First, Dev Siegen: *Nectaspis peltata* Wängsjö, and *Acrotomaspis instabilis* Wängsjö, Kapp Kjeldsen Div., Wood Bay Series, Spitzbergen (Wängsjö 1952).

Last, Dev Ems or Eifel: *Acrotomaspis* sp. "2", Grey Hoek Series, Spitzbergen (Wängsjö 1952) .

Superorder ANASPIDA

Order JAMOYTIIFORMES

First and **Last,** Sil Wenl: *Jamoytius kerwoodi* White, "Downtonian", Lesmahagow, Lanarkshire, Scotland. Primitive anaspid from which lampreys and typical anaspids derived (see also under Protochordata, Chapt. 23).

Order ENDEIOLEPIDIFORMES Berg. 1940

First and **Last,** Dev Frasn: *Endeiolepis aneri* Stensiö, and *Euphanerops longaevus* Woodward, Escuminac Beds, Scaumenac Bay, Quebec, Canada (Ørvig 1957b). *Euphanerops* which is included in a separate family within the order Birkeniida by Obruchev (1964), and as a separate but independent family within the anaspids by Stensiö (1964) in all probability represents an immature individual of *Endeiolepis*.

Order LASANIIFORMES Berg 1940

First and **Last,** Sil Wenl: *Lasanius problematicus* Traquair, "Downtonian", Lesmahagow, Lanarkshire, Scotland (Obruchev 1964).

Chapter 25: Agnatha

Order BIRKENIIFORMES Berg 1940

General comments: The following are here included within the Order Birkeniiformes although Stensiö (1964) made them independent groups of the Anaspida: Birkeniidae, Rhyncholepididae, Pterolepididae (= Pterygolepididae), Pharyngolepididae.

First, Sil Wenl: *Birkenia elegans* Traquair, "Downtonian", Lesmahagow, Lanarkshire, Scotland (Obrucher 1964).

Last, Dev Gedinn: Anaspid scales, *Traquairaspis symondsi* Z., Dittonian (*sensu* Allen and Tarlo). Welsh Borderland, England (Ball and Dineley 1961).

Superorder GALEASPIDA

Order GALEASPIDIFORMES Liu 1965

First and **Last,** Dev (L.): *Galeaspis changi* Liu and *Polybranchiaspis liaojaoshanensis* Liu, L.Dev, nr Chutsing, Yunnan, China (Liu 1965).

Superorder PETEROMYZONIDA (PETROMYZONES)

Order PETROMYZONIFORMES Berg 1940

No known fossil record. *Scaumenella mesacanthus* Graham-Smith, Dev Frasn, Escuminac Beds, Scaumenac Bay, Quebec, Canada, may possibly represent a larval lamprey (Tarlo 1960).

Extant. (See also under Anaspida: Jamoytiiformes).

Subclass HYPEROTRETI (MYXINI)

Order MYXINIFORMES Berg 1940

No known fossil record. *Palaeospondylus gunni* Traquair, Dev Givet, Caithness Flags, Achanarras, Caithness, Scotland, may possibly represent a larval hagfish. **Extant.**

REFERENCES

ALLEN, J. R. L. & TARLO, L. B. H. 1963. The Downtonian and Dittonian facies of the Welsh Borderland. *Geol. Mag.*, **100**, 129–155.

BALL, H. W. & DINELEY, D. L. 1961. The Old Red Sandstone of Brown Clee Hill and the adjacent area. I. Stratigraphy. *Bull. Br. Mus. (Nat. Hist.) Geol.*, **5**, 175–242.

BERG, L. S. 1955. Classification of fishes and fish-like animals, both recent and fossil. *Trudy zool. Inst., Leningr.*, **20**, 1–286.

DENISON, R. H. 1951. Evolution and Classification of the Osteostraci. *Fieldiana, Geol.*, **11**, 155–196.

—— 1952. Early Devonian fishes from Utah. Part 1. Osteostraci. *Ibidem.*, **11**, 163–287.

—— 1953. Early Devonian fishes from Utah. Part 2. Heterostraci. *Ibidem.*, **11**, 289–335.

—— 1963. New Silurian Heterostraci from Southeastern Yukon. *Ibidem.*, **14**, 105–141.

—— 1964. The Cyathaspididae a family of Silurian and Devonian jawless vertebrates. *Ibidem.*, **13**, 307–473.

DINELEY, D. L. 1955. Some Devonian fish remains from North Central Vestspitsbergen. *Geol. Mag.*, **92**, 255–260.

FRIEND, P. F. 1961. The Devonian stratigraphy of North and Central Vestspitsbergen. *Proc. Yorks. geol. Soc.*, **33**, 77–118.

GROSS, W. 1962. 1962. Neuuntersuchung der Stensioellida (Arthrodira Unterderon). *Notizbl. hess Landesamt. Bodenforsch. Wiesbaden*, **90**, 48–86.

KARATAJUTE-TALIMAA, V. 1964. Data on Lower Devonian Stratigraphy of the Southern Baltics. 21–39. *in Questions of Stratigraphy and Palaeogeography of the Devonian Baltics.* Vilnius.

KOSSOVOI, L. S. & OBRUCHEV, D. 1962. The Lower Devonian of Central Timan. *Dolk. Akad. nauk. SSSR.* **147**, 1147–1150.

Liu, Y.-H. 1965. New Devonian agnathans of Yunnan. *Vertebr. Palasiat.* **9,** 125–134.

Obruchev, D. 1948. On the evolution of the exoskeleton in fishes. *Izv. Akad. nauk SSSR.* Ser. Biol., **3,** 281–286.

—— 1956. Cephalaspids from the Lower Devonian of Tuva. *Dokl. Akad. nauk. SSSR.*, **106,** 917–919.

—— 1958. On the Biostratigraphy of the Lower and Middle Palaeozoic Ichthyofaunas of the USSR. *Sov. Geol.*, **11,** 40–53.

—— 1964. Agnatha. *Mater. osnov. Paleont.*, **11,** 34–116.

Ørvig, T. 1957a. Notes on some Paleozoic lower vertebrates from Spitsbergen and North America. *Norsk. geol. tidsskr.*, **37,** 285–353.

—— 1957b. Remarks on the vertebrate fauna of the Lower Upper Devonian of Escuminac Bay, P.Q., Canada, with special reference to the Porolepiform Crossopterygians. *Ark. Zool.*, **10,** 367–426.

—— 1958. Pycnaspis splendens, new genus, new species, a new ostracoderm from the Upper Ordovician of North America. *Proc. U.S. natn. Mis.*, **108,** 1–23.

—— 1965. Palaeohistological notes 2. Certain comments on the phyletic significance of acellular bone tissue in early lower vertebrates. *Ark. Zool. ser. 2*, **16,** 551–556.

Stensiö, E. A. 1927. The Downtonian and Devonian Vertebrates of Spitsbergen, Part I. Family Cephalaspidae. *Skr. Sralbard Ishavet*, **12,** xii + 391, 112 pls.

—— 1932. 1932. *The Cephalaspids of Great Britain*. British Museum (Nat. Hist.). xiv + 220.

—— 1964. Les Cyclostomes fossiles ou Ostracodermes. *Traité de Paléontologie.*, **4** (1), 96–382.

Tarlo, L. B. H. 1960. The invertebrate origins of the vertebrates. *21st Int. geol. Congr.*, **22,** 113–123.

—— 1961. Rhinopteraspis cornubica (McCoy), with notes on the classification and evolution of the pteraspids. *Acta palaeont. pol.*, **6,** 367–402.

—— 1962. The classification and evolution of the Heterostraci. *Ibidem.*, **7,** 249–290.

—— 1964. Psammosteiformes (Agnatha)—a review with descriptions of new material from the Lower Devonian of Poland. 1. General Part. *Palaeont pol.*, **13,** vii + 1 − 135.

—— 1965. Psammosteiformes (Agnatha)—a review with descriptions of new material from the Lower Devonian of Poland 2. Systematic Part. *Palaeont. pol.*, **15,** ix + 1 − 168.

—— & Gurr, P. R. 1966. New cephalaspids from the Lower Devonian of Kerrera, Argyllshire, Scotland (in the press).

Wängsjö, G. 1952. Morphologic and systematic studies of the Spitzbergen cephalaspids. *Skr. Svalbard Ishavet*, **97,** 1–611.

Westoll, T. S. 1951. The Vertebrate-bearing Strata of Scotland. *18th Int. geol. Congr.*, **11,** 5–21.

L. B. H. Tarlo, d.sc. ph.d. f.l.s. f.a.z. f.g.s.

Department of Geology, The University, Reading, Berkshire.

CHAPTER 26

Pisces

Contributors: S. M. ANDREWS, B. G. GARDINER, R. S. MILES
& C. PATTERSON

Introduction. The fishes are traditionally divided into two major groups—the Chondrichthyes or cartilaginous fish and the Osteichthyes or bony fish. Watson (1937) proposed that the Acanthodii and Arthrodira (Placodermi) should, by virtue of their possession of a free hyoid, be placed in a new class the Aphetohyoidea, but in view of recent evidence that these animals did not have a free hyoid, this opinion can no longer be sustained (Miles 1964). The systematic position of these two fossil groups is still, however, a matter of considerable controversy. Stensiö (1963) and Jarvik (1960, 1965) unite them with the cartilaginous fish as Elasmobranchiomorphi, whilst Miles (1965) has produced convincing evidence that the acanthodians are related to the bony fish. Ørvig (1960, 1962) on the other hand has indicated that a living group of cartilaginous fish—the Holocephali—were derived from a specialised line of arthrodires, although Patterson (1965) has disputed this. In view of the current state of debate, it is preferable to retain the Acanthodii and Placodermi as independent classes to avoid any unnecessary phylogenetic implications, consequent upon linking either of them to the cartilaginous or bony fish.

With regard to the cartilaginous fish, the Selachii and Holocephali reveal no evidence of common ancestry and they are thus here placed in separate classes. The problem of the bony fish is somewhat comparable, but now seems to be resolved. There are two major divisions—the Actinopterygii or ray-finned fish and the "Sarcopterygii" or lobe-finned fish. This latter group was formerly called the "Choanichthyes", but this is an inappropriate term since the majority of forms included are devoid of a choana or third nostril. In fact the "Sarcopterygia" consists of two quite unrelated groups—the Crossopterygii (Rhipidistia and Actinistia or Coelacanthi) and the Dipnoi or lung-fish.

The old class "Pisces" is nowadays recognized to be merely a convenient holdall for all primary aquatic jawed vertebrates, which actually belong to seven classes (viz. Acanthodii, Placodermi, Crossopterygii, Dipnoi, Actinopterygii, Selachii and Holocephali). [L.B.H.T.]

Class ACANTHODII

Order CLIMATIIFORMES

Suborder CLIMATIOIDEI Miles 1966

First, Sil Lldov-Wenl: *Nostolepis* Pander, Liteň Bds (E$_a$), Czechoslovakia (Gross 1950).

Last, Carb Tourn: *Gyracanthides murrayi* Woodward, Mansfield, Victoria, Australia (Woodward 1906, Edgworth David 1950). *Gyracanthus* Agassiz, type species *G. formosus* Agassiz, Bashk, which is

The Fossil Record, pp. 637–683. Geological Society of London, 1967. Printed in Northern Ireland.

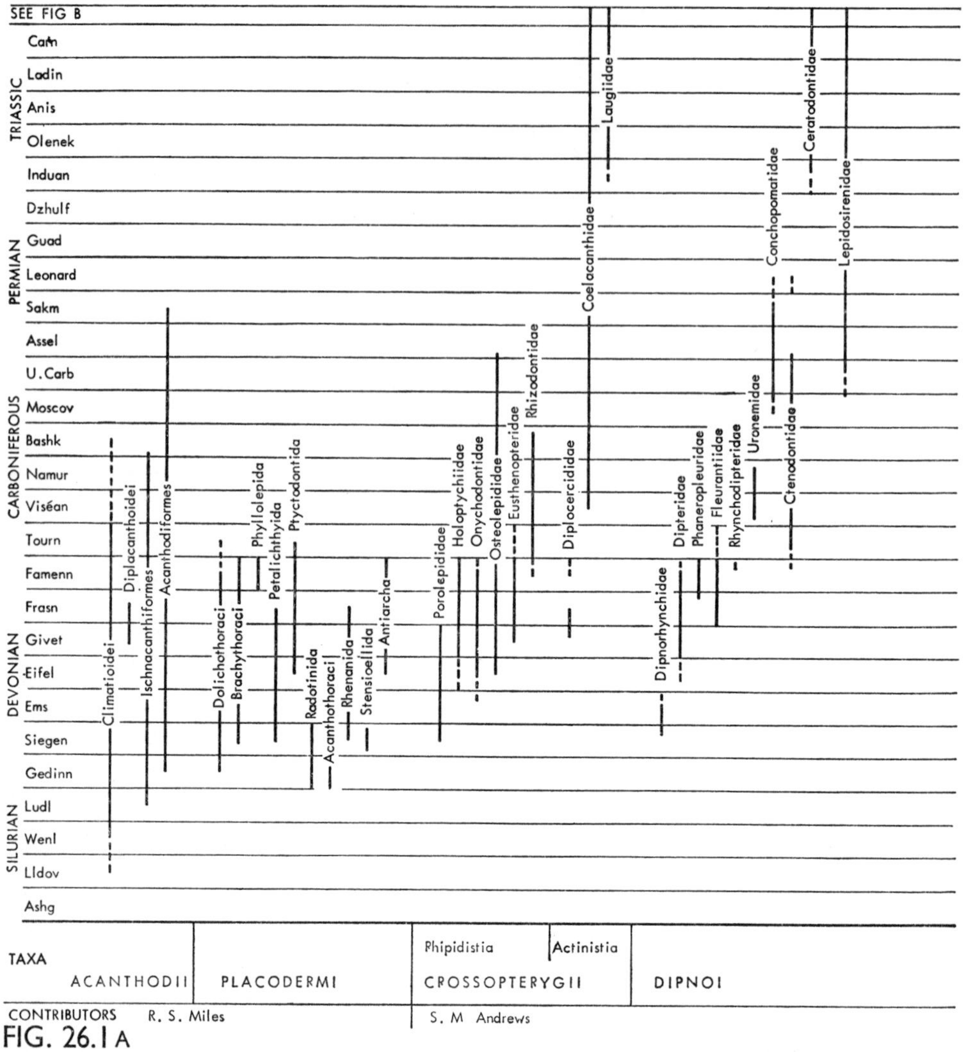

FIG. 26.1 A

widely distributed in the Coal Measures, may belong to this suborder, but this is not certain (Miles 1966).

Suborder DIPLACANTHOIDEI Miles 1966

First, Dev Givet: *Diplacanthus striatus* Agassiz and *Rhadinacanthus longispinus* (Agassiz), Achanarras band, Moray Firth Nodule Beds, Sandwick Fish-Bd, Scotland (Woodward 1891, Traquair 1888). Identity of undescribed specimens noted as "cf. *Diplacanthus*", Dittonian, England requires investigation (Denison 1956).

Last, Dev Frasn: *Diplacanthus horridus* Woodward, Escuminac Fm, Canada (Russell 1951).

Order ISCHNACANTHIFORMES Berg 1940

First, Sil Ludl: *Gomphodus* Pander (scales) and *Onchus* Agassiz (spines), K$_3$ Bds., Oesel (Hoppe 1931). *Onchus* spines, Liteň Beds, Czechoslovakia (Lldov or Wenl) are of uncertain identity and systematic position (Gross 1950).

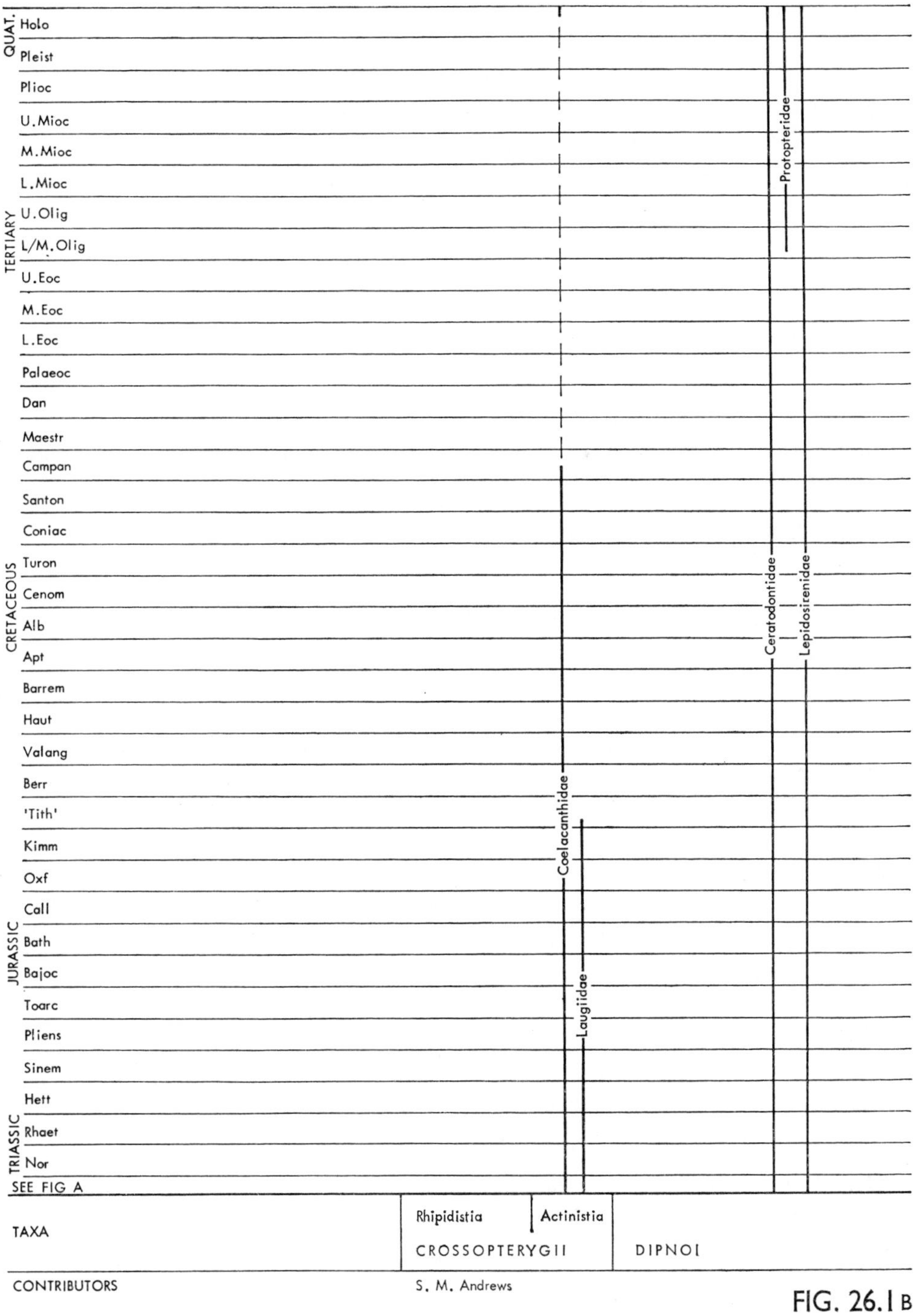
QUAT.
Holo
Pleist
TERTIARY
Plioc
U.Mioc
M.Mioc
L.Mioc
U.Olig
L/M.Olig
U.Eoc
M.Eoc
L.Eoc
Palaeoc
CRETACEOUS
Dan
Maestr
Campan
Santon
Coniac
Turon
Cenom
Alb
Apt
Barrem
Haut
Valang
Berr
JURASSIC
'Tith'
Kimm
Oxf
Call
Bath
Bajoc
Toarc
Pliens
Sinem
Hett
TRIASSIC
Rhaet
Nor
SEE FIG A
Coelacanthidae
Laugiidae
Protopteridae
Ceratodontidae
Lepidosirenidae
TAXA
Rhipidistia
Actinistia
CROSSOPTERYGII
DIPNOI
CONTRIBUTORS
S. M. Andrews

FIG. 26.1 B

Last, Carb Bashk: *Acanthodopsis wardi* Hancock & Atthey, similispulchra Z, Great Britain (Hancock & Atthey 1868, Miles 1966.)

Order ACANTHODIFORMES Berg 1940

First, Dev Gedinn: *Mesacanthus mitchelli* (Egerton), Carmillie Group and above, Scotland (Traquair 1888, Watson, 1937).

Last, Perm Sakm: *Acanthodes bronni* Agassiz and *Acanthodes gracilis* (Beyrich), Lebach Beds and equivalent, Germany and Czechoslovakia (Roemer 1857, Fritsch 1889, Reis 1896). *Acanthodes* also described from L. Perm of N. America (Dunkle & Mamay 1956).

Class PLACODERMI

(Classification of Denison 1958 used here without prejudice)

Superorder ARTHRODIRA

Order EUARTHRODIRA

Suborder DOLICHOTHORACI Stensiö 1944

First, Dev Gedinn: *Kujdanowiaspis* Stensiö, Dittonian, Great Britain, Old Red Stage 1, Ukraine (Denison 1958).

Last, Dev Famenn-Carb Tourn: *Groenlandaspis mirabilis* Heintz, Groenlandaspis Series, E. Greenland (Jarvik 1961). Also said to occur in uppermost Dev of Australia (Rade 1964).

Suborder BRACHYTHORACI Gross 1932

First, Dev Siegen: *Euleptaspis depressa* (Gross), Taunus quartzite, Germany (Gross 1937, Ørvig 1960).

Last, Dev Famenn: *Dunkleosteus* Lehman and at least eight other genera, Cleveland sh, N. America (Hoover 1960).

Order PHYLLOLEPIDA Stensiö 1934

First and Last, Dev Famenn: *Phyllolepis* Agassiz, Phyllolepis Series and base of Remigolepis Series E. Greenland; Rosebrae Beds and Dura Den Beds, Scotland; also occurs in England, Belgium, Russia, N. America and Australia (Stensiö 1934, 1936, 1939; Jarvik 1950*b*).

Order PETALICHTHYIDA Gross 1932

First, Dev Siegen: *Lunaspis broilii* Gross and *Lunaspis heroldi* Broili, Hunsrückschiefer, Germany (Gross 1937, 1961). *L. broilii* has been reported from Siegen rocks in Rhineland which are slightly older than the Hunsrückschiefer, but identification requires confirmation. The specimen of *Macropetalichthys* recorded by King (1925, 1934) from the Downtonian of England is a clay gall (Brit. Mus. (Nat. Hist.) P. 14436-7).

Last, Dev Frasn: *Epipetalichthys wildungensis* Stensiö, Manticoceras Bds, Germany (Stensiö 1925a).

Order PTYCTODONTIDA Gross 1932

First, Dev Eifel: Unnamed tooth-plates, U. Nohn Bds, Germany (Ørvig *in* Schmidt 1961).

Last, Carb Tourn: *Ptyctodus calceolus* Newberry, Bushberg Sst, N. America (Branson *et al.* 1938).

Order RADOTINIDA Gross 1950

First, Dev Gedinn: *Radotina kosorensis* Gross, Radotin Lst, Czechoslovakia (Gross 1958, 1959).

Last, Dev Siegen: *Radotina tuberculata* Gross, Taunus quartzite, Germany (Gross 1937, 1958).

Order ACANTHOTHORACI Stensiö 1944

First, Dev Gedinn: *Kosoraspis peckai*, Radotin Lst, Czechoslovakia (Gross 1959).

Last, Dev Gedinn: *Palaeacanthaspis vasta* Brotzen and *Dobrowlania podolica* Stensiö, Czortkow Stg, Ukraine (Stensiö 1944, Boucot & Pankiwskyj 1962).

Chapter 26: Pisces

Superorder RHENANIDA Broili 1930

First, Dev Siegen: *Gemuendina stuertzi* Traquair, Hunsrückschiefer, Germany (Gross 1963).

Last, Dev Frasn: *Jagorina pandora* Jaekel, Manticoceras Bds, Germany (Jaekel 1921, Stensiö 1925).

Superorder STENSIOELLIDA White 1952

First and Last, Dev Siegen: *Stensioella heintzi* Broili, *Pseudopetalichthys problematicus* Moy-Thomas, *Paraplesiobatus heinrichsi* Broili and *Nessariostoma granulosum* Broili, Hunsrückschiefer, Germany (Gross 1962). *Cratoselache pruvosti* Woodward (L. Carb, Belgium), sometimes placed in this group, is most probably an elasmobranch (Woodward 1924).

Superorder ANTIARCHA Cope 1885

First, Dev Eifel: *Gerdalepis rhenana* (Beyrich), Mühlenberg Bds and above, Germany (Thienhaus 1940, Gross 1941). *Yunnanolepis chii* Liu from China is said to be from L. Dev, but age requires confirmation (Liu 1963).

Last, Dev Famenn: *Remigolepis* Stensiö, Remigolepis Series, E. Greenland (Stensiö 1931, Jarvik 1961). Genus also recorded from U. Dev of Australia (see Hills 1958).   [R.S.M.]

Class CROSSOPTERYGII

Subclass RHIPIDISTIA

Order HOLOPTYCHIIDA

Family POROLEPIDIDAE Berg 1940

First, Dev Siegen: *Porolepis siegenensis* Gross, and *P. hefteri* Gross, Taunusquarzit, Rhineland, Germany (Gross 1936). Other species of *Porolepis* are recorded from beds of probably similar age, e.g. Wood Bay Series, Spitsbergen (Jarvik 1942; Friend 1962), and U. Siegen, Taimyr Peninsula, N. Siberia (Obruchev 1940; Vorobjeva 1963).

Last, Dev Givet: *Porolepis posnaniensis* Kade, Pernau Stufe, Torgel, (Teufelshöhle), Baltic (Gross 1942; Westoll 1951), and *P. uralensis* Obruchev, from beds of similar age, Rivers Vilva and Kosva, Urals (Obruchev 1939).

Family HOLOPTYCHIIDAE Owen 1860.

First, Dev Eifel-Givet: *Glyptolepis leptopterus* Agassiz, Tynet Burn Fish Bed, Tynet Burn, Morayshire, Scotland (Westoll 1951), and *G. paucidens* (Agassiz), Achanarras Fish Bed, Achanarras Quarry, Caithness, Scotland (Rayner 1963).

Last, Dev Famenn: *Holoptychius nobilissimus* Agassiz, Rosebrae Beds, Morayshire, Scotland, and *H. flemingi* Agassiz, Dura Den, Fifeshire, Scotland (Westoll 1951). Many "species" of *Holoptychius* are also described from Dev Famenn, Catskill and Chemung Fms, Eastern U.S.A. (see Hay 1929), and the genus is recorded from U. Old Red Sst of Australia, Antarctica, Greenland, Russia and elsewhere.

Family ONYCHODONTIDAE Woodward 1891

First, Dev Ems-Eifel: *Onychodus* sp. Ørvig, Grey Hoek Series, Spitsbergen (Ørvig 1957, p. 393, Friend 1961). Records from earlier beds refer to teeth probably pertaining to acanthodians (e.g. Woodward 1888).

Last, Dev Famenn: *Onychodus hopkinsi* Newberry, Chemung Fm, Franklin, Delaware Co, New York (Newberry 1889), and *O. dellei* Gross, h-Stufe, Kapsehden, Liban, Baltic (Gross 1942).

Order OSTEOLEPIDIDA

Family OSTEOLEPIDIDAE Cope 1889.

First, Dev Eifel: *Thursius macrolepidotus* (Sedgwick & Murchison), Wick Beds, Caithness, Scotland (Jarvik 1948; Westoll 1951).

Last, Perm Assel: *Ectosteorhachis nitidus* Cope, Wichita Group, Baylor Co, Texas (Romer 1937, Thomson 1964), and *Megalichthys* sp. Heintz, L. Perm, Semsvik, Oslo, Norway (Heintz 1934).

Family EUSTHENOPTERIDAE Berg 1955

First, Dev Givet: *Tristichopterus alatus* Egerton, John O'Groat's Sst, Caithness, and Eday Flags, Deerness, Orkney (Traquair 1875).

Last, Dev Famenn-Carb Tourn: *Eusthenodon wängsjöi* Jarvik, Remigolepis Series, Gauss Halvö and Ymers Ö, E. Greenland (Jarvik 1952).

Family RHIZODONTIDAE Traquair 1881

First, Dev Famenn: *Sauripterus taylori* Hall, Catskill Fm, Blossburgh, Pennsylvania (Newberry 1889). Other species of *Sauripterus* from Dev Frasn, Alves, Morayshire, Scotland (Traquair 1897; Woodward 1891) are of doubtful affinities.

Last, Carb Bashk: *Strepsodus sauroides* (Binney), *S. sulcidens* (Hancock & Atthey), and *Rhizodopsis sauroides* (Williamson), Low Main Coal Shale (upper M. Coal Measures), Newsham, Northumberland, and elsewhere in British coalfields (Woodward 1891, Panchen & Walker 1960).

Subclass ACTINISTIA (COELACANTHI)

Order DIPLOCERCIDIDA

Family DIPLOCERCIDIDAE Stensiö 1922

First, Dev Givet: *Dictyonosteus arcticus* Stensiö, Asterolepis Series, Wijde Bay, Spitsbergen (Stensiö 1918, Friend 1961), and *Euporosteus eifeliensis* Jaekel, M. Dev, Gerolstein, Germany (Jaekel 1927, Gross 1950), although its age has been questioned by Stensiö who prefers a lower U. Dev age (Stensiö 1937).

Last, Dev Frasn: *Diplocercides kayseri* (v. Koenen) and *D. jaekeli* Stensiö, lower U. Dev, Müllenborn and Ense, Wildungen, Germany (Stensiö 1937). *Chagrinia enodis* Schaeffer, from Dev Famenn, Chagrin Sh, Euclid Creek, Ohio, U.S.A., is tentatively referred to this group, mainly on the structure of the tail (Schaeffer 1962).

Order COELACANTHIDA

Family COELACANTHIDAE Agassiz 1843

First, Carb Viséan: *Rhabdoderma ardrossense* Moy-Thomas, Calciferous Sst Series, Ardross Castle, Fifeshire, and *R. huxleyi* (Traquair), L. Carb, Glencartholm, Dumfriesshire, Scotland. (Moy-Thomas 1937, Westoll 1951).

Last, Cret Campan: *Macropoma mantelli* Agassiz, U. Chalk, Quadrata Z, Lewes, Sussex, and elsewhere in S.E. England (Woodward 1909, Jukes-Browne 1904).

Family LATIMERIIDAE Berg 1940

No fossil record. *Latimeria chalumnae* Smith, Comores Archipelago, Indian Ocean (Millot 1954, Millot & Anthony 1958).

Order LAUGIIDA

Family LAUGIIDAE Berg 1940

First, Trias Induan: *Laugia groenlandica* Stensiö, Otoceras-Ophiceras Beds, Clavering Ö, East Greenland (Stensiö 1932).

Last, Jur 'Tith': *Coccoderma suevicum* Quenstedt, Lithographic Stone, Württemberg and Bavaria, Germany (Woodward 1891). This genus was previously thought to be a coelacanthid, but the presence of anteriorly placed pelvic fins shows that it must be united with *Laugia* (White 1954).

Chapter 26: Pisces

Class DIPNOI

Order DIPTERIDA

Suborder DIPTEROIDEI

Family DIPNORHYNCHIDAE Berg 1940

First, Dev Siegen: *Dipnorhynchus lehmanni* Westoll, Hunsrückschiefer, Schmeidenberg Quarry, Bundenbach, Germany (Lehmann & Westoll 1952).

Last, Dev Ems: *Dipnorhynchus süssmilchi* (Etheridge), Murrumbidgee Series, Taemas, N.S.W., Australia (Hills 1941, Philip & Pedder 1964). The genera *Ganorhynchus* and *Holodipterus* are doubtfully referred to this family: species of *Ganorhynchus* are recorded from Dev Famenn, Chemung and Catskill Fms, Eastern U.S.A., and *Holodipterus kiprijanowi* (Pander) is recorded from Famenn, Orla region, Poland.

Family DIPTERIDAE Owen 1846

First, Dev Eifel-Givet: *Dipterus platycephalus* (Agassiz), Achanarras Fish Bed, Achanarras Quarry, Caithness, Scotland (Westoll 1949, 1951).

Last, Dev Famenn: *Dipterus nelsoni* Newberry, Chemung Fm, Warren, Pennsylvania (Newberry 1889), and other species from the Chemung and Catskill Fms, Eastern U.S.A. (see Hay 1929). *Dipterus* and *Conchodus* have also been recorded from Dev Famenn, h-Stufe, Kapsehden, Liban, Baltic (Gross 1942, Westoll 1951).

Suborder PHANEROPLEUROIDEI

Family PHANEROPLEURIDAE Huxley 1861

First, Dev Frasn: *Scaumenacia curta* (Whiteaves), Scaumenac Bay Fm, Scaumenac Bay, Quebec, Canada (Whiteaves 1881, Westoll 1949).

Last, Dev Famenn: *Phaneropleuron andersoni* Huxley, Dura Den, Fifeshire (Traquair 1873; Westoll 1951). *Oervigia nordica* Lehman, Dev Famenn-Carb Tourn, Remigolepis Series, Mt. Celsius, East Greenland, is also tentatively referred to this family (Lehman 1959).

Family FLEURANTIIDAE Berg 1940

First, Dev Frasn: *Fleurantia denticulata* Graham-Smith & Westoll, Scaumenac Bay Fm, Scaumenac Bay, Quebec, Canada (Graham-Smith & Westoll 1937).

Last, Dev Famenn-Carb Tourn: *Jarvikia arctica* Lehman, Remigolepis Series, East Greenland (Lehman 1959). However, this genus is doubtfully referred to this family.

Family RHYNCHODIPTERIDAE Berg 1940

First and **Last,** Dev Famenn: *Rhynchodipterus elginensis* Säve-Söderbergh, Rosebrae Beds, Rosebrae, Morayshire Scotland (Säve-Söderbergh 1937, Westoll 1951).

Comment: *Soederberghia groenlandica* Lehman, Dev Famenn-Carb Tourn, Remigolepis Series, Nathorsts Fjeld, East Greenland (Lehman 1959) has doubtful affinities with this group.

Suborder CTENODONTOIDEI

Family URONEMIDAE Traquair 1890

First, Carb Viséan: *Uronemus lobatus* Agassiz, Burdiehouse Lst, Oil sh Group, Burdiehouse, Midlothian, Scotland (Traquair 1873, Westoll 1951).

Last, Carb Namur: *Uronemus splendens* Traquair, Borough Lee (Loanhead No. 2) Ironstone, Loanhead, Midlothian, Scotland (Watson & Gill 1923).

Family CONCHOPOMATIDAE Berg 1940

First, Carb Moscov: *Conchopoma anthracina* (Cope), Freeport Group, Late Westphalian, Linton, Ohio (Romer 1930, Westoll 1944).

Last, Perm Sakm-Leonard: *Conchopoma gadiforme* Kner, Rothliegende, Lebach, Saarbrücken, Germany (Weitzel 1926).

Family CTENODONTIDAE Woodward 1891

First, Dev Famenn-Carb Tourn: *Proceratodus wagneri* (Newberry), Cleveland Sh, Cleveland, Ohio, (Newberry 1889; Romer and Smith 1934), and *Ctenodus breviceps* Woodward, Lowermost Carb, Mansfield, Victoria, Australia (Woodward 1906, Hills 1958). *Nielsenia nordica* Lehman, Dev Famenn, Phyllolepis Series, Ymers Ö, East Greenland (Lehman 1959), is tentatively classified here.

Last, Perm Assel: *Sagenodus dialophus* Cope, and two other species, Wichita Group, Texas (Romer & Smith 1934). *"Ctenodus" tardus* Fritsch, Perm Leonard, Brandschiefer, Koschtialov, Bohemia, has doubtful affinities with this group (Watson & Gill 1923).

Order CERATODONTIDA

Suborder CERATODONTOIDEI

Family CERATODONTIDAE Gill 1872

First, Trias Induan-Olenek: *Gosfordia truncata* Woodward, Lower Hawkesbury Beds, Narrabeen Group, Gosford, N.S.W., Australia (Hills 1958, Voisey 1952). *Ceratodus* and *Epiceratodus* are also known from L. Trias, Lake Bogdo, U.S.S.R. (Kabakov 1947). **Extant.**

Comment: Only living species, *Epiceratodus forsteri* (Krefft), Burnett and Mary Rivers, Queensland, Australia.

Suborder LEPIDOSIRENOIDEI

Family PROTOPTERIDAE Günther 1872

First, Tert L. Olig: *Protopterus libycus* Stromer, and two other species based on toothplates, L. Olig, Fäyûm, Egypt (Greenwood 1951). **Extant.**

Comment: *Protopterus annectens* (Owen), and two other species, living in the fresh waters of Central Africa.

Family LEPIDOSIRENIDAE Bonaparte 1841

First, Carb ?U.Carb: *Gnathorhiza pusilla* (Cope), late Pennsylvanian, Danville, Illinois (Romer & Smith 1934). **Extant.**

Comment: Only living species, *Lepidosiren paradoxa* Fitzinger, Amazon Basin. Fossils are unknown after the Perm. [S.M.A.]

Class ACTINOPTERYGII

Subclass CHONDROSTEI

Order PALAEONISCIFORMES

Family CHEIROLEPIDIDAE Pander 1860

First, Dev Eifel-Givet: *Cheirolepis trailli* Agassiz 1835, M. ORS, Scotland.

Last, Dev Frasn: *Cheirolepis canadensis* Whiteaves 1881, Escuminac Bay, Quebec, Canada.

Family STEGOTRACHELIDAE Gardiner 1963

First, Dev Eifel-Givet: *Stegotrachelus* Woodward & White 1926, *Moythomasia* Gross 1950, *Orvikuina* Gross 1953, M. ORS Europe; *Moythomasia* Famenn U.S.A. (Gardiner 1963).

Last, Carb Tourn-Viséan: *Kentuckia deani* (Eastman 1905), Waverly Sh, Kentucky.

Family OSORIOICHTHYIDAE Gardiner 1967

First and **Last,** Dev Frasn-Famenn: *Osorioichthys marginis* (Casier 1952), Belgium.

Chapter 26: Pisces

Family TEGEOLEPIDIDAE Romer 1945

First, Dev Famenn: *Tegeolepis clarki* (Newberry 1888), Cleveland Sh, Ohio.
Last, Trias ?Nor: *Elpisopholis dunstani* Woodward 1908, Wianamatta Sh, St. Peter's, Australia.

Family RHADINICHTHYIDAE Romer 1945

First, Carb Tourn: *Rhadinichthys* Traquair 1877, *Cycloptychius* Young 1866, *Rhadinoniscus* White 1937, *Aetheretmon* White 1937, *Strepheoschema* White 1937, Scotland and elsewhere; *Cycloptychius* and *Rhadinichthys* also in U. Carb.
Last, ?Perm/Trias: *Rhadinichthys tellecheai* Rusconi 1948, Argentina, South America.

Family CANOBIIDAE Aldinger 1937

First and **Last,** Carb Tourn: *Canobius* Traquair 1881, *Mesopoma* Traquair 1890, Scotland; Whiteichthys Moy-Thomas 1942, Carb, Greenland.

Family AEDUELLIIDAE Romer 1945

First and **Last,** Perm Assel-Leonard: *Aeduella blainvillei* (Agassiz 1833), *Westollia crassus* (Pholig 1892), Europe.

Family ELONICHTHYIDAE Aldinger 1937

First, Carb Tourn: *Elonichthys* Giebel 1848, many species, Europe and U.S.A.
Last, Perm Guad-Dzhulf: *Elonichthys davidi* Mitchell 1914, Tarro, New South Wales, Australia.

Family GONATODIDAE Gardiner 1967

First, Carb Tourn: *Gonatodus punctatus* (Agassiz 1835), *Protamblypterus macrolepis* (Traquair 1877), Scotland.
Last, Carb U. Carb: *Drydenius molyneuxi* (Traquair 1877), England, France and Germany.

Family ACROLEPIDIDAE Aldinger 1937

First, Carb Tourn-Viséan: *Acrolepis* Agassiz 1833, several spp., Europe and U.S.A.
Last, Trias Rhaet: *Hyllingea swanbergi* Aldinger 1937, Sweden.

Family BOREOSOMIDAE Gardiner 1967

First, Trias Induan: *Boreosomus* Stensiö 1921, several spp., Spitsbergen, Madagascar and Greenland.
Last, Trias Ladin: *Leptogenichthys longus* Wade 1935, *Mesembroniscus longisquamosus* Wade 1935, Brookvale, Hawkesbury Sst, New South Wales, Australia.

Family CARBOVELIDAE Romer 1945

First and **Last,** Carb Tourn-Viséan: *Carboveles ovensi* White 1927, *Phanerosteon mirabile* Traquair 1881, Scotland.

Family RHABDOLEPIDIDAE Gardiner 1963

First and **Last,** Perm Sakm-Leonard: *Rhabdolepis macropterus* (Bronn 1829), *Rhabdolepis saarbrueckensis* Gardiner 1964, Germany.

Family COSMOPTYCHIIDAE Gardiner 1963

First and **Last,** Carb Tourn: *Watsonichthys pectinatus* (Traquair 1877), *Cosmoptychius striatus* (Agassiz 1835), Scotland.

Family PYGOPTERIDAE Aldinger 1937

First, Carb Tourn: *Nematoptychius greenocki* (Traquair 1866), Scotland.
Last, Trias Induan: *Pygopterus de geeri* Stensiö 1921, Spitsbergen, *Pygopterus crecelli* Wilser 1923, Germany.

Family COMMENTRYIDAE Gardiner 1963

First and **Last,** Carb Bashk: *Commentrya traquairi* Sauvage 1888, France.

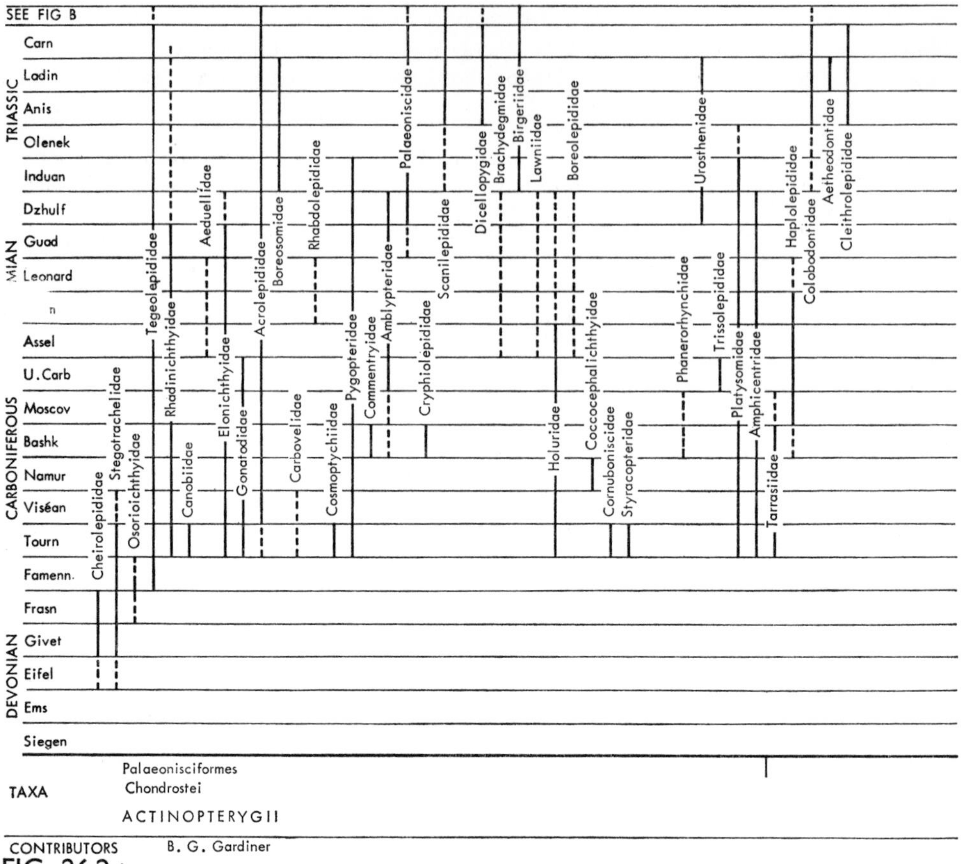

FIG. 26.2 A

Family AMBLYPTERIDAE Romer 1945

First, Carb Bashk-U. Carb: *Paramblypterus decorus* Egerton 1850, France.

Last, Perm Dzhulf: *Amblypterus* Agassiz 1833, *Amblypterina* Berg 1940, Europe and South Africa.

Family PALAEONISCIDAE Vogt 1852

First, Perm Guad-Dzhulf: *Palaeoniscum* Blainville 1818, *Trachelacanthus* Waldheim 1850, Greenland, Europe and U.S.A.

Last, Trias Carn-Nor: *Turseodus acutus* Leidy 1857, U.S.A.

Family CRYPHIOLEPIDIDAE Moy-Thomas 1939

First and **Last,** Carb Bashk: *Cryphiolepis striatus* (Traquair 1881), Edge Coal ser, Scotland.

Family SCANILEPIDIDAE Romer 1945

First, Trias Induan-Anis: *Evenkia eunotoptera* Berg 1941, Siberia.

Last, Trias Rhaet: *Scanilepis dubia* (Woodward 1893), Sweden.

Family COCCOLEPIDIDAE Berg 1940

First, Jur Sinem: *Coccolepis liassica* Woodward 1890, England.
Last, Cret Berr/Cenom: *Sunolepis yumenensis* Liu 1957, China, *Coccolepis macroptera* Traquair 1911, Berr, Belgium. *Coccolepis* is widely distributed and is also recorded from Turkestan, Russia and Australia.

Family DICELLOPYGIDAE Romer 1945

First, Trias Anis: *Dicellopyge macrodentata* Brough 1931, *Dicellopyge lissocephala* Brough 1931, Bekkers Kraal, Rouseville, South Africa.
Last, Trias Carn-Nor: *Aneurolepis* White & Moy-Thomas 1941, several species, Italy.

Family BRACHYDEGMIDAE Gardiner 1967

First and **Last,** Perm: *Brachydegma caelatum* Dunkle 1939, Texas.

Family BIRGERIIDAE Aldinger 1937

First, Trias Induan: *Birgeria* Stensiö 1919, several spp., Europe, Madagascar and Greenland.
Last, Jur Toarc: *Ohmdenia multidentata* Hauf 1953, Germany. This doubtfully belongs.

Family LAWNIIDAE Gardiner 1967

First and **Last,** Perm: *Lawnia taylorensis* Wilson 1953, Texas.

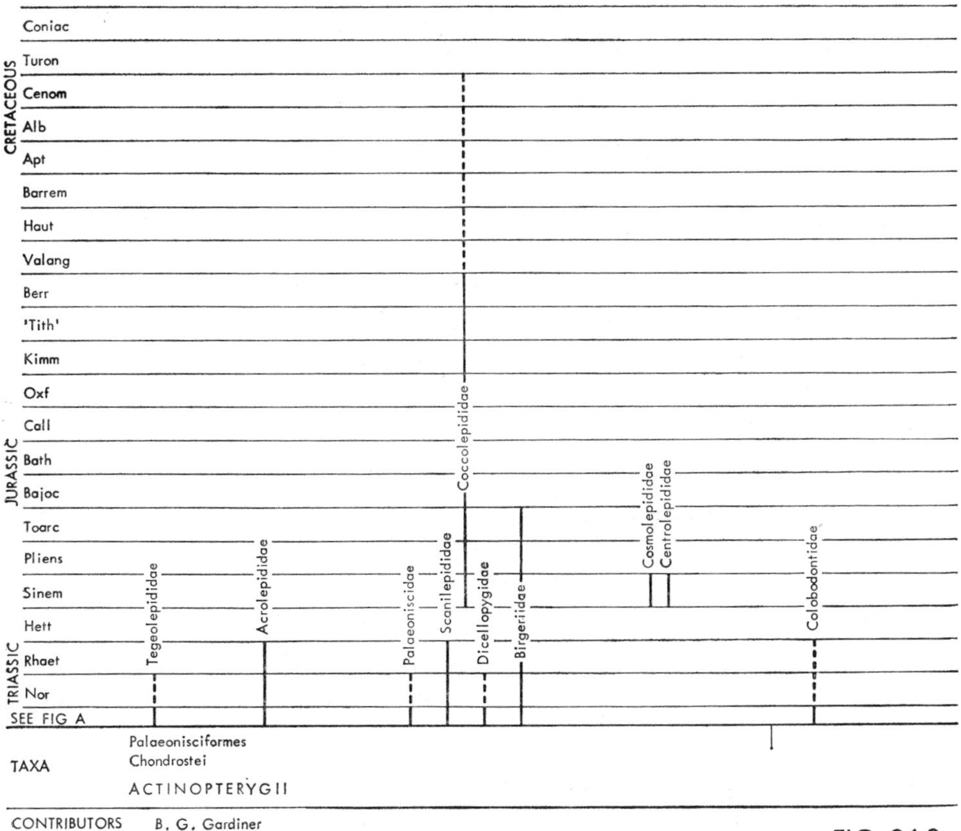

FIG. 26.2 B

647

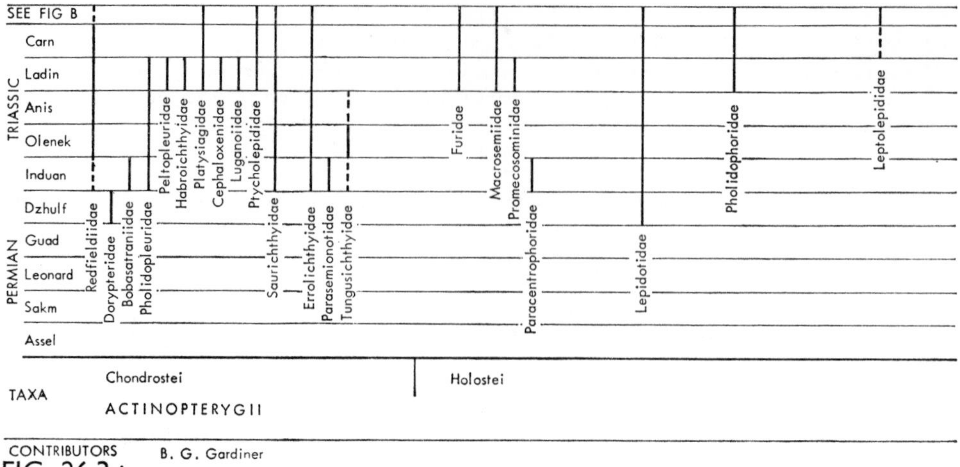

SEE FIG B		

TRIASSIC: Carn, Ladin, Anis, Olenek, Induan
PERMIAN: Dzhulf, Guad, Leonard, Sakm
Assel

Families (vertical labels): Redfieldiidae, Dorypteridae, Bobasatraniidae, Pholidopleuridae, Peltopleuridae, Habroichthyidae, Platysiagidae, Cephaloxenidae, Luganoiidae, Ptycholepididae, Saurichthyidae, Errolichthyidae, Parasemionotidae, Tungusichthyidae, Furidae, Macrosemiidae, Promecosominidae, Paracentrophoridae, Lepidotidae, Pholidophoridae, Leptolepididae

Chondrostei	Holostei

TAXA — ACTINOPTERYGII

CONTRIBUTORS   B. G. Gardiner

FIG. 26.3 A

Family HOLURIDAE Moy-Thomas 1939

First, Carb Tourn: *Holurus parki* Traquair 1881, Scotland.
Last, Perm: *Holuropsis yavorskyi* Berg 1947, Russia.

Family BOREOLEPIDIDAE Aldinger 1937

First and **Last,** Perm: *Boreolepis jenseni* Aldinger 1937, Greenland.

Family COCCOCEPHALICHTHYIDAE Romer 1945

First and **Last,** Carb Namur: *Coccocephalichthys wildi* (Watson, 1925), England.

Family CORNUBONISCIDAE White 1939

First and **Last,** Carb Tourn: *Cornuboniscus budensis* White, 1939, Cornwall, England.

Family STYRACOPTERIDAE Moy-Thomas 1939

First and **Last,** Carb Tourn: *Styracopterus fulcatus* Traquair 1890, Scotland, *Benedenius deneensis* (Traquair 1878), Belgium.

Family COSMOLEPIDIDAE Gardiner 1967

First and **Last,** Jur Sinem: *Cosmolepis ornatus* (Egerton 1854), *Cosmolepis egertoni* Egerton 1858, England.

Family CENTROLEPIDIDAE Gardiner 1960

First and **Last,** Jur Sinem: *Centrolepis aspera* Agassiz 1844, England.

Family PHANERORHYNCHIDAE Stensiö 1932

First and **Last,** Carb Bashk-Moscov: *Phanerorhynchus armatus* Gill 1923, Lancashire, England.

Family UROSTHENIDAE Woodward 1931

First, Perm Dzhulf: *Urosthenes latus* Woodward 1931, New South Wales, Australia.
Last, Trias Ladin: *Urosthenes australis* Dana 1848, Hawkesbury series, New South Wales, Australia.

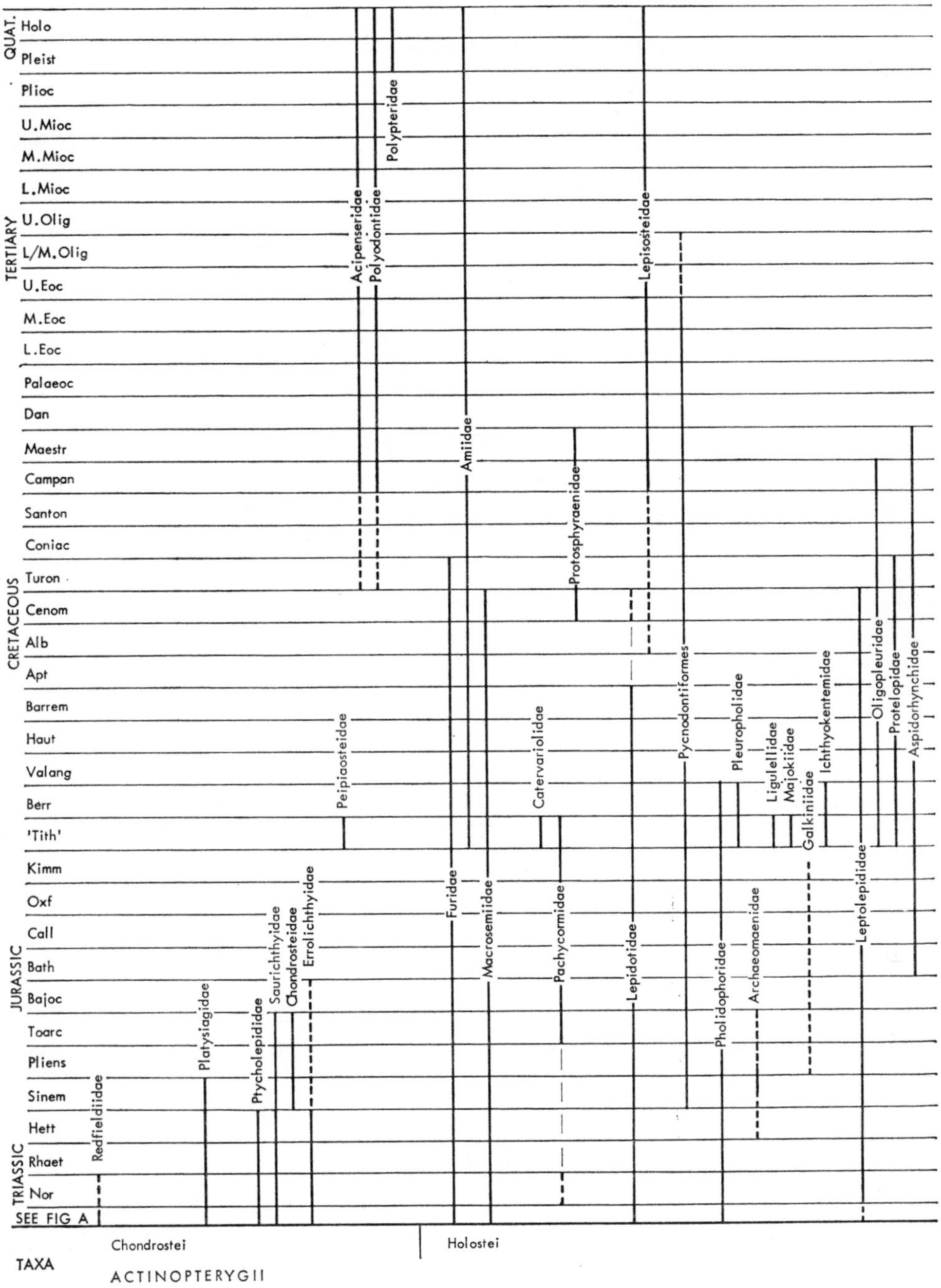

FIG. 26.3 B

CONTRIBUTORS   B. G. Gardiner

Family TRISSOLEPIDIDAE Frič 1893

First and **Last,** Carb U.Carb: *Sceletophorus biserialis* Frič 1894, *Sphaerolepis kounoviensis* Frič 1877, Germany.

Family PLATYSOMIDAE Young 1866

First, Carb Tourn: *Mesolepis* Young 1866, *Paramesolepis* Moy-Thomas & Dyne 1938, *Wardichthys* Traquair 1875, *Platysomus* Agassiz 1833, Europe.

Last, Trias ?Olenek: *Caurichthys ornatus* Broom 1913, South Africa.

Family AMPHICENTRIDAE Moy-Thomas 1939

(CHEIRODIDAE Moy-Thomas 1939)

First, Carb Tourn: *Cheirodopsis geikiei* Traquair 1881, Scotland.
Last, Perm Dzhulf: *Eurynotoides cypriorion* Berg 1940, Russia.

Order TARRASIIFORMES

Family TARRASIIDAE Traquair 1881

First, Carb Tourn: *Tarrasius problematicus* Traquair 1881, Scotland.
Last, Carb Bashk-Moscow: *Palaeophichthys parvulus* Eastman 1908, Illinois.

Order HAPLOLEPIFORMES

Family HAPLOLEPIDIDAE Westoll 1944

First, Carb Bashk-Moscov: *Haplolepis* Miller 1892, several spp., Europe and U.S.A.
Last, Perm Assel-Leonard: *Pyritocephalus sculptus* Frič 1894, Germany.

Order PERLEIDIFORMES

Family COLOBODONTIDAE Stensiö 1916

First, Trias Induan-Anis: *Colobodus* Agassiz 1844, *Perleidus* Deeke 1911, *Meidiichthys* Brough 1931, *Tripelta* Wade 1940, *Chrotichthys* Wade 1940, *Zeuchthiscus* Wade 1940, *Pristisomus* Woodward 1890, collectively a world-wide distribution.
Last, Trias Carn-Nor: *Colobodus* Agassiz 1844, several spp., Italy. [Not Rhaet, Fig. 26.2B].

Family AETHEODONTIDAE Brough 1939

First and **Last,** Trias Ladin: *Aetheodontus besanensis* Brough 1939, Italy.

Family CLEITHROLEPIDIDAE Wade 1935

First, Trias Anis: *Cleithrolepis granulata* Egerton 1864, *Cleithrolepis alta* Wade 1935, Narrabeen Shs, Gosford, New South Wales, Australia.
Last, Trias Carn: *Dipteronotus cyphus* Egerton 1854, England.

Order REDFIELDIIFORMES

Family REDFIELDIIDAE Berg 1940

First, Trias ?Induan: *Sakamenichthys germaini* Nauche 1959, Madagascar; *Brookvalia* Wade 1935, *Dictyopyge* Egerton 1847, ?Anis, Narrabeen Shs, Gosford, New South Wales; *Atopocephala* Brough 1934, *Daedalichthys* Brough 1930, *Helichthys* Broom 1909, Olenek, Cynognathus Z, Bekkers Kraal, South Africa.
Last, Trias Carn-Nor: *Redfieldius* Hay 1902, several spp., Carn? U.S.A.; *Dictyopyge* Egerton 1847, Carn-Nor, U.S.A., England, Ireland, Germany and Australia.

Chapter 26: Pisces

Order DORYPTERIFORMES

Family DORYPTERIDAE Gill 1926

First and **Last,** Perm Guad: *Dorypterus hoffmanni* Germar 1842, *?Dorypterus althausi* (Münster 1842), England and Germany *Dorypterus* sp. Liu & Tseng 1964, Perm Touling Coal Ser, Central China. [Not Dzhulf, Fig. 26.3A].

Order BOBASATRANIIFORMES

Family BOBASATRANIIDAE Stensiö 1932

First and **Last,** Trias Induan: *Bobasatrania* White 1932, several spp., Greenland, Madagascar and Canada; *Ecrinesomus dixoni* Wood 1910, Madagascar.

Order PHOLIDOPLEURIFORMES

Family PHOLIDOPLEURIDAE Wade 1932

First, Trias Induan: *Australosomus* Stensiö 1932, several spp., Greenland, Madagascar; *Arctosomus sibiricus* Berg 1941, Induan/Anis, Siberia.
Last, Trias Ladin: *Pholidopleurus typus* Bronn 1858, Italy.

Order PELTOPLEURIFORMES

Family PELTOPLEURIDAE

First and **Last,** Trias Ladin: *Peltopleurus* Kner 1866, Italy and China; *Placopleurus* Brough 1939, Italy.

Family HABROICHTHYIDAE Gardiner 1967

First and **Last,** Trias Ladin: *Habroichthys minimus* Brough 1929, Italy.

Order PLATYSIAGIFORMES

Family PLATYSIAGIDAE Brough 1939

First, Trias Ladin: *Platysiagum minus* Brough 1939, Italy.
Last, Jur Sinem: *Platysiagum sclerocephalum* Egerton 1872, England.

Order CEPHALOXENIFORMES

Family CEPHALOXENIDAE Brough 1939

First and **Last,** Trias Ladin: *Cephaloxenus macropterus* Brough 1939, Italy.

Order LUGANOIIFORMES

Family LUGANOIIDAE Brough 1939

First and **Last,** Trias Ladin: *Luganoia* Brough 1939, several spp., *Besania micrognathus* Brough 1939, Italy.

Order PTYCHOLEPIFORMES

Family PTYCHOLEPIDIDAE Brough 1939

First, Trias Ladin: *Ptycholepis barboi* Brough 1939, Italy.
Last, Jur Hett: *Ptycholepis bollensis* Agassiz 1833, England, Germany and France.

Order SAURICHTHYIFORMES

Family SAURICHTHYIDAE Goodrich 1909 (= Belonorynchidae Woodward 1888)

First, Trias Induan: *Saurichthys* Agassiz 1834, several spp., Germany, Madagascar and Spitsbergen.
Last, Jur Toarc: *Saurorhynchus brevirostris* (Woodward 1895), England and Germany.

651

Order CHONDROSTEIFORMES

Family CHONDROSTEIDAE Traquair 1877

First, Jur Sinem: *Chondrosteus acipenseroides* Egerton 1844, *Chondrosteus pachyurus* Egerton 1858, England.

Last, Jur Toarc: *Strongylosteus hindenburgi* (Pompeckz 1914), Germany; *Gyrosteus mirabilis* Egerton 1858, England.

Family ERROLICHTHYIDAE Lehman 1952

First, Trias Induan: *Errolichthys mirabilis* Lehman 1952, Magadascar.
Last, Jur?: *Psilichthys selwyni* Hall 1900, Carrapook, Victoria, Australia.

Order PARASEMIONOTIFORMES

Family PARASEMIONOTIDAE Stensiö 1932

First and **Last,** Trias Induan: *Broughia* Stensiö 1932, *Helmolepis* Stensiö 1932, *Ospia* Stensiö 1932, Greenland; *Jacobulus* Lehman 1952, *Stensionotus* Lehman 1952, *Thomasinotus* Lehman 1952, *Watsonulus* Brough 1939, *Parasemionotus* Piveteau 1929, Madagascar.

Family TUNGUSICHTHYIDAE Berg 1940

First and **Last,** Trias Induan-Anis: *Tungusichthys acentrophoroides*, *T. derjungini* Berg 1940, Siberia.

Order ACIPENSERIFORMES

Family PEIPIAOSTEIDAE Liu & Zhou 1965

First and **Last,** Jur 'Tith': *Peipiaosteus pani* Liu & Zhou 1965, China.

Family ACIPENSERIDAE Bonaparte 1831

First, Cret Turon-Campan: *Protoscaphirhynchus squamosus* Wilimovsky 1956, Montana.
Extant.

Family POLYODONTIDAE Bonaparte 1838

First, Cret Turon-Campan: *Paleopsephurus wilsoni* McAlpin 1941, Montana.   **Extant.**

Order POLYPTERIFORMES

Family POLYPTERIDAE

First, Quat Pleist: *Polypterus bichir ornatis* Arambourg 1947, Kenya.   **Extant.**

Subclass HOLOSTEI

Division Holosteans

Order AMIIFORMES

Family FURIDAE Jordan 1923

First, Trias Ladin: *Eoeugnathus megalepis* Brough 1939, Italy; *Sinoeugnathus kusichowensis* Su 1959, China.

Last, Cret Turon: *Neorhombolepis excelsus* Woodward 1888, England.

Family AMIIDAE Bonaparte 1837

First, Jur 'Tith': *Urocles* Jordan 1919, *Ionoscopus* Costa 1953, *Liodesmus* Wagner 1859, Germany and France.   **Extant.**

Chapter 26: Pisces

Family MACROSEMIIDAE Cope 1889

First, Trias Ladin: *Ophiopsis lepturus* (Bellotti 1857), Italy.
Last, Cret Cenom: *Petalopteryx syriacus* Pictet 1850, *Aphaneygus dorsalis* (Davis 1887), Mt Lebanon, Syria; *Aphanepygus elegans* Bassani 1879, Cenom, Dalmatia, Yugoslavia.

Family PROMECOSOMINIDAE Wade 1941

First and **Last,** Trias ?Ladin: *Promecosomina formosa* (Woodward 1905), Hawkesbury Sst, Brookvale, New South Wales, Australia.

Family PARACENTROPHORIDAE Obruchev 1964

First and **Last,** Trias Induan: *Paracentrophorus madagascariensis* Piveteau 1941, Madagascar.

Family CATERVARIOLIDAE Saint-Seine 1955

First and **Last,** Jur 'Tith': *Signeuxelle premonti* Saint-Seine 1955, *Catervariolus* Saint-Seine 1955, *Lombardina* Saint-Seine 1955, Congo.

Order PACHYCORMIFORMES

Family PACHYCORMIDAE Woodward 1895

First, Jur Toarc: *Sauropsis* Agassiz 1832, several spp., Germany; *Prosauropsis elongatus* (Sauvage 1875), France; *Hypsocormus* Wagner 1860 is very doubtfully recorded from Trias Nor, Germany.
Last, Jur 'Tith': *Hypsocormus beaugrandi* Sauvage 1905, *Hypsocormus combesi* Sauvage 1905, France.

Family PROTOSPHYRAENIDAE Nicholson & Lydekker 1889

First, Cret Cenom: *Protosphyraena* Leidy 1857, several spp., England and Italy.
Last, Cret Maestr: *Protosphyraena* Leidy 1857, several spp., Belgium and United States.

Order SEMIONOTIFORMES

Family LEPIDOTIDAE Owen 1860

First Perm Dzhulf: *Acentrophorus varians* (Kirkby 1862), Magnesian 1st, England.
Last Cret Barrem: *Lepidotes mantelli* Agassiz 1833, England; *Lepidotes? pustulatus* Woodward 1895, Cret, Cenom, England, doubtfully a *Lepidotes*.

Family LEPISOSTEIDAE Cuvier 1825

First, Cret Alb/Campan: *Paralepidosteus africanus* Aramburg & Joleaud 1943, West Africa.
Extant.

Order PYCNODONTIFORMES

First, Jur Sinem: *Eomesodon liassicus* (Egerton 1854), England and France, but Pycnodont remains do occur in the Nor/Rhaet.
Last, Tert Eoc (M. Eoc): *Palaeobalistum orbiculatum* Blainville 1818, *Pycnodus* Agassiz 1833, several spp, Monte Bolca, Italy. ?Koch 1904 records Pycnodont remains from L/M. Olig.

Division Halecostomes

Order PHOLIDOPHORIFORMES

Family PHOLIDOPHORIDAE Woodward 1890

First, Trias Ladin: *Pholidophorus* Agassiz 1833, several spp., *Prohalecites* Deecke 1889, several species, Italy, Austria, England. *Pholidophorus* sp., Ladin, Europe (Gardiner 1960) is the earliest record.
Last, Cret Berr: *Pholidophorus granulatus* Egerton 1854, England and Germany; *Ceramurus macrocephalus* Egerton 1854, *Pholidophoristion ornatus* (Agassiz 1843), England.

Family PLEUROPHOLIDAE Saint-Seine 1955

First, Jur 'Tith': *Austropleuropholis lombardion* Saint-Seine 1955. *Parapleurophokis* Saint-Seine 1955, several spp., Congo; *Pleuropholis* Egerton 1858, several spp., 'Tith', Germany and France. **Last,** Cret Berr: *Pleuropholis* Egerton 1858, several species, England, France and Africa.

Family ARCHAEOMAENIDAE Wade 1941

First and **Last,** Jur ?Hett-Toarc: *Aetheolepis* Woodward 1895, *Aphnelepis* Woodward 1895, *Madariscus* Wade 1941 and *Archaeomaene* Woodward 1895 all come from the L. Jur, Talbragar River, New South Wales.

Family LIGULELLIDAE Saint-Seine 1955

First and **Last,** Jur 'Tith': *Ligulella sluysi* Saint-Seine 1955, Congo.

Family MAJOKIIDAE Saint-Seine 1955

First and **Last,** Jur 'Tith': *Majokia brasseuri* Saint-Seine 1955, Congo.

Family GALKINIIDAE Yakovlev 1962

First and **Last,** Jur: *Galkinia nuda* Berg 1948, Russia.

Family ICHTHYOKENTEMIDAE Griffith & Patterson 1963

First and **Last,** Jur 'Tith'-Cret Berr: *Ichthyokentema purbeckensis* (Davis 1887), England.

Order LEPTOLEPIFORMES

Family LEPTOLEPIDIDAE Nicholson & Lydekker 1889

First, Trias Carn/Nor: *Leptolepis africana* Gardiner 1960, Tanzania; *Leptolepis* sp. Gardiner 1960, Ladin, Seefeld, Austria is the earliest known occurrence.
Last, Cret Cenom: *Clupavus* Aramburg 1955, several spp., Dalmatia, Yugoslavia; and Morocco.

Family OLIGOPLEURIDAE Woodward

First, Jur 'Tith': *Oligopleurus esocinus* Thiollière 1850, Germany.
Last, Cret Campan: *Spathiurus dorsalis* Davis 1887, Mt. Lebanon, Syria; this is probably an amioid.

Family PROTELOPIDAE Saint-Seine 1949

First, Jur 'Tith': *Eoprotelops vireti* Saint-Seine 1949, Cerin, France.
Last, Cret Turon: *Protelops* Laube 1885, several spp., England and Germany. This is a very poorly known family but both *Protelops* and *Eoprotelops* appear to be Halecostomes rather than Teleosts.

Family ASPIDORHYNCHIDAE Nicholson & Lydekker 1889

First, Jur Bath: *Aspidorhynchus crassus* Woodward 1890, England.
Last, Cret Maestr: *Belonostomus longirostris*(Lambe 1902), Lance Fm, Wyoming and Montana.

[B.G.G.]

Subclass TELEOSTEI

General Comment. The palaeontology of the teleosts is still in a rather rudimentary state and many of the following listings are tentative. In particular much work remains to be done on the holostean-teleostean transition (whether this took place once, several or many times, what groups were involved, and where the line between the two groups should be drawn) and on the Jur and

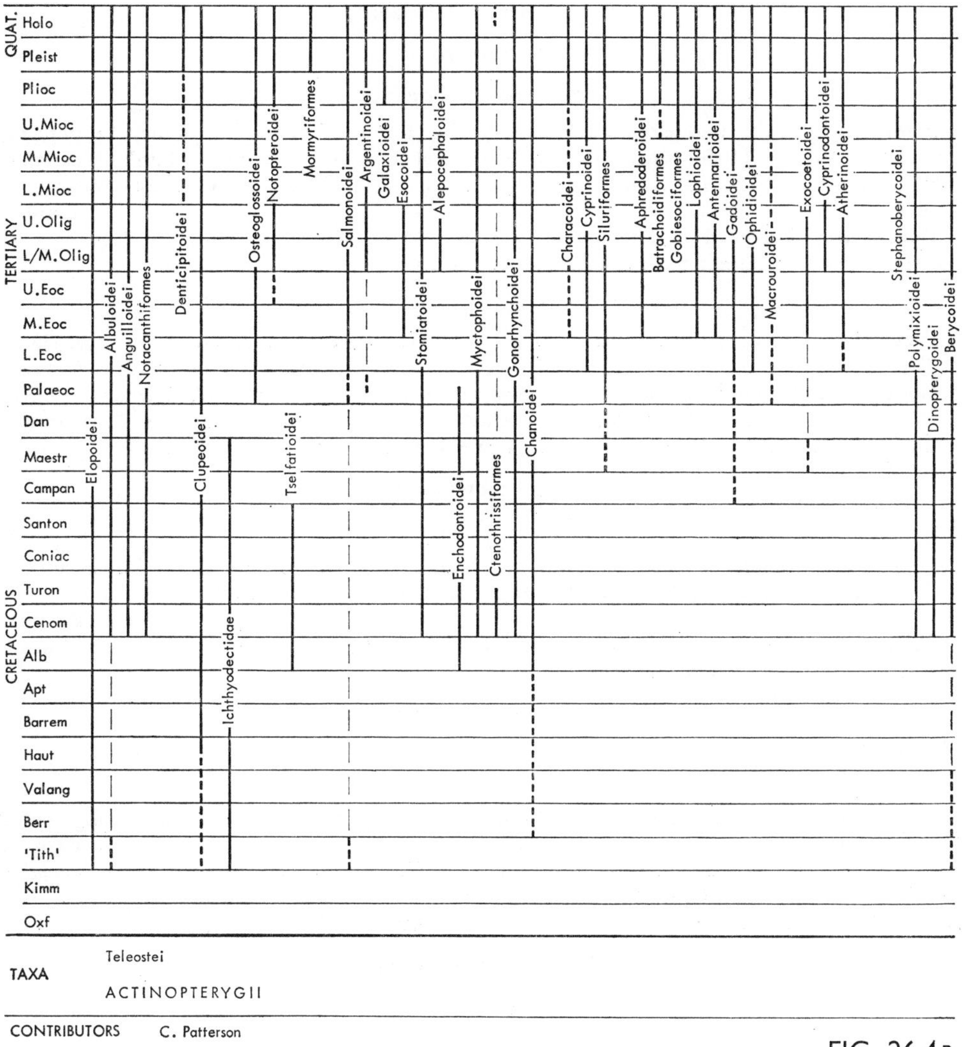
QUAT.
Holo
Pleist
Plioc
U.Mioc
M.Mioc
L.Mioc
TERTIARY
U.Olig
L/M.Olig
U.Eoc
M.Eoc
L.Eoc
Palaeoc
Dan
Maestr
Campan
Santon
Coniac
CRETACEOUS
Turon
Cenom
Alb
Apt
Barrem
Haut
Valang
Berr
'Tith'
Kimm
Oxf
Elopoidei
Albuloidei
Anguilloidei
Notacanthiformes
Denticipitoidei
Clupeoidei
Ichthyodectidae
Osteoglossoidei
Notopteroidei
Tselfatioidei
Mormyriformes
Salmonoidei
Argentinoidei
Galaxioidei
Esocoidei
Stomiatoidei
Alepocephaloidei
Enchodontoidei
Myctophoidei
Ctenothrissiformes
Gonorhynchoidei
Chanoidei
Characoidei
Cyprinoidei
Siluriformes
Aphredoderoidei
Batrachoidiformes
Gobiesociformes
Lophioidei
Antennarioidei
Gadoidei
Ophidioidei
Macrouroidei
Exocoetoidei
Cyprinodontoidei
Atherinoidei
Stephanoberycoidei
Polymixioidei
Dinopterygoidei
Berycoidei
TAXA
Teleostei
ACTINOPTERYGII
CONTRIBUTORS
C. Patterson

FIG. 26.4B

Cret fossils, especially in regard to their relationships to Tert and living forms. There appear to have been two major radiations in teleost history, one at about the middle of the Cret (Alb or Apt?) in which many of the orders at pre-percoid level arose, and one at the Cret Tert boundary in which the majority of living suborders, including percoids, were differentiated.

A difficulty in compiling records of teleost history is that many fossil species and genera are based on isolated scales and on otoliths: since these (especially otoliths) can generally be identified only by comparison with living forms, the reliance which can be placed on them decreases with increasing age. In the following I have based the first record on skeletal remains in most cases, mentioning otolith or scale records where these are markedly earlier.

The classification followed is that of Greenwood, Rosen, Weitzman & Myers (1966). Suborders are documented.

Superorder ELOPOMORPHA

Order ELOPIFORMES

Suborder ELOPOIDEI

First, Jur 'Tith': undescribed elopid (Nybelin 1961), Lithographic Stone, Nusplingen, Germany. Nybelin (1964) suggests that *Pachythrissops propterus* (Wagner), 'Tith', Bavaria, is close to *Megalops*. *Eoprotelops vireti* Saint-Seine 1949, 'Tith', Cerin, France, does not appear to be an elopoid. **Extant.**

Comment: derived from Pholidophoridae according to Nybelin, who holds *Elops* to be a holostean. Several extinct genera in L. and U. Cret.

Suborder ALBULOIDEI

First, Cret Cenom: *Hajula multidens* Woodward 1942 (Albulidae), U.Cenom fish beds, Hakel & Hajula, Lebanon. **Extant.**

Comment: Albuloid (pterothrissid) otoliths are recorded from Jur 'Tith', Germany (Martin & Weiler 1957): tooth plates of '*Pisodus*' (= *Albula*, otherwise unknown before Tert Palaeoc) are doubtfully recorded from Cret L. Cenom, Baharîje Stufe, Egypt (Stromer 1936).

Order ANGUILLIFORMES

Suborder ANGUILLOIDEI

First, Cret Cenom: *Urenchelys hakelensis* (Davis 1887), *U.germanus* Hay 1903, *Anguillavus bathshebae* Hay, *Enchelion montium* Hay, U.Cenom fish beds, Hakel & Hajula, Lebanon. **Extant.**

Comment: These and other Cret forms differ from Tert and living eels in a number of ways. Extant families of eels do not appear until Tert L.Eoc.

Suborder SACCOPHARYNGOIDEI

No fossil record.

Order NOTACANTHIFORMES

First, Cret Cenom: *Enchelurus anglicus* Woodward 1901 (Halosauridae), L.Chalk, subglobosus Z. Kent, England. **Extant.**

Comment: Other halosaur genera and species in U.Cret, group rare in Tert. *Pronotacanthus sachelalmae* (Davis 1887), Cret Maestr, Lebanon, normally held to be the first notacanthid, is a stomiatoid (Arambourg 1954) and no fossil notacanthids are known with certainty.

Superorder CLUPEOMORPHA

Order CLUPEIFORMES

Suborder DENTICIPITOIDEI

First, Tert: *Palaeodenticeps tanganikae* Greenwood 1960, M/U. Tert, lacustrine sh, Tanzania. **Extant.**

Suborder CLUPEOIDEI

First, Cret Haut: '*Clupea*' *antiqua* Pictet 1858, Calcaire des Hivernages, Voirons, Switzerland. **Extant.**

Comment: Clupeoid otoliths are recorded from Jur 'Tith', Germany (Martin & Weiler 1954). Arambourg (1954 etc.) includes in Clupeidae *Clupavus* (first, Jur 'Tith': *C.brodiei* (Agassiz), L.Purbeck, Wiltshire, England), but this genus is closer to the leptolepids (Patterson 1967a). Most authors (Nybelin 1964, Bardack 1965b) include the Jur 'Tith' genera *Thrissops* and *Allothrissops* (Lithographic Stone, Bavaria and Cerin, France) in the clupeoid family Chirocentridae and hold that the suborder is derived diphyletically from leptolepids and pholidophorids, but relationship between *Chirocentrus* and these Jur forms is unlikely (Greenwood *et al.* 1966, Patterson 1966b; see Ichthyodectidae, below, under Tselfatioidei).

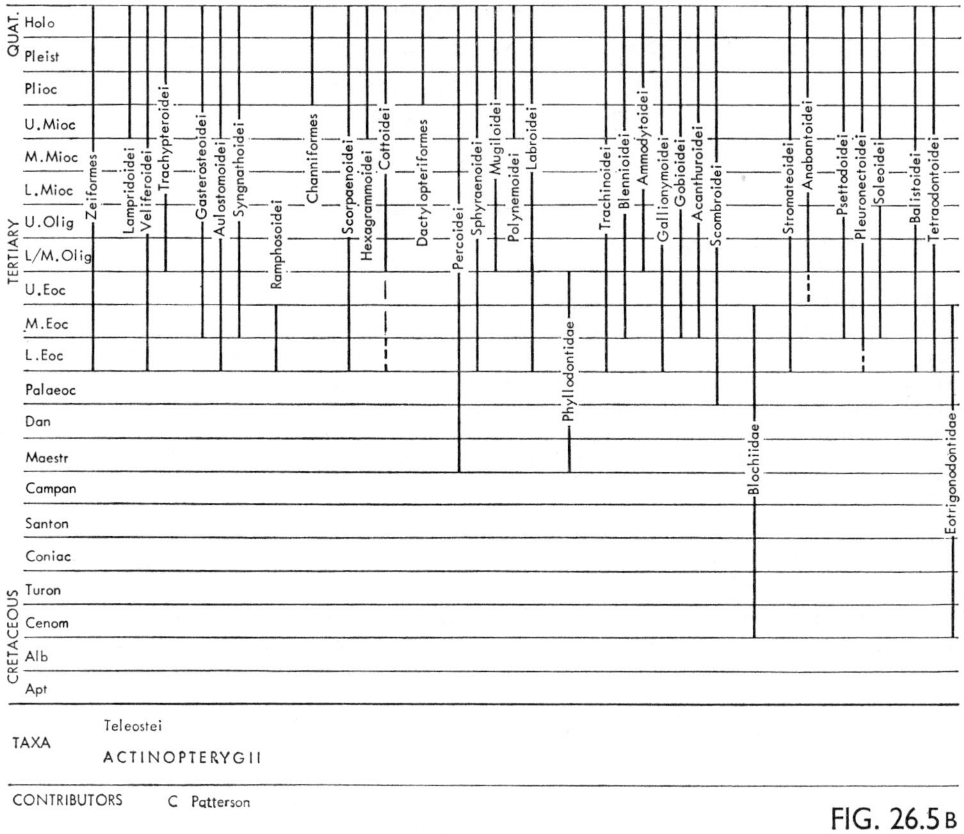

FIG. 26.5 B

CONTRIBUTORS C. Patterson

TAXA Teleostei
ACTINOPTERYGII

Superorder OSTEOGLOSSOMORPHA

Order OSTEOGLOSSIFORMES

Suborder OSTEOGLOSSOIDEI

First, Tert Palaeoc: *Brychaetus muelleri* Woodward 1901, Landana, Cabinda, Congo (Dartevelle & Casier 1959). **Extant.**

Comment: According to Greenwood *et al.* (1966) *Brychaetus* is not certainly an osteoglossoid: the first osteoglossoids would then be Tert M.Eoc: *Phareodus* spp., Green River Shs, Wyoming (Hussakof 1908).

Suborder NOTOPTEROIDEI

First, Tert U.Eoc-L./M.Olig: *Notopterus notopterus* (Pallas), Fish Shs, Sumatra (Sanders 1934). **Extant.**

Suborder TSELFATIOIDEI (PLETHODONTIDAE & PROTOBRAMIDAE, Patterson 1967b)

First, Cret Alb: *Plethodus expansus* Dixon 1850, Gault, Kent, England.

Last, Cret Santon: *Ananogmius* and other genera, Niobrara Fm, Kansas; Chalk, S. E. England) is probably related to the Osteoglossiformes (Bardack 1965a; Patterson 1967b).

Comment: The extinct family Ichthyodectidae [**First,** Jur 'Tith': *Thrissops* spp., *Allothrissops* spp., Lithographic Stone, Bavaria and Cerin, France, (possibly also in Jur Bath-Oxf, Nybelin 1964, Bardack 1965b): **Last,** Cret Maestr: several genera in Europe, N. Africa and N. America] is normally placed in or near the Chirocentridae, suborder Clupeoidei, but is more probably related to the Osteoglossiformes (Greenwood *et al.* 1966).

657

Order MORMYRIFORMES

First, Quat L.Pleist: *?Hyperopisus* sp., N. shore of L.Edward, Congo (Greenwood 1959).
Extant.

Superorder PROTACANTHOPTERYGII

Order SALMONIFORMES

Suborder SALMONOIDEI

First, Tert L.Eoc: undescribed salmonid, Mo-clay, N. Jutland, Denmark (Bonde 1965).
Extant.

Comment: Otoliths referred to Salmonoidei are recorded from Jur 'Tith', Germany (Martin & Weiler 1954) and from Tert Palaeoc, Thanetian, Kent (Stinton 1965). Supposed salmonoid scales from Cret, are named *Leucichthyops vagans* Cockerell 1919 (Cenom-Campan, Colorado, Wyoming), *Natlandia ornata* David 1946 (Maestr, Moreno Fm, California) and *Goudkoffia delicata* David 1946 (Maestr, Moreno Fm, California). The Tert M.Eoc *Thaumaturus spannuthi* Voigt 1934 (Braunkohle, Geiseltale, Germany) is generally held to be the first salmonoid, but Weitzman (1960a), who places other M.Eoc forms in the Thaumaturidae, suggests that this family is myctophoid.

Suborder ARGENTINOIDEI

First, Tert L/M.Olig: *Proargentina inclinata* Daniltshenko 1960, Maikop Beds, Caucasus.
Extant.

Comment: Argentinoid otoliths are described from Tert Palaeoc (Thanet Sands, Kent, England) and Tert L.Eoc (Woolwich Beds, S. E. England) by Stinton (1965, 1966).

Suborder GALAXIOIDEI

First, Tert Plioc: *Galaxias* sp., diatomaceous sh, nr. Dunedin, New Zealand (Whitley 1956).
Extant.

Suborder ESOCOIDEI

First, Tert M.Eoc: *Palaeoesox fritzschei* Voigt 1934, (Palaeoesocidae), Braunkohle, Geiseltale, Germany. **Extant.**

Suborder STOMIATOIDEI

First, Cret Cenom: *Idrissia jubae* Arambourg 1954, *Paravinciguerra praecursor* Arambourg 1954 (both Gonostomoidae) and *Protostomias maroccanus* Arambourg 1943 (Astronesthoidae or Stomiatoieae), L.Cenom fish shs, Djebel Tselfat, Morocco **Extant.**

Suborder ALEPOCEPHALOIDEI

First, Tert L/M.Olig: *Palaeotroctes strictus* Daniltshenko 1960, Maikop Beds, Caucasus.
Extant.

Suborder ENCHODONTOIDEI

First, Cret ? Alb: *Apateodus glyphodus* (Blake 1863), teeth and fragments of jaws, Gault, S. E. England, seems to be the only L.Cret enchodent. By L.Cenom enchodonts are abundant in the Mediterranean area.

Last, Tert L.Palaeoc: *Enchodus elegans* Dartevelle & Casier 1949, Montian Phosphates, Morocco (Arambourg 1952). Apart from these isolated teeth enchodonts are unknown above Cret Maestr, where there are several genera and many species in Europe, W. Asia, Africa and N. America. The *? Cimolichthya*, Cret Berr-Alb, Patagonia, recorded by d'Erasmo (1934), is doubtfully an enchodont.

Suborder BATHLYACONOIDEI

No fossil record.

Chapter 26: Pisces

Suborder MYCTOPHOIDEI

First, Cret Cenom: *Dactylopogon* ? sp., *Cassandra* spp., ? *Nematonotus* sp., all from L.Cenom, Carso Triestino, Jugoslavia (d'Erasmo 1946); *Ichthyotringa* sp., L.Cenom fish shales, Jebel Tselfat, Morocco (Arambourg 1954). **Extant.**

Comment: A large and important group in the U.Cret, with many extinct genera which are doubtfully related to Tert and living forms.

Order CETOMIMIFORMES

Contains four small suborders of deep-sea forms without fossil record.

Order CTENOTHRISSIFORMES

First, Cret Cenom: *Ctenothrissa* spp., *Pateroperca* sp., U.Cenom fish beds, Hakel & Hajula, Lebanon; *Ctenothrissa* spp., *Aulolepis* sp., Chalk, subglobosus Z., England (Patterson 1964).

Last, Cret Turon: *Ctenothrissa radians* (Agassiz), lata Z., Chalk, England. The living *Macristium* is included in the ctenothrissoids by Marshall (1961), a conclusion doubted by Patterson (1964).

Order GONORHYNCHIFORMES

Suborder GONORHYNCHOIDEI

First, Cret Cenom: *Charitosomus hakelensis* (Davis 1887), U.Cenom fish beds, Hakel, Lebanon. **Extant.**

Comment: Chabanaud (1931) reviews fossil gonorhynchoids.

Suborder CHANOIDEI

First, Cret Berr-Alb: *Chanopsis lombardi* Casier 1961, couches de la Loia (?Neocomian), Congo, tentatively placed in Chanidae; *Parachanos aethiopicus* (Weiler 1922), Coco-beach Fm, (Alb), Gabon and Spanish Guinea (Dartevelle & Casier 1949). **Extant.**

Comment: *Prochanos rectifrons* Bassani, recorded as Neocomian in Daniltshenko (1964), is L.Cenom.

Superorder OSTARIOPHYSI

Order CYPRINIFORMES

Suborder CHARACOIDEI

First, Tert: *Procharax minor* Santos & Travassos 1956, ?'L.Tert', bituminous shs, Nova York, Brazil. **Extant.**

Comment: Weitzman (1960a,b) reviews records of fossil characins. Scales (*Erythrinolepis mowriensis* Cockerell 1919) from Cret Cenom, Mowry shale, Wyoming, have been referred to this suborder without good reason.

Suborder GYMNOTOIDEI

No fossil record.

Suborder CYPRINOIDEI

First, Tert L.Eoc: *Blicca croydonensis* White 1931, Woolwich Beds, Surrey, England. **Extant.**

Order SILURIFORMES

First, Tert Palaeoc: '*Arius*' sp., Montian, Landana, Cabinda, Congo (Casier 1960). **Extant.**

Comment: Frizzell (1965) describes ?siluroid otoliths (*Vorhisia vulpes*) from Cret Maestr, Fox Hills Sst, S. Dakota.

Superorder PARACANTHOPTERYGII

Order PERCOPSIFORMES

Suborder AMBLYOPSOIDEI

No fossil record.

Suborder APHREDODEROIDEI

First, Tert M.Eoc: *Amphiplaga brachyptera* Cope 1877, *Erismatopterus* spp. Cope, *Asineops* spp. Cope, Green River shs, Wyoming. **Extant.**

Comment: Modern work on these forms is necesary to confirm their position in this suborder.

Suborder PERCOPSOIDEI

No fossil record.

Order BATRACHOIDIFORMES

First, Tert U.Mioc-Plioc: *Batrachoides didactylus* Bloch & Schneider, 'Sahelian', Oran, Algeria (Arambourg 1927). **Extant.**

Order GOBIESOCIFORMES

First, Tert? U.Mioc: *Bulbiceps raninus* Jordan 1919, Soledad, California, said to be possibly a gobiesocid by Jordan (1921), no other record. **Extant.**

Order LOPHIIFORMES

Suborder LOPHIOIDEI

First, Tert M.Eoc: *Lophius brachysomus* Agassiz 1835, Lutetian fish beds, Monte Bolca, Italy. **Extant.**

Comment: Further work on this species is necessary to confirm its position. L.Eoc teeth have been referred to this suborder under various names but without good reason.

Suborder ANTENNARIOIDEI

First, Tert M.Eoc: *Histionotophorus bassani* (Zigno 1887), Lutetian fish beds, Monte Bolca, Italy (Eastman 1904). **Extant.**

Suborder CERATIOIDEI

No fossil record.

Order GADIFORMES

Suborder MURAENOLEPOIDEI

No fossil record.

Suborder GADOIDEI

First, Tert L.Eoc: *Rhinocephalus planiceps* Casier 1966 (Merlucciidae), London Clay, Kent, England. An undescribed *Rhinocephalus* also occurs in the basal Eoc, Mo-clay, N. Jutland, Denmark (Bonde 1966). **Extant.**

Comment: Dunkle (1958) refers scales from Cret Campan/Maestr (*Paractichthys fibrillatus* Cockerell 1919, Blair Fm, Wyoming; Fox Hills sandstone, Colorado) to the Gadidae. Several species of gadoid otoliths from Tert Palaeoc, Thanetian, Kent, England, are described by Stinton (1965).

Suborder OPHIDIOIDEI

First, Tert L.Eoc: otoliths referred to seven living genera from London Clay, S. E. England and Argile d'Ypres, Belgium (Stinton 1966). **Extant.**

Comment: Skeletal remains of ophidioids are rare: *Ophidium voltianum* Massalongo 1859, Lutetian fish beds, Monte Bolca, Italy, is a very doubtful record; *Protobrotula sobijevi* (Daniltschenko 1960), L/M. Olig, Maikop Beds, Caucasus, is the earliest reliable record.

Chapter 26: Pisces

Suborder ZOARCOIDEI

No fossil record.

Suborder MACROUROIDEI

First, Tert U.Mioc: *Bolbocara gyrinus* Jordan 1927, Lompoc, California; *Trichiurichthys incertus* Sauvage 1873, Licata, Sicily. **Extant.**

Comment: Scales from Cret Santon-Campan (*Rankinia macrouriformis* David 1946, Panoche Fm., California) are referred to this suborder by David. Otoliths from Cret U. Senon, near Siegsdorf, Bavaria, are named *O.(Macruridarum) bavaricus* by Koken (1891): known by otoliths in Tert Palaeoc (*Archemacruroides ornatus* Stinton 1965, Thanetian, Kent, England) and in U.Eoc and Olig.

Superorder ATHERINOMORPHA

Order ATHERINIFORMES

Suborder EXOCOETOIDEI

First, Tert M.Eoc: *Hemirhamphus edwardsii* Bassani 1876, Lutetian fish beds, Monte Bolca, Italy. **Extant.**

Comment: The record of *Belone flava* Delvaux (1867), L.Eoc (L.Ypresian, Belgium), is very doubtful (Casier 1946). Scales from Cret Maestr (*Hemilampronites hesperius* Cockerell 1919, Fox hills sandstone, Colorado) are exocoetoid according to Cockerell and to Dunkle (1958).

Suborder CYPRINODONTOIDEI

First, Tert L/M.Olig: *Prolebias cephalotes* (Agassiz 1839), Serie d'Aix, Aix-en-Provence, France; other genera and spp. in Olig, Puy-de-Dôme (Piton 1934) and California (Miller 1945). **Extant.**

Comment: Romer's (1945) record of *?Cobitopsis* in the U.Cret of W. Asia is based on Woodward's (1901) description of B.M.N.H. 46540, an indeterminable caudal region from Sahel Alma (Cret Maestr), Lebanon.

Suborder ATHERINOIDEI

First, Tert M.Eoc: *Atherina macrocephala* Woodward 1901, *Rhamphognathus paralepoides* Agassiz 1844, and *R.sphyraenoides* Agassiz 1844, Lutetian fish beds, Monte Bolca, Italy. **Extant.**

Comment: An atherinid otolith (*Leuresthes distans* Stinton 1966) is recorded from the L.Eoc London Clay, Kent, England.

Superorder ACANTHOPTERYGII

Order BERYCIFORMES

Suborder STEPHANOBERYCOIDEI

First, Tert U.Mioc: *Scopelogadus ?capistraensis* Ebeling 1962, diatomaceous shs, Capistrano Beach, California. **Extant.**

Suborder POLYMIXIOIDEI

First, Cret Cenom: *Omosoma simum* Arambourg 1954, L.Cenom fish shs, Jebel Tselfat, Morocco. **Extant.**

Comment: Group fairly abundant in U.Cret in Europe, Lebanon, N. Africa, California (scales only), much reduced in Tert.

Suborder DINOPTERYGOIDEI

First, Cret Cenom: *Aipichthys pretiosus* Steindachner 1860, L.Cenom, Carso Triestino, Comen Lesina & Volci, Dalmatia, Yugoslavia.

Last, Cret Maestr: *Dinopteryx spinosus* (Davis 1887), fish beds, Sahel Alma, Lebanon.

Comment: Group contains four U.Cret genera, probably not closely related, resembling various groups of percoids (Patterson 1964).

Suborder BERYCOIDEI

First, Cret Cenom: *Acrogaster anceps* Arambourg 1954, *Caproberyx polydesmus* (Arambourg 1954), L.Cenom fish shs, Jebel Tselfat, Morocco; *Hoplopteryx stachei* (Kramberger 1895), *Lobopterus pectinatus* Kramberger 1895, '*Beryx*' spp., Carso Triestino, Dalmatia and Lesina, Yugoslavia **Extant.**

Comment: Berycoid otoliths are recorded from Jur 'Tith'-Cret Valang of Germany by Martin &Weiler (1954, 1957). A pelvic fin from Cret U.Apt of Armenkov Island, S. Georgia, is referred to Berycomorphi by Weiler (1947).

Order ZEIFORMES

First, Tert L.Eoc: undescribed zeid, Mo-clay, N. Jutland, Denmark (Bonde 1966).
Extant.

Comment: *Palaeocentrotes boeggildi* Kühne 1941 (L.Eoc Mo-clay, Denmark), normally recorded as the first zeoid, is a lampridiform (Bonde 1965).

Order LAMPRIDIFORMES

Suborder LAMPRIDOIDEI

First, Tert U.Mioc: *Lampris zatima* Jordon & Gilbert 1919, diatomaceous shs, Lompic, California. **Extant.**

Suborder VELIFEROIDEI

First, Tert L.Eoc: *Palaeocentrotes boeggildi* Kühne 1941 (Palaeocentrotidae) and an undescribed veliferid, Mo-clay, N. Jutland, Denmark (Bonde 1966). **Extant.**

Suborder TRACHYPTEROIDEI

First, Tert L/M.Olig: *Protolophotes elami* (Arambourg 1943), Elam beds, Luristan, Persia.
Extant.

Suborder STYLEPHOROIDEI

No fossil record.

Order GASTEROSTEIFORMES

Suborder GASTEROSTEOIDEI

First, Tert M.Eoc: *Protaulopsis bolcensis* Woodward 1901 (Aulorhynchidae), Lutetian fish beds, Monte Bolca, Italy. **Extant.**
Comment: The Gasterosteidae do not appear until the M. or U.Mioc (Siberia, California).

Suborder AULOSTOMOIDEI

First, Tert L.Eoc: undescribed centriscoid, Mo-clay, N. Jutland, Denmark (Bonde 1966).
Extant.

Comment: The Cret L.Cenom *Protriacanthus gortanii* d'Erasmo 1946, Carso Triestino, Comen, Yugoslavia, is possibly related to the aulostomoids or gasterosteoids (Patterson 1964).

Suborder SYNGNATHOIDEI

First, Tert M.Eoc: *Calamostoma breviculum* (Blainville 1818), *Syngnathus* spp., *Solenostomus* sp. (Jungersen 1910), Lutetian fish beds, Monte Bolca, Italy; *Solenorhynchus elegans* Heckel 1854, Lutetian fish beds, Monte Postale, Italy. **Extant.**
Comment: All these Lutetian forms are poorly known and more work on them is necessary.

incertae sedis Suborder RAMPHOSOIDEI

First, Tert L.Eoc: *Ramphosus rosenkrantzi* Nielsen 1960, Mo-clay, N. Jutland, Denmark.

Last, Tert M.Eoc: *Ramphosus rastrum* Volta 1796, *R.biserratus* Bassani 1876, Lutetian fish beds, Monte Bolca, Italy.

Chapter 26: Pisces

Order CHANNIFORMES

First, Tert Plioc: *Ophiocephalus* sp. (Lydekker 1886), Siwalik Beds, Siwalik Hills, India. Also in Pleist, Java (Boesemann 1949). **Extant.**

Order SYNBRANCHIFORMES

Contains two suborders, Alabetoidei and Synbranchoidei, both without fossil record.

Order SCORPAENIFORMES

Suborder SCORPAENOIDEI

First, Tert L.Eoc: *Ampheristus toliapicus* König 1825 (Scorpaenidae), London Clay, Kent (Casier 1966); *Eosynanceja brabantica* Casier 1946 (Synancejidae), Argile des Flandres, Belgium. There are two undescribed scorpaenids in the basal Eoc Mo-clay, N. Jutland, Denmark (Bonde 1966). **Extant.**

Comment: Otoliths of scorpaenids, triglids and peristedids are described from Tert L.Eoc, London Clay, S. E. England, by Stinton (1966).

Suborder HEXAGRAMMOIDEI

First, Tert ?U.Mioc: *Achrestogrammus achrestus* Jordon & Gilbert 1919, diatomaceous shs, Lompoc, California, tentatively referred to Hexagrammidae by David (1943); *Aneoscorpius* (= *Eoscorpius*) *primaevus* (Jordan & Gilbert 1919), Mioc, Bairdstown, California, later referred to Scombridae by Jordan (1923), is possibly an aplopomid according to Berg (1955). **Extant.**

Suborder PLATYCEPHALOIDEI

No fossil record.

Suborder HOPLICHTHYOIDEI

No fossil record.

Suborder CONGIOPOIDEI

No fossil record.

Suborder COTTOIDEI

First, Tert L./M.Olig: *Cottus cervicornis* Storms 1894, U.Rupelian, Belgium (Leriche 1910); *Cottopsis gaudryi* Priem 1908, Pouchtikouh, Luristan, Persia, described as U.Cret, is in fact Olig(?M.)(Arambourg 1939). **Extant.**

Comment: Otoliths referred to *Enophrys*, *Agonus* and *Scorpaenichthys* from L.Eoc London Clay are described by Stinton (1966). The M.Eoc *Eocottus veronensis* (Volta 1796), Lutetian, Monte Bolca, Italy, is a gobioid according to Tate Regan (1913) (Eleotridae *fide* J. R. Norman, m.s.). The L.Olig-L.Mioc *Lepidocottus* is also gobioid according to Tate Regan: this is confirmed for the L.Mioc *L. multipinnatus* (Meyer 1848) by Weiler (1955).

Order DACTYLOPTERIFORMES

First, Tert ?Plioc: *Dactylopterus pliocenicus* Lawley 1886 (*nom. nud.*), L.Plioc, Orciano, Italy, said to be identical with *D. volitans;* no other record. **Extant.**

Order PEGASIFORMES

No fossil record.

Order PERCIFORMES

Suborder PERCOIDEI

First, Cret Maestr: *Platacodon nanus* Marsh 1889 (Sciaenidae), Lance Fm., Wyoming (Estes 1964), known only by pharyngeals. The first moderately well known percoids are Tert Dan, *Proserranus lundensis* (Davis 1890) (?Serranidae) and *Bathysoma lutkeni* Davis 1890 (Menidae), Danian, Limhamn, S. Sweden (Patterson 1964). Supposed carangid scales from Cret Maestr, Moreno Fm, California, have been described by David (1946). **Extant.**

Comment: This extremely large and important suborder contains about seventy families. Most of the supposed percoids recorded from Cret are beryciforms (*Aipichthys*, *Pharmacichthys*), members of more primitive groups (*Pateroperca*, *Protobrama*) or *incertae sedis* (*Protriacanthus*, *Pseudo-egertonia*, *Eodiaphyodus*, etc.) (Patterson 1964).

Suborder SPHYRAENOIDEI

First, Tert L.Eoc: *Sphyraena striata* Casier 1946, *S.bognorensis* Casier 1966, London Clay, S. E. England, and Ypresian, Belgium. **Extant.**

Suborder MUGILOIDEI

First, Tert L./M.Olig: *Mugil princeps* Agassiz 1844, Série d'Aix, Aix-en-Provence, France; *M.latus* Svichenskaya 1957, Maikop Beds, Causasus (Daniltshenko 1960). **Extant.**

Suborder POLYNEMOIDEI

First, Tert U.Mioc: *Polydactylus fossilis* Daniltshenko 1958, L.Pontian, Krasnodar, USSR. **Extant.**

Suborder LABROIDEI

First, Tert L.Eoc: *Labrus eocaenus* Casier 1946, Ypresian, Belgium; *Labrodan paucidens* Priem 1901, Ypresian, Marne, France; *Pseudosphaerodon antiqueus* Casier 1966, London Clay, Kent, England. **Extant.**

Comment: The three Ypresian species are known only by pharyngeals and are not certainly labroid. The first complete labroid is M.Eoc, *Eolabroides szajnochae* (Zigno 1887), Lutetian, Monte Bolca, Italy. The extinct family Phyllodontidae (**First,** Cret Maestr: *Pseudoegertonia bebianoi* Dartevelle & Casier 1949, Maestr Phosphates, Roseifa, Jordan (Signeux 1959); **Last,** Tert U.Eoc: *Egertonia stromeri* Weiler 1929, Sagha Stufe, Fâyum, Egypt), known only by tooth plates, is commonly referred to the Labroidei without real justification.

Suborder TRACHINOIDEI

First, Tert L.Eoc: *Trachinus* sp. (Casier 1946), Ypresian, Belgium, Stinton (1966) describes a uranoscopid otolith (*Uranoscopus rotundus* Stinton) from L.Eoc, London Clay, Surrey, England. **Extant.**

Suborder NOTOTHENOIDEI

No fossil record.

Suborder BLENNIOIDEI

First, Tert M.Eoc: *Pterygocephalus paradoxus* Agassiz 1839 (Clinidae), ?*Oncolepis isseli* Bassani (1898), Lutetian fish beds, Monte Bolca, Italy. **Extant.**

Suborder ICOSTEOIDEI

No fossil record.

Suborder SCHINDLEROIDEI

No fossil record.

Suborder AMMODYTOIDEI

First, Tert L/M.Olig: *Ammodytes antipae* Pauca 1929, Olig, Suslanesti, Rumania; Menelith Schiefer, Hungary (Weiler 1933); Maikop Beds, Caucasus (Daniltshenko 1960). **Extant.**

Suborder CALLIONYMOIDIEI

First, Tert L.Eoc: *Callionymus eocaenus* Casier 1946, Ypresian, Belgium. **Extant.**

Suborder GOBIOIDEI

First, Tert M.Eoc: *Eocottus veronensis* (Volta 1796) (Eleotridae), Lutetian fish beds, Monte Bolca, Italy. **Extant.**

Chapter 26: Pisces

Suborder KURTOIDEI

No fossil record.

Suborder ACANTHUROIDEI

First, Tert M.Eoc: *Zanclus brevirostris* Agassiz 1835, *Acanthurus* spp., *Naso* spp., Lutetian fish beds, Monte Bolca (Randall 1955). **Extant.**

Suborder SCOMBROIDEI

First, Tert Palaeoc: *Landanichthys lusitanicus* Dartevelle & Casier 1949, *L.moutai* Dartevelle & Casier 1949, and other genera, L.Palaeoc, Landana, Cabinda, Congo. **Extant.**

Comment: A large and important group in L.Tert, with many extinct genera in the London Clay.

incertae sedis Family BLOCHIIDAE

First, Cret Cenom: *Cylindracanthus libanicus* (Woodward 1942), U.Cenom fish beds, Hajula, Lebanon; *C.cretaceus* (Dixon 1850), Subglobosus Z, Chalk, Sussex, England.

Last, Tert Eoc (M.Eoc): *Blochius longirostris* Volta 1796, Lutetian fish beds, Monte Bolca, Italy: *Cylindracanthus* spp., Lutetian, widely distributed in Africa, Europe, N. America (Arambourg 1952).

Comment: Previously associated with the scombroids, but of unknown affinities.

Suborder STROMATEOIDEI

Comment: No genuine fossil stromateoids have yet been described, but Bonde (1966) has found two undescribed stromateoids in the Tert L.Eoc, Mo-clay, N. Jutland, Denmark. Le Danois (1964) incorrectly describes the Cret Maestr *Omosoma sahelalmae* Costa 1857 (Polymixiidae) as a stromateid.

Suborder ANABANTOIDEI

First, Tert U.Eoc-L./M.Olig: *Osphronemus goramy* Lacépède 1802, fish shs, Sumatra (Sanders 1934). **Extant.**

Suborder LUCIOCEPHALOIDEI

No fossil record.

Suborder MASTACEMBELOIDEI

No fossil record.

Order PLEURONECTIFORMES

Suborder PSETTODOIDEI

First, Tert M.Eoc: *Joleaudichthys sadeki* Chabanaud 1937 (Joleaudichthyidae), L.Mokattam Fm., Tourah, Egypt. **Extant.**

Suborder PLEURONECTOIDEI

First, Tert M.Eoc: *Eobothus minimus* (Agassiz 1842), Lutetian fish beds, Monte Bolca, Italy; *E. vialovi* Berg 1941, Alai Series, M.Haudag, Uzbekistan, U.S.S.R.; *Imhoffius lutetianus* Chabanaud 1940, Calcaire Grossier, Paris Basin (all Bothidae). Also known by otoliths (bothids, citharids, pleuronectids) in the L.Eoc London Clay, S.E. England (Stinton 1966). **Extant.**

Suborder SOLEOIDEI

First, Tert M.Eoc: *Eobuglossus eocenicus* (Woodward 1910), *Turahbuglossus cuvillieri* Chabanaud 1937 (Eobuglossidae), L.Mokattam Fm., Tourah, Egypt. **Extant.**

Order TETRAODONTIFORMES

Suborder BALISTOIDEI

First, Tert L.Eoc: *Ostracion clavatus* Casier 1946, Ypresian, Belgium. Also known by otoliths (*Amanses sulcifer* Stinton 1966, Monacanthidae) in L.Eoc London Clay, Kent, England. **Extant.**

Suborder TETRAODONTOIDEI

First, Tert L.Eoc: *Triodon antiquus* Leriche 1903, Ypresian, Belgium and Germany (Casier 1946). **Extant.**

Comment: The extinct family Eotrigonodontidae, known only by teeth [**First,** Cret Cenom: *Stephanodus* sp. (Weiler 1935), Baharîje Stufe, Egypt, *Eotrigonodon tabroumiti* Tabaste 1964, Gara Tabroumith (?Apt-Alb) S. Morocco.; **Last,** Tert M.Eoc: *Eotrigonodon* spp. Lutetian, Cabinda and Angola (Dartevelle & Casier 1959), Egypt (Priem 1908), Belgium (Leriche 1906)], is commonly placed in the Tetraodontiformes but is *incertae sedis*. *Protriacanthus gortanii* d'Erasmo 1946, Cret L. Cenom, Carso Triestino, is probably unrelated to this order (Patterson 1964).

ELASMOBRANCHII (CHONDRICHTHYES)

General Comment. The elasmobranchs will be treated as two separate classes, Selachii and Holocephali, since these two groups appear to have been separate throughout their history. Many Palaeozoic elasmobranch spines are *incertae sedis* and are not recorded here.

Class SELACHII

General Comment. The classification followed is that of Berg (1955) with additional families taken from later authors. Families are documented, but among the Palaeozoic groups the characters used in separating families (commonly the pectoral fin skeleton) are preserved in so few specimens that familial distinctions can rarely be maintained in the fragmentary materials on which stratigraphic limits are often based.

Order CLADOSELACHIFORMES

Family CLADOSELACHIDAE Dean 1894

First, Dev Ems: *Ohiolepis* cf. *newberryi* Wells 1944 (isolated scales), U.Heisdorf Beds (U.Ems), Wetteldorf, Germany (Ørvig, pers. commn).

Last, Carb Tourn: *Cladoselache pachypterygius* Dean 1909, Waverly Group, Kentucky.

Comment: Scales (*Cladolepis, Ohiolepis*) in Eifel, Givet, N. America (Wells, 1944), complete fishes in U. Fammen, Cleveland Sh, Ohio. Origins unknown, perhaps only distantly related to other sharks (Harris 1951). May extend higher as isolated teeth ('*Cladodus*').

Family DENAEIDAE Berg 1940

First and **Last,** Carb Viséan: *Denaea fournieri* Pruvost 1922, Marbre noir (L. Viséan), Denée, Belgium.

Order CLADODONTIFORMES

Family CLADODONTIDAE Nicholson & Lydekker 1889

First, Dev Eifel: *Cladodus prototypus* Eastman 1907, Columbus Lst, Columbus, Ohio. Whether this and the many U.Dev species based on isolated teeth are true cladodonts (or cladoselachids or ctenacanthids) is impossible to tell.

Last, Perm Guad-Dzhulf: *Cladodus* sp. (Nielsen 1932), Foldvik Creek Fm, E.Greenland. Again, this species is not definitely a member of this family.

Comment: Origin unknown, and relationships of this and the next family with contemporary and later groups obscure: possibly ancestral to Hexanchiformes.

Chapter 26: Pisces

Family SYMMORIIDAE Dean 1909

First and **Last;** Carb Moscov-U.Carb: *Symmorium reniforme* Cope 1893, Coal Measures, Galesburg, Illinois.

Family CORONODONTIDAE Romer 1945

First, Dev Frasn: *Coronodus reimanni* Bryant 1923, Genesee conodont bed (L.Frasn), New York State.

Last, Dev Famenn: *Diademodus hydei* Harris 1951, Cleveland Sh (U.Famenn), Ohio.

Comment: *Phoebodus floweri* Wells 1944 and *P. ?bryanti* Wells 1944, U.Givet, E.Liberty bone-bed, Ohio, and Kiddville bone-bed, Kentucky, may belong in this family.

incertae sedis Family CRATOSELACHIDAE Woodward 1924

First and **Last,** Carb Viséan: *Cratoselache pruvosti* Woodward 1924, Marbre noir (L.Viséan), Denée, Belgium.

Comment: Commonly recorded as arthrodiran but probably selachian: re-examination of the only specimen is necessary.

Order XENACANTHIFORMES

Family XENACANTHIDAE Fritsch 1889

First, Dev Givet-Frasn: *Dittodus priscus* (Eastman 1899), *D.striatus* (Eastman 1899), *D.grabaui* Hussakof & Bryant 1918, *Anodontacanthus pusillus* Hussakof & Bryant 1918, Genesee conodont bed (U.Givet-L.Frasn), New York State (Hussakof & Bryant 1918).

Last, Trias Carn-Nor *Dittodus moorei* (Woodward 1899), Keuper, Somerset, and Gipskeuper, Württemburg, Germany (Seilacher 1943); *Xenacanthus parvidens* (Woodward 1908), Hawkesbury Ss, New South Wales, Australia.

Comment: Origin unknown, probably distantly related to other sharks; abundant and widely distributed in fresh water in Carb and Perm. *Phoebodus floweri* Wells 1944 and *P. ?bryanti* Wells 1944 (U.Givet, E.Liberty bone-bed, Ohio, and Kiddville bone-bed, Kentucky) were placed in this family by Wells but may be Coronodontidae.

Order HETERODONTIFORMES

Family CTENACANTHIDAE Dean 1909

First, Dev Givet: *Ctenacanthus wrighti* Newberry 1884, *C. nodocostatus* Hussakof & Bryant 1918, Hamilton Group, New York State.

Last, Perm Guad: *Ctenacanthus browni* Branson 1916, *C.mutabilis* Branson 1933, Phosphoria Fm, Wyoming.

Comment: Origin unknown, generally held to be the stem group of the hybodonts and modern sharks.

Family HYBODONTIDAE Owen 1846

Separation of this family from the Palaeozoic ctenacanthids and cladodontids is difficult. In the typical Jur hybodontids there are one or two pairs of spines ('*Sphenonchus*') above the orbits in males: these structures are apparently absent in the more completely known Palaeozoic forms commonly assigned to Hybodontidae ("*Petrodus patelliformis* M'Coy" Moy-Thomas 1935, Carb, ?Viséan, Yorkshire, England; *Wodnika althausi* (Münster 1840), Perm Guad, Kupferschiefer, Germany).

The **First** occurrences of such structures are Perm Guad-Dzhulf: *Arctacanthus uncinatus* Nielsen 1932, Foldvik Creek Fm, E.Greenland; *A.wyomingensis* Branson 1934, Phosphoria Fm, Wyoming.

Last, Cret Maestr: *Lonchidion selachos* Estes 1964, Lance Fm, Wyoming; *Hybodus* sp., *Asteracanthus aegyptiacus* Stromer, Mt. Igdaman, Sahara (Tabaste 1964); *Asteracanthus* sp., Ait Nafane, Sahara (Tabaste 1964).

Comment: Derived from near ctenacanthids, abundant in marine Trias & Jur, commoner in fresh water than marine in Cret.

Family TRISTYCHIIDAE Moy-Thomas 1939

First and **Last,** Carb Tourn-Namur: *Tristychius arcuatus* Agassiz 1837, Calciferous Sst Series-Lst Coal Group, Scotland.

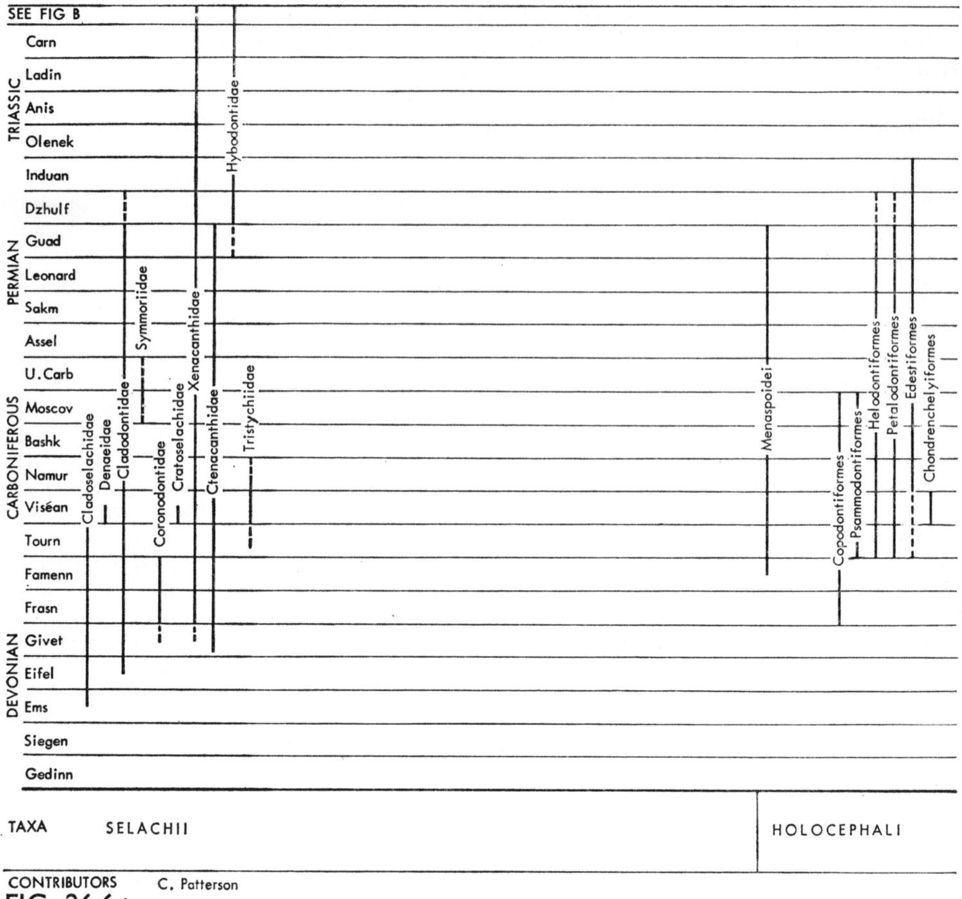

SEE FIG B

TRIASSIC
- Carn
- Ladin
- Anis
- Olenek
- Induan

PERMIAN
- Dzhulf
- Guad
- Leonard
- Sakm
- Assel

CARBONIFEROUS
- U.Carb
- Moscov
- Bashk
- Namur
- Viséan
- Tourn

DEVONIAN
- Famenn
- Frasn
- Givet
- Eifel
- Ems
- Siegen
- Gedinn

Taxa labels: Hybodontidae, Symmoriidae, Xenacanthidae, Cladodontidae, Cladoselachidae, Denaeidae, Coronodontidae, Cratoselachidae, Ctenacanthidae, Tristychiidae, Menaspoidei, Copodontiformes, Psammodontiformes, Helodontiformes, Petalodontiformes, Edestiformes, Chondrenchelyiformes

| TAXA | SELACHII | HOLOCEPHALI |

CONTRIBUTORS   C. Patterson

FIG. 26.6 A

Family PTYCHODONTIDAE Jaekel 1898

First, Cret Barrem: *Hylaeobatis ornatus* (Woodward 1889), Weald Clay, S. E. England (Patterson 1966a).

Last, Tert Dan: *Ptychodus decurrens* Agassiz 1839, *P.mammillaris* Agassiz 1839, Dan, S. Sweden (Davis 1890).

Comment: Derived from hybodontids (Casier 1953), perhaps originating in fresh water from near *Lonchidion* (Patterson 1966). Abundant and widespread throughout U.Cret.

Family PALAEOSPINACIDAE Regan 1906

First, Jur Sinem: *Palaeospinax priscus* (Agassiz 1843), L.Lias, Lyme Regis, Dorset, England. Also possibly in Trias Rhaet, Somerset (Woodward 1889).

Last, Tert Palaeoc: *Synechodus eocaenus* Leriche 1902, *S.subulatus* Leriche 1951, Landenian, Belgium.

Comment: *S.clarkei* Eastman 1901, M.Eoc, Aquia Fm, Maryland, is derived (Leriche 1942).

Family HETERODONTIDAE Gill 1862

First, Jur 'Tith': *Heterodontus falcifer* (Wagner 1847), *H.semirugosus* (Pleininger 1847), Lithographic stone, Bavaria, Germany (Schweizer 1964). **Extant.**

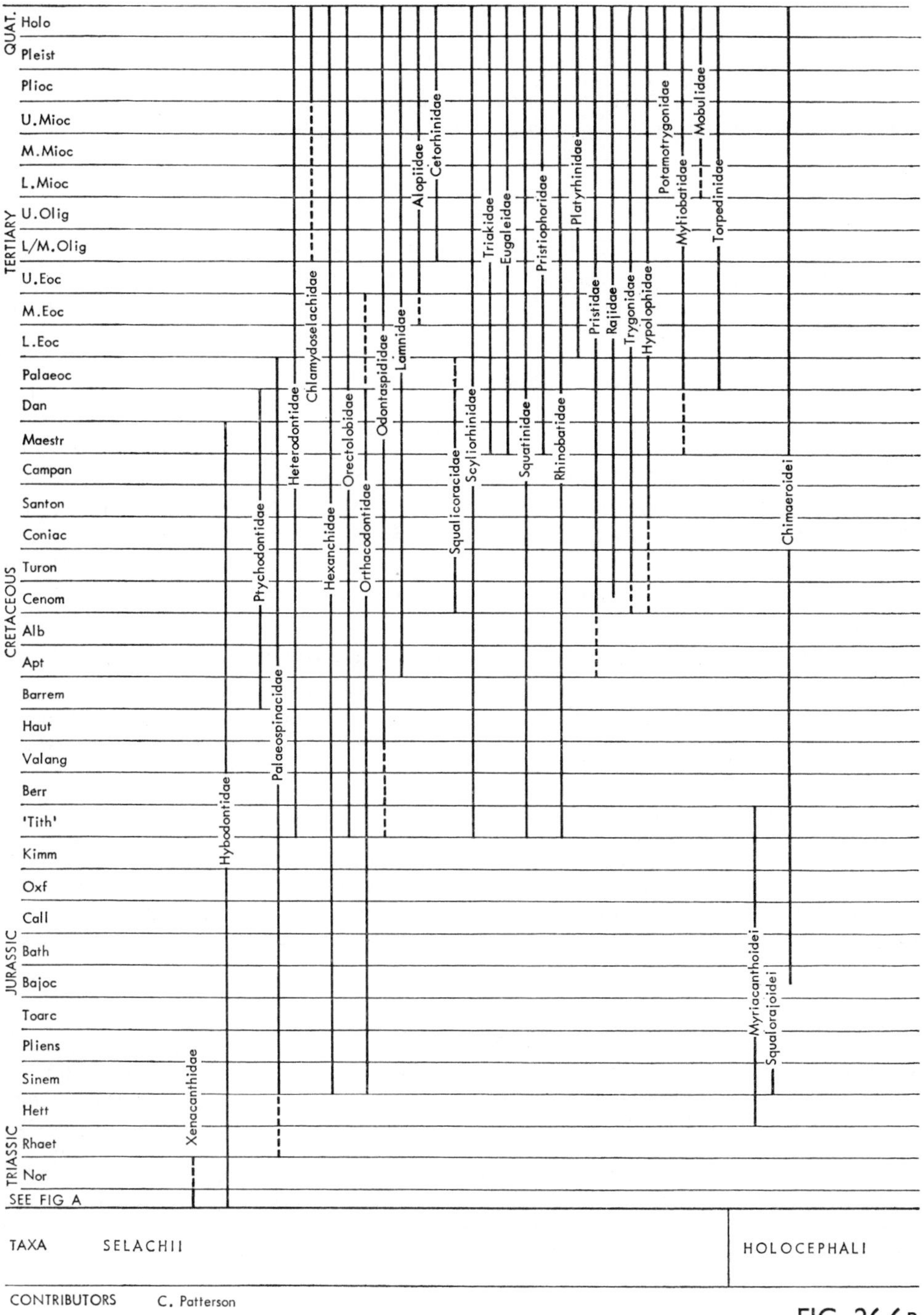
QUAT.
Holo
Pleist
TERTIARY
Plioc
U.Mioc
M.Mioc
L.Mioc
U.Olig
L/M.Olig
U.Eoc
M.Eoc
L.Eoc
Palaeoc
Dan
CRETACEOUS
Maestr
Campan
Santon
Coniac
Turon
Cenom
Alb
Apt
Barrem
Haut
Valang
Berr
'Tith'
JURASSIC
Kimm
Oxf
Call
Bath
Bajoc
Toarc
Pliens
Sinem
Hett
TRIASSIC
Rhaet
Nor
SEE FIG A
Xenacanthidae
Hybodontidae
Ptychodontidae
Palaeospinacidae
Heterodontidae
Chlamydoselachidae
Hexanchidae
Orectolobidae
Orthacodontidae
Odontaspididae
Lamnidae
Alopiidae
Cetorhinidae
Squalicoracidae
Scyliorhinidae
Triakidae
Eugaleidae
Squatinidae
Pristiophoridae
Rhinobatidae
Platyrhinidae
Pristidae
Rajidae
Trygonidae
Hypolophidae
Potamotrygonidae
Myliobatidae
Mobulidae
Torpedinidae
Chimaeroidei
Myriacanthoidei
Squalorajoidei
TAXA
SELACHII
HOLOCEPHALI
CONTRIBUTORS
C. Patterson

FIG. 26.6B

The Fossil Record, Part II

Order HEXANCHIFORMES

Suborder CHLAMYDOSELACHOIDEI

Family CHLAMYDOSELACHIDAE Garman 1884

First, Tert L/M.Olig-U.Mioc: *Chlamydoselachoides tableri* (Leriche 1929), unknown Fm, Trinidad. **Extant.**

Suborder HEXANCHOIDEI

Family HEXANCHIDAE Gill 1885

First, Jur Sinem: *Notidanus arzoensis* de Beaumont 1960, Lotharingien, Switzerland.
Extant.

Comment: Origin perhaps from Cladodontidae.

Order LAMNIFORMES

Suborder LAMNOIDEI

Family ORECTOLOBIDAE Regan 1906

First, Jur 'Tith': *Crossorhinus jurassicus* Woodward 1919, Lithographic Stone, Bavaria; *Phorcynis catulina* Thiollière 1854, *Corysodon cerinensis* Saint-Seine 1949, Lithographic Stone, Cerin, France. **Extant.**

Family RHINCODONTIDAE Garman 1913

No fossil record.

Family ORTHACODONTIDAE de Beaumont 1960 (= Paraorthacodidae Glikman 1958)

First, Jur Sinem: *Orthacodus helveticus* de Beaumont 1960, Lotharingien, Arzo, Switzerland.
Last, Tert Dan: *Orthacodus lundgreni* Davis 1890, Danian, S. Sweden. Glikman (1957) makes this species the type of a new genus *Eychlaodus* and considers that the orthacodontids extend into the M.Eoc Tykbutaksk Ser, Kazak, USSR (*Paraorthacodus turgaicus* Glikman 1964).

General Comment. The remaining lamnoids are a difficult group in which large samples of fossil teeth, allowing reconstruction of the dentition, are often necessary before genera can be reliably separated. In most general classifications only two families are recognised (Odontaspididae (= Carchariidae) and Lamnidae (= Isuridae)) but Glikman has recently (1964) published a radically different classification, based largely on fossils, in which the group is divided among 2 orders, 4 suborders and 12 families: this work has not yet been evaluated and I follow the traditional classification, noting some of Glikman's families in passing.

Family ODONTASPIDIDAE Muller & Henle 1839

First, Jur 'Tith': *Palaeocarcharias stromeri* de Beaumont 1960, Lithographic Stone, Bavaria, Germany: tentatively referred to this family, as are a few questionable records of teeth in U.Jur (de Beaumont 1960). Otherwise unknown before Cret Valang-Haut: *Odontaspis macrorhiza* mut. *infracretacea* Leriche (1911), '*O.*' *studeri* Pictet 1858, Mont Salève and St Croix, Switzerland.
Extant.

Comment: The Scapanorhynchidae, sometimes considered a separate family and made a separate suborder by Glikman (but see Signeux 1949), are unknown with certainty before Cret Maestr, *Scapanorhynchus* spp., fish beds, Sahel Alma, Lebanon: many teeth in Cret Alb-Cenom which are commonly placed in *Scapanorhynchus* could as well be *Odontaspis*.

Family LAMNIDAE Muller & Henle 1839

First, Cret Apt: *Isurus mantelli* (Agassiz 1843), jacobi Z., Folkestone, Kent (Casey 1961). This and other spp. (especially *Oxyrhina macrorhiza* Pictet & Campiche 1858) widespread in Alb in Europe. Glikman (1958) places *O.macrorhiza* in a new genus *Paraisurus* and *I. mantelli* in a new genus *Cretoxyrhina*, these genera being placed in a new family Cretoxyrhinidae ranging from Alb-Dan. According to Glikman true lamnids do not appear until Tert Mioc: he places the Cret and early Tert forms in several new families.   **Extant.**

Family ALOPIIDAE Gill 1885

First, Tert M/U.Eoc: *Alopias latidens* (Leriche 1908), U.Eoc, Alabama and S. Carolina (White 1956); *A.smithwoodwardi* Böhm 1926, M.-U.Eoc, S. W. Africa.   **Extant.**

Family CETORHINIDAE Gill 1872

First, Tert L/M.Olig: *Cetorhinus parvus* Leriche 1908, Rupelian, Belgium, Rumania, Switzerland, Germany, France.   **Extant.**

Family SQUALICORACIDAE nom. nov. (= ANACORACIDAE Casier 1947)

First, Cret Cenom: *Squalicorax falcatus* (Agassiz 1843) and other spp., Cenom, W. Europe, Lithuania, USSR, N. Africa, Madagascar, etc.
Last, Tert Dan: *Squalicorax lindstromi* (Davis 1890), Danian, S. Sweden. Possibly in Tert Palaeoc, Fort Union Fm, Wyoming (Applegate 1964).

Suborder SCYLIORHINOIDEI

Family SCYLIORHINIDAE Gill 1862

First, Jur 'Tith': *Palaeoscyllium formosum* Wagner 1857, *'Galeus' hassei* (Woodward 1889), Lithographic Stone, Bavaria, Germany.   **Extant.**

Family TRIAKIDAE White 1936

First, Cret Maestr: *Triakis curtirostris* (Davis 1887), fish beds, Sahel Alma, Lebanon (Signeux 1949).   **Extant.**

Family EUGALEIDAE Gurr 1963

First, Cret Maestr: *Palaeogaleus gomphoriza* premut. *prior* (Arambourg 1952), Maestr Phosphates, Ouled Abdoun, Morrocco.   **Extant.**

Family CARCHARHINIDAE Garman 1913

First, Tert Palaeoc: *Physodon tertius* (Winkler 1874), Thanetian Phosphates, Ouled Abdoun, Morocco (Arambourg 1952).   **Extant.**
[N.B. This family and the following 5 were inadvertently omitted from the chart. Ed.]

Family SPHYRNIDAE Gill 1874

First, Tert M.Eoc: *Sphyrna itoriensis* White 1926, Lutetian, Nigeria; *S.africana* Dartevelle & Casier 1959, Insono, Cabinda, Congo.   **Extant.**

Suborder SQUALOIDEI

Family PROTOSPINACIDAE Woodward 1919

First and **Last,** Jur 'Tith': *Protospinax annectens* Woodward 1919, Lithographic Stone, Bavaria, Germany.

Family SQUALIDAE Bonnaterre 1831

First, Cret Cenom: *Squalus appendiculatus* (Leriche 1929), Cenom, Lithuania (Dalinkevičius 1935).   **Extant.**

671

Family DALATIIDAE Gill 1892

First, Tert Palaeoc: *Isistius trituratus* (Winkler 1874), Thanetian Phosphates, Ouled Abdoun, Morocco (Arambourg 1952); *Dalatias turkmenicus* Glikman 1964, Chaaldzhinsk Series, Turkmenia. **Extant.**

Comment: Both Romer (1945) and Glikman (1964) record dalatiids as present in U.Cret but no definite occurrence can be found.

Family ECHINORHINIDAE Garman 1913

First, Tert Eoc (L.Eoc): *Echinorhinus priscus* Arambourg 1952, Ypresian Phosphates, Ouled Abdoun, Morocco. **Extant.**

Suborder SQUATINOIDEI

Family SQUATINIDAE Muller & Henle 1837

First, Jur 'Tith': *Squatina alifera* (Münster 1842), *S.speciosa* (Meyer 1856), *S.acanthoderma* Fraas (1854), Lithographic Stone, Bavaria, Germany. **Extant.**

Order PRISTIOPHORIFORMES

Family PRISTIOPHORIDAE Bleeker 1859

First, Cret Maestr: *Propristiophorus tumidens* Woodward 1932, fish beds, Sahel Alma, Lebanon. **Extant.**

Order RAJIFORMES

Suborder RHINOBATOIDEI

Family RHINOBATIDAE Muller & Henle 1841

First, Jur 'Tith': *Spathobatis bugesiacus* Thiollière 1849, Lithographic Stone, Cerin, France & Bavaria, Germany (Saint-Seine 1949); *Belemnobatis sismondae* Thiollière 1854, Lithographic Stone, Cerin, France (Saint-Seine 1949); *Asterodermus platypterus* Agassiz 1843, Lithographic Stone, Bavaria, Germany. **Extant.**

Comment: Normally held to be derived from a shark-like ancestor, direct derivation from arthrodire-like forms proposed by Holmgren (1942) and Jarvik (1964).

Family PLATYRHINIDAE Norman 1926

First, Tert L.Eoc: *Platyrhina bruxelliensis* Casier 1946, Ypresian, Belgium. **Extant.**

Suborder PRISTOIDEI

Family PRISTIDAE Muller & Henle 1837

First, Cret Cenom: *Marckgrafia libyca* Weiler 1935, *Ischyrhiza* sp. (Arambourg 1941), Baharîje Stufe (L.Cenom), Egypt; ?Apt-Alb: *Onchopristis numidus* (Haug), Djoua, S. Morocco (Tabasti 1964). **Extant.**

Comment: Other genera and species in Cenom Lebanon & N. Africa, all Ganopristinae: Pristinae do not appear until Tert L.Eoc (Schaeffer 1963).

Suborder RAJOIDEI

Family RAJIDAE Bonaparte 1831

First, Cret Cenom: *Raja expansa* (Davis 1887), *R.whitfieldi* Hay 1903, *Cyclobatis oligodactylus* Egerton 1844, *C.major* Davis 1887, *C.longicaudatus* Woodward 1942, U.Cenom fish beds, Hakel and Hajula, Lebanon. **Extant.**

Chapter 26: Pisces

Family TRYGONIDAE Muller & Henle 1837

First, Cret Cenom-Turon: 'cf. *Trygon*' (Stromer 1927), L.Cenom, Baharîje Stufe, Egypt (doubtful); cf. *Dasyatis* (Schaeffer 1963), El Molino Fm (?Cenom), Bolivia; *Ptychotrygon triangularis* (Reuss 1845), 'Plänerkalk' (Turon), Czechoslovakia (Jaekel 1893). **Extant.**

Family HYPOLOPHIDAE Leriche 1913

First, Cret Cenom-Campan: cf. *Rhombodus* (Schaeffer 1963), El Molino Fm. (?Cenom), Bolivia; *Parapalaeobates* sp., Santonian, USSR (Glikman 1964); *Parapalaeobates atlanticus* Arambourg 1952, *Hypolophites* sp., Senonian, Congo and Cabinda (Dartevelle & Casier 1959); *Myledaphus bipartitus* Cope 1876, Campan, Mesaverde Fm, Wyoming (Estes 1964). 'cf. *Hypolophites*' doubtfully recorded from L.Cenom, Baharîje Stufe, Egypt (Stromer 1927). **Extant.**

Family POTAMOTRYGONIDAE Garman 1913

First, ?Tert: The only records of this freshwater family are Quat Pleist: *Potamotrygon africana* Arambourg 1947, Lake Rudolph, Ethiopia and '*Dynatobatis*' spp. (dermal tubercles) from unknown Tert Fm, Rio Parana, Brazil (Larrazet 1886). **Extant.**

Family MYLIOBATIDAE Muller & Henle 1837

First, Cret Maestr-Tert Palaeoc: *Myliobatis* spp., Maestr, Mt. Igdaman, Sahara (Tabaste 1964), Montian Phosphates, Ouled Abdoun, Morocco (Arambourg 1952), L. Palaeoc, Congo and Cabinda (Dartevelle & Casier 1959), Brazil, U.S.S.R. (Glikman 1964), N. Dakota (Leriche 1942). **Extant.**

Comment: None of the other supposed Cret records of myliobatids seem reliable. *Apocopodon sericeus* Cope 1886 and *Rhinoptera prisca* Woodward 1897, both from Maria Farinha, Pernambuco, Brazil, are commonly recorded as U.Cret but are Palaeoc in age. 'cf. *Rhinoptera*', L.Cenom, Baharîje Stufe, Egypt (Stromer 1929), is a doubtful myliobatid.

Family MOBULIDAE Garman 1913

First, Tert L.M.Mioc: *Manta unios* (Leidy 1877), Hawthorn Fm, S.Carolina. The only record. **Extant.**

Order TORPEDINIFORMES

Family TORPEDINIDAE Bonaparte 1837

First, Tert Palaeoc: *Eotorpedo hilgendorfi* (Jaekel 1904), Landenian, Cabinda (Dartevelle & Casier 1959), Montian Phosphates, Ouled Abdoun, Morocco (Arambourg 1952). **Extant.**

Class HOLOCEPHALI

General Comment. The classification followed is that of Patterson (1965). Orders are documented except within the Chimaeriformes, where suborders are listed.

Order CHIMAERIFORMES

Suborder MENASPOIDEI (including Cochliodontidae)

First, Dev Famenn: *Thoralodus cabrieri* Lehman 1953, U. Famenn, Montagne Noire, Cabrières, France.

Last, Perm Guad: *Menaspis armata* Ewald 1848, Kupferschiefer, Mansfeld, Germany.

Comment: Origin unknown but probably related to arthrodires (Patterson 1965). Group rare in U.Dev & Perm, abundant in Carb.

Suborder MYRIACANTHOIDEI

First, Jur Hett: *Myriacanthus paradoxus* Agassiz 1837, 'Grés infraliasique,' Hettange, France (Terquem 1855).

Last, Jur 'Tith': *Chimaeropsis paradoxa* Zittel 1887, Lithographic Stone, Bavaria, Germany.
Comment: Origin from ptyctodont arthrodires suggested by Ørvig (1962), from Menaspoidei by Patterson (1965). Group rare throughout Jur.

Suborder SQUALORAJOIDEI

First and **Last,** Jur Sinem: *Squaloraja polyspondyla* Agassiz 1836 and *S.tenuispina* Woodward 1886, L.Lias, Lyme Regis, Dorset, England.
Comment: Origin unknown, presumably from near ancestry of Chimaeroidei.

Suborder CHIMAEROIDEI

First, Jur Bajoc: *Ischyodus aalensis* Riess 1887, *I.ferrugineus* Riess 1887, *I.personati* Quenstedt 1853, Braun Jura β, Württemburg, Germany (Heimberg 1949).   **Extant.**
Comment: Origin from ptyctodont arthrodires according to Ørvig (1962), from Myriacanthoidei according to Patterson (1965). Group common in Mesozoic from Jur Bath, declining in Tert.

Order COPODONTIFORMES

First, Dev Frasn: *Acmoniodus clarkei* Hussakof & Bryant 1918, Genesee conodont bed (L. Frasn), New York State.
Last, Carb Moscov: *Solenodus crenulatus* Trautschold 1874, Mjatshckovo, USSR.
Comment: Origin unknown, known only by isolated tooth plates.

Order PSAMMODONTIFORMES

First, Carb Tourn: *Psammodus* spp., L.Tourn, Belgium, Great Britain, U.S.A., U.S.S.R., etc.
Last, Carb Moscov: *Lagarodus angustus* (Romanovsky 1864), Mjatshckovo, USSR.
Comment: Origin unknown, appearance and extinction sudden, widely distributed and common in L.Carb. Known only by tooth plates. *Psammodus antiquus* Newberry 1857, Dev Eifel, Delaware Lst, Ohio, is a very doubtful record.

Order HELODONTIFORMES

First, Carb Tourn: *Helodus* spp., L.Tourn, Great Britain, U.S.A., U.S.S.R. etc.
Last, Perm Guad-Dzhulf: *Helodopsis* spp., *Psephodus* spp., U.Productus Lst, Salt Range, Pakistan (Waagen 1879).
Comment: Origin unknown. Abundant throughout Carb, rarer in Perm. Supposed Dev records of group reviewed by Patterson (1965).

Order PETALODONTIFORMES

First, Carb Tourn: *Petalodus* and other genera, L.Tourn, Great Britain, Belgium, U.S.A., U.S.S.R. etc.
Last, Perm Guad-Dzhulf: *Petalorhynchus indicus* Waagen 1897, U.Productus Lst, Salt Range, Pakistan; *Janassa bituminosa* (Schlotheim 1823), *Ctenoptychius korni* Weigelt 1930, Kupferschiefer, Germany; *Janassa kochi* Nielsen 1932, ?Foldvik Creek Fm, E. Greenland.
Comment: Origin unknown, possibly from Helodontiformes (Patterson 1965). Common in Carb and more abundant in Perm than other groups listed above. Newberry's records of *Polyrhizodus* spp. (1889) from Dev Famenn, Cleveland Sh, Ohio, are probably Carb Tourn, Sunbury Sh (Kindle 1912).

Order EDESTIFORMES

First, Carb Tourn: *Orodus* spp., L.Tourn, Great Britain, Belgium, U.S.A., etc. *Orodus* contains teeth which in shape and structure agree exactly with the lateral teeth of later edestiform genera, but the specialised symphysial teeth which characterise true edestids are unknown with certainty before Carb Namur: *Edestus newtoni* Woodward 1917, Gastrioceras Z, Millstone Grit, Yorkshire, England.

Chapter 26: Pisces

Last, Trias Induan: *Parahelicampodus sparcki* Nielsen 1952, Fish Z. II, Cape Stosch, E. Greenland.

Comment: Origin unknown, possibly from helodonts (Patterson 1965). Group more abundant and varied in Perm than in Carb. Records of *Edestus* from L.-M. Namur, British Isles are the ? cladodont *Dicrenodus dentatus* Agassiz (Yates 1962, Eumorphoceras Z, Co Antrim, Ireland; Chatwin 1936, Homoceras Z, Staffordshire - specimen not traced). Dev records of edestiforms, reviewed by Patterson (1965), are all doubtful.

Order CHONDRENCHELYIFORMES

First and **Last,** Carb Viséan: *Chondrenchelys problematicus* Traquair 1888, *Eucentrurus paradoxus* Traquair 1901, Calciferous Sst Series, Scotland.

Comment: Obruchev (1964) makes a new holocephalan family Pseudodontichthyidae for *Pseudodontichtys* Skeels 1962, but this is a phyllocarid crustacean (Dunkle 1965, Rolfe & Denison 1966).

[C.P]

REFERENCES

Agassiz, L. 1833–44. *Recherches sur les Poissons Fossiles.* 5 vols., 1420 pp., 396 pls., with supplement. Neuchâtel.

—— 1844–45. *Monographie des Poissons fossiles du Vieux Grès Rouge ou Système Dévonien (Old Red Sandstone) des Îles Brittaniques et de Russie.* xxxvi + 171 pp., 43 pls., Neuchâtel.

Applegate, S. P. 1964. First record of the extinct shark *Squalicorax falcatus* from California. *Bull. Sth. Calif. Acad. Sci.,* **63,** 42–43, 1 fig.

Arambourg, C. 1927. Les poissons fossiles d'Oran. *Bull. Serv. Carte géol. Algér., Paléont.* (1) **6,** 1–298, 46 pls.

—— 1939. Sur des Poissons fossiles de Perse. *C.r. hebd. Séanc. Acad. Sci., Paris.,* **209,** 898–899.

—— 1941. Le groupe des Ganopristinés. *Bull. Soc. géol. Fr.* (5), **10,** 127–147, pls. 3–4.

—— 1943. Note préliminaire sur quelques Poissons fossiles nouveaux. *Bull. Soc. géol. Fr.* (5), **13,** 281–285, 1 pl.

—— 1952. Les Vertébrés Fossiles des Gisements de Phosphates (Maroc, Algérie, Tunisie). *Notes Mém. Serv. géol. Maroc,* **92,** 1–372, 44 pls.

—— 1954. Les poissons crétacés du Jebel Tselfat (Maroc). *Notes Mém. Serv. géol. Maroc,* **118,** 1–188, 20 pls.

Bardack, D. 1965. New Upper Cretaceous teleost fish from Texas. *Paleont. Contr. Univ. Kansas,* Paper **1,** 1–9, 2 figs.

—— 1965b. Anatomy and evolution of chirocentrid fishes. *Paleont. Contr. Univ. Kansas,* Vertebrata, **10,** 1–88, 2 pls.

Beaumont, G. de 1960a. Contribution à l'Étude des Genres *Orthacodus* Woodw. et *Notidanus* Cuv. (Selachii). *Schweiz. palaeont. Abh.,* **77,** 1–46, pls. 1–3.

—— 1960b. Observations preliminaires sur trois Sélaciens nouveaux du Calcaire lithographique d'Echstätt (Bavière) *Éclog. geol. Helv.,* **53,** 315–328, pl. 1.

Berg, L. S. 1955. Classification of fishes and fish-like vertebrates, living and fossil. Second edition, corrected and enlarged. *Trudy zool. Inst., Leningr.,* **20,** 1–286, 263 figs. (In Russian.)

Boeseman, M. 1949. On Pleistocene remains of *Ophicephalus* from Java, in the 'Collection Dubois'. *Zool. Meded., Leiden,* **30,** 83–94, pls. 3–5.

Böhm, J. 1926. Über Tertiäre versteinerungen von den Bogenfelser diamantfelden, pp. 55–87, pls. 31–34 in Kaiser, E. *Die Diamantenwüste Südwest Africas,* **2.** Berlin, Reimer.

Bonde, N. 1966. The Fishes of the Mo-clay Formation (Lower Eocene). *Meddr. dansk geol. Foren.,* **16,** 198–202.

Boucot, A. J. & Pankiwskyj, K. 1962. Llandoverian to Gedinnian stratigraphy of Podolia and adjacent Moldavia in 2 *Internationalische Arbeitstagung über die Silur/Devon-Grenze und die Stratigraphie von Silur und Devon, Bonn-Bruxelles* (1960). Symposiums-Bands, 1–11.

Branson, C. C. 1933. Fish fauna of the Middle Phosphoria Formation. *J. Geol.,* **41,** 174–183.

—— 1934. Permian sharks of Wyoming and of East Greenland. *Science N.Y.,* **79,** 431.

BRANSON, E. B. *et al.* 1938. Stratigraphy and paleontology of the Lower Mississippian of Missouri. Pt. 2. *Univ. Mo. Stud.*, **13**, 1–242.

BROUGH, J. 1939. *The Triassic Fishes of Besano, Lombardy.* ix + 117 + xiv pp., 7 pls., London, Brit. Mus. (Nat. Hist.).

CASEY, R. 1961. The Stratigraphical palaeontology of the Lower Greensand. *Palaeontology*, **3**, 487–621, pls. 77–84.

CASIER, E. 1946. La faune ichthyologique de l'Yprésien de la Belgique. *Mém. Mus. r. Hist. nat. Belg.*, **104**, 1–267, pls. 1–6.

—— 1953. Origine des Ptychodontes. *Mém. Inst. r. Sci. nat. Belg.*, (2), **49**, 1–51, 2 pls.

—— 1960. Note sur la collectiond es poissons Paléocènes et Éocènes de l'Enclave de Cabinda (Congo). *Ann. Mus. r. Congo Belge*, AIII, **1**, 2, 1–48, 2 pls.

—— 1961. Matériaux pour la faune ichthyologique éocrétacique du Congo. *Ann. Mus. r. Afr. Cent., Ser.* 8vo (Sci. Géol.), **39**, xii + 96 pp., 12 pls.

—— 1966. *Faune ichthyologique du London Clay.* xiv + 496 pp., 68 pls. London, Brit. Mus. (Nat. Hist.).

CHABANAUD, P. 1931. Affinités morphologique, répartition stratigraphique et géographique des poissons fossiles et actuelles de la famille des Gonorhynchidés. *Bull. Soc. géol. Fr.* (5), **1**, 497–517, pl. 22.

—— 1937. Les Téléostéens dyssymétriques du Mokattam inférieur de Tourah. *Mém. Inst. Égypte*, **32**, 1–121, 4 pls.

—— 1940. Un nouveau téléostéen dyssymétrique fossile, originaire du Lutétien du bassin de Paris. *Archs Mus. natn. Hist. nat., Paris* (6), **16**, 5–33, 2 pls.

CHATWIN, C. P. 1938. Report of Palaeontological Department. *Summ. Progr. Geol. Surv. U.K.* for 1937, 76–82.

COCKERELL, T. D. A. 1919. Some American Cretaceous fish-scales, with notes on the classification and distribution of Cretaceous fishes. *Prof. Pap. U.S. Geol. Surv.*, **120**, 165–188, 7 pls.

DALINKEVIČIUS, J. A. 1935. On the Fossil Fishes of the Lithuanian Chalk. I. Selachii. *Liet. Univ. Mat. Gamtos Fak. Darb.*, **9**, 245–305, pls. 1–5.

DANILTSHENKO, P. T. 1958. [Two new species of fish from the Tertiary deposits of the Caucasus.] *Mater. Osnov. Paleont.*, **2**, 95–98, 1 pl. (Russian).

—— 1960. [Bony fishes of the Maikop Beds of the Caucasus.] *Trudÿ paleont. Inst.*, **78**, 208 pp., 28 pls. (Russian).

—— 1964. Superorder Teleostei, pp. 396–472, pls 5–14 *in* Obruchev, D. B. (Editor) *Osnovy Paleontologii*, **11**: Beschelyustnye, Ryby. Akad. Nauk. SSSR, Moscow (Russian).

DARTEVELLE, E. & CASIER, E. 1949. Les Poissons fossiles du Bas-Congo et des régions voisines (2me partie). *Ann. Mus. r. Congo Belge*, AIII, **2**, 201–256, pls. 17–22.

—— & —— 1959. Les Poissons fossiles du Bas-Congo et des régions voisines (3me partie). *Ann. Mus. r. Congo Belge*, AIII, **3**, 257–568, pls. 23–39.

DAVID, L. R. 1943. Miocene fishes of Southern California. *Spec. Pap. geol. Soc. Am.*, **43**, xiii + 193 pp., pls. 1–16.

—— 1946. Upper Cretaceous Fish Remains from the Western Border of the San Joaquin Valley, California. *Publs Carnegie Instn*, **551**, 81–112, 3 pls.

DAVIS, J. W. 1890. On the fossil fish of the Cretaceous formations of Scandinavia. *Scient. Trans. R. Dubl. Soc.*, **4**, 363–434, pls. 38–46.

DEAN, B. 1909. Studies on fossil fishes (sharks, chimaeroids and arthrodires). *Mem. Am. Mus. nat. Hist.*, **9**, 211–287, pls. 26–41.

DENISON, R. H. 1956. A review of the habitat of the earliest vertebrates. *Fieldiana: Geol.*, **11**, 359–457.

—— 1958. Early Devonian fishes from Utah. Pt. 3. Arthrodira. *Fieldiana: Geol.*, **11**, 461–551.

DUNKLE, D. H. 1958. Three North American Cretaceous fishes. *Proc. U.S. natn Mus.*, **108**, 269–277, 3 pls.

—— 1965. The presumed holocephalan fish *Pseudodontichthys whitei* Skeels. *Sci. Publ. Cleveland Mus. nat. Hist.*, (N.S.) **4**, 1–10, pl. 1.

—— & MAMAY, S. H. 1956. An acanthodian fish from the Lower Permian of Texas. *J. Wash. Acad. Sci.*, **46**, 308–310.

EASTMAN, C. R. 1904. Descriptions of Bolca Fishes. *Bull. Mus. comp. Zool. Harv.*, **46**, 1–36, 2 pls.

—— 1907. Devonic Fishes of the New York formations. *Mem. N.Y.St. Mus.*, **10**, 1–235, pls 1–15.

EBELING, A. W. 1962. *Scopelogadus* (?) *capistraensis*, a new fossil melamphaid (Pisces, Teleostei) from Capistrano Beach, California. *Postilla*, **71**, 1–6, 1 fig.

EDGWORTH DAVID, T. W. 1950. *The Geology of the Commonwealth of Australia* (Edited and much supplemented by BROWN, W. R.). 1. London.

D'ERASMO, G. 1934. Sopra alcuni avanzi di vertebrati fossili della Patagonia raccolti dal dott. E. Feruglio. *Atti Accad. Sci. fis. mat., Napoli* (2), **2**, 8, 1–26.

—— 1946. L'ittiofauna cretacea di Comeno nel Carso Triestino. *Atti Accad. Sci. fis. mat., Napoli* (3a), **2**, 8, 136 pp., 1 pl.

ESTES, R. D. 1964. Fossil vertebrates from the late Cretaceous Lance Formation, Eastern Wyoming. *Univ. Calif. Publs Bull. Dep. Geol.*, **49**, 1–187, pls. 1–5.

FRIEND, P. F. 1961. The Devonian Stratigraphy of North and Central Vestspitsbergen. *Proc. Yorks. Geol. Soc.*, **33**, 77–118, pl. 6.

FRITSCH, A. J. 1889. *Fauna der Gaskóhle und der Kalksteine Permformation Böhems.* 2. Prague.

FRIZZELL, D. L. 1965. Otoliths of new fish (*Vorhisia vulpes*, n. gen., n. sp., Siluroidei?) from Upper Cretaceous of South Dakota. *Copeia*, 1965, 178–181, 3 figs.

GARDINER, B. G. 1963. Certain palaeoniscoid fishes and the evolution of the snout in actinopterygians. *Bull. Brit. Mus. nat. Hist., Geol.*, **8**, no. 6, 255–325, 2 pls.

—— 1967. Further notes on palaeoniscoid fishes with a classification of the Chondrostei. *Bull. Brit. Mus. nat. Hist., Geol.*, **14**, no 5 (in press).

GLIKMAN, L. S. 1958. [The rate of evolution in lamnoid sharks.] *Dokl. Akad. nauk SSSR*, **123**, 568–571 (Russian).

—— 1964a. [*Palaeogene sharks and their stratigraphical significance.*] 229 pp., 31 pls. Akademii Nauk SSSR, Moscow (Russian).

—— 1964b. Subclass Elasmobranchii, pp. 196–237, pls. 1–6, *in* Obruchev, D. V. (Editor) *Osnovy Paleontologii*, **11**, Beschelyustyne, Ryby. Akad. Nauk SSSR, Moscow (Russian).

GRAHAM-SMITH, W. G. & WESTOLL, T. S. 1937. On a new long-headed Dipnoan fish from the Upper Devonian of Scaumenac Bay, P.Q., Canada. *Trans. R. Soc. Edinb.*, **59**, 241–256.

GREENWOOD, P. H. 1951. Fish Remains from Miocene Deposits of Rusinga Island and Kavirondo Province, Kenya. *Ann. Mag. nat. Hist.* (12), **4**, 1192–1201.

—— 1959. Quaternary fish fossils. *Explor. Parc Natn. Albert Miss. J. de Heinzelin de Braucourt*, **4**, 1–80, 14 pls.

—— 1960. Fossil denticipitid fishes from East Africa. *Bull. Brit. Mus. (nat. Hist.), Geol.*, **5**, 1–11, pls. 1–3.

——, ROSEN, D. E., WEITZMAN, S. H. & MYERS, G. S. 1966. Phyletic studies of teleostean fishes with a provisional classification of living forms. *Bull. Am. Mus. nat. Hist.*, **131**, 339–456, pls. 21–23.

GROSS, W. 1936. Beiträge zur Osteologie baltischer und rheinischer Devon-Crossopterygier. *Paläont. Z.*, **18**, 129–155, pl. 7–8.

—— 1937. Die Wirbeltiere des rheinischen Devons 2. *Abh. preuss. geol. Landesanst.*, **176**, 5–83.

—— 1941. Neue Beobachtungen an *Gerdalepis rhenana* (Beyrich). *Palaeontographica.*, **93A**, 193–212.

—— 1942. Die Fischfaunen des baltischen Devons und ihre biostratigraphische Bedeutung. *Korrespbl. des Naturf Ver. Riga*, **64**, 373–436.

—— 1950. Die paläontologische und stratigraphische Bedeutung der Wirbeltier-faunen des Old Reds und der marinen altpaläozoischen Schichten. *Abh. dt. Akad. Wiss. Berlin*, for 1949, 1–130.

—— 1958. Über die älteste Arthrodiren-Gattung. *Notizbl. hess. Landesamt Bodenforsch, Wilsbaden* 86, 7–30.

—— 1959. Arthrodiren aus dem Obersilur der Prager Mulde. *Palaeontographica.*, **133A**, 1–35.

—— 1961. *Lunaspis broilli* und *Lunaspis heroldi* aus dem Hunsrückschiefer (Unterdevon, Rheinland). *Notizbl. hess. Landesamt Bodenforsch. Wiesbaden*, **89**, 1–43.

—— 1962. Neuuntersuchung der Stensiöellida (Arthrodira, Unterdevon). *Notizbl. hess. Landesamt Bodenforsch. Wiesbaden*, 90, 48–86.

—— 1963. *Gemuendina stuertzi* Traquair. Neuuntersuchung. *Notizbl. hess. Landesamt Bodenforsch. Wiesbaden*, **91**, 36–73.

GURR, P. R. 1963. A New Fish Fauna from the Woolwich Bottom Bed (Sparnacian) of Herne Bay, Kent. *Proc. geol. Ass.*, **73**, 419–447, pls. 17–26.

HANCOCK, A. & ATTHEY, T. 1868. Notes on the remains of some reptiles and fishes from the shales of the Northumberland coal field. *Ann. Mag. nat. Hist.* (4), **1**, 266–278.

HARRIS, J. E. 1951. *Diademodus hydei*, a new fossil shark from the Cleveland Shale. *Proc. zool. Soc. Lond.*, **120**, 683–697, pls. 1–3.

HAY, O. P. 1903. On a collection of Upper Cretaceous fishes from Mount Lebanon, Syria, with descriptions of four new genera and nineteen new species. *Bull. Am. Mus. nat. Hist.*, **19**, 395–452, 14 pls.

—— 1929. *Second Bibliography and Catalogue of Fossil Vertebrata of North America, Vol.* 1. Carnegie Institute, Washington.

HEIMBERG, G. 1949. Neue Fischfunde aus dem Weissen Jura von Württemberg. *Palaeontographica*, **97A**, 75–98, pls. 5–8.

HEINTZ, A. 1934. Fischreste aus dem Unterperm Norwegens. *Norsk geol. Tidsskr.*, **14**, 176–194.

HILLS, E. S. 1941. The Cranial Roof of *Dipnorhynchus süssmilchi* (Eth. fil.). *Rec. Aust. Mus.*, **21**, No. 1, 45–55.

—— 1958. A brief review of Australian fossil vertebrates. in WESTOLL, T. S. (Editor), *Studies on fossil vertebrates*. 86–107. London.

HOLMGREN, N. 1942. Studies on the head in fishes, Part III. *Acta zool., Stockh.*, **23**, 129–261, 54 figs.

HOOVER, K. V. 1960. Devonian-Mississippian shale sequence in Ohio. *Inf. Circ. Div. geol Surv. Ohio*, **27**, 1–154.

HOPPE, K. -H. 1931. Die Coelolepiden und Acanthodier des Obersilurs der Insel Ösel. Ihre Paläobiologie und Paläontologie. *Palaeontographica*, **76**, 35–94.

HUSSAKOF, L. & BRYANT, W. L. 1918. Catalog of the fossil fishes in the Museum of the Buffalo Society of Natural Sciences. *Bull. Buffalo Soc. nat. Sci.*, **12**, 346 pp., 70 pls.

JAEKEL, O. 1921. Paläontologische Berichte: Die Stellung der Paläontologie zu einigen Problemen der Biologie und Phylogenie. *Paläont. Z.*, **3**, 217–221.

—— 1927. Der Kopf der Wirbelthiere. *Ergebn. Anat. EntwGesch.*, **27**, 815–974.

JARVIK, E. 1942. On the Structure of the Snout of Crossopterygians and Lower Gnathostomes in General. *Zool. Bidr. Upps.*, **21**, 235–675, pl. 1–17.

—— 1948. On the Morphology and Taxonomy of the Middle Devonian Osteolepid Fishes of Scotland. *K. Svenska VetenskAkad. Handl.*, **25**, No. 1, 1–301, pl. 1–37.

—— 1950a. On Some Osteolepiform Crossopterygians from the Upper Old Red Sandstone of Scotland. *K. Svenska VetenskAkad. Handl.*, **2**, No. 2, 1–35, pl. I–X.

—— 1950b. Middle Devonian vertebrates from Canning Land and Wegeners Halvo (East Greenland). Pt. 2. Crossopterygii. *Meddr. Grønland*, **96**, 1–132.

—— 1952. On the Fish-like Tail in the Ichthyostegid Stegocephalians. *Meddr Grønland*, **114**, no. 12, 1–90, pl. 1–21.

—— 1960. *Théories de l'évolution des vertébrés*, 104 pp. Paris.

—— 1961. Devonian Vertebrates. in RAASCH, G. O. (Editor), *Geology of the Arctic*, 197–204. Toronto.

—— 1964. Specializations in early vertebrates. *Annls Soc. r. zool. Belg.*, **94**, 11–95, 28 figs.

JORDAN, D. S. 1921. The Fish Fauna of the California Tertiary. *Stanford Univ. Publs* (Biol. Sci.), **1**, 233–300, pls. 1–57.

—— 1927. The fossil fishes of the Miocene of Southern California. Contribution No. IX. *Stanford Univ. Publs* (Biol. Sci.), **5**, 85–99, 4 pls.

—— & GILBERT, J. Z. 1919. Fossil Fishes of Southern California. *Leland Stanford jr Univ. Publs Univ. Ser.*, 64 pp., 31 pls.

JUKES-BROWNE, A. J. 1904. The Cretaceous Rocks of Britain. Vol. III, The Upper Chalk of England. *Mem. geol. Surv. U.K.*, 1904.

KABAKOV, A. V. 1947. Ob Ostatkach Dvoyakodyshastchich (Fam. Ceratodontidae) iz Nizhnego Triasa Gory Bogdo. *Trudy̆ Paleozool. Inst.* for 1947, no. 1, 45–55.

KING, W. W. 1925. Notes on the "Old Red Sandstone" of Shropshire. *Proc. geol. Ass.*, **36,** 383–389.

—— 1934. The Downtonian and Dittonian strata of Great Britain and North-western Europe. *Q. Jl geol. Soc. Lond.*, **90,** 526–566.

KÜHNE, W. G. 1941. A new zeomorph fish from the Palaeocene Moler of Denmark. *Ann. Mag. nat. Hist.* (11), **7,** 374–386, 3 figs.

LE DANOIS, Y. 1964. Remarques ostéo-myologiques sur certains poissons de l'Ordre des Scombres. *Mém. Inst. franç. Afr. noire*, **68,** 109–152, 31 figs.

LEHMAN, J-P. 1952. Étude complémentaire des Poissons de l'Eotrias de Madagascar. *K. svenska VetenskAkad. Handl.*, **2,** no. 6, 1–210, 48 pls.

—— 1953. Notes paléoichthyologiques. *Annls Paléont.*, **38,** 59–67, pl. 1.

—— 1959. Les Dipneustes du Dévonien Supérieur du Groenland. *Meddr Grønland*, **160,** no. 4, 1–58, pl. 1–21.

LEHMANN, W. & WESTOLL, T. S. 1952. A Primitive Dipnoan Fish from the Lower Devonian of Germany. *Proc. R. Soc.*, **140B,** 403–421.

LERICHE, M. 1910. Les Poissons oligocènes de la Belgique. *Mém. Mus. r. Hist. nat. Belg.*, **5,** 1–363, pls. 1–27.

—— 1929. Sur une forme nouvelle du genre *Chlamydoselachus* rejetée par le volcan de boue de Chogonary (Île de la Trinite, Petites-Antilles). *Bull. Soc. belge Géol. Paléont. Hydrol.*, **38,** 55–58.

—— 1942. Contribution à l'étude des faunes ichthyologiques marines des terrains tertiaires de la plaine côtière atlantique et du Centre des États-Unis. *Mém. Soc. géol. Fr.*, (n.s.), **45,** 1–112, pls. 1–8.

—— 1951. Les Poissons tertiaires de la Belgique (Supplément). *Mém. Inst. r. Sci. nat. Belg.*, **118,** 475–600, pls. 42–47.

LIU, Y.-H. 1963. On the Antiarchi from Chutsing, Yunnan. *Vertebr. Palasiat.*, **7,** 39–46.

MARSHALL, N. B. 1961. A young *Macristium* and the Ctenothrissid fishes. *Bull. Brit. Mus. nat. Hist., Zool.*, **7,** 353–370, 4 figs.

MARTIN, G. P. R. & WEILER, W. 1954. Fisch-Otolithen aus dem deutschen Mesozoikum (Dogger bis Wealden). *Senckenberg. leth.*, **35,** 119–192, pls. 1–4.

—— & —— 1957. Das Aldorfer Otolithen- "Pflaster" und seine Fauna. *Senckenberg. leth.*, **38,** 211–250, pls. 1–3.

MILES, R. S. 1964. A reinterpretion of the visceral skeleton of Acanthodes. *Nature, Lond.* **204,** 457–459.

—— 1965. Some features in the cranial morphology of acanthodians and the relationships of the Acanthodii. *Acta zool.Stockh.*, **46,** 233–255.

—— 1966. The acanthodian fishes of the Devonian Plattenkalk of the Paffrath trough in the Rhineland. With an appendix containing a classification of the Acanthodii and a revision of the genus *Homalacanthus*. *Ark. Zool*, Ser. 2, **18,** (9), 147–194.

MILLER, R. R. 1945. Four new species of fossil cyprinodont fishes from eastern California. *J. Wash. Acad. Sci.*, **35,** 315–321, 4 figs.

MILLOT, J. 1954. Le Troisième Coelacanthe. *Naturaliste malgache*, Premier Suppl., 26 pp., 50 pl.

—— & ANTHONY, J. 1958. *Anatomie de* Latimeria chalumae, 1. *Squelette, muscles et formation de Soutien*, 122 pp., 80 pls. Paris, Centre National de la Recherche Scientifique.

MOY-THOMAS, J. A. 1935. On the Carboniferous shark, *Petrodus patelliformis* M'Coy. *Proc. Leeds phil. lit. Soc. (Sci. Sect.)*, **3,** 68–72, 1 pl.

—— 1937. The Carboniferous Coelacanth Fishes of Great Britain and Ireland. *Proc. zool. Soc. Lond.*, B, Pt. 3, 383–415, pl. I–IV.

—— 1939. The early evolution and relationships of the elasmobranchs. *Biol. Rev.*, **14,** 1–26,12 figs.

NEWBERRY, J. S. 1889. The Paleozoic Fishes of North America. *Monog. U.S. geol. Surv.*, **16**, Washington.

NIELSEN, E. 1932. Permo-Carboniferous fishes from East Greenland. *Meddr Grønland*, **86**, no. 3, 1–63, pls. 1–16.

—— 1952. On new or little known Edestidae from the Permian and Triassic of East Greenland. *Meddr Grønland*, **144**, no, 5, 1–55, pls. 1–13.

—— 1960. A new Eocene Teleost from Denmark. *Meddr dansk geol. Foren.*, **14**, 247–252, 3 figs.

NYBELIN, O. 1961. Über die Frage der Abstammung der rezenten primitiven Teleostier. *Paläont. Z.*, **35**, 114–117.

—— 1964. Versuch einer taxonomischen Revision der jurassischen Fischgattung *Thrissops* Agassiz. *Göteborgs K. Vetensk.- o. VitterhSamh. Handl.* (B), **9**, 4, 1–44, 9 pls.

OBRUCHEV, D. 1939. [Discovery of a Lower Devonian Fish Fauna in the U.S.S.R.] *Dokl. Akad. nauk SSSR*, **22**, no. 5, 287–288 (Russian).

—— 1940. [Devonian Fishes of Siberia and Central Asia.] *Dokl. Akad. nauk SSSR*, **27**, no. 8, 889–892 (Russian).

—— 1964. Subclass Holocephali pp. 238–266, pls. 1–4. *In* OBRUCHEV, D. V. (Editor) *Osnovy Paleontologii*, **11**, Beschelyustnye, Ryby. Akad. Nauk SSSR, Moscow (Russian).

ØRVIG, T. 1957. Remarks on the Vertebrate Fauna of the Lower Upper Devonian of Escuminac Bay, P.Q., Canada, with Special Reference to the Porolepiform Crossopterygians. *Ark. Zool.*, Ser. 2, **10**, no. 6, 367–426.

—— 1960. New finds of acanthodians, arthrodires, crossopterygians, ganoids and dipnoans in the Upper Middle Devonian Calcareous Flags (Oberer Plattenkalk) of the Bergisch Gladbach-Paffrath Trough. Pt. 1. *Paläont. Z.*, **34**, 295–335.

—— 1962. Ya-t-il une relation directe entre les arthrodires ptyctodontides et les holocéphales? *Colloques int. Cent. natn. Rech. Scient.*, **104**, 49–61, pl. 1.

PANCHEN, A. L. & WALKER, A. D. 1960. British Coal Measure Labyrinthodont Localities. *Ann. Mag. nat. Hist.* (13), **3**, 321–332.

PATTERSON, C. 1964. A review of Mesozoic acanthopterygian fishes, with special reference to those of the English Chalk. *Phil. Trans. R. Soc.* **247B**, 213–482, pls. 2–5.

—— 1965. The Phylogeny of the Chimaeroids. *Phil. Trans. R. Soc.*, **249B**, 101–219, pls. 22–28.

—— 1966. British Wealden Sharks. *Bull. Brit. Mus. nat. Hist., Geol.*, **11**, 283–350, 5 plates.

—— 1967a. Are the teleosts a polyphyletic group? *Colloques int. Cent. natn. Rech. Scient.* (in press).

—— 1967b. A second specimen of the Cretaceous teleost *Protobrama* and the relationships of the suborder Tselfatioidei. *Ark. Zool.*, [in press].

PHILIP, G. M. & PEDDER, A. E. H. 1964. A Re-assessment of the Age of the Middle Devonian of South-Eastern Australia. *Nature, Lond.*, **202**, 1323–1324.

PITON, L. 1934. Les Cyprinodontes fossiles du Puy de Corent (Puy-de-Dôme). *Bull. mens. Soc. linn. Lyon*, **3**, 162–167, 1 fig.

PRUVOST, P. 1922. Description de *Denaea fournieri*, sélacien nouveau du Marbre noir de Denée. *Bull. Acad. r. Belg. Cl. Sci.* for 1922, 213–218, 1 fig.

RADE, J. 1964. Upper Devonian fish from the Mt. Jack area of New South Wales, Australia. *J. Paleont.*, **38**, 929–931.

RANDALL, J. E. 1955. An analysis of the genera of Surgeon fishes (Family Acanthuridae). *Pacif. Sci.*, **9**, 359–367.

RAYNER, D. H. 1963. The Achanarras Limestone of the Middle Old Red Sandstone, Caithness, Scotland. *Proc. Yorks. geol. Soc.*, **34**, 117–138.

REGAN, C. TATE. 1913. The Osteology and Classification of the Teleostean Fishes of the Order Scleroparei. *Ann. Mag. nat. Hist.* (8), **9**, 169–184, 5 figs.

REIS, O. M. 1896. Über *Acanthodes bronni* Agassiz. *Morphologische Arbeit, G. S̄chwalbē.*, **6**, 143–220.

ROEMER, F. 1857. Ueber Fisch- und Pflanzen-führende Mergelschiefer des Rothliegenden bei Klein-Neundorf unweit Löwenberg, und im Besonders über *Acanthodes gracilis*, den am häufigsten in denselben vorkommenden Fische. *Z. dt. geol. Ges.*, **9**, 51–83.

ROLFE, W. D. I. & DENISON, R. H. 1966. The supposed fish *Pseudodontichthys* Skeels, 1962, is the Phyllocarid crustacean *Dithyrocaris*. *J. Paleont.*, **40**, 214–215.

ROMER, A. S. 1930. The Pennsylvanian Tetrapods of Linton, Ohio. *Bull. Amer. Mus. nat. Hist.*, **59**, 77–147.

—— 1937. The Braincase of the Carboniferous Crossopterygian *Megalichthys nitidus*. *Bull. Mus. comp. Zool. Harv.*, **82**, 1–73.

—— 1945. *Vertebrate Palaeontology* (2nd edition), viii + 687 pp., Univ. Chicago Press.

—— & SMITH, H. J. 1934. American Carboniferous Dipnoans. *J. Geol.*, **42**, 700–719.

RUSSELL, L. S. 1951. Acanthodians of the Upper Devonian Escuminac Formation, Maguasha, Quebec. *Ann. Mag. nat. Hist.* (12), **4**, 401–407.

SAINT-SEINE, P. DE 1949 Les Poissons des Calcaires Lithographiques de Cerin (Ain). *Nouv. Archs Mus. Hist. nat. Lyon*, **2**, vii + 357 pp., 26 pls.

SANDERS, M. 1934. Die fossilen Fische der alttertiären Süsswasserablagerungen aus Mittel-Sumatra. *Verh. geol.-mijnb. Genoot. Ned.*, **11**, 1–143, pls. 1–9.

SANTOS, R. da S. & TRAVASSOS, H. 1956. *Procharax*, um novo gênero fóssil de caracídeo dos folhelos de Nova York, Estado do Maranhão. *Anais Acad. bras. Cienc.*, **28**, 297–322, pls. 1–7.

SÄVE-SÖDERBERGH, G. 1937. On *Rhynchodipterus elginensis* n.g., n.sp. *Ark. Zool.*, **29B**, No. 10, 1–5.

SCHAEFFER, B. 1962. A Coelacanth Fish from the Upper Devonian of Ohio. *Scient. Publs Cleveland Mus. nat. Hist.* (new Ser.), **1**, 1–13, pl. 1–4.

—— 1963. Cretaceous Fishes from Bolivia, with Comments on Pristid Evolution. *Am. Mus. Novit.*, **2159**, 20 pp., 6 figs.

SCHMIDT, W. 1961. Neue Vertebraten-Faunen in den Laucher und den Oberen Nohner Schichten (Devon, Eifelium) der Eifel. *Senckenberg. leth.*, **42**, 255–264.

SEILACHER, A. 1943. Elasmobranchier-Reste aus dem oberen Muschelkalk und dem Keuper Würtemburgs. *Neues Jb. Miner. Geol. Paläont. Mh.* (B), for 1943, 256–292, 50 figs.

SIGNEUX, J. 1949. Notes Paléoichthyologiques. *Bull. Mus. natn. Hist. nat., Paris*, **21**, 633–638, 3 figs.

—— 1959. Poissons et Reptiles marins du Gisement des phosphates maëstrichtiens de Roseifa (Jordanie). *Notes Mém. Moyen-Orient.*, **7**, 223–228, pl. 7.

SKEELS, M. A. 1962. Two new fishes from the Middle Devonian Silica formation, Lucas County, Ohio. *J. Paleont.*, **36**, 1039–1045, pl. 147.

STENSIÖ, E. A. 1918. Notes on a Crossopterygian Fish from the Upper Devonian of Spitzbergen. *Bull. geol. Instn Univ. Upsala*, **16**, 115–124, pl. 4–6.

—— 1921. *Triassic Fishes from Spitsbergen*, Part I. 307 pp., 35 pls. Vienna.

—— 1925a. On the head of the macropetalichthyids with certain remarks on the head of the other arthrodires. *Publs Field Mus. nat. Hist. geol. Series*, **232**, 91–197.

—— 1925b. Triassic fishes from Spitsbergen, Part II. *K. svenska VetenskAkad. Handl.*, (3), **2**, no. 1, 261 pp., 33 pls.

—— 1931. Upper Devonian vertebrates from East Greenland collected by the Danish Greenland Expeditions in 1929 and 1930. *Meddr Grønl.* **86**, no. 1, 212 pp.

—— 1932. Triassic Fishes from East Greenland collected by the Danish expeditions in 1929–31. *Meddr Grønl.*, **83**, no. 3, 345 pp.

—— 1934. On the Placodermi of the Upper Devonian of East Greenland. 1. Phyllolepida and Arthrodira. *Meddr Grønl.*, **97**, no. 1, 1–58.

—— 1936. On the Placodermi of the Upper Devonian of East Greenland Supplement to Part 1. *Meddr Grønl.*, **97**, no. 2, 1–52.

—— 1937. On the Devonian Coelacanthids of Germany with Special Reference to the Dermal Skeleton. *K. Svenska VetenskAkad. Handl.*, **16**, No. 4, 1–56, pl. I–XII.

—— 1939. On the Placodermi of the Upper Devonian of East Greenland. Second supplement to Part 1. *Meddr Grønl.*, **97**, No. 3. 1–33.

—— 1944. Contributions to the knowledge of the vertebrate fauna of the Silurian and Devonian of Western Podolia. 2. Notes on two arthrodires from the Downtonian of Podolia. *Ark. Zool.*, **35A**, 1–83.

—— 1963. The brain and cranial nerves in fossil, lower craniate vertebrates. *Skr. norske Vidensk-Akad*, **13**, 1–12.

STINTON, F. C. 1965. Teleost otoliths from the Lower London Tertiaries. *Senckenberg leth.*, **46a**, 389–425. pls 30–33.

—— 1966. *Fish Otoliths from the London Clay.* pp. 404–464, pls. 66–68 *in* Casier, E., *Faune Ichthyologique du London Clay.* London, British Museum (Natural History).

STROMER, E. 1927. Ergebnisse der Forschungsreisen Prof. E. Stromers in den Wüsten Ägyptens. II. Wirbeltier-Reste der Baharîje-Stufe (Unterstes Cenoman). 9. Die Plagiostomen. *Abh. bayer. Akad. Wiss.*, **31**, 5, 1–64, pls. 1–3.

—— 1936. Ergebnisse der Forschungsreisen Prof. E. Stromers in den Wüsten Ägyptens. VII. Baharîje-Kessel und -Stufe mit deren Fauna und Flora. *Abh. bayer. Akad. Wiss.* (N.F.), **33**, 102 pp., 1 pl.

THIENHAUS, R. 1940. Die Faziesverhältnisse im Südwestteil der Attendorner Mulde und ihre Bedeutung für die Stratigraphie des Bergisch-Sauerländischen Mittledevons. *Abh. Reichstelle Bodenforsch.*, **199**, 1–77.

THOMSON, K. S. 1964. Revised Generic Diagnoses of the Fossil Fishes *Megalichthys* and *Ectosteorhachis* (family Osteolepidae). *Bull. Mus. comp. Zool. Harv.*, **131**, 285–311, pl. 1.

TRAQUAIR, R. H. 1873. On *Phaneropleuron andersoni* (Huxley) and *Uronemus lobatus* (Agassiz). *J. Geol. Soc. Ireland*, **13**, 41–47, pl. V.

—— 1875. On the Structure and Affinities of *Tristichopterus alatus* Egerton. *Trans. Soc. Edinb.*, **27**, 383–396.

—— 1877–1914. The ganoid fish of the British Carboniferous formations. Part 1. Palaeoniscidae *Palaeontogr. Soc.* [*Monogr.*], **31**, 1–186, 40 pls., 14 text-figs.

—— 1888. Notes on the nomenclature of the fishes of the Old Red Sandstone of Great Britain. *Geol. Mag.*, **5**, 507–517.

—— 1897. Additional Notes on the Fossil Fishes of the Upper Old Red Sandstone of the Moray Firth Area. *Proc. R. phys. Soc. Edinb.*, **13**, 376–385.

VOIGT, E. 1934. Die Fisch aus der mitteleozänen Braunkohle des Geiselales. *Nova Acta Leopoldina* N.F., **2**, 21–146, pls. 1–13.

VOISEY, A. H. 1952. The Gondwana System in New South Wales. *19th Int. geol. Congr.* Symposium sur les Séries de Gondwana, Alger, 50–55.

VOROBJEVA, E. I. 1963. O Kisteperych Rybach Roda *Porolepis* iz Devona, S.S.S.R. *Paleont. Zh.* for 1963, no. 2, 83–92.

WATSON, D. M. S. 1937. The acanthodian fishes. *Phil. Trans. R. Soc.*, **228B**, 49–146.

—— & GILL, E. L. 1923. The Structure of Certain Palaeozoic Dipnoi. *J. Linn. Soc.* (**Zool.**), **35**, 163–216.

WEIGELT, J. 1930. Wichtige Fischreste aus dem Mansfelder Kupferschiefer. *Leopoldina*, **6**, 601–624, pls. 1–8.

WEILER, W. 1933. Zwei oligozäne Fischfaunen aus dem Königreich ungarn. *Geol. hung.*, Palaeont. series, **11**, 1–54, 3 pls.

—— 1935. Ergebnisse der Forschungsreisen Prof. E. Stromers in den Wüsten Ägyptens. II. Wirbeltierreste der Baharîje-Stufe (unterstes Cenoman). 16. Neue Untersuchungen an dem Fischresten. *Abh. bayer. Akad. Wiss.* N.F., **32**, 1–57, pls. 1–3.

—— 1947. Fische, pp. 17–18 *in* WILCKENS, O. Paläontologische und geologische Ergebnisse der Reise von Kohl-Larsen (1928–29) nach Sud-Georgien. *Abh. senckenb. naturforsch. Ges.*, **474**, 1–75, 7 pls.

—— 1955. Untersuchungen an der Fischfauna von Unter- und Oberkirchberg bei Ulm vornehmlich an Hand von Otolithen in situ. *Paläont. Z.*, **29**, 88–102, pl. 8.

WEITZEL, K. 1926. *Conchopoma gadiforme* Kner, ein Lungenfisch aus dem Rotliegenden. *Abh. senckenb. naturforsch. Ges.*, **40**, 159–178.

WEITZMAN, S. H. 1960a. The systematic position of Piton's presumed characid fishes from the Eocene of Central France. *Stanford ichthyol. Bull.*, **7**, 114–123, 2 figs.

—— 1960b. Further notes on characid fossils. *Stanford ichthyol. Bull.*, **7**, 215–216.

Wells, J. W. 1944. Fish remains from the Middle Devonian Bone Beds of the Cincinnati Arch region. *Palaeontogr. Am.*, **3,** 99–160, pls. 7–14.

Westoll, T. S. 1944. The Haplolepidae, a New Family of Late Carboniferous Bony Fishes. *Bull. Am. Mus. nat. Hist.*, **83,** Art. 1, 1–121.

—— 1949. On the Evolution of the Dipnoi *in*, G. L. Jepsen, G. G. Simpson, & E. Mayr (Editors) *Genetics, Palaeontology, and Evolution.* 121–184. Princeton University Press.

—— 1951. The Vertebrate-Bearing Strate of Scotland. *18th Int. geol. Cong.*, Pt. 9, 5–21.

White, E. I. 1926. Eocene Fishes from Nigeria. *Bull. geol. Surv. Nigeria*, **10,** 1–87, pls. 1–18.

—— 1931. *The Vertebrate faunas of the English Eocene. Vol.* 1. *From the Thanet Sands to the Basement Bed of the London Clay.* xiv + 123 pp., 1 pl. London, British Museum Natural History.

—— 1954. More about the Coelacanths. *Discovery*, **15,** 332–335.

—— 1957. The Eocene fishes of Alabama. *Bull. Am. Paleont.*, **36,** 123–150, pl. 1.

Whiteaves, J. F. 1881. On Some Remarkable Fossil Fishes from the Devonian Rocks of Scaumenac Bay, P.Q., with Descriptions of a New Genus, and three New Species. *Canadian Naturalist*, **10,** (2), 27–35.

Whitley, G. P. 1956. The Story of *Galaxias*. *Aust. Mus. Mag.*, **12,** 30–34, 3 figs.

Woodward, A. S. 1888. Note on the Occurrence of a Species of *Onychodus* in the Lower Old Red Sandstone Passage Beds of Ledbury, Herefordshire. *Geol. Mag.*, **25,** 500–501.

—— 1889. *Catalogue of the fossil fishes in the British Museum (Natural History).* **1,** xlvii + 474 pp., 17 pls. London, British Museum (Natural History).

—— 1891. *Catalogue of the fossil fishes in the British Museum (Natural History).* **2,** xliv + 567 pp., 16 pls. London, British Museum (Natural History).

—— 1895. *Catalogue of the fossil fishes in the British Museum (Natural History).* **3.** xliii + 544 pp., 18 pls. London, British Museum (Natural History).

—— 1901. *Catalogue of the fossil fishes in the British Museum (Natural History).* **4.** xxxviii 636 pp., 19 pls. London, British Museum (Natural History).

—— 1906. On a Carboniferous Fish Fauna from the Mansfield District, Victoria. *Mem. natn Mus., Melb.*, No. 1, 1–32, pl. I–XI.

—— 1909. The Fishes of the English Chalk. Pt. V. *Palaeontographical Soc.* [*Monogr.*], **63,** No. 3, 153–184, 6 pl.

—— 1917. On a New Species of *Edestus* from the Upper Carboniferous of Yorkshire. *Q. Jl. geol. Soc. Lond.*, **72,** 1–5, pl. 1.

—— 1919. On two new Elasmobranch Fishes (*Crossorhinus jurassicus*, sp. nov., and *Protospinax annectans*, gen. et sp. nov.) from the Upper Jurassic Lithographic Stone of Bavaria. *Proc. zool. Soc. Lond.*, for 1918, 231–235, pl. 1.

—— 1924. Un nouvel Elasmobranche (*Cratoselache pruvosti* gen. et sp. nov.) du calcaire carbonifère inférieur de Denée. *Liège. Soc. Géol. Belg. Livre jubilaire*, 59–62.

—— 1932. A Cretaceous Pristiophorid Shark. *Ann. Mag. Nat. Hist.* (10), **10,** 476–478, pl. 18.

—— 1942. Some new and little known Upper Cretaceous fishes from Mount Lebanon. *Ann. Mag. Nat. Hist.* (11), **9,** 537–568, pls. 3–7.

—— & Sherborn, C. D. 1890. *A catalogue of British Fossil Vertebrata.* xxxv + 396 pp. London.

Yates, P. J. 1962. The Palaeontology of the Namurian rocks of Slieve Anierin, Co. Leitrim, Eire. *Palaeontology*, **5,** 355–443, pls. 51–62.

S. M. Andrews, m.a.
Department of Geology, The University, Newcastle-upon-Tyne.

B. G. Gardiner, ph.d. a.r.c.s. f.g.s.
Department of Biology, Queen Elizabeth College, Campden Hill Road, London w 8.

R. S. Miles, ph.d.
Department of Geology, Royal Scottish Museum, Edinburgh 1, Scotland.

C. Patterson, ph.d.
Department of Palaeontology, British Museum (Natural History), Cromwell Road, London s w 7.

CHAPTER 27

Amphibia

Contributor: A. L. PANCHEN

Introduction. The Palaeozoic Amphibia ('Stegocephalia') are divided into two subclasses on the character of their vertebrae—the Labyrinthodontia and the Lepospondyli. The relationship of the three extant orders—Salientia, Urodela and Apoda—to the stegocephalians and to one another is a matter of debate.

The Salientia are often included with the labyrinthodonts as Apsidospondyli, while the Urodela and Apoda are included in the lepospondyls (Watson 1940, Romer 1947). A wider dichotomy is proposed by Jarvik (1942, 1965) who concludes that the urodeles (and possibly the Apoda) are descended from a group of rhipidistian fishes distinct from that which gave rise to the remaining Amphibia and all other tetrapods. This view has been opposed by Thomson (1962, 1964a, 1964b) amongst others.

The arrangement adopted here is based on the assumption that the living orders are fairly closely related to one another and may be grouped as the Lissamphibia (Parsons and Williams 1963). Evidence of the relationship of the Lissamphibia to the stegocephalians is unsatisfactory and it is therefore preferable to recognise three independent subclasses: Labyrinthodontia, Lepospondyli and Lissamphibia (Baird 1965).

Subclass LABYRINTHODONTIA Owen 1861

Order ICHTHYOSTEGALIA Säve-Söderbergh 1932

First, Dev Famenn or Carb Tourn: *Ichthyostega* and *Ichthyostegopsis* spp. Säve-Söderbergh 1932 and *Acanthostega gunnari* Jarvik 1952, Remigolepis Series, E. Greenland (Jarvik 1952, Westoll 1940). *Elpistostege watsoni* Westoll 1938, Dev Frasn, may be an ichthyostegid ancestor (fish or amphibian). *Otocratia modesta* Watson 1929, Carb Viséan, may be an ichthyostegid. *Colosteus* and *Erpetosaurus*, Carb Moscov, are not ichthyostegids (Jarvik 1952, Romer 1947).

Last, all forms attributed to the Ichthyostegalia are noted above.

Constituent families: Ichthyostegidae Säve-Söderbergh; Acanthostegidae Jarvik.

Order TEMNOSPONDYLI Zittel 1889
(Classification, to families, as in Romer 1947 unless otherwise noted.)

Suborder RHACHITOMI

Superfamily LOXOMMOIDEA

Family LOXOMMIDAE

First, Carb Viséan: *Loxomma allmanni* Huxley 1862, Gilmerton Ironstone, Scotland (Watson 1929).

The Fossil Record, pp. 685–694. Geological Society of London, 1967. Printed in Northern Ireland.

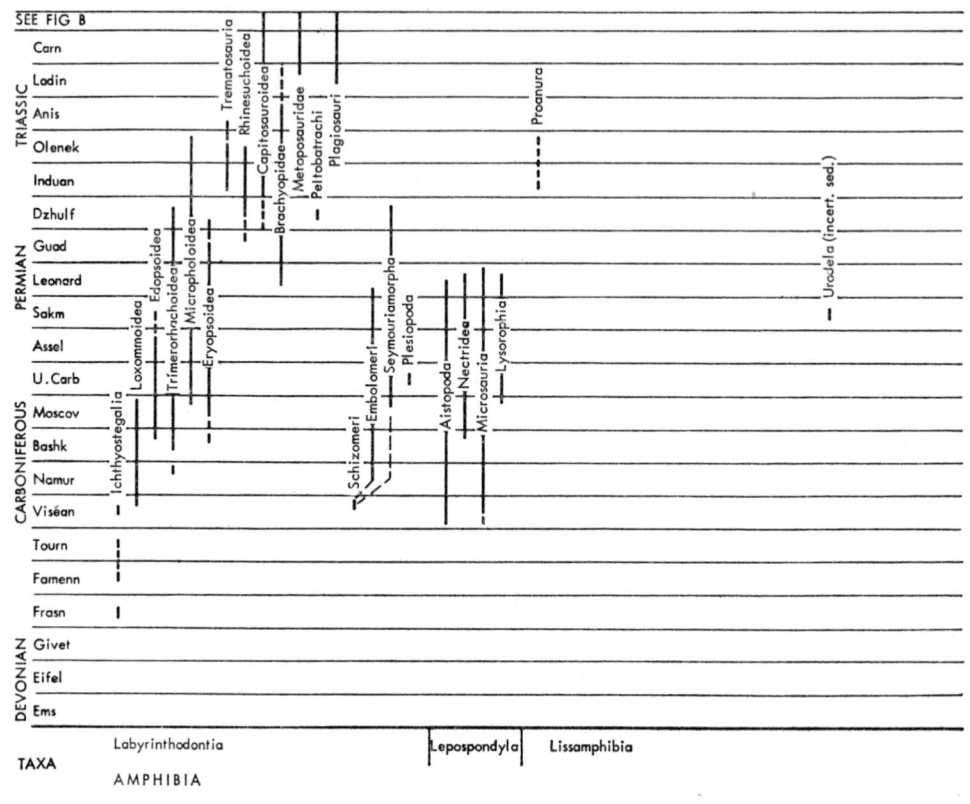

TAXA   Labyrinthodontia   Lepospondyla   Lissamphibia

AMPHIBIA

CONTRIBUTORS   A. L. Panchen

FIG. 27.1 A

Last, Carb Moscov: *Megalocephalus lineolatus* (Cope) and *M.* sp., U. Freeport Coal, Linton, Ohio and Gaskohle, Nýřany, Czechoslovakia (Steen 1938, Baird 1957).

Superfamily EDOPSOIDEA

First, Carb Bashk: *Dendrerpeton acadianum* Owen 1853 (*Dendryazouza, Dendrysekos, Platystegos* are probably congeneric), Joggins Fm, Nova Scotia (Steen 1934, Baird 1962).

Last, Perm Assel or Sakm: *Edops craigi* Romer 1936, Moran Fm, Texas (Romar & Witter 1942).

Constituent families: Edopsidae, Carb Moscov-Perm Assel; Dendrerpetontidae, Carb Bashk; Cochleosauridae, Carb Moscov.

Superfamily TRIMERORHACHOIDEA

First, Carb Bashk: *Eugyrinus wildi* (Woodward 1891), Bullion Coal, Lancs., England (Panchen & Walker 1961). Smithsonian specimen U.S.N.M. 22576, Carb Namur, Hinton Shales, W. Virginia, is a possible trimerorhachoid (Romer 1941, Hotton, pers. comm.).

Last, Perm Dzhulf: *Dvinosaurus primus* Amalitsky 1924, Sarma Fm (Z. IV), Dvina Basin, U.S.S.R. (Bystrow 1938, Romer 1947).

Constituent families: Peliontidae, Carb Bashk-Carb Moscov; Trimerorhachidae, ?Carb Namur-Perm Guad; Dvinosauridae, Perm Dzhulf; ?Colosteidae Cope 1875, Carb Moscov.

Superfamily MICROPHOLOIDEA

First, Carb Moscov: *Potamochoston limnaios* Steen 1938, Gaskohle, Nýřany, Czechoslovakia (Steen 1938).

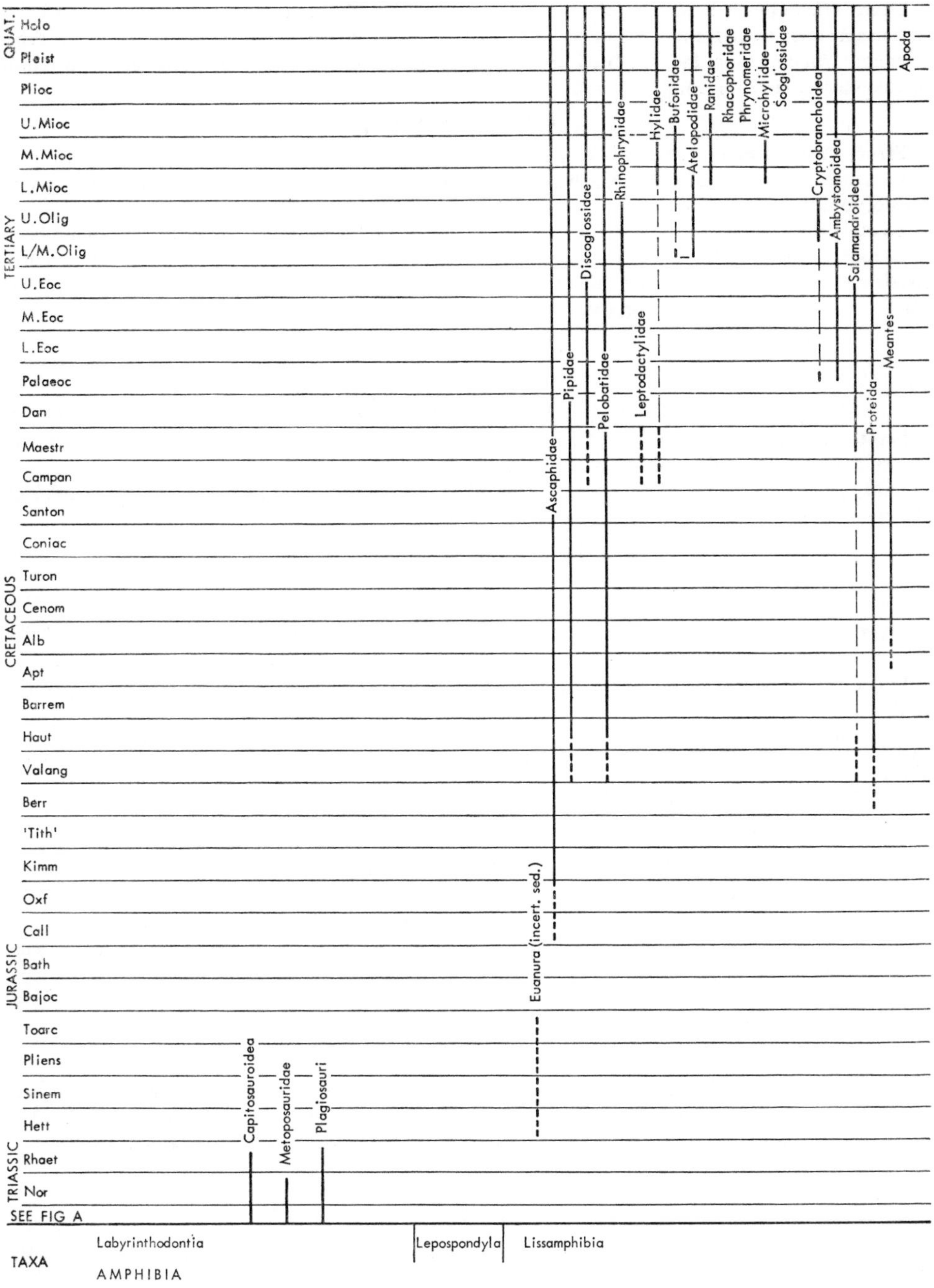

FIG. 27.1 B

Last, Trias Olenek: *Micropholis stowi* Owen 1876, Procolophon Z., S. Africa (Romer 1947)·
Constituent families: Lysipterygiidae, Carb Moscov-Perm ?Sakm; Micropholidae, Trias Olenek; Chenoprosopidae, Carb Moscov-Perm Assel or Sakm; Archegosauridae, Perm Sakm or Leonard-Guad or Dzhulf.

Superfamily ERYOPSOIDEA

First, Carb Moscov: *Amphibamus grandiceps* Cope 1865, Nodule Bed, Mazon Creek, Illinois. *Arkanserpeton arcuatum* Lane 1932, Carb Bashk or Moscov, Paris Shale, Kansas may be an Eryopsoid (Dissorophid) (Carroll 1964).
Last, Perm Guad or Dzhulf: c.f. *Zygosaurus* Eichwald 1848 sp., Z. III, U.S.S.R. (Romer 1947).
Constituent families: Eryopsidae, Perm Assel-Sakm or Leonard; Trematopsidae, Perm Assel or Sakm-Leonard; Dissorophidae, Carb Bashk or Moscov-Perm Guad or Dzhulf; Zatrachydidae, Carb Moscov-Perm Leonard.

Suborder TREMATOSAURIA

Family TREMATOSAURIDAE

First, Trias Induan: *Gonioglyptus kokeni* Huene 1920, Prionolobus Z., India, and *Stoschiosaurus nielseni* Säve-Söderbergh 1935, "Eotrias", E. Greenland (Piveteau 1955).
Last, Trias Olenek or Anis: *Trematosuchus sobeyi* (Haughton 1915), Cynognathus Z., S. Africa (Piveteau 1955). [Not Anis, Fig. 27.1A.]

Suborder STEREOSPONDYLI

Superfamily RHINESUCHOIDEA

First, Perm Guad or Dzhulf: *Rhinesuchus avenanti* Boonstra 1940, *R. whaitsi* Broom 1908, *Rhinesuchoides tenuiceps* Olson and Broom 1937, Tapinocephalus Z., S. Africa (Romer 1947).
Last, Trias Olenek: *Sclerothorax hypselonotus* Huene 1932, Bunter, Hessen, Germany (Romer 1947).
Constituent families: Rhinesuchidae, Guad or Dzhulf-Dzhulf, Tapinocephalus-Endothiodon (?Kistecephalus) Z.; Lydekkerinidae, Trias Induan or Olenek, Lystrosaurus Z.; Uranocentrodontidae, Kistecephalus-Lystrosaurus Z.; Sclerothoracidae, Induan-Olenek.

Superfamily CAPITOSAUROIDEA

First, Perm ?Dzhulf: *Gondwanosaurus bijorensis* Lydekker 1885, Damuda Series, India (Romer 1947).
Last, Trias Rhaet: c.f. *Cyclotosaurus* (*"Hercynosaurus"* Jaekel 1914), Halberstadt, Germany. *Australopelor wadleyi* Longman 1941 is a jaw fragment ?capitosaur, ?Jur., Marburg Series, Queensland, Australia (Romer 1947).
Constituent families: Benthosuchidae, Perm Dzhulf-Trias Olenek; Capitosauridae, Trias Induan or Olenek-Rhaet.

Superfamily BRACHYOPOIDEA

General comments: The plagiosaurs have here been removed from the Brachyopoidea of Romer's (1947) classification in agreement with Nilsson (1939) and Panchen (1959). The remaining two families are probably not closely related, and are treated separately.

Family BRACHYOPIDAE

First, Perm Leonard: *Eobrachyops townendae* Watson 1956, Clear Fork, Texas (Watson 1956).
Last, Trias ?Ladin: *Pelorocephalus mendozensis* Cabrera 1944, Cacheuta Beds, Mendoza, Argentina (Romer 1947).

Family METOPOSAURIDAE

First, Trias Ladin: *"Trigonosternum latum"* Schmidt 1931, Lettenkohle, Thuringia, Germany (Romer 1947).

Last, Trias Nor: *Metoposaurus diagnosticus* ("*M. stuttgartiensis*" Fraas 1913) Lehrbergstufe, nr. Stuttgart, Germany. All other metoposaurs are from the Keuper (s.s.) or Keuper equivalents, thus Carn-Nor (Colbert & Imbrie 1956, Romer 1947).

Order PLAGIOSAURIA Nilsson 1939

Suborder PELTOBATRACHI Panchen 1959

First and **Last,** Perm Dzhulf: *Peltobatrachus pustulatus* Panchen 1959, "Lower Bone Bed", Ruhuhu, Tanzania (Panchen 1959).

Suborder PLAGIOSAURI Jaekel 1914

Family PLAGIOSAURIDAE Romer 1947

First, Trias Ladin: *Plagiosuchus pustuloglomeratus* Huene 1922, Crailsheim Bonebed, U. Muschelkalk, Swabia, Germany. *Plagiosternum* (same locality and horizon) may not be a plagiosaur (Romer 1947, Panchen 1959).

Last, Trias Rhaet: *Gerrothorax rhaeticus* Nilsson 1934, above "L. Coal Measures", Scania, Sweden (Nilsson 1946).

Order ANTHRACOSAURIA Watson 1917

Suborder SCHIZOMERI Romer 1964

First and **Last,** Carb Viséan: *Pholidogaster pisciformis* Huxley 1862, Gilmerton Ironstone, Scotland (Romer 1964).

Suborder EMBOLOMERI Cope 1885

First, Carb Namur: "*Pholiderpeton*" *bretonense* Romer 1958, Pt. Edward Fm, Nova Scotia, also undescribed anthracosaur material Hinton Shales, W. Virginia (Romer 1941, 1963).

Last, Perm Leonard: *Archeria* Case 1915 sp., Clyde Fm, Clear Fork Group, Texas (Romer 1947, 1958).

Constituent families: the natural division of embolomeres into families requires new comparative treatment of the material.

Suborder SEYMOURIAMORPHA Watson 1917

First, Carb Moscov: *Diplovertebron punctatum* Fritsch 1889, Gaskohle, Nýřany, Czechoslovakia, and *Diplovertebron digitatum* (Cope 1875), U. Freeport Coal, Linton, Ohio (Romer 1947). *Diplovertebron = Gephyrostegus = "Solenodonsaurus"* of Pearson = *Eusauropleura*, non *Solenodonsaurus* Broili (Baird 1964 & per. comm.).

Last, Perm Dzhulf: *Kotlassia prima* Amalitsky 1921 Sarma Fm, (Zone IV) Dvina basin, U.S.S.R. *Buzulukia butsuri* Viushkov 1957, *Kotlassia* sp., Pronkino (Zone IV) Chkalov Province, U.S.S.R. *Bystrowiana permira* Viushkov 1957, Vyazniki (Zone IV), Vladimir Province, U.S.S.R. and *Kotlassia* spp. in Zone IV, other localities, U.S.S.R. (Bystrow 1944, Viushkov 1957, Olson 1957).

Constituent families: Diplovertebrontidae, Carb Moscov; Discosauriscidae, Perm Assel or Sakm-?Guad; Seymouriidae, Perm Assel or Sakm-?Guad; Kotlassiidae, Perm Dzhulf; ?Lanthanosuchidae Efremov 1947, Perm Guad; Waggoneriidae Olson 1951, Perm Leonard; Bystrowianidae Viushkov 1957, Perm Dzhulf. (Families as Romer 1947 or as stated).

Order PLESIOPODA Eaton & Stewart 1960

First and **Last,** Carb U. Carb: *Hesperoherpeton garnettense* Peabody 1958, Rock Lake Sh, Stanton Fm, Garnett, Kansas (Eaton & Stewart 1960).

The Fossil Record, Part II

Subclass LEPOSPONDYLI Zittel 1889

Order AÏSTOPODA Miall 1875

First, Carb Viséan: "*Ophiderpeton*" sp. of Stock 1882, L. Oil Shale Group, Wardie, nr. Edinburgh, Scotland (Baird 1964).

Last, Perm Leonard: *Phlegothontia* Cope 1981 sp., Arroyo Fm, Clear Fork Group, Fort Sill, Oklahoma (Baird 1964).

Constituent families: Ophiderpetontidae, Carb Bashk-U. Carb; Phlegothontiidae, Carb Bashk-Perm Leonard (Baird 1964).

Order NECTRIDEA Miall 1875

First, Carb Bashk: *Batrachiderpeton lineatum* Hancock & Atthey 1870 and *Keraterpeton reticulatum* (Hancock & Atthey 1869), Low Main Seam, Newsham, Northumberland, England (Piveteau 1955, Steen 1938).

Last, Perm Leonard: *Diplocaulus recurvatus* Olson 1952, Choza Fm, Clear Fork Group, Texas (Olson 1958).

Constituent families: Lepterpetontidae, Carb Bashk-?Perm Assel or Sakm; Keraterpetontidae, Carb Bashk-Perm Leonard; Urocordylidae, Carb Bashk-Perm Assel or Sakm (Piveteau 1955, Olson 1958).

Order MICROSAURIA Dawson 1863

First, Carb Viséan: *Dolichopareias disjectus* Watson 1929, Burdiehouse, Scotland. An earlier unnamed lepospondyl, Carb Viséan, Pumpherston No. 3 Curley Shale, Scotland, may also be a microsaur (Westoll 1951).

Last, Perm Leonard: *Cymatorhiza kittsi* Olson & Barghusen 1962, Flowerpot Fm, Kingfisher Co., Oklahoma (Olson & Barghusen 1962).

Constituent families: Dolichopareiidae, Carb Viséan; Adelogyrinidae, Carb Viséan; Microbrachidae, Carb Bashk-Moscov; Gymnarthridae, Perm Sakm-Leonard (Piveteau 1955).

Order LYSOROPHIA Williston 1908

Family LYSOROPHIDAE

First, Carb Moscov; *Cocytinus gyrinoides* Cope 1871, *Molgophis* Cope 1868 sp. (? = *Pleuroptyx clavatus* Cope 1875), U. Freeport Coal, Linton, Ohio (Steen 1931).

Last, Perm Leonard: *Lysorophus ?tricarinatus* Cope 1877, Choza Fm, Clear Fork Group, Texas (Olson 1958).

Subclass LISSAMPHIBIA Haeckel 1866

Order SALIENTIA Laurenti 1768 (ANURA Duméril 1806)

Suborder PROAN(O)URA Piveteau 1937

First and **Last,** Trias "L. Trias" ? stage (derived): *Protobatrachus massinoti* Piveteau 1937, Madagascar (Piveteau 1955). *Amphibamus* (= *Miobatrachus* = *Mazonerpeton*), ("Suborder Eoanura", Romer 1945) Carb Moscov, is not a salientian or, probably a salientian ancestor (Gregory 1950). Possible salientian footprints occur Perm Leonard, Ecca Fm, S. Africa (Griffiths 1963).

Comment: unique *Protobatrachus* type may be a larval form, thus questionably separable from other Anura (Griffiths 1963), or possibly not related to other Anura (Hecht 1962).

Suborder EUAN(O)URA Piveteau 1937

General Comments: The accepted major subdivisions of the Euanura are unsatisfactory: recent families as in Griffiths 1963. In the present state of knowledge all fossil frogs not referable to extant families must be *incertae sedis* (Griffiths 1963, Hecht 1963).

Chapter 27: Amphibia

Family INCERTAE SEDIS

First, Jur "Lias": *Vieraella herbstii* Reig 1961, Roca Blanca Fm, Patagonia, Argentina (Reig 1961).

Family ASCAPHIDAE Fejérváry 1923

First, Jur ?Call or Oxf: *Notobatrachus deguistoi* Reig 1957, Matilde Fm, Patagonia, Argentina (Griffiths 1963). **Extant.**

Family PIPIDAE Günther 1858

First, Cret ?Valang: unnamed pipid Nevo 1956, Lacustrine deposits, Makhtesh Ramon, Negev, Israel (Nevo 1956, 1964, Griffiths 1963 Addendum). *Eobatrachus agilis* Marsh 1887, Jur Kimm or "Tith", may be a pipid (Hecht & Ester 1960). **Extant.**

Family DISCOGLOSSIDAE Günther 1858

First, Cret "late Cret.": unnamed discoglossid, Wyoming (Hecht 1963). *Eodiscoglossus santonjae* Villalta, U. Jur. N. Spain may be discoglossid or ascaphid (Hecht 1963). **Extant.**

Family PELOBATIDAE Lataste 1879

First, Cret ?Valang: unnamed ?pelobatid tadpole Nevo 1956, Lacustrine deposits, Makhtesh Ramon, Negev, Israel (Nevo 1956, 1964). Pelobatids may also occur in the late Cret. of Wyoming (Hecht 1963). **Extant.**

Family RHINOPHRYNIDAE Günther 1858

First, Tert M. Eoc: *Eorhinophrynus septentrionalis* Hecht 1959, locality 5, late Bridgerian, Tabernacle Butte, Wyoming (Hecht 1959). **Extant.**

Family LEPTODACTYLIDAE Stejneger & Barbour 1917

First, Tert L. Eoc: *Eophractus casamayorensis* Schaeffer 1949, "Bird Clay", Casamayoran Stage, nr. Pass Niemann, Argentina (Schaeffer 1949). *Comobatrachus aenigmatis* Hecht & Estes 1960, Jur Kimm or "Tith", may have leptodactyloid affinity also leptodactylids may also occur in late Cret., Wyoming (Hecht 1963, Hecht & Estes 1960). [Not Cret, Fig. 27.1B]. **Extant.**

Family HYLIDAE Günther 1858

First, Tert L. Mioc: *Hyla goini* Auffenberg 1956 and *Proacris mintoni* Holman 1961, Thomas Farm deposits, Hawthorne Fm, Gilchrist Co., Florida (Auffenberg 1956, Holman 1961). Hylids may possibly occur in the late Cret. of Wyoming (Hecht 1963). **Extant.**

Family BUFONIDAE Hogg 1841

First, Tert L. Mioc: *Bufo praevius* Tihen 1962, Thomas Farm deposits, Hawthorne Fm, Gilchrist County, Florida (Tihen 1962). *Neoprocoela edentata* Schaeffer 1949, Tert L. Olig, Argentina, has been interpreted as a bufonid (Tihen 1962). **Extant.**

Family ATELOPODIDAE Fitzinger 1843

First, Tert L/M.Olig: *Neoprocoela edentata* Schaeffer 1949, Sarmientan Group, Sierra Canquel, Patagonia, Argentina (Schaeffer 1949, Griffiths 1963). This species, though probably an atelopodid ancestor, has been interpreted as a bufonid. (*Bufo edentatus* Tihen) and a leptodactylid (Tihen 1962, Hecht 1963). **Extant.**

Family RANIDAE Linn. 1758

First, Tert L. Mioc: *Rana* sp. ("*pipiens* group") Thomas Farm deposits, Hawthorne Fm, Gilchrist County, Florida (Auffenberg 1956). **Extant.**

Family RHACOPHORIDAE

No known fossil record.

Family PHRYNOMERIDAE

No known fossil record.

Family MICROHYLIDAE Günther 1858

First, Tert L. Mioc: *Microhyla* sp., Thomas Farm deposits, Hawthorne Fm, Gilchrist Co., Florida (Auffenberg 1956). **Extant.**

Family SOOGLOSSIDAE Griffiths 1963

No known fossil record.

Order URODELA Fischer 1813 (CAUDATA Duméril 1806).
(Classification as in Noble 1931).

Suborder INCERTAE SEDIS

First, Perm Sakm: ?urodele vertebrae etc. in coprolite, Cutler Fm, Welles Quarry, Arroyo de Agua, Rio Arriba Co., New Mexico (Vaughn 1963).

Suborder CRYPTOBRANCHOIDEA Dunn 1922

First, L/M. Olig: *Andrias scheuchzeri* (Holl 1831), "Blätterkohle", Bonn, Germany (Westphal 1958). *Wolterstorffiella wiggeri*, Tert Palaeoc, has been interpreted as a cryptobranchoid (hynobiid). **Extant.**

Constituent families: Cryptobranchidae, Tert L/M. Olig-Holo; Hynobiidae, ?Tert Palaeoc-Holo.

Suborder AMBYSTOMOIDEA

Family AMBYSTOMATIDAE Hallowell 1858

First. Tert Palaeoc, *Ambystomichnus montanensis* (Gilmore 1928), Fort Union beds, Bear Butte, Sweetgrass Co., Montana (Peabody 1954), and *Wolterstorffiella wiggeri* Herre 1950, Walbeck, Germany (Herre 1950). **Extant.**

Suborder SALAMANDROIDEA Cope 1890

First, Cret Maestr: *Opisthotriton kayi* Auffenberg 1961, Lance Fm, Niobrara Co., Wyoming (Auffenberg 1961). Specimens from Cret ?Valang, Negev, Israel, may be salamandroids (Nevo 1964). **Extant.**

Constituent families: Salamandridae, Cret Maestr-Holo; Plethodontidae, Tert Palaeoc-Holo; Amphiumidae, Pleist-Holo (Goin & Goin 1962).

Suborder PROTEIDA Cope 1866

Family PROTEIDAE Tschudi 1839

First, Cret Berr or Valang: *Hylaeobatrachus croyii* Dollo 1884, Wealden facies, Bernissart, Belgium (Piveteau 1955). *Comonecturoides marshi,* Jur Kimm or "Tith", Quarry Nine, Como Bluff. Wyoming may be a proteid (Hecht & Estes 1960). **Extant.**

Suborder MEANTES Linn. 1766

Family SIRENIDAE Gray 1825

First, Cret Apt or Alb: *Prosiren elinorae* Goin & Auffenberg 1958, Trinity beds, nr. Forestburg, Montague Co., Texas (Goin & Auffenberg 1958). **Extant.**

Order APODA Oppel 1811 (GYMNOPHIONA Müller 1831)

Family CAECILIIDAE Hoffman 1878

No known fossil record.

REFERENCES

Auffenberg, W. 1956. Remarks on some Miocene anurans from Florida, with a description of a new species of *Hyla. Breviora,* **52,** 1–11.

—— 1961. A new genus of fossil salamander from North America. *Am. Midl. Nat.,* **66,** 456–465.

Baird, D. 1957. Rhachitomous vertebrae in the loxommid amphibian *Megalocephalus. Bull. geol. Soc. Am.,* **68,** 1698.

—— 1962. A haplolepid fish fauna in the early Pennsylvanian of Nova Scotia. *Palaeontology,* **5,** 22–29.

—— 1964. The aistopod amphibians surveyed. *Breviora,* **206,** 1–17.

—— 1965. Paleozoic lepospondyl amphibians. *Am. Zool. Utica,* **5,** 287–294.

Bystrow, A. P. 1938. *Dvinosaurus* als neotenische Form der Stegocephalen. *Acta zool., Stockh.,* **19,** 209–295.

—— 1944. *Kotlassia prima* Amalitzky. *Bull. geol. Soc. Am.,* **55,** 379–416.

Carroll, R. L. 1964. Early evolution of the dissorophid amphibians. *Bull. Mus. comp. Zool. Harv.,* **131,** 161–250.

Colbert, E. H. & Imbrie, J. 1956. Triassic metoposaurid amphibians. *Bull. Am. Mus. nat. Hist.,* **110,** 403–452.

Eaton, T. H. & Stewart, P. L. 1960. A new order of fishlike Amphibia from the Pennsylvanian of Kansas. *Univ. Kans. Publs Mus. nat. Hist.,* **12,** 217–240.

Goin, C. J. & Auffenberg, W. 1958. New salamanders of the family Sirenidae from the Cretaceous of North America. *Fieldiana: Geol.,* **10,** 449–459.

—— & Goin, O. B. 1962. *Introduction to Herpetology.* San Francisco & London: Freeman.

Gregory, J. T. 1950. Tetrapods of the Pennsylvanian nodules from Mazon Creek, Illinois. *Am. J. Sci.,* **248,** 833–873.

Griffiths, I. 1963. The phylogeny of the Salientia. *Biol. Rev.,* **38,** 241–292.

Hecht, M. K. 1959. Amphibia and Reptiles *in* McGrew, P. O. The geology and paleontology of the Elk Mountain and Tabernacle Butte area, Wyoming. *Bull. Am. Mus. nat. Hist.,* **117,** 130–146.

—— 1962. A reevaluation of the early history of the frogs. Part I. *Syst. Zool.,* **11,** 39–44.

—— 1963. A reevaluation of the early history of the frogs. Part II. *Syst. Zool.,* **12,** 20–35.

—— & Estes, R. 1960. Fossil amphibians from Quarry Nine. *Postilla,* **46,** 1–19.

Herre, W. 1950. Schwanzlurche aus dem Paleocän von Walbeck. *Zool. Anz.,* **145,** *Supplement,* 286–301.

Holman, J. A. 1961. A new hylid genus from the Lower Miocene of Florida. *Copeia,* **1961,** 354–355.

Jarvik, E. 1942. On the structure of the snout of crossopterygians and lower gnathostomes in general. *Zool. Bidr. Upps.,* **21,** 235–675.

—— 1952. On the fish-like tail in the ichthyostegid stegocephalians. *Meddr Grønl.,* **114,** No. 12, 1–90.

—— 1965. Specialisation in early vertebrates. *Annls Soc. r. zool. Belg.,* **94,** 11–95.

Nevo, A. R. (or E.) 1956. Fossil frogs from a Lower Cretaceous bed in southern Israel. *Nature, Lond.,* **178,** 1191–1192.

—— 1964. Fossil urodeles in early Lower Cretaceous deposits of Makhtesh Ramon, Israel. *Nature, Lond.,* **201,** 415–416.

Nilsson, T. 1939. Cleithrum und Humerus der Stegocephalen und rezenten Amphibien. *Acta Univ. lund.* (2), **35,** (10) 1–39.

—— 1946. A new find of *Gerrothorax rhaeticus* Nilsson a plagiosaurid from the Rhaetic of Scania. *Acta Univ. lund* (2), **42,** 1—42.

Noble, G. K. 1931. *The Biology of the Amphibia.* New York: McGraw-Hill.

Olson, E. C. 1957. Catalogue of localities of the Permian and Triassic terrestrial vertebrates of the territories of the U.S.S.R. *J. Geol.,* **65,** 196–226.

—— 1958. Fauna of the Vale and Choza: 14: Summary, review, and integration of the geology and the faunas. *Fieldiana: Geol.,* **10,** 397–448.

—— & Barghusen, H. 1962. Permian vertebrates from Oklahoma and Texas. Pt. I. Vertebrates from the Flowerpot Formation. *Circ. Okla. geol., Surv.*, **59**, 1–48.

Panchen, A. L. 1959. A new armoured amphibian from the Upper Permian of East Africa. *Phil. Trans. R. Soc.*, **242B**, 207–281.

—— & Walker, A. D. 1961. British Coal Measure labyrinthodont localities. *Ann. Mag. nat. Hist.* (13), **3**, 321–332.

Parsons, T. S. & Williams, E. E. 1963. The relationships of the modern Amphibia: a re-examination. *Q. Rev. Biol.*, **38**, 26–53.

Peabody, F. E. 1954. Trackways of an ambystomid salamander from the Paleocene of Montana. *J. Palaeont.*, **28**, 79–83.

Piveteau, J. (Editor) 1955. *Traité de Paléontologie*, **5**. Paris: Masson.

Reig, O. A. 1961. Noticia sobre un nuevo anuro fosil del Jurasico de Santa Cruz (Patagonia). *Ameghiniana*, **11**, (5) 73–78.

Romer, A. S. 1941. Earliest land vertebrates of this continent. *Science, N.Y.*, **94**, 279.

—— 1947. Review of the Labyrinthodontia. *Bull. Mus. comp. Zool. Harv.*, **99**, 1–368.

—— 1958. The Texas Permian Redbeds and their vertebrate fauna in *Studies on fossil vertebrates presented to D.M.S. Watson*. London: Athlone Press.

—— 1963. The larger embolomerous amphibians of the American Carboniferous. *Bull. Mus. comp. Zool. Harv.*, **128**, 415–454.

—— 1964. The skeleton of the Lower Carboniferous labyrinthodont *Pholidogaster pisciformis*. *Bull. Mus. comp. Zool. Harv.*, **131**, 129–159.

—— & Witter, R. V. 1942. *Edops* a primitive rhachitomous amphibian from the Texas red beds. *J. Geol.*, **50**, 925–960.

Schaeffer, B. 1949. Anurans from the early Tertiary of Patagonia. *Bull. Am. Mus. nat. Hist.*, **93**, 45–68.

Steen, M. C. 1931. The British Museum collection of Amphibia from the Middle Coal Measures of Linton, Ohio. *Proc. zool. Soc. Lond.*, **1930**, 949–891.

—— 1934. The amphibian fauna from the South Joggins, Nova Scotia. *Proc. zool. Soc. Lond.*, **1934**, 465–504.

—— 1938. On the fossil Amphibia from the Gas Coal of Nýřany and other deposits in Czechoslovakia. *Proc. zool. Soc. Lond.* (B), **108**, 205–283.

Thomson, K. S. 1962. Rhipidistian classification in relation to the origin of the tetrapods. *Breviora*, **177**, 1–12.

—— 1964a. The ancestry of the tetrapods. Sci. Progr., **52**, 451–459.

—— 1964b. The comparative anatomy of the snout in rhipidistian fishes. *Bull. Mus. comp. Zool. Harv.*, **131**, 313–357.

Tihen, J. A. 1962. A review of New World fossil bufonids. *Am. Midl. Nat.*, **67**, 157–183.

Vaughn, P. P. 1963. New information on the structure of Permian lepospondylous vertebrae—from an unusual source. *Bull. Sth. Calif. Acad. Sci.*, **62**, 150–158.

Viushkov, B. P. 1957. [New Kotlassiomorpha from the Tatar formations of European Russia]. *Trudý palaeont. Inst.* **68**, 89–108 (Russian).

Watson, D. M. S. 1929. The Carboniferous Amphibia of Scotland. *Palaeont. hung.* **1**, 219–252.

—— 1940. The origin of frogs. *Trans. R. Soc. Edinb.*, **60**, 195–231.

—— 1956. The brachyopid labyrinthodonts. *Bull. Br. Mus. nat. Hist. Geol.*, **2**, 315–391.

Westoll, T. S. 1940. (In Discussion on the boundary between the Old Red Sandstone and the Carboniferous) *Advmt. Sci., Lond.*, **1**, 258.

—— 1951. The vertebrate-bearing strata of Scotland. *18th Int. Geol. Congr.*, **11**, 5–21.

Westphal, F. 1958. Die tertiären und rezenten eurasiatischen Riesensalamander (genus *Andrias*, Urodela, Amphibia). *Palaeontographica*, **110**, 20–92.

A. L. Panchen, ph.d

Department of Zoology, The University, Newcastle upon Tyne.

CHAPTER 28

Reptilia

Contributors: R. M. APPLEBY, A. J. CHARIG, C. B. COX, K. A. KERMACK & L. B. H. TARLO

Introduction. The Reptilia are frequently divided into subclasses on the basis of the temporal openings in the skull roofing bones: Anapsida (no openings, incl. Chelonia and Cotylosauria), "Parapsida" (upper opening, Ichthyosauria and Plesiosauria), Synapsida (lower, mammal-like reptiles), Diapsida (both upper and lower, Lepidosauria and Archosauria). Although this classification is perfectly adequate for living reptiles, it cannot be satisfactorily applied to the fossil groups. Unfortunately at present it is not possible to give a classification which is acceptable to all workers in the field, and in consequence that employed here represents a compromise between two basically opposed views.

One school of thought believes that the reptiles are monophyletic and that most groups can be derived from the captorhinomorph cotylosaurs. The other school claims that they are polyphyletic and that several groups had separate origins from the Amphibia. Thus Watson (1957) from his study of the ear region concluded that the cotylosaurs included the ancestors of the sauropsids and the theropsids—the captorhinomorphs belonging to the latter group. In this context the position of the millerosaurs is critical, and in the interests of neutrality they are included in the documentation as submitted. Thus they appear both as captorhinomorphs (C.B.C) and as lepidosaurs (L.B.H.T.)!

In the classification the following separate subclasses are recognized: Anapsida, Ichthyopterygia, Sauropterygia, Placodontia, Proganosauria, Incertae sedis (for the orders Araeoscelidia, Trilophosauria, Proterosauria), Lepidosauria, Archosauria and Synapsida.   [L.B.H.T.]

Subclass ANAPSIDA

Order COTYLOSAURIA

Origin: from unknown, very early seymouriamorph amphibians? (see Fox & Bowman 1966).

Family ROMERIIDAE Price 1937

The most primitive family, probably ancestral to all other cotylosaur families.

First, Carb Bashk: *Hylonomus lyelli* Dawson 1860 and *Archerpeton anthracos* Carroll 1964, Joggins Fm, Nova Scotia, Canada (Carroll 1964).

Last, Carb U. Carb: *Protorothyris archeri* Price 1937, Moran Fm, Wichita Group, Texas (Price 1937).

The Fossil Record, pp. 695–731. Geological Society of London, 1967. Printed in Northern Ireland.

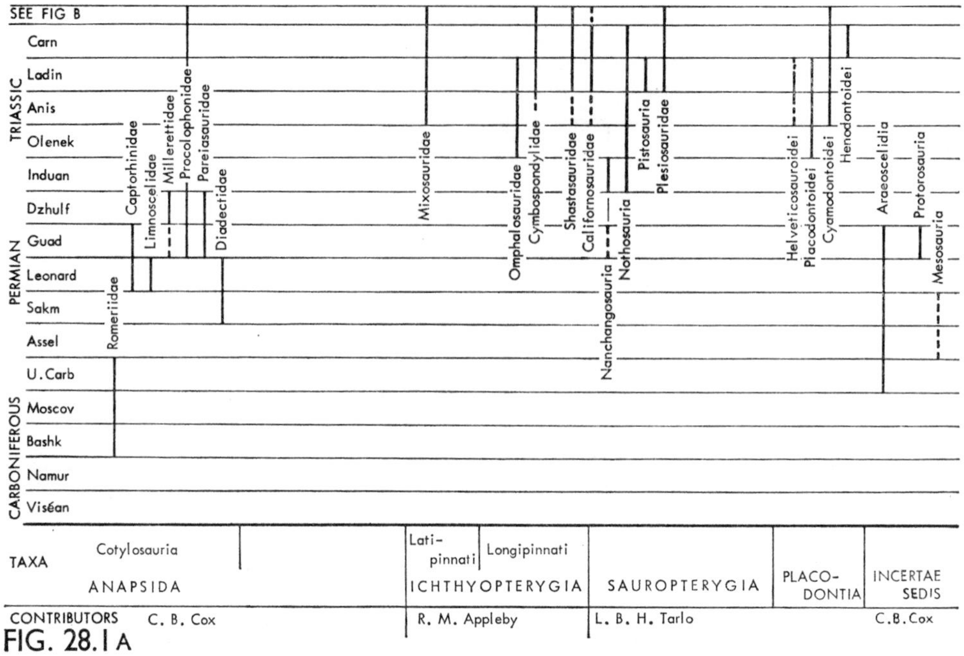

SEE FIG B
Carn
Ladin
Anis
Olenek
Induan
Dzhulf
Guad
Leonard
Sakm
Assel
U.Carb
Moscov
Bashk
Namur
Viséan
TRIASSIC
PERMIAN
CARBONIFEROUS
Captorhinidae
Limnoscelidae
Millerettidae
Procolophonidae
Pareiasauridae
Diadectidae
Romeriidae
Mixosauridae
Omphalosauridae
Cymbospondylidae
Shastasauridae
Californosauridae
Nanchangosauria
Nothosauria
Pistosauria
Plesiosauridae
Helveticosauroidei
Placodontoidei
Cyamodontoidei
Henodontoidei
Araeoscelidia
Protorosauria
Mesosauria
TAXA
Cotylosauria
ANAPSIDA
Latipinnati
Longipinnati
ICHTHYOPTERYGIA
SAUROPTERYGIA
PLACODONTIA
INCERTAE SEDIS
CONTRIBUTORS
C. B. Cox
R. M. Appleby
L. B. H. Tarlo
C.B.Cox

FIG. 28.1 A

Family CAPTORHINIDAE Case 1911

First, Perm Leonard: *Captorhinus aguti* Cope 1882, Admiral Fm, Wichita Group, Texas (Fox & Bowman 1966).

Last, Perm Guad: *Rothia multidonta* Olson & Beerbower 1953, San Angelo and Flower Pot Fms, Pease River Group, Texas U.S.A. (Seltin 1959, Olson & Barghusen 1962) and *Hecatogomphius kavejevi* Vjushkov & Chudinov 1957, Belebei Suite, Zone II, Bashkir Rep, U.S.S.R. (Olson 1962).

Family LIMNOSCELIDAE Romer 1945

First and **Last,** Perm Leonard: *Limnoscelis paludis* Williston 1911, Abo Fm, New Mexico (Romer 1946, Vaughn 1963).

Family MILLERETTIDAE Romer 1956

First and **Last,** Perm Dzhulf: Six genera from the Tapinocephalus Z, Beaufort Ser, S. Africa (Watson 1957). *Mesenosaurus* Efremov 1938 from Perm, Guad, Zone II, Archangel Prov, U.S.S.R. is a possible earlier representative (Watson 1957).

Comment: See also under Subclass Lepidosauria, Order Millerosauria p. 701.

Family PROCOLOPHONIDAE Cope 1889

First, Perm Guad: *Nyctiphruretus acudens* Efremov 1938 and *Nycteroleter ineptus* Efremov 1938, Zone II, Archangel Prov, U.S.S.R. (Olson 1962).

Last, Trias Nor: *Hypsognathus fenneri* Colbert 1946 and *Sphodrosaurus pennsylvanicus* Colbert 1960, Brunswick Fm, Newark Gp, Eastern U.S.A. and *Leptopleuron lacertinum* Owen 1851, Lossiemouth Beds, Elgin, Scotland (Colbert 1946, Walker 1961).

Family PAREIASAURIDAE Cope 1896

Origin: from procolophonids? (Chudinov 1957, Olson 1962, 1965).

First, Perm Guad: *Rhipeosaurus* Efremov 1940 and *Leptoropha* Chudinov 1955, both from Zone II, Bashkir Rep. and Kirov Prov, U.S.S.R. (Olson 1962).

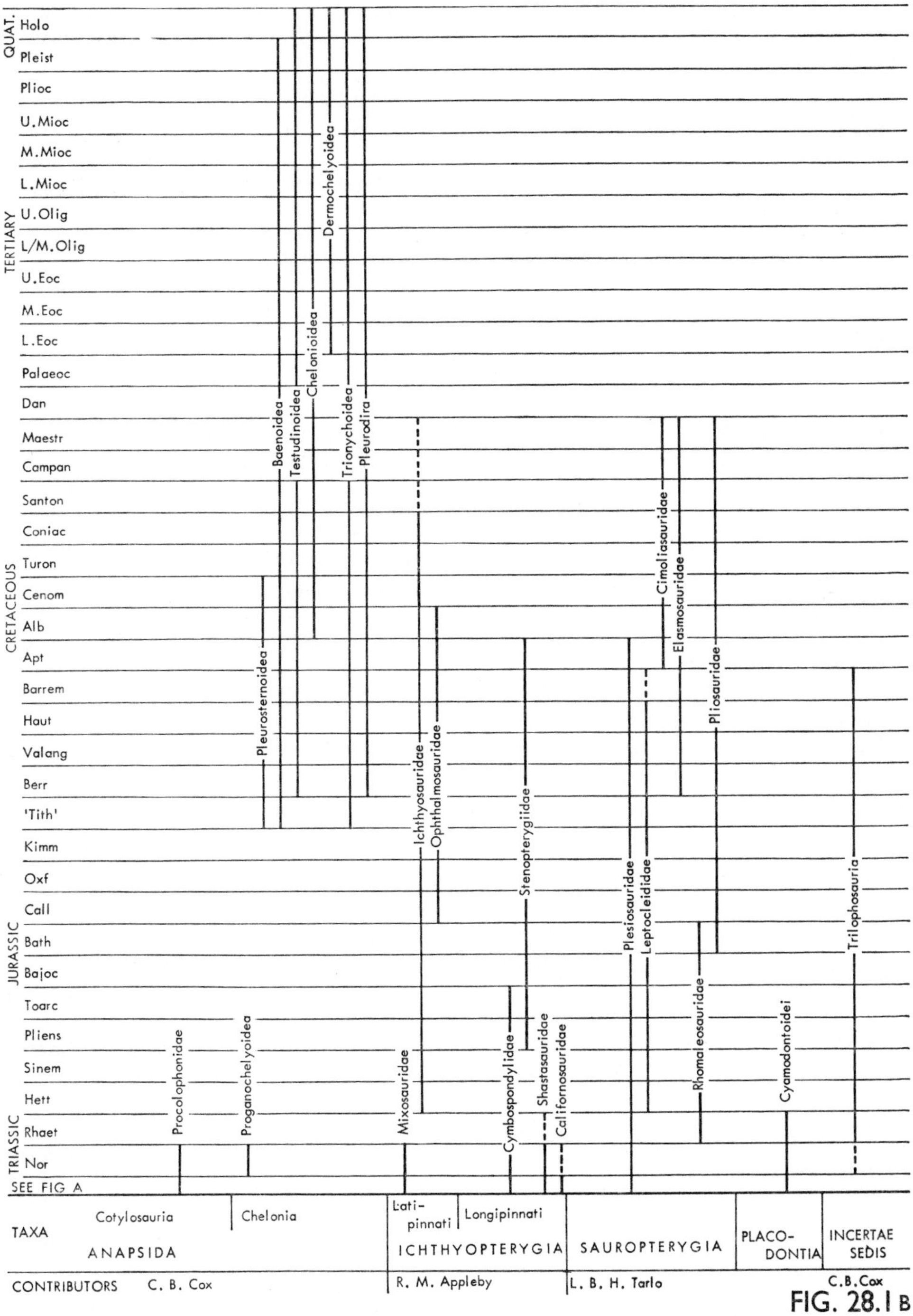
QUAT.
Holo
Pleist
TERTIARY
Plioc
U.Mioc
M.Mioc
L.Mioc
U.Olig
L/M.Olig
U.Eoc
M.Eoc
L.Eoc
Palaeoc
CRETACEOUS
Dan
Maestr
Campan
Santon
Coniac
Turon
Cenom
Alb
Apt
Barrem
Haut
Valang
Berr
JURASSIC
'Tith'
Kimm
Oxf
Call
Bath
Bajoc
Toarc
Pliens
Sinem
Hett
TRIASSIC
Rhaet
Nor
SEE FIG A
Baenoidea
Testudinoidea
Chelonioidea
Dermochelyoidea
Trionychoidea
Pleurodira
Pleurosternoidea
Procolophonidae
Proganochelyoidea
Ichthyosauridae
Ophthalmosauridae
Stenopterygiidae
Mixosauridae
Cymbospondylidae
Shastasauridae
Californosauridae
Cimoliasauridae
Elasmosauridae
Pliosauridae
Plesiosauridae
Leptocleididae
Rhomaleosauridae
Cyamodontoidei
Trilophosauria
TAXA
Cotylosauria
Chelonia
ANAPSIDA
Lati-pinnati
Longipinnati
ICHTHYOPTERYGIA
SAUROPTERYGIA
PLACO-DONTIA
INCERTAE SEDIS
CONTRIBUTORS
C. B. Cox
R. M. Appleby
L. B. H. Tarlo
C.B.Cox

FIG. 28.1 B

Last, Perm Dzhulf: several genera from Tapinocephalus, Endothiodon and Kistecephalus Z., Beaufort Series, S. Africa (Haughton & Brink 1955) and formations of similar age in East Africa and Europe.

Family DIADECTIDAE Cope 1880

First, Perm Sakm: *Desmatodon hollandi* Cope 1908, Dunkard Group, Pennsylvania (Olson 1947).

Last, Perm Leonard: *Phanerosaurus naumanni* von Meyer 1861, M. Rothliegende, Zwickau, Saxony, Germany (Olson 1947).

Comment: This family is normally placed in the Cotylosauria, but is now thought to belong in the labyrinthodont Amphibia (Romer 1964, Olson 1965, 1966).

Order CHELONIA

Suborder PROGANOCHELYDIA

Superfamily PROGANOCHELYOIDEA Romer 1956

First and **Last,** Trias Nor: *Proganochelys quenstedtii* Baur 1887, Stubensandstein, Wurtemberg, Germany (? = *Triassochelys dux* Jaekel 1918, see Parsons & Williams 1961).

Suborder AMPHICHELYDIA

Superfamily PLEUROSTERNOIDEA Hay 1930

First, Jur "Tith": *Platychelys oberndorferi* Wagner 1853, Lithographic Lst, Regensburg, Bavaria, Germany.

Last, Cret Cenom: *Helochelys danubina* von Meyer 1854, Chalk, Kelheim, Bavaria, Germany.

Superfamily BAENOIDEA Romer 1956

First, Jur "Tith": several genera from Morrison Fm, Colorado, U.S.A. (Hay 1908).

Last, Quat Pleist: *Meiolania platyceps* Owen 1886, Lord Howe Is, S. Pacific, and Australia (Anderson 1925).

Suborder CRYPTODIRA

Superfamily TESTUDINOIDEA Baur 1893

First, Cret Berr: *Tretosternon punctatum* Owen 1842, M. Purbeck Beds, Dorset, England (Delair 1958). **Extant.**

Superfamily CHELONIOIDEA Baur 1889

First, Cret Alb: *Rhinochelys* spp. Lydekker 1889, Gault, S.E. England (Zangerl 1960).

Extant.

Superfamily DERMOCHELYOIDEA Romer 1956

First, Tert L. Eoc: *Cosmochelys dolloi* Andrews 1919, Ombiall District, S. Nigeria. **Extant.**

Superfamily CARETTOCHELYOIDEA Romer 1956

First, Jur "Tith": *Palaeochelys novemcostatus* Valenciennes 1863, Kimmeridgian Fm, Le Havre, France. [This superfamily inadvertently omitted from chart, Ed.] **Extant.**

Superfamily TRIONYCHOIDEA Gray 1870

First, Jur "Tith": *Trionyx primoevus* Bergounioux 1937, Kimmeridgian Fm, Le Havre, France. **Extant.**

Suborder PLEURODIRA Cope 1870

First, Cret Berr: *Platycheloides nyasae* Haughton 1928, Mwakasyunguti, Malawi. **Extant.**
[C.B.C.]

Chapter 28: Reptilia

Subclass ICHTHYOPTERYGIA

Order ICHTHYOSAURIA

Suborder LATIPINNATI Huene 1951

First, Trias Anis: *Mixosaurus atavus* (Quenstedt), Wellendolomit, Black Forest, Germany (Huene, 1956).

Last, Cret Coniac or Maestr: *Myopterygius campylodon* (Carter) U. Chalk, England (Huene, 1956).

Constituent families: Mixosauridae, Trias Anis—Nor; Ichthyosauridae Jur Hett—Coniac or Maestr; Ophthalmosauridae, Jur Call—Cret Alb.

Suborder LONGIPINNATI Huene 1951

First, Trias Olenek: *Grippia longirostris* Wiman 1928, Grippia Bed, Spitsbergen (Wiman 1928, Buchan *et al.* 1965).

Last, Cret Apt: *Platypterygius platydactylus* (Broili) 1907, Deshayesites Z, Hannover, Germany (Broili 1907).

Constituent families: Omphalosauridae, Trias Olenek-Ladin; Cymbospondylidae, Trias Anis or Ladin—Jur Toarc; Stenopterygiidae, Jur Pliens—Cret Apt; Shastasauridae, Trias Anis or Ladin—Nor or Rhaet. Californosauridae, Trias Anis or Ladin—Carn or Nor.   [R.M.A.]

Subclass SAUROPTERYGIA

Order NANCHANGOSAURIA Wang 1959

First and **Last,** Trias Induan: *Nanchangosaurus suni* Wang, L. Trias, Tayieh Lst, Hupeh, Nanchang district, China (Wang 1959). *Nothosauravus geraensis* Kuhn, Perm Guad, Kupferschiefer, central Germany, may belong to this order (Kuhn 1964a).

Order NOTHOSAURIA Zittel 1889

First, Trias Induan: *Metanothosaurus nipponicus* Yabe and Shikama, L. Trias, Isihu, Janaigu, Japan; *Kwangsisaurus orientalis* Young L. Trias, Kwangsi, China; and nothosaur, Panchet Beds, Lystrosaurus Z., India. (Young 1959a, Tarlo 1959).

Last, Trias Carn: *Nothosaurus* sp., Gipskeuper (Estherien-schicht.), Bayreuth, Germany (Schmidt 1928, 1938).

Order PLESIOSAURIA

Suborder PISTOSAURIA Edinger 1935

First and **Last,** Trias Ladin: *Pistosaurus grandaevus* Meyer, and *P. longaevus* Meyer, U. Muschelkalk, Bayreuth, Germany, and Muschelkalk, Mont, N.E. France (Persson 1963).

Suborder DOLICHODEIRA

Family PLESIOSAURIDAE Gray 1825

First, Trias Ladin: *Plesiosaurus? baruthicus* Kuhn, U. Muschelkalk, Bayreuth, Germany (Persson 1963).

Last, Cret Apt: *"Plesiosaurus" latispinus* Owen, L. Greensand, Maidstone, England (Persson 1963).

Family LEPTOCLEIDIDAE White 1940

First, Jur Hett: *Eurycleidus arcuatus* (Owen), L. Lias, Psiloceras planorbe Z., Bitton, England (Persson 1963).

Last, Cret Haut or Barrem: *Leptocleidus superstes* Andrews, U. Wealden, Berwick, Sussex, England (Persson 1963).

Family CIMOLIASAURIDAE Delair 1959

First, Cret Apt: *Cimoliasaurus maccoyi* Etheridge, Roma Series, White Cliffs, New South Wales, Australia (Persson 1963).

Last, Cret Maestr: *Aristonectes parvidens* Cabrera, U. Cret Maestr, Cañadon del Loro, Chubut, Argentina, S. America; and undescribed specimen from Maestr, Cabinda, N. Congo River Estuary, S.W. Africa (Persson 1963).

Family ELASMOSAURIDAE Cope 1869

First, Cret Berr: *Brancasaurus brancai* Wegner, Wealden, Gronau, Westphalia, Germany (Welles 1962).

Last, Cret Maestr: *Plesiosaurus mauretanicus* Arambourg, Maestr, Djebel Tilda, Morocco; *Leurospondylus ultimus* Brown, Edmonton Fm, Red Deer River, Alberta, Canada: *Aphrosaurus furlongi* Welles, *Fresnosaurus drescheri* Welles, *Hydrotherosaurus alexandrae* Welles, and *Morenosaurus stocki* Welles, U. Campani-L.Maestr, Moreno Fm, Panoche Hills, California (Persson 1963).

Suborder BRACHYDEIRA

Family RHOMALEOSAURIDAE Kuhn 1961

First, Trias Rhaet: *Eretmosaurus rugosus* Owen, *"Plesiosaurus" costatus* Owen, *"P". hawkinsi* Owen, and *Termatosaurus alberti* Plieninger, Rhaetic Bone Bed, Aust Cliff, England (Persson 1963).

Last, Jur Bath: *Plesiosaurus? erraticus* Phillips, L. Oolite, Stonesfield, England (Persson 1963).

Family PLIOSAURIDAE Seeley 1874

First, Jur Bath: *Liopleurodon pachydeirus* (Seeley), Ecouche, N.W. France (Persson 1963).

Last, Cret Maestr: *"Plesiosaurus" traversii* Hector, and *Polycotylus tenuis* Hector, Amuri Beds, Amuri Bluff, S. Is, New Zealand (Welles 1962).

Subclass PLACODONTIA

Comment: The Placodonts have been shown by Kuhn-Schnyder (1963) to be unrelated to the Sauropterygia with which they are classically associated. It is for this reason that the Placodontia are here raised to the status of independent subclass.

Order HELVETICOSAUROIDEI Peyer & Kuhn-Schnyder 1955

First and **Last,** Trias Anis–Ladin: *Helveticosaurus zollingeri* Peyer, Bitumenhoriz., Mt. San Giorgio, Tessin, Switzerland (Kuhn-Schnyder 1964).

Order PLACODONTOIDEI Peyer & Kuhn-Schnyder 1955

First, Trias Olenek: *Placodus impressus* Agassiz, U. Buntsandstein, Alsace, Germany (Huene 1956).

Last, Trias Ladin: *Placodus gigas* Agassiz, U. Muschelkalk, Bayreuth, Germany (Huene 1956).

Order CYAMODONTOIDEI Peyer & Kuhn-Schnyder 1955

First, Trias Anis: *Saurosphargis voltzi* Drevermann, L. Muschelkalk, Gorny Slask, S.W. Poland (Huene 1956).

Last, Trias Rhaet: *Psephosaurus anglicus* (Meyer), Rhaetic Bone Bed, Aust Cliff, and Frome, Somerset, England, and *Psephoderma alpinus* Meyer, Rhaet, Bavaria, Germany (Huene 1956). *Placochelys placodonta* Jaekel, Jur Hett-Sinem, Arzo, Tessin, Switzerland, is probably a derived fossil (Huene 1956).

Order HENODONTOIDEI Kuhn 1961

First and **Last,** Trias Carn: *Henodus chelyops* Huene, U. Gipskeuper, Lustnau, Tübingen, Germany (Huene 1956).

Chapter 28: Reptilia

Subclass INCERTAE SEDIS

Order ARAEOSCELIDIA Willston 1913

First, Carb U. Carb: *Petrolacosaurus kansensis* Lane, Konemo Series, Kansas (Tatarinov 1964).

Last, Perm Guad, *Weigeltisaurus jaekeli* (Weigelt), Kupferschiefer, Zeichstein, Germany. *Aenigmasaurus grallator* Parrington, Trias Induan, Lystrosaurus Z, E. Africa, is tentatively assigned to this order by Tatarinov (1964).

Order TRILOPHOSAURIA Romer 1956

First, Trias Nor–Rhaet: *Trilophosaurus buettneri* Case, Kansas; *Variodens inopinatus* Robinson, fissures in Carboniferous Lst, Mendips, England (Tatarinov 1964).

Last, Cret Barrem: *Toxolophosaurus cloudi* Olson, Kootenai Fm, Montana (Olson 1960). This order is included in the Lepidosauria by Kuhn (1961a) but there seems no real justification for this procedure.

Order PROTOROSAURIA Huxley 1871

First and **Last,** Perm Guad: *Protorosaurus spenceri* Meyer, Kupferschiefer, Thuringia, Germany.

Comment: According to Huene (1956) Watson (1957), Kuhn (1961a) and Tatarinov (1964) this group is equivalent to or included within the Prolacertilia. However there is, as yet, no evidence to suggest that the protorosaurs were even diapsid let alone part of the basic stock from which the Squamata evolved! For this reason the Protorosauria are retained as an independent order separate from the Lepidosauria. [L.B.H.T.]

Subclass PROGANOSAURIA

Order MESOSAURIA

First and **Last,** Perm Assel/Sakm: *Mesosaurus tenuidens* Gervais 1865, Upper Shales, Dwyka Series, S. Africa. The genus is also found in the Irati Fm, Passa Dois Series, S. America, of similar age. [C.B.C.]

Subclass LEPIDOSAURIA

Order MILLEROSAURIA Watson 1957

First, Perm Guad: *Mesenosaurus romeri* Efremov, L. Mesen, Zone II, Archangel Distr., Soviet Union (Tatarinov 1964).

Last, Perm Dzhulf: *Milleretta rubidgei* (Broom), *Millerosaurus ornatus* Broom, *M. pricei* Watson, *M. nuffieldi* Watson, and four other genera, Kistecephalus Z., Karroo, S. Africa (Watson 1957). At present there is insufficient evidence to assign *Microcnemus efremovi* Huene, Trias Induan, to this order.

Order EOSUCHIA Broom 1911

First and **Last,** Perm Dzhulf: *Palaeagama vielhaueri* Broom, *Youngina capensis* Broom, *Youngoides romeri* Olson and Broom, *Y. minor* Broom and Robinson, *Youngopsis kitchingi* Broom, *Y. rubidgei* Broom and Robinson, Kistecephalus Z, Karroo, S. Africa (Watson 1957). *Hovasaurus* Piveteau, Perm Dzhulf, Madagascar, and *Tangasaurus* Haughton, Perm Dzhulf, E. Africa, probably belong to this order (Huene 1956, Romer 1956).

Order PROLACERTILIA Huene 1940

First, Trias Induan: *Prolacerta broomi* Parrington, and *Pricea longiceps* Broom and Robinson, Lystrosaurus Z., Karroo, S. Africa (Watson 1957). *Santaisaurus* Koh, Trias Induan, Lystrosaurus Z., Sinkiang, probably belongs to this order (Hoffstetter 1962).

Last, Trias Olenek: *Paliguana whitei* Broom, Procolophon Z., Karroo, S. Africa (Huene 1956).

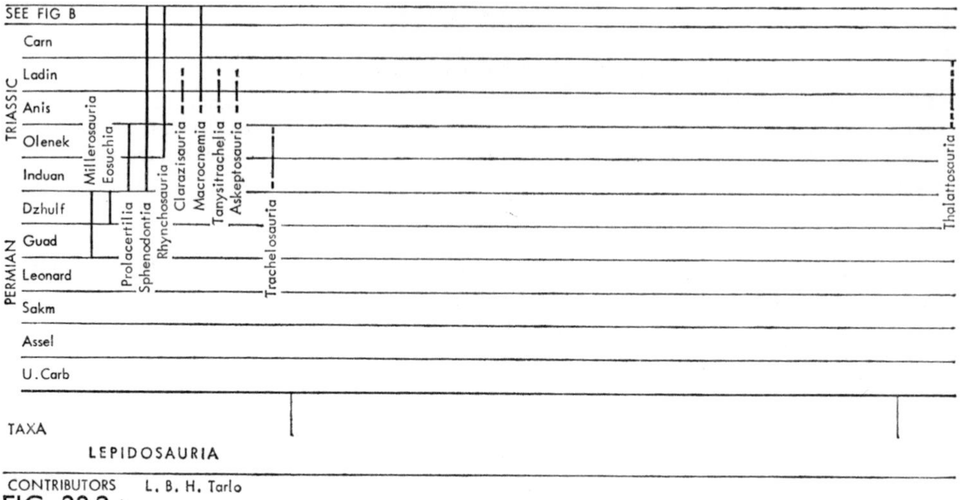

FIG. 28.2 A

Order RHYNCHOCEPHALIA

Suborder SPHENODONTIA Nopcsa 1923

First, Trias Induan: *Schargengia enigmatica* Huene, Benthosuchus Z., Zone V, Vologodskaya Distr., Soviet Union (Tatarinov 1964). **Extant.**

Suborder RHYNCHOSAURIA Osborn 1903

First, Trias Olenek: *Mesosuchus browni* Watson, and *Howesia browni* Broom, Cynognathus Z., Karroo, S. Africa (Tatarinov 1964).
Last, Trias Nor: *Hyperodapedon gordoni* Huxley, Lossiemouth Beds, Elgin, Scotland (Walker 1961).

Suborder CLARAZISAURIA Hoffstetter 1955

First and **Last,** Trias Anis–Ladin: *Clarazia schinzi* Peyer, and *Hescheleria ruebeli* Peyer, Grenzbitumenhoriz., Mt. San Giorgio, Tessin, Switzerland (Kuhn-Schnyder 1964).

Order SQUAMATA

Suborder MACROCNEMIA Kuhn 1946

First, Trias Anis–Ladin: *Macrocnemus bassanii* Nopcsa, Grenzbitumenhoriz., Mt. San Giorgio, Tessin, Switzerland (Kuhn-Schnyder 1964).
Last, Trias Nor–Rhaet: undescribed lizard remains, fissures in Carboniferous Lst., Bristol, Mendips, England, and S. Wales.

Suborder TANYSITRACHELIA Peyer 1931

First and **Last,** Trias Anis-Ladin: *Tanystropheus longobardicus* (Bassani), Grenzbitumenhoriz., Mt. San Giorgio, Tessin, Switzerland; L. Muschelkalk, Gorny Slask, Poland (Kuhn-Schnyder 1964).

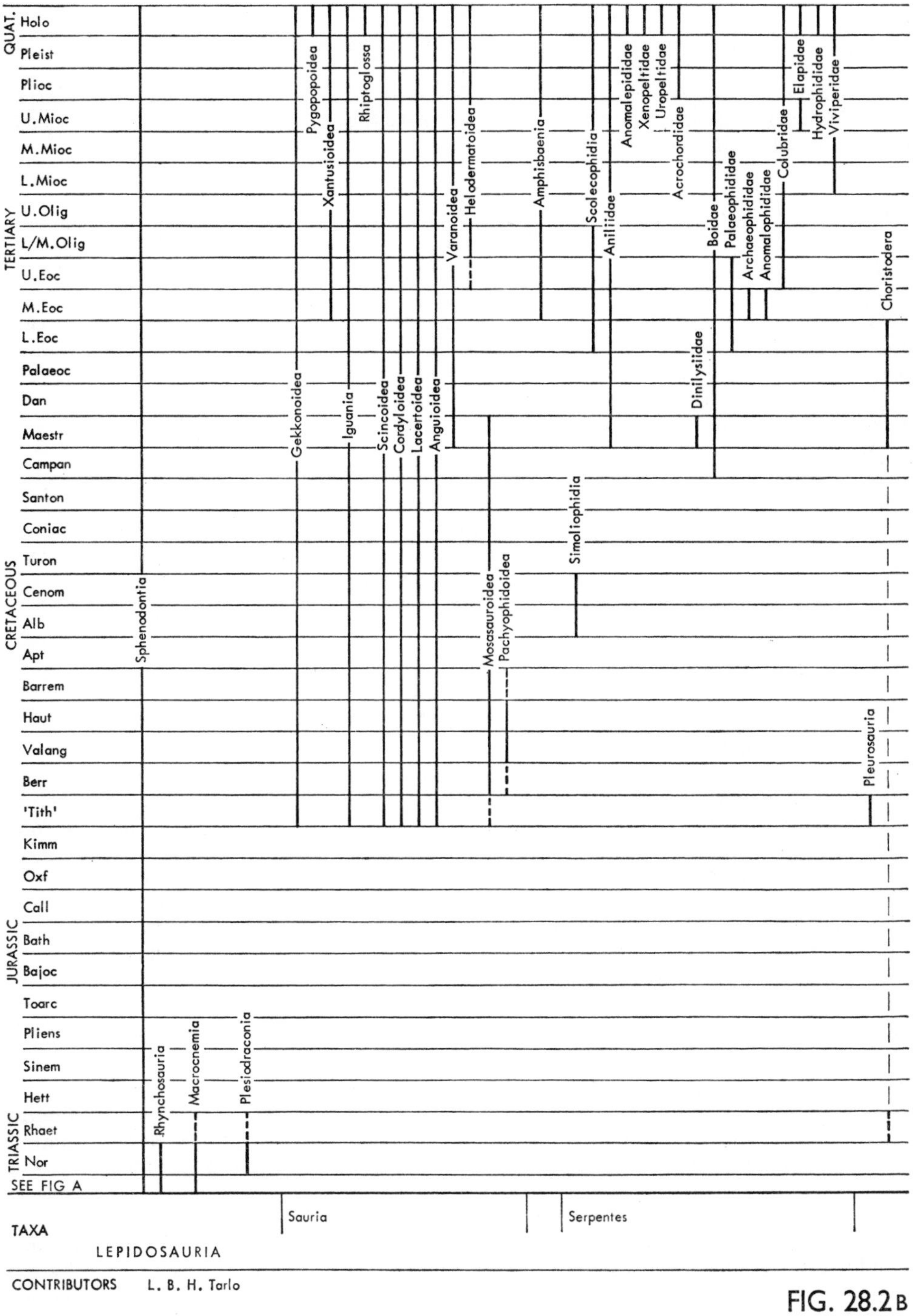
QUAT.
Holo
Pleist
Plioc
U.Mioc
M.Mioc
L.Mioc
TERTIARY
U.Olig
L/M.Olig
U.Eoc
M.Eoc
L.Eoc
Palaeoc
Dan
Maestr
Campan
Santon
Coniac
CRETACEOUS
Turon
Cenom
Alb
Apt
Barrem
Haut
Valang
Berr
'Tith'
Kimm
Oxf
Call
JURASSIC
Bath
Bajoc
Toarc
Pliens
Sinem
Hett
TRIASSIC
Rhaet
Nor
SEE FIG A
Sphenodontia
Rhynchosauria
Macrocnemia
Plesiodraconia
Gekkonoidea
Pygopopoidea
Xantusioidea
Iguania
Rhiptoglossa
Scincoidea
Cordyloidea
Lacertoidea
Anguioidea
Varanoidea
Helodermatoidea
Mosasauroidea
Pachyophidoidea
Amphisbaenia
Simoliophidia
Scolecophidia
Aniliidae
Anomalepididae
Xenopeltidae
Uropeltidae
Acrochordidae
Dinilysiidae
Boidae
Palaeophiidae
Archaeophiidae
Anomalophiidae
Colubridae
Elapidae
Hydrophiidae
Viviperidae
Choristodera
Pleurosauria
TAXA
Sauria
Serpentes
LEPIDOSAURIA
CONTRIBUTORS L. B. H. Tarlo

FIG. 28.2B

The Fossil Record, Part II

Suborder ASKEPTOSAURIA Kuhn-Schnyder 1952 emend.

First and **Last,** Trias Anis-Ladin: *Askeptosaurus italicus* Nopcsa, Grenzbitumenhoriz., Mt. San Giorgio, Tessin, Switzerland (Kuhn-Schynder 1964).

Comment: This group was previously included in the Thalattosauria but since *Thalattosaurus* Merrian is clearly not a squamate, the Askeptosauridae are raised to independent subordinal status within the Squamata.

Suborder EOLACERTILIA Romer 1966 emend.

First and **Last,** Trias Nor: *Kuehneosaurus latus* Robinson, *Kuehneosuchus latissimus* (Robinson), fissures in Carb Lst, Mendips and S. Gloucester, England; and *Icarosaurus siefkeri* Colbert, Granton Q., Newark Gp., New Jersey. [Shown incorrectly in Fig. 28.2B as Suborder Plesiodraconia.]

Comment: The known species of gliding lizards belong to the three monotypic genera cited above, united in the family Kuehneosauridae (Kuhn 1964b, 1966; Robinson 1967). This family, placed in a suborder indet. of the Prolacertilia by Kuhn (1966) and in the infraorder Eolacertilia of the suborder Lacertilia (Sauria) by Romer (1966), is here considered to merit independent subordinal status within the Squamata.

Suborder TRACHELOSAURIA Broili 1917

First and **Last,** Trias Induan–Olenek: *Trachelosaurus fischeri* Broili, M. Bundsandstein, Bernberg, Germany. This group is variously assigned (Kuhn 1961a): independent order; Tatarinov 1964: suborder Prolacertilia with *Macrocnemus;* Huene 1956: fam. Askeptosauridae with *Macrocnemus;* here tentatively retained as independent suborder of Squamata of which it would be earliest fossil record.

Suborder SAURIA (LACERTILIA)

Infraorder GEKKOTA

Superfamily GEKKONOIDEA Underwood 1954

First, Jur "Tith"; *Ardeosaurus brevipes* (Meyer), *A. digitatellus* (Grier), *Eichstaettisaurus schroederi* (Broili), Lithographic Lst., L. Portland., Bavaria, Germany: *Yabeinosaurus tenuis* Endo and Shikama, *Y. youngi* Hoffstetter, Tsaotzushan Fm., N.E. China (Hoffstetter 1964). **Extant.**

Comment: *Bavarisaurus* Hoffstetter and *Palaeolacerta* Cocude-Michel, Jur "Tith", Bavaria, Germany, previously tentatively assigned to the Iguania and Scincoporpha (Lacertoidea) respectively by Hoffstetter (1962) and Cocude-Michel (1963), and now placed by Hoffstetter (1964) close to the Gekkonoidea with the rider that they may represent "proto-iguanians". *Changisaurus* Young, Jur "Tith", S. Chekiang, China, previously described as a probable gekkonid (Young 1959b) has been shown by Baird (1964) to be a thalassemydid chelonian.

Superfamily PYGOPOPOIDEA Gill 1885

No known fossil record.

Superfamily XANTUSIOIDEA Camp 1923

First, Tert M. Eoc: *Palaeoxantusia fera* Hecht, U. Bridgerian, Wyoming (Hecht 1959). **Extant.**

Comment: This superfamily is placed in the Scincomorpha by Kuhn (1963b) and Tatarinov (1964) but Hoffstetter's (1962) views that it belongs to the Gekkota is here accepted.

Infraorder IGUANIA Cuvier 1817 (Cope 1864)

First, Jur "Tith": *Euposaurus thiollierei* Lortet, *E. cerinensis* Lortet, *E. lorteti* Hoffstetter, Lithographic Lst, U. Kimmeridge., Cerin, Ain, France (Hoffstetter 1964). **Extant.**

Comment: *Bavarisaurus* Hoffstetter and *Palaeolacerta* Cocude-Michel, Jur "Tith", Bavaria, Germany, are tentatively assigned to the Gekkonoidea, although they may be "pre- or proto-iguanians" (Hoffstetter 1964). *Polyglyphanodon* Gilmore, U. Cret, Utah, United States, is included

Chapter 28: Reptilia

in this infra order by Romer (1956) and Tatarinov (1964), Hoffstetter's (1962) placing of this genus in the Scincomorpha (Lacertoidea) is here accepted.

Infraorder RHIPTOGLOSSA Wiegmann 1834 (Cope 1864)

No certain fossil record.

Comment: The chamaeleons were probably derived from the agamids (Iguania), and although several genera have been assigned to this infraorder, they all are probably agamids (e.g. *Tinosaurus* Marsh, Tert M. Eoc, Wyoming, United States; *Palaeochamaelo* Stefano, Tert Eoc or Olig, France; *Mimeosaurus* Gilmore, Cret. Maestr, Mongolia) (Hoffstetter 1962).

Infraorder SCINCOMORPHA

Superfamily SCINCOIDEA Oppel 1811 (Camp 1923)

First, Jur "Tith": *Becklesisaurus scincoides* Hoffstetter, Lulworth Beds, Purbeck, Dorset, England (Hoffstetter 1967). **Extant.**

Superfamily CORDYLOIDEA Fitzinger (Hoffstetter 1962)

First, Jur "Tith": *Macellodus brodiei* Owen, and *Saurillus obtusus* Owen, Lulworth Beds, Purbeck, Dorset, England (Hoffstetter 1964). **Extant.**

Comment: This group is frequently included in the Lacertoidea (Kuhn 1963b, Chudinov 1964) but Hoffstetter's (1962) separation of the Cordyloidea as an independent superfamily is here accepted.

Superfamily LACERTOIDEA Fitzinger 1826

First, Jur "Tith": *Durotrigia triconidens* Hoffstetter, Lulworth Beds, Purbeck, Dorset, England (Hoffstetter 1967). **Extant.**

Comment: *Palaeolacerta* Cocude-Michel, Jur "Tith", Bavaria, Germany, was included in this group by Cocude-Michel (1961), but Hoffstetter (1964) has shown that it approximates more closely to the Gekkota and Iguania.

Infraorder ANGUIMORPHA

Superfamily ANGUIOIDEA Fitzinger 1826 (Camp 1923)

First, Jur "Tith": *Dorsetisaurus purbeckensis* Hoffstetter, and *D. hebetidens* Hoffstetter, Lulworth Beds, Purbeck, Dorset, England (Hoffstetter 1967). **Extant.**

Superfamily VARANOIDEA Gill 1885 (Camp 1923)

First, Cret Maestr: *Parasaniwa wyomingensis* Gilmore, Lance Fm, Wyoming; *Telmaseurus grangeri* Gilmore, U. Cret. Mongolia. (Hecht 1959). *Chilingosaurus chingshankouensis* Young, "U. Cret", Chiling, China (Young 1961), is of doubtful stratigraphical and systematic position (Hoffstetter *in litt.*). **Extant.**

Superfamily HELODERMATOIDEA Gray 1837 (Gill 1885)

First, Tert Eoc-Olig: *Eurheloderma gallicum* Hoffstetter, Phosphorites du Quercy (U. Eoc-L. Olig) France (Hoffstetter 1957b). **Extant.**

Comment: This group is included in the Varanoidea by Hoffstetter (1962), but Tatarinov (1964) gives it separate superfamily status.

Superfamily MOSASAUROIDEA Camp 1923

First, Jur "Tith": *Proaigialosaurus huenei* Kuhn, Lithographic Lst., Bavaria, Germany (Kuhn 1958). Hoffstetter (*in litt.*) thinks this fossil might be a poorly observed pleurosaurian!

Last, Cret Maestr: Numerous genera (e.g. *Mosasaurus* Conybeare, *Globidens* Gilmore) with world wide distribution.

Comment: Mosasaurs were an important group of marine reptiles during Cret and are frequently included in the Varanoidea. Since this procedure obscures their importance and gives a false impression of the stratigraphic range of the varanids, this group is here given the independent rank of superfamily.

Superfamily PACHYOPHIDOIDEA Tarlo 1967

First and **Last,** Cret Berr-Barrem: *Pachyophis woodwardi* Nopcsa, and *Mesophis nopcsai* Bolkay, Neocomian, Herzegovinia (Jugoslavia).

Comment: This group is usually united with *Simoliophis* Sauvage, Cret Cenom, France, in the infraorder Cholophidia, which is variously assigned to the Sauria (Romer 1956, Tatarinov 1964) and Serpentes (Kuhn 1963a). These small snake-like aquatic forms are probably highly specialised varanoideans. There is insufficient evidence to assign them to the snakes and they are therefore tentatively referred to the Anguimorpha, as an independent superfamily.

Suborder AMPHISBAENIA Gray 1844

First, Tert M. Eoc: *Lestophis anceps* Marsh, and *L. crassus* Marsh, U. Bridgerian, Wyoming, United States (Hecht 1959). *Omoiotyphlops priscus* Rochebrune, Phosphorites du Quercy (U. Eoc–L. Olig) France (Hoffstetter 1962). **Extant.**

Comment: Zangerl's (1944) view that this group should be given separate subordinal status and no longer included in the Sauria is here accepted.

Suborder SERPENTES (OPHIDIA)

Infraorder SIMOLIOPHIDIA Tarlo 1967

First, Cret Alb: *Lapparentophis defrennei* Hoffstetter, "continental intercalaire", In Akhamil, Sahara, Algeria (Hoffstetter 1959).

Last, Cret Cenom: *Simoliophis rochebrunei* Sauvage, France, Portugal, Egypt (Hoffstetter 1962).

Comment: This group is usually united with *Pachyophis* Nopcsa, Cret Neocomian Jugoslavia, in the infraorder Cholophidia which is variously assigned to the Sauria (Romer 1956, Tatarinov 1964) and Serpentes (Kuhn 1963a). In this instance Hoffstetter (1959) has demonstrated that the two genera included in the Simoliophidia are true snakes (the later form having become secondarily aquatic). In view of this the Simoliophidia are given independent infraordinal status within the Serpentes.

Infraorder SCOLECOPHIDIA Dumeril and Bribron 1844 (Cope 1864)

First, Tert L. Eoc: undescribed material, Belgium (Hoffstetter 1962). **Extant.**

Comment: This infraorder includes the Typhlopidae and Leptotyphlopidae: the former is classed as an independent infraorder Typhlopidia, the latter is included in the Aniliida by Tatarinov (1964). Unfortunately it is not possible to distinguish these two groups on isolated vertebrae (all that is known fossil) and therefore following Hoffstetter (1962) these two groups are retained in a single taxon. Tatarinov (1964) has resolved the problem by arbitrarily placing all the fossil material in the Typhlopidia and giving the Leptotyphlopidae no fossil record!

Infraorder ANILIIDIA

Family ANILIIDAE Amaral 1929

First, Cret Maestr: *Coniophis precedens* Marsh, Lance Fm, Wyoming (Hecht 1959). **Extant.**

Family ANOMALEPIDIDAE

No known fossil record.

Family XENOPELTIDAE Cope 1864

No known fossil record.

Family UROPELTIDAE Müller 1832

No known fossil record.

Family ACROCHORDIDAE Bonaparte 1838

First, Test Plioc: giant *Acrochordus*, Siwalika, Pakistan (Hoffstetter & Gayrard, 1965.)

Extant.

Chapter 28: Reptilia

Family DINILYSIIDAE Romer 1956

First and **Last,** Cret Maestr: *Dinilysia patagonica* Woodward, U. Cret, Argentina, S. America.

Infraorder ALETHINOPHIDIA

Superfamily BOOIDEA

Family BOIDAE Bonaparte 1831

First, Cret Campan: *Madtsoia madagascariensis* Hoffstetter, Maevarono Sands, N.W. Madagascar (Hoffstetter 1961a). **Extant.**
Comment: The family Bolyeridae is here included in the Boidae, following Hoffstetter (1960).

Family PALAEOPHIDIDAE Boulenger

First, Tert L. Eoc: *Palaeophis toliapicus* Owen, and several other species, L.-M. Eoc, England, Morocco, Nigeria, Sudan.
Last, Tert U. Eoc: *Pterosphenus schucherti* Lucas, U. Eoc, Alabama; *P. sheppardi* Hoffstetter, U. Eoc, Ecuador, S. America; *P. schweinfurthi* (Andrews), U. Eoc, Egypt, Libya (Hoffstetter 1961b).

Superfamily COLUBROIDEA

Family ARCHAEOPHIDIDAE Janesch 1906

First and **Last,** Tert M. Eoc: *Archaeophis proavus* Massalongo, Monte Bolca Lst., nr. Verona, Italy (Auffenberg 1959, Hoffstetter *in litt.*).

Family ANOMALOPHIDIDAE Affenberg 1959

First and **Last,** Tert M. Eoc: *Anomalophis bolcensis* (Massalongo), Monte Bolca Lst., nr. Verona, Italy (Auffenberg 1959, Hoffstetter *in litt.*).

Family COLUBRIDAE Gray 1825

First, Tert U. Eoc: *"Coluber" beggiatoi* Zigno, U. Eoc, Venetia, Italy. **Extant.**
Comment: Although this record is of a genuine colubrid, Hoffstetter (1962) is suspicious of the stratigraphic age, since elsewhere this family only appears in U. Olig.

Family ELAPIDAE Boie 1827

First, Tert U. Mioc: *Palaeonaja romani* Hoffstetter, *P. crassa* Hoffstetter, and *P. depereti* Hoffstetter, La Grive, U. Mioc, France; undescribed material, U. Mioc, Beni Mellal, Morocco (Hoffstetter 1962). **Extant.**

Family HYDROPHIDIDAE Swainson 1839

No known fossil record.

Family VIPERIDAE Gray 1825

First, Tert L. Mioc: *Laophis crotaloides* Owen, Mioc, Salonika, Greece (Hoffstetter 1962). **Extant.**

Order PLEUROSAURIA Fitzinger 1843

First and **Last,** Jur "Tith": *Pleurosaurus goldfussi* Meyer, Lithographic Lst, Portland, Bavaria, Germany, and Cerin, Ain, France. Tatarinov's (1964) assignation of this group to the order Araeoscelidia is not here accepted.

Order CHORISTODERA Cope 1876

First, Cret Maestr: *Champsosaurus profundus* Cope, *C. Iaramiensis* Brown, U. Cret, Montana, United States, Alberta, Canada; *Simoedosaurus lemoinei* Gervais, U. Cret, Belgium, France: U. Cret. Timor, Indonesia.

Last, Tert L. Eoc: *Champsosaurus profundus* Cope, *C. Laramiensis* Brown, Montana, United States, Alberta, Canada. *Simoedosaurus lemoinei* Gervais, L. Eoc, Belgium, France.

Comment: *Pachystropheus rhaeticus* Huene, Trias Rhaet, Rhaetic Bone Bed, Wurttemberg, Germany, and Somerset, England may possibly belong to this order, but the group is only adequately known from beds of Cret Maestr and Tert L. Eoc age.

Order THALATTOSAURIA Merriam 1904

First and **Last,** Trias Anis–Ladin: *Thalattosaurus shastensis* Merriam, Hosselkus Lst, Shasta, California.

Comment: This order was previously taken to include the Askeptosauridae but this family is clearly squamate whereas *Thalattosaurus* is not. For this reason the Askeptosauridae are raised to independent subordinal rank within the Squamata, while the Thalattosauria are retained as a separate order. [L.B.H.T.]

Subclass ARCHOSAURIA

Order THECODONTIA

Comment: The many Triassic footprints generally assigned to this order cannot be certainly correlated with the skeletal remains and are not considered here.

Suborder PROTEROSUCHIA

(= PELYCOSIMIA = ERYTHROSUCHIA)

Family PROTEROSUCHIDAE von Huene 1908

(= CHASMATOSAURIDAE Haughton 1924)

First, Perm Dzhulf: *Archosaurus rossicus* Tatarinov 1960, Zone IV, U.S.S.R.
Last, Trias Olenek: *Chasmatosaurus ultimus* Young 1964a, Ehrmaying Series, China.

Family ERYTHROSUCHIDAE Watson 1917

First, Trias Induan: *Garjainia prima* Ochev 1958, Zone V, U.S.S.R.
Last, Trias Olenek: *Erthyrosuchus africanus* Broom 1905, Cynognathus Z., S. Africa; *Vjushkovia triplicostata* von Huene 1960, Zone, VI–VII, U.S.S.R.; *Shansisuchus* spp. Young 1964a, Ehrmaying Series, China.

Suborder PSEUDOSUCHIA

(= AETOSAURIA)

Comment: Generally considered to be ancestral to all later archosaurs (but see Krebs 1963). Most genera inadequately known; classifications into families vary to an extraordinary degree. Arrangement below, best which can be made at present, does not provide families for many poorly known forms.

Family EUPARKERIIDAE von Huene 1920

First and **Last,** Trias Olenek: *Euparkeria capensis* Broom 1913, Cynognathus Z., S. Africa (Ewer 1965); *Wangisuchus tzeyii* Young 1964a, Ehrmaying Series, China.
Comment: Earliest, most "typical" of all pseudosuchians.

Family PALLISTERIIDAE Charig 1967

First and **Last,** Trias Anis: *Pallisteria angustimentum* Charig 1967, Manda Fm, Tanzania.
Comment: Possibly close to line of ancestry of crocodilians.

Chapter 28: Reptilia

Family TELEOCRATERIDAE Charig 1967

First and **Last,** Trias Anis: *Teleocrater rhadinus* Charig 1967, Manda Fm, Tanzania.
Comment: Probably ancestral to coelurosaurs.

Family PRESTOSUCHIDAE Charig 1967

First, Trias Anis: *Mandasuchus tanyauchen* Charig 1967, *Stagonosuchus major* (Haughton 1932), Manda Fm, Tanzania; *Ticinosuchus ferox* Krebs 1965, Grenzbitumenhorizont, Switzerland.

Last, Trias Carn: *Saurosuchus galilei* Reig 1959, Ischigualasto Fm, Argentina. [Submitted as Ladin, altered by Ed. L.B.H.T.]

Comment: Probably ancestral to sauropodomorphs. Approximately equivalent to family Rauisuchidae von Huene 1942 but with genus *Rauisuchus* excluded.

Family AETOSAURIDAE Baur 1887

(= STAGONOLEPIDAE von Huene 1908)

First, Trias Carn: *Aetosauroides scagliai* and *Argentinosuchus bonapartei* both Casamiquela 1960, Ischigualasto Fm, Argentina. [Submitted as Ladin, altered by Ed. L.B.H.T.]

Last, Trias Nor: *Aetosaurus* spp., Stubensandstein, Germany; *Stagonolepis robertsoni* Agassiz 1844, Lossiemouth Beds, Scotland; *Stegomus arcuatus* Marsh 1896, New Haven Arkose, Connecticut and lower Brunswick Fm, New Jersey; *Typothorax* spp., *Desmatosuchus haplocerus* (Cope 1892), Petrified Forest Mr, Arizona and New Mexico; cf. *Typothorax*, Maleri Fm, India (Chowdhury 1965).

Family PEDETICOSAURIDAE van Hoepen 1915

First, Trias Nor: *Saltoposuchus connectens, S. longipes* both von Huene 1921, Stubensandstein, Germany; *Hesperosuchus agilis* Colbert 1952, Petrified Forest Mr, Arizona; *Sphenosuchus acutus* Haughton 1915, upper Red Beds, S. Africa.

Last, Trias Rhaet: *Pedeticosaurus leviseuri* van Hoepen 1915, Cave Sandstone, S. Africa.

Comments: *Saltoposuchus* and *Hesperosuchus* hitherto regarded as pseudosuchians; *Sphenosuchus* as a pseudosuchian transitional to Crocodilia (denied by Reig 1959); *Pedeticosaurus* generally as a crocodilian. But Walker (verb. comm.) believes that all these forms may be crocodilian.

Family SCLEROMOCHLIDAE von Huene 1914

First and **Last,** Trias Nor: *Scleromochlus taylori* Smith Woodward 1907, Lossiemouth Beds, Scotland.

Comments on Pseudosuchia: Family Ornithosuchidae (Nor), generally regarded as "typical" and ancestral to dinosaurs, is based on *Ornithosuchus* which Walker (1964) has shown to be a theropod dinosaur. Family Erpetosuchidae (Nor) is based on *Erpetosuchus* which Walker (verb. comm.) considers to be a crocodilian. Possible pseudosuchians in Rhaet: *Microchampsa scutata* Young 1951, *Platyognathus hsui* Young 1944, L. Lufeng Series, Yunnan.

Suborder PARASUCHIA

(= PHYTOSAURIA)

Family PHYTOSAURIDAE Lydekker 1888

First, Trias Carn or Nor: several spp. *Paleorhinus, Angistorhinus, Phytosaurus* (*Brachysuchus*) from Blasensandstein, Germany; Maleri Fm, India; Popo Agie Fm, Wyoming; basal Dockum Group, Texas.

Last, Trias Rhaet: *Rutiodon rutimeyeri* (von Huene 1911), Switzerland and Germany; *Pachysuchus imperfectus* Young 1951, L. Lufeng Series, Yunnan.

Comments: Nature and horizon of *Mesorhinus fraasi* Jaekel 1910, supposedly L. Trias, Germany, highly dubious (Gregory 1962); but *Phytosaurus arenaceus* (Fraas 1896), Schilfsandstein, Germany, probably parasuchian and earlier in Carn than forms listed above. Only in Northern Hemisphere except for a few scutes and teeth from Madagascar (see Gregory 1962).

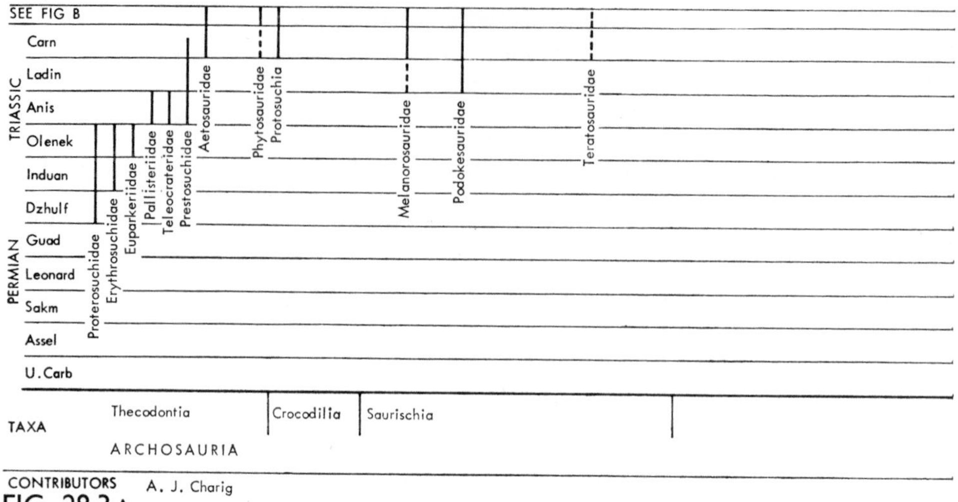

FIG. 28.3 A

CONTRIBUTORS A. J. Charig

Order CROCODILIA

Suborder PROTOSUCHIA Mook 1934

First, Trias Carn: *Proterochampsa barrionuevoi* Reig 1959, Ischigualasto Fm, Argentina. [Submitted as Ladin, altered by Ed. L.B.H.T.]

Last, Trias Rhaet: *Protosuchus richardsoni* (Brown 1933), Dinosaur Canyon Sst, Arizona; *Notochampsa istedana* Broom 1904, Cave Sst, S. Africa; possibly also unnamed crocodilian (Kermack 1956), fissure filling in Carboniferous Lst, S. Wales.

Comments: Stem suborder, itself possibly polyphyletic. No clear distinction between some Pseudosuchia and Protosuchia (see "Pseudosuchia" above, pp. 708–9, especially Pedeticosauridae and final Comments); but inclusion of doubtful forms would not extend stratigraphical range of Protosuchia.

Suborder MESOSUCHIA Huxley 1875

First, Jur Toarc: *Steneosaurus brevior* Blake 1876, Jet Rock Series, Yorkshire, England.

Last, Tert M. Eoc: *Dyrosaurus* sp. (see Arambourg & Signeux 1952), Lutetian, Niger Basin.

Suborder THALATTOSUCHIA E. Fraas 1901

First, Jur Call: *Metriorhynchus blainvillei* (Eudes-Deslongchamps 1868), *Metriorhynchus* sp. Kuhn-Schnyder 1961, L. Call, France.

Last, Cret Haut: *Dakosaurus maximus* (Plieninger 1846), base of Haut, France; *Dakosaurus* sp. Corroy 1922, Haut, France.

Comment: The only fully marine crocodilians.

Suborder EUSUCHIA Huxley 1875

First, Cret Valang: *Bernissartia fagesi* Dollo 1883, L. Wealden, Belgium. **Extant.**

Comments: Supposedly eusuchian vertebra in Berr (M. Purbeck, Dorset, England; see Seeley 1887) almost certainly mesosuchian. Originated from Mesosuchia in U. Jur or L. Cret. Present distribution, tropics and sub-tropics everywhere; lakes and rivers, except *Crocodylus porosus*, which is estuarine and occasionally marine.

Chapter 28: *Reptilia*

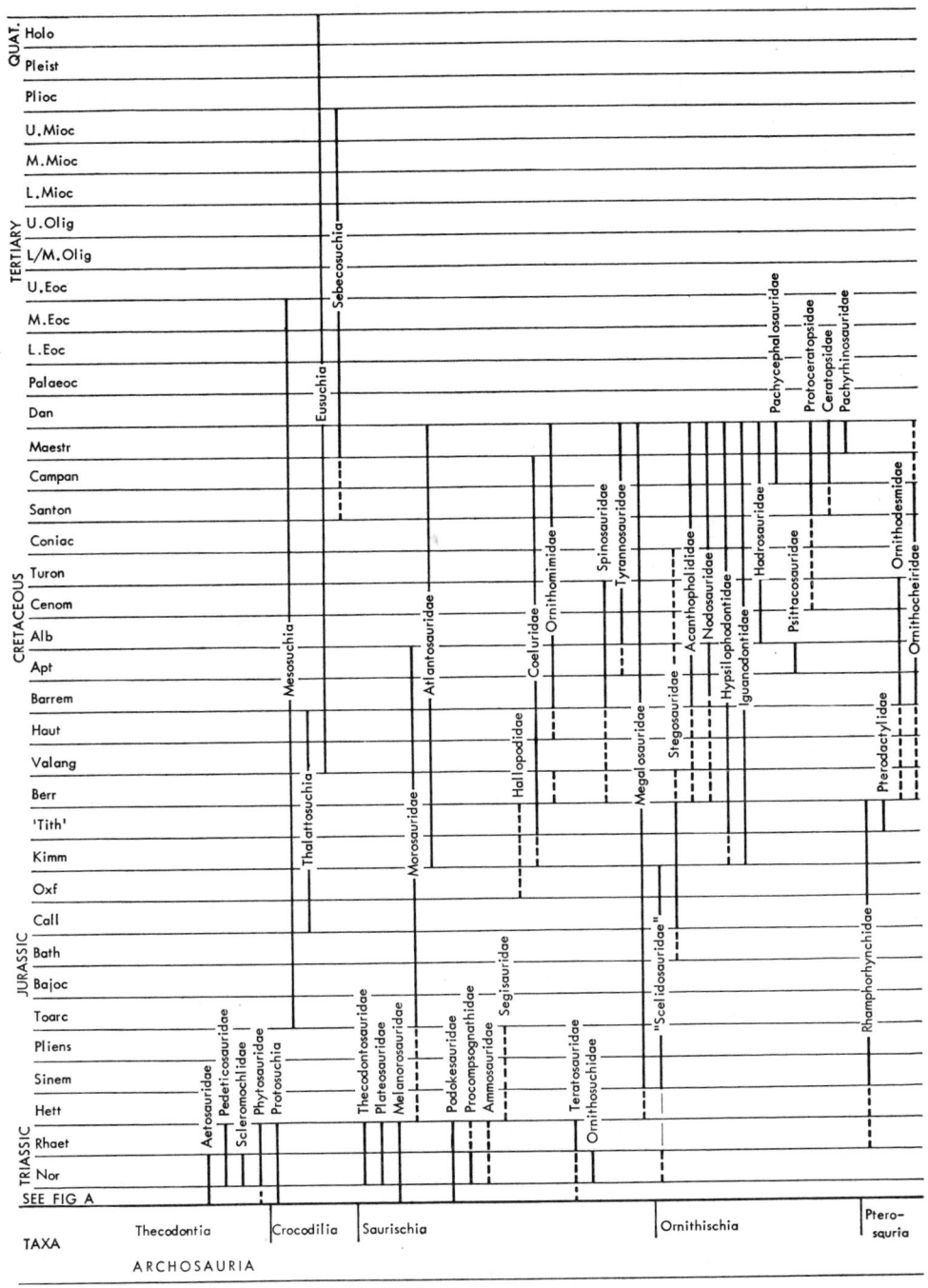

The Fossil Record, Part II

Suborder SEBECOSUCHIA Simpson 1937

First, U. Cret: *Baurusuchus pachecoi* Price 1945, *Peirosaurus torminni* Price 1955, Baurú Series, Minas Gerais, Brazil.

Last, Tert U. Mioc: *Sebecus* sp. nov. Savage 1951, Honda Fm, Colombia (see Langston 1956).

Comments: *Hsisosuchus chungkingensis* Young & Chow 1953, "Red Beds", China, probably U. Jur, shows certain strong similarities to Sebecosuchia and cannot be referred to any other existing suborder. Supposedly sebecosuchian teeth found also in Tert of Europe, E. Africa and N. America (see Langston 1956). Otherwise S. America only.

Order SAURISCHIA

(Suborders and infraorders as in Charig *et al.* 1965)

Suborder SAUROPODOMORPHA

Infraorder PROSAUROPODA

(Arrangement of families as in Charig *et al.* 1965)

Family THECODONTOSAURIDAE von Huene 1908

First, Trias Nor: *Palaeosauriscus diagnosticus* (von Huene 1932), Stubensandstein, Germany; *Thecodontosaurus browni* (Seeley 1895), *T. minor* Haughton 1918, *Massospondylus* spp., *Dromicosaurus gracilis* van Hoepen 1920, *Gryponyx africanus* Broom 1911, *G. taylori* Haughton 1924, *Aetonyx palustris* Broom 1911, upper Red Beds, S. Africa (and some of these also in Forest Sst, Rhodesia).

Last, Trias Rhaet: *Thecodontosaurus dubius* Haughton 1924, *Gyposaurus capensis* Broom 1911, *G. erectus* (van Hoepen 1920), *G. skirtopodus* (Seeley 1894), Cave Sst, S. Africa; *G. sinensis* Young 1941, L. Lufeng Series, Yunnan.

Comments: Earlier prosauropod in Trias Anis, probably thecodontosaurid: *Nyasasaurus cromptoni* Charig 1967, Manda Fm, Tanzania. Similar, in Anis or Ladin, but might still be prestosuchid pseudosuchian: *Spondylosoma absconditum* von Huene 1942, Santa Maria Fm, Brazil. Supposed *Thecodontosaurus* spp. in Anis (Muschelkalk) of Germany, Lorraine and Silesia later referred (Huene 1931) to *Tanystropheus; Thecodontosaurus alophos* Haughton 1932 in Anis (Manda Fm) of Tanzania referred (Charig 1967) to the pseudosuchian *Teleocrater*. Probably derived directly from prestosuchid pseudosuchians.

Family PLATEOSAURIDAE Marsh 1895

First, Trias Nor: *Plateosaurus gracilis* von Huene 1908, *"Teratosaurus" minor* von Huene 1908, *"T." trossingensis* von Huene 1908, Stubensandstein, Germany.

Last, Trias Rhaet: *Plateosaurus* several spp., *Gresslyosaurus ingens* Rütimeyer 1857, U. Keuper, Germany; *Plateosaurus poligniensis* (Pidancet & Chopard 1862), Marnes Irisées, France; *Lufengosaurus huenei* Young 1941, *L. magnus* Young 1947, *Yunnanosaurus huangi* Young 1942, *Y. robustus* Young 1951, L. Lufeng Series, Yunnan.

Comment: "Teratosauridae" based on post-cranial remains now referred to this family (or, in a few cases, to Melanorosauridae).

Family MELANOROSAURIDAE von Huene 1929

First, Trias Ladin or Carn: *Melanorosaurus readi* Haughton 1924, *Plateosauravus stormbergensis* (Broom 1915), *P. cullingworthi* (Haughton 1924), *Euskelosaurus browni* Huxley 1866, *E. africanus* Haughton 1924, *Eucnemesaurus fortis* van Hoepen 1920, Passage Beds and lower Red Beds, S. Africa.

Last, Trias Rhaet: *Avalonianus sanfordi* (Seeley 1898), Somerset; *"Sinosaurus triassicus"* Young 1948 (post-cranial), L. Lufeng Series, Yunnan, China.

Comments: Rhaetic material listed above, previously classed as Teratosauridae, now referred to this family. "Blikana dinosaur" (Charig *et al.* 1965), Ladin or Carn (Passage Beds) of S. Africa, probably represents a new family.

712

Chapter 28: Reptilia

Infraorder SAUROPODA

Family MOROSAURIDAE Marsh 1882
(= BRACHIOSAURIDAE Riggs 1904)

First, L. Jur: *Rhoetosaurus brownei* Longman 1926, Walloon Coal Measures, Queensland, Australia.

Last, Cret Apt: *Pelorosaurus mackesoni* (Owen 1884), bowerbanki Z., L. Greensand, Kent, England.

Comments: Earlier record of probable sauropod footprints, presumably attributable to this family, in Trias Ladin or Carn?: "Soebeng trackways", Passage Beds, Lesotho (see Charig *et al.* 1965). Another record of bones in L. Jur: sauropod gen. indet., Kota Fm, Deccan (see Jain *et al.* 1962). Possible later records of this family in Cret, Alb or L. Cenom: *Rebbachisaurus garasbae* Lavocat 1954, Morocco; *R. tamesnensis* Lapparent 1960, Tunisia and Central Sahara; *Astrodon* sp. Lapparent 1960, Central Sahara. Doubtful last record in U. Cret, only a tooth: *Chiayusaurus lacustris* Bohlin 1953, Chia-yü-kuan, N.W. China.

Family ATLANTOSAURIDAE Marsh 1877
(= TITANOSAURIDAE Marsh 1895)

First, Jur Kimm: *Atlantosaurus alenquerensis* (Lapparent & Zbyszewski 1957), U. Lusitanian, Portugal. Middle Saurian Bed, Tanzania, with *Barosaurus africanus* (Fraas 1908) and *Dicraeosaurus hansemanni* Janensch 1914, reported as "Tith" but possibly extending down into Kimm.

Last, Cret Maestr: *Magyarosaurus* spp., "Danian", Transylvania (see Huene 1932); *Titanosaurus indicus* Lydekker 1877, France (see Lapparent 1947); *Hypselosaurus priscus* Matheron 1869, various fms, France and Spain; *Titanosaurus* cf. *indicus*, *Hypselosaurus* sp. nov., Spain (see Lapparent & Aguirre 1956); *Alamosaurus sanjuanensis* Gilmore 1922, Ojo Alamo Fm, New Mexico and North Horn Fm, Utah.

Comment: Cretaceous genera all Titanosaurinae, other subfamilies restricted to U. Jur.

Suborder THEROPODA

Infraorder COELUROSAURIA

Family PODOKESAURIDAE von Huene 1914

First, Trias Ladin: *Avipes dillstedtianus* von Huene 1932, Lettenkohle, Germany; *Triassolester romeri* Reig 1963, Ischigualasto Fm, Argentina. [Ischigualasto Fm submitted as Ladin, altered to Carn by Ed. L.B.H.T.]

Last, Trias Rhaet: *Lukousaurus yini* Young 1948, L. Lufeng Series, Yunnan.

Comment: Probably derived directly from teleocraterid pseudosuchians.

Family PROCOMPSOGNATHIDAE von Huene 1929

First, Trias Nor: *Procompsognathus triassicus* E. Fraas 1913, *Halticosaurus longotarsus* von Huene 1908, cf. *H. orbitoangulatus* von Huene 1932, Stubensandstein, Germany.

Last, Trias Nor or Rhaet: *Halticosaurus liliensterni* von Huene 1934, Knollenmergel, Germany.

Family AMMOSAURIDAE von Huene 1914

First and **Last,** Trias Nor or Rhaet: *Ammosaurus major* (Marsh 1889), *A. solus* (Marsh 1892), Portland Fm, Connecticut.

Comment: Classification as coelurosaur is doubtful.

Family SEGISAURIDAE Camp 1936

First and **Last,** L. Jur: *Segisaurus halli* Camp 1936, Navajo Sst, Arizona.

Family HALLOPODIDAE Marsh 1881

First and **Last,** U. Jur: *Hallopus victor* (Marsh 1877), Hallopus Beds, Colorado (beds of uncertain age, also claimed as U. Trias or L. Jur; see Schuchert 1939).

Family COELURIDAE Marsh 1881

First, Jur "Tith": *Coelurus fragilis* Marsh 1879, *C. hermanni* (Osborn 1903), Morrison Fm, Wyoming; *C. agilis* Marsh 1884, Morrison Fm, Colorado; *Compsognathus longipes* Wagner 1859, Solnhofener Schiefer, Bavaria, Germany; *Elaphrosaurus bambergi* Janensch 1921, Middle Saurian Bed, Tanzania; *Sinocoelurus fragilis* Young 1942, Kuangyuan Series, Szechuan, China.

Last, Cret Campan: *Dromaeosaurus albertensis* Matthew & Brown 1922, *Chirostenotes pergracilis* Gilmore 1924, Oldman Fm, Alberta, Canada.

Comment: Possible earlier record in Jur Kimm: *Caudocoelus sauvagei* von Huene 1932, U. Malm, France (1 distal caudal vertebra only). Age of M. Saurian Bed, Tanzania, with *Elaphrosaurus bambergi*, may also be Kimm rather than "Tith".

Family ORNITHOMIMIDAE Marsh 1890

First, Cret Haut–Barrem: *Ornithomimus affinis* Gilmore 1920, Arundel Fm, Maryland.

Last, Cret Maestr: *Ornithomimus velox* Marsh 1890, Denver Fm, Colorado and Hell Creek Fm, Montana; *O. sedens, O. minutus* both Marsh 1892, Lance Fm, Wyoming; *Ornithomimus* spp., Frenchman Fm, Saskatchewan and elsewhere in Maestr of N. America; ornithomimids gen. indet., Nemegetu Fm, Mongolia (Rozhdestvenskii 1957).

Comment: A few ornithomimid remains found by Young in lowermost Cret (Berr?) of Shantung, China, reported by von Huene 1956.

Infraorder CARNOSAURIA

(Superfamilies and families as in Walker 1964, except that first two families not regarded as one)

Superfamily TYRANNOSAUROIDEA

Family TERATOSAURIDAE Nopcsa 1923

First, Trias Carn–Nor: *Teratosaurus suevicus* von Meyer 1861, M. Keuper, Germany.

Last, Trias Rhaet: *Sinosaurus triassicus* Young 1948 (skull only), L. Lufeng Series, Yunnan, China.

Comments: Earlier records in Anis (Muschelkalk) and Ladin (Lettenkohle) of Germany based on highly doubtful material (jaw fragment and teeth). "Teratosauridae" based on post-cranial remains (inc. post-cranial *Sinosaurus triassicus*) referred to Plateosauridae or Melanorosauridae (Charig *et al.* 1965).

Family ORNITHOSUCHIDAE von Huene 1908

First and Last, Trias Nor: *Ornithosuchus longidens* (Huxley 1877), Lossiemouth Beds, Scotland.
Comment: Previously regarded as pseudosuchian (Walker 1964).

Family SPINOSAURIDAE Stromer 1915

First, L. Cret: *"Altispinax"* sp. (von Huene 1926), Wealden, Sussex, England.

Last, Cret Cenom: *Spinosaurus aegyptiacus* Stromer 1915, Baharia Fm, Egypt.

Comment: *Hypselorhachis mirabilis* Charig 1966, Manda Fm, Tanzania (Trias Anis) possibly ancestral to this family.

Family TYRANNOSAURIDAE Osborn 1906

First, Cret ?Alb: *Alectrosaurus olseni* Gilmore 1933, Iren Dabasu Fm, Mongolia.

Last, Cret Maestr: *Aublysodon lancensis* (Gilmore 1946), Hell Creek Fm, Montana; *Tyrannosaurus rex* Osborn 1905, Lance Fm, Montana, Wyoming, S. Dakota (?) and in Canada; *Aublysodon lancinator* (Maleev 1955), *A. novojilovi* (Maleev 1955), *Tyrannosaurus bataar, Tarbosaurus efremovi* both Maleev 1955 Nemegetu Fm, Mongolia.

Comment: Possible earlier record in Cret Apt? teeth only: *Prodeinodon mongoliensis* Osborn 1924, Oshih Fm, Mongolia.

Superfamily MEGALOSAUROIDEA

Family MEGALOSAURIDAE Huxley 1869

First, Jur Sinem: *Sarcosaurus woodi* Andrews 1921, bucklandi Z., L. Lias, Warwickshire, England (von Huene 1932).

Last, Cret Maestr: *Dryptosaurus aquilunguis* (Cope 1866), Navesink Fm, New Jersey.

Comments: Probably a heterogeneous assemblage. Possible earlier records in Jur Hett: *Sarcosaurus andrewsi* von Huene 1932, angulatum Z., L. Lias, Warwickshire, England; megalosaurid gen. indet. *terquemi* von Huene 1926, angulatum Z., Lorraine, France. ("*Megalosaurus*" *wetherilli* Welles 1954, Kayenta Fm, Arizona is probably Trias Rhaet but probably not a megalosaurid s.s.). Possible later records in Cret Maestr, mostly isolated teeth: *Megalosaurus pannoniensis* Seeley 1881, France (Lapparent 1947); *M.* cf. *pannoniensis*, Portugal (Lapparent & Zbyszewski 1957); *Megalosaurus* spp. indet., Transylvania (see Nopcsa 1915) and Ariyalur Stage, India (Lydekker 1877); *Chingkankousaurus fragilis* Young 1958a, U. Cret, Wangshih Series, Shantung.

Order ORNITHISCHIA

(Suborders and families approximately as in Romer 1956)

Comments: Ornithischians in U. Trias as yet insufficiently known to be referred with certainty to any of the existing families or even suborders. Possible "scelidosaurid" in Nor: *Fabrosaurus australis* Ginsburg 1964, upper Red Beds, Lesotho. Probable ornithopods in Rhaet: *Heterodontosaurus tucki* Crompton & Charig 1962, *Geranosaurus atavus* Broom 1911, Cave Sst, S. Africa. *Nanosaurus agilis* Marsh 1877, Hallopus Beds, Colorado, probably U. Jur (see Schuchert 1939). *Poposaurus gracilis* Mehl 1915, Popo Agie Fm, Wyoming and Dockum Group, Texas, probably a saurischian (see Colbert 1961). Many dinosaur-bearing beds of U. Cret, previously regarded as Tert Dan and now generally accepted as Maestr (e.g. "Danian" of Transylvania), may be even older (Jeletzky 1960, 1962); but dating of these continental deposits is itself based largely upon correlation of their very inadequately known dinosaur faunas, and the semi-conservative view that they are of Maestr age is generally adopted here.

Suborder STEGOSAURIA

Family "SCELIDOSAURIDAE" Huxley 1869

First, Jur Sinem: "*Scelidosaurus harrisoni*" Owen 1861, L. Lias, Dorset, England (i.e., the fairly complete skeleton; Lydekker's lectotype, a knee-joint, is a megalosaurid saurischian, see Newman 1967 *in press*); *Lusitanosaurus liasicus* Lapparent & Zbyszewski 1957, Lias, Portugal.

Last, Jur Oxf: *Sarcolestes leedsi* Lydekker 1893, Oxford Clay, Peterborough, England.

Comments: Known only from three genera mentioned, two of which are merely jaw fragments. Possibly ancestral to ankylosaurs as well as to stegosaurs. [See Ornithischia comment above, ed.]

Family STEGOSAURIDAE Marsh 1880

First, Jur Call: *Lexovisaurus durobrivensis* (Hulke 1887), England, *L.* cf. *durobrivensis*, France (see Hoffstetter 1957a).

Last, Jur "Tith": *Stegosaurus* spp., Morrison Fm, Colorado and Wyoming; *Kentrosaurus aethiopicus* Hennig 1915, U. Saurian Bed, Tanzania.

Comments: Possible earlier records in Bath: un-named dermal plates, Chipping Norton Lst, Gloucestershire, England (Reynolds 1939); *Dacentrurus vetustus* (von Huene 1910), Great Oolite, Oxfordshire, England (only a femur). Possible later records in Cret, all based on rather inadequate material: *Echinodon becklesi* Owen 1861, M. Purbeck (Berr), Dorset, England; *Craterosaurus pottonensis* Seeley 1874, Potton Sands (Neocomian), Bedfordshire, England; *Priconodon crassus* Marsh 1888, Potomac Fm (Neocomian), Maryland; *Paranthodon oweni* Nopcsa 1929, L. Cret, S. Africa; "*Stegosaurus*" *madagascariensis* Piveteau 1926, Turon, Madagascar. All well known forms are from U. Jur, cosmopolitan, highly specialised and presumably without descendants.

Suborder ANKYLOSAURIA

Family ACANTHOPHOLIDIDAE Nopcsa 1915

First, L. Cret: *Hylaeosaurus armatus* Mantell 1833, *H. northamptoni* (Mantell 1848), Wealden, Sussex and Isle of Wight, England.

Last, Cret Maestr: *Struthiosaurus transylvanicus* Nopcsa 1915, "Danian", Transylvania; *Rhodanosaurus ludgunensis* Nopcsa 1929, L. Rognacian, France.

Comments: From Europe and Mongolia only. The more primitive ankylosaurs, smaller and less heavily armoured. The U. Cret *Syrmosaurus* is considered by some to suggest ankylosaur-stegosaur affinities.

Family NODOSAURIDAE Marsh 1890

First, L. Cret (pre-Apt): *Polacanthus foxi* Hulke 1882, Wealden, Isle of Wight, England; *Polacanthoides ponderosus* Nopcsa 1929, Wealden, Isle of Wight and Sussex, England.

Last, Cret Maestr: *Euoplocephalus magniventris* (Brown 1908), Hell Creek Fm, Montana; *Palaeoscincus latus* Marsh 1892, Lance Fm, Wyoming; *Talarurus plicatospineus* Maleev 1952, Bain Shire, Mongolia.

Comments: Other records in U. Cret which may be Maestr: *Heishansaurus pachycephalus*, *Peishansaurus philemys* both Bohlin 1953, N.W. China. Very heavily armoured.

Suborder ORNITHOPODA

Family HYPSILOPHODONTIDAE Dollo 1882

First, Jur Kimm or ?"Tith": *Dysalotosaurus lettow-vorbecki* Pompeckj 1920, M. Saurian Bed, Tanzania. Also in "Tith": *Laosaurus* spp., Morrison Fm, U.S.A.; *Nanosaurus rex* Marsh 1877, Morrison Fm, Colorado.

Last, Cret Maestr: *Thescelosaurus neglectus* Gilmore 1913, Lance Fm, Wyoming and Frenchman Fm, Saskatchewan; *T. edmontonensis* Sternberg 1940, upper Edmonton Fm, Alberta.

Comment: Apparently the most primitive ornithopods, with teeth in premaxilla; but certain hypsilophodontids antedating more specialised iguanodontids not yet known.

Family IGUANODONTIDAE Huxley 1869

First, Jur Kimm: *Camptosaurus prestwichi* (Hulke 1880), Kimmeridge Clay, Oxfordshire, England; also from France.

Last, Cret Maestr: *Mochlodon priscus* (Matheron 1869), "Danian", Transylvania, and various fms, France and Spain.

Comments: Earlier records in Jur Oxf, based on rather inadequate material: *Camptosaurus leedsi* Lydekker 1889, Oxford Clay, Peterborough, England; *Cryptodraco eumerus* (Seeley 1875), Oxford Clay, Huntingdonshire and Dorset, England. The "typical" ornithopods, apparently most abundant in U. Jur and L. Cret. Presumably the ancestors of the hadrosaurs, and, through the psittacosaurids, of the ceratopsians.

Family HADROSAURIDAE Cope 1870

First, Cret ?Alb: *Bactrosaurus johnsoni* Gilmore 1933, Iren Dabasu Fm, Mongolia. Cret Cenom: *B. prynadi*, *Jaxartosaurus aralensis* both Ryabinin 1939, Kyrk-kuduk, Kazakhstan; "*Trachodon*" *cantabrigiensis* Lydekker 1888, Cambridge Greensand, England.

Last, Cret Maestr: *Anatosaurus* spp., Lance Fm, Wyoming, Montana, S. Dakota and in Frenchman Fm, Saskatchewan; *Thespesius occidentalis* Leidy 1856, Lance Fm, S. Dakota; *Edmontosaurus* sp. nov.? Rohrer & Konizeski 1960, Hell Creek Fm, Montana; *Kritosaurus navajovius* Brown 1910, *Parasaurolophus tubicen* Wiman 1931, Ojo Alamo Fm, New Mexico; *Telmatosaurus transsylvanicus* (Nopcsa 1899), "Danian", Transylvania, also France (see Lapparent 1947); *Orthomerus dolloi* Seeley 1883, Maastricht Beds, Netherlands; *Saurolophus angustirostris* Rozhdestvenskii 1952, Nemegetu Fm, Mongolia.

Comments: Other records in U. Cret, possibly Maestr: *Tanius chingkankouensis*, *Tsintaosaurus spinorhinus* both Young 1958, upper Wangshih Series, Shantung, China. Highly specialised; semiaquatic; very abundant in upper part of U. Cret.

Family PACHYCEPHALOSAURIDAE Sternberg 1945

First, Cret Campan: *Stegoceras validus* Lambe 1902, *S. brevis* Lambe 1919, *S. sternbergi* (Brown & Schlaikjer 1943), *S. lambei* Sternberg 1945, Oldman Fm, Alberta, Canada. Also in U. Cret: *S. bexelli* (Bohlin 1953), Tsondolein-khuduk, N.W. China.

Last, Cret Maestr: *Pachycephalosaurus wyomingensis* (Gilmore 1931), Lance Fm, Wyoming; *P. grangeri* Brown & Schlaikjer 1943, Lance Fm, Montana; *P. reinheimeri* Brown & Schlaikjer 1943, Lance Fm, S. Dakota.

Comment: Includes only the two aberrant genera mentioned above.

Chapter 28: Reptilia

Family PSITTACOSAURIDAE Osborn 1923

First, Cret ?Apt: *Protiguanodon mongoliensis* Osborn 1923, Ondai Sair Fm, Mongolia.

Last, Cret ?Apt: *Psittacosaurus mongoliensis* Osborn 1923, Ashile (= Oshih) Fm, Mongolia.

Comments: *Protiguanodon* cf. *mongoliensis* and *Psittacosaurus* spp. in beds of presumably equivalent age in Shantung, China (Young 1958a, Chao 1962), and N.W. China (Young 1931, Bohlin 1953). Possible earlier record: *Stenopelix valdensis* von Meyer 1857, Wealden, Germany. Otherwise family apparently restricted to upper L. Cret, E. Asia. Seems to represent intermediate stage in evolution of Ceratopsia from Ornithopoda, reverting from bipedality to quadrupedality.

Suborder CERATOPSIA

Family PROTOCERATOPSIDAE Granger & Gregory 1923

First, Cret ?Cenom-Coniac: *Protoceratops andrewsi* Granger & Gregory 1923, Djadochta Fm, Mongolia.

Last, Cret Maestr: *Leptoceratops gracilis* Brown 1914, upper Edmonton Fm, Alberta, Canada.

Comments: *Microceratops* spp. Bohlin 1953, N.W. China, based on inadequate material of possibly Maestr age. Small primitive ceratopsians without proper horns, apparently restricted to N. America and China.

Family CERATOPSIDAE Marsh 1888

First, Cret Campan: *Brachyceratops* spp., *Ceratops* spp., *Chasmosaurus* spp., *Eoceratops canadensis* (Lambe 1902), *Monoclonius* spp., *Styracosaurus* spp., Judith River and Two Medicine Fms, Montana, and Oldman Fm, Alberta, Canada (these genera restricted to Campan). Also in Oldman Fm: *Anchiceratops* spp. indet. Langston 1959.

Last, Cret Maestr: *Torosaurus latus* Marsh 1891, *T. gladius* Marsh 1896, *Triceratops horridus* Marsh 1889, top of Lance Fm, Wyoming; *Torosaurus latus* also in Hell Creek Fm, S. Dakota (see Colbert & Bump 1947).

Comments: Earlier record of ceratopsian tooth fragment in Cret Santon: cf. *Brachyceratops* sp., U. Milk River Fm, Alberta, Canada (see Russell 1935). The horned dinosaurs of the U. Cret; restricted to N. America except for one fragment from Mongolia and one from Argentina.

Family PACHYRHINOSAURIDAE Sternberg 1950

First and **Last,** Cret Maestr: *Pachyrhinosaurus canadensis* Sternberg 1950, St Mary River Fm, Alberta.

Comment: One single aberrant species.

Order PTEROSAURIA

Suborder RHAMPHORHYNCHOIDEA

Family RHAMPHORHYNCHIDAE Seeley 1870

First, Jur Sinem: *Dimorphodon macronyx* (Buckland 1829), L. Lias, Dorset.

Last, Jur "Tith": *Rhamphorhynchus* spp., *Odontorhynchus aculeatus* Stolley 1936, *Scaphognathus crassirostris* (Goldfuss 1831), Solnhofener Schiefer, Bavaria, Germany; ?*Rhamphorhynchus tendagurensis* Reck 1931, Upper Saurian Bed, Tanzania. Also in U. Jur *Batrachognathus volans* Ryabinin 1948, Paper Shs, Kazakhstan.

Comment: Evidence of indeterminate pterosaurs—fragmentary bones and impressions— begins in Rhaet, Germany.

Suborder PTERODACTYLOIDEA

Family PTERODACTYLIDAE C. L. Bonaparte 1840

First and **Last,** Jur "Tith": *Pterodactylus* spp., *Anurognathus ammoni* Döderlein 1923, ?*Belonochasma aenigmaticum* Broili 1939, *Ctenochasma gracile* Oppel 1862, *Germanodactylus kochi* (Wagner 1837) (see Young 1964b), Solnhofener Schiefer, Bavaria, Germany; ?*Pterodactylus* spp. Reck 1931, U. Saurian Bed, Tanzania.

Comment: Fragmentary, possibly pterodactylid remains may extend range from Oxf to L. Cret.

Family ORNITHODESMIDAE Hooley 1913

First, L. Cret: *Ornithodesmus cluniculus* Seeley 1887, *O. latidens* Seeley 1901, Wealden, Isle of Wight, England.

Last, Cret Cenom: Un-named humeri (Hooley 1913), L. Chalk, Kent, England.

Family ORNITHOCHEIRIDAE Seeley 1870

(= PTERANODONTIDAE Marsh 1876)

First, L. Cret: *Coloborhynchus clavirostris* Owen 1874, Hastings Sands, Sussex, England.

Last, Cret Santon: *Ornithocheirus cuvieri* (Bowerbank 1851), *O. giganteus* (Bowerbank 1846), U. Chalk, Kent, England; *Pteranodon* spp., *Nyctosaurus gracilis* Marsh 1876, *N. nanus* (Marsh 1881), Niobrara Chalk, Kansas.

Comment: Two later records of fragmentary pterosaurs, probably ornithocheirid, in Cret Maestr: *Nyctosaurus lamegoi* Price 1953, Gramame Fm (or possibly Itamaracá Fm, Campan), Brazil; *Titanopteryx philadelphiae* Arambourg 1959, Phosphates de Roseifa, Jordan.   (A.J.C.)

Subclass SYNAPSIDA

Order PELYCOSAURIA

All the suborders are most common in the L. Perm of N. America, but are also known from Europe.

Suborder OPHIACODONTIA

Family OPHIACODONTIDAE Nopsca 1923

First, Carb Bashk: *Protoclepsydrops haplous* Carroll, 1964, Joggins Fm, Nova Scotia, Canada (Carroll 1964).

Last, Perm Leonard: *Varanosaurus acutirostris* Broili 1904, Arroyo Fm, Clear Fork Gp, Texas (Romer & Price 1940).

Family EOTHYRIDIDAE Romer & Price 1940

First, Carb U. Carb: *Stereorhachis dominans* Gaudry 1880, U. Steph, Autun, France (Romer & Price 1940).

Last, Perm Leonard: *Eothyris parkeyi* Romer 1937, Belle Plains Fm, Wichita Group, Texas (Romer & Price 1940).

Suborder SPHENACODONTIA

Family VARANOPSIDAE Romer & Price 1940

First and **Last,** Perm Leonard: *Varanops brevirostris* (Williston 1914), Arroyo Fm, Clear Fork Group, Texas (Romer & Price 1940).

Comment: This is the only certain varanopsid, but possible later forms include *Elliotsmithia* Broom 1937 and *Anningia* Broom 1927, both from Perm, Dzhulf, Tapinocephalus Z., Beaufort Series, S. Africa, and *Mesenosaurus* Efremov 1938 from Perm, Guad, Zone II, Archangel Prov., U.S.S.R. Alternatively these forms may be related to millerettid captorhinomorphs (Watson 1957), see above under Lepidosauria.

Family SPHENACODONTIDAE Williston 1912

First, Carb U. Carb: *Macromerion schwarzenbergi* Fritsch 1879, Steph, Gaskohle, Kounova, Czechoslovakia (Romer 1945).

Last, Perm Guad: *Dimetrodon angelensis* Olson 1962, San Angelo Fm, Pease River Group, Texas (Olson 1962).

Chapter 28: Reptilia

Suborder EDAPHOSAURIA

Family EDAPHOSAURIDAE Case 1907

First, Carb U. Carb: *Edaphosaurus ecordi* Peabody 1957, Missourian Series, Kansas (Peabody 1957).

Last, Perm Leonard: *Edaphosaurus pogonias* Cope 1882, Arroyo Fm, Clear Fork Group, Texas (Romer & Price 1940).

Family NITOSAURIDAE Romer & Price 1940

First and **Last,** Perm Leonard: *Nitosaurus jacksonorum* Romer 1937, Abo Fm, New Mexico, and *Mycterosaurus longiceps* Williston 1915, Clyde Fm, Clear Fork Group, Texas (Romer & Price 1940).

Family LUPEOSAURIDAE Romer & Price 1940

First and **Last,** Perm, Leonard: *Lupeosaurus kayi* Romer 1937, Moran Fm, Wichita Group, Texas (Romer & Price 1940).

Suborder CASEOIDEA

Family CASEIDAE Williston 1912

First, Perm Leonard: *Casea broilii* Williston 1910, Vale Fm, Clear Fork Froup, Texas (Romer & Price 1940). *Colobomycter pholeter* Vaughn 1958 is a slightly earlier possible caseid from fissure deposits in Oklahoma, which may indicate that the group originated from eothyrids (Vaughn 1958, Langston 1965).

Last, Perm Guad, *Ennatosaurus tecton* Vjushkov 1955, Zone II, Archangel Prov. U.S.S.R. (Olson 1962).

Order THERAPSIDA

Origin: from sphenacodont Pelycosauria.

Suborder DEINOCEPHALIA

Infraorder EODEINOCEPHALIA Olson 1962

Known from N. America and U.S.S.R. only.

First, Perm Guad: *Mastersonia driverensis* Olson 1962, San Angelo Fm, Pease River Group, Texas (Olson 1962).

Last, Perm Guad: *Deuterosaurus biarmicus* Eichwald 1861, Zone II, Molotov (Perm) Prov., U.S.S.R. (Olson 1957).

Infraorder EUDEINOCEPHALIA

Superfamily TITANOSUCHOIDEA Olson 1962

First and **Last,** Perm Dzhulf: numerous spp., Tapinocephalus Z., Beaufort Series, S. Africa (Haughton & Brink 1955).

Comment: Origin from estemennosuchid Eodeinocephalia (Olson 1962).

Superfamily TAPINOCEPHALOIDEA Olson 1962

First, Perm, Guad: *Ulemosaurus svijagensis* Riabinin 1938, Zone II, Tatar Rep., U.S.S.R. (Olson 1957).

Last, Perm, Dzhulf: numerous spp., Tapinocephalus Z., Beaufort Ser., S. Africa (Haughton & Brink 1955).

Comment: Origin from deuterosaurid Eodeinocephalia (Olson 1962).

719

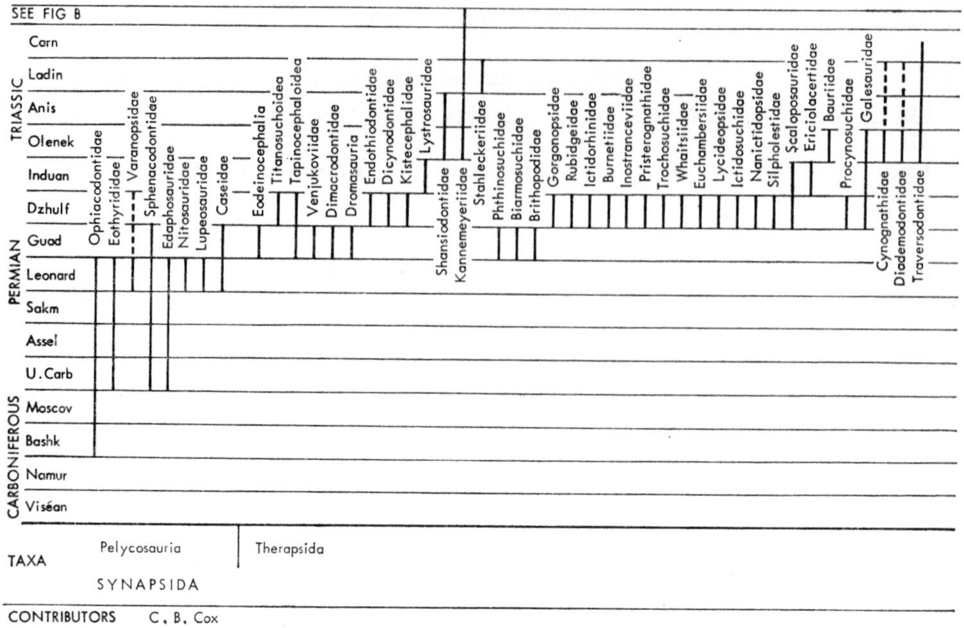

SEE FIG B

Chart axes — left margin periods and stages:

TRIASSIC: Carn, Ladin, Anis, Olenek, Induan

PERMIAN: Dzhulf, Guad, Leonard, Sakm, Assel

U.Carb

CARBONIFEROUS: Moscov, Bashk, Namur, Viséan

Taxa columns (left to right): Ophiacodontidae, Eothyrididae, Varanopsidae, Sphenacodontidae, Edaphosauridae, Nitosauridae, Lupeosauridae, Caseidae, Eodeinocephalia, Titanosuchoidea, Tapinocephaloidea, Venjukoviidae, Dimacrodontidae, Dromasauria, Endothiodontidae, Dicynodontidae, Kistecephalidae, Lystrosauridae, Shansiodontidae, Kannemeyeriidae, Strahleckeriidae, Phthinosuchidae, Biarmosuchidae, Brithopodidae, Gorgonopsidae, Rubidgeidae, Ictidorhinidae, Burnetiidae, Inostranceviidae, Pristerognathidae, Trochosuchidae, Whaitsiidae, Euchambersiidae, Lycideopsidae, Ictidosuchidae, Nanictidopsidae, Silpholestidae, Scaloposauridae, Ericiolacertidae, Bauriidae, Procynosuchidae, Galesauridae, Cynognathidae, Diademodontidae, Traversodontidae

TAXA   Pelycosauria | Therapsida

SYNAPSIDA

CONTRIBUTORS   C. B. Cox

FIG. 28.4 A

Suborder ANOMODONTIA

Infraorder VENJUKOVIOIDEA

Family VENJUKOVIIDAE Efremov 1940

First, Perm Guad: *Otsheria netzvetajevi* Chudinov 1960, Zone I, Ezhovo, Molotov Prov., U.S.S.R. (Olson 1962).

Last, Perm Guad: *Venjukovia* Amalitzky 1922, Zone II, Isheevo, Tatar Rep., U.S.S.R. (Olson 1957).

Family DIMACRODONTIDAE Olson & Beerbower 1953

First and **Last,** Perm Guad: *Dimacrodon hottoni* Olson & Beerbower 1953, San Angelo Fm, Pease River Group, Texas (Olson 1962).

Infraorder DROMASAURIA Broom 1907

First and **Last,** Perm Guad: *Galeops whaitsi* Broom 1912, Tapinocephalus Z., Beaufort Series, S. Africa, and two other genera (*Galechirus scholtzi* Broom 1907 and *Galepus jouberti* Broom 1910) of uncertain stratigraphic origin within the Beaufort Ser. (Haughton & Brink 1955).

Infraorder DICYNODONTIA

Origin: probably from venjukovii anomodonts. Known from Africa and Eurasia in U. Perm; world-wide in Trias (exc. Australia), though only one very late record in N. America.

Family ENDOTHIODONTIDAE Lydekker 1890

First and **Last,** Perm Dzhulf: numerous spp., Tapinocephalus, Endothiodon, and Kistecephalus Z., Beaufort Ser., A. Africa, and fs of similar age in Central and E. Africa (Haughton & Brink 1955, Cox 1964).

Family DICYNODONTIDAE Owen 1860

First and **Last,** Perm Dzhulf: numerous spp., Tapinocephalus, Endothiodon and Kistecephalus Z., Beaufort Series, S. Africa, and formations of similar age in Central and E. Africa, Gt. Britain, U.S.S.R. and China (Haughton & Brink 1955).

Family KISTECEPHALIDAE Seeley 1895

First and **Last,** Perm Dzhulf: numerous spp., Kistecephalus Z., Beaufort Series, S. Africa, and formations of similar age in Central and East Africa (Haughton & Brink 1955).

Family LYSTROSAURIDAE Broom 1903

First and **Last,** Trias Induan: *Lystrosaurus* spp., Lystrosaurus Z., Beaufort Series, S. Africa, and formations of similar age in India and China (Cox 1965).

Family SHANSIODONTIDAE Cox 1965

First, Trias Olenek: *Shansiodon wangi* Yeh 1959, Er-ma-ying Series, Shansi, China (Yeh 1959).

Last, Trias Anis: *"Dicynodon" njalilus* von Huene 1942, Manda Fm, E. Africa (Cox 1965).

Family KANNEMEYERIIDAE von Huene 1948

First, Trias Olenek: *Kannemeyeria* Seeley 1909, Cynognathus Z., Beaufort Series, S. Africa (Haughton & Brink 1955). The family is known also from L. Trias formations in China and U.S.S.R., and from M. Trias formations in E. Africa and S. America (Cox 1965).

Last, Trias Nor: *Placerias* Lucas 1904, Chinle Fm, Arizona (Camp & Wells 1956, Cox 1965).

Family STAHLECKERIIDAE Cox 1965

First and **Last,** Trias Ladin: *Stahleckeria* von Huene 1935 and *Dinodontosaurus* Romer 1943, both from Santa Maria Fm, Brazil, S. America (Cox 1965).

Suborder THERIODONTIA

Infraorder EOTHERIODONTA

Known from N. America and U.S.S.R. only.

Family PHTHINOSUCHIDAE Efremov 1954

First, Perm Guad: *Eotitanosuchus olsoni* Tchudinov 1960, Zone I, Ezhovo, Molotov Prov., U.S.S.R. (Olson 1962).

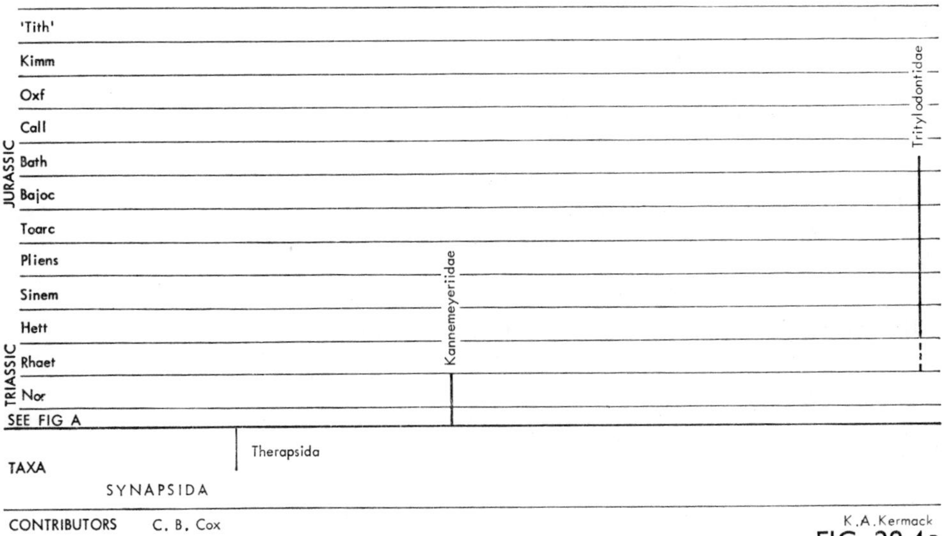

FIG. 28.4B

Last, Perm Guad: *Phthinosuchus discors* Efremov 1954, Zone II, Kluchevsky, Bashkir Rep., U.S.S.R. (Olson 1962).

Family BIARMOSUCHIDAE Olson 1962

First and **Last,** Perm Guad: *Biarmosuchus tener* Chudinov 1960 and *Biarmosaurus antecessor* Chudinov 1964, both from Zone I, Ezhovo, Molotov Prov., U.S.S.R. (Olson 1962).

Family BRITHOPODIDAE Efremov 1954

First, Perm Guad: *Archaeosyodon praeventor* Chudinov 1960, Zone I, Ezhovo, Molotov Prov., U.S.S.R. (Olson 1962).

Last, Perm Guad: *Titanophoneus potens* Efremov 1938 and *Doliosuchus yanshinovi* both from Zone II, Isheevo, Tatar Rep., U.S.S.R. (Olson 1962).

Infraorder EUTHERIODONTA

Superfamily GORGONOPSIA

Known only from Africa, except for two genera from the U.S.S.R.

Family GORGONOPSIDAE Lydekker 1890

Origin: from phthinosuchid Eotheriodonta.

First and **Last,** Perm Dzhulf: numerous spp., Tapinocephalus, Endothiodon or Kistecephalus Z., Beaufort Series, S. Africa, and formations of similar age in Central and E. Africa (Haughton & Brink 1955).

Family RUBIDGEIDAE Broom 1938

First, Perm Dzhulf: *Smilesaurus ferox* Broom 1948, Endothiodon Z., Beaufort Series, S. Africa (Haughton & Brink 1955).

Last, Perm Dzhulf: several spp., Kistecephalus Z., Beaufort Series, S. Africa (Haughton & Brink 1955).

Family ICTIDORHINIDAE Boonstra 1952

First, Perm Dzhulf: *Hipposaurus boonstrai* Haughton 1929 and *H. major* Boonstra 1952, both from Tapinocephalus Z., Beaufort Series, S. Africa (Haughton & Brink 1955).

Last, Perm Dzhulf: several spp., Kistecephalus Z., Beaufort Series, S. Africa (Haughton & Brink 1955).

Family BURNETIIDAE Broom 1923

First and **Last,** Perm Dzhulf: *Burnetia mirabilis* Broom 1923, Kistecephalus Z., Beaufort Series, S. Africa (Haughton & Brink 1955).

Family INOSTRANCEVIIDAE Pravoslavlev 1927

First and **Last,** Perm Dzhulf: *Amalitzkia* Pravoslavlev 1927 and *Inostrancevia* Amalitzky 1922, both from Zone IV, Archangel and Vologda Provs, U.S.S.R. (Watson & Romer 1956, Olson 1957).

Superfamily THEROCEPHALIA Broom 1903

Known only from Africa, except for one genus from U.S.S.R.

Family PRISTEROGNATHIDAE Broom 1908

First and **Last,** Perm Dzhulf: Several spp., Tapinocephalus Z., Beaufort Series, S. Africa (Watson & Romer 1956).

Family TROCHOSUCHIDAE Watson & Romer 1956

First and **Last,** Perm Dzhulf: Several spp., Tapinocephalus Z., Beaufort Series, S. Africa (Watson & Romer 1956).

Chapter 28: Reptilia

Family WHAITSIIDAE Haughton 1918

First, Perm Dzhulf: *Hofmeyria atavus* Broom 1935, Endothiodon Z., Beaufort Series, S. Africa (Haughton & Brink 1955).

Last, Perm Dzhulf: Several spp., Kistecephalus Z., Beaufort Series S. Africa and formations of similar age in Central and E. Africa (Watson & Romer 1956) and U.S.S.R. (Tatarinov 1963).

Family EUCHAMBERSIIDAE Boonstra 1934

First and **Last,** Perm Dzhulf: *Euchambersia mirabilis* Broom 1931, Kistecephalus Z., Beaufort Series, S. Africa (Watson & Romer 1956).

Superfamily BAURIAMORPHA Watson 1917

Origin: from Therocephalia. Known only from Africa, except for one record in the U.S.S.R.

Family LYCIDEOPSIDAE Boonstra 1934

First and **Last,** Perm Dzhulf: *Lycideops longiceps* Broom 1931, Kistecephalus Z., Beaufort Series, S. Africa (Watson & Romer 1956).

Family ICTIDOSUCHIDAE Broom 1903

First and **Last,** Perm Dzhulf: *Ictidosuchus primaevus* Broom 1900, Endothiodon Z., Beaufort Series, S. Africa (Watson & Romer 1956).

Family NANICTIDOPSIDAE Watson & Romer 1956

First and **Last,** Perm Dzhulf: Several spp., Kistecephalus Z., Beaufort Series, S. Africa (Watson & Romer 1956).

Family SILPHOLESTIDAE Watson & Romer 1956

First and **Last,** Perm Dzhulf: Several spp., Endothiodon or Kistecephalus Zones, Beaufort Series, S. Africa (Watson & Romer 1956).

Family SCALOPOSAURIDAE Broom 1914

First, Perm Dzhulf: *Icticephalus polycynodon* Broom 1915, Tapinocephalus Z., Beaufort Series, S. Africa (Watson & Romer 1956).

Last, Trias Induan: *Tetracynodon darti* Sigogneau 1963, Lystrosaurus Z., Beaufort Series, S. Africa (Sigogneau 1963).

Family ERICIOLACERTIDAE Watson & Romer 1956

First and **Last,** Trias Induan: *Ericiolacerta* spp., Lystrosaurus Z., Beaufort Series, S. Africa (Watson & Romer 1956) and formations of similar age in the U.S.S.R. (Vjushkov 1964).

Family BAURIIDAE Watson 1914

First and **Last,** Trias Olenek: Several genera, Cynognathus Z., Beaufort Series, S. Africa (Watson & Romer 1956).

Superfamily CYNODONTIA Owen 1860

Origin: from early Bauriamorpha? (Brink 1961). Known from Africa, S. America, U.S.S.R and China.

Family PROCYNOSUCHIDAE Broom 1937

First and **Last,** Perm Dzhulf: Several spp., Kistecephalus Z., Beaufort Series, S. Africa and formations of similar age in E. Africa and U.S.S.R. (Watson & Romer 1956).

Family GALESAURIDAE Lydekker 1890

First, Perm Dzhulf: *Cynosaurus suppostus* (Owen 1876), Kistecephalus Z., Beaufort Series, S. Africa (Watson & Romer 1956).

Last, Trias Olenek: *Sysphinctostoma smithi* Broili & Schröder 1936 and *S. gracilis* Broom 1950, both from Cynognathus Z., Beaufort Series, S. Africa (Watson & Romer 1956) and *Sinognathus gracilis* Young 1959 from formation of similar age in Shansi, China (Young 1959c).

Family CYNOGNATHIDAE Seeley 1895

First and **Last,** Trias Olenek: Several genera, Cynognathus Z., Beaufort Series, S. Africa (Watson & Romer 1956). *Chiniquodon* von Huene 1936 and *Belesodon* von Huene 1936, from probably Ladinian Rio do Rasto beds of Brazil, may be later survivors (Watson & Romer 1956).

Family DIADEMODONTIDAE Haughton 1925

First and **Last,** Trias Olenek: Several genera, Cynognathus Z., Beaufort Series, S. Africa, and formations of similar age in Central Africa and China (Watson & Romer 1956, Brink 1963, Young 1961a). A specimen from E. Africa, and *Gomphodontosuchus* von Huene 1928 from probably Ladin, Rio do Rasto beds of Brazil, may be later survivors (Crompton & Ellenberger 1957).

Family TRAVERSODONTIDAE von Huene 1936

First, Trias Olenek: *Trirachodon* Seeley 1894, Cynognathus Z., Beaufort Series, S. Africa (Crompton & Ellenberger 1957).

Last, Trias Carn: several genera from the Ischigualasto beds of Argentina (Bonaparte 1963). [C.B.C.]

Infra-order TRITYLODONTIA

Family TRITYLODONTIDAE Cope

First, Trias Rhaet-Jur Hett.: *Chalepotherium* Simpson, prob. Schlosslemuhle, Württemberg, Germany.

Last, Jur Bath: *Stereognathus* Charlesworth, Stonesfield Slate, Oxfordshire, England.

Constituent genera: *Archaeodon?*, F. von Huene, *Bienotherium* Young, *Chalepotherium* Simpson, *Eoraetia?* Dietrich, *Likhoelia* Ginsberg, *Lufengia* Chow & Hu, *Mucrotherium* F. von Huene, *Oligokyphus* Hennig, *Stereognathus* Charlesworth, (*Triglyphus*) Fraas, *Tritylodon* Owen, *Unitherium* F. von Huene, undescribed from Arizona (Lewis 1955).

Comment: some of the other genera may be older than *Chalepotherium*. None, however, would be older than the Upper Trias. *Eoraetia* is an ulna. If it is tritylodontid it is the earliest dateable member of the family—L. Rhaet.

Infra-order ICTIDOSAURIA

Not included in the time charts.

Family TRITHELODONTIDAE Broom

First and **Last,** U. Trias–L. Jur: *Trithelodon* Broom, Red Beds (Stormberg), Griqualand East, S. Africa.

Comment: *Pachygenelus* Watson is probably a synonym of *Trithelodon;* closer dating of *Trithelodon* is impossible.

Family DIARTHROGNATHIDAE Crompton

First and **Last,** U. Trias–L. Jur: *Diarthrognathus* Crompton, Cave Sandstone (Stormberg), Ladybrand, South Africa.

Comment: Classification follows Crompton (1958). May be better classified as a mammal. Cannot be more closely dated.

Family indeterminate

First and **Last,** U. Trias–L. Jur: *Kunminia* Young, Lu Feng Beds, Yunnan, China.

Comment: Cannot be more closely dated. May be a mammal.

Chapter 28: Reptilia

Infra-order indeterminate

Family DROMOTHERIIDAE Osborn

First and **Last,** Trias? Rhaet.: *Dromatherium* Emmons, *Microconodon* Osborn, both from Egypt, N. Carolina.

Infra-class indeterminate

Family indeterminate

First and **Last,** Trias Rhaet–Jur Hett.: *Tricuspes* F. von Huene, Bone-bed, Gaisbrunnen, Württemburg, Germany.

Comment: May be mammal.   [K.A.K.]

REFERENCES

ANDERSON, C. 1925. Notes on the extinct chelonian *Meiolania*, with a record of a new occurrence. *Rec. Aust. Mus.*, **14,** 223–242.

APPLEBY, R. M. 1961. On the cranial anatomy of the ichthyosaurs. *Proc. zool. Soc. Lond.*, **137,** 333–370.

ARAMBOURG, C. 1959. *Titanopteryx philadelphiae* nov. gen., nov. sp., ptérosaurien géant. *Notes Mém. Moyen-Orient*, **7,** 229–234.

—— & SIGNEUX, J. 1952. Les vertébrés fossiles des Gisements de Phosphates (Maroc—Algérie—Tunisie). *Notes Mém. Serv. Mines Carte géol. Maroc*, **92,** 1–372.

AUFFENBERG, W. 1959. *Anomalophis bolcensis* (Massalongo), a new genus of fossil snake from the Italian Eocene. *Breviora*, **114,** 1–16.

BAIRD, D. 1964. *Changisaurus* reinterpreted as a Jurassic turtle. *J. Paleont.*, **38,** 126–127.

BOHLIN, B. 1953. Fossil reptiles from Mongolia and Kansu. *Rep. scient. Exped. N.W. Prov. China*, **6,** (6), 1–113.

BONAPARTE, J. F. 1963. La familia traversodontidae. *Acta geol. Lilloana*, **4,** 163–94.

BRINK, A. S. 1961. A new type of primitive cynodont. *Palaeont. afr.*, **7,** 119–54.

—— 1963. Two cynodonts from the Ntawere Formation in the Luangwa Valley of Northern Rhodesia. *Palaeont. afr.*, **8,** 77–96.

BROILI, F. 1907–8. Ein neuer *Ichthyosaurus* aus der norddeutschen Kreide. *Palaeontographica*, **54,** 139–162.

BUCHAN, S. H., CHALLINOR A., HARLAND, W. B. & PARKER, J. R. 1965. The Triassic stratigraphy of Svalbard. *Skr. Norsk Polarinst.*, **135,** Oslo 1965.

CAMP, C. L. & WELLES, S. P. 1956. Triassic dicynodont reptiles. Part I. The North American genus *Placerias*. *Mem. Univ. Calif.*, **13,** 255–304.

CARROLL, R. L. 1964. The earliest reptiles. *J. Linn. Soc.* Zool. series, **45,** 61–83.

CASAMIQUELA, R. M. 1960. Noticia preliminar sobre dos nuevos estagonolepóideos argentinos. *Ameghiniana*, **2,** 3–9.

—— 1961. Dos nuevos estagonolepóideos argentinos (de Ischigualasto, San Juan). *Revta Asoc. geol. argent.*, **16,** 143–203.

CHAO, S.-T. 1962. O novom vide psittakozavrov iz Laiyana, Shan'dun. *Vertebr. palasiat.*, **6,** 349–364.

CHARIG, A. J. 1967. Preliminary note on the archosaurs in the Manda Formation (Middle Trias) of Tanzania. *Palaeontology*, In press.

——, ATTRIDGE, J. & CROMPTON, A. W. 1965. On the origin of the sauropods and the classification of the Saurischia. *Proc. Linn. Soc. Lond.*, **176,** part 2, 197–221.

—— & REIG, O. A. 1967. The classification of the Proterosuchia. *Proc. Linn. Soc. Lond.* (in the press).

CHOWDHURY, T. R. 1965. A new metoposaurid amphibian from the Upper Triassic Maleri formation of Central India. *Phil. Trans. R. Soc.*, **250B,** 1–52.

CHUDINOV, P. K. 1957. Cotylosaurians from the Upper Permian Red Beds of the Pre-Ural region. *Trav. Inst. paléozool. Acad. Sci. U.R.S.S.*, **68**, 19–88.

—— 1964. Superfamily Lacertoidea *in Osnovy Paleontologii*, **12**, 468–469.

COCUDE-MICHEL, M. 1961. Les Sauriens des calcaires lithographiques de Baviere, d'age portlandien inferieur. *Bull. Soc. Geol. France*, set 7, **2**, 707–710.

—— 1963. Les Rhynchocéphales et les Sauriens des calcaires lithographiques (Jurassique supérieur) d'Europe occidentale. *Thèse Univ. Nancy Fac. Sci.*, 187 pp.

COLBERT, E. H. 1946. *Hypsognathus*, a Triassic reptile from New Jersey. *Bull. Am. Mus. Nat. Hist.* **86**, 229–274.

—— 1958. Relationships of the Traissic Maleri fauna. *Journ. palaeont. Soc. India*, **3**, 68–81.

—— 1961. The Triassic reptile, *Poposaurus*. *Fieldiana: Geol.*, **14**, 59–78.

—— 1963. Relationships of the Triassic reptilian faunas of Brazil and South Africa. *A. Afr. J. Sci.*, **59**, 248–253.

—— 1966. A gliding reptile from the Triassic of New Jersey. *Am. Mus. Novit.*, **2246**, 1–23.

—— & BUMP, J. D. 1947. A skull of *Torosaurus* from South Dakota and a revision of the genus. *Proc. Acad. nat. Sci. Philad.*, **99**, 93–106.

COX, C. B. 1964. On the palate, dentition, and classification of the fossil reptile *Endothiodon* and related genera. *Am. Mus. Novit.* **2171**, 1–26.

—— 1965. New triassic dicynodonts from South America, their origins and relationships. *Phil. Trans. R. Soc.*, **248**B, 457–516.

CROMPTON, A. W. 1958. The cranial morphology of a new genus and species of ictidosaurian. *Proc. zool. Soc. Lond.*, **130**, 183.

—— & CHARIG, A. J. 1962. A new ornithischian from the Upper Triassic of South Africa. *Nature, Lond.*, **196**, 1074–1077.

—— & ELLENBERGER, F. 1957. On a new cynodont from the Molteno Beds and the origin of the tritylodontids. *Ann. S. Afr. Mus.* **44**, 1–14.

DEBELMAS, J. 1957. Sur la persistance du genre *Dacosaurus* dans le Néocomien de la Haute-Provence. *C.r. hebd. Séanc. Acad. Sci., Paris*, **244**, 1238–1240.

DELAIR, J. B. 1958. The Mesozoic reptiles of Dorset. *Proc. Dorset nat. Hist. Soc.*, **79**, 47–72.

EUDES–DESLONGCHAMPS, J. A. 1868. Note sur un groupe de vertèbres et d'écailles rapportées au *Teleosaurus hastifer* etc. *Bull. Soc. linn. Normandie* (2), **1**, 146–156.

EWER, R. F. 1965. The anatomy of the thecodont reptile *Euparkeria capensis* Broom. *Phil. Trans. R. Soc.* **248**B, 379–435.

FOX, R. C. & BOWMAN, M. C. 1966. Osteology and relationships of *Captorhinus aguti* (Cope) (Reptilia, Captorhinomorpha). *Paleont. Contr. Univ. Kans.*, **11**, 1–38.

FRAAS, E. 1902. Die Meer-Crocodilier (Thalattosuchia) des oberen Jura unter specieller Berück-sichtigung von *Dacosaurus* und *Geosaurus*. *Palaeontographica* **49**, (1) 1–72.

GINSBURG, L. 1964. Découverte d'un scélidosaurien (dinosaure ornithischien) dans le Trias supérieur du Basutoland. *C.r. hebd. Séanc. Acad. Sci., Paris*, **258**, 2366–2368.

GREGORY, J. T. 1953. *Typothorax* and *Desmatosuchus*. *Postilla*, **16**, 1–27.

—— 1957. Significance of fossil vertebrates for correlation of late Triassic continental deposits of North America. *20th Int. geol. Congr.*, Sec. 2, 7–25.

—— 1962. The genera of phytosaurs. *Am. J. Sci.*, **260**, 652–690.

HAUGHTON, S. H. 1924. The fauna and stratigraphy of the Stormberg Series. *Ann. S. Afr. Mus.*, **12**, 323–497.

—— & BRINK, A. S. 1955. A bibliographical list of Reptilia from the Karroo beds of Africa. *Palaeont. afr.*, **2**, 1–187.

HAY, O. P. 1908. The fossil turtles of North America. *Publs Carnegie Instn Wash.*, **75**, 1–568.

HECHT, M. K. 1959. Amphibians and Reptiles. *in* McGREW, P. O. The Geology and Paleontology of the Elk Mountain and Tabernacle Butte area. *Bull. Am. Mus. nat. Hist.*, **117**, 130–146.

HOFFSTETTER, R. 1957a. Quelques observations sur les stégosaurinés. *Bull. Mus. Hist. nat., Paris*, (2), **29**, 537–547.

—— 1957b. Un saurien helodermatide (Eurheloderma gallicum nor. gen. et sp.) dans la faune fossile des Phosphorites du Quercy. *Bull. Soc. géol. Fr.* (6), **7**, 775–786.

—— 1958. Un serpent marin du genre Pterosphenus (*Pt. sheppardi* nov. sp.) dans l'Eocene Superieur de l'Equateur (Amerique du Sud). *Bull. Soc. géol. Fr.* (6), **8**, 45–50.

—— 1959. Un serpent terrestre dans le Cretace inferieur du Sahara. *Bull. Soc. géol. Fr.* (7), **1**, 897–902.

—— 1960. Sur la classification des Boides de Madagascar et des Mascareignes. *Bull. Mus. natn. Hist. nat., Paris*, **32**, 131–138.

—— 1961a. Nouveaux restes d'un serpent boide (Madtsoia madagascariensis nov. sp.) dans le Cretace superieur de Madagascar. *Bull. Mus. natn. Hist. nat., Paris*, **33**, 152–160.

—— 1961b. Nouvelles recoltes de serpents fossiles dans l'Eocene superieur du Desert Libyque. *Bull. Mus. natn. Hist. nat., Paris*, **33**, 326–331.

—— 1962. Revue des recentes acquisitions concernant l'historie et la systematique des Squamates. *in* Problemes actuels de Paléontologie (Évolution des Vertébrés). *Colloques int. Cent. natn. Rech. scient.*, **104**, 243–279.

—— 1964. Les Sauria du Jurassique superieur et specialement les Gekkota de Baviere et de Mandchourie. *Senckenberg. biol.*, **45**, 281–324.

—— 1967. Coup d'oeil sur les Sauriens (= Lacertiliens) des couches de Purbeck (Jurassique supérieur d'Angleterre). *Colloques int. Cent. natn. Rech. scient.*, **163**, in press.

—— & GAYRARD, Y. 1965. Observations sur l'osteologie et la classification des Acrochordidae (Serpentes). *Bull. Mus. natn. Hist. nat., Paris*, **36**, 677–696.

HOOLEY, R. W. 1913. On the skeleton of *Ornithodesmus latidens*; an ornithosaur from the Wealden Shales of Atherfield (Isle of Wight). *Q. Jl geol. Soc. Lond.*, **69**, 372–422.

HUENE, F. VON 1907–1908. Die Dinosaurier der europäischen Triasformation, mit Berücksichtigung der aussereuropäischen Vorkomnisse. *Geol. paläont. Abh.*, Suppl. **1**, i–xii, 1–419.

—— 1914. Beiträge zur Geschichte der Archosaurier. *Geol. palaont. Abh.* new series, **13**, 1–53.

—— 1926. The carnivorous Saurischia in the Jura and Cretaceous formations, principally in Europe. *Revta Mus. La Plata*, **29**, 35–114.

—— 1931. Über *Tanystropheus* und verwandte Formen. *Neues Jb. Miner. Geol. Paläont. BeilBd.* Abt. B, **67**, 65–86.

—— 1932. Die fossile Reptil-Ordnung Saurischia, ihre Entwicklung und Geschichte. *Monogrn. Geol. Paläont.*, (1), **4**, i–viii, 1–361.

—— 1956. *Paläontologie und Phylogenie der niederen Tetrapoden.* xii + 716 pp., Jena.

HUGHES, B. 1963. The earliest archosaurian reptiles. *S. Afr. J. Sci.*, **59**, 221–241.

JAIN, S. L., ROBINSON, P. L. & CHOWDHURY, T. K. R. 1962. A new vertebrate fauna from the early Jurassic of the Deccan, India. *Nature, Lond.*, **194**, 755–757.

JELETZKY, J. A. 1960. Youngest marine rocks in western interior of North America and the age of the *Triceratops*-Beds; with remarks on comparable dinosaur-bearing beds outside North America. *21st Int. geol. Congr.*, Sect 5, (5) 25–40.

—— 1962. The allegedly Danian dinosaur-bearing rocks of the globe and the problem of the Mesozoic-Cenozoic boundary. *J. Paleont.*, **36**, 1005–1018.

KERMACK, K. A. 1956. An ancestral crocodile from South Wales. *Proc. Linn. Soc. Lond.*, **166**, 1–2.

KREBS, B. 1963. Bau und Funktion des Tarsus eines Pseudosuchiers aus der Trias des Monte San Giorgio (Kanton Tessin, Schweiz). *Paläont. Z.*, **37**, 88–95.

—— 1965. *Ticinosuchus ferox* nov. gen. nov. sp. Ein neuer Pseudosuchier aus der Trias des Monte San Giorgio. *Schweiz. palaeont. Abh.*, **81**, 1–140.

KUHN, O. 1934. Ichthyosauria. *Fossilium Catalogus, 1 Animalia*, Berlin.

—— 1958. Ein neuer Lacertilier aus dem frankischen Lithographie-schiefer. *N. Jb. Geol. Paläont., Monatsh.* for **1958**, 380–382.

—— 1961a. *Die Familien der rezenten und fossilen Amphibien und Reptilien.* 79 pp. Bamberg.

—— 1961b. Die Tier- und Pflanzenwelt des Solnhofener Schiefers. *Geologica bav.*, **48**, 1–68.

—— 1963a. Serpentes (Supplementum 1). *Fossilium Catalogus*, **103**, 1–45. Berlin.

—— 1963b. Sauria (Supplementum 1). *Fossilium Catalogus*, **104**, 1–87. Berlin.

—— 1964a. Die Familien der rezenten und fossilen Amphibien und Reptilien. 79 pp. Bamberg.

—— 1964b. Ungeloste Probleme der Stammesgeschichte der Amphibien und Reptilien. *Jh. Ver. vaterl. Naturkde. Wurttemberg*, **118/119**, 293–325.

—— 1966. *Die Reptilien*. 154 pp. Munich.

KUHN-SCHNYDER, E. 1961. Ein Schädelfragment von *Metriorhynchus* aus dem unteren Callovien von La Voulte-sur-Rhône (Ardèche, France). *Eclog. geol. Helv.*, **53**, (2), 793–804.

—— 1963. Wege der Reptiliensystematik. *Paläont. Z.*, **37**, 61–87.

—— 1964. Die Wirbeltierfauna der Trias der Tessiner Kalkalpen. *Geol. Rundsch.*, **53**, 393–412.

LANGSTON, W. 1956. The Sebecosuchia: cosmopolitan crocodilians? *Am. J. Sci.*, **254**, (10), 605–614.

—— 1959. *Anchiceratops* from the Oldman Formation of Alberta. *Nat. Hist. Pap. natn. Mus. Can.*, **3**, 1–11.

—— 1965. *Oedaleops campi* (Reptilia: Pelycosauria), a new genus and species from the Lower Permian of New Mexico, and the family Eothyrididae. *Bull. Texas Mem. Mus.*, **9**, 1–47.

LAPPARENT, A. F. DE 1947. Les dinosauriens du Crétacé Supérieur du Midi de la France. *Mém. Soc. géol. Fr.*, n.s., **56**, 1–54.

—— 1960. Les dinosauriens du "Continental intercalaire" du Sahara Central. *Mém. Soc. géol. Fr.* new series, **88a**, 1–57.

—— & AGUIRRE, E. 1956. Présence de dinosauriens dans le Crétacé supérieur du bassin de Tremp (province de Lérida, Espagne). *C.r. Séanc. Soc. géol. Fr.* for 1956, no. 14, 261–262.

LAPPARENT, A. F. DE & ZBYSZEWSKI, G. 1957. Les dinosauriens du Portugal. *Mém. Servs géol. Port.*, (n.s.) **2**, 1–63.

LEWIS, G. E. 1955. *News Bull. Soc. vertebr. Paleont.*, **43**, 21. [No title.]

LONGMAN, H. A. 1926. A giant dinosaur from Durham Downs, Queensland. *Mem. Qd Mus.*, **8**, (3), 183–194.

LULL, R. S. & WRIGHT, N. E. 1942. Hadrosaurian dinosaurs of North America. *Spec. Pap. geol. Soc. Am.*, **40**, 1–242.

LYDEKKER, R. 1877. Notices of new and other Vertebrata from Indian Tertiary and Secondary rocks. *Rec. geol. Surv. India*, **10**, (1), 30–43.

—— 1889. *Catalogue of the fossil Reptilia and Amphibia in the British Museum (Nat. Hist.).* 2 *The Orders Ichthyopterygia and Sauropterygia*. London, British Museum (Natural History).

MALEEV, E. A. 1952. Novyi ankilozavr iz verkhnego mela Mongolii. *Dokl. Akad. Nauk SSSR*, **87**, (2), 273–276.

—— 1955a. Gigantskie khishchnȳe dinozavrȳ Mongolii. *Dokl. Akad. Nauk SSSR*, **104**, (4), 634–637.

—— 1955b. Novȳe khishchnȳe dinozavrȳ iz verkhnego mela Mongolii. *Dokl. Akad. Nauk SSSR*, **104**, (5), 779–782.

MARSH, O. C. [1870–1898. A great number of publications on Saurischia and Ornithischia, mostly in *Am. J. Sci.*]

MOOK, C. C. 1934. The evolution and classification of the Crocodilia. *J. Geol.*, **42**, (3), 295–304.

NEWMAN, B. H. 1967. The Jurassic dinosaur *Scelidosaurus harrisoni*, Owen. *Palaeontology*, In press.

NOPCSA, F. 1915 Die Dinosaurier der siebenbürgischen Landesteile Ungarns. *Mitt. Jb. K. ung. geol. Anst.*, **23**, (1), 1–24.

OLSON E. C. 1947. The family Diadectidae and its bearing on the classification of reptiles. *Fieldiana: Geol.*, **11**, 1–53.

—— 1957. Catalogue of localities of Permian and Triassic terrestrial vertebrates of the territories of the U.S.S.R. *J. Geol*, **65**, 196–226.

—— 1960. A trilophosaurid reptile from the Kootenai Formation (Lower Cretaceous). *J. Paleont.*, **34**, 551–555.

—— 1962. Late Permian terrestrial vertebrates, U.S.A. and U.S.S.R. *Trans. Am. phil. Soc.*, **52**, 1–224.

—— 1965. Relationship of *Seymouria*, *Diadectes* and Chelonia. *Am. Zool.*, **5**, 295–307.

—— 1966. Relationships of *Diadectes*. *Fieldiana: Geol.*, **14**, 199–227.

—— & BARGHUSEN, H. 1962. Permian vertebrates from Oklahoma and Texas. Part I—Vertebrates from the Flowerpot Formation, Permian of Oklahoma. *Circ. Okla. geol. Surv.* **59,** 1–48.

PARSONS, T. S. & WILLIAMS, E. E. 1961. Two Jurassic turtle skulls: a morphological study. *Bull. Mus. comp. Zool. Harv.,* **125,** 43–107.

PEABODY, F. E. 1957. Pennsylvania reptiles of Garnett, Kansas: edaphosaurs. *J. Paleont.,* **31,** 947–49.

PERSSON, P. O. 1963. A revision of the classification of the Plesiosauria with a synopsis of the stratigraphical and geographical distribution of the group. *Acta Univ. lund.,* **59,** 1–60.

PIVETEAU, J. (Editor) 1955. *Traité de Paléontologie,* **5,** Amphibiens, Reptiles, Oiseaux. 1113 pp. Paris, Masson.

POMPECKJ, J. F. 1920. Das angebliche Vorkommen und Wandern des Parietalformens bei Dinosauriern. *Sber. Ges. naturf. Freunde Berl.,* **1920,** (3), 109–129.

PRICE, L. I. 1937. Two new cotylosaurs from the Permian of Texas. *Proc. New Engl. zool. Club,* **16,** 97–102.

—— 1950. Os crocodilídeos da fauna da formação Baurú, do Cretáceo terrestre do Brasil meridional. *Anais Acad. bras. Cienc.* **22,** (4), 473–490.

—— 1953. A presença de Pterosáuria no Cretáceo Superior do Estado da Paraíba. *Notas prelim. Estud. Div. Geol. Miner. Bras.* **71,** 1–10.

—— 1955. Novos crocodilídeos dos arenitos da série Baurú, Cretáceo do Estado de Minas Gerais. *Anais Acad. bras. Cienc.,* **27** (4), 487–498.

—— 1963. A presença de Pterosáuria no Cretáceo Superior do Estado da Paraíba. *Notas prelim. Estud. Div. Geol. Miner. Bras.,* **71,** 1–10.

QUENNELL, A. M., McKINLAY, A. C. M. & AITKEN, W. G. 1919. Summary of the geology of Tanganyika. Part 1: Introduction and stratigraphy. *Mem. geol. Surv. Dep. Tanganyika* **1,** 1–264.

RECK, H. 1931. Die deutschostafrikanischen Flugsaurier. *Zentbl. Miner. Geol. Paläont.* Abt. B, 321–336.

REIG, O. A. 1959. Primeros datos descriptivos sobre nuevos reptiles arcosaurios del Triásico de Ischigualasto (San Juan, Argentina). *Revta Asoc. geol. argent.,* **13,** 257–270.

—— 1961. Acerca de la posición sistemática de la familia Rauisuchidae y del género *Saurosuchus* (Reptilia, Thecodontia). *Publnes Mus. munic. Cienc. nat. tradic. Mar del Plata,* **1,** 73–114.

—— 1963. La presencia de dinosaurios saurisquios en los 'Estratos de Ischigualasto' (Mesotriásico superior) de las Provincias de San Juan y La Rioja (República Argentina). *Ameghiniana,* **3,** (1), 3–20.

REYNOLDS, S. H. 1939. On a collection of reptilian bones from the Oolite of Stow-on-the-Wold, Gloucestershire. *Geol. Mag.,* **76,** 193–214.

ROBINSON, P. L. 1967. Triassic vertebrates from lowland and upland. *Sci. Cult.,* **33,** 169–173.

ROHRER, W. L. & KONIZESKI, R. 1960. On the occurrence of *Edmontosaurus* in the Hell Creek Formation of Montana. *J. Paleont.,* **34,** 464–466.

ROMER, A. S. 1945. The late Carboniferous vertebrate fauna of Kounova (Bohemia) compared with that of the Texas redbeds. *Am. J. Sci.,* **243,** 417–42.

—— 1946. The primitive reptile *Limnoscelis* restudied. *Am. J. Sci.* **244,** 149–188.

—— 1956. *Osteology of the Reptiles.* xxi + 772 pp. Chicago.

—— 1964. *Diadectes* an amphibian? *Copeia,* **1964,** 718–719.

—— 1966. *Vertebrate Paleontology.* 3rd edn. ix + 468 pp. Chicago.

—— & PRICE, L. I. 1940. Review of the Pelycosauria. *Spec. Pap. geol. Soc. Am.,* **28,** 1–538.

ROZHDESTVENSKII, A. K. 1952. Novȳi predstavitel' utkonosȳkh dinozavrov iz verkhnemelovȳkh otlozhenii Mongolii. *Dokl. Akad. nauk SSSR,* **86,** (2), 405–408.

—— 1957. Kratkie itogi izucheniya iskopaemȳkh pozvonochnȳkh Mongolii po materialam Mongol'skoi Paleontologicheskoi Ekspeditsii Akademii Nauk SSSR v 1946–1949 gg. *Vertebr. palasiat.,* **1,** (3), 169–185.

RUSSELL, L. S. 1935. Fauna of the Upper Milk River Beds, Southern Alberta. *Trans. R. Soc. Can.* (3), **29,** (4), 115–128.

—— 1964. Cretaceous non-marine faunas of northwestern North America. *Contr. Life Sci. Div. R. Ont. Mus.*, **61**, 1–24.

RYABININ, A. N. 1939. Fauna pozvonochnȳkh iz verkhnego mela yuzhnogo Kazakhstana. *Trudȳ tsent. nauchno-issled. geologo-izv. Inst.*, **118**, 1–40.

—— 1948. Zametka o letayushchem yashchere iz yurȳ Kara-tau. *Trudȳ paleont. Inst.*, **15**, 86–93.

SAVAGE, D. E. 1951. Report on fossil vertebrates from the Upper Magdalena Valley, Colombia. *Science, N.Y.*, (n.s.), **114**, 186–187.

SCHMIDT, M. 1928. *Die Lebewelt unserer Trias.* 461 pp. Ohringen.

—— 1938. *Die Lebewelt unserer Trias*, Nachtrag. 143 pp. Oehringen.

SCHUCHERT, C. 1939. The geological horizon of the dinosaurs *Hallopus* and *Nanosaurus agilis*. *Am. J. Sci.*, **237**, (1), 19–26.

SEELEY, H. G. 1887. On *Heterosuchus valdensis* Seeley, a procoelian crocodile from the Hastings Sand of Hastings. *Q. Jl geol. Soc. Lond.*, **43**, 212–215.

—— 1901. *Dragons of the air*, xiii + 239 pp. London (Methuen & Co.).

SELTIN, R. J. 1959. A review of the family Captorhinidae. *Fieldiana: Geol.*, **10**, 461–509.

SIGOGNEAU, D. 1963. Note sur une nouvelle éspèce de Scaloposauridae. *Palaeont. afr.*, **8**, 13–37.

STOLLEY, E. 1936. *Odontorhynchus aculeatus* n. g. n. sp., ein neuer Rhamphorhynchide von Solnhofen. *Neues Jb. Miner. Geol. Paläont. BeilBd.* Abt. B, **75**, 543–564.

TARLO, L. B. H. 1959. Fossil Reptiles from the Panchet Beds of India. *Nature, Lond.*, **183**, 912–913.

—— 1967. An outline classification of the Squamata. (In the press.)

TATARINOV, L. P. 1961. Materialȳ po psevdozukhiyam SSSR. *Paleont. Zh.*, **1**, 117–132.

—— 1963. New Upper Permian Therocephalians. *Paleont. Zh.*, **4**, 76–94.

—— 1964. Order Placodontia: Subclass Lepidosauria, *in Osnovy Paleontologii*, **12**, 332–338, 439–493.

VAUGHN, P. P. 1958. On a new pelycosaur from the Lower Permian of Oklahoma, and on the origin of the family Caseidae. *J. Paleont.*, **32**, 981–91.

—— 1963. The age and locality of the Late Paleozoic vertebrates from El Cobre Canyon, Rio Arriba County, New Mexico. *J. Paleont.*, **37**, 283–286.

VYUSHKOV, B. P. 1964. A Triassic theriodont from the U.S.S.R. *Paleont. Zh.*, **2**, 158–60.

WALKER, A. D. 1961. Triassic reptiles from the Elgin area: *Stagonolepis, Dasygnathus* and their allies. *Phil. Trans. R. Soc.*, **244**B, 103–204.

—— 1964. Triassic reptiles from the Elgin area: *Ornithosuchus* and the origin of carnosaurs. *Phil. Trans. R. Soc.*, **248**B, 53–134.

WANG, K-M. 1959. Ueber eine neue fossil Reptilform von Provinz Hupeh, China. *Acta palaeont. sin.*, **7**, 367–378.

WATSON, D. M. S. 1957. On *Millerosaurus* and the early history of the sauropsid reptiles. *Phil. Trans. R. Soc.*, **140**B, 325–400.

—— & ROMER, A. S. 1956. A classification of therapsid reptiles. *Bull. Mus. comp. Zool. Harv.*, **114**, 37–89.

WELLES, S. P. 1954. New Jurassic dinosaur from the Kayenta Formation of Arizona. *Bull. geol. Soc. Am.*, **65**, 591–598.

—— 1962. A new species of elasmosaur from the Aptian of Colombia and a review of the Cretaceous plesiosaurs. *Univ. Calif. Publs geol. Sci.*, **44**, 1–96.

WESTPHAL, F. 1962. Die Krokodilier des deutschen und englischen Oberen Lias. *Palaeontographica* Abt. A, **118**, 23–118.

WIMAN, C. 1928. Eine neue marine Reptilien-Ordnung aus der Trias Spitzbergens. *Bull. geol. Instn Upsale*, **22**, 183–196.

YEH, H-K. 1959. New dicynodont from *Sinokannemeyeria* fauna from Shansi. *Vert. Palasia.* **3**, 187–204.

YOUNG, C.-C. 1931. On some new dinosaurs from western Suiyuan, Inner Mongolia. *Bull. geol. Soc. China*, **11**, 259–266.

—— 1948. On two new saurischians from Lufeng, Yunnan. *Bull. geol. Soc. China*, **28**, (1–2), 75–90.

—— 1951. The Lufeng saurischian fauna in China. *Palaeont. sin.*, **134**, 1–96.

—— 1958a. The dinosaurian remains of Laiyang, Shantung. *Palaeont. sin.*, **142**, 53–138.

—— 1958b. On new Pachypleurosauroidea from Keichow, South-West China. *Vertebr. palasiat.*, **2**, 69–81.

—— 1959a. On a new Nothosauria from the Lower Triassic beds of Kwangsi. *Vertebr. palasiat.*, **3**, 73–78.

—— 1959b. On a new Lacertilia from Chingning, Chekiang, China. *Sci. Rec. Acad. sin.*, **3**, 520–523.

—— 1959c. Note on the first cynodont from the *Sinokannemeyeria* faunas in Shansi, China. *Vertebr. palasiat.*, **3**, 124–31.

—— 1961a. On a new cynodont from N. W. Shansi. *Vertebr. palasiat.*, **5**, 109–14.

—— 1961b. On two new fossil lizards of China. *Vertebr. palasiat.* **1961**, 115–120.

—— 1964a. The pseudosuchians in China. *Palaeont. sin.*, **151**, 1–205.

—— 1964b. On a new pterosaurian from Sinkiang, China. *Vertebr. palasiat.*, **8**, 221–256.

—— & CHOW, M.-C. 1953. New fossil reptiles from Szechuan China. *Acta scient. sin.*, **2**, (3), 216–243.

ZANGERL, R. 1944. Contribution to the osteology of the skull of the Amphisbaenidae. *Am. Midl. Nat.*, **31**, 417–454.

—— 1960. The vertebrate fauna of the Selma Formation of Alabama. Part V. An advanced cheloniid sea turtle. *Fieldiana, Geol. Mem.*, **3**, 281–312.

R. M. APPLEBY, M.SC. PH.D. F.G.S.
Department of Geology, University College, Cathays Park, Cardiff, Wales.

A. J. CHARIG, M.A. PH.D. F.G.S.
Department of Palaeontology, British Museum (Natural History), Cromwell Road, London S W 7.

C. B. COX, M.A. PH.D. F.Z.S.
Department of Zoology, King's College, Strand, London W C 2.

K. A. KERMACK, PH.D. F.G.S.
Department of Zoology, University College, Gower Street, London W C 1.

L. B. H. TARLO, D.SC. PH.D. F.L.S. F.A.Z. F.Z.S. F.G.S.
Department of Geology, The University, Reading, Berkshire.

CHAPTER 29

Aves

Contributor: J. FISHER

Introduction. Birds are perhaps the most successful group of living vertebrates, and yet their fossil record is by far the poorest. The identification of birds from isolated skeletal fragments poses incredible difficulties and it is therefore not surprising that specialists in this subject are extremely thin on the ground. At the same time, as James Fisher points out, "nature can scarcely ever have given us a proper sample of the avifauna of any time at any horizon; the favoured candidates were nearly always the bigger birds—the marsh-birds, water-birds, shore-birds and continental-shelf sea-birds, and the birds of prey that preyed upon them". These problems notwithstanding, Fisher has produced a remarkably complete picture of the fossil record of birds. It is to be hoped that as a result of his two contributions to this volume, this history will in future receive the prominence it clearly merits. [L.B.H.T.]

Subclass SAURIURAE

Order ARCHAEOPTERYGIFORMES

Family ARCHAEOPTERYGIDAE

First and **Last,** Jur "Tith": *Archaeopteryx lithographica* H. von Meyer 1861; syn *A. siemensii* Dames 1897, Solnhofener Plattenkalk (= M. Kim.), Bavaria, Germany.

Comment: Wetmore (1960) and Brodkorb (1963) would recognize 2 spp. (de Beer 1954, Heller 1960).

Subclass ODONTOHOLCAE

Order HESPERORNITHIFORMES

Family ENALIORNITHIDAE

First and **Last,** Cret Alb: *Enaliornis* Seeley 1869, U. Greensand, Cambridgeshire, England.

Comment: Two spp., on hind-limb material. Family has been lately referred (Brodkorb 1963) to stem of Gaviiformes, a view resisted by Storer (1965).

Family BAPTORNITHIDAE

First, Cret Coniac: *Baptornis advenus* Marsh 1877, Smoky Hill Chalk, Niobrara Fm, Kansas.

Last, Cret Maestr: *Neogaeornis wetzeli* Lambrecht 1929, Quiriquina beds, Prov. Concepción, Chile.

Comment: Two spp., on hind-limb material. Family has been lately referred (Brodkorb 1963) to stem of Podicipitiformes.

The Fossil Record, pp. 733–762. Geological Society of London, 1967. Printed in Northern Ireland.

Family HESPERORNITHIDAE

First, Cret Coniac: *Hesperornis* Marsh 1872, 3 spp. Smoky Hill Chalk, Niobrara Fm, Kansas.
Last, Cret Campan: *Coniornis altus* Marsh 1893, U. Claggett Fm, Montana.
Comment: Family has above 4 spp., only (Gregory 1952).

Subclass ORNITHURAE

Superorder ICHTHYORNITHES

Order ICHTHYORNITHIFORMES

Family ICHTHYORNITHIDAE

First and **Last,** Cret Coniac: *Ichthyornis* Marsh 1872, 6 spp. Smoky Hill Chalk, Niobrara Fm, Kansas, 1 sp. McKinney (cf. Austin) Chalk, Texas (Gregory 1952).

Family APATHORNITHIDAE

First and **Last,** Cret Coniac: *Apatornis celer* (Marsh 1873), Smoky Hill Chalk, Niobrara Fm, Kansas.

Superorder IMPENNES

Order SPHENISCIFORMES

Family SPHENISCIDAE

First, Tert L. Eoc: Gen. and sp. undescribed, Marples 1952, Heretaungan stage, Cheviot, New Zealand.   **Extant.**
Comment: Family has 34 palaeospecies, 15 neospecies of which oldest named is *Palaeeudyptes marplesi* Brodkorb 1963, U. Eoc. Burnside marl, Otago, New Zealand; S. Hemisphere only (Simpson 1946).

Superorder RATITAE

Order STRUTHIONIFORMES

Family ELEUTHERORNITHIDAE

First and **Last,** Tert L. Eoc.: *Eleutherornis helveticus* Schaub 1940, Egerkingen gamma, Bohnerz, Switzerland.
Comment: Fragmentary pelvis only; could be in Diatrymiformes.

Family STRUTHIONIDAE

First, Tert Plioc: *Struthio asiaticus* Milne-Edwards 1871, Siwalik series, United Provinces, India.   **Extant.**
Comment: Family has 6 palaeospecies, 1 neospecies; Ethiopian-Palearctic-Oriental.

Order AEPYORNITHIFORMES

Family AEPYORNITHIDAE

First, Tert L. Eoc: *Eremopezus eocaenus* Andrews 1904, Birket-el-Qurun stage, Fayum Fm, Egypt.
Last, Quat Holo: *Aepyornis maximus* I. Geoffroy-Saint-Hilaire 1851 probably survived in S. Madagascar to *c.* 1649.
Comment: Family has 8 palaeospecies and (by virtue of survival after 1600) 1 neospecies; known with certainty from Egypt and Madagascar only.

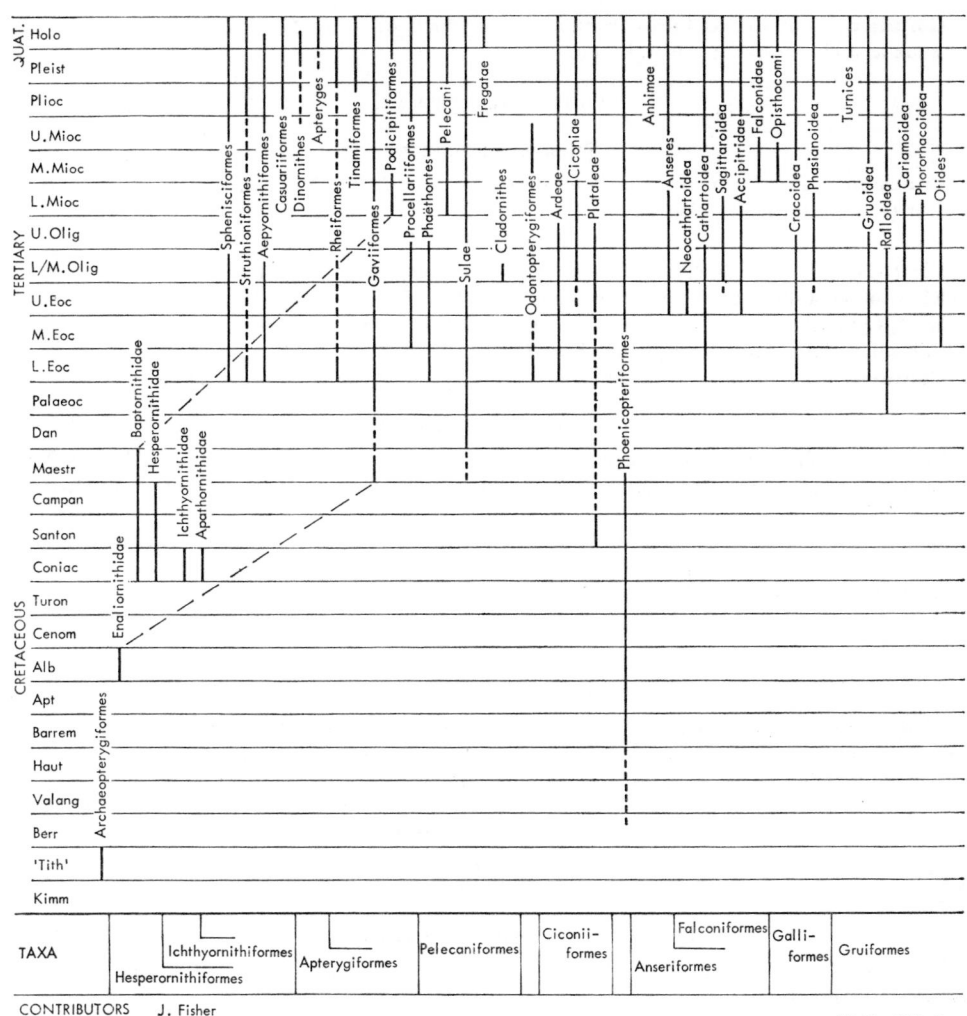

FIG. 29.1 B

Order CASUARIIFORMES

Family DROMICEIIDAE

First, Tert Plioc: *Dromiceius ocypus* A. H. Miller 1963, Mampu Wordu Sands (L. Plioc), L. Palankarinna, South Australia. **Extant.**

Comment: Family has 3 (some make 4) palaeospecies, 1 neospecies; Australia.

Family DROMORNITHIDAE

First and **Last,** Quat Pleist: *Dromornis australis* Owen 1872, Chinchilla beds (U. Pleist), Queensland; and *Genyornis newtoni* Stirling and Zeitz 1896 from other U. Pleist Fms, South Australia and New South Wales. No other spp.

Family CASUARIIDAE

First, Quat Pleist: *Casuarius lydekkeri* Rothschild 1911, U. Pleist cave deposits, Wellington Valley, New South Wales. **Extant.**

Comment: Family has 3 neospecies, in one of which, *C. bennetti* Gould 1857, the above could be sunk as a chrono-race; Australia-Papua.

Order APTERYGIFORMES

Suborder DINORNITHES

Comment: Has been given ordinal status by Brodkorb (1963), see also Archey (1941), Oliver (1949), and Duff (1956).

Family EMEIDAE

First, Tert U. Mioc or ?Plioc: *Anomalopteryx antiquus* Hutton 1892, Fm (clay under lava flow) beleived of Mioc-Plioc threshold, near Timaru, S. Island, New Zealand.

Last, Quat Holo: *Megalapteryx didinus* (Owen 1883), survived Takahé Valley, S.I., N.Z., to 18th century A.D., probably after 1785, by C_{14}.

Comment: Family has 17 palaeospecies, 2 extinct neospecies; New Zealand.

Family DINORNITHIDAE

First, Tert ?Plioc: *Dinornis novaezealandiae* Owen 1843, Nukumaru Beach, N. Island, New Zealand, cf. early Plioc by Oliver; but first certain Dinornithid, uppermost Pleist-Holo threshold.

Last, Quat Holo: *Dinornis torosus* Hutton 1891, survived Pyramid Valley, S.I., N.Z. to 17th century A.D., *c.* 1670 by C_{14}.

Comment: Family has 7 palaeospecies, 1 extinct neospecies; New Zealand.

Suborder APTERYGES

Family APTERYGIDAE

First, ?Quat Uppermost Pleist or Holo: sole palaeospecies *Pseudapteryx gracilis* Lydekker 1891 from unknown site New Zealand based on tarsometatarsus of subfossil appearance, may not antedate Quat (probably all Holo) remains of all 3 living neospecies N. and S. Is., N.Z.

Extant.

Order RHEIFORMES

Family RHEIDAE

Subfamily OPISTHODACTYLINAE

First and **Last,** Tert L. Eoc: *Opisthodactylus patagonicus* Ameghino 1891, Casamayor Fm, S. Patagonia, Argentina.

Comment: Has been given familial status by Brodkorb (1963) but may not earn it.

Subfamily RHEINAE

First, Tert Plioc: *Heterorhea dabbenei* Rovereto 1914, Monte Hermoso Fm (U. Plioc), prov. Buenos Aires, Argentina. **Extant.**

Comment: Subfamily has 3 palaeospecies, 2 neospecies, Southern S. America.

Superorder DROMAEOGNATHAE

Order TINAMIFORMES

Family TINAMIDAE

First, Tert Plioc: *Tinamisornis intermedius* Rovereto 1914, *Cayetanornis parvulus* (Rovereto 1914) and *Querandiornis romani* Rusconi 1958, Monte Hermoso Fm (U. Plioc), prov. Buenos Aires, Argentina. **Extant.**

Comment: Family has 4 palaeospecies, 42 neospecies, Neotropical.

Chapter 29: Aves

Superorder CARINATAE

Order GAVIIFORMES

Family LONCHODYTIDAE

First and **Last,** Cret Maestr: *Lonchodytes* Brodkorb 1964, 2 spp., Lance Fm, Niobrara Co., Wyoming. May be Hesperornithiform, near Enaliornithidae.

Family GAVIIDAE

First, Tert Paleoc: *Eupterornis remensis* Lemoine 1878, Cernay conglomerate, Marne, France.
Extant.
Comment: Family has 8 palaeospecies, 4 neospecies, Holarctic. May have Charadriiform connection (Storer 1956).

Order PODICIPITIFORMES

Family PODICIPITIDAE

First, Tert L. Mioc: *Podiceps oligocaenus* (Shufeldt 1915), uppermost John Day Fm, Malheur Co., Oregon. **Extant.**
Comment: Family has 7 palaeospecies, 17 neospecies, cosmopolitan.

Order PROCELLARIIFORMES

Family DIOMEDEIDAE

First, Tert M. Eoc: *Gigantornis eaglesomei* Andrews 1916, Ameki Fm, Ombialla district, Nigeria. **Extant.**
Comment: Family has 5 palaeospecies, 12 neospecies, southern-cosmopolitan.

Family PROCELLARIIDAE

First, Tert L/M Olig: *Puffinus raemdonckii* (van Beneden 1871), Rupelian sand (M. Olig), prov. Antwerp, Belgium. **Extant.**
Comment: Family has 13 palaeospecies, 47 neospecies, cosmopolitan.

Family OCEANITIDAE

First, Tert U. Mioc: *Oceanodroma hubbsi* L. Miller 1951, Capistrano Fm, Orange Co., California.
Extant.
Comment: Family has 1 palaeospecies, 19 neospecies, cosmopolitan. Hydrobatidae has been widely used.

Family PELECANOIDIDAE

First, Quat Pleist or Holo: neospecies *Pelecanoides garnotii* (Lesson 1828), guano deposits, Islas Lobos de Afuera, Peru, and (probably later) neospecies *P. urinatrix* (Gmelin 1789), Maori midden (XIV–XVI C. A.D.), Ototara, S.I., and (?late) Holo, Chatham Is., New Zealand.
Extant.
Comment: Family has 4 neospecies, southern hemisphere.

Order PELECANIFORMES

Suborder PHAËTHONTES

Family PHAËTHONTIDAE

First, Tert L. Eoc.: *Prophaethon shrubsolei* Andrews 1899, London Clay, Sheppey, Kent, England. **Extant.**
Comment: Family has 1 palaeospecies, 3 neospecies, now tropical.

Suborder PELECANI

Family PELECANIDAE

First, Tert L. Mioc: *Pelecanus gracilis* Milne-Edwards 1863, Aquitainian, Allier, France.
Extant.
Comment: Family has 10 palaeospecies, 6 neospecies, cosmopolitan.

Family CYPHORNITHIDAE

First, Tert L. Mioc: *Cyphornis magnus* Cope 1894, Carmanah Point beds, Vancouver I.
British Columbia.
Last, Tert L. Mioc: *Palaeochenoides mioceanus* Shufeldt 1916 and *Tympanonesiotes wetmorei* Hopson
1964, Hawthorne Fm, Charleston Co., South Carolina.
Comment: 3 paleospecies, Brodkorb (1963) would place in suborder Cladornithes; Hopson
(1964) finds good reasons for preferring Odontopterygiformes (Odontopterygia).

Suborder SULAE

Family PELAGORNITHIDAE

First, Tert L. Mioc: *Pelagornis miocaenus* Lartet 1857, silt of Léognan (Burdigalian), Gironde,
France.
Last, Tert M. Mioc: cf. same species, silt of Armagnac, Gers, France.
Comment: Brodkorb (1963) would refer to Odontopterygiformes (Odontopterygia).

Family SULIDAE

First, Tert L/M Oligoc: *Sula ronzoni* Milne-Edwards 1867, calc. marl of Ronzon (L. Olig),
Haute-Loire, France. **Extant.**
Comment: Family has 18 palaeospecies, 7 neospecies, cosmopolitan.

Family ELOPTERYGIDAE

First, Cret Maestr or Dan: *Elopteryx nopcsai* Andrews 1913, Transylvanian freshwater 1st,
near Hatszeg, Rumania.
Last, Tert M. Eoc: *Eostega lebedinskyi* Lambrecht 1929, coarse chalk of Steinbruch, near
Kolozsvár, Rumania.
Comment: 3 palaeospecies, all European.

Family PHALACROCORACIDAE

First, Cret Maestr: *Graculavus* Marsh 1872, 2 spp. Hornerstown marl, Monmouth Co., New
Jersey. **Extant.**
Comment: Family has 25 palaeospecies, 27 neospecies, cosmopolitan.

Family ANHINGIDAE

First, Tert ?M Eoc: *Protoplotus beauforti* Lambrecht 1930, freshwater fish beds, Sipang,
Sumatra. **Extant.**
Comment: Family has 5 palaeospecies, 1 neospecies, tropical

Suborder FREGATAE

Family FREGATIDAE

First, Quat Holo: *Fregata* Lacépède 1799, 3 neospp., middens W. Indies and guano, Ascension
I. and St. Helena. **Extant.**
Comment: Family has 5 neospecies, tropical.

Chapter 29: Aves

Suborder CLADORNITHES

Family CLADORNITHIDAE

First and **Last,** Tert L/M. Olig: *Cladornis pachypus* Ameghino 1894, Deseado Fm (L. Olig), Santa Cruz, Argentina.

Order ODONTOPTERYGIFORMES

Comment: Brodkorb (1963) and some previous authorities would demote to suborder of Pelecaniformes.

Family ODONTOPTERYGIDAE

First and **Last,** Tert L. Eoc: *Odontopteryx toliapicus* Owen 1873, London Clay, Sheppey, Kent, England.

Family PSEUDODONTORNITHIDAE

First, Tert. L. Mioc: *Pseudodontornis longirostris* (Spulski 1910), type skull from unknown horizon (?Mioc) and locality (?Brazil); but dentary from Hawthorne Fm, Charleston Co, S. Carolina, is fully referrable (Hopson 1964).

Last, Tert U. Mioc: *Osteodontornis orri* Howard 1957, Monterey Sh, Santa Barbara and Los Angeles Cos. California.

Order CICONIIFORMES

Comment: Ardeiformes may be preferred

Suborder ARDEAE

Family ARDEIDAE

First, Tert L. Eoc: *Proherodius oweni* Lydekker 1891, London Clay, London, England.
Extant.

Comment: includes monotypic Cochleariidae on views of Bock (1956) that *Cochlearius cochlearius* (Linnaeus 1766) may be an aberrant Nycticoracine Ardeidid. With this, family has 14 palaeospecies, 64 neospecies, cosmopolitan.

Suborder CICONIAE

Superfamily SCOPOIDEA

Family SCOPIDAE

No fossil known.
Comment: Family (monotypic) is held in Ardeae by Brodkorb (1963) who suppresses superfamily. Ethiopian.

Superfamily CICONOIDEA

Family CICONIIDAE

First, Tert U. Eoc or L. Oligoc: *Pelargopappus* Stejneger 1885 2 spp. and *Propelargus cayluxensis* Lydekker 1891, phosphorites of Quercy and Bach, France.
Extant.
Comment: Family has 24 palaeospecies, 17 neospecies, cosmopolitan.

Family BALAENICIPITIDAE

No fossil known.
Comment: Family (monotypic) is held in Ardeae by Brodkorb (1963). Ethiopian.

Suborder PLATALEAE

Family PLEGADORNITHIDAE

First and **Last,** Cret Santon: *Plegadornis antecessor* Wetmore 1962, Selma Chalk, near Boligee, Greene Co., Alabama.

Family PLATALEIDAE

First, Tert U. Eoc: *Ibidopsis hordwelliensis* Lydekker 1891, L. Headon beds, Hordle, Hampshire, England. **Extant.**

Comment: Threskiornithidae has been widely used. Family has 7 palaeospecies, 30 neospecies, cosmopolitan.

Order PHOENICOPTERIFORMES

Comment: Brodkorb (1963) and others would reduce to suborder of Ciconiiformes (Ardeiformes) as Phoenicopteri. Parasitic and behavioral evidence, however, favours a closer relationship to Anseriformes, and the adoption of a fully ordinal intermediate position.

Family TOROTIGIDAE

First, Cret ?Valang: *Gallornis straeleni* Lambrecht 1931, "Neocomian", Auxerre, Yonne, France.

Last, Cret Maestr: *Torotix clemensi* Brodkorb 1964, Lance Fm, Niobrara Co., Wyoming.

Comment: 3 species; other is *Parascaniornis stensioi* Lambrecht 1933, Cret Campan lst, Ivö, Sweden.

Family SCANIORNITHIDAE

First and **Last,** Tert Dan: *Scaniornis lundgreni* Dames 1890, Saltholm Chalk, Annetorp, Limhamn, Sweden.

Family TELMABATIDAE

First and **Last,** Tert L. Eoc: *Telmabates antiquus* Howard 1955, Casamayor Fm, Cañadón Hondo, Chubut, Argentina.

Family AGNOPTERIDAE

First, Tert U. Eoc.: *Agnopterus hantoniensis* Lydekker 1891, L. Headon beds, Hordle, Hampshire, England.

Last, Tert U. Olig *Agnopterus turgaiensis* Tugarinov 1940, *Indricotherium* beds, L. Chelkar-Teniz, Kazakhstan, U.S.S.R.

Comment: 3 species; other is Tert U. Eoc. *A. laurillardi* Milne-Edwards 1868, Montmartre gypsum, Seine, France.

Family PALAELODIDAE

First, Tert L. Mioc: *Palaelodus* Milne-Edwards 1863, 5 spp., Aquitainian, of Allier, Somme and Puy-de-Dôme, France.

Last, Tert Plioc: *Megapaloelodus opsigonus* Brodkorb 1961, Juntura beds (L. Plioc), Malheur Co., Oregon.

Comment: 8 spp., Europe and N. America.

Family PHOENICOPTERIDAE

First, Tert U. Eoc: *Elornis anglicus* Lydekker 1891, L. Headon beds, Hordle, Hampshire, England. **Extant.**

Comment: Family has 12 palaeospecies, 5 neospecies, cosmopolitan.

Order ANSERIFORMES

Suborder ANHIMAE

Family ANHIMIDAE

First, Quat Pleist: neospecies *Chauna torquata* (Oken 1816), Luján (U. Pleist), Argentina.

Comment: Family has 3 neospecies, Neotropical. **Extant.**

Chapter 29: Aves

Suborder ANSERES

Family ANATIDAE

First, Tert U. Eoc: *Eonessa anaticula* Wetmore 1938, horizon C, Uinta Fm, Duchesne Co., Utah. **Extant.**

Comment: Including monotypic Paranyrocini (which has been offered as full family) taxon has 93 palaeospecies, 151 neospecies, cosmopolitan.

Order FALCONIFORMES

Comment: Brodkorb (1964) prefers Accipitriformes.

Suborder CATHARTAE

Comment: Brodkorb (1964) prefers Sarcoramphi.

Superfamily NEOCATHARTOIDEA

Comment: Brodkorb (1964) would suppress this taxon.

Family NEOCATHARTIDAE

First and **Last,** Tert U. Eoc: *Neocathartes grallator* (Wetmore 1944), level B, Washakie Fm, Sweetwater Co., Wyoming.

Superfamily CATHARTOIDEA

Comment: Brodkorb (1964 June) would suppress this taxon.

Family CATHARTIDAE

First, Tert L. Eoc: *Lithornis vulturinus* Owen 1841, London Clay, Sheppey, Kent. **Extant.**

Comment: Family has 15 palaeospecies (6 W. Europe to L. Mioc), 6 neospecies, now confined to New World. Brodkorb (1964) prefers Vulturidae.

Family TERATORNITHIDAE

First, Quat Pleist: *Teratornis incredibilis* Howard 1952, upper part Palm Spring Fm (M. Pleist), Vallecito Creek, San Diego Co., California.

Last, Quat Holo: *T. merriami* L. Miller 1909, tarpit No. 10, Rancho La Brea, California (tarpits mostly Uppermost Pleist but No. 10 has human bones probably not earlier than fifth millenium B.C. at same horizon as the teratorn).

Comment: 3 palaeospecies; Brodkorb (1964) holds as subfamily of Cathartidae (Vulturidae).

Suborder FALCONES

Comment: Brodkorb (1964) prefers Accipitres.

Superfamily SAGITTAROIDEA

Comment: Brodkorb (1964) would suppress this taxon. Others might even transfer it to Cariamae!

Family SAGITTARIIDAE

First, Tert U. Eoc or L. Oligoc: *Amphiserpentarius schlosseri* Gaillard 1908, Quercy phosphorites, Lot, France. **Extant.**

Comment: Family has 2 palaeospecies, 1 neospecies presently Ethiopian, which Quercy avifauna seems also to have been.

Superfamily FALCONOIDEA

Family ACCIPITRIDAE

First, Tert U. Eoc: *Palaeocircus cuvieri* Milne-Edwards 1871, L. Headon beds, Hordle, Hampshire, England and Montmartre gypsum, Seine, France.   **Extant.**

Comment: Family has 63 palaeospecies, 208 neospecies, cosmopolitan.

Family PANDIONIDAE

First, Quat Pleist: *Pandion haliaetus* (Linnaeus 1758). A number of Quat U. Pleist records Europe and N. America of which earliest probably in 3 Pamlico Fm deposits Florida, cf. early U. Pleist, mid Sangamonian (by describer late U. Pleist., mid Wisconsinian).   **Extant.**

Comment: Monotypic, cosmopolitan. With Accipitridae, may deserve superfamilial status as Accipitroidea.

Family FALCONIDAE

First, Tert M.Mioc: *Badiostes patagonicus* Ameghino 1895, Santa Cruz Fm, Patagonia, Argentina and *Falco ramenta* Wetmore 1936, *Merychippus* zone, Sheep Creek Fm, Dawes Co, Nebraska.   **Extant.**

Comment: Family has 11 palaeospecies, 59 neospecies, cosmopolitan.

Order GALLIFORMES

Suborder OPISTHOCOMI

Comment: Brodkorb (1964) suppresses this taxon; but see remarks under Musophagiformes (p. 749).

Family OPISTHOCOMIDAE

First, Tert M. Mioc: *Hoazinoides magdalenae* A. H. Miller 1963, La Venta beds, Honda group, Huila, Colombia.   **Extant.**

Comment: Family has 1 palaeospecies, 1 neospecies, Neotropical

Suborder GALLI

Comment: Brodkorb (1964) suppresses this taxon.

Superfamily CRACOIDEA

Comment: Brodkorb (1964) suppresses this taxon.

Family GALLINULOIDIDAE

First, Tert M.Eoc: *Gallinuloides wyomingensis* Eastman 1900, Green River shs, Lincoln Co., and Bridger Fm, Uinta Co., Wyoming.

Last, Tert L. Mioc: *Taoperdix* Milne-Edwards 1869, 3 spp. from Aquitainian of Langy and St. Gérand-le-Puy, Allier, France.

Comment: Brodkorb (1964) following Tordoff and Macdonald (1957) demotes the Gallinuloididae to a subfamily and proposes a new subfamily Filholornithinae for *Filholornis* Milne-Edwards 1892 (3 spp from U.Eoc-L.Oligoc threshold, Chaux phosphate, Caylux and Escamps, of Tarn-et-Garonne and Lot, France), placing both taxa in Cracidae. Taxon here embraces these two subfamilies only, and has 15 palaeospecies, known only from Wyoming, S. Dakota and France.

Family CRACIDAE

First, Tert L. Eoc: *Palaeophasianus meleagroides* Shufeldt 1913, Willwood Fm, Elk Creek, Big Horn Co., Wyoming.   **Extant.**

Comment: Embracing the subfamilies Cracinae and Penelopinae (in Brodkorb 1964), this family has 9 palaeospecies, 39 neospecies, New World.

Family MEGAPODIIDAE

First, Quat Pleist: *Chosornis praeteritus* DeVis 1889, Darling Downs beds (U. Pleist), Queensland.   **Extant.**

Comment: Family has 1 palaeospecies, 10 neospecies, Australasian.

Chapter 29: Aves

Superfamily PHASIANOIDEA

Comment: Brodkorb (1964) suppresses this taxon. [Not ?U.Eoc, Fig. 29.1B].

Family TETRAONIDAE

First, Tert L. Mioc: *Palaealectoris incertus* Wetmore 1930, L. Harrison beds, Arikaree Fm, Sioux Co, Nebraska and *Tympanuchus stirtoni* A. H. Miller 1944, Rosebud Fm, Bennett Co., South Dakota. **Extant.**

Comment: Brodkorb (1964) demotes this taxon to a subfamily of the Phasianidae with some justification as wild hybridization is beyond doubt. Taxon here has 10 palaeospecies, 17 neospecies, Holarctic.

Family PHASIANIDAE

First, Tert L/M Olig: *Nanortyx inexpectatus* Weigel 1963, Cypress Hills Fm (L. Olig), Calf Creek, Saskatchewan. **Extant.**

Comment: Family has 44 palaeospecies, 175 neospecies, cosmopolitan.

Family NUMIDIDAE

First, Quat Holo: neosp. *Numida meleagris* (Linnaeus 1758), six sites, Hungary, Czechoslovakia and Germany, most of which have U. Pleist horizons, but all also late Holo material, of which that in the Hallstatt site at Takács-Menyhért, Hungary, may have the earliest guineafowl. The German record from loess at Sasbach, cf. *Numida* sp., needs re-investigation. There is also a "subRecent" African record. **Extant.**

Comment: Family has 7 neospecies, Ethiopian with Palearctic outlier.

Family MELEAGRIDIDAE

First, Quat Pleist: *Agriocharis progenes* Brodkorb 1964, Rexroad Fm, Meade Co., Kansas and San Pedro Valley Fm, Cochise Co., Arizona (surely both =Villafranchian). **Extant.**

Comment: Family has 7 paleospecies, 2 neospecies, Nearctic with Neotropical outlier. Brodkorb (1964) demotes it to a subfamily of the Phasianidae.

Order GRUIFORMES

Suborder MESITORNITHES

Family MESITORNITHIDAE

No fossil known: 3 neospecies, Madagascar.

Suborder TURNICES

Family TURNICIDAE

First, Quat Pleist: *Turnix* neosp. recorded from China. **Extant.**

Comment: Taxon incorporates monotypic Pedionomidae and has 16 neospecies, Old World.

Suborder GRUES

Superfamily GRUOIDEA

Family GERANOIDIDAE

First and **Last,** Tert L. Eoc: *Geranoides jepseni* Wetmore 1933, Willwood Fm, Bighorn Co., Wyoming.

Family EOGRUIDAE

First, Tert U. Eoc: *Eogrus aeola* Wetmore 1934, Irdin Manha Fm, Shara Murun, Inner Mongolia.

Last, Tert U.Mioc: *Eogrus* sp. Wetmore 1934, Tung Gur beds, near Iren Dabasu, Inner Mongolia.

Comment: No other spp. named (though also *Eogrus* sp. Wetmore 1934, Ardyn Obo Fm, Outer Mongolia).

Family GRUIDAE

First, Tert L. Eoc: *Paragrus prentici* (Loomis 1906), Willwood Fm, Bighorn Co., Wyoming.
Extant.

Comment: Family has 20 palaeospecies, 14 neospecies, cosmopolitan (not Neotropical).

Family ARAMIDAE

First, Tert L. Olig: *Aminornis excavatus* Ameghino 1899, Deseado Fm, Patagonia.
Extant.

Comment: Family has 5 palaeospecies, 1 neospecies, New World.

Family PSOPHIIDAE

No fossil known: 3 neospecies, Neotropical.

Family ERGILORNITHIDAE

First and **Last,** Tert L/M Olig: *Ergilornis rapidus* Kozlova 1960 and *Proergilornis minor* Kozlova 1960, Érgil'-Obo, S.E. Gobi desert, Outer Mongolia.

Superfamily RALLOIDEA

Family ORTHOCNEMIDAE

First and **Last,** Tert U. Eoc. or L. Olig: *Orthocnemus* Milne-Edwards 1892 4 spp. and *Elaphrocnemus* Milne-Edwards 1892, 3 spp., phosphorites of Quercy in Lot and Tarne-et-Garonne, France.

Family RALLIDAE

First, Cret Maestr: *Telmatornis* Marsh 1870, 2 spp. Navesink Fm, Hornerstown, New Jersey.
Extant.

Comment: Family has 53 palaeospecies, 131 neospecies, cosmopolitan.

Suborder HELIORNITHES

Family HELIORNITHIDAE

No fossil known, 3 neospecies, tropical.

Suborder RHYNOCHETI

Family RHYNOCHETIDAE

No fossil known, Monotypic, New Caledonia.

Suborder EURYPYGAE

Family EURYPYGIDAE

No fossil known, Monotypic, Neotropical.

Suborder CARIAMAE

Superfamily CARIAMOIDEA

Family BATHORNITHIDAE

First, Tert L/M Olig: *Bathornis veredus* Wetmore 1927, Chadronian, Horsetail Creek facies (L. Olig), Weld Co., Colorado and near Crawford, Nebraska, and Pennington Co., South Dakota.

Last, Tert U.Olig: *Bathornis geographicus* Wetmore 1942, Upper Brule Fm, *Protoceras-Leptauchenia* beds, Washington Co., S. Dakota.
Comment: 4 palaeospecies, Middle West U.S.

Family CARIAMIDAE

First, Tert L/M Olig: *Riacama caliginea* Ameghino 1899, Guaranítica Fm (L. Olig), Patagonia, Argentina.   **Extant.**
Comment: Family has 1 palaeospecies, 2 neospecies, s. Neotropical.

Superfamily PHORORHACOIDEA

Comment: Phorusrhacoidea may be preferable. (Analysis Patterson and Kraglievich 1960).

Family PSILOPTERIDAE

First, Tert L.Mioc: *Psilopterus tubulatus* (Ameghino 1895). Patagonian Fm, Monte Leone, Argentina.
Last, Quat Pleist: *Hermosiornis rapax* (Kraglievich 1946), Chapadmalalian Fm (L. Pleist), prov. Buenos Aires, Argentina.
Comment: Dryornithidae may be preferable. Family has 12 palaeospecies, S. Neotropical.

Family PHORORHACIDAE

First, Tert L/M Olig: *Andrewsornis affinis* (Ameghino 1899), Guaranítica Fm, Patagonia, Argentina and *Andrewsornis abbotti* Patterson 1941, Deseado Fm, Chubut, Argentina, both L. Olig.
Last, Quat Pleist: *Titanis walleri* Brodkorb 1963, U. Pleist, Santa Fé R., boundaries Gilchrist and Columbia Cos., Florida.
Comment: Original spelling of genus *Phorusrhacos* Ameghino 1887 makes Phorusrhacidae preferable. Family has 13 palaeospecies, S. Neotropical with exception of single Florida species.

Family BRONTORNITHIDAE

First, Tert L/M Olig: *Aucornis* Ameghino 1899, 2 spp., Deseado Fm, Chubut, Argentina and *Pseudolarus guaraniticus* Ameghino 1899, Guaranítica Fm, Patagonia, Argentina, both L. Olig.
Last, Tert M.Mioc: *Brontornis burmeisteri* Moreno and Mercerat 1891, *Rostrornis minor* Saez 1927, *Pseudolarus eocaenus* Ameghino 1891, *Lophiornis obliquus* Ameghino 1891 and *Staphylornis gallardoi* Mercerat 1897, Santa Cruzian Fm, Argentina.
Comment: Family has 12 palaeospecies, S. Neotropical.

Family CUNAMPAIIDAE

First and **Last,** Tert L/M Olig: *Cunampaia simplex* Rusconi 1946, Atala Fm, division Largo, Mendoza, Argentina.
Comment: Incertae sedis; Patterson and Kraglievich (1960) are doubtful whether this curiosity belongs to this superfamily.

Suborder OTIDES

Family OTIDIDAE

First, Tert M. Eoc: *Palaeotis weigelti* Lambrecht 1928, lignite (Braunkohle), Geiseltal, Merseburg, Germany.   **Extant.**
Comment: Family has 3 palaeospecies, 22 neospecies, Ethiopian, Palearctic and Australian.

Order DIATRYMIFORMES

Family GASTORNITHIDAE

First, Tert Paleoc: *Gastornis* Hébert 1855, 3 spp., L. Sparnacian (Landenian), Rheims and Paris, France and Woolwich-Reading beds Croydon, London, England and *Remiornis minor* (Lemoine 1881), Lower Sparnacian, Mouchard, France.

Last, Tert U. Eoc: *Macrornis tanaupus* Seeley 1866, L. Headon beds, Hordle, Hampshire, England.
Comment: Family has 6 palaeospecies, W. Europe.

Family DIATRYMIDAE

First, Tert L. Eoc: *Diatryma* Cope 1876, 4 spp., *Teredina* sand, Ypresian Fm, Epernay, France, and Wasatch Fm, Wyoming, and New Mexico; and *Omorhamphus storchii* Sinclair 1928, L. Gray Bull horizon, L. Wasatch Fm, Big Horn Co., Wyoming.
Last, Tert M. Eoc: *Barornis regens* Marsh 1894, "Squankum", Monmouth Co., New Jersey and *Diatryma cotei* Gaillard 1937, Mont d'Or, Rhône, France, may be from later Eocene horizons than the others; and *Diatryma* sp. Fischer 1962, lignite (Braunkohle), Geiseltal, Merseburg, Germany is M. Eoc.
Comment: Family has these 7 palaeospecies, W. Europe and U.S.

Order CHARADRIIFORMES

Suborder CHARADRII

Superfamily JACANOIDEA

Family JACANIDAE

First, Quat Pleist: neospecies *Jacana spinosa* (Linnaeus 1758), Lagoa Santa (U.Pleist), Minas Geraës, Brazil. **Extant.**
Comment: Family has 7 neospecies, tropical.

Superfamily CHARADRIOIDEA

Family RHEGMINORNITHIDAE

First and **Last,** Tert L. Mioc: *Rhegminornis calobates* Wetmore 1943, Hawthorne Fm, near Bell, Gilchrist Co. Florida.

Family ROSTRATULIDAE

First, Tert M.Eoc: *Rhynchaeites messelensis* Wittich 1899, Lutetian, Darmstadt, Germany. **Extant.**
Comment: Family has 1 palaeospecies, 2 neospecies, cosmopolitan (not Nearctic).

Family HAEMATOPODIDAE

First, Tert L. Mioc: *Paractiornis perpusillus* Wetmore 1930, Harrison Fm, Sioux Co., Nebraska. **Extant.**
Comment: Family has 2 palaeospecies, 4 neospecies, cosmopolitan.

Family CHARADRIIDAE

First, Tert L Oligoc: *Dolicopterus viator* Aymard 1856, Sannoisian Ronzon, Haute-Loire, France. **Extant.**
Comment: Family has 5 palaeospecies, 60 neospecies, cosmopolitan.

Family SCOLOPACIDAE

First, Cert Maestr: *Palaeotringa* Marsh 1870, 2 spp., Navesink Fm, Hornerstown, New Jersey. **Extant.**
Comment: Family has 30 palaeospecies, 76 neospecies, cosmopolitan.

Family RECURVIROSTRIDAE

First, Tert L. Eoc: *Coltonia recurvirostra* Hardy 1959, Colton Fm, Ephraim Canyon, Sanpete Co., Utah. **Extant.**
Comment: Family has 1 palaeospecies, 7 neospecies, cosmopolitan.

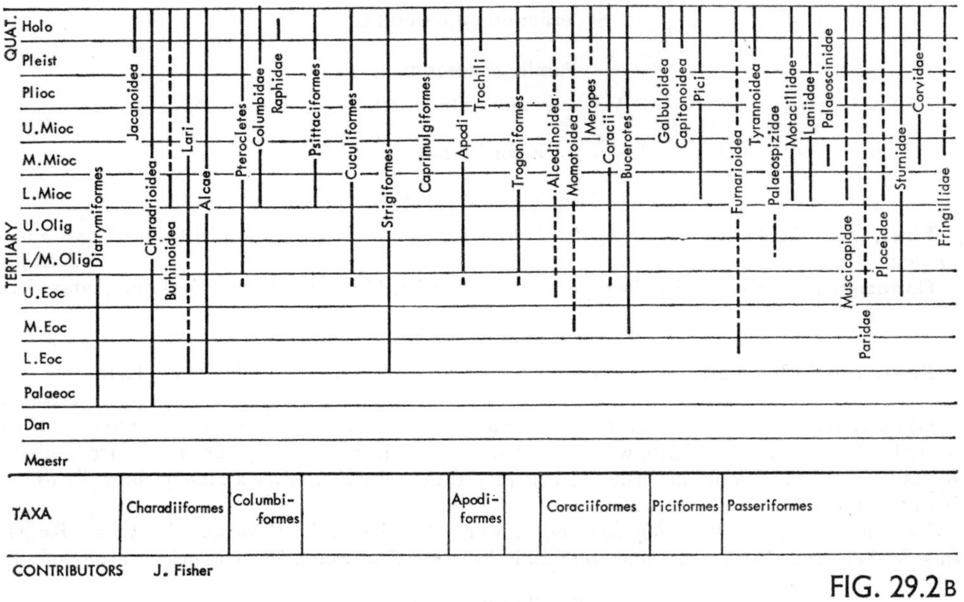

TAXA	Charadiiformes	Columbi-formes		Apodi-formes	Coraciiformes	Piciformes	Passeriformes

CONTRIBUTORS   J. Fisher

FIG. 29.2 B

[No family in Passeres shown unless represented before Pliocene.]

Family PRESBYORNITHIDAE

First and **Last,** Tert L. Eoc: *Presbyornis pervetus* Wetmore 1926, L. Green River Fm, White River, Utah.

Family PHALAROPODIDAE

First, Quat Pleist: neospecies *Phalaropus lobatus* (Linnaeus 1758), Fossil Lake (M. Pleist, Fossil Lake Fm), Oregon.   **Extant.**
Comment: Family has 3 neospecies, Holarctic.

Superfamily DROMADOIDEA

Family DROMADIDAE

No fossil known, Monotypic, shores Indian Ocean.

Superfamily BURHINOIDEA

Family BURHINIDAE

First, Tert L. Mioc: *Milnea gracilis* Lydekker 1891, Aquitainian, Allier, France.   **Extant.**
Comment: Reference of *Milnea* to this family has been queried by Wetmore (1927); next earliest is Quat Pleist: *Burhinus nanus* Brodkorb 1959, (possibly early Sangamonian; pre-Pamlico, U. Pleist), New Providence I., Bahamas. Including *Milnea*, family has 2 palaeo-species, 9 neospecies, cosmopolitan (not Nearctic).

Family GLAREOLIDAE

No fossil known, 16 neospecies, Old World.

Superfamily THINOCOROIDEA

Family THINOCORIDAE

No fossil known, 4 neospecies, Neotropical.

The Fossil Record, Part II

Superfamily CHIONIDOIDEA

Family CHIONIDIDAE

No fossil known, 2 neospecies, Antarctic and Subantarctic.

Suborder LARI

Family STERCORARIIDAE

First, Quat Pleist: *Stercorarius shufeldti* Howard 1946, Fossil Lake (M. Pleist, Fossil Lake Fm), Oregon. **Extant.**

Comment: Family has 1 palaeospecies, 4 neospecies, Holarctic, Neotropical and Antarctic.

Family LARIDAE

First, Tert L. Eoc: *Halcyornis toliapicus* (König 1838), London Clay, Sheppey, Kent.
Extant.

Comment: As *Larus toliapicus*, *Halcyornis* was the first palaeospecies of bird ever to have been formally described. Since 1846, when Owen transferred it to the Halcyonidae (= Alcedinidae), it has been held familially uncertain, but is placed now, by many, back among the gulls where it was first put.

Next oldest is L/M Olig: *Rupelornis definitus* van Beneden 1871, Rupelian (M. Olig), Rupelmonde, Belgium. With *Halcyornis*, the family has 14 paleospecies, 78 neospecies, cosmopolitan.

Family RYNCHOPIDAE

No fossil known, 3 neospecies, basically tropical.

Suborder ALCAE

Family ALCIDAE

First, Tert L. Eoc: *Nautilornis* Wetmore 1926, 2 spp. L. Green River Fm, White River, Utah. **Extant.**

Comment: Taxon here includes Mancallinae, until lately widely held as full family, but doubtfully meriting that status, and has 14 palaeospecies, 20 neospecies, Holarctic.

Order COLUMBIFORMES

Suborder PTEROCLETES

Family PTEROCLIDAE

First, Tert U. Eoc or L. Olig: *Pterocles* Temminck 1815, 2 spp. Milne-Edwards 1892, phosphorites of Quercy and Mouillac, Lot and Tarn-et-Garonne, France. **Extant.**

Comment: Family has 3 palaeospecies, 16 neospecies, Old World. (Not Australasia).

Suborder COLUMBAE

Family COLUMBIDAE

First, Tert L. Mioc: *Gerandia calcaria* (Milne-Edwards 1871), Aquitainian, St.-Gérand-le-Puy, Allier, France. **Extant.**

Comment: Family has 7 palaeospecies, 291 neospecies, cosmopolitan.

Family RAPHIDAE

First and **Last,** Quat Holo: two of the three extinct neospecies are known from subfossil material: *Raphus cucullatus* (Linnaeus 1758), Mauritius and *Pezophaps solitaria* (Gmelin 1789), Rodriguez.

Comment: This remarkable flightless Mascarene Is. family (the third was *R. solitarius* (de Sélys-Longchamps 1846), Réunion) is rather traditionally regarded as Columban, but may even be Ralloid (Lüttschwager 1961). (Full account Hachisuka 1953). The islands may be of Mioc volcanic origin.

Order PSITTACIFORMES

Family PSITTACIDAE

First, Tert L. Mioc: *Archaeopsittacus verreauxi* (Milne-Edwards 1870). Aquitainian, Langy and St.-Gérand-le-Puy, Allier, France. **Extant.**
Comment: Family has 4 palaeospecies, 336 neospecies, cosmopolitan (not Holarctic fauna).

Order MUSOPHAGIFORMES

Comment: P. R. Lowe (1943) and Verheyen (1956), summarized by Moreau (1958), show that the traditional ordinal uniting of the Musophagidae and Cuculidae may have even less justification than the uniting of Opisthocomidae and Musophagidae in one order or higher taxon, for which there is a case. The present taxon is retained here in celebration of the patent fact that detection of some similarities based on convergence from some based on common ancestry is beyond present zoologists' skills.

Family MUSOPHAGIDAE

No fossil known, 18 neospecies, Ethiopian.

Order CUCULIFORMES

Family CUCULIDAE

First, Tert U.Eoc or L. Olig: *Dynamopterus velox* Milne-Edwards 1892, phosphorite of Caylux, Tarn-et-Garonne, France. **Extant.**
Comment: Family has 4 palaeospecies, 126 neospecies, cosmopolitan.

Order STRIGIFORMES

Family TYTONIDAE

First, Tert L.Mioc: *Tyto antiqua* (Milne-Edwards 1871), St.-Gérand-le-Puy and *T. arvernenis* (Milne-Edwards 1863), Langy; both Aquitainian, Allier, France. **Extant.**
Comment: Vaurie (1965) sinks taxon as subfamily of Strigidae, a judgment to be respected; has 6 palaeospecies, 11 neospecies, cosmopolitan.

Family PROTOSTRIGIDAE

First, Tert L. Eoc: *Protostrix mimica* Wetmore 1938, Wasatch Fm, near Worland, Wyoming.
Last, Tert M. Eoc: *Protostrix* Wetmore 1933, 3 spp., Bridger Fm, Wyoming.
Comment: These 4 palaeospecies only; the taxon may be ancestral to the previous and next and probably deserves but subfamilial status.

Family STRIGIDAE

First, Tert U. Eoc or L. Olig: *Strigogyps dubius* Gaillard 1908, *Necrobyas* Milne-Edwards 1892 2 spp., *Bubo incertus* Milne-Edwards 1892 and *Asiohenrici* Milne-Edwards 1891, phosphorites of Escamps and Quercy, Lot, and of Mouillac, Tarn-et-Garonne, France. **Extant.**
Comment: Family has 22 palaeospecies, 123 neospecies, cosmopolitan.

Order CAPRIMULGIFORMES

Suborder STEATORNITHES

Family STEATORNITHIDAE

No fossil known, Monotypic, Neotropical.

Suborder CAPRIMULGI

Family AEGOTHELIDAE

No fossil known, 5 neospecies, Australasian.

Family PODARGIDAE

No fossil known, 12 neospecies, Oriental and Australasian.

Family CAPRIMULGIDAE

First, Quat Pleist: neospecies *Caprimulgus europaeus* Linnaeus 1758, Biharian fauna, Cromerian (L.Pleist), Betfia, Rumania. **Extant.**

Comment: Family has 69 neospecies, cosmopolitan.

Family NYCTIBIIDAE

First, Quat Pleist: *Nyctibius* Vieillot 1816 sp. Winge 1888, Lapa da Escrivania (U. Pleist), prov. Minas Geraës, Brazil. **Extant.**

Comment: Family has 5 neospecies, Neotropical.

Order APODIFORMES

Suborder APODI

Family AEGIALORNITHIDAE

First and **Last,** Tert U. Eoc or L. Oligoc: *Aegialornis* Lydekker 1891, 2 spp., phosphorites of Caylux and Quercy, Tarn-et-Garonne and Lot, France.

Family APODIDAE

First, Tert U. Eoc or L. Oligoc: *Cypselavus gallicus* Gaillard 1908, phosphorite of Mouillac, Tarn-et-Garonne, France. **Extant.**

Comment: Family has 4 palaeospecies, 65 neospecies, cosmopolitan.

Family HEMIPROCNIDAE

No fossil known, 3 neospecies, Oriental and Papuan.

Suborder TROCHILI

Family TROCHILIDAE

First, Quat Pleist: Gen. and sp. indet. Winge 1888, Lapa da Escrivania (U. Pleist), prov. Minas Geraës, Brazil. **Extant.**

Comment: Family has 314 neospecies, New World.

Order COLIIFORMES

Family COLIIDAE

No fossil known, 6 neospecies, Ethiopian.

Order TROGONIFORMES

Family TROGONIDAE

First, Tert U. Eoc. or L. Olig: *Archaeotrogon* Milne-Edwards 1892, 3 spp., phosphorites of Quercy, Lot and Caylux and Mouillac, Tarn-et-Garonne, France. **Extant.**

Comment: Family has 4 paleospecies (Quercian to L. Mioc. France, doubtless then an Ethiopian fauna), 35 neospecies, Neotropical, Ethiopian and Oriental.

Chapter 29: Aves

Order CORACIIFORMES

Suborder ALCEDINES

Superfamily ALCEDINOIDEA

Family ALCEDINIDAE

First, Tert U. Eoc: *Protornis* H. von Meyer 1854, 2 spp. in fish-bearing and Matt schists, Glarus, Switzerland. **Extant.**

Comment: *Protornis* is referred to this family following Storer (1960) and the advice of Pierce Brodkorb (*litt.* 1962 Nov. 2). Lambrecht (1933) held the genus in Passeriformes inc. sed., as did Swinton (1958) after considering Stussi's (1958) mathematical corrections of the bone distortions. With it, the family has the two palaeospecies and 87 neospecies, cosmopolitan. If *Protornis* be removed, 6 neospecies are known from Quat. U. Pleist Israel, France, England, Florida and Brazil.

Superfamily TODOIDEA

Family TODIDAE

No fossil known, 5 neospecies, West Indies.

Superfamily MOMOTOIDEA

Family MOMOTIDAE

First, Tert M. Eoc: *Uintornis lucaris* Marsh 1872, Bridger Fm, near Henry's Fork, Wyoming. **Extant.**

Comment: Marsh suggested *Uintornis* was a Picid; Shufeldt (1915) believed it not so, and *inc. sed.*, as did Wetmore (1956) and Storer (1960). Swinton (1958) favoured a Picid. I hold the palaeospecies here on the advice of Brodkorb; apart from it the family has 8 neospecies, presently Neotropical, of which *Baryphthengus ruficapillus* (Vieillot 1818) is known from Lagoa Santa (U. Pleist), prov. Minas Geraës, Brazil.

Suborder MEROPES

Family MEROPIDAE

First, Quat Pleist: neospecies *Merops apiaster* Linnaeus 1758, Don Valley (Mid? Pleist alluvium), between Novocherkassk and Nijni-Tchirskaya, U.S.S.R. **Extant.**

Comment: Family has 25 neospecies, Old World.

Suborder CORACII

Family CORACIIDAE

First, Tert U. Eoc or L. Oligoc: *Geranopterus alatus* Milne-Edwards 1892, phosphorite of Escamps, Lalbenque, in Lot, France. **Extant.**

Comment: Family has 1 palaeospecies, 11 neospecies, Old World.

Family BRACHYPTERACIIDAE

No fossil known, 5 neospecies, Madagascar.

Family LEPTOSOMATIDAE

No fossil known, Monotypic, Madagascar and Comoros.

Family UPUPIDAE

First, Quat Pleist: neospecies *Upupa epops* Linnaeus 1758, Middle Acheulean (M. Pleist, U. Holsteinian), Mugharet-Oumm-Qatafa, Israel. **Extant.**

Comment: Monotypic, Paleartic, Ethiopian and Oriental.

Family PHOENICULIDAE

First, Tert L. Mioc: *Limnatornis paludicola* Milne-Edwards 1871, Aquitainian, St.-Gérand-le-Puy, Allier, France. **Extant.**

Comment: Family has 1 palaeospecies (doubtless in Miocene France in an Ethiopian fauna) and 6 neospecies, Ethiopian.

Suborder BUCEROTES

Family BUCEROTIDAE

First, Tert M. Eoc: *Geisleroceros robustus* Lambrecht 1935, Lutetian Fm, Halle, Germany. **Extant.**

Comment: Family has 2 palaeospecies (above and another U. Eoc France, which doubtless then belonged to the Ethiopian fauna) and 44 neospecies, Ethiopian, Oriental and Papuan.

Order PICIFORMES

Suborder GALBULAE

Superfamily GALBULOIDEA

Family GALBULIDAE

No fossil known, 15 neospecies, Neotropical.

Family BUCCONIDAE

First, Quat Pleist: neospecies *Nystalus chacuru* (Vieillot 1816) and *Malacoptila striata* (Spix 1824), Lagoa Santa (U. Pleist), prov. Minas Geraës, Brazil. **Extant.**

Comment: Family has 30 neospecies, Neotropical.

Superfamily CAPITONOIDEA

Family CAPITONIDAE

First, Quat Pleist: *Capito* Vieillot 1816 sp., prob. neospecies *C. niger* (P.L.S. Müller 1776), Curvallo or Lagoa Santa (U. Pleist), prov. Minas Geraës, Brazil. **Extant.**

Comment: Family has 72 neospecies, Neotropical, Ethiopian and Oriental.

Family INDICATORIDAE

No fossil known, 14 neospecies, Ethiopian and Oriental.

Family RAMPHASTIDAE

First, Quat Pleist: *Ramphastos* Linnaes 1758, 2 spp. Lagoa Santa, (U. Pleist), prov. Minas Geraës, Brazil. **Extant.**

Comment: Family has 37 neospecies, Neotropical.

Suborder PICI

Family PICIDAE

First, Tert L. Mioc: *Palaeopicus* Lambrecht 1933, 2 spp. Aquitainian, Langy and St.-Gérand-le-Puy, Allier, France. **Extant.**

Comment: Family has 4 palaeospecies, 213 neospecies, cosmopolitan (only marginally Australasian).

Order PASSERIFORMES

Comment: Within this vast order, which embraces nearly 60 per cent of the neospecies in the Class, the classification continues as that of Fisher & Peterson (1964), with minor modifications. This strove to bring the widely accepted arrangement of Wetmore (1960) into line with the views of a committee set up by the Eleventh International Ornithological Congress (Mayr & Greenway 1956) and fundamentally adopted by Mayr, Greenway and their colleagues in the compilation of the later volumes of the Peters *Check-list of [living] birds of the world.* As a result, a number of the Passerine families of Wetmore have been demoted to subfamilial status. Since many working ornithologists still use a practical systema based on Wetmore the larger and more important of these taxa are therefore listed and analysed in what follows.

Suborder EURYLAIMI

Family EURYLAIMIDAE

No fossil known, 14 neospecies, Ethiopian and Oriental.

Suborder TYRANNI

Superfamily FURNARIOIDEA

Family FURNARIIDAE

Subfamily DENDROCOLAPTINAE

First, Quat Pleist: neospecies *Xiphocolaptes albicollis* (Vieillot 1818) and *Lepidocolaptes angustiros-tris* (Vieillot 1818), Lagoa Santa (U.Pleist), prov. Minas Geraës, Brazil.　　**Extant.**
Comment: Taxon has 47 neospecies, Neotropical.

Subfamily FURNARIINAE

First, Quat Pleist: remains of 2 indet. spp. of different genera (Lund 1841) in Curvallo or Lagoa Santa (U. Pleist). prov. Minas Geraës, Brazil.　　**Extant.**
Comment: Taxon has 215 neospecies, Neotropical.

Family FORMICARIIDAE

First, Quat Pleist: neospecies *Chamaeza campanisona* (Lichtenstein 1823), Lagoa Santa (U. Pleist), Minas Gerais, Brazil.　　**Extant.**
Comment: Family has 224 neospecies, Neotropical.

Family CONOPOPHAGIDAE

No fossil known, 11 neospecies, Neotropical.

Family RHINOCRYPTIDAE

First, Tert (? L or M) Eoc: *"Hebe" schucherti* Shufeldt 1913, 5 mi. W. of Green River, Wyoming.　　**Extant.**
Comment: *Hebe* Shufeldt 1913 is preoccupied by the crustacean genus *Hebe* Risso 1826, as was pointed out by Wetmore (1940, 1956) who puts the species in full *inc. sed.* and suggests that a new name for the genus can wait until the relationships are cleared up. However, Lambrecht (1933) referred it to the Pteroptochidae (= Rhinocryptidae), and Brodkorb (*litt.* 1962 Nov. 2) carries it "with query" in the Scytalopidae (= Rhinocryptidae). If valid it is the sole known palaeospecies in the family, with 29 neospecies, presently Neotropical.

Superfamily TYRANNOIDEA

Family PITTIDAE

No fossil known, 25 neospecies, Old World.

Family PHILEPITTIDAE

No fossil known, 4 neospecies, Madagascar.

Family ACANTHISITTIDAE

No fossil known, 4 neospecies, New Zealand.

Family TYRANNIDAE

First, Quat Pleist: neospecies *Tyrannus tyrannus* (Linnacus 1758), Reddick beds (Illinoian, M. Pleist), Reddick, Florida.

Comment: Family has 364 neospecies, New World. This taxon includes the monotypic Oxyruncinae, raised by some to familial status.

Family PIPRIDAE

No fossil known, 61 neospecies, Neotropical.

Family COTINGIDAE

No fossil known, 91 neospecies, Neotropical.

Family PHYTOTOMIDAE

No fossil known, 3 neospecies, Neotropical.

Suborder MENURAE

Family MENURIDAE

No fossil known, 2 neospecies, Australian.

Family ATRICHORNITHIDAE

No fossil known, 2 neospecies, Australian.

Suborder PASSERES

Comment: Alternative: Oscines.

Family ALAUDIDAE

First, Tert Plioc: *Alauda* 2 spp. Portis 1887 from Messiniano (L. Plioc), Sinigaglia, and from Gabbro, near Leghorn (also L. Plioc), Italy. **Extant.**

Comment: Family has 3 palaeospecies, 75 neospecies, cosmopolitan (1 native species only New World).

Family PALAEOSPIZIDAE

First and **Last,** Tert M. or U. Oligoc: *Palaeospiza bella* J. A. Allen 1878, Florissant Lake beds, Colorado.

Family HIRUNDINIDAE

First, Quat Pleist: neospecies *Hirundo rustica* Linnaeus 1758 and *Delichon urbica* (Linnaeus 1758), Biharian Fauna, Cromerian (L. Pleist), Betfia, Rumania, earlier than sole paleospecies *Tachycineta speleodytes* Brodkorb 1957, Illinoian (M. Pleist), Reddick, Marion Co., Florida.

Extant.

Comment: Family has 1 palaeospecies, 79 living species, cosmopolitan.

Family MOTACILLIDAE

First, Tert L. Mioc: *Motacilla* 2 spp. Milne-Edwards 1871, Aquitainian, Langy, Allier. France. **Extant.**

Comment: Family has 3 palaeospecies, 53 neospecies, cosmopolitan.

Family CAMPEPHAGIDAE

No fossil known, 70 neospecies, Old World.

Family PYCNONOTIDAE

First, Quat Pleist: neospecies *Pynconotus barbatus* (Desfontaines 1789), Acheulian (U. Holsteinian, M. Pleist), Mugharet-Oumm-Qatafa, Israel. **Extant.**

Comment: Family has 119 neospecies, Old World.

Family IRENIDAE

No fossil known, 14 neospecies, Oriental.

Family LANIIDAE

First, Tert L. Mioc: *Lanius miocaenus* Milne-Edwards 1871, Aquitainian, Langy, Allier, France. **Extant.**

Comment: Taxon includes Prionopinae, preferred by some as family, and has 1 palaeospecies, 74 neospecies, cosmopolitan (not Neotropical and only marginally Australasian).

Family VANGIDAE

No fossil known, 13 neospecies, Madagascar and Comoros.

Family BOMBYCILLIDAE

First, Quat Pleist: neospecies *Bombycilla garrulus* (Linnaeus 1758), probably Eemian (U. Pleist), Grotte Grimaldi, Monaco. **Extant.**

Comment: Family has 8 neospecies, Holarctic.

Family DULIDAE

No fossil known, monotypic, Hispaniola.

Family CINCLIDAE

First, Quat Pleist: neospecies *Cinclus cinclus* (Linnaeus 1758), Gudenus Cave (U. Pleist), Lower Austria. **Extant.**

Comment: Family has 4 neospecies, cosmopolitan (not Neotropical, Australasian).

Family PALAEOSCINIDAE

First and **Last,** Tert M. Mioc: *Palaeoscinis turdirostris* Howard 1957, Mohnian, Monterey Fm, Tepusquet Creek, Santa Barbara Co., California.

Family TROGLODYTIDAE

First, Quat Pleist: *Cistothorus brevis* Brodkorb 1957, Illinoian (M. Pleist), Reddick, Marion Co., Florida. **Extant.**

Comment: Family has 1 palaeospecies, 59 neospecies, Neotropical and Holarctic.

Family MIMIDAE

First, Quat Pleist: neospecies *Mimus gundlachii* Capanis 1855, pre-Pamlico cave deposits (cf. early Sangamonian, U. Pleist), New Providence I., Bahamas. Bones have been provisionally referred to this family from Chihuahua, Mexico (M. Plioc). **Extant.**

Comment: Family has 31 neospecies, New World.

Family PRUNELLIDAE

First, Quat Pleist: neospecies *Prunella modularis* (Linnaeus 1758), Chudleigh Cave, Devon, England, may be from Riss 2 horizon (M. Pleist); if not, earliest known fossil is probably *Prunella collaris* (Scopoli 1869), probably Eemian (U. Pleist), Grotte Grimaldi, Monaco.

Extant.

Comment: Family has 12 neospecies, Palearctic.

The Fossil Record, Part II

Family MUSCICAPIDAE

Subfamily TURDINAE

First, Tert Plioc; cf. neospecies *Monticola solitarius* (Linnaeus 1758), Astian (U. Plioc), Fort du Serrat, near Perpignan, France. **Extant.**
Comment: Taxon has 303 neospecies, cosmopolitan.

Subfamily ORTHONYCHINAE

No fossil known, 17 neospecies, Australasia.

Subfamily TIMALIINAE

First, Quat Pleist: neospecies *Turdoides squamiceps* (Cretzschmar 1826), Upper Acheulian (U. Holsteinian, M. Pleist), Mugharet-Oumm-Qatafa, Israel, **Extant.**
Comment: Taxon has 249 neospecies, Old World, with W. Nearctic outpost.

Subfamily PANURINAE

No fossil known, 19 neospecies, Palearctic and Oriental.

Subfamily PICATHARTINAE

No fossil known, 2 neospecies, West Africa.

Subfamily POLIOPTILINAE

No fossil known, 11 neospecies, New World.

Subfamily SYLVIINAE

First, ?Tert L. Mioc: *Sylvia* sp ? Lambrecht 1933, is reported from the Aquitainian, France. Pending re-investigation of this, earliest fossils are neospecies *Acrocephalus palustris* (Bechstein 1798) and *Sylvia communis* Latham 1787, Biharian Fauna, Cromerian (L. Pleist), Betfia, Rumania. **Extant.**
Comment: Taxon has ? 1 palaeospecies, 322 neospecies, cosmopolitan (only marginally Nearctic).

Subfamily MALURINAE

No fossil known, 83 neospecies, Australasian and Oriental.

Subfamily REGULINAE

First, Quat Pleist: neospecies *Regulus regulus* (Linnaeus 1758), probably Gudenus Cave (U. Pleist) or a neighbour in Lower Austria. **Extant.**
Comment: Taxon has 3 (some systematists hold 4) neospecies, Holarctic with Neotropical outpost.

Subfamily MUSCICAPINAE

First, Quat Pleist: neospecies *Muscicapa striata* Pallas 1764, U. Acheulian (U. Holsteinian, M. Pleist), Mugharet-Oumm-Qatafa, Israel. **Extant.**
Comment: Taxon has 286 neospecies. Old World.

Subfamily MONARCHINAE

No fossil known, 63 neospecies, Old World, only marginally Palearctic.

Subfamily PACHYCEPHALINAE

First, Quat Holo: neospecies *Turnagra capensis* (Sparrman 1787), prehistoric (*c.* 1000 B.C.– 1670 A.D.), Pyramid Valley, S.I., New Zealand. **Extant**
Comment: Taxon has 49 neospecies, Australasian and Oriental.

756

Chapter 29: Aves

Family PARIDAE

First, Tert U. Eoc: *Palaegithalus cuvieri* (Gervais 1852), Ledian, Montmartre, France.
Extant.
Comment: Besides typical subfamily, taxon here includes Remizinae, perhaps nearer Dicaeidae, and Aegithalinae, perhaps nearer Panurinae in Muscicapidae and by some erected to familial rank; sole palaeospecies is only tentatively assigned, following Storer (1960); otherwise earliest fossils are *Parus* Linnaeus 1758, 3 spp., and *Aegithalus caudatus* (Linnaeus 1758), Biharian Fauna, Cromerian (L. Pleist), Betfia, Rumania. Family as here has 62 neospecies, cosmopolitan, though but marginally Neotropical and Australasian.

Family SITTIDAE

First, Tert Plioc: *Sitta senogalliensis* Portis 1887, Messiniano Fm (L. Plioc), Sinigaglia, Italy
Extant.
Comment: Taxon here has 1 palaeospecies, 31 neospecies, Holarctic, Oriental, Australasian and marginally Neotropical. Climacterinae, 6 Australian species (no fossil known), are promoted by some to family status.

Family CERTHIIDAE

First, Quat Pleist: neospecies *Certhia familiaris* Linnaeus 1758, Biharian Fauna, Cromerian (L. Pleist), Betfia, Rumania. **Extant.**
Comment: Family has 7 neospecies, Holarctic, Oriental, Ethiopian and marginally Neotropical.

Family DICAEIDAE

No fossil known, 57 neospecies, Oriental and Australasian.

Family NECTARINIIDAE

No fossil known, 105 neospecies, Old World, though only marginally Palearctic.

Family ZOSTEROPIDAE

No fossil known, 79 neospecies, Old World, though only marginally Palearctic.

Family MELIPHAGIDAE

First, Quat Holo: neospecies *Prosthemadera novaeseelandiae* (Gmelin 1788), prehistoric (*c.* 1000 B.C.–1670 A.D.), Pyramid Valley, S.I., New Zealand. **Extant.**
Comment: Family has 162 neospecies, Australasian with South African outpost.

Family EMBERIZIDAE

Comment: See remarks under Fringillidae, p. 758.

Subfamily EMBERIZINAE

First, Tert Plioc: *Palaeostruthus hatcheri* (Shufeldt 1913), equiv. Ogallala Fm (L. Plioc), near Long Island, Kansas and *P. eurius* Brodkorb 1963, also L. Plioc, near Haile, Alachua Co., Florida.
Extant.
Comment: Taxon has 3 palaeospecies, 211 neospecies, cosmopolitan, though not naturally Australasian and only marginally Oriental.

Subfamily CARDINALINAE

First, Quat Pleist: neospecies *Pyrrhuloxia cardinalis* (Linnaeus 1758), Arredondo clay member, Wicomico Fm (Illinoian, M. Pleist), Arredondo, Alachua Co, Florida. **Extant.**
Comment: Some authorities prefer Richmondeninae for taxon, which has 110 neospecies, New World.

The Fossil Record, Part II

Subfamily CATAMBLYRHYNCHINAE

No fossil known, Monotypic, N. Andes of South America.

Subfamily TANAGRINAE

First, Quat Holo: neospecies *Spindalis zena* (Linnaeus 1766) and *Nesospingus speculiferus* (Lawrence 1875), cave deposits (early Holo), Puerto Rico.   **Extant.**
Comment: Some authorities prefer Thraupinae for taxon, which has 191 neospecies, New World.

Subfamily TERSININAE

First, Quat Pleist: neospecies *Tersina viridis* (Illiger 1811) Lagoa Santa, (U. Pleist), prov. Minas Geraës, Brazil.   **Extant.**
Comment: Monotypic, Neotropical.

Subfamily COEREBINAE

First, Quat Holo: neospecies *Coereba flaveola* (Linnaeus 1758), cave deposits (early Holo), Puerto Rico.   **Extant.**
Comment: Taxon may be artificial and has been divided into two tribes, 26 Dacnini with believed Tanagrine affinities, and 10 Coerebini with believed Parulid affinities; has 36 neospecies, Neotropical, marginally Nearctic.

Family PARULIDAE

First, Quat Pleist: neospecies *Geothlypis trichas* (Linnaeus 1766), Reddick beds (Illinoian, M.Pleist), Reddick, Marion Co., Florida.   **Extant.**
Comment: Family has 113 neospecies, New World.

Family DREPANIDIDAE

No fossil known, 22 neospecies, Hawaiian archipelago.

Family VIREONIDAE

First, Quat Pleist: neospecies *Cyclarhis gujanensis* (Gmelin 1789) and another indet. sp., Lagoa Santa (U. Pleist), prov. Minas Geraës, Brazil.   **Extant.**
Comment: Family has 42 neospecies, New World.

Family ICTERIDAE

First, Quat Pleist: *Pandanaris floridana* Brodkorb 1957 and 3 neospecies, Reddick, Marion Co., and *Cremaster tytthus* Brodkorb 1959 and 2 of the Reddick neospecies, Arrendondo, Alachua Co., all Illinoian (M.Pleist), Florida.   **Extant.**
Comment: Family has 6 palaeospecies, 88 neospecies, New World.

Family FRINGILLIDAE

First, Tert ?M. Mioc: *Fringilla* sp. de Villalta 1963, Vindobonian, Spain; otherwise earliest are neospecies *Fringilla coelebs* Linnaeus 1758 and *Coccothraustes coccothraustes* (Linnaeus 1758), Biharian Fauna, Cromerian (L. Pleist), Betfia, Rumania.   **Extant.**
Comment: Family has 124 neospecies, cosmopolitan, not native Australasia. Unnamed material referred to Fringillidae *sensu lato* (i.e. perhaps including Emberizinae and Ploceidae) has been recorded from the Quercian (Eoc-Olig), France; from the M.Mioc, France (*c.* 13 forms Helvetian) and Germany (Vindobonian); and from Plioc or Villafranchian Pleist horizons, Italy and Arizona. [N.B. This family appears last on chart.]

Family ESTRILDIDAE

No fossil known, 107 neospecies, Ethiopian, Oriental and Australasian.

Family VIDUIDAE

No fossil known, 8 neospecies, Ethiopian.

Family PLOCEIDAE

First, Tert? L. Mioc: *Passer* sp.? Lambrecht 1933, Aquitainian, France. Pending re-investigation of this, earliest fossil is neospecies *Passer montanus* (Linnaeus 1758), Biharian Fauna, Cromerian (L.Pleist), Betfia, Rumania, earlier than palaeospecies *Passer predomesticus* Tchernov 1962, M. Acheulian (U. Holsteinian, M.Pleist), Mugharet-Oumm-Qatafa, Israel. **Extant.**

Comment: Subfamilies Bubalornithinae (2 Ethiopian neospecies) and Passerinae (37 neospecies) are raised by some to family rank. Taxon here has 2 (or 1) palaeospecies, 134 neospecies, cosmopolitan, though New World and Australasia by introduction. See remarks under Fringillidae.

Family STURNIDAE

First, Tert U. Eoc: *Laurillardia* Milne-Edwards 1871, 3 spp., Ledian, Montmartre and Montmorency, France. **Extant.**

Comment: Family has 3 palaeospecies, 111 neospecies, Old World, Nearctic by introduction.

Family ORIOLIDAE

First, Quat Pleist: cf. neospecies *Oriolus oriolus* (Linnaeus 1758), L. Levalloiso-Mousterian layer (= Eemian, U.Pleist), Kebara Cave, Israel. **Extant.**

Comment: Family has 28 neospecies, Old World.

Family DICRURIDAE

First, Quat Pleist: a record from China (Brodkorb *in litt*). **Extant.**

Comment: Family, held by some close to Muscicapidae, has 19 neospecies, Ethiopian, Oriental and Australasian.

Family CALLAEIDAE

First, Quat Holo: records of 3 neospecies, all in deposits formed at least partly since Polynesian colonization *c*. 950 A.D. Earliest may be extinct *Heteralocha acutirostris*, Waingongoro, N.I., New Zealand. **Extant.**

Comment: Family has 3 neospecies, New Zealand.

Family GRALLINIDAE

No fossil known, 4 neospecies, Australia and Papua.

Family ARTAMIDAE

No fossil known, 10 neospecies, Australasian and Oriental.

Family CRACTICIDAE

No fossil known, 10 neospecies, Australasian.

Family PTILONORHYNCHIDAE

No fossil known, 17 neospecies, Papua and Australia.

Family PARADISAEIDAE

No fossil known, 40 neospecies, Papua and Australia.

Family CORVIDAE

First, Tert M. Mioc: *Miocorvus larteti* (Milne-Edwards 1871), Helvetian, Sansan, Gers, France **Extant.**

Comment: Family has 10 palaeospecies, 102 neospecies, cosmopolitan.

REFERENCES

AMADON, D. 1957. Remarks on the classification of the perching birds [order Passeriformes]. *Proc. zool. Soc. Calcutta* (Mookerjee Mem. Volume) 259–68.

—— 1959. Behavior and classification: some reflections. *Vjschr. naturf. Ges., Zurich* **104**, 73–78.

AMEGHINO, F. 1891. Enumeración de las aves fósiles de la República Argentina. *Rev. Argent. Hist. nat.* **1**, 441–53.

ARCHEY, G. 1941. The moa. *Bull. Auckland Inst. Mus.* **1**, 1–145.

BAIRD, D. 1967. Age of fossil birds from the greensands of New Jersey. *Auk*, **84**, 260–62. [Not used in this compilation.]

BEER, G. DE 1954. *Archaeopteryx lithographica.* A study based upon the British Museum specimen. London (British Museum (Nat. Hist.)).

BROCK, W. J. 1956. A genetic review of the family Ardeidae (Aves). *Am. Mus. Novit.* No. 1779, 1–49.

BRODKORB, P. 1963. Catalogue of fossil birds, Part 1 (Archaeopterygiformes through Ardeiformes). *Bull. Florida St. Mus. biol. Sci.*, **7**, 179–293.

—— 1964A. Birds from the Upper Cretaceous of Wyoming. *Int. orn. Congr.* **13**, 55–70.

—— 1964. Catalogue fossil birds, Part 2 (Anseriformes through Galliformes). *Bull. Florida St. Mus. biol. Sci.*, **8**, 195–335.

—— 1967 (for 1966). Catalogue of fossil birds, Part 3 (Ralliformes, Ichthyorniformes, Charadriiformes). *Bull. Florida St. Mus. Biol. Sci.*, **11**, 99–220. [Not used in this compilation.]

DELACOUR, J. & VAURIE, C. 1957. A classification of the Oscines (Aves). *Contr. Sci.* **16**, 1–6.

DUFF, R. 1956. The moa-hunter period of Maori culture. *Canterbury Mus. Bull.* **1**, 1–400. (2nd edn.)

FISHER, J. & PETERSON, R. T. 1964. *The world of birds.* London (Macdonald).

FLEMING, C. A. 1962A. History of the New Zealand land bird fauna. *Notornis* **9**, 270–4.

—— 1962B. The extinction of moas and other animals during the Holocene period. *Notornis* **10**, 113–7.

FLINT, R. F. 1957. *Glacial and Pleistocene geology.* New York (John Wiley).

FRIEDMANN, H. E. 1955. Recent revisions in classification and their geological significance. In WOLFSON, A. (Ed.): *Recent studies in avian biology.* Urbana (University of Illinois Press).

GREGORY, J. T. 1952. The jaws of the Cretaceous toothed birds, *Ichthyornis* and *Hesperornis*. *Condor* **54**, 73–88.

HACHISUKA, M. 1953. *The dodo and kindred birds.* London (Witherby).

HELLER, F. 1960. Der dritte *Archaeopteryx*-fund aus den Solnhofener Plattenkalken des oberen Malm Frankens. *J. Orn. Lpz.* **101**, 7–28.

HOWARD, H. 1947. A preliminary survey of trends in avian evolution from Pleistocene to Recent time. *Condor* **49**, 10–13.

—— 1950. Fossil evidence of avian evolution. *Ibis* **92**, 1–21.

KUHN, O. 1965. *Die fossilen Vögel.* Krailling-München (Verlag Oeben).

LAMBRECHT, K. 1933. *Handbuch der Palaeornithologie.* Berlin (Borntraeger).

LOWE, P. R. 1943. Some notes on the anatomical differences obtaining between the Cuculidae and the Musophagidae. *Ibis* **85**, 490–575.

LÜTTSCHWAGER, J. 1961. *Die Dronte Vögel.* Wittenberg Lutherstadt (Ziemsens Neue Brehm Bücherei).

LYDEKKER, R. 1891. *Catalogue of the fossil birds in the British Museum.* London (British Museum (Nat. Hist.)).

—— 1896. Fossil birds. In NEWTON, A. (Ed.): *A dictionary of birds.* London (Black), pp. 277–89.

MARSHALL, A. J. (Ed.) 1960. *Biology and comparative physiology of birds*, Vol. 1. New York (Academic Press).

MAYR, E. 1955. Comments on some recent studies of song bird phylogeny. *Wilson Bull.* **67**, 33–44.

—— 1963. *Animal species and evolution.* Cambridge, Mass. (Harvard University Press).

—— & AMADON, D. 1957. A classification of recent birds. *Am. Mus. Novit.* No. 1496, 1–42.

MAYR, E. & GREENWAY, J. C. JR. 1956. Sequence of Passerine families (Aves). *Breviora* **58**, 1–11.

METCALF, M. M. 1929. Parasites and the aid they give in problems of taxonomy, geographical distribution and paleogeography. *Smithson. Misc. Collns* **81** (8).

MILLER, A. H. 1955. Concepts and problems of avian systematics in relation to evolutionary processes. In WOLFSON, A. (Ed.): *Recent studies in avian biology.* Urbana (University of Illinois Press), pp. 1–22.

MILNE-EDWARDS, A. 1867–71. *Recherches anatomiques et paléontologiques pourservir a l'histoire des oiseaux fossiles de la France,* Vols. 1 & 2.

MOREAU, R. E. 1958. Some aspects of the Musophagidae. *Ibis* **100,** 67–112, 238–70.

MORENO, F. P. & MERCERAT, A. 1891. Catálogo de los Pájaros fósiles de la República Argentina. *An. Mus. La Plata Sec. Paleont.* part 1.

NEWTON, A. and others. 1896. *A dictionary of birds.* London (Black).

OLIVER, W. R. B. 1949. The moas of New Zealand and Australia. *Dom. Mus. Bull.* **15,** 1–206.

PATTERSON, B. & KRAGLIEVICH, J. L. 1960. Sistemática y nomenclatura de las aves Forracoideas del Plioceno argentino. *Publnes Mus. munic. Cienc. nat. tradic. Mar del Plata* **1,** 1–51.

PETERS, J. L. *et al.* 1931–64. *Check-list of birds of the world.* Cambridge, Mass. (Harvard University Press Museum of Comparative Zoology). [Published to date, Vols. **1–7** (1931–51); **9–10** (1960, 1964); **15** (1962); after **7** edited by E. MAYR and others.]

ROTHSCHILD, M. & CLAY, T. 1961. *Fleas, flies and cuckoos.* London (Arrow Books). [First edn. 1952.]

SALOMONSEN, F. 1960. Report of the standing committee on ornithological nomenclature. *Int. orn. Congr.* **12,** 30–43.

SHUFELDT, R. W. 1915. Fossil birds in the Marsh collection of Yale University. *Trans. Conn. Acad. Arts Sci.* **19,** 1–110.

SIBLEY, C. G. 1960. The electrophoretic patterns of avian egg-white proteins as taxonomic characters. *Ibis* **102,** 215–84.

SIMPSON, G. G. 1945. The principles of classification and a classification of mammals. *Bull. am. Mus. nat. Hist.,* **85,** 1–350.

—— 1946. Fossil penguins. *Bull. am. Mus. nat. Hist.* **87,** 1–100.

STORER, R. W. 1956. The fossil loon, *Colymbordes minutus. Condor* **58,** 413–26.

—— 1956. The arrangement of songbird families. *Condor* **61,** 152–53.

—— 1960. Adaptive radiation in birds *and* The classification of birds. In Marshall, A. J. (Ed.): *Biology and comparative physiology of birds.* London (Black), pp. 15–93.

—— 1965. *Auk* **82,** 657–8. [Review of Brodkorb 1963, 1964, *q.v.*]

STÜSSI, F. 1958. Die Entzerrung von Fossilien am Beispiel des *Protornis glaronensis. Abh. Schweiz. paläont. Ges.* **73,** 1–16.

SWINTON, W. E. 1958. *Fossil birds.* London (British Museum (Nat. Hist.)).

TORDOFF, H. B. 1954. Relationships in the New World nine-primaried Ocines. *Auk.* **71,** 273–84.

—— & MACDONALD, J. R. 1957. A new bird (family Cracidae) from the early Oligocene of South Dakota. *Auk.* **74,** 174–84.

VAURIE, C. 1959. *The birds of the palearctic fauna: a systematic reference: Order Passeriformes.* London (Witherby).

—— 1965. *The birds of the palearctic fauna: a systematic reference: Non-Passeriformes.* London (Witherby).

VERMEYEN, R. 1956. Contribution à l'anatomie et à la systematique des touracos (Musophagi) et des coucous (Cuculiformes). *Bull. Inst. r. Sci. nat. Belg.* **32,** 1–31.

WETMORE, A. 1928. Prehistoric ornithology in North America *J. Wash. Acad. Sci.* **18,** 145–58.

—— 1929. Birds of the past in North America. *Rep. Smithson. Inst.* (1928), 377–89.

—— 1940. A check-list of the fossil birds of North America. *Smithson. misc. Collns,* **99,** 1–81.

—— 1951. [Presidential address]. Recent additions to our knowledge of prehistoric birds 1933–1949. *Int. Orn. Congr.* **10,** 51–74.

—— 1956. A check-list of the fossil and prehistoric birds of North America and the West Indies. *Smithson. misc. Collns* **131,** 1–105.

—— 1959. Birds of the Pleistocene in North America. *Smithson. misc. Collns.* **138,** 1–24.

—— 1960. A classification for the birds of the world. *Smithson. misc. Collns.* **139,** 1–37.

WOLFSON, A. (Ed.) 1955. *Recent studies in avian biology.* Urbana (University of Illinois Press).

The Fossil Record, Part II

JAMES M. McC. FISHER, M.A. F.R.G.S. F.L.S. F.Z.S.
Ashton Manor, Northampton.

Note added in proof: Brodkorb (1967)—published too late to be used in this compilation—significantly alters the systema in some important orders; it puts important groups of taxa back from Palaeoc to Maestr, major radiation of modern families thus being provedly earlier than was previously thought.

J. F.

CHAPTER 30

Mammalia

Contributors: P. M. BUTLER, W. A. CLEMENS, S. F. GRAHAM,
D. A. HOOIJER, K. A. KERMACK, B. PATTERSON, W. D. L. RIDE,
D. E. RUSSELL, R. J. G. SAVAGE, E. L. SIMONS, L. B. H. TARLO,
L. THALER & T. WHITWORTH

Introduction. The classification employed here and the order of taxa listed are essentially those given by Simpson (1945). The only additions are the subclass Eotheria and the following orders of Metatheria: Marsupicarnivora, Paucituberculate, Peramelina and Diprotodonta, and of Eutheria: Deltatheridia, Trigonostylopoidea, Xenungulata and Desmostylia.

The only serious problem encountered in compiling the documentation was with the early and hence more primitive members of certain orders. Thus the arctocyonids are listed as the first creodont carnivores and also as condylarths. The earliest members of the Deltatheridia are also listed as insectivores and the latest as creodont carnivores. Rather than impose an arbitrary system of classification that would at the same time necessitate major changes in stratigraphical range, the various taxa are listed as submitted by contributors. Thus certain groups have a multiple documentation. This situation seems genuinely to reflect the real difficulty of assigning the small generalised mammals from the late Mesozoic and basal Tertiary to clearly defined orders. The uncertainty in this aspect of the documentation is therefore retained without apology.
[L.B.H.T.]

Subclass EOTHERIA

Order DOCODONTA

Family MORGANUCODONTIDAE Kühne

First and **Last,** Trias Rhaet or Jur Hett: *Morganucodon* Kühne, Glamorgan, Wales.
Constituent genera: *Morganucodon* Kühne, *Sinoconodon* (in part) Patterson and Olson, *Erythrotherium* Crompton, *Eozostrodon* Parrington, *Tricuspes* F. von Huene.
Comment: *Morganucodon* also comes from the Lu Feng Beds of Yunnan China, *Erythrotherium* from the Basutoland 'Red Beds' and *Eozostrodon* from Somerset, England. None of these localities can be dated more closely than U. Trias-L. Jur. They have not been included in the time-chart.

Family DOCODONTIDAE Simpson

First and **Last,** Cret Berr: *Docodon* Marsh, Morrison Fm, Wyoming.
Comment: *Peraiocynodon* Simpson, Purbeck, England, probably young *Docodon*. [K.A.K.]

The Fossil Record, pp. 763–787. Geological Society of London, 1967. Printed in Northern Ireland.

The Fossil Record, Part II

Subclass PROTOTHERIA

Order MONOTREMATA

First, Tert? Plioc: *Zaglossus [Proechidna] robusta* (Dun, 1895), gold bearing wash, 1st cavern 'Canadian Lead', Gulong, New South Wales, Australia (J. A. Mahoney, *pers. comm.*). **Extant.**
[W.D.L.R.]

Subclass ALLOTHERIA

Order MULTITUBERCULATA

Suborder PLAGIAULACOIDEA Simpson, 1928

First, Jur Kimm: Un-named form, Leira, Portugal (Kühne 1961). [K.A.K.]

Last, Cret Alb: One or, possibly, two as yet undescribed species mentioned by Patterson (1956), Trinity Sand, Texas.

Comments: Plagiaulacoidea is used here to include only the Plagiaulacidae and provide a taxon of rank equivalent to those proposed by Sloan and Van Valen (1965) for U. Cret and Tert multituberculates. Wealden plagiaulacids were described by Simpson (1928a) and Clemens (1963). [W.A.C.]

Suborder PTILODONTOIDEA Gregory and Simpson, 1926

First, Cret Campan: *Mesodma? primaevus* (Lambe, 1902), Oldman Fm, Alberta. Descriptions of U. Cret ptilodontoids and taeniolabidoids (see below) given by Simpson (1929b), Clemens (1964), and Sloan & Van Valen (1965).

Last, Tert U. Eoc: *Ectypodus* sp., Tepee Trail Fm, Badwater area, Natrona Co., Wyoming (Robinson, Black & Dawson 1964).

Suborder TAENIOLABIDOIDEA Granger and Simpson, 1929

First, Cret Campan: *Cimolomys major* Russell, 1937, Oldman Fm, Alberta. *Djadochtatherium* Simpson, 1925, from the Djadokhta local fauna, Mongolia, is probably of Late Cret age and might be older than *Cimolomys major*.

Last, Tert L. Eoc: *Neoliotomus* Jepsen, Wyoming. [Shown in Fig. 30.1B only extending to Palaeoc. Ed.] [W.A.C.]

Subclass uncertain

Order TRICONODONTA

Family AMPHILESTIDAE Kühne

First, Jur, Bath: *Amphilestes* Owen, *Phascolotherium* Owen, Stonesfield Slate, Oxfordshire, England.

Last, Cret Berr: *Aploconodon* Simpson, *Phascolodon* Simpson, Morrison Fm, Wyoming.

Family TRICONODONTIDAE Marsh.

First, Cret Berr: *Triconodon* Owen, Purbeck of Dorset, England; *Priacodon* Marsh, Morrison Fm, Wyoming; *Trioracodon* Simpson, both localities. [K.A.K.]

Last, Cret Alb: *Astroconodon* Patterson, Trinity Sands, Texas. [K.A.K. & W.A.C.]

Subclass THERIA

Infraclass PANTOTHERIA

Order EUPANTOTHERIA Kermack & Mussett

Family unnamed

First and **Last,** Trias Rhaet or Jur Hett: unnamed Welsh forms (Kermack & Mussett 1959) Glamorgan, Wales.

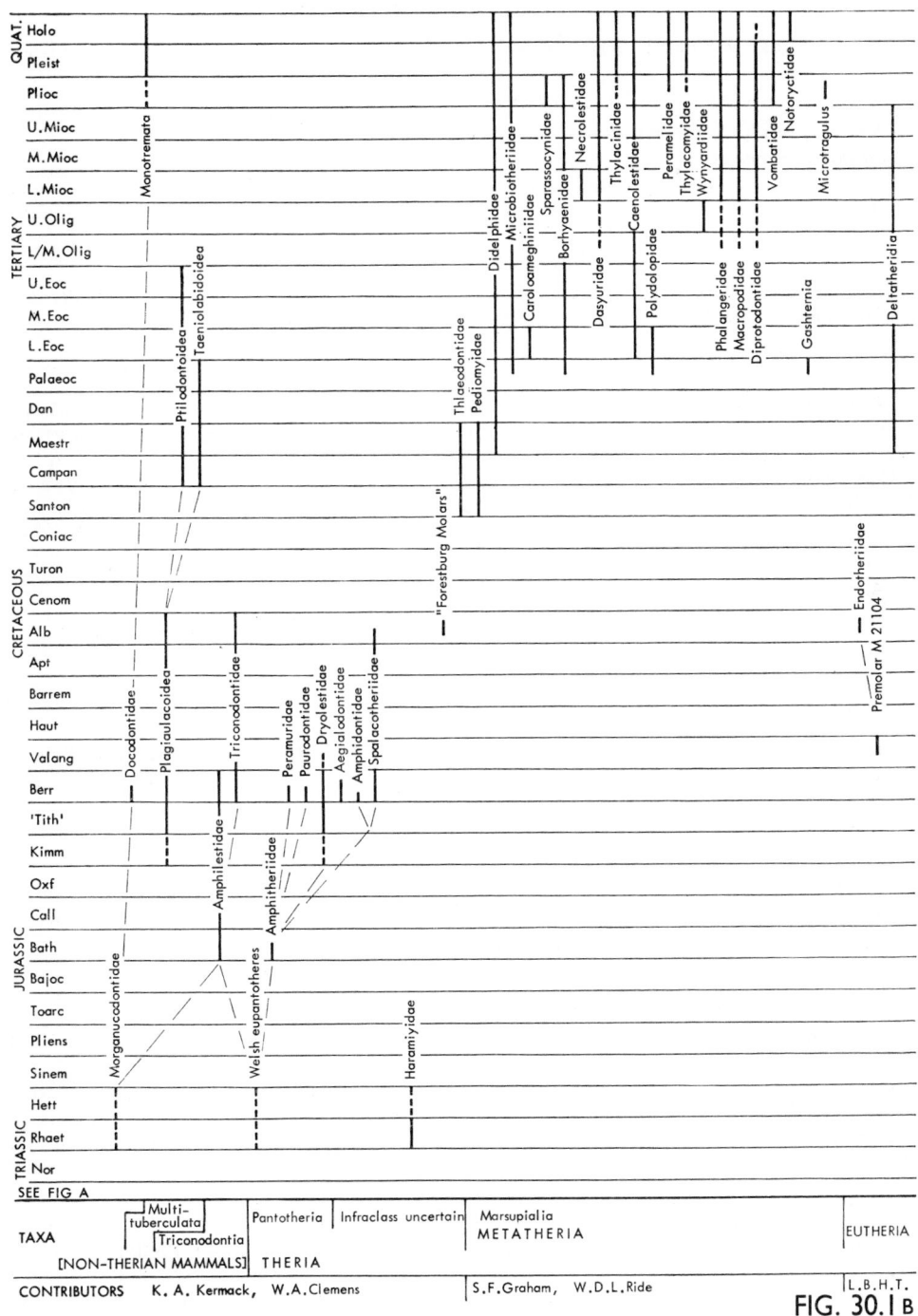

FIG. 30.1 B

Family AMPHITHERIIDAE Owen

First and **Last,** Jur Bath: *Amphitherium* Blainville, Stonesfield Slate of Oxfordshire, England.

Family PERAMURIDAE Kretzoi

First and **Last,** Cret Berr: *Peramus* Owen, Purbeck of Dorset, England.
Constituent genera: *Peramus* Owen, *Brancatherulum?* Dietrich.
Comment: *Brancatherulum* comes from the Upper Dinosaur Horizon, Tendaguru, Tanzania, and cannot be dated more closely than U. Jur-L. Cret. It has not been included in the time-chart.

Family PAURODONTIDAE Marsh

First and **Last,** Cret Berr: *Araeodon* Simpson, *Archaeotrigon* Simpson, *Paurodon* Marsh, *Tathiodon* Simpson, all Morrison of Wyoming, U.S.A.

Family DRYOLESTIDAE Marsh

First, Jur Kimm: un-named form Kühne 1961, Leira, Portugal. [K.A.K.]
Last, Cret Berr or Valang; cf. *Melanodon goodrichi* Simpson, (M21101) fragment of upper molar Cliff End Bone-Bed, Sussex, England (Clemens 1963). [W.A.C. & K.A.K.]
Constituent genera: *Amblotherium* Owen, *Dryolestes* Marsh, *Euthalastus* Simpson, *Herpetairus* Simpson, *Kepolestes* Simpson, *Kurtodon* Osborn, *Laolestes* Simpson, *Malthacolestes* Simpson, *Melanodon* Simpson, cf. *Melanodon* (M21101) Clemens 1963, *Miccylotyrans* Simpson, *Pelicopsis* Simpson, *Paraspalax* Owen, *Phascolestes* Owen, un-named form Kühne 1961.

Infra-class uncertain

Order indeterminate

Family AEGIALODONTIDAE Kermack 1966

First and **Last,** Cret Berr: *Aegialodon* Kermack, Lees & Mussett, Cliff End Bone Bed, Sussex, England.
Comment: intermediate in dental character between Pantotheria and Eutheria. [K.A.K.]

Family PAPPOTHERIIDAE Slaughter 1965

First and **Last,** Cret Alb: *Pappotherium* Slaughter, Trinity Sands, Texas [charted as: Forestburg Molars, ed.]. [B.P. & D.E.R.]

Order SYMMETRODONTA

Family AMPHIDONTIDAE Simpson

Only, Cret Berr: *Amphidon* Simpson, *Eurylambda* Simpson, *Tinodon* Marsh, all Morrison of Wyoming.
Constituent genera: *Amphidon* Simpson, *Eurylambda* Simpson, *Manchurodon* Yabe & Shikama, *Tinodon* Marsh.
Comment: No useful date can be given for *Manchurodon*, Husin Coal Series, Manchuria. It has not been included in the time chart.

Family SPALACOTHERIIDAE Marsh

First, Cret Berr: *Peralestes* Owen, *Spalacotherium* Owen, Purbeck of Dorset, England; [K.A.K.]
Last, Cret Alb: *Spalacotheroides* Patterson, Trinity Sands, Texas, U.S.A. [W.A.C. & K.A.K.]
Constituent genera: *Peralestes* Owen, *Spalacotherium* Owen, cf. *Spalacotherium* (M.21103, Clemens, 1963), *Spalcotherioides* Patterson. [K.A.K.]

Subclass indeterminate

Order undefined

Family HARAMIYIDAE (MICROLESTIDAE) Simpson

First, Trias Rhaet: *Hypsiprymnopsis* Dawkins, Watchet, Somerset, England.

Last, Trias Rhaet or Jur. Hett.: *Thomasia* Poche, Schlösslemühle, Württemburg, Germany; un-named specimens Peyer (1956), Hallau, Schaffhausen, Switzerland.

Constituent genera: *Haramiya* (*Microlestes, Microcleptes*) Simpson, *Hypsiprymnopsis* Dawkins, *Thomasia* (*Plieningeria*) Poche.

Comment: May well be synapsid reptiles. *Haramiya*, fissure at Holwell, Somerset, England, cannot be dated satisfactorily. [K.A.K.]

Infraclass METATHERIA

Superorder MARSUPIALIA

Order MARSUPICARNIVORA Ride, 1964

First, Cret Santon: *Eodelphis, Delphodon*, Oldman Fm, N. Amer.

Extant, N. Amer., S. Amer., Aust.

Constituent families: Stagodontidae Marsh [listed as Thlaeodontidae in Fig. 30.1B. Ed.], Cret Santon, *Eodelphis*, Oldman Fm, N. America (Russell 1952, classification here W. A. Clemens 1966)–Cret Maestr, *Didelphodon*, etc., Lance Fm and equivalents, N. America (Simpson 1929b).

Pediomyidae Simpson, Cret Santon, *Delphodon?*, Oldman Fm. (Russell, 1952)–Cret Maestr, *Pediomys*, etc., Lance Fm and equivalents, N. America (Simpson 1929b).

Didelphidae Gray, Didelphinae Simpson, Cret Maestr, *Alphadon*, Lance Fm and equivalents, N. America (classification, W. A. Clemens 1966); probable first in Europe, Tert Palaeoc, unnamed marsupial tooth (Russell 1964, Pl. 16, fig. 3b), Cernay; first in S. America Tert Palaeoc, *Protodidelphis*, etc. (Paula Couto 1952c), Riochican, Itaborai. **Extant** N. and S. America, last in Europe Tert L.Mioc, *Peratherium* (Simpson 1930).

Glasbiinae Clemens, Cret Maestr, *Glasbius*, Lance Fm, and equivalents, N. America (Clemens 1966). [Omitted from Fig. 30.1B. Ed.]

Microbiotheriinae Ameghino, Tert Palaeoc, *Schaefferi? Guggenheimia* and Riochican, Itaborai, S. America (Paula Couto 1952): **extant** S. America (Reig 1955a).

Caroloameghiniinae Ameghino, Tert L.Eoc, *Caroloameghinia*, Casamayor, Patagonia (Simpson 1948).

Sparassocyninae Reig, Tert Plioc, *Sparassocynus*, Chapadmalalan, Argentina (Reig 1958b).

Borhyaeninae Ameghino, Tert Palaeoc, *Patene*, Riochican, Patagonia (Simpson 1948)–Tert Plioc, *Notocynus*, Chapadmalalan, Argentina (Reig 1958b).

Necrolestidae Ameghino, Tert L.Mioc, *Necrolestes*, Santacrucian, Patagonia (Patterson 1958).

Dasyuridae Goldfuss, Tert ? Olig or Mioc (see Ludbrook 1963), unnamed (Stirton *et al.* 1961), Etadunna Fm, Ngapakaldi Fauna, Australia; **extant,** Australia, N. Guinea.

Thylacinidae Bensley, Tert ? Plioc, *Thylacinus*, Chinchilla Sand, Australia (Ride 1964); **extant,** Australia (Tasmania only).

Comment: It is possible that the oldest marsupial fossils are the "Forestburg Molars" (Patterson 1956) Cret Alb, N. America, classified by Patterson as Theria of "Metatherian-Eutherian Grade". Tert correlations are in accordance with Simpson (1947); and the age of European forms through comparison of Simpson (1930) and Papp & Thenius (1959). [See Pappotheriidae above.] [Subfamilies shown as families in Fig. 30.1B, Ed.]

Order PAUCITUBERCULATA Ameghino, 1894

First, Tert Palaeoc: *Epidolops* Paula Couto, Riochican, S. Amer; **extant,** S. America.

Constituent families: Caenolestidae Trouessart, Tert L.Eoc: *Progarzonia*, Casamayoran, Patagonia (Simpson 1948) **extant,** S. America.

Polydolopidae Ameghino, Tert Palaeoc: *Epidolops* (Paula Couto 1952b), *Polydolops, Seumadia* (Simpson 1948), Riochican, S. America. *Polydolops*, Tert L.Eoc: Casamayoran, S. America.

Groeberiidae Patterson, Tert L/M. Olig: *Groeberia*, Divisadero Largo Fauna, approximately early Deseadan, Argentina (Simpson, Minoprio & Patterson 1962) [Inadvertently omitted from chart, Ed.]

Order PERAMELINA Gray, 1825

First, Tert Plioc: unnamed Grange Burn, Australia.   **Extant.**
Constituent families: Peramelidae Waterhouse, Tert Plioc: unnamed (Turnbull *et al.* 1965) Grange Burn, Australia; **extant,** Australia, N. Guinea.
Thylacomyidae Bensley, Tert ? Plioc: *Ischnodon*, Etadunna Fm, Palankarinna Fauna (Stirton *et al.* 1961, Ride 1964); **extant,** Australia.

Order DIPROTODONTA Owen, 1866

First, Tert Olig: *Wynyardia*, Janjukian Sta., Australia (Tasmania).
Extant, Australia, N. Guinea, Solomon Is., Celebes.
Constituent families: Wynyardiidae Osgood, Tert Olig: *Wynyardia* (Gill 1957, Ride 1964) Janjukian Stage, Tasmania.

Phalangeridae Thomas, Tert ? Olig or Mioc (Ludbrook 1963): *Perikoala*, Etadunna Fm, Ngapakaldi Fauna, Australia. (Stirton *et al.* 1961); **extant,** Australia, N. Guinea, Solomon Is., Celebes.

Macropodidae Gray, Tert ? Olig or Mioc (Ludbrook 1963): unnamed (Stirton *et al.* 1961), Etadunna Fm, Ngapakaldi Fauna, Australia; **extant,** Australia, N. Guinea.

Diprotodontidae Gill, Tert ? Olig or Mioc (Ludbrook 1963): unnamed (Stirton *et al.* 1961), Etadunna Fm, Ngapakaldi Fauna, Australia; or Tert U.Mioc: "unnamed Notothere" Cheltenhamian Stage, Australia (Gill 1957, Stirton 1957)–Quat ? Holo: *Diprotodon* (Grant-Taylor & Rafter 1963) Callabonna, Australia.

Vombatidae Iredale & Troughton, Tert Plioc: "*Phascolomys pliocenus*" (McCoy 1874, age pers. comm. E. D. Gill) Dunolly Gold Drift, Australia–**extant** Australia.

MARSUPIALIA *incertae sedis*

Notoryctidae Ogilby: Fossils unknown. *Notoryctes*, Australia,   **Extant.**

? MARSUPIALIA

Tert Palaeoc: *Gashternia*, Riochican, Patagonia (Simpson 1948).
Tert Plioc: *Argyrolagus* [= *Microtragulus*], S. America (Simpson 1945). [S.F.G. & W.D.L.R.] (N.B. This is probably a caenolestid (paucituberculate) and should be *Microtragulus* although still Argyrolagidae! *Argyrolagus* is the jaw and *Microtragulus* the metatarsals of one species (Reig 1955b, 1958a).   [B.P.])

Infraclass EUTHERIA

Order indeterminate.

Family ENDOTHERIIDAE Shikama

First and **Last,** Cret Alb: un-named specimens (PM 583, 660, 884, 886, 887, 922, 930, 931, 948, 965, 966, 999, 1005, 1075, 1287) Patterson 1956, Trinity Sands, Texas. [See Pappotheriidae above, p. 766]
Constituent genera: Trinity specimens, *Endotherium* Shikama.
Comment: *Endotherium* comes from the Husin Coal Bearing Series, Manchuria. Estimates of the age of these beds range from the L. Jur to post-Wealden. On the internal evidence of the specimen itself Apt or Alb is most probable. *Endotherium* has not been included in the time-chart.
                                                                                    [K.A.K.]
This mammal might be a eupantothere, an early eutherian or represent an intermediate group. (See also under Insectivora and Marsupialia).   [W.A.C.]

Family indeterminate

First and **Last,** Cret Haut: Un-named premolar (M21104) Clemens 1963, Paddockhurst Park Bone-Bed, Sussex, England.
Comment: may be closer to Eutheria than Pantotheria in character. [Not Valang, Fig. 30.1B]   [K.A.K.]

Chapter 30: Mammalia

Order DELTATHERIDIA Van Valen 1965

First, Cret Maestr: *Cimolestes* Marsh, 1889, Lance and Hell Creek Fms, Wyoming and Montana. *Deltatheridium, Deltatheroides* and *Hyotheridium* from the Djadokhta local fauna are probably late Cret, and may be older than *Cimolestes*. [data from W.A.C.]

Last, Tert U. Mioc: *Dissopsalis carnifex* Pilgrim, 1910, Chinji Stage, Salt Range, Siwalik Hills, Pakistan; *D. pyroclasticus* Savage, 1965, Maboko Is., Kenya. [data from R.J.G.S.]

Comments: This order was erected by Van Valen (1965a) and discussed by him in more detail recently (1966). It comprises the Palaeoryctoidea which are generally included in the Insectivora, as well as the Oxyaenoidea (Oxyaenidae, Hyaenodontidae), which are usually classified in the Carnivora, suborder Creodonta.

The remaining creodonts the Arctocyonidae and Mesonychidae are also now removed from the Carnivora being placed by Van Valen (1966) in the Condylarthra. Even though the new scheme introduced by Van Valen considerably alters the classification and hence stratigraphical range of the groups affected, it is not proposed to amend the documentation presented by the contributors dealing with the groups concerned. Nevertheless it is felt necessary to include this new order in the documentation. [L.B.H.T.]

Cohort UNGUICULATA

Order INSECTIVORA

Suborder MENOTYPHLA Haeckel 1866 emend.

First, Cret ? Alb *Endotherium niinomii* Shikama 1947, Husin Fm, Manchuria (Patterson 1956, Chow 1953). **Extant.**

Comments: Suborder admittedly artificial, includes a number of primitive and poorly understood Eutheria which cannot be placed in clearly-established orders. Comprises as superfamilies Deltatheridioidea Simpson 1931, Cret Maestr-Tert Olig; Pantolestoidea Cope 1887, Tert M. Palaeoc-M.Eoc; Apatemyoidea Saban 1954, Tert M. Palaeoc-M.Eoc; Leptictoidea Butler 1956, ? Cret Alb, Cret Campan-Tert M.Olig; Macroscelidoidea Gill 1872, Tert L.Olig-present. Maximum development in Palaeoc, decline in Eoc; only African Macroscelididae survive into Mioc and later. On Cret insectivores also see Simpson 1951, Clemens 1960, 1961, Russell 1962, Sloan & Van Valen 1965. [Deltatheridia now removed from Insectivora]

Suborder LIPOTYPHLA Haeckel 1866

First, Tert Palaeoc: *Leptacodon ladae* Simpson 1935, Crazy Mountain Fort Union Fm, Montana (equivalent in part to Torrejon stage). **Extant.**

Comments: Early erinaceoids, known only from jaw fragments, are not clearly distinguished from leptictoids (Menotyphla); discussion by McKenna (1960a, 1960b). Major radiation probably M.Eoc-Olig, when living families Erinaceidae, Soricidae, Talpidae in N. Hemisphere acquired their distinctive features. In Africa, Tenrecidae and Chrysochloridae known from Rusinga Beds (?L.Mioc). Solenodontidae in W. Indies unknown before Pleist.

Order DERMOPTERA Illiger 1811

First, Tert Palaeoc: *Planetetherium mirabile* Simpson 1928b, Bear Creek Fm, Montana (equivalent to Tiffany stage). **Extant,** S.E. Asia.

Comment: Reference of *Planetetherium* and *Plagiomene* to the Dermoptera rests only on characters of the cheek-teeth; see Matthew & Granger 1918, Simpson 1929a. No other fossils known.

Order CHIROPTERA

Suborder MICROCHIROPTERA Dobson 1875

First, Tert L. Eoc.: *Icaronycteris index* Jepsen 1966, Green River Fm. (Wasatchian), S.W. Wyoming. First European appearance M. Eoc. (Revilliod 1917). **Extant.**

The Fossil Record, Part II

Suborder MEGACHIROPTERA Dobson 1875

First, Tert L. Olig; *Archaeopteropus transiens* Meschinelli 1902, Monteviale, Italy (Sannoisian stage). **Extant.**

Comments: Fossil record of Chiroptera very incomplete. Existing families were well established by Olig. *Zanycteris* Matthew 1917 is not chiropteran (McGrew and Patterson 1962).

[P.M.B.]

Order PRIMATES

Suborder PROSIMII Illinger, 1811.

First, Cret Maestr: *Purgatorius* Van Valen and Sloan, 1965, Tullock Fm, (early Palaeoc) and Hell Creek Fm, both in Montana. In the event that this genus should not be generally accepted as belonging to Primates, then the earliest occurrences would be: *Pronothodectes* Gidley, 1923, Ft. Union Fm (M. Palaeoc), Montana; *Palenochtha* Simpson 1935, Ft. Union (M. Palaeoc), Montana; *Plesiolestes* Jepsen, 1930, "Torrejon Sandstone" (M. Palaeoc), Wyoming; *Paromomys* Gidley, 1923, Ft. Union Fm (M. Palaeoc), Montana; *Elphidotarsius* Gidley, 1923, Ft. Union Fm (M. Palaeoc), Montana; *Plesiadapis* Gervais, 1877, fissure deposit (U. Palaeoc), Walbeck, Germany; *Saxonella* Russell, 1964, fissure deposit (M. Palaeoc), Walbeck, Germany; *Mckennatherium* Van Valen [= *Leptacodon*], 1965 (possibly not a primate) Lebo Fm (M. Palaeoc), Montana [definitely not, B.P.]. **Extant.**

Comments: Not common in fossil faunas, Palaeoc forms known almost exclusively from jaws and isolated teeth. The exceptions are *Palaechthon* and *Plesiadapis* for which well-preserved cranial and, in the latter case, postcranial materials are known. Prosimians became extinct in the New World with the disappearance of *Ekgmowechashala* species after early Mioc times. All known early Tert families are Holarctic or N. Hemisphere, suggesting possible northern origin of order. Arrival in Africa in or before late Eocene, South America in or before late Olig times. Present distributions: Madagascar, Africa, India, and S.E. Asia.

Suborder ANTHROPOIDEA Mivart, 1864.

First, Tert U.Eoc: *Pondaungia* Pilgrim, 1927, *Amphipithecus* Colbert, 1937, both from Pondaung Fm, Burma. In the event that these genera cannot be sustained as belonging to suborder Anthropoidea, first occurrences are: *Apidium*, Osborn, 1908; *Propliopithecus*, Schlosser, 1910; *Parapithecus*, Schlosser, 1910; *Oligopithecus*, Simons, 1962; *Aegyptopithecus*, Simons, 1965; *Aelopithecus*, Simons, 1965.

Comments: Primate status of *Pondaungia* and *Amphipithecus* has been questioned but, if not Anthropoidea, they almost certainly represent advanced prosimians. Numerous extinct taxa have been described, but few are known from cranial and postcranial finds. The distribution of ceboids has been entirely limited to the New World where they are first abundant in South America deposits of Mioc age. Similarly the distribution of cercopithecoids and hominoids have been limited to the Old World (except *Homo*). Fossil remains of both superfamilies, with the exception of the problematic Burmese specimens, are unknown before early Olig times; they appear for the first time well-differentiated in the Olig deposits of the Fayum, Egypt. The paucity of associated whole skeletons is possibly due to their typical occupation of forest and grassland habitats where the probability of fossilisation is low.

Extant catarrhine Anthropoidea apparently derive from an African radiation, members of which reached Eurasia in Mioc times. Hominoidea evidently radiated in the late Eoc (earlier than Cercopithecoidea), but contains members of a more advanced grade. Ancestors of living Cercopithecoidea evidently did not establish a firm foothold in Eurasia much before early Plioc times, and are not abundant as fossils until the late Plioc. [E.L.S.]

Order TILLODONTIA

First, Tert L. Eoc: *Esthonyx*, N. America, Europe. Origin possibly from Condylarthra, Arctocyonidae. Distribution holarctic. One family, Esthonychidae.

Last, Tert U.Eoc: *Adapidium*, China (Gazin 1953, Chow 1963a, Van Valen 1963).

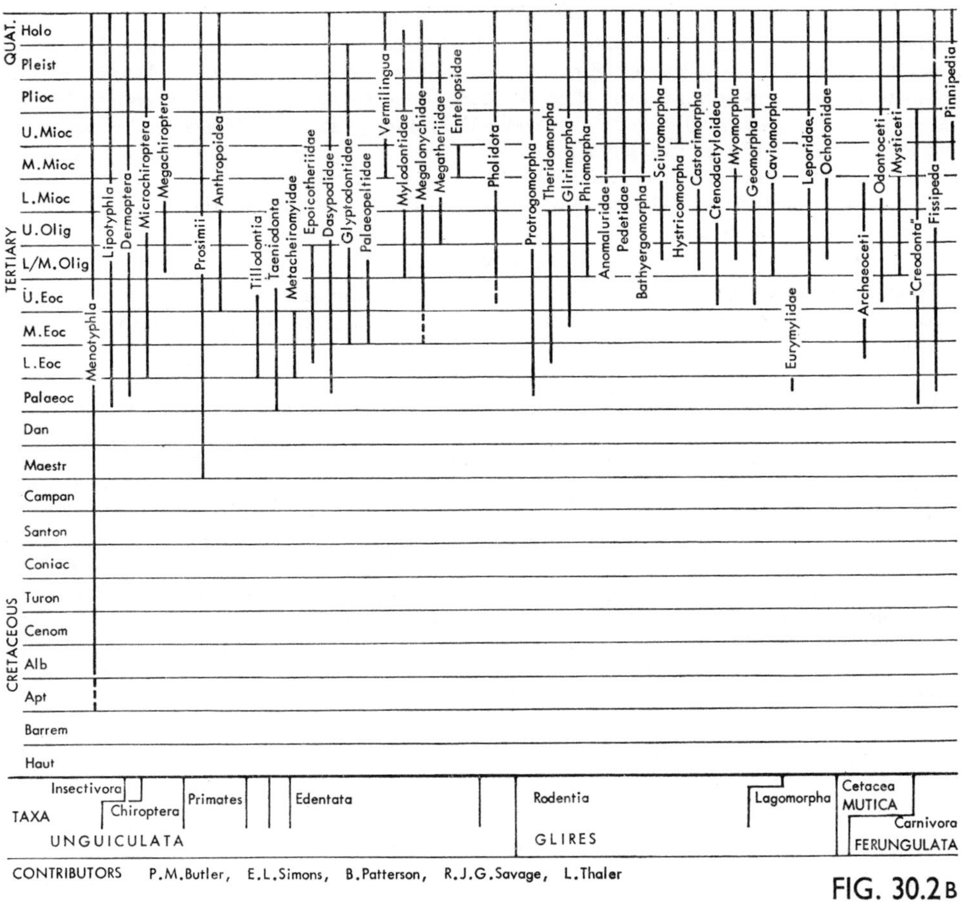

FIG. 30.2 B

CONTRIBUTORS   P.M.Butler,   E.L.Simons,   B.Patterson,   R.J.G.Savage,   L.Thaler

Order TAENIODONTA

First, Tert Palaeoc: *Onychodectes, Wortmania,* N. America.
Last, Tert U.Eoc: *Stylinodon.* N. America.
Comment: Origin unknown. Distribution N. America. One family, Stylinodontidae.
(Patterson 1949)

Order EDENTATA

Suborder PALAEANODONTA

First, Tert L.Eoc: *Palaeanodon,* N. Amer. (the "Clark Fork" *P. parvulus* is L.Eoc., not Palaeoc., R. C. Wood *in press*). Distribution N. America. Similar to but rather more primitive than the Xenarthra. (Gazin 1952).
Last, Tert M.Olig: *Xenocranion.*
Constituent families: Metacheiromyidae, L.-M. Eoc; Epoicotheriidae, L. Eoc-M. Olig.

Suborder XENARTHRA

First, Tert Palaeoc: S. Amer. Distribution predominantly S. America. Three infraorders.
Extant, N. and S. America.

Infraorder CINGULATA

First, Tert Palaeoc: Dasypodidae inc. sed., Patagonia. Distribution predominantly S. America, reaching N. America in Pleist. The peltephilines are a subfamily of the Dasypodidae, a group with numerous subdivisions. The Glyptodontidae probably arose from chlamytheriine dasypodids. *Palaeopeltis*, with which *Pseudorophodon* Hofstetter 1954 (= "*Orophodon*" Kraglievich and Rivas, *nec*. Ameghino) is closely related if not identical, represents a third family. (Simpson 1948, James 1957, Patterson and Pascual 1963). **Extant,** S. and N. America.

Constituent families: Dasypodidae, Palaeoc-extant; Glyptodontidae, M. Eoc-Pleist; Palaeopeltidae, M. Eoc-L. Olig.

Infraorder VERMILINGUA

First, Tert M.Mioc: *Promyrmephagus*, Patagonia. Distribution predominantly S. America, reaching C. America probably in Pliest. One family, Myrmecophagidae. **Extant,** S. and C. America.

Infraorder PILOSA

First, Tert M.Eoc: *Proplatyarthrus*, Patagonia (sole known specimen possibly derived from overlying L.Olig; infraorder definitely present in L.Olig. Patagonia: *Orophodon, Octodontotherium*, "*Hapalops*" *antistis*). Distribution predominantly S. America; megalonychids reached N. America and Antilles by rafting, possibly during Mioc; mylodontids and megatheriids reached N. America in Pleist. Two superfamilies: Mylodontoidea for the Mylodontidae, Megalonychoidea for the remainder. *Octodontotherium*, surely, and *Orophodon*, very possibly, are Mylodontidae. The nothrotheriines are a subfamily of the Megatheriidae, not of the Megalonychidae. The tree sloths have no fossil record. They are megalonychoids and possibly diphyletic, *Choloepus* showing resemblances to the Megalonychidae, *Bradypus* to the Megatheriidae. The peculiar, poorly known *Entelops* may belong to the Pilosa (Pascual 1960). *Chungchienia*, U.Eoc. China, referred to the Megalonychoidea by Chow (1963b), is of uncertain affinities. *Protobradys*, L. Eoc, Patagonia, is neither a pilosan nor an edentate. (Simpson 1948, *in press*, Hofstetter 1956, Matthew and Paula Couto 1959, Patterson and Pascual 1963, Hooijer 1963.) **Extant,** S. and C. America.

Constituent families: Mylodontidae, L. Olig-Holo; Megalonychidae, M. Eoc?-Holo (kitchen middens in Hispaniola, Curaçao); Megatheriidae, U. Olig-Pleist.

Inc. sed. Entelopsidae, M. Mioc. [B.P.]

Order PHOLIDOTA Weber 1904

First, Tert Olig: *Necromanis quercyi* Filhol 1894; *Leptomanis edwardsi* Filhol 1894, Phosphorites de Quercy (U.Eoc-M.Olig), S. France. Helbing (1938) described but did not name a fragmentary manid humerus from Tert M.Olig of St. André, near Marseilles, France. **Extant.**

Comment: Order known from Tert M.Olig, Europe, but remains so fragmentary that little can be deduced from these. Fossil record very poor: further fragments in the U.Olig-L.Mioc, Europe, and Pleist, India and S.E. Asia. [R.J.G.S.]

Cohort GLIRES

Order RODENTIA

Many subordinal groups of unequal systematic volume. For systematic and taxonomic discussions see Wood (1955, 1958), Simpson (1961), Lavocat (1962), and Thaler (1966).

Suborder PROTROGOMORPHA Zittel 1893

First, Tert Palaeoc: *Paramys* Leidy, 1871. Tiffanian, approximately late, but not latest, Palaeoc, N.America (McKenna 1961). **Extant.**

Suborder THERIDOMORPHA Lavocat 1955

First, Tert L.Eoc: *Masillamys* Tobien, 1954, "Zone biochronologique de Cuis", late L.Eoc, Europe (Thaler 1966, pp. 26, 218).

Last, Tert U.Olig: *Archaeomys* Laizer and Parieu, 1839; *Issiodoromys* Gervais, 1848; *Columbomys* Thaler, 1962. "Zone biochronologique de Coderet", late Olig, Europe (Thaler 1966, p. 218).

Chapter 30: Mammalia

Suborder GLIRIMORPHA Thaler 1966.

First, Tert M.Eoc: *Gliravus* Stehlin and Schaub, 1951. "Zone biochronologique d'Issel", late M.Eoc, Europe (Thaler 1966, p. 102). **Extant.**

Suborder PHIOMORPHA Lavocat (in press)

First, Tert L.Olig: *Phiomys* Osborn, 1908; *Metaphiomys* Osborn, 1908. L.Olig, Egypt (Lavocat 1962). **Extant.**

Comment: *Thryonomys, Petromys*. These two genera classically not placed near the Phiomyidae are here considered as the extant representatives of the suborder.

Suborder not named = Family ANOMALURIDAE Gill 1872

First, Tert Mioc: Anomaluridae gen. nov. not named, Mioc, E. Africa (Lavocat 1962). **Extant.**

Suborder not named = Family PEDETIDAE Owen 1847

First, Tert Mioc: *Parapedetes* Stromer 1926, Mioc, South West Africa; *Megapedetes* McInnes 1957, Mioc, E. Africa (Lavocat 1962). **Extant.**

Suborder BATHYERGOMORPHA Roberts 1951

First, Tert Mioc: *Bathyergoides* Stromer 1926 Mioc, South West Africa; and gen. nov. not named, Mioc, E. Africa (Lavocat 1962 & Wood 1955). **Extant.**

Suborder SCIUROMORPHA Brandt 1855.

First, Tert M.Olig: *Protosciurus* Black 1963, Lower Orellan, M. Olig, North America; and Sciuridae indet., "zone biochronologique de La Sauvetat", M.Olig, Europe (Black 1963 & Thaler 1966, p. 216). **Extant.**

Suborder HYSTRICOMORPHA Brandt 1855

First, Tert U.Mioc: *Sivacanthion* Colbert 1933, U.Miocene, India (Colbert 1933b). **Extant.**

Suborder CASTORIMORPHA Wood 1955

First, Tert L.Olig: *Agnotocastor* Stirton 1935, L.Olig, N. America; *Steneofiber* Geoffroy 1833, Early M.Olig, Europe (Schaub *in* Piveteau 1958 & Thaler 1966, p. 210). **Extant.**

Suborder not named = superfamily CTENODACTYLOIDEA Simpson 1945

First, Tert U.Eoc: *Advenimus* Dawson 1964, Late Eoc, Inner Mongolia (Dawson 1964). **Extant.**

Suborder MYOMORPHA Brandt 1855

First, Tert L.Olig: *Eucricetodon* Thaler 1966, Early M.Olig, Europe; and *Eumys* Leidy 1856, M.Olig, N. America (Thaler 1966, p. 210). **Extant.**

Suborder GEOMORPHA Thaler 1966

First, Tert U.Eoc: *Protadjidaumo* Burke 1934, U.Eoc, N. America. **Extant.**

Suborder CAVIOMORPHA Wood & Patterson 1955

First, Tert L.Olig: *Platypittamys* Wood, 1949; *Deseadomys* Wood and Patterson, 1959; *Scotamys* Loomis, 1914; *Cephalomys* Ameghino, 1897; *Litodontomys* Loomis, 1914; *Asteromys* Ameghino, 1897; *Chubutomys* Wood and Patterson, 1959; *Protosteiromys* Wood and Patterson, 1959. Deseadan, L. Oligocene, S. America (Wood & Patterson 1959). **Extant.**

Order LAGOMORPHA

Family EURYMYLIDAE Matthew, Granger & Simpson 1929

First and **Last,** Tert Palaeoc: *Eurymylus* Matthew and Granger 1925, U. Palaeoc, Inner Mongolia (Wood 1942).
Comment: Studies in progress cast some doubt on *Eurymylus* being a lagomorph.

Family LEPORIDAE Gray 1821

First, Tert U.Eoc: *Shamolagus* Burke, 1941 and *Gobiolagus* Burke 1941, Late Eoc, Inner Mongolia; *Mytonolagus* Burke 1934, Late Eoc, N. America (Dawson 1958). **Extant.**

Family OCHOTONIDAE Thomas 1897

First, Tert M.Olig: *Desmatolagus* Matthew and Granger 1923, M.Olig, Asia (Dawson 1959). **Extant.**
[L.T.]

Cohort MUTICA

Order CETACEA

Suborder ARCHAEOCETI Flower 1883

First, Tert L.Eoc: *Anglocetus beatsoni* Tarlo 1964, London Clay, Isle of Sheppey, Kent, England.
Last, Tert L.Mioc: *Phococetus vasconum* (Delfortrie 1874), L. Burdigalian, St. Medard-en-Jalle, Bordeaux, France; and *Kekenodon onamata* Hector 1881, Ototaran Stage, Waitaki Valley, Otago, New Zealand.

Suborder ODONTOCETI Flower 1867

First, Tert U.Eoc: *Agorophius pygmaeus* (Leidy 1869) and *Xenorophus sloanii* Kellogg 1923, both from Ashley Marl, Jackson Group, Charleston, S. Carolina. **Extant.**

Suborder MYSTICETI Flower 1864

First, Tert L. Olig: *Mauicetus parki* (Benham 1937), *M. lophocephalus, M. waitakiensis* and *M. brevicollis* Marples 1956, all from Duntroonian Fm, N. Otago, New Zealand. **Extant.**
Comment: Cetacea fully developed on first appearance on 3 continents (Amer, Afr and Eur) in Tert Eoc, implying long unknown history. M.Eoc of Egypt with good fauna of Archaeoceti. Origins of Odontoceti and Mysticeti from Archaeoceti not clear. Reviews of Cetacea in Kellogg (1928, 1936) and Slijper (1936).

Cohort FERUNGULATA

Superorder FERAE

Order CARNIVORA

Comments: The order classically comprises three suborders, Creodonta, Fissipeda and Pinnipedia. The Creodonta have 4 families; Van Valen (1966) has removed the Oxyaenidae and the Hyaenodontidae to his new order Deltatheridia (see above). He further proposed the placing of Arctocyonidae and the Mesonychidae in the order Condylarthra, thus abolishing the suborder Creodonta. The probable diphyletic origin of the Pinnipedia (Savage 1957 and McLaren 1960) undermines this suborder, but no author has yet reallocated the families.

Suborder 'CREODONTA' Cope 1875

First, Tert Palaeoc: *Oxyclaenus* Scott 1892; *Loxolophus* Cope 1885; *Carcinodon* Scott 1892; *Protogonodon* Scott 1892; *Eoconodon* Matthew & Granger 1921; all from the Nacimiento Fm, S.W.U.S.A. *Baioconodon* Gazin 1941 from L. Denver Fm, Colorado, equivalent of Nacimiento Fm. Detailed treatment of all except last genus in Matthew (1937).
Last, Tert U. Mioc: *Dissopsalis carnifex* Pilgrim 1910 & 1914: *D. ruber* Pilgrim 1910 & 1914; both from Chinji Stage, Chinji, Salt Range, Siwalik Hills, Pakistan; *Dissopsalis pyroclasticus* Savage 1965, Maboko ls., Kenya.

Comments: All seven genera listed for the first occurrences belong to the Arctocyonidae. Creodonts are well known from Tert Palaeoc of N. America, plentiful and varied in Eoc and Olig of N. America, Europe and Asia; rarer in Mioc, last records in Mioc of Africa and Asia: gradually replaced during Mid Tert by fissiped carnivores. (The contributor follows Van Valen (1965a, 1966) in rejecting the suborder Creodonta as a valid taxon. However, in view of its familiarity, and admitted usefulness in uniting all the archaic carnivorous placentals, it is retained in the documentation.—Ed.).

Suborder FISSIPEDA Blumenbach 1791

First, Tert Palaeoc: Two miacid genera from U.S.A. *Protictis haydenianus* (Cope 1882), Nacimiento Fm (M.Palaeoc), New Mexico; *P. tenuis* (Simpson 1935), Lebo Fm, Montana; *P. microlestes* (Simpson 1935), Fort Union Fm, Montana; *Ictidopappus mustelinus* Simpson 1935, Lebo Fm, Montana. Isolated tooth referred to ? *Ictidopappus* sp. MacIntyre 1966 from early Puercan, L. Palaeoc, New Mexico, if confirmed will become earliest fissiped.   **Extant.**

Comments: The ancestral Miacidae family currently being revised by MacIntyre (1966). Rare in Palaeoc and Eoc, suborder becomes increasingly abundant in Neogene. World-wide (Australia by introduction).

Suborder PINNIPEDIA Illiger 1811

First, Tert M.Mioc: *Allodesmus* Kellogg 1922 and *Neotherium* Kellog 1931, Temblor Fm, California and *Desmatophoca* Condon 1906, Astoria Fm, Oregon (both equivalents to Hemingfordian Stage).   **Extant.**

Comments: Few records. Earliest records all otarids from N. Pacific coasts; phocids appear in Tert M.Mioc of Europe and N. Atlantic; odobenids also N. Atlantic. *Semantor*, morphologically most primitive is Tert L. Plioc, W. Siberia. Present distribution, all oceans.   [R.J.G.S.]

Superorder PROTUNGULATA

Order CONDYLARTHRA Cope 1881

First, Cret Maestr: *Protungulatum* Sloan & Van Valen 1965, Hell Creek Fm, Montana, Tert L.Palaeoc: *Tiznatzinia* Simpson 1936; *Choeroclaenus* Simpson 1937; *Oxyacodon* Osborn & Earle 1895; *Conacodon* Matthew 1897; *Hemithlaeus* Cope 1882; *Anisonchus* Cope 1881; *Haploconus* Cope 1882; *Ectoconus* Cope 1884; *Carsioptychus* Simpson 1936; *Desmatoclaenus* Gazin 1941; all of the immediately preceding from the Puerco Fauna, or equivalents, of W. U.S.A. (Nacimiento Fm, New Mexico; Polecat Bench Fm, Wyoming; North Horn Fm, Utah). Detailed treatment of most of the genera in Matthew (1937); for the last 5 genera see also Gazin (1941).

South America: *Asmithwoodwardia* Ameghino 1901; *Ernestokokenia* Ameghino 1901; *Lamegoia* de Paula Couto 1952; all from U.Palaeoc fissure fillings, Saõ José de Itaborai, S. Brazil. Detailed account in Paula Couto (1952a).

Europe: *Paratricuspiodon* Russell 1964; *Louisina* Russell 1964; both from M. or U. Palaeoc fissure filling, Walbeck, Germany.

Asia: *Phenacolophus* Matthew & Granger 1925, U.Palaeoc Gashato Fm, Mongolia.

Comment: Whether the Arctocyonidae are considered as Carnivora or Condylarthra *Protungulatum*, placed in that family with some admitted arbitrariness, is described as being "a very satisfactory annectant type" between the Arctocyonidae and the condylarth families Hyopsodontidae and Periptychidae. It is probably the oldest presently known ungulate.

Last, Tert M.Eoc: *Almogaver* Crusafont & Villalta 1954, from the M.Eoc continental series of the Montllobar Fm, Lérida prov., Spain; and *Dulcidon gandaensis* (Dehm & Oettingen-Spielberg 1958), M.Eoc Lower Chharat series, Pakistan.

S. America: *Megalodus* McKenna 1956, San Nicolás unit, Honda group (Tert U.Mioc), Colombia.

North America: *Hyopsodus* Leidy 1876, U.Eoc, Uinta Fm, Utah, and the Swift Current Beds of Saskatchewan.

Comment: Forms possibly related to the mioclaenine Hyopsodontidae, *Pugiodens* ('*Vulpavoides*') Matthes 1952, and *Kopidodon* Weitzel 1933 (both M.Eoc of Germany), *Paroxyclaenus* Teilhard de Chardin 1922 (Quercy, U.Eoc or L.Olig, France), and *Kochictis* Kretzoi 1943 (M. or

U. Olig, Hungary), constitute perhaps the youngest European condylarths; they have been questionably referred to the Insectivora by Van Valen 1965b.

Condylarths typify the earliest Tertiary mammalian faunas; by the end of early Eoc time their numbers and diversity markedly decreased. The abundantly represented N. American M.Eoc *Hyopsodus*, however, provides an exception to this generality. Other genera that occur in younger horizons are usually known from isolated, single specimens. Palaeoc condylarths are generally considered as ancestral to younger Tert ungulates, although transitional forms are still poorly demonstrable.

Constituent families: Hyoposodontidae, Palaeoc–U. Eoc/?L. Olig; Phenacodontidae, Palaeoc–M. Eoc; Didolodontidae, Palaeoc–U. Mioc; Periptychidae, Palaeoc; Meniscopheriidae, Palaeoc–L. Eoc; Tricuspiodontidae, Palaeoc; *Phenacolophus*, Palaeoc; ? Arctocyonidae, Cret Maestr.   [D.E.R.]

Order LITOPTERNA

First, Tert Palaeoc: *Wainka, Josepholeidya* sp., *?Ricardolydekkeria* sp., *?Victorlemoinea* sp., Patagonia; *Anisolambda prodromus, Victorlemoinea prototypica*, Brazil; Origin from Condylarthra., Distribution S. America, abundant during Tert. (Simpson 1948, Paula Couto 1952a, Simpson *et al.* 1962.)

Last, Quat Pleist: *Macrauchenia*.

Constituent families: Proterotheriidae, Palaeoc-Plioc; Macraucheniidae Palaeoc-Pleist; Adianthidae, L. Olig (U. Eoc?)-M. Mioc.

Order NOTOUNGULATA

Comment: Origin uncertain. A very abundant, highly diversified group, especially in Eogene. Distribution predominantly S. America. Four suborders and numerous families.

Suborder NOTIOPROGONIA

First, Tert Palaeoc: *Palaeostylops*, Mongolia; *Henricosbornia waitehor, H. minuta, ?Othnielmarshia* sp., *?Peripantostylops orehor, Seudenius*, Patagonia; *?Homalostylops atavus*, Brazil. Suborder contains the only known northern Eogene forms, *Palaeostylops*, and *Arctostylops* of the L.Eoc, N. America (Simpson 1948, Paula Couto 1954).

Last, Tert M. Eoc: *Otronia*, Patagonia.

Constituent families: Arctostylopidae Palaeoc-L. Eoc; Henricosborniidae, Palaeoc-L. Eoc; Notostylopidae, Palaeoc-M. Eoc.

Suborder TYPOTHERIA

First, Tert Palaeoc: *Kibenikhoria, ?Notopithecus* sp., *?Transpithecus* sp., Patagonia; *Colbertia*, Brazil; Palaeoc, S. America (Paula Couto 1952d, Stirton 1953a, Francis 1960, Simpson (1967, *in press*).

Last, Quat Pleist *Mesotherium*, S. America.

Constituent families: Oldfieldthomasiidae, Palaeoc-M. Eoc; the L. Olig (U. Eoc?) *Brachystephanus, Xenostephanus* and *Allalmeia* may be referable (Simpson *et al.* 1962); Archaeopithecidae, L. Eoc; Interatheriidae, Palaeoc-Plioc; Mesotheriidae, L. Olig (U. Eoc?)-Pleist.

Suborder HEGETOTHERIA

First, Tert L. Eoc: *Eohyrax rusticus, E. praerusticus*, L. Eoc, Patagonia. Distribution S. America (Simpson *et al.* 1962, Simpson (1966) *in press*).

Last, Quat Pleist *Paedotherium*, S. America.

Constituent families: Archaeohyracidae, L. Eoc-L. Olig; Hegetotheriidea, L. Olig-Pleist.

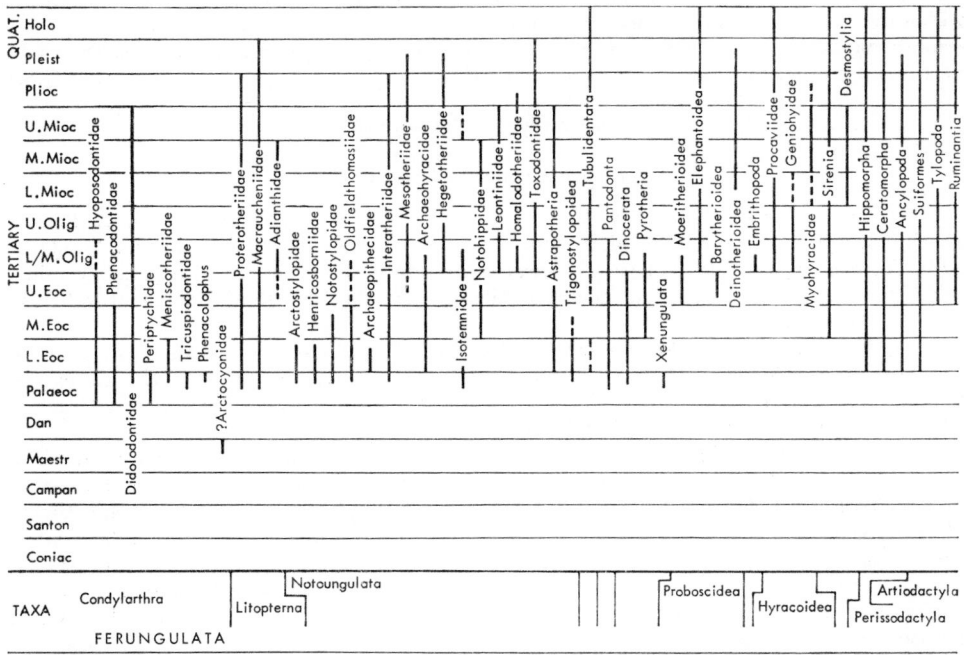

FIG. 30.3 B

Suborder TOXODONTA

First, Tert Palaeoc: *Isotemnus haugi, ?I. ctalego,* Palaeoc, Patagonia. Distribution predominantly S. America, reaching C. America in Pleist. Isotemnidae broadly ancestral to other families (Stirton 1953b, Ringuelet 1957, van Frank 1957, Pascual 1965, Simpson (1967, *in press*).

Last, Quat Pleist *Toxodon,* S. America, *Mixotoxodon,* S. and C. America, Pleist.

Constituent families: Isotemnidae, Palaeoc-L. Olig (possibly to U. Mioc, McKenna 1956); Notohippidae, M. Eoc-M. Mioc; Leontiniidae, L. Olig-U. Mioc; Homalodotheriidae, L. Olig-Plioc; Toxodontidae, L. Olig-Pleist.

Order ASTRAPOTHERIA

First, Tert L. Eoc: *Scaglia,* Patagonia. Origin possibly from Condylarthra. One family, Astrapotheriidae, S. America (Simpson 1957, 1967 *in press*).

Last, Tert U. Mioc: *Uruguaytherium, Xenastrapotherium,* Uruguay, Colombia.

Order TRIGONOSTYLOPOIDEA

First, Tert Palaeoc: *"Trigonostylops" apthomasi,* Brazil. Origin possibly from Condylarthra. Distribution S. America. One family, Trigonostylopidae. *Shecenia,* Palaeoc, Patagonia may be referable. (Paula Couto 1952a, Simpson (1967) *in press*).

Last, Tert L. Eoc: *Albertogaudrya, Trigonostylops wortmani,* Patagonia; *T. gegenbauri* possibly M. Eoc.

Comment: Formerly a suborder of Astrapotheria, raised to ordinal rank by Simpson (1967, *in press*). [B.P.]

Order TUBULIDENTATA Huxley 1872

First, Tert ? L. Eoc: *Palaeorycteropus quercyi Filhol* 1893 and *Archaeorycteropus gallicus* Ameghino 1905, both from the Phosphorites de Quercy (U. Eoc-M. Olig), France. *Tubulodon taylori* Jepsen

777

1932 from the Lost Cabin zone, Wind River Fm, Wyoming (Tert L. Eoc) was placed by Jepsen within the Tubulidentata, but its relationships are in dispute (see Colbert 1941b). **Extant.**
Comment: Poor fossil record; Colbert favoured condylarth ancestry. L. Mioc record in East Africa and U. Mioc records from Tethyan fringes. [R.J.G.S.]

Superorder PAENUNGULATA

Order PANTODONTA Cope 1873

First, Tert Palaeoc: *Pantolambda* Cope, 1882; common to Nacimiento Fm, N.M., Polecat Bench Fm, Wyoming, upper part of Lebo Fm., Crazy Mountain Field, and Melville Fm., Montana, all in Torrejonian stage (M. Palaeoc). *Caenolambda* Gazin, 1956; Polecat Bench Fm., Wyoming, and Upper Saunders beds, Saunders Series, Alberta, Canada, from the Tiffanian stage (M. to early U. Palaeoc).

Last, Tert M. Olig: *Coryphodon* Owen, 1845, common to latest Wasatch stage (L. Eoc), N. America; Sparnacian stage (L. Eoc), Europe; and M. (?) Eoc, Shantung, China. *Eudinoceras* Osborn, 1924, Irdin Manha Fm. (U. Eoc), Mongolia. *Hypercoryphodon* Osborn and Granger, 1932, Houldjin gravels (M. Olig), Mongolia.

Comments: Detailed account of the Palaeoc and earliest Eocene pantodonts of N. America is given by Simons (1960). Members of the Pantolambdidae, and Titanoideidae are restricted in distribution to the Palaeoc of N. America. One genus of Barylambdidae, *Haplolambda*, occurs in U. Palaeoc of N. America and in ?L. Eoc of Mongolia. Other barylambdids *Barylambda*, *Leptolambda* and *Ignaciolambda* are exclusively N. American. The Coryphodontidae are the only survivors of this order to persist as abundant faunal elements from late Palaeoc into Eoc times. Although the earliest pantodonts were about the size of a fox, later forms were typically tapir or hippopotamus-sized and were apparently slow-moving, relatively unspecialized herbivores. Competitive displacement by the adaptive radiations of various Eoc ungulate groups is a probable cause of extinction. [E.L.S.]

Order DINOCERATA

First, Tert Palaeoc: *Probathyopsis newbilli*, *Bathyopsoides*, N. Amer.; *Prodinoceras*, Mongolia. Origin uncertain, possibly from Condylarthra. One family, Uintatheriidae. Distribution N. America, Asia. (Flerov 1957, Dorr 1958, Wheeler 1961, Chow 1960, Chow & Tung 1962.)
Last, Tert U. Eoc: *Eobasileus*, *Tetheopsis*, N. America; *Gobiatherium*, Mongolia; U. Eoc.

Order PYROTHERIA

First, Tert M. Eoc: *Propyrotherium*, Patagonia. Origin possibly from Condylarthra. Distribution S. America. One family, Pyrotheriidae. *Carolozittelia*, L. Eoc, Patagonia, may be referable. (Simpson (1967), *in press.*)
Last, Tert L. Olig: *Pyrotherium*, Patagonia.

Order XENUNGULATA

First and **Last,** Tert Palaeoc: *Carodnia*, Brazil and Patagonia, is the only certainly known representative. Origin possibly from Condylarthra. *Griphodon* from beds of unknown, but surely later age in Peru may be referable. (Paula Couto 1952a, Simpson 1967 *in press*.) [B.P.]

Order PROBOSCIDEA

Suborder MOERITHERIOIDEA Osborn 1921

First, Tert U. Eoc: *Moeritherium lyonsi* Andrews 1901 and *M. gracile* Andrews 1902, both from the Qasr-el-Sagha Series (U. Mokattam), Fayûm, Egypt: *M.* cf *gracile* from In Tafidet, Gao, Mali, Africa; *Moeritherium* sp., Lutetian or Bartonian Lst, M'Bodione Dadera, Senegal, Africa.
Last, Tert L. Olig: *Moeritherium trigonodon* Andrews 1904 and *M. andrewsi* Schlosser 1911, both Fluvio-marine Fm, Fayûm, Egypt.

Comment: Moeritherioidea known only from U. Eoc and L. Olig of Africa. Considered by Andrews (1906) and many later writers (e.g. Obsorn 1936) as ancestral to other proboscideans. Recent discoveries by Simons in Egypt and Savage in Libya substantiate doubts on proboscidean affinity.

Suborder ELEPHANTOIDEA Osborn 1921

First, Tert L. Olig: *Palaeomastodon beadnelli* Andrews 1901, *P. parvus* Andrews 1905, *P. intermedius* Matsumoto 1922; *Phiomia minor* (Andrews 1904), *P. wintoni* (Andrews 1905) and *P. osborni* Matsumoto 1922; all above species from Fluvio-marine Fm, Fayûm, Egypt.   **Extant.**

Suborder BARYTHERIOIDEA Simpson 1945

First and **Last,** Tert U. Eoc: *Barytherium grave* Andrews 1901, Qasr-el-Sagha Beds, Fayûm, Egypt.

Suborder DEINOTHERIOIDEA Osborn 1921

First, Tert L. Mioc: *Deinotherium hobleyi* Andrews 1911, Karungu Beds (= Argillaceous Series), Karungu, Kavirondo Gulf, Lake Victoria, Kenya; *D. bavaricum* von Meyer 1831, Burdigalian of France (e.g. Sables de l'Orleanais (Orleanais), Sables de la Romieu (Aquitaine)), Spain (Catalonia), Portugal, Tunisia and Algeria (*vide* Bergounioux & Crouzel 1962); *D. maricum* Pilgrim 1908 Bugti Beds, Bugti Hills, Baluchistan, Pakistan.

Last, Quat M. Pleist: *Deinotherium bozasi* Arambourg 1934, l. part of Bed II, Olduvai Gorge, Tanzania.

Comment: Remarkable suborder (?order) comprising only one genus in which the species vary essentially only in size from L. Mioc to M. Pleist. Much of the dating is by cross reference on size comparison.

Order EMBRITHOPODA Andrews 1906

First and **Last,** Tert. L. Olig: *Arsinoitherium* Beadnell 1902, Fluvio-marine Series (Sannoisian), Fayûm, Egypt.

Comment: The only two known species *A. zitteli* and *A. andrewsi*, occur in the Fayûm; detailed description in Andrews 1906. Order probably of African origin but no continental beds of earlier age known in Africa and no other known occurrence of the order.

Order SIRENIA Illiger 1811

First, Tert M. Eoc: *Prorastomus sirenoides* Owen 1855, Yellow Lst Group, Freeman's Hall Estate, Jamaica; *Eotheroides aegyptiacum* (Owen 1875), *E. abeli* Sickenberg 1934, *E. majus* Zdansky 1938 and *Protosiren fraasi* Abel 1904, all from L. Mokattam Beds, Mokattam Hills, Cairo, Egypt; *P. ?dubia* (Cuvier 1821), Blaye Lst (Lutetian), S.W. France. *Prototherium veronense* de Zigno 1875, U. Lutetian. N. Italy.

Comments: Widespread distribution in Tethyan area from M. Eoc onwards. Reviews in Abel (1904, 1913), Simpson (1932) and Sickenberg (1934).

Order DESMOSTYLIA Reinhardt 1953

First, Tert L. Mioc: *Desmostylus hesperus* Marsh 1888, Tappu Fm, Tesio Prov. Hokkaido, Japan and Hattyorei Fm Honto-mati, S. Sakhalin, Japan; *Cornwallius sookensis* (Cornwall 1922), Sooke Fm, Vancouver Is, B.C., Canada.

Last, Tert U. Mioc: *Desmostylus hesperus* Marsh 1888, Branch Canyon Fm, Cuyama Valley, California and Astoria Fm, Grays Harbour County, Washington; *Paleoparadoxia tabatai* (Tokunaga 1939) from Sado Is, Honshû, Japan, and *Paleoparadoxia* sp., Santa Margarita Fm, Santa Cruz, California.

Comments: Desmostylia separated from Sirenia to contain Pacific M. Tert amphibious forms in genera *Desmostylus*, *Cornwallius*, *Vanderhoofius* and *Paleoparadoxia*. Age correlations of the American and Japanese fms uncertain. Reviews in Vanderhoof (1937) and Reinhardt (1959).

[R.J.G.S.]

The Fossil Record, Part II

Order HYRACOIDEA Huxley, 1869

Family PROCAVIIDAE Thomas, 1892 (incl. Pliohyracidae Osborn, 1899; in part = Saghatheriidae Andrews, 1906).

First, Tert L. Olig: *Saghatherium* Andrews & Beadnell, 1902, Fayûm, Egypt. **Extant.**

Comments: Conservative group of moderately large to small hyracoids, possessing short snouts and selenolophodont to lophodont cheek teeth. Persistent throughout Cainozoic, but never prolific.

Family GENIOHYIDAE Matsumoto, 1926 (incl. Titanohyracidae Matsumoto, 1926; in part-Saghatheriidae Andrews, 1906).

First, Tert L. Olig: *Megalohyrax* Andrews, 1903; *Geniohyus* Andrews, 1904; *Bunohyrax* Schlosser, 1911; *Pachyhyrax* Schlosser, 1911; *Titanohyrax* Matsumoto, 1921, Fayûm, Egypt.

Last, Tert ?L. Mioc: *Megalohyrax* and *Bunohyrax*, Kenya.

Comments: Large to medium-sized, long-snouted, probably cursorial, hyracoids, with bunoselenodont to selenolophodont cheek teeth. Sudden appearance of numerous forms in Olig followed by rapid depletion and extinction.

Family MYOHYRACIDAE Andrews, 1914

First, Tert ?L. Mioc: *Myohyrax oswaldi* Andrews, 1914 (-*M. doederleini* Stromer, 1922); Kenya.

Last, Tert ?U. Mioc or Plioc: *Myohyrax oswaldi* Andrews, 1914; *M. beetzi* (Stromer), 1922, Namib, S.W. Africa.

Comments: Very small, long-snouted hyracoids, showing pronounced rodent-like specializations of dentition and jaws. Sudden appearance and brief span; relationships to other hyracoids obscure. [Transferred by Patterson (1965) to Macroscelidae as subfamily, B.P.]

General Comment: Origins and affinities of Hyracoidea unknown, although superficial resemblances to S. American Notoungulata and N. American Condylarthra have been noted. Association within Paenungulata arbitrary. Abundant genera and species appear suddenly in L. Olig, greatly reduced from Mioc onwards. All known hyracoids restricted to Africa, Arabia, and Mediterranean region. [T.W.]

Superorder MESAXONIA

Order PERISSODACTYLA

Suborder HIPPOMORPHA Wood 1937

First, Tert L. Eoc: *Hyracotherium* Owen 1840, Europe, U.S.A. (Simpson 1952, Kitts 1956); *Propachynolophus* Lemoine 1891, Teredine Sands nr. Epernay, France; *Lambdotherium* Cope 1880, Lost Cabin, Wind River, Knight fm, late Wasatchian, U.S.A. **Extant.**

Suborder CERATOMORPHA Wood 1937

First, Tert L. Eoc: *Homogalax* Hay 1899, U.S.A. (Radinsky 1963), Wutu fm, Shantung, China (Chow & Li 1965); *Hyrachyus* Leidy 1871, Lost Cabin, Knight fm, late Wasatchian, U.S.A. and Teredine Sands, nr. Epernay, France (Savage, Russell & Louis, 1966). **Extant.**

Suborder ANCYLOPODA Cope 1889

First, Tert L. Eoc: *Paleomoropus* Radinsky 1964, Lower Gray Bull Beds, early Wasatchian, U.S.A.; *Lophiaspis* Depéret 1910, Palette, Aix-en-Provence, France (Radinsky 1964).

Last, Quat Pleist: *Ancylotherium* Gaudry 1863, L. Pleist S. & E. Africa (George 1950, Butler *in* Leakey 1965, p. 26); *Nestoritherium* Kaup 1859, M. Pleist S.E. Asia (Hooijer 1964).

Comment: Perissodactyls have a rather good fossil record, that of the horses being known best. In the late Eoc the order was much diversified, including among the brontotheres ("titanotheres") some of the largest land mammals of their time. The earliest ceratomorph *Homogalax* has just been shown to appear simultaneously in the New and the Old World, as does the earliest hippomorph. The Olig-Mioc paraceratheres ("*Baluchitherium*") comprise the largest land mammals ever. Mioc rhinocerotids of Africa will soon become better known. Chalicotheres, long thought to have appeared only by late Eoc times, have recently been traced back to the early Eoc of N. America as well as France (Radinsky 1964).

Superorder PARAXONIA Marsh 1884

Order ARTIODACTYLA Owen 1848

Suborder SUIFORMES Jaeckel 1911

First, Tert L. Eoc: *Diacodexis* Cope 1882, *Wasatchia* Sinclair 1914, *Bunophorus* Sinclair 1914, *Hexacodus* Gazin 1952, all Wind River, Knight fm, Wasatchian, U.S.A.; *Protodichobune* Lemoine 1891, Teredine Sands, nr. Epernay, France.   **Extant.**

Suborder TYLOPODA Illiger 1811

First, Tert U. Eoc: *Protylopus* Wortman 1898, *Poebrodon* Gazin 1955, Uinta fm, Uinta Basin, U.S.A.   **Extant.**

Suborder RUMINANTIA Scopoli 1777

First, Tert U. Eoc: *Protoreodon* Scott & Osborn 1887, *Leptotragulus* Scott & Osborn 1887, *Oromeryx* Marsh 1894, *Leptoreodon* Wortman 1898, all Uinta fm, Uinta Basin, U.S.A.; *Simimeryx* Stock 1934, Sespe fm, Calif., Duchesne River fm, Utah, U.S.A.; *Archaeomeryx* Matthew & Granger 1925, Shara Murun fm, Mongolia; *Indomeryx* Pilgrim 1928, Pondaung Sandstones, Burma; *Lophiomeryx* Pomel 1854, Apt, Quercy phosphorites, France; *Phaneromeryx* Schlosser 1886, Gely nr. Montpellier, France; *Cryptomeryx* Schlosser 1886, Quercy phosphorites, France.   **Extant.**

Comment: Artiodactyls are mostly well-documented cranially and dentally. Only non-ruminants have yet been dated back to the early Eoc (chart no. 1 in Gazin 1955). *Poebrodon* is perhaps the first true camelid to be known from the Eocene (Gazin 1955, p. 78); of the families appearing in the Olig only the pigs and peccaries survive to this day. The ruminants, a very abundant group dominant since the Mioc, have been classified in various ways (Colbert 1941a). Much work still needs to be done before their early history will be clarified.   [D.A.H.]

REFERENCES

ABEL, O. 1904. Die Sirenen der mediterranen Tertiarbildungen Oesterreichs. *Abh. geol. Reichsanst., Wien,* **19,** 1–223.
—— 1913. Die eocanen Sirenen der Mittelmeerregion. *Paleontographica,* **59,** 289–360.
ANDREWS, C. W. 1903. Notes on an Expedition to the Fayûm, Egypt, with Description of some New Mammals. *Geol. Mag.,* **40,** 337–343.
—— 1904. Further Notes on the Mammals of the Eocene of Egypt, III. *Geol. Mag.,* **41,** 211–215.
—— 1906. *Catalogue of the Tertiary Vertebrata of the Fayûm, Egypt.* xxxvii + 324 pp. Brit. Mus. (Nat. Hist.), London.
—— 1914. On the Lower Miocene Vertebrates from British East Africa, collected by Dr Felix Oswald. *Quart. J. Geol. Soc. Lond.,* **70,** 163–186.
—— & Beadnell, H. J. L. 1902. *A Preliminary Note on some new Mammals from the Upper Eocene of Egypt.* 9 pp., Survey Dept., Cairo.
BERGOUNIOUX, F. M. & CROUZEL, F. 1962. Les Deinothérides d'Europe. *Annls Paléont.,* **48,** 11–56.
BLACK, C. C. 1963. A review of the North American Tertiary Sciuridae. *Bull. Mus. comp. Zool. Harv.,* **130** (3), 109–248.
CASAMIQUELA, R. M. 1961. Sobre la presencia de un mammifero en el primer elenco (icnológico) de vertebrados del Jurásico de la Patagonia. *Physis, B. Aires,* **22,** 225–33.

Chow, M. C. 1953. Remarks on the two mesozoic mammals from the north-eastern provinces. *Acta palaeont. sin.* **1**, 151–6. 1960. *Prodinoceras* and a summary of mammalian fossils of Sinkiang. *Vertbr. palasiat.*, **4**, 99–102.

—— 1963a. Tillodont materials from Eocene of Shantung and Honan. *Vertbr. palasiat.*, **7**, 97–104.

—— 1963b. A xenarthran-like mammal from the Eocene of Honan. *Scientia sin.*, **12**, 1889–1893.

—— & Li, C.-K. 1965. *Homogalax* and *Heptodon* of Shantung. *Vertbr. palasiat.*, **9**: 15–21.

—— & Tung, Y. S. 1962. Notes on some new uintathere materials of China. *Vertbr. palasiat.*, **6**, 368–374.

Clemens, W. A. 1960. Stratigraphy of the type Lance Formation. *21st Int. geol. Congr.*, Part V, 7–13.

—— 1961. Late Cretaceous mammals from the Lance Formation (abstract) *in International Colloquium on Evolution of lower and non-specialised mammals*, 127–8. Kon. Vlaamse Academie Wetenschappen.

—— 1963. Wealden mammalian fossils. *Palaeontology*, **6**, 55–69.

—— 1964. Fossil Mammals of the Type Lance Formation, Wyoming. Part I. Introduction and Multituberculata. *Univ. Calif. Publs. geol. Sci.* **48**, 1–105.

—— 1966. Fossil Mammals of the Type Lance Formation, Wyoming. Part II. Marsupialia. *Ibid.*, **62**, 1–122.

Colbert, E. H. 1933a. The skull of *Dissopsalis carnifex* Pilgrim, a Miocene creodont from India. *Am. Mus. Novit.*, **603**, 1–8.

—— 1933b. Two new rodents from the Lower Siwalik beds of India. *Ibid.*, **633**, 1–6.

—— 1941a. The osteology and relationships of *Archaeomeryx*, an ancestral ruminant. *Am. Mus. Novit.*, **1135**, 1–24.

—— 1941b. A study of *Orycteropus gaudryi* from the island of Samos. *Bull. Am. Mus. nat. Hist.*, **78**, 305–351.

Dawson, M. R. 1958. Later Tertiary Leporidae of North America. *Paleont. Contr. Univ. Kans.*, **6**, 1–75.

—— 1959. *Paludotona etruria*, a new ochotonid from the Pontian of Tuscany. *Verh. naturf. Ges. Basel*, **70**, 157–166.

—— 1964. Late Eocene Rodents (Mammalia) from Inner Mongolia. *Am. Mus. Novit.*, **2191**, 1–15.

Dorr, J. A. 1958. *Prouintatherium*, new uintathere genus, earliest Eocene, Hoback Formation, Wyoming, and the phylogeny of Dinocerata. *J. Paleont.*, **32**, 506–516.

Filhol, H. 1894. Observations concernant quelques mammifères nouveaux du Quercy. *Annls. Sci. nat.*, (7), **16**, 129–150.

Flerov, K. K. 1957. [The Dinocerata of Mongolia]. *Trudy. Palaeont. Inst.*, **67**, 1–82. (In Russian.)

Francis, J. C. 1960. Análisis de algunos factores de confusión en la sistemática genérica de los Mesotheriinae (Notoungulata, Typotheria). *Ameghiniana*, **2**, 29–36.

Gazin, C. L. 1941. The mammalian faunas of the Paleocene of central Utah, with notes on the geology. *Proc. U.S. natn. Mus.*, **91**, 1–53.

—— 1952. The Lower Eocene Knight Formation of Wyoming and its mammalian faunas. *Smithson. Misc. Collns*, **117** (18), 1–82.

—— 1953. The Tillodontia: an early Tertiary order of mammals. *Smithson. Misc. Collns*, **121**, (10), 1–110.

—— 1955. A review of the Upper Eocene Artiodactyla of North America. *Smithson. Misc. Collns*, **128**, (8), 1–96.

George, M. 1950. A chalicothere from the Limeworks Quarry of the Makapan Valley, Potgietersrust District. *S. Afr. J. Sci.*, **46**, 241–242.

Gill, E. D. 1957. The stratigraphical occurrence and palaeoecology of some Australian Tertiary marsupials. *Mem. natn. Mus. Viet.*, **21**, 135–203.

Grant-Taylor, T. L. & Rafter, T. A. 1963. New Zealand natural radiocarbon measurements I–V. *Radiocarbon*, **5**, 143, 161.

HOFFSTETTER, R. 1954. Les gravigrades cuirassés du Déséadian de Patagonie (note préliminaire). *Mammalia*, **18**, 159–169.

—— 1956. Contribution a l'étude des Orophodontoidea, gravigrades cuirassés de la Patagonie. *Annls Paléont*, **42**, 27–64.

HOOIJER, D. A. 1963. Mammalian remains from an Indian site on Curaçao. *Stud. Fauna Curaçao*, **14**, 119–122.

—— 1964. New records of mammals from the Middle Pleistocene of Sangiran, Central Java. *Zool. Meded., Leiden*, **40**, (10), 73–88.

JAMES, G. T. 1957. An edentate from the Pleistocene of Texas. *J. Paleont.*, **31**, 796–808.

JEPSEN, G. L. 1932. *Tubulodon taylori*, a Wind River Eocene tubulidentate from Wyoming. *Proc. Am. Phil. Soc.*, **71**, 255–274.

—— 1966. Early Eocene bat from Wyoming. *Science, N.Y.* **154**, 1333–1338.

KELLOGG, R. 1928. The history of whales—their adaptation to life in water. *Q. Rev. Biol.*, **3**, 29–76, 174–208.

—— 1936. A review of the Archaeoceti. *Publs Carnegie Instn*, **482**, 1–366.

KERMACK, K. A. & MUSSETT, F. (1959). The jaw articulation in Mesozoic mammals. *15th Int. zool., Congr.* Sect. V.

KITTS, D. B. 1956. American Hyracotherium (Perissodactyla, Equidae). *Bull. Am. Mus. nat. Hist.*, **110**, 1–60.

KRAGLIEVICH, J. L. & RIVAS, S. 1951. *Orophodon* Amegh., representante de una nueva super-familia Orophodontoidea del subordern Xenarthra (Nota preliminar). *Comun. Inst. nac. Invest. cienc. nat., B. Aires*, Zool. series **2**, 9–28.

KÜHNE, W. G. 1961. A mammalian fauna from the Kimmeridgian of Portugal. *Nature, Lond.*, **192**, 274.

LAVOCAT, R. 1962. Réflexions sur l'origine et la structure du groupe des Rongeurs. *Colloques int. Cent. natn. Rech. scient.*, **104**, 287–290.

LEAKEY, L. S. B. 1965. Olduvai Gorge 1951–61. I. A preliminary report on the geology and fauna. I–XIV, 1–118, Cambridge, University Press.

LEWIS, G. E. 1955. *Soc. Vertebrate Paleontol. News Bull.*, **42**, 21.

LUDBROOK, N. H. 1963. Correlations of the Tertiary rocks of South Australia. *Trans. R. Soc. S. Aust.*, **87**, 5–15.

McCOY, F. 1874. *Prodromus of the palaeontology of Victoria*... Decade I. Geol. Survey Victoria, 21–22.

McGREW, P. O. & PATTERSON, B. 1962. A picrodontid insectivore(?) from the Paleocene of Wyoming. *Breviora*, **175**, 1–9.

MACINTYRE, G. T. 1966. The Miacidae, (Mammalia, Carnivora). Part 1. The systematics of *Ictidopappus* and *Protictis*. *Bull. Am. Mus. Nat. Hist.*, **131**, (2), 115–210.

McKENNA, M. C. 1956. Survival of primitive notoungulates and condylarths into the Miocene of Colombia. *Am. J. Sci.*, **254**, 736–743.

—— 1960a. Fossil Mammalia from the Early Wasatchian Four Mile fauna, Eocene of North-west Colorado. *Univ. Calif. Publs geol. Sci.*, **37**, 1–130.

—— 1960b. The Geolabidinae: a new subfamily of Early Cenozoic erinaceoid insectivores. *Univ. Cal. Publs geol. Sci.*, **37**, 131–64.

—— 1961. A note on the origin of Rodents, *Am. Mus. Novit.*, **2037**, 1–5.

——, ROBINSON, P. & TAYLOR, D. W. 1962. Notes on Eocene Mammalia and Mollusca of Tabernacle Butte, Wyoming. *Am. Mus. Novit.*, **2102**.

McLAREN, I. A. 1960. Are the Pinnipedia biphyletic? *Syst. Zool.* **9**, 18–28.

MATSUMOTO, H. 1921. A revision of the Hyracoids from the Fayum, Egypt. *Proc. zool. Soc. Lond.*, **1921**, 839–850.

—— 1926. Contribution to the knowledge of the fossil Hyracoidea of the Fayum, Egypt, with description of several new species. *Bull. Am. Mus. Nat. Hist.*, **56**, 253–350.

MATTHEW, W. D. 1917. A Paleocene bat. *Bull. Am. Mus. Nat. Hist.*, **37**, 569–71.

—— 1937. Paleocene faunas of the San Juan Basin, New Mexico. *Trans. Am. phil. Soc.* New series, **30**, i–viii, 1–510.

—— & GRANGER, W. 1918. A revision of the Lower Eocene Wasatch and Wind River faunas. Part V. Insectivora (continued), Glires, Edentata. *Bull. Am. Mus. Nat. Hist.*, **38**, 565–657.

—— & PAULA COUTO, C. DE, 1959. The Cuban edentates. *Bull. Am. Mus. Nat. Hist.*, **117**, 1–56.

MESCHINELLI, L. 1902. Un nuovo Chirottero fossile delle Lignite di Monteviale. *Atti Ist. veneto Sci.*, **62**, 1329–44.

OSBORN, H. F. 1899. *Pliohyrax kruppi* from the lower Pliocene of Samos. *4th Int. zool. Congr.*, 172–173.

—— 1936 & 1942. *Proboscidea* (2 vols.). New York, American Museum Natural History.

PAPP, A. & THENIUS, E. 1959. Tertiär: *Handbuch der stratigraphischen Geologie.* III Bd., 2 Teil. Stuttgart.

PASCUAL, R. 1960. Una nueva superfamilia Entelopsoidea. Descripción de la neuva especie *Entelops parodii. Acta geol. Lilloana*, **3**, 127–146.

—— 1965. Los Toxodontidae (Toxodonta, Notoungulata) de la formación Arroyo Chasicó (Plioceno inferior) de la Provincia de Buenos Aires. *Ameghiniana*, **4**, 101–129.

PATTERSON, B. 1949. Rates of evolution in taeniodonts. In *Genetics, Paleontology and Evolution* (Ed. Jepsen, G. L., Simpson, G. G. and Mayr, E.). Princeton, Princeton University Press.

—— 1956. Early Cretaceous mammals and the evolution of mammalian molar teeth. *Fieldiana, Geol.*, **13**, 1–105,

—— 1958. Affinities of the Patagonian fossil mammal *Necrolestes. Breviora*, **94**, 1–14.

—— & PASCUAL, R. 1963. The extinct land mammals of South America. *16th Int. zool. Congr.*, Program Vol., 138–148.

PAULA COUTO, C. DE, 1952a. Fossil mammals from the beginning of the Cenozoic in Brazil. Condylarthra, Litopterna, Xenungulata, and Astrapotheria. *Bull. Am. Mus. Nat. Hist.*, **99**, 355–394.

—— 1952b. Fossil mammals from the beginning of the Cenozoic in Brazil. Marsupialia: Polydolopidae and Borhyaenidae. *Am. Mus. Novit.*, **1959**, 1–27.

—— 1952c. Fossil mammals from the beginning of the Cenozoic in Brazil. Marsupialia: Didelphidae. *Am. Mus. Novit.*, **1567**, 1–26.

—— 1952d. Fossil mammals from the beginning of the Cenozoic in Brazil. Notoungulata. *Am. Mus. Novit.*, **1568**, 1–16.

—— 1954. On a notostylopid from the Paleocene of Itaborai, Brazil. *Am. Mus. Novit.*, **1693**, 1–5.

—— 1962. Didelfídeos fósiles del Paleoceno de Brasil. *Revta Mus. argent. cienc. nat. Bernardino Rivadavia Inst. nac. Invest. Cienc. nat.* Zool. series, **8**, 135–166.

PEYER, P. 1956. Über Zähne von Haramiyden, von Triconodonten und von Wahrscheinlich synapsiden Reptilien aus dem Rhät von Hallan, Kt. Schaffhausen, Schweiz. *Schweiz. palaont. Abh.*, **72.**

PILGRIM, G. E. 1932. The fossil Carnivora of India. *Mem. geol. Surv. India, Palaeont. Indica*, **18**, 1–232.

RADINSKY, L. 1963. Origin and early evolution of North American Tapiroidea. *Bull. Peabody Mus. nat. Hist.*, **171**, 1–106.

—— 1964. *Paleomoropus*, a new Early Eocene chalicothere (Mammalia, Perissodactyla), and a revision of Eocene chalicotheres. *Am. Mus. Novit.*, **2179**, 1–29.

REIG, O. 1955a. Noticia preliminar sobre la presencia de microbiotherinos vivientes en la fauna sudamericana. *Investnes zool. chil.*, **2**, 121–130.

—— 1955b. Un neuvo género y especie de caenolestinos del Plioceno de la Provincia de Buenos Aires (República Argentina). *Rev. Assoc. Geol. Argent.*, **10**, 60–71.

—— 1958a. Conocimiento de la fauna de la formacion Chapadmalal. 1. List faunistica preliminar. *Acta geol. Lilloana*, **2**, 241–253.

—— 1958b. Notas para una actualización del conocimiento de la fauna de la formación Chapadmalal II. *Acta. geol. Lilloana*, **2**, 255–283.

REINHARDT, R. H. 1959. A review of the Sirenia and Desmostylia. *Univ. Calif. Publs geol. Sci.*, **36**, 1–146.

REVILLIOD, P. 1917. Fledermäuse aus der Braunkohle von Messel bei Darmstadt. *Abh. geol. Landesanst. Darmstadt*, **7**, 157–96.

RIDE, W. D. L. 1964. A review of Australian fossil marsupials. *J. Proc. R. Soc. West. Aust.*, **47**, 97–131.

RINGUELET, A. B. DE. 1957. Estudio del género *Chasicotherium* Cabrera y Kraglievich 1931 (Notoungulata-Homalodotheriidae). *Ameghiniana*, **1**, 7-14.

ROBINSON, P., BLACK, C. C. & DAWSON, M. R. 1964. Late Eocene multituberculates and other mammals from Wyoming. *Science, N.Y.*, **145**, 809–811.

RUSSELL, L. S. 1952. Cretaceous mammals of Alberta. *Bull. natn. Mus. can.*, **126**, 110–119.

—— 1962. Mammal teeth from the St. Mary River formation (Upper Cretaceous) at Scabby Butte, Alberta. *Nat. Hist. Pap. natn. Mus. Can.*, **14**, 1–4.

—— 1964. Cretaceous Non-marine Faunas of Northwestern North America. *Contr. Life Sci. Div. R. Ont. Mus.*, **61**, 1–24.

RUSSELL, D. E. 1964. Les Mammifères Paléocènes d'Europe. *Mém. Mus. Natn. Hist. Nat., Paris*, **13**, 1–324.

SAVAGE, R. J. G. 1965. The Miocene Carnivora of East Africa. *Bull. Brit. Mus. (Nat. Hist.)* (Geol), **10**, 239–316.

SCHAUB, S. *in* PIVETEAU, é. 1958. *Traité de Paléontologie*, **6** (2), 659–818

SCHLOSSER, M. 1911. Beiträge zur Kenntniss der oligozänen Landsäugetiere aus dem Fayum (Ägypten). *Beitr. Paläont. Geol. Öst-Ung.*, **24**, 51–167,

SHIKAMA, T. 1947. *Teilhardosaurus* and *Endotherium*, new Jurassic Reptilia and Mammalia from the Husin Coalfield, South Manchuria. *Proc. Japan Acad.*, **23**, 76–84.

SICKENBERG, O. 1934. Beiträge zur Kenntnis Tertiären Sirenen. *Mém. Mus. r. Hist. nat. Belg.*, **63**, 1–352.

SIMONS, E. L. 1960. The Paleocene Pantodonta. *Trans. Am. phil. Soc.*, **50**, 1–81.

SIMPSON, G. G. 1928a. *A catalogue of the Mesozoic Mammalia in the Geological Department of the British Museum*, x + 215 pp. London, British Museum (Nat. Hist.).

—— 1928b. A new mammalian fauna from the Fort Union of southern Montana. *Am. Mus. Novit.* **297.**

—— 1929a. A collection of Paleocene mammals from Bear Creek, Montana. *Ann. Carneg. Mus.*, **19**, 115–22.

—— 1929b. American Mesozoic Mammalia. *Mem. Peabody Mus. Yale*, **3** (1) xv + 1–171.

—— 1930. Post-Mesozoic Marsupialia. *Fossilium Catalogus* I. *Animalia* Pars 47. W. Junk, Berlin.

—— 1932. Fossil Sirenia of Florida and the evolution of the Sirenia. *Bull. Am. Mus. nat. Hist.*, **59**, 419–503.

—— 1935. New Paleocene mammals from the Fort Union of Montana. *Proc. U.S. nat. Mus.* **83**, 221–44.

—— 1945. The principles of classification and a classification of mammals. *Bull. Am. Mus. nat. Hist.*, **85**, 1–350.

—— 1947. A continental Tertiary time chart. *J. Paleont.*, **21**, 480–483.

—— 1948. The beginning of the Age of Mammals in South America. Part 1. Introduction. Systematics: Marsupialia, Edentata, Condylarthra, Litopterna, and Notioprogonia. *Bull. Am. Mus. nat. Hist.*, **91**, 1–232.

—— 1950. History of the fauna of Latin America. *Am. Scient.*, **38**, 361–389.

—— 1951. American Cretaceous insectivores. *Am. Mus. Novit.*, **1541.**

—— 1952. Notes on British hyracotheres. *J. Linn. Soc. Lond.*, (*Zool*), **42**, 195–206.

—— 1957. A new Casamayor astropothere. *Revta Mus. munic. Cienc. nat. Mar del Plata*, **1**, 11–18.

—— 1961. *Principles of animal taxonomy*, 259 pp. Columbia Univ. Press.

—— 1967. The beginning of the Age of Mammals in South America. Part 2. Systematics: Notoungulata concluded (Typotheria, Hegetotheria, Toxodonta, Notoungulata *incertae sedis*); Astrapotheria; Trigonostylopoidea; Pyrotheria; Xenungulata; Mammalia *incertae sedis*. *Bull. Am. Mus. nat. Hist.*, In press.

——, Minoprio, J. L. & Patterson, B. 1962. The mammalian fauna of the Divisadero Largo Formation, Mendoza, Argentina. *Bull. Mus. comp. Zool. Harv.*, **127**, 237–293.

Slijper, E. J. 1936. Die Cetaceen: Vergeichend-anatomisch und systemisch. *Capita zool.*, **7**, 1–590.

Sloan, R. E. & Van Valen, L. 1965. Cretaceous mammals from Montana. *Science, N.Y.*, **148**, 220–7.

Stirton, R. A. 1953a. A new genus of interatheres from the Miocene of Colombia. *Univ. Calif. Pubs geol. Sci.*, **29**, 265–348.

—— 1953b. Vertebrate paleontology and continental stratigraphy in Columbia. *Bull. geol. Soc. Am.*, **64**, 603–622.

—— 1957. Tertiary marsupials from Victoria, Australia. *Mem. natn. Mus. Vict.* **21**, 121–134.

——, Tedford, R. H. & Miller, A. H. 1961. Cenozoic stratigraphy and vertebrate paleontology of the Tirari desert, South Australia. *Rec. S. Aust. Mus.*, **14**, 19–61.

Stromer, E. 1922. Erste Mitteilung über tertiäre Wirbeltier-Reste aus Deutsch-Südwestafrika. *Sber. bayer. Akad. Wiss.*, 1921, **21**, 331–340.

Thaler, L. 1966. Les Rongeurs fossiles du Bas-Languedoc dans leurs rapports avec l'histoire des faunes et la stratigraphie du Tertiaire d'Europe. *Mém. Mus. natn Hist. nat. Paris*, n.s., série C, **17**, 295 p., 25 figs., 27 pl.

Thomas, O. 1892. On the Species of the Hyracoidea. *Proc. zool. Soc. Lond.*, **1892**, 50–76, pl. 3.

Turnbull, W. D., Lundelius, E. L. & McDougall, I. 1965. A Potassium/Argon dated Pliocene marsupial fauna from Victoria, Australia. *Nature, Lond.*, **206**, 816.

Vanderhoof, V. L. 1937. A study of the Miocene sirenian *Desmostylus*. *Univ. Calif. Publs geol. Sci.*, **24**, 169–262.

Van Frank, R. 1957. A fossil collection from northern Venezuela. 1. Toxodontidae (Mammalia, Notoungulata). *Am. Mus. Novit*, **1850**, 1–38.

Van Valen, L. 1963. The origin and status of the mammalian order Tillodontia. *J. Mammal.* **44**, 364–373.

—— 1964. A possible origin for rabbits. *Evolution, Lancaster, Pa.*, **18**, 484–91.

—— 1965a. Some European Proviverrini (Mammalia, Deltatheridia). *Palaeontology*, **8**, 838–665.

—— 1965b. Paroxyclaenidae, an extinct family of Eurasian mammals. *J. Mammal.*, **46**, (3), 388–397.

—— 1966. Deltatheridia, a new order of mammals. *Bull. Am. Mus. nat. Hist.*, 132, (1), 1–126.

Wheeler, W. H. 1961. Revision of the uintatheres. *Bull. Peabody Mus. nat. Hist.*, **14**, i–vi, 1–93.

Wood, A. E. 1942. Notes on the paleocene lagomorph, *Eurymylus*. *Am. Mus. Novit.*, **1162**, 1–7.

—— 1955. A revised classification of the Rodents. *J. Mammal.*, **36** (2), 165–187.

—— 1958. Are there Rodent suborders? *Syst. Zool.*, **7** (4), 169–173.

—— & Patterson, B. 1959. The Rodents of the Deseadan Oligocene of Patagonia and the beginnings of South American rodent evolution. *Bull. Mus. comp. Zool. Harv.*, **120** (3).

Wood, R. C. 1967. A review of the Clark Fork vertebrate fauna. *Breviora*, In press.

[Professor] P. M. Butler, M.A. PH.D.
'Alderhurst', Royal Holloway College, Bakeham Lane, Englefield Green, Surrey.

W. A. Clemens, PH.D.
Department of Zoology, University of Kansas, Lawrence, Kansas, U.S.A.

S. F. Graham, M.A.
American Museum of Natural History, Central Park West at 79th Street, New York City, U.S.A.

D. A. Hooijer, D.PHIL.
Rijksmuseum van Natuurlijke Historie, Raamsteeg 2, Leiden, Netherlands.

K. A. Kermack, PH.D. F.G.S.
Department of Zoology, University College, Gower Street, London WC 1.

[Professor] B. Patterson,
Museum of Comparative Anatomy, Harvard University, Cambridge Mass. 02138, U.S.A.

Chapter 30: Mammalia

W. D. L. RIDE, M.A. D.PHIL. F.L.S. F.Z.S.
  Director, Western Australia Museum, Perth, Western Australia.
D. E. RUSSELL, DR. ÈS SC.
  Institut de Paléontologie, 8 rue Buffon, Paris V^e, France.
R. J. G. SAVAGE, PH.D. F.L.S. F.G.S.
  Department of Geology, The University, Bristol 8.
E. L. SIMONS, PH.D. D.PHIL.
  Peabody Museum of Natural History, Yale University, New Haven, Conn., U.S.A.
L. B. H. TARLO, D.SC. PH.D. F.L.S. F.A.Z. F.G.S.
  Department of Geology, The University, Reading, Berks.
L. THALER, DR. ÈS SC.
  Université de Montpellier, Montpellier, Faculté des Sciences, 34 Montpellier, France.
T. WHITWORTH, M.A. D.PHIL. F.G.S.
  The Master's Lodging, Hatfield College, Durham.

The Fossil Record

Part III

Computer analysis

Numerical analysis of *The Fossil Record*

JOHN LOUIS CUTBILL & BRIAN MICHAEL FUNNELL

CONTENTS

SUMMARY

A numerical analysis has been carried out based on the ranges of taxa as shown in Part II of *The Fossil Record*. The numbers of first occurrences, last occurrences and totals have been calculated for groups of related taxa for each stratigraphical sub-division. Relative and net changes across all sub-division boundaries have also been calculated. Results for selected groupings are presented in the form of combined histograms and graphs. Smoothing techniques have been applied to some results, and some other numerical measures calculated.

1. Introduction

This article describes the methods adopted and results obtained from a numerical analysis of the data presented in the range-charts included as figures in Part II of *The Fossil Record*.

It was originally hoped that this analysis could be delayed until all the figures in Part II of the volume were in proof, so that there would be absolutely no doubt as to the data which formed the basis of our calculations and so that the results would then form, in effect, a numerical index to the volume. Unfortunately this has not proved quite possible. Our files had to be closed for the purpose of computation on 18 October 1966. At that date only the Plantae figures had been finally passed for press; the Vertebrata and Invertebrata figures had all been draughted but were still liable to occasional minor amendment on checking against corrected proofs of the text. It is unlikely that any such amendments would have any perceptible effect on our computations; nevertheless we cannot unequivocally state that our calculations are based entirely on the figures as published, although in the circumstances we believe we have approached as closely as possible to that ideal.

The Fossil Record, pp. 791–820. Geological Society of London, 1967. Printed in Northern Ireland.

2. Methods

For the purposes of computation the stratigraphical sub-divisions of the charts were coded numerically from 0 (pre-Varangian) to 73 (Holocene). The beginnings and ends of ranges of taxa were annotated according to this code directly onto copies of the figures. (None of the occurrences shown as restricted to the Holocene were included in the calculations.) Pecked ranges, indicating stratigraphical or taxonomic uncertainty, were taken alternately to their earlier or later limits; no distinction was made between the two types of uncertainty. Each occasion this was done was checked off so as to ensure consistency in alternation, but some interruptions in this sequence were introduced by later amendments and by the overlap of taxa between the A and B parts of the figures. (For convenience the A and B figures were annotated sequentially and not jointly.) Taxa on the figures were also coded for rank, from 0 (Class) to 9 (Genus), and the working copies of the figures annotated accordingly. Tapes were punched directly from the annotated figures.

For each selected grouping the numbers of the different taxonomic ranks and total numbers of taxa were accumulated (Table 1). For each stratigraphical sub-division the following measures were determined:
For the jth unit:

F_j—the number of taxa appearing for the first time;
L_j—the number of taxa appearing for the last time;
P_j—the number of taxa present in the sub-division;
E_j—the number of extant taxa present in the sub-division;
$(F_j - L_j)$—the net loss or gain in the sub-division;
$100F_j/P_j$—the percentage of first occurrences among those present;
$100L_j/P_j$—the percentage of last occurrences among those present;
$100E_j/P_j$—the percentage of extant taxa among those present;
$100(F_j + L_j)/P_j$—measure of relative change in the sub-division;
DF_j—average duration in number of sub-divisions of taxa appearing for first time in the sub-division;
DL_j—average duration of taxa occurring for last time in the sub-division.

For the boundary between the $(j - 1)$th and jth sub-divisions:

$(F_j - L_{j-1})$—net loss or gain across boundary;
$100(F_j + L_{j-1})/(P_{j-1} + F_j)$—measure of relative change across boundary.

As discussed below some of the fluctuation in the values of these measures from sub-division to sub-division may be due to a variety of extraneous factors. We have therefore thought it legitimate to apply curve-smoothing methods to measures in order to bring the broad trends out more clearly. The degree of smoothing that it is appropriate to use is a matter of opinion. We selected four measures— number of first occurrences, number of last occurrences, relative rate of change across boundaries and net loss or gain across boundaries—and for several of the larger groups applied various degrees of smoothing. For smoothing we used the expression:

$$x_j = [nx_j + (n-1)(x_{j-1} + x_{j+1}) + \cdots + (1)(x_{j-n+1} + x_{j+n-1})]/$$
$$\{n + 2[(n-1) + (n-2) + \cdots + 1]\}$$

and calculated new values for the measures for $n = 2, 3, \ldots, 7$.

3. Reservations

Throughout our analysis of the *Fossil Record* data we have been well aware of its inherent shortcomings from the point of view of numerical treatment. Nevertheless we think the exercise will have been well worth while *so long as the deficiencies of the data input are kept clearly in mind* when attempting to interpret the results. We do not regard the present results as in any sense permanent or sacrosanct, but in so far as the patterns they reveal may promote closer investigation of their generating causes a useful purpose will have been served.

Before presenting our results we would like to draw attention to some of the more universal deficiencies in the input data, i.e. those which most seriously and consistently influence the nature of the output. Other deficiencies of both general and particular application will no doubt occur to our readers, although we hope we have not overlooked too many that exert a major influence.

(A) COMPLETENESS OF DOCUMENTATION

As we have specified above it has been our intention to define our coverage of data as being the same as that provided by the figures in Part II of this volume. This coverage is in our opinion a uniquely comprehensive and authoritative compilation, but nevertheless can in no sense be regarded as a *complete* documentation of the fossil record. In particular the taxonomic level of documentation is very variable from group to group—a point which we now consider separately.

(B) TAXONOMIC LEVEL OF DOCUMENTATION

Of the 2526 taxa included in our computation, 11 are Classes, 18 Subclasses, 6 Superorders, 275 Orders, 335 Suborders, 25 Divisions, 150 Superfamilies, 1407 Families, 40 Subfamilies and 259 Genera. With only two exceptions this represents the level of documentation adopted on the Part II figures: (*i*) some Trilobita data at family level present on an early version of the figures has been omitted, because it seemed that its retention would have seriously distorted the record of that group (which is otherwise only documented at a superfamily level), and (*ii*) the Mesozoic and Tertiary larger Foraminifera have been computed at family level (not as genera as given in the figures), in order to obtain consistency of treatment with the other Foraminifera.

We would have liked to have selected a particular taxonomic level throughout for the purposes of computation, but in practice this would only have been possible at a very high taxonomic level. Moreover we are not at all convinced that there is any real equivalence in rank even between nominally equivalent taxa. We would like to think that the level to which contributors were prepared to document their taxa on the charts has imposed a certain uniformity of treatment, but we know in fact that certain groups are represented at particularly high (e.g. molluscs) and others at particularly low (e.g. certain protozoans) taxonomic levels for purely fortuitous reasons. On the whole, as might be expected, uniformity of treatment is greater within groups than between them. Therefore the results for individual groupings are probably less seriously affected by this factor than those for higher combinations.

Finally we would like to point out that in fact almost 60 per cent of the documentation accepted for computation is at the family level, and that, in theory at least, this might be regarded as the least objectionable level at which to attempt an exercise of this kind.

(c) UNRELIABILITY OF STRATIGRAPHICAL RANGES

Uncertainties regarding stratigraphical ranges arise from numerous sources, but mainly from difficulties of taxonomic attribution, difficulties of correlation and collection failure. The effects of these may in general be randomly distributed, but in particular instances prejudiced taxonomy or correlations may have a systematic effect, and collection failure usually tends to produce bunched and shortened ranges. It seems to us that the number of taxa shown in our figures as commencing or ending their ranges at major Era or System boundaries may well be influenced, at least in part, by preconceptions on the part of systematists on the limiting effect of these boundaries. Also there are several clear examples where collection failure largely determines the form of our graphs and histograms (e.g. reptiles and insects), although it should be remembered in this connexion that *The Fossil Record* is concerned principally with the *fossil* ranges of taxa as preserved in rocks, rather than with their notional range in time. Thus the record is as much one of preservation as it is of evolution.

(d) INFLUENCE OF EXTANT RECORDS

The one exception to the procedure of recording the *fossil* range of taxa in *The Fossil Record* lies in the practice of giving the last occurrence as 'extant' if the taxon is known living, rather than recording the last fossil occurrence. It seems to us that the chances of finding a taxon living are considerably greater than those of finding it fossil, and in our opinion this factor has probably consistently influenced both the total number of taxa and the number of extinctions that we have plotted for the late Mesozoic and Cainozoic. There is no way of eliminating this influence from our calculations, without requiring a complete re-documentation of the last occurrences of extant taxa on a different basis, but in order to draw attention to the potential nature and magnitude of its influence we have characterized the extant taxa separately in the total taxa histograms.

(e) DURATION OF STRATIGRAPHICAL DIVISIONS

For any of the numerical data to be mutually comparable in a time direction the duration of the stratigraphical divisions should be at least approximately equal.

The form of presentation we have adopted arbitrarily represents these divisions as if they were exactly equal. We know that this is in fact not so, but when we investigated the possibility of constructing a proportional scale we found that the information available for doing so was totally inadequate. In general divisions back to and including the Trias approximate 5 to 6 m. y. (although where durations are probably best known—in the Tertiary—considerable variation about this mean is obvious), and before that, back to and including the Devonian, 5 to 10 m. y. is more characteristic. Most of the Cambrian to Silurian divisions are however somewhat longer, falling in the range 15 to 30 m. y. This effect may to some extent account for some of the comparatively high rates of change and large numbers of taxa indicated for the lower Palaeozoic. We have not attempted to scale our figures to eliminate this effect (there is insufficient information in existence to do this), but the ages of the bases of systems in m. y. is given on all of our figures, so that some allowance can be made for it when examining them.

These then are in our opinion the *main* deficiencies in the data which we have processed, and should be continuously borne in mind in any attempt to interpret the results.

4. Results

In Table 1 we show all the groupings which we have computed separately, together with the numbers of each taxonomic rank included in each grouping. A full set of the values for all of the measures described in section 2 (Methods) above is deposited in the Library of the Geological Society of London[1]. For the purposes of this article we have restricted our illustrations to a standard form of presentation by histogram and graph, representing six measures for each of twenty selected groupings. Each figure shows (*i*) the number of taxa occurring for the first time in each sub-division (F_j) = 'firsts', (*ii*) the number occurring for the last time (L_j) = 'lasts', (*iii*) the number of extant taxa in each sub-division (E_j) = 'extants', and (*iv*) the total number of taxa in each (P_j) = 'totals'—all shown as histograms; (*v*) the relative change in taxa across boundaries between stratigraphical sub-divisions $[100(F_j + L_{j-1})/(P_{j-1} + F_j)]$ = 'relative turnover', (*vi*) the net change across boundaries ($F_j - L_{j-1}$) = 'net profit and loss'—both shown as graphs.

We do not intend to comment in detail on the figures, but to leave readers to make their own observations and draw their own conclusions as they see fit. There are just a few general points, mainly regarding the plot of all groups, to which we would like to call attention: (*a*) the Palaeozoic plateau in total taxa (most marked in the Invertebrata), (*b*) the progressive rise in total taxa during the Mesozoic and Cainozoic (showing an increasing proportion of extants), (*c*) the reduction of total taxa at the end of the Palaeozoic, brought about by a high proportion of 'lasts' (extinctions) rather than by any fall-off in 'firsts',

---

[1] Copies of these are available at a price representing the cost of Xerox reproduction and postage for the sections required. Application should be made to the Librarian, Geological Society, Burlington House, Piccadilly, London w 1.

TABLE 1: *Source, taxonomic composition and illustration references of computed data*

Grouping	Chapter(s)	No. of Taxa	Classes	Subclasses	Superorders	Orders	Suborders	Divisions	Superfamilies	Families	Subfamilies	Genera	Figure in this paper
Thallophyta 1	1	63	1	—	—	19	—	—	—	41	2	—	—
Thallophyta 2	2	247	—	—	—	—	—	—	—	28	—	219	—
Thallophyta 1 + 2	1,2	310	1	—	—	19	—	—	—	69	2	219	1
Pteridophyta 1–2	4,5	70	—	—	—	3	—	—	—	55	8	4	2
Gymnospermae	6	58	—	—	—	16	—	—	—	29	—	13	3
Angiospermae	7	167	—	—	—	—	—	—	—	167	—	—	16*b*
PLANTAE	1–7	623	1	4	—	42	—	—	—	330	10	236	4
Protozoa	8	131	—	1	—	1	—	—	1	121	7	—	5
Coelenterata	10	163	—	—	—	12	8	—	—	143	—	—	6
Brachiopoda	12	109	—	—	—	—	1	—	20	88	—	—	7
Mollusca 1–5	13–17	115	1	—	—	41	10	—	48	7	8	—	8
Arthropoda 1–3	18–20	291	1	7	3	66	65	11	52	85	—	1	9
Arthropoda 2 (Insecta)	19	135	1	3	—	39	50	6	35	—	—	1	10
Echinodermata 1–2	21–22	184	5	6	—	9	32	—	—	129	3	—	11
INVERTEBRATA	8–24	1205	10	14	3	145	143	11	121	709	30	19	12
Agnatha	25	36	—	—	—	13	23	—	—	—	—	—	—
Pisces	26	242	—	—	3	23	70	—	—	146	—	—	—
Agnatha + Pisces	25,26	278	—	—	3	36	93	—	—	146	—	—	13
Amphibia	27	40	—	—	—	6	13	—	7	14	—	—	14
Reptilia	28	171	—	—	—	16	22	14	4	115	—	—	15*b*
Aves	29	76	—	—	—	18	22	—	18	18	—	—	45*a*
Mammalia	30	133	—	—	—	12	42	—	—	75	—	4	16*a*
VERTEBRATA	25–30	698	—	—	3	88	192	14	29	368	—	4	17
ALL GROUPS	1–30	2526	11	18	6	275	335	25	150	1407	40	259	18

(*d*) the more or less random incidence of 'firsts' (except for the Plantae), (*e*) the consistent association of maximum numbers of 'lasts' with the ends of various systems, (*f*) the variable relationship between relative 'turnover' and net 'profit and loss'—sometimes high 'turnover' coincides with negligible profit or loss, at other times with either a high 'profit' or a high 'loss'.

The Palaeozoic/Mesozoic boundary appears from our results to fall in the middle of a fairly protracted period of crisis characterized by a normal rate of accession of new taxa, but an abnormally high rate of extinction, leading eventually to an over-all decrease in the total taxa from the 'plateau' conditions of the Palaeozoic. The Mesozoic/Cainozoic boundary seems to be marked by a brief period of crisis characterized by an abnormally high rate of extinction, followed by a higher than usual rate of accession, so that the curve of progressive increase in total taxa, which typifies the post-Palaeozoic, is first set back and then goes on to rise even more steeply than before during the early part of the Cainozoic.

In addition to the figures referred to above, a number of smoothed profiles have been illustrated for particular measures and groupings. These show the major patterns more clearly by reducing short-term variation, some of which at least is almost certainly due to uncertainties in correlation or collection failure. As before the full set of values obtained by these smoothing operations is deposited in the Library of the Geological Society of London[1].

We give here (Fig. 19) only a possible meaning for the curves showing the net profit and loss for all taxa. The raw data show considerable short-term fluctuations. High and low values alternate and the curve has 42 peaks and troughs. By considering the values in two stratigraphical sub-divisions above and below each sub-division, we hope to derive a curve in which the sources of error have been randomly distributed. The resulting curve ($n = 3$) shows only 16 peaks and troughs, and may be a better representation of the actual distribution of taxa in time. More intense smoothing will amost certainly obliterate genuine variation. The curve derived by considering four sub-divisions above and below ($n = 5$), has 13 peaks and troughs, many of them of minor importance, and probably shows trends whose duration is comparable with that of a geological system. The most intense smoothing ($n = 7$), since it takes into account 6 sub-divisions above and below a particular sub-division, should obliterate all but the very long-term trends. The least that can be said about a pattern which survives such intense smoothing is that it demands some explanation.

ACKNOWLEDGEMENTS. The computations which form the basis of this article were carried out using the *Titan* computer at the University of Cambridge Mathematical Laboratory, according to programmes devised by J. L. C. Mr Charles Harkness draughted the figures in the Department of Geology, University of Cambridge.

---

[1] See footnote on p. 795.

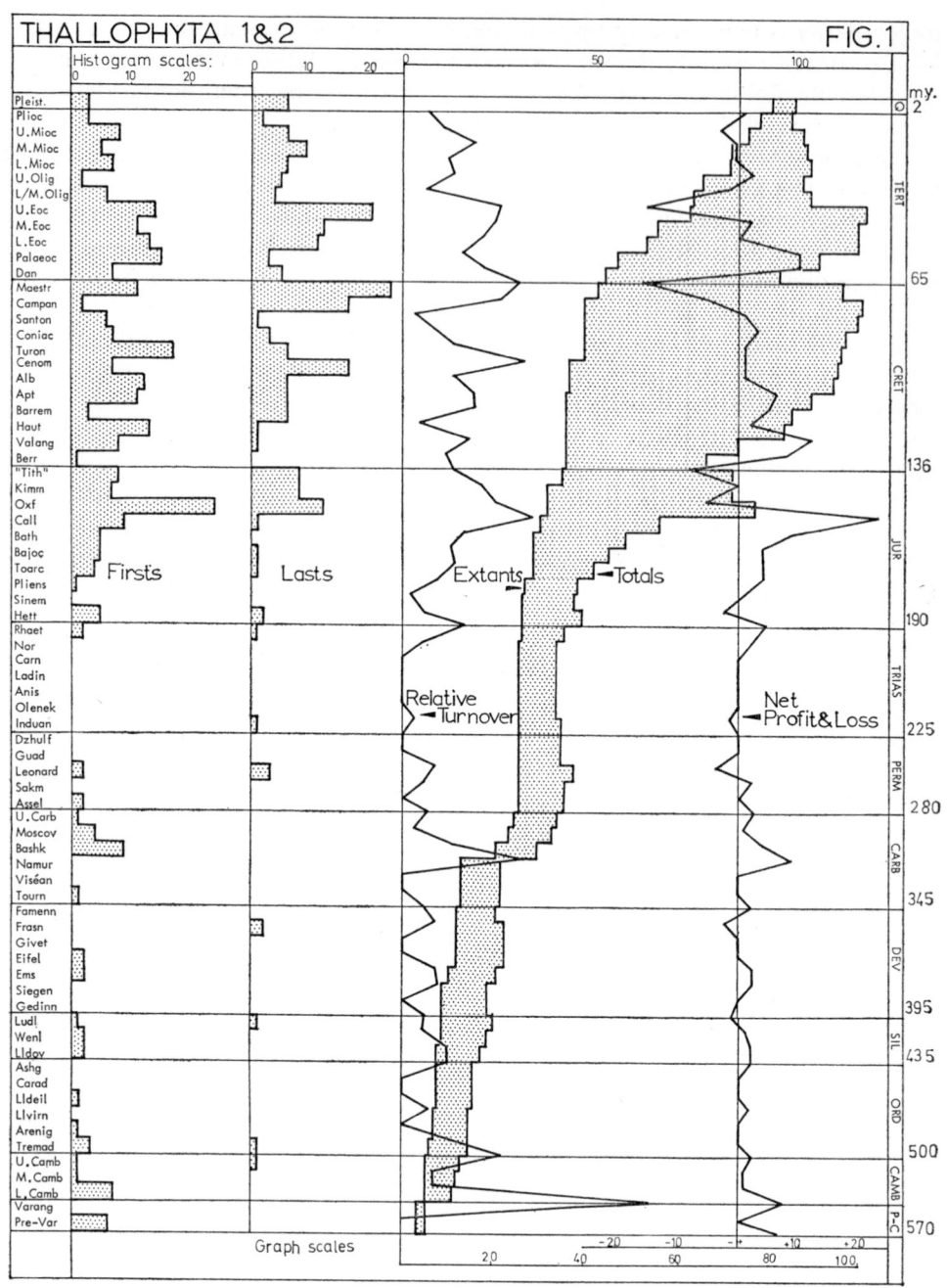

THALLOPHYTA 1&2 — FIG.1

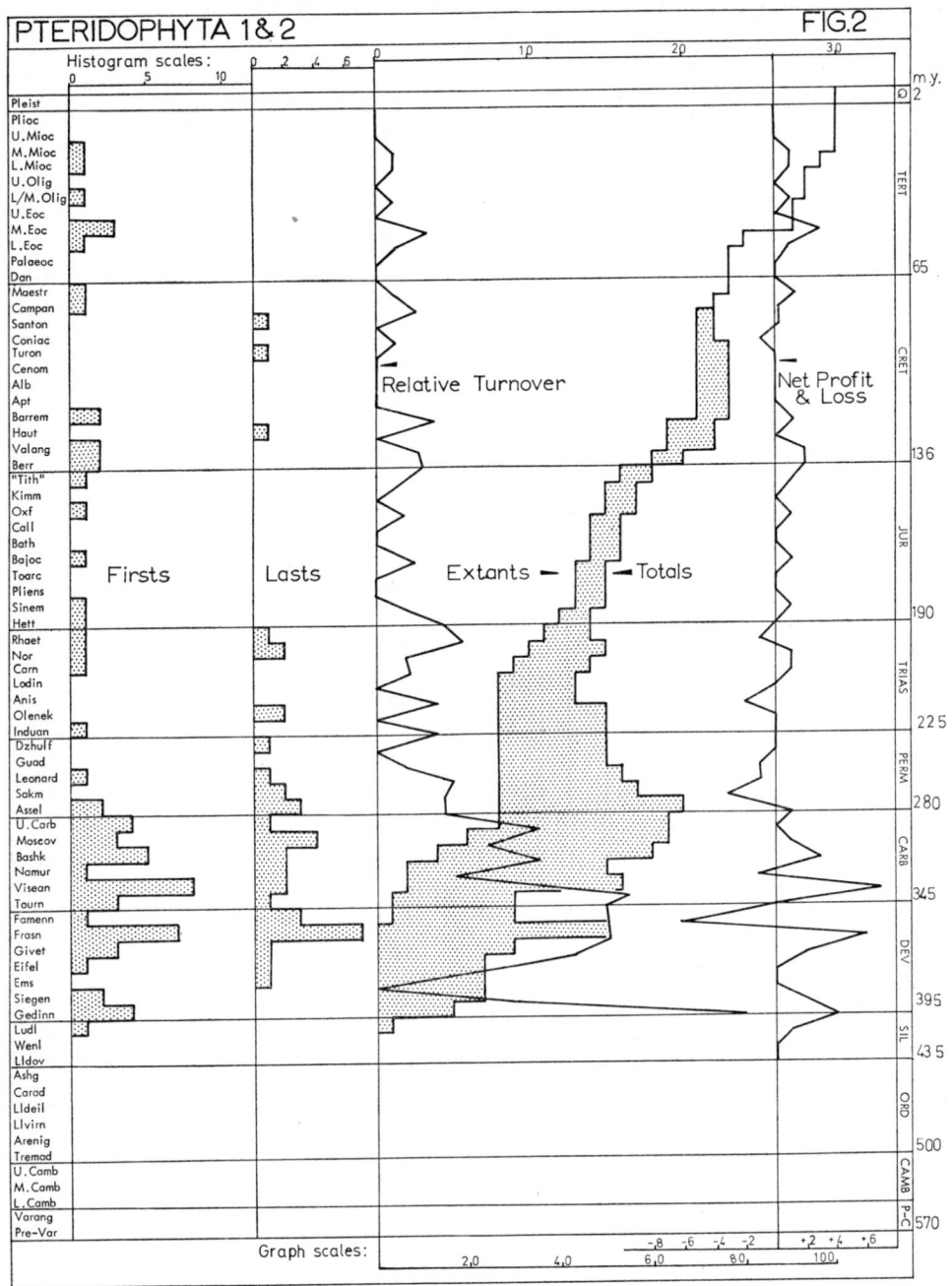

PTERIDOPHYTA 1 & 2   FIG.2

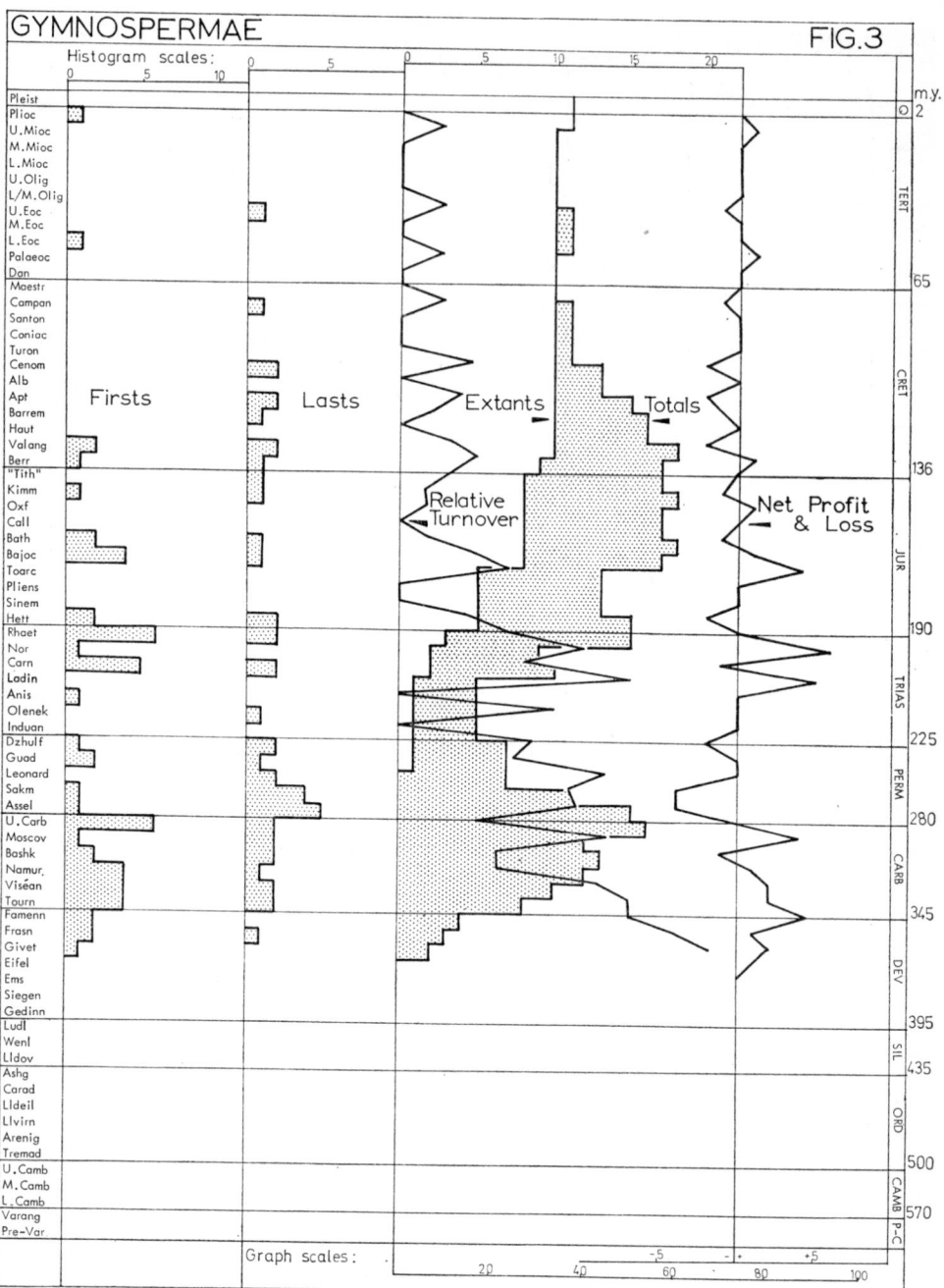

GYMNOSPERMAE   FIG.3

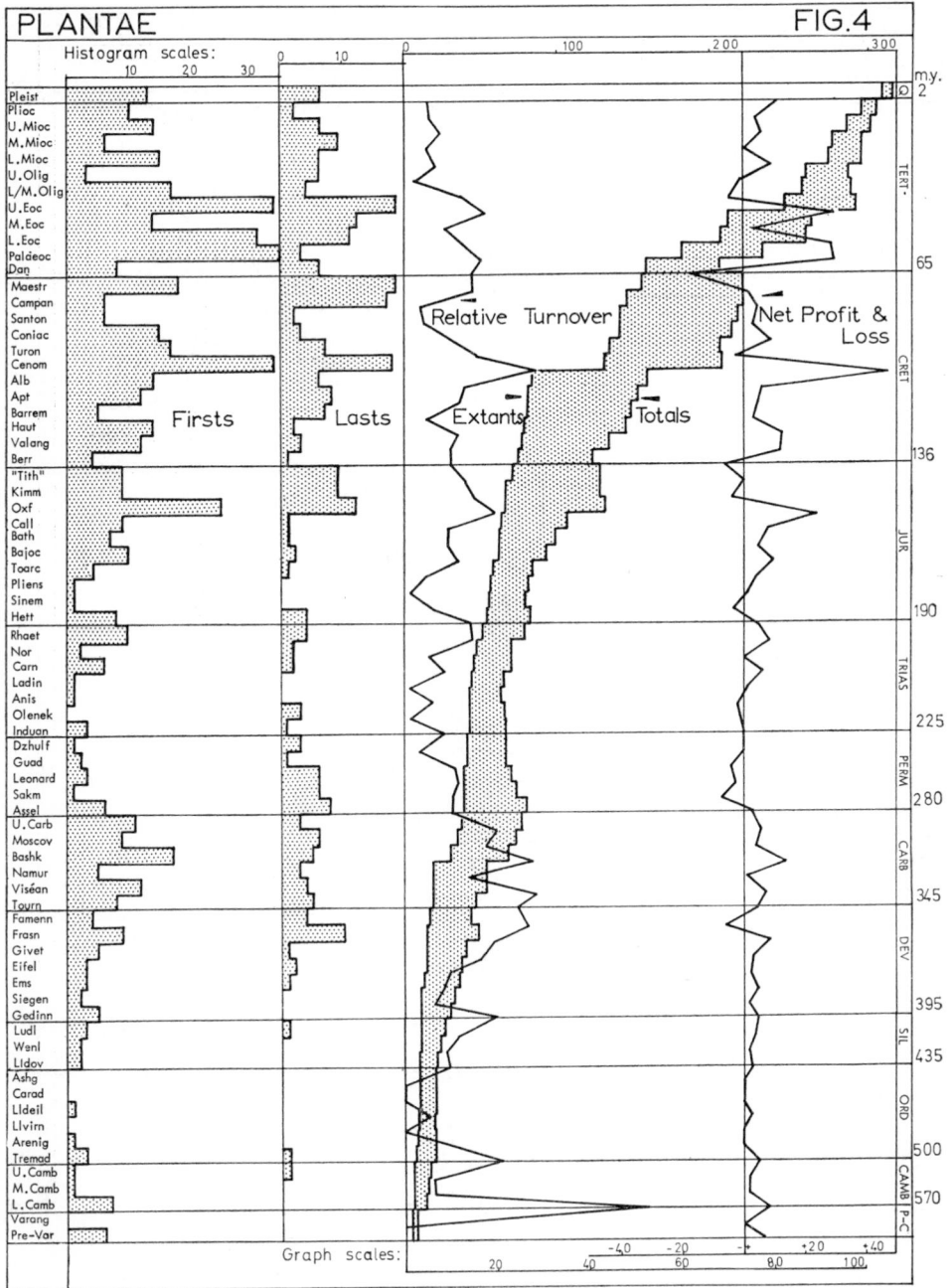

PLANTAE — FIG.4

Histogram scales: Firsts, Lasts

Relative Turnover — Extants, Totals

Net Profit & Loss

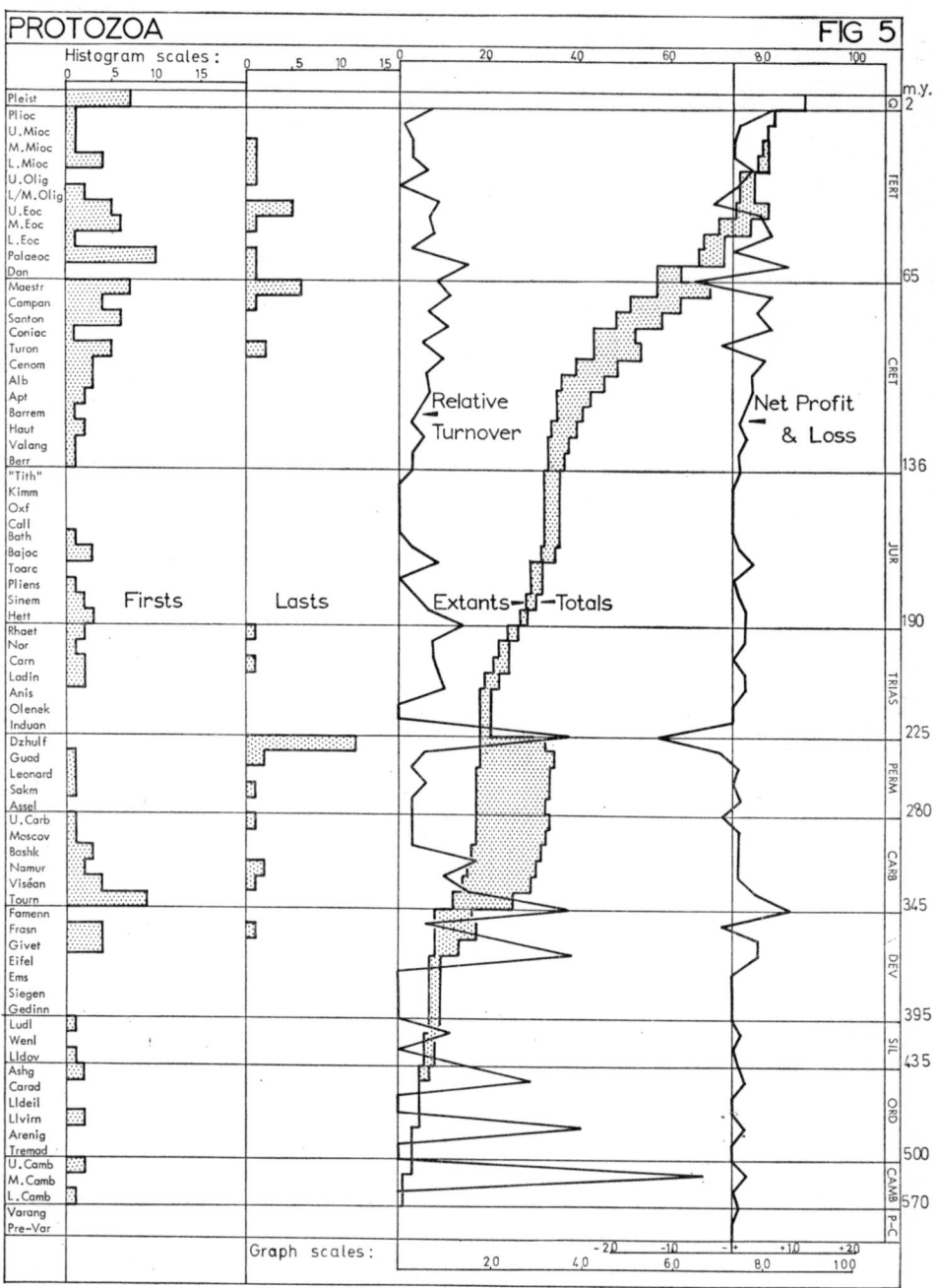

PROTOZOA   FIG 5

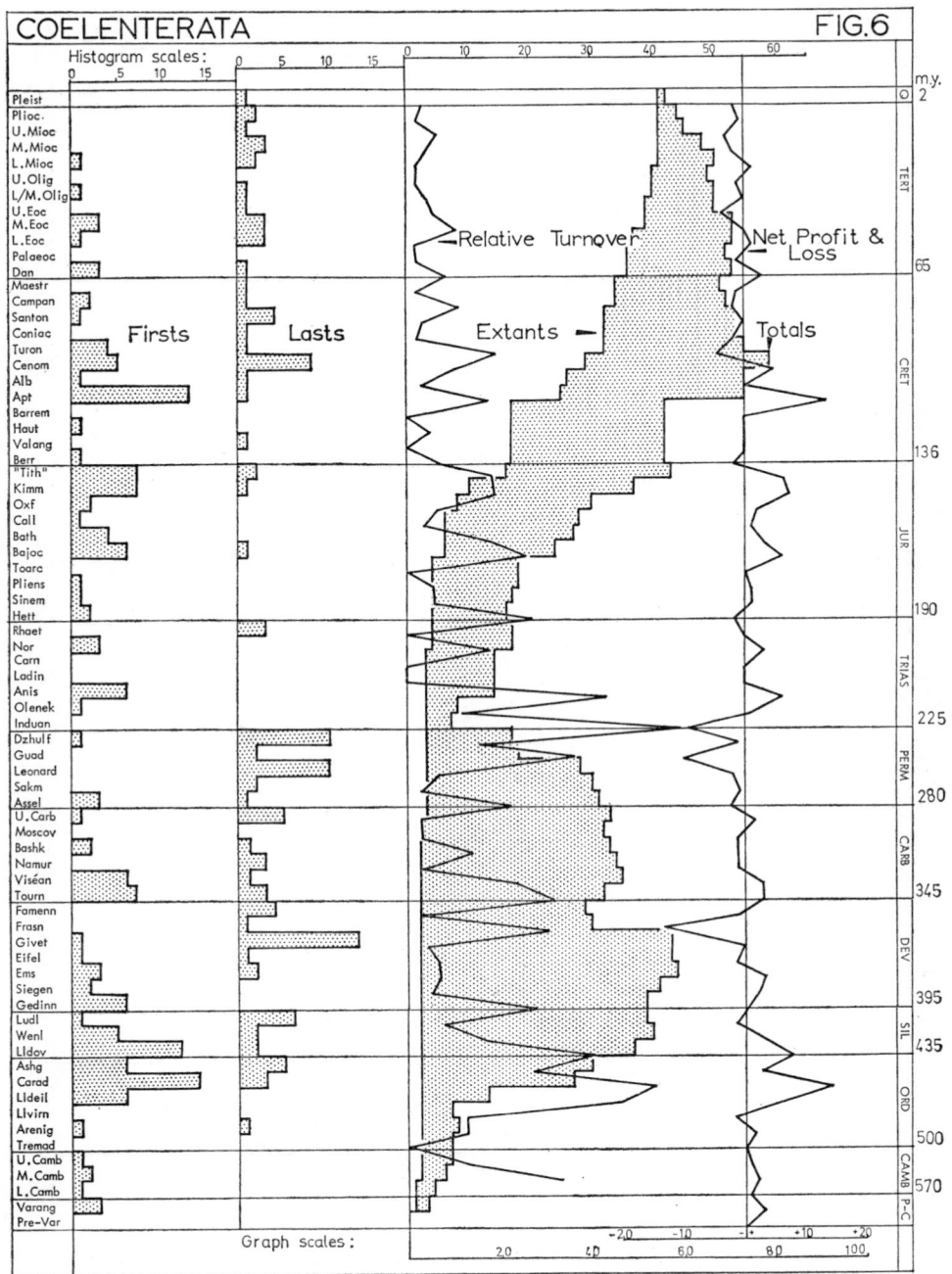

COELENTERATA   FIG.6

803

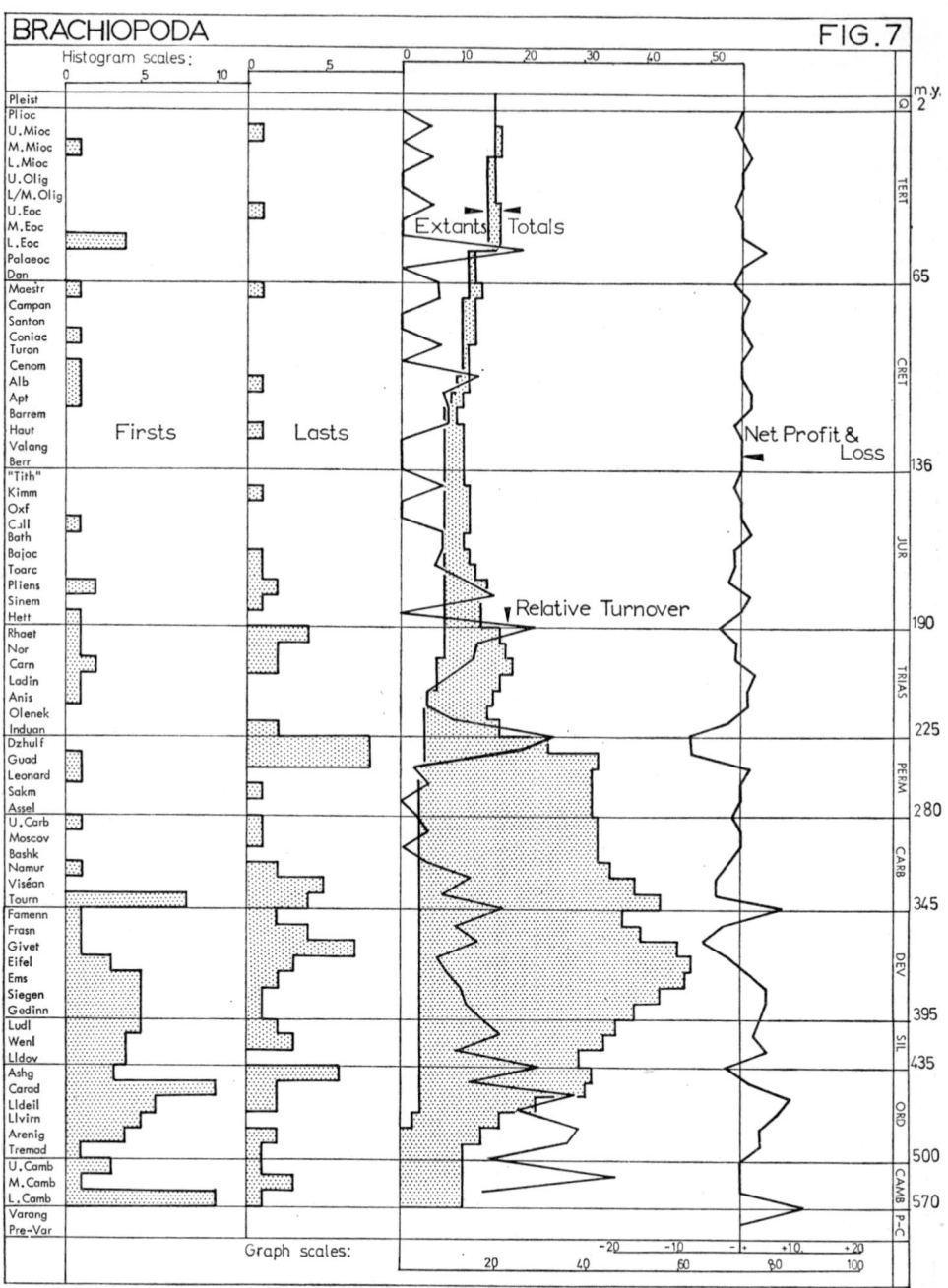

BRACHIOPODA   FIG.7

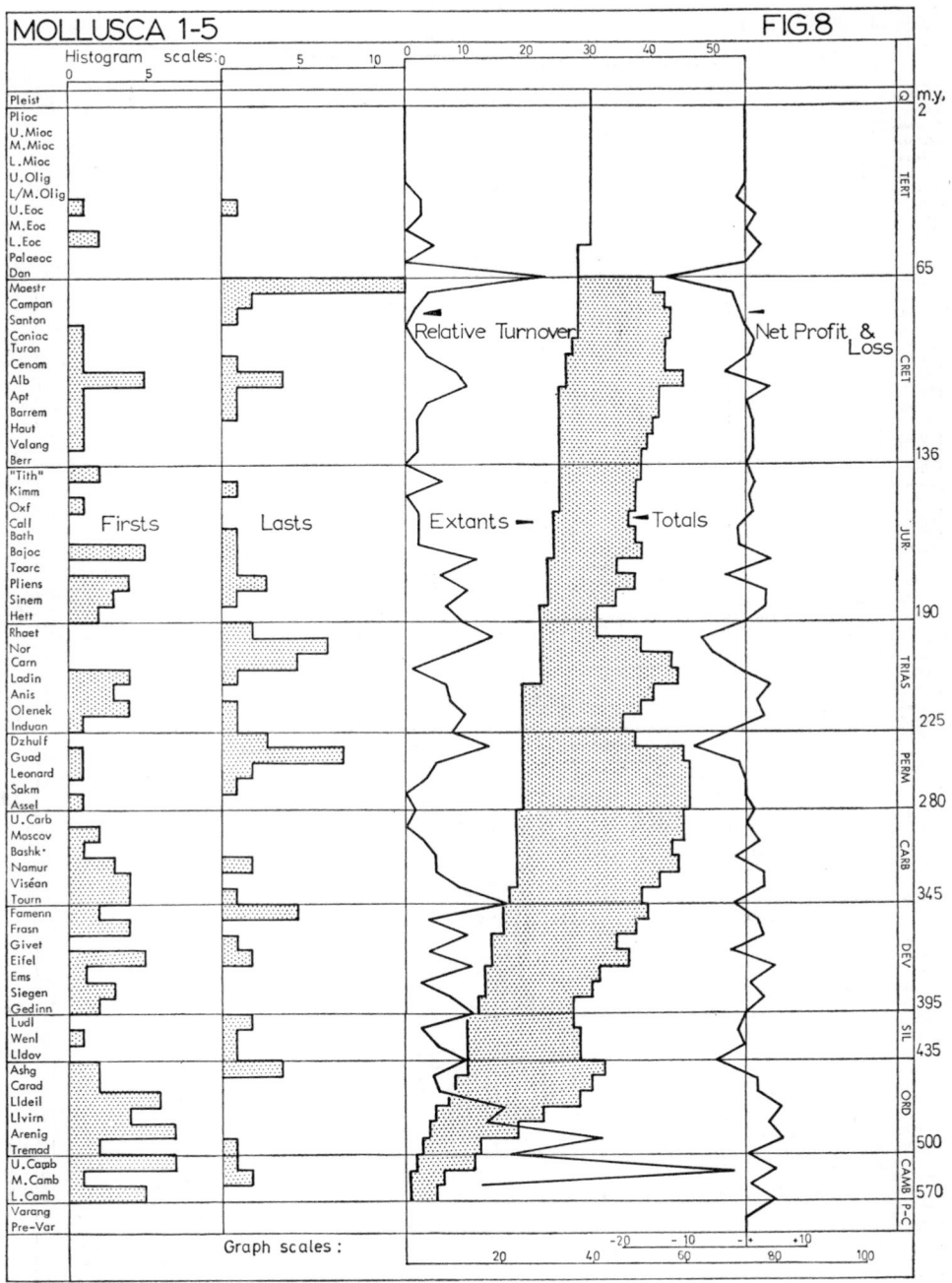

MOLLUSCA 1-5   FIG.8

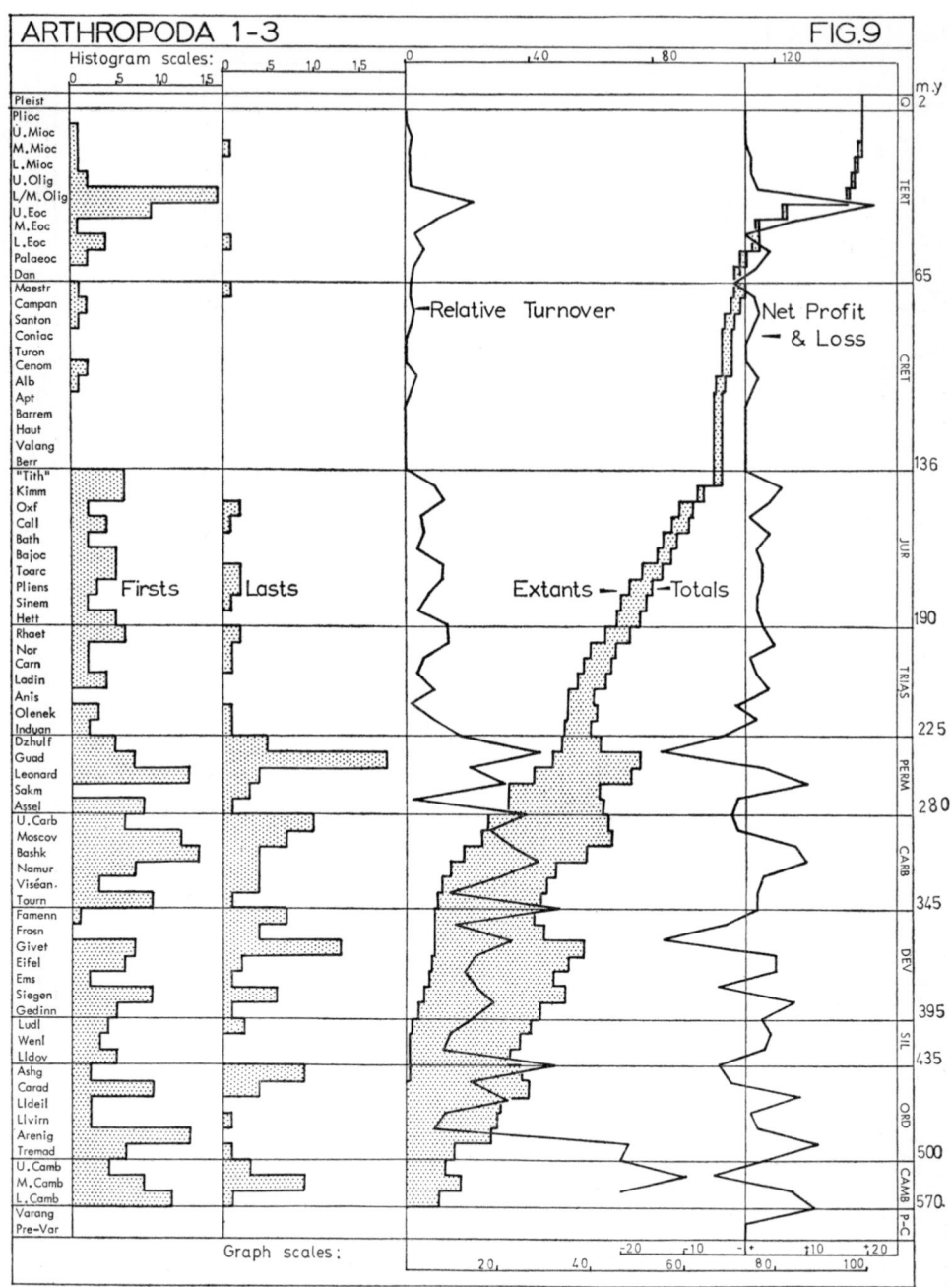

ARTHROPODA 1-3   FIG.9

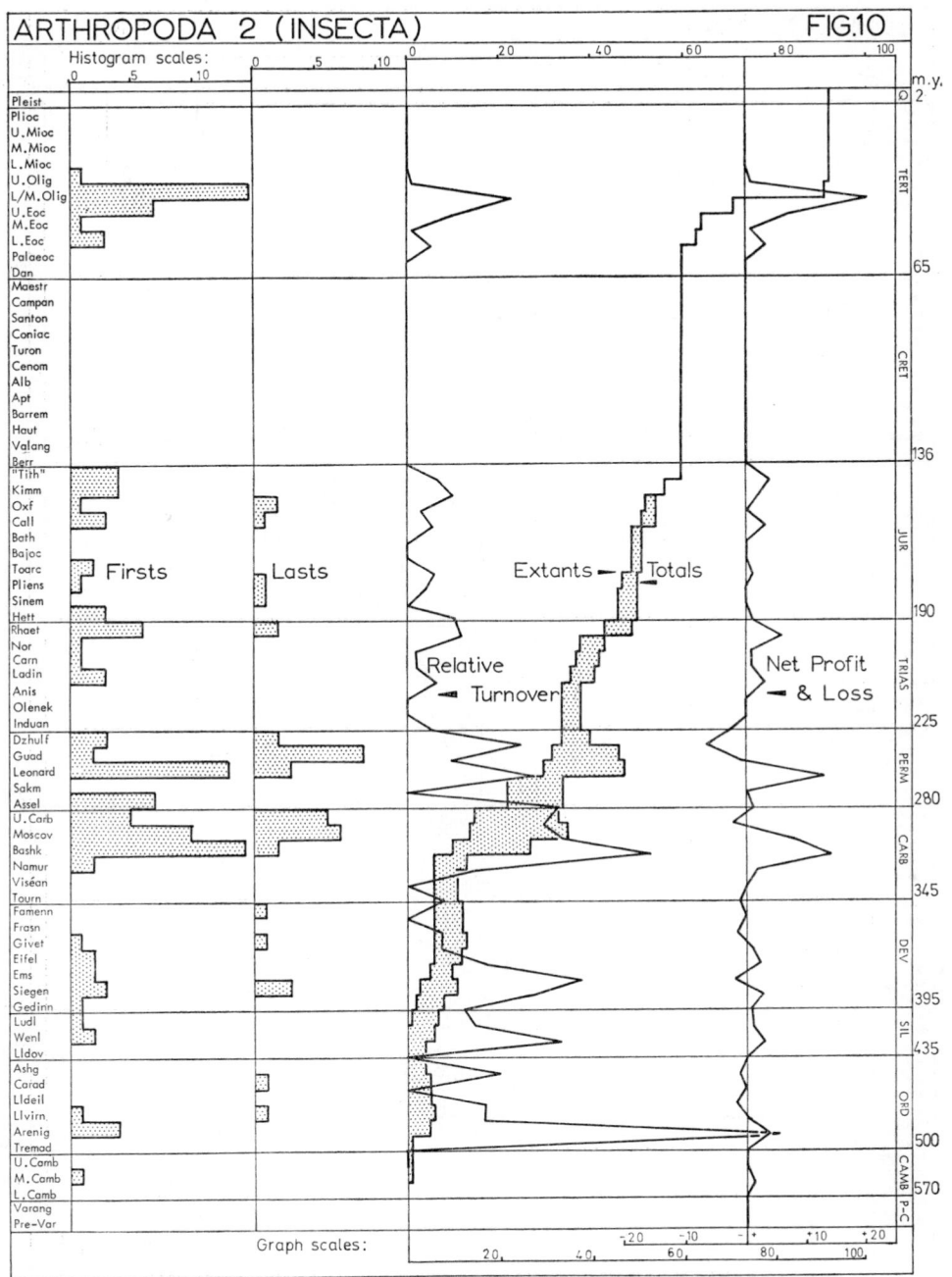

ARTHROPODA 2 (INSECTA)   FIG.10

Firsts   Lasts   Extants — Totals

Relative — Turnover   Net Profit — & Loss

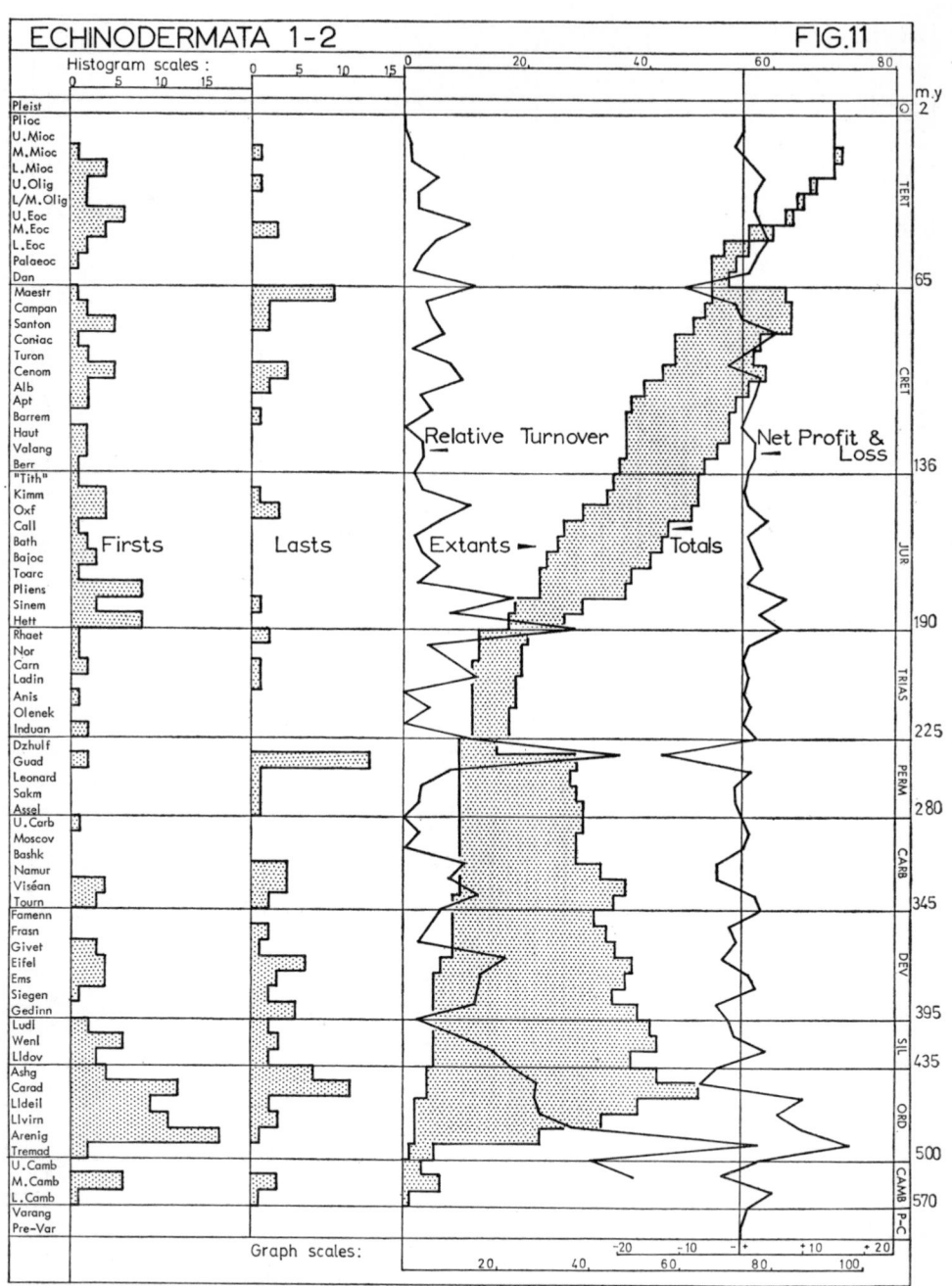

ECHINODERMATA 1-2   FIG.11

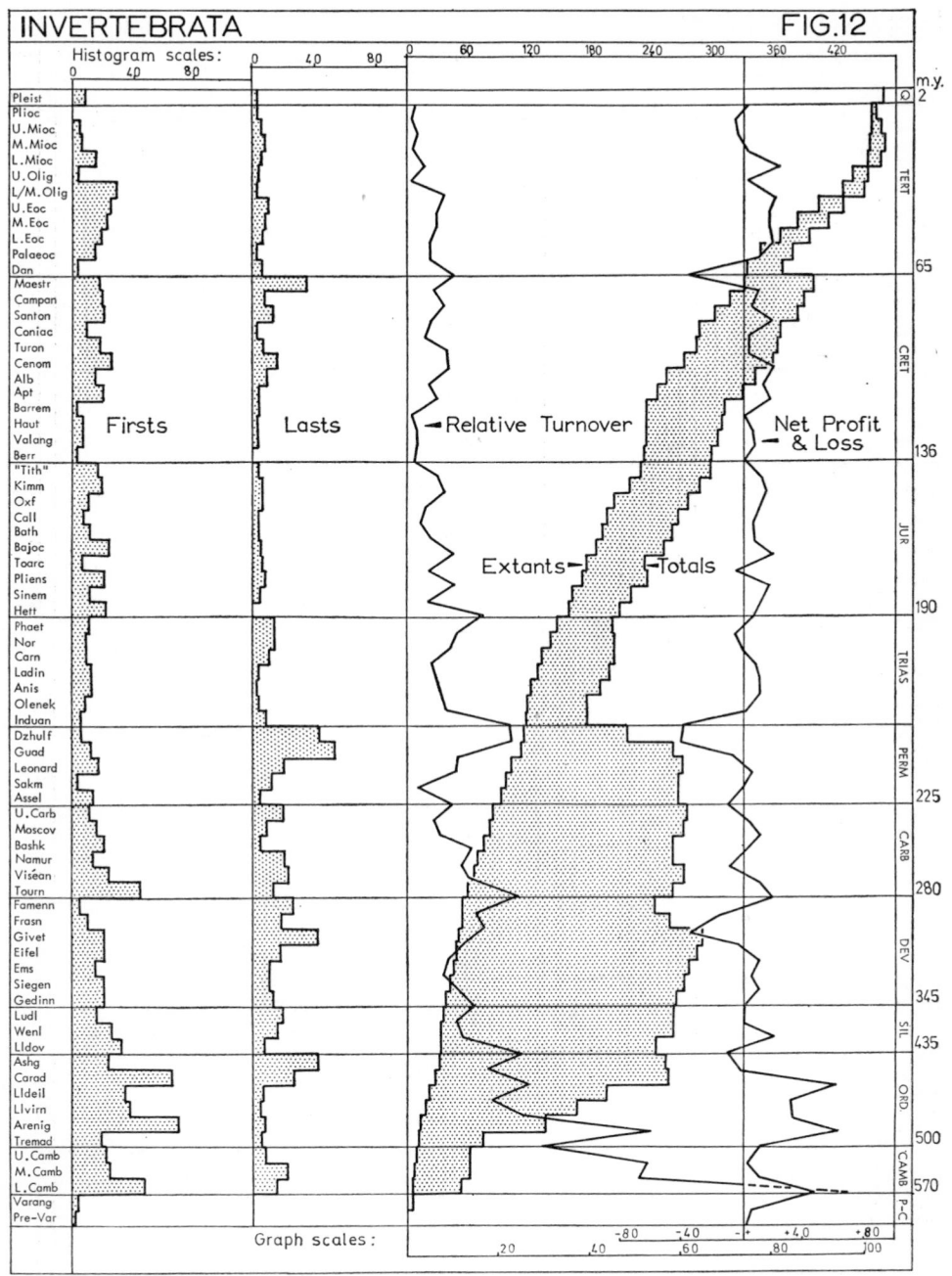

FIG.12 — INVERTEBRATA

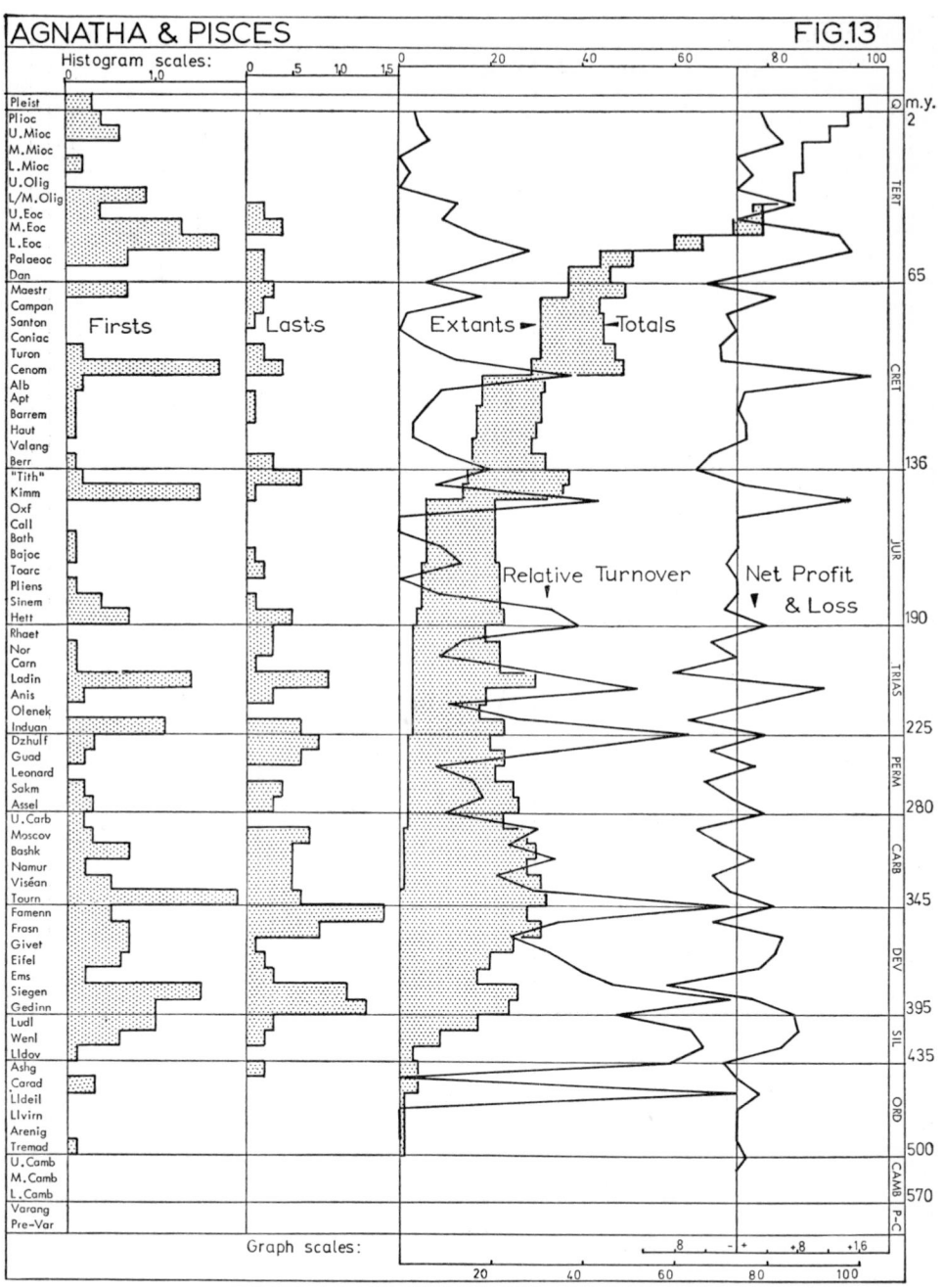

AGNATHA & PISCES

FIG.13

Histogram scales:

Firsts

Lasts

Extants ► ◄ Totals

Relative Turnover

Net Profit & Loss

Graph scales:

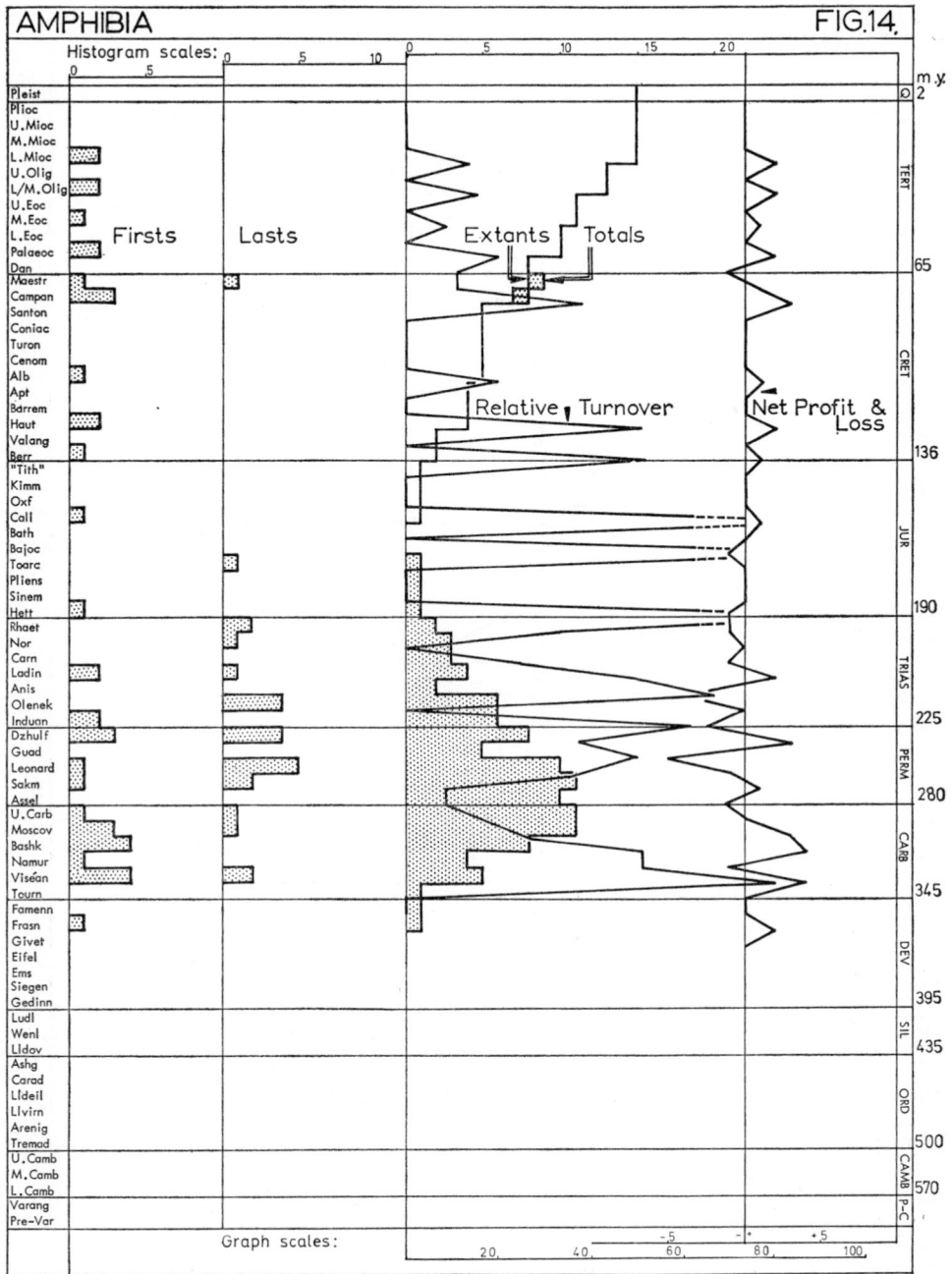

AMPHIBIA   FIG.14.

Firsts   Lasts   Extants Totals

Relative Turnover   Net Profit & Loss

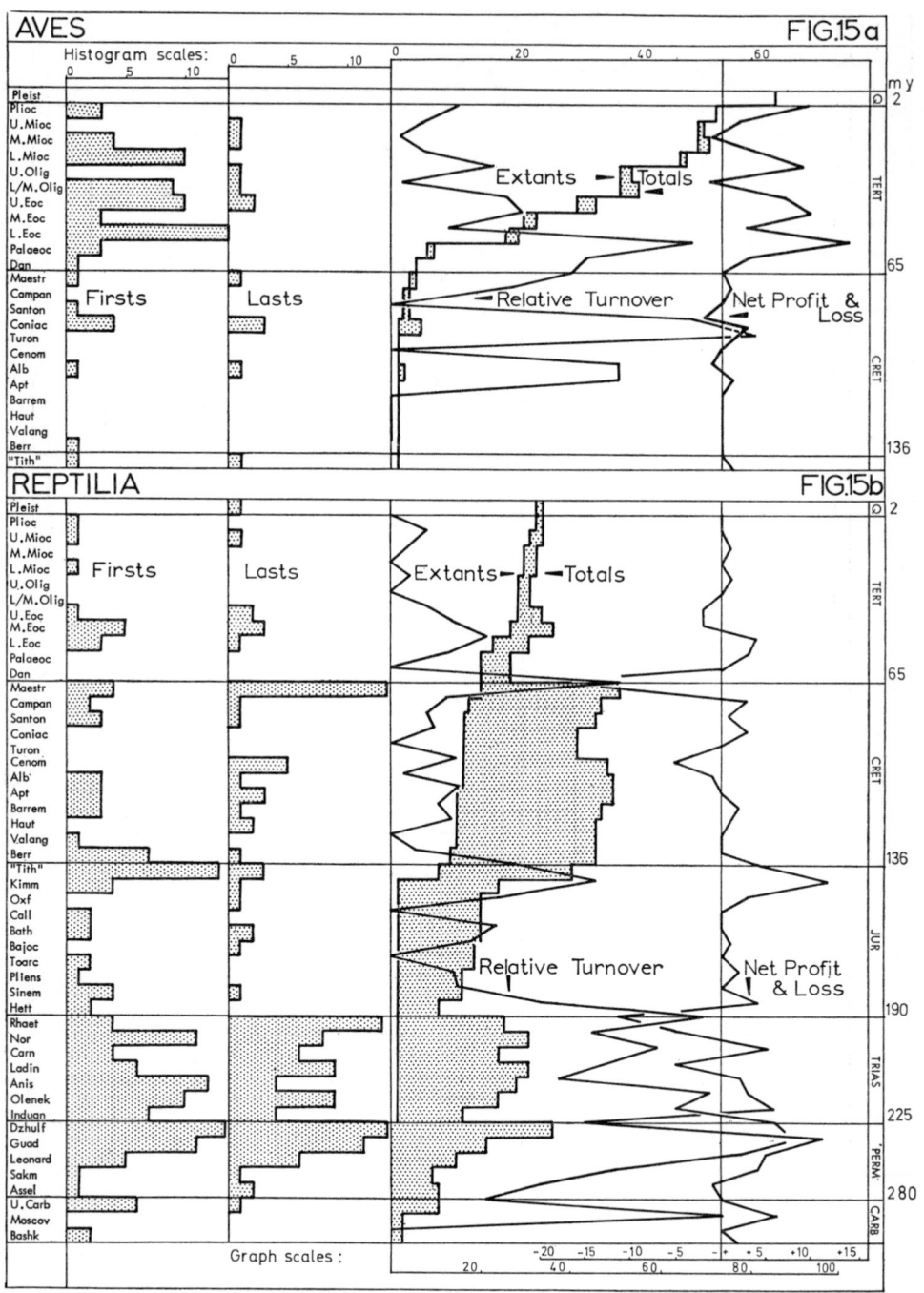

AVES — FIG.15a

Histogram scales:

Firsts Lasts Extants Totals

Relative Turnover Net Profit & Loss

REPTILIA — FIG.15b

Firsts Lasts Extants — Totals

Relative Turnover Net Profit & Loss

Graph scales:

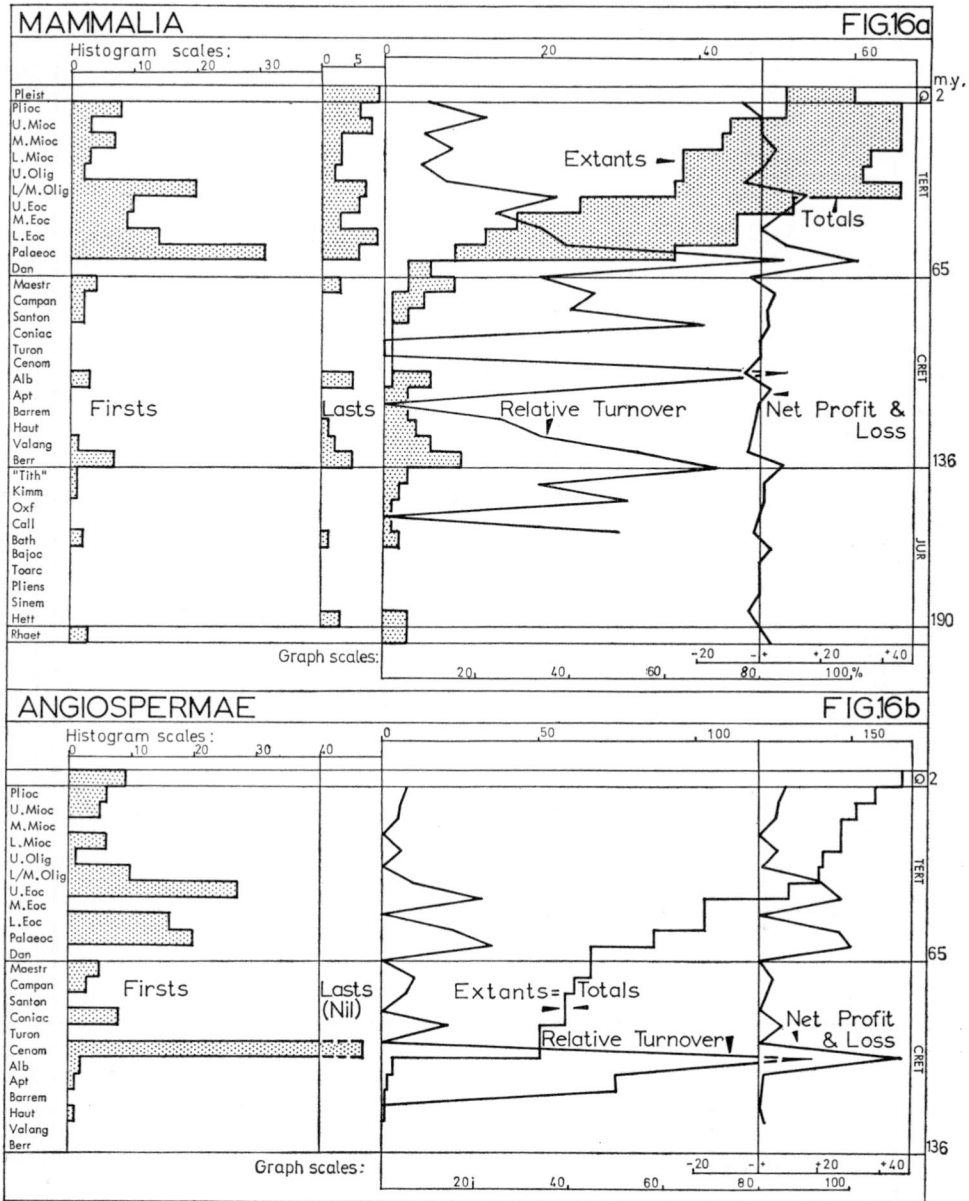

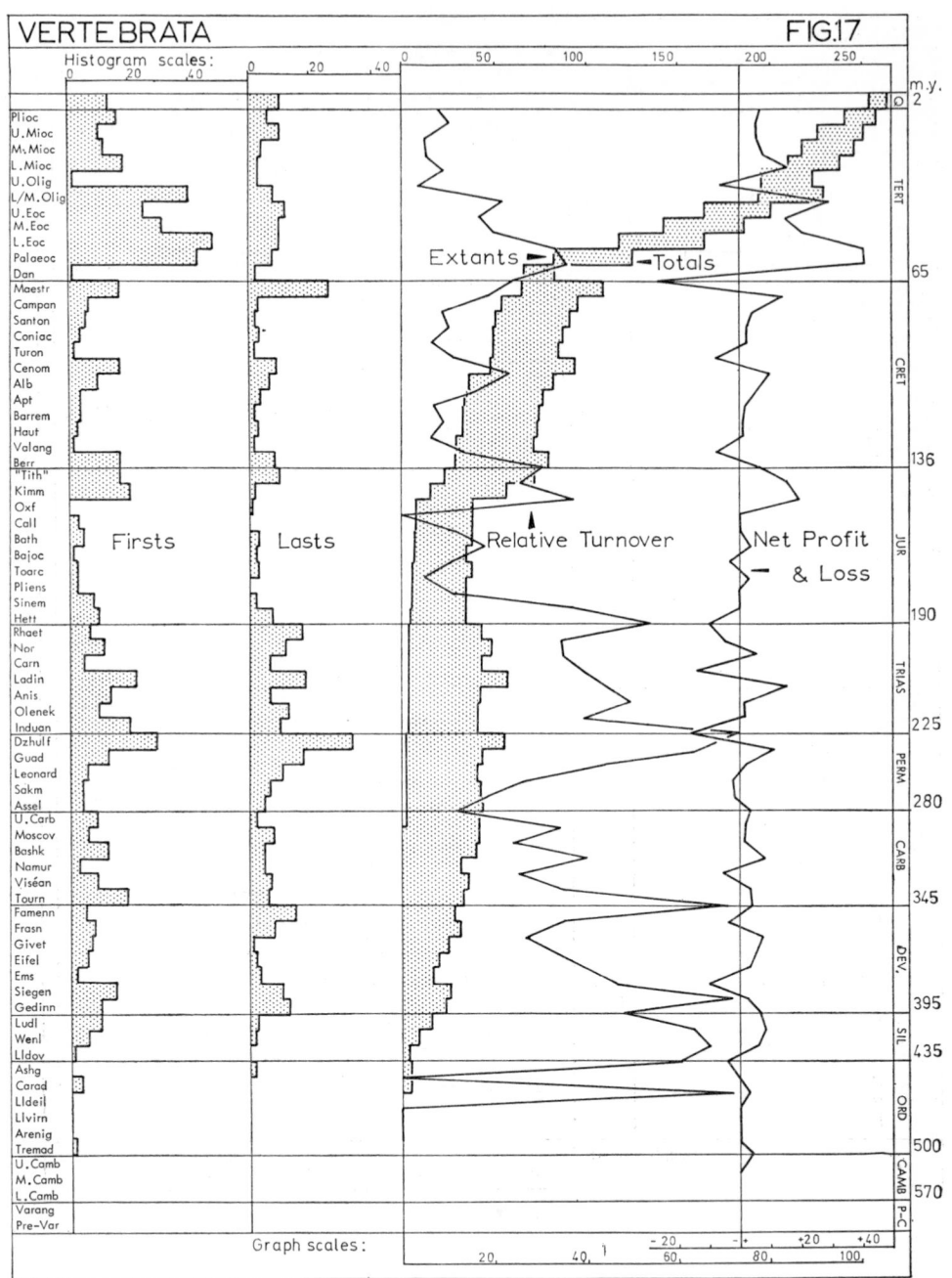

VERTEBRATA   FIG.17

Histogram scales:
0   20   40   0   20   40   0   50   100   150   200   250
                                                                        m.y.
                                                                        2

Plioc
U.Mioc
M.Mioc
L.Mioc
U.Olig
L/M.Olig
U.Eoc
M.Eoc
L.Eoc
Palaeoc
Dan   Extants   Totals   65
Maestr
Campan
Santon
Coniac
Turon
Cenom
Alb
Apt
Barrem
Haut
Valang
Berr   136
"Tith"
Kimm
Oxf
Call
Both   Firsts   Lasts   Relative Turnover   Net Profit JUR
Bajoc
Toarc   & Loss
Pliens
Sinem
Hett   190
Rhaet
Nor
Carn
Ladin   TRIAS
Anis
Olenek
Induan   225
Dzhulf
Guad
Leonard   PERM
Sakm
Assel   280
U.Carb
Moscov
Bashk   CARB
Namur
Viséan
Tourn   345
Famenn
Frasn
Givet
Eifel   DEV.
Ems
Siegen
Gedinn   395
Ludl
Wenl   SIL 435
Lldov
Ashg
Carad
Lldeil   ORD
Llvirn
Arenig
Tremad   500
U.Camb
M.Camb   CAMB 570
L.Camb
Varang   P-C
Pre-Var

Graph scales:
                              20,   40, 1   -20, -+- +20, +40,
                                                  60,   80,   100,

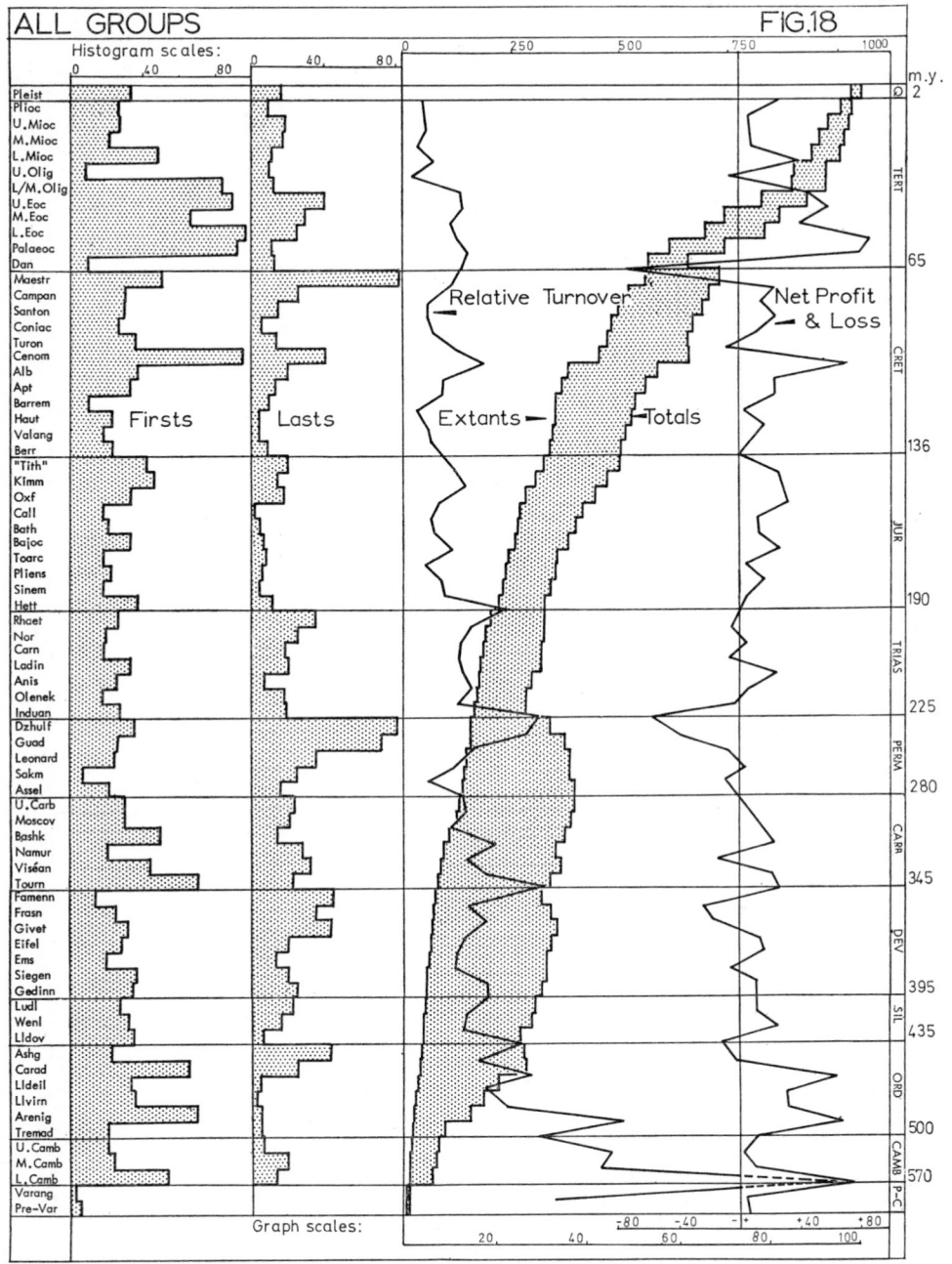

ALL GROUPS   FIG.18

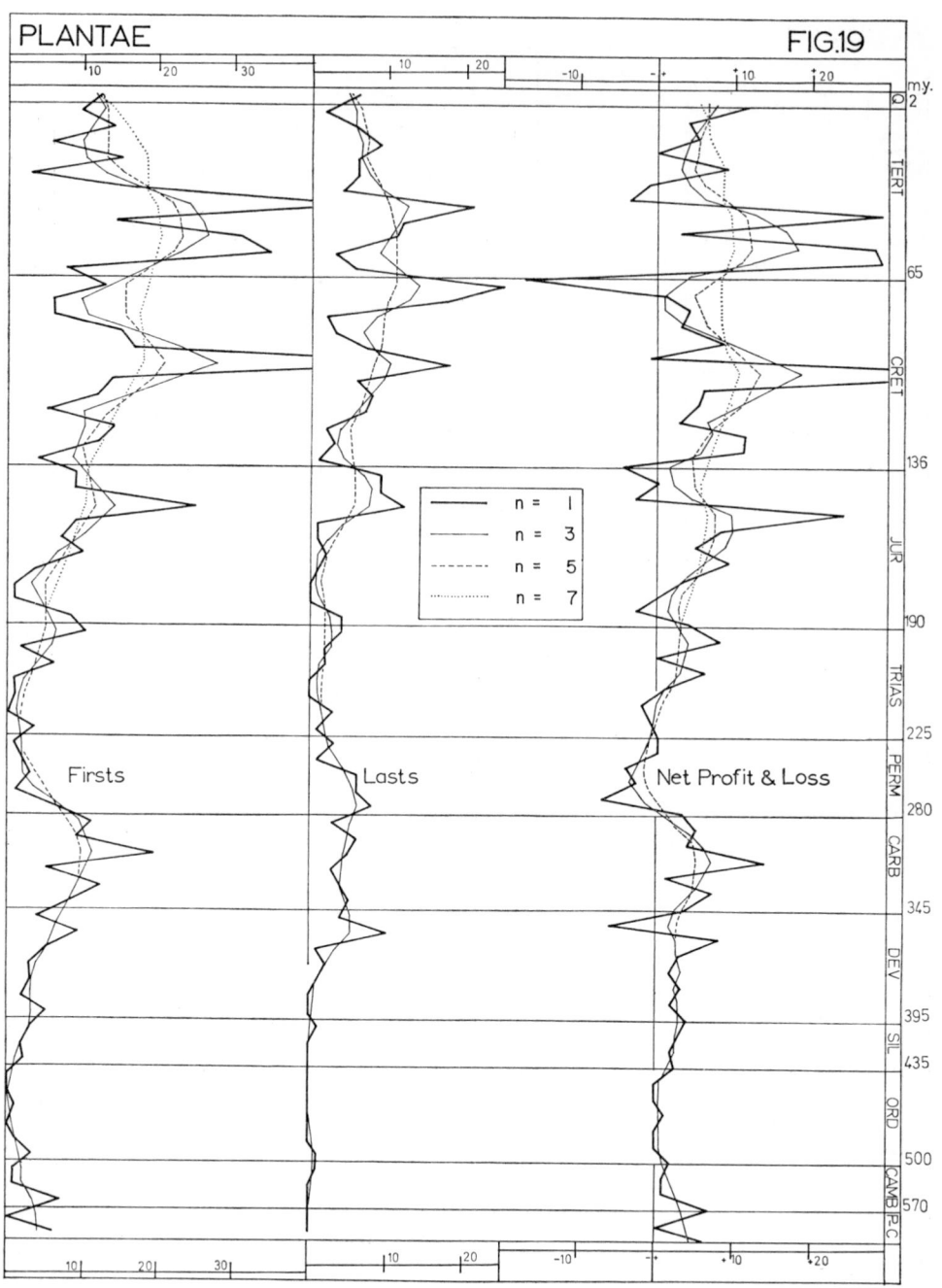

PLANTAE   FIG.19

Firsts

Lasts

Net Profit & Loss

n = 1
n = 3
n = 5
n = 7

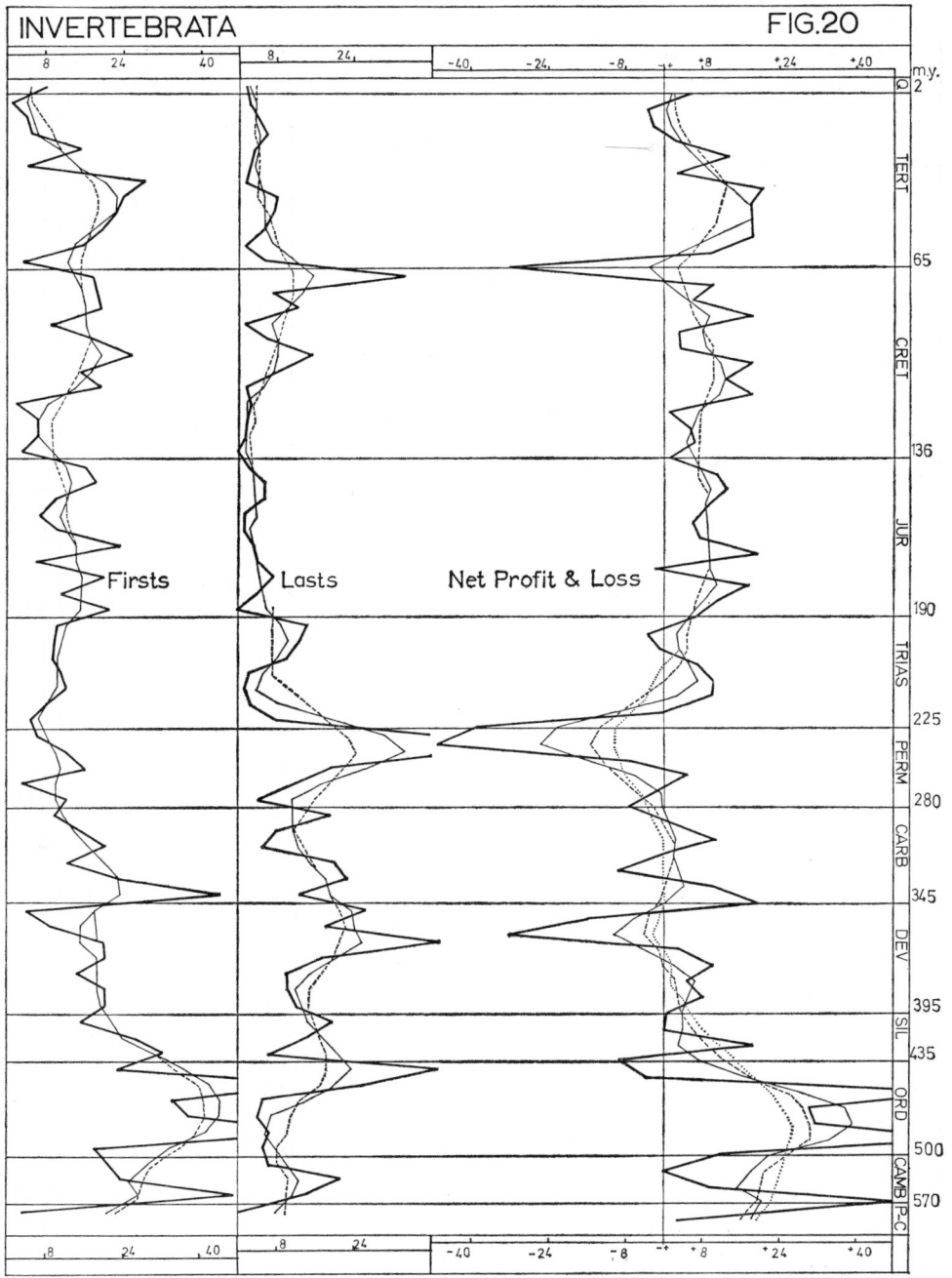

INVERTEBRATA   FIG.20

Firsts

Lasts

Net Profit & Loss

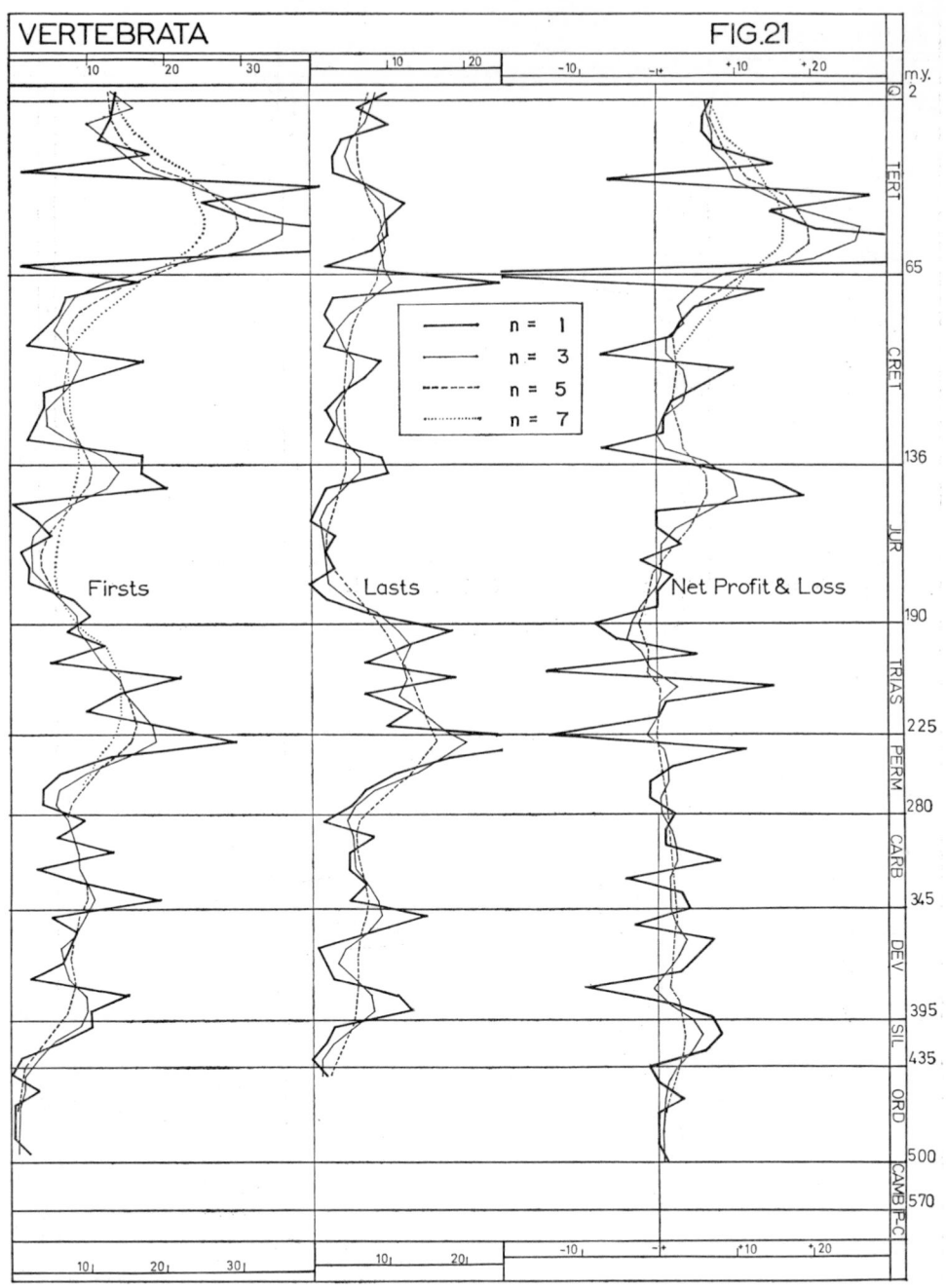

VERTEBRATA   FIG.21

	n = 1
	n = 3
	n = 5
	n = 7

Firsts   Lasts   Net Profit & Loss

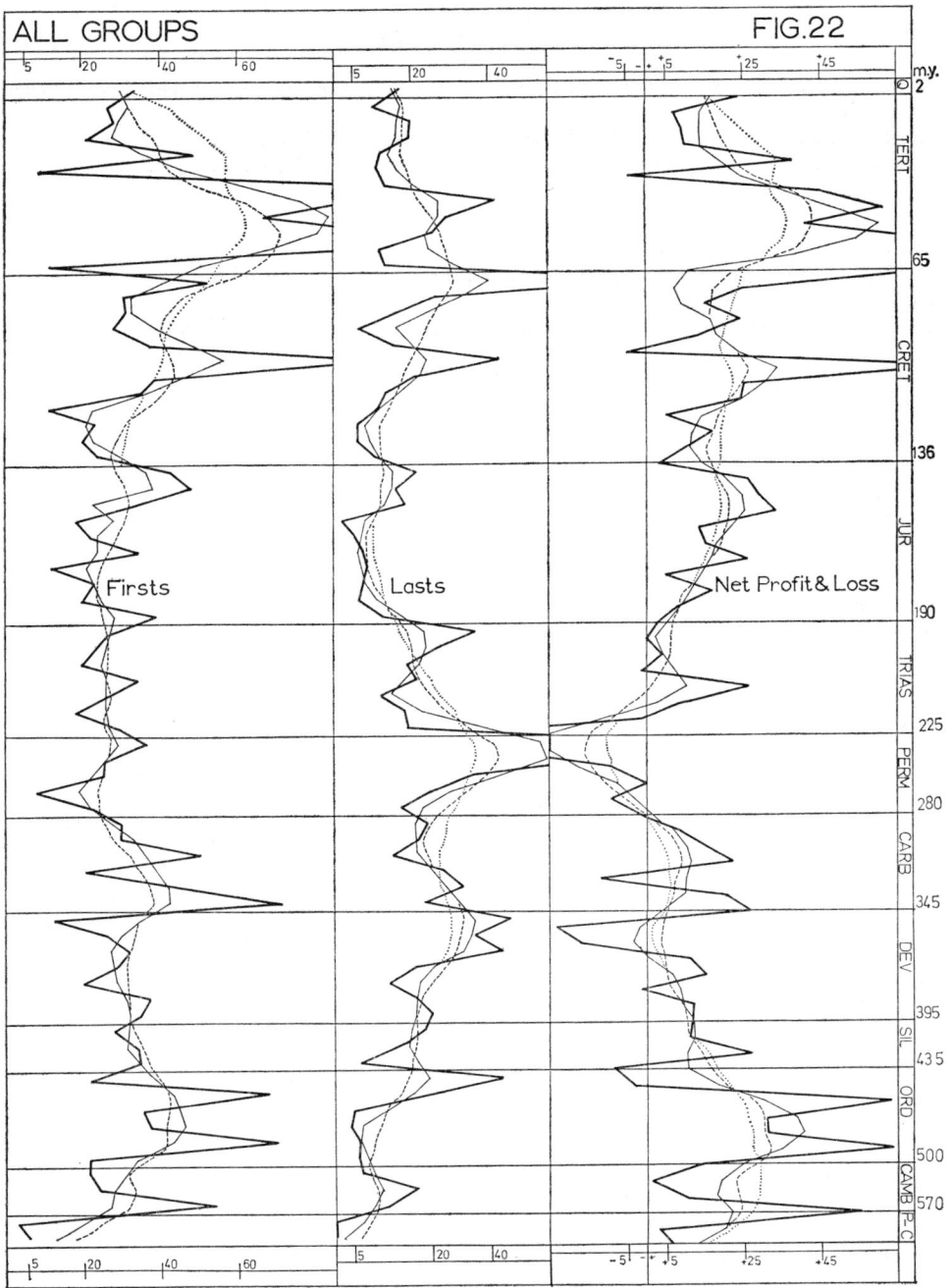

ALL GROUPS   FIG.22

Firsts   Lasts   Net Profit & Loss

5. References

MÜLLER, A. H. 1961. *Grossabläufe der Stommesgeschichte—Erscheinungen and Probleme.* Jena (Fischer Verlag).

NEWELL, N. D. 1963. Crises in the history of life. *Sci. Amer.* **208,** 77.

SIMPSON, J. F. 1966. Evolutionary pulsations and geomagnetic polarity. *Bull. geol. Soc. Amer.* **77,** 197–203, pl. 1.

J. L. Cutbill, M.A. PH.D. F.G.S.
    Department of Geology, Sedgwick Museum, Downing Street, Cambridge.
B. M. Funnell, M.A. PH.D. F.G.S.
    Department of Geology, Sedgwick Museum, Downing Street, Cambridge.

The Fossil Record

Index

Index

The numbers below refer to pages. Only one page reference is given in each chapter or paper, to the most convenient page in it. Names of persons refer only to those concerned with this volume as contributors or editors. Only familiar groups of plants or animals, anglicized and with the formal names of taxa in brackets where necessary, are indexed. The systematic arrangement of taxa in Part II is not repeated in the index which, however, does include some synonyms, groups of uncertain systematic position and groups not treated in this volume. Stratigraphical names, and discussion of them, are to be found in the Introduction, pp. 3–11. Editors of the chapters comprising Part II are listed on p. 827.

EDITORS OF CHAPTERS IN PART II

chapters

C. H. HOLLAND	8, 18, 19, 20, 23
M. R. HOUSE	13, 14, 15, 16, 17, 24
N. F. HUGHES	1, 2, 3, 4, 5, 6, 7
M. J. S. RUDWICK	9, 10, 11, 12, 21, 22
L. B. H. TARLO	25, 26, 27, 28, 29, 30